Algebra 1 *Teacher's Edition Contents*

Teacher Handbook

VOLUME 1

VOLUME 2

Series *Authors*

Randall I. Charles, Ph.D., is Professor Emeritus in the Department of Mathematics and Computer Science at San Jose State University, San Jose, California. He began his career as a high school mathematics teacher, and he was a mathematics supervisor for five years. Dr. Charles has been a member of several NCTM committees and is the former Vice President of the National Council of Supervisors of Mathematics. Much of his writing and research has been in the area of problem solving. He has authored more than 75 mathematics textbooks for kindergarten through college.

Dan Kennedy, Ph.D., is a classroom teacher and the Lupton Distinguished Professor of Mathematics at the Baylor School in Chattanooga, Tennessee. A frequent speaker at professional meetings on the subject of mathematics education reform, Dr. Kennedy has conducted more than 50 workshops and institutes for high school teachers. He is coauthor of textbooks in calculus and precalculus, and from 1990 to 1994 he chaired the College Board's AP Calculus Development Committee. He is a 1992 Tandy Technology Scholar and a 1995 Presidential Award winner.

Basia Hall currently serves as Manager of Instructional Programs for the Houston Independent School District. With 33 years of teaching experience, Ms. Hall has served as a department chair, instructional supervisor, school improvement facilitator, and professional development trainer. She has developed curricula for Algebra 1, Geometry, and Algebra 2 and co-developed the Texas state mathematics standards. A 1992 Presidential Awardee, Ms. Hall is past president of the Texas Association of Supervisors of Mathematics and is a state representative for the National Council of Supervisors of Mathematics (NCSM).

Consulting *Authors*

Stuart Murphy is a visual learning author and consultant. He is a champion of developing visual learning skills and using related strategies to help children become more successful students. He is the author of MathStart, a series of children's books that presents mathematical concepts in the context of stories. A graduate of the Rhode Island School of Design, he has worked extensively in educational publishing and has been on the authorship teams of a number of elementary and high school mathematics programs. He is a frequent presenter at meetings of the National Council of Teachers of Mathematics, the International Reading Association, and other professional organizations.

Grant Wiggins, Ed.D., is the President of Authentic Education in Hopewell, New Jersey. He earned his Ed.D. from Harvard University and his B.A. from St. John's College in Annapolis. Dr. Wiggins consults with schools, districts, and state education departments on a variety of reform matters; organizes conferences and workshops; and develops print materials and Web resources on curricular change. He is perhaps best known for being the coauthor, with Jay McTighe, of *Understanding by Design* and *The Understanding by Design Handbook*, the award-winning and highly successful materials on curriculum published by ASCD. His work has been supported by the Pew Charitable Trusts, the Geraldine R. Dodge Foundation, and the National Science Foundation.

Program *Authors*
Algebra 1 and Algebra 2

Allan E. Bellman, Ph.D., is a Lecturer/Supervisor in the School of Education at the University of California, Davis. Before coming to Davis, he was a mathematics teacher for 31 years in Montgomery County, Maryland. He has been an instructor for both the Woodrow Wilson National Fellowship Foundation and the T^3 program. He has been involved in the development of many products from Texas Instruments. Dr. Bellman has a particular expertise in the use of technology in education and speaks frequently on this topic. He was a 1992 Tandy Technology Scholar and has twice been listed in Who's Who Among America's Teachers.

Sadie Chavis Bragg, Ed.D., is Senior Vice President of Academic Affairs at the Borough of Manhattan Community College of the City University of New York. A former professor of mathematics, she is a past president of the American Mathematical Association of Two-Year Colleges (AMATYC), co-director of the AMATYC project to revise the standards for introductory college mathematics before calculus, and an active member of the Benjamin Banneker Association. Dr. Bragg has coauthored more than 50 mathematics textbooks for kindergarten through college.

William G. Handlin, Sr., is a classroom teacher and Department Chairman of Technology Applications at Spring Woods High School in Houston, Texas. Awarded Life Membership in the Texas Congress of Parents and Teachers for his contributions to the well-being of children, Mr. Handlin is also a frequent workshop and seminar leader in professional meetings throughout the world.

Geometry

Laurie E. Bass is a classroom teacher at the 9–12 division of the Ethical Culture Fieldston School in Riverdale, New York. A classroom teacher for more than 30 years, Ms. Bass has a wide base of teaching experience, ranging from Grade 6 through Advanced Placement Calculus. She was the recipient of a 2000 Honorable Mention for the Radio Shack National Teacher Awards. She has been a contributing writer for a number of publications, including software-based activities for the Algebra 1 classroom. Among her areas of special interest are cooperative learning for high school students and geometry exploration on the computer. Ms. Bass is a frequent presenter at local, regional, and national conferences.

Art Johnson, Ed.D., is a professor of mathematics education at Boston University. He is a mathematics educator with 32 years of public school teaching experience, a frequent speaker and workshop leader, and the recipient of a number of awards: the Tandy Prize for Teaching Excellence, the Presidential Award for Excellence in Mathematics Teaching, and New Hampshire Teacher of the Year. He was also profiled by the Disney Corporation in the American Teacher of the Year Program. Dr. Johnson has contributed 18 articles to NCTM journals and has authored over 50 books on various aspects of mathematics.

Reviewers *National*

Tammy Baumann
K-12 Mathematics Coordinator
School District of the City
 of Erie
Erie, Pennsylvania

Sandy Cowgill
Mathematics Department Chair
Muncie Central High School
Muncie, Indiana

Kari Egnot
Mathematics Teacher
Newport News High School
Newport News, Virginia

Sheryl Ezze
Mathematics Chairperson
DeWitt High School
Lansing, Michigan

Dennis Griebel
Mathematics Coordinator
Cherry Creek School District
Aurora, Colorado

Bill Harrington
Secondary Mathematics
 Coordinator
State College School District
State College, Pennsylvania

Michael Herzog
Mathematics Teacher
Tucson Small School Project
Tucson, Arizona

Camilla Horton
Secondary Instruction Support
Memphis School District
Memphis, Tennessee

Gary Kubina
Mathematics Consultant
Mobile County School System
Mobile, Alabama

Sharon Liston
Mathematics Department Chair
Moore Public Schools
Oklahoma City, Oklahoma

Ann Marie Palmeri Monahan
Mathematics Supervisor
Bayonne Public Schools
Bayonne, New Jersey

Indika Morris
Mathematics Department Chair
Queen Creek School District
Queen Creek, Arizona

Jennifer Petersen
K-12 Mathematics Curriculum
 Facilitator
Springfield Public Schools
Springfield, Missouri

Tammy Popp
Mathematics Teacher
Mehlville School District
St. Louis, Missouri

Mickey Porter
Mathematics Teacher
Dayton Public Schools
Dayton, Ohio

Steven Sachs
Mathematics Department Chair
Lawrence North High School
Indianapolis, Indiana

John Staley
Secondary Mathematics
 Coordinator
Office of Mathematics, PK-12
Baltimore, Maryland

Robert Thomas, Ph.D.
Mathematics Teacher
Yuma Union High School
 District #70
Yuma, Arizona

Linda Ussery
Mathematics Consultant
Alabama Department of
 Education
Tuscumbia, Alabama

Denise Vizzini
Mathematics Teacher
Clarksburg High School
Montgomery County,
 Maryland

Marcia White
Mathematics Specialist
Academic Operations,
 Technology and Innovations
Memphis City Schools
Memphis, Tennessee

Merrie Wolfe
Mathematics Department Chair
Tulsa Public Schools
Tulsa, Oklahoma

Contents *in Brief*

Welcome to Pearson's *Prentice Hall Algebra 1* student book. Throughout this textbook, you will find content that has been developed to cover all of the Algebra 1 Standards in Indiana's Academic Standards for Mathematics. The **IN Chapter** offers timely review and practice to help you prepare for the Algebra 1 End-of-Course Assessment (ECA). The End-of-Course Assessment, modeled after the American Diploma Project's (ADP) Algebra 1 test can provide additional practice.

ENGAGE ME

HELP ME

ENCOURAGE ME

Change
the way students see math.

Prentice Hall Algebra 1 helps students see math like never before. This blended print and digital curriculum provides an environment where you can engage students, teach for understanding, and promote mastery—for success today and through life. It's a whole new way to look at math. See for yourself.

Algebra 1

Geometry

Algebra 2

PowerAlgebra.com

Using the latest in digital instructional technology, PowerAlgebra.com provides a pedagogically relevant interface to support your math classroom. PowerAlgebra.com can be used as a stand-alone digital course or integrated with print materials to provide a balanced classroom environment for you and your students to engage in the study of math. This online learning environment is designed to enable you to easily access resources, plan lessons, incorporate presentation tools, assign student work and support student understanding.

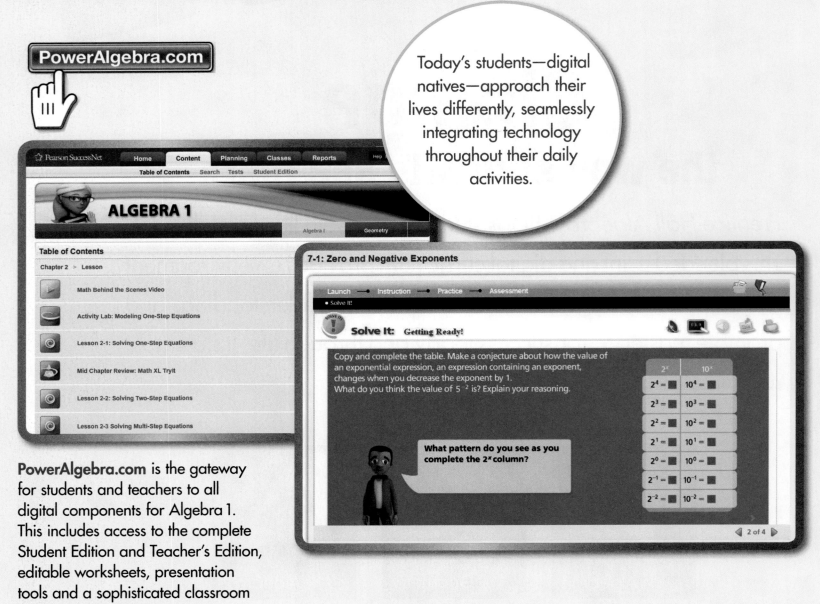

Today's students—digital natives—approach their lives differently, seamlessly integrating technology throughout their daily activities.

PowerAlgebra.com is the gateway for students and teachers to all digital components for Algebra 1. This includes access to the complete Student Edition and Teacher's Edition, editable worksheets, presentation tools and a sophisticated classroom management system.

"Today's students are digital natives. These students are not merely technology-savvy; they are approaching their lives differently as they integrate digital technologies seamlessly throughout their daily activities. Let's not have them power-down when they get to math class."

—Laurie Bass

PEARSON
video ▶ challenge

My Math Videos are student-produced videos that engage students in math concepts and are relevant to their lives. Through the Pearson Video Challenge, students can generate and submit their own videos to be included on PowerAlgebra.com.

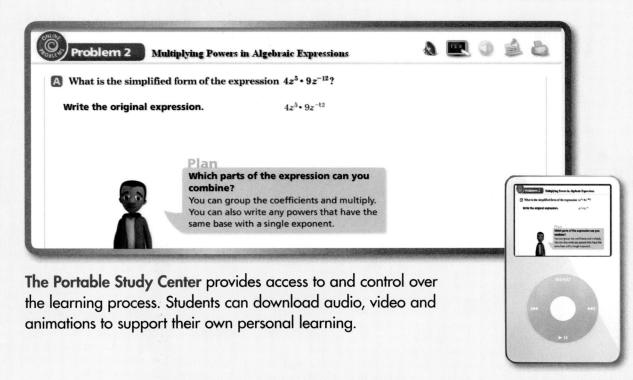

The Portable Study Center provides access to and control over the learning process. Students can download audio, video and animations to support their own personal learning.

Visual *Learning*

Visual learning is about acquiring and communicating information. By presenting concepts visually, and through different media, students can understand the importance of a mathematical idea and the context in which it is useful.

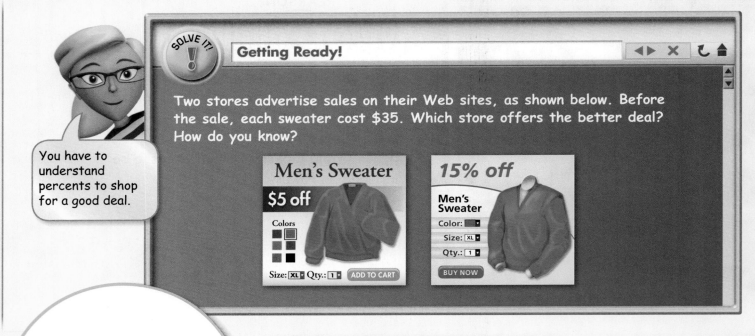

You have to understand percents to shop for a good deal.

Visual learning strategies increase the learning potential of all students.

The Solve It! at the start of each lesson makes use of engaging visuals to help students tap into their prior knowledge and connect it to important concepts in the lesson.

"Through visual models, students interact with mathematical concepts, process information, observe change, reflect on their experiences, modify their thinking, and draw conclusions. They learn."

—*Stuart Murphy*

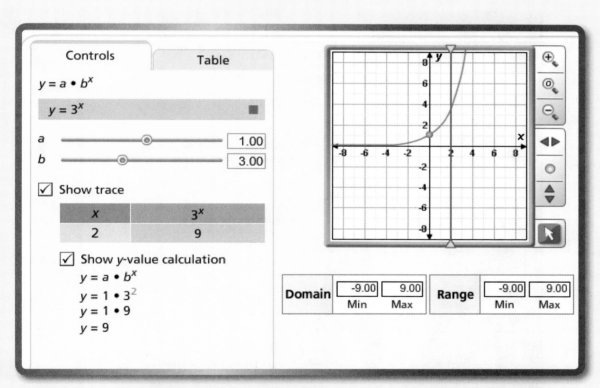

Dynamic Activities at PowerAlgebra.com provide an interactive way for students to explore lesson concepts. Additionally, Math Tools enable students and teachers to utilize the functionality of tools such as a graphing calculator, algebra tiles, and geometry software.

Big *Ideas*

Big Ideas are the organizing ideas for all of the lessons in the program. They appear in every lesson and throughout the chapters and courses. These Big Ideas help students focus on the key mathematical concepts they will be studying.

BIG ideas focus student learning.

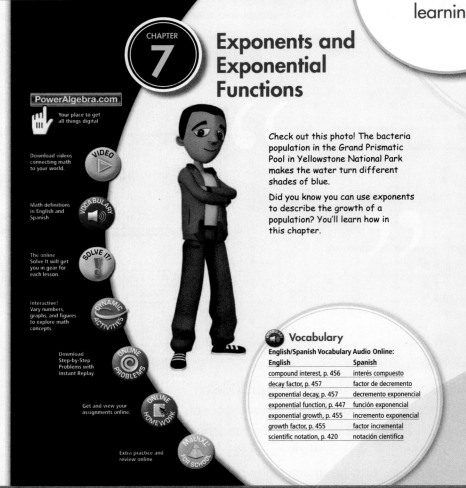

Chapter 7 Overview

UbD **Understanding by Design**

Chapter 7 expands on students' understandings and skills related to exponential expressions. In this chapter, students will develop the answers to the Essential Questions posed on the opposite page as they learn the concepts and skills bulleted below.

BIG idea **Equivalence**

ESSENTIAL QUESTION How can you represent very large and very small numbers?
• Students will learn to write numbers in scientific notation.

BIG ideas **Properties**

ESSENTIAL QUESTION How can you simplify expressions involving exponents?
• Students will define and use zero and negative exponents.
• Students will learn the rules for multiplying powers.
• Students will learn the rules for dividing powers.

BIG idea **Functions**

ESSENTIAL QUESTION What are characteristics of exponential functions?
• Exponential functions may show growth or decay.

CHAPTER 7

Exponents and Exponential Functions

PowerAlgebra.com
Your place to get all things digital

VIDEO Download videos connecting math to your world.

VOCABULARY Math definitions in English and Spanish

SOLVE IT! The online Solve It will get you in gear for each lesson.

DYNAMIC ACTIVITIES Interactive! Vary numbers, graphs, and figures to explore math concepts.

ONLINE PROBLEMS Download Step-by-Step Problems with Instant Replay

ONLINE HOMEWORK Get and view your assignments online.

MathXL FOR SCHOOL Extra practice and review online

Check out this photo! The bacteria population in the Grand Prismatic Pool in Yellowstone National Park makes the water turn different shades of blue.

Did you know you can use exponents to describe the growth of a population? You'll learn how in this chapter.

Vocabulary

English/Spanish Vocabulary Audio Online:

English	Spanish
compound interest, p. 456	interés compuesto
decay factor, p. 457	factor de decremento
exponential decay, p. 457	decremento exponencial
exponential function, p. 447	función exponencial
exponential growth, p. 455	incremento exponencial
growth factor, p. 455	factor incremental
scientific notation, p. 420	notación científica

Understanding by Design uses backward design to create a comprehensive curriculum. By starting with the end results in mind, instruction can be planned more effectively.

Essential Questions help students think about the Big Ideas presented in the lesson.

"A Big Idea is a way of seeing better and working smarter, not just another piece of knowledge."

—*Grant Wiggins*

7 Chapter Review

Connecting **BIG** ideas and Answering the Essential Questions

1 Equivalence
One way to represent numbers is in scientific notation. This form uses powers of ten to write very large or very small numbers.

Zero and Negative Exponents (Lesson 7-1)
$$10^0 = 1$$
$$10^{-3} = \frac{1}{10^3}$$

Scientific Notation (Lesson 7-2)
$$175{,}000{,}000{,}000{,}000$$
$$= 1.75 \times 10^{14}$$
$$0.0000568 = 5.68 \times 10^{-5}$$

2 Properties
Just as there are properties that describe how to rewrite expressions involving addition and multiplication, there are properties that describe how to rewrite and simplify exponential expressions.

Properties of Exponents (Lessons 7-3, 7-4, and 7-5)
$$5^2 \cdot 5^4 = 5^{2+4} = 5^6$$
$$(3^7)^4 = 3^{7 \cdot 4} = 3^{28}$$
$$(6x)^4 = 6^4 x^4$$
$$\frac{7^8}{7^5} = 7^{8-5} = 7^3$$
$$\left(\frac{y}{2}\right)^5 = \frac{y^5}{2^5}$$

3 Functions
The family of exponential functions has equations of the form $y = a \cdot b^x$. They can be used to model exponential growth or decay.

Exponential Functions (Lesson 7-6)
$$y = 2 \cdot \left(\frac{5}{4}\right)^x$$
$$y = 3 \cdot \left(\frac{1}{4}\right)^x$$

Exponential Growth and Decay (Lesson 7-7)
Exponential growth is modeled by the function $y = a \cdot b^x$, where $a > 0$ and $b > 1$. Exponential decay is modeled by the function $y = a \cdot b^x$, where $a > 0$ and $0 < b < 1$.

In the Chapter Review, students will find answers to the Essential Questions for the Big Ideas. The Chapter Review also provides a comprehensive set of notes for student reference.

Problem *Solving*

Problem solving strategies are an integral part of the program and are embedded throughout each lesson. The worked-out problems model effective thinking and reasoning strategies and can help foster students' mathematical reasoning. These important skills can help students score well on the Algebra 1 End-of-Course exam.

 Problem 2 **Simplifying an Expression With Powers**

What is the simplified form of $y^3(y^5)^{-2}$?

Plan

What is the first step in simplifying the expression?
By the order of operations, you simplify powers before you multiply.

Think

You multiply exponents when raising a power to a power.

You add exponents when multiplying powers with the same base.

Write the expression using only positive exponents.

Write

$$y^3(y^5)^{-2} = y^3 y^{5 \cdot (-2)}$$
$$= y^3 y^{-10}$$
$$= y^{3 + (-10)}$$
$$= y^{-7}$$
$$= \frac{1}{y^7}$$

Think-Write Boxes guide students' thinking and reasoning by modeling the problem solving process. Students gain a deeper understanding of the problem and learn how to arrive at the solution.

Problem solutions are stepped out to help students develop mathematical thinking and reasoning skills.

"Research shows that understanding develops during the process of solving problems in which important math concepts and skills are embedded."

—*Randy Charles*

Online Problems at PowerAlgebra.com provide students with step-by-step instruction at their own pace—and include guided support from an avatar. These problems can be used for in-class presentation or assigned to students on their own.

Differentiated *Instruction*

Differentiating instruction helps all students develop conceptual understanding, fosters mathematical reasoning, and refines problem solving strategies. The program offers options for differentiating instruction at the start of each chapter and throughout the lessons.

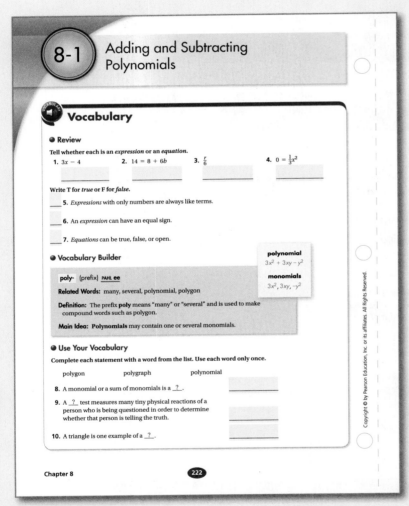

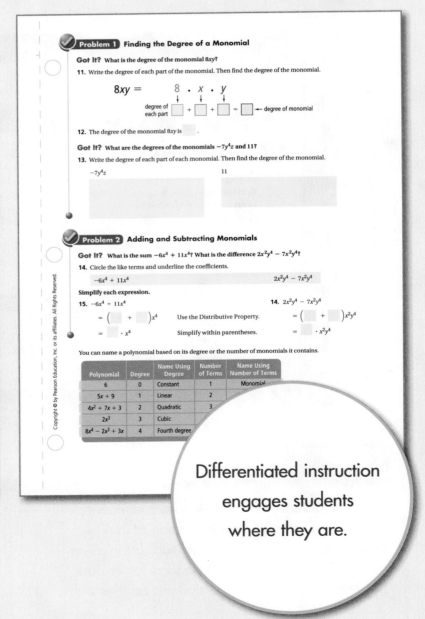

The Student Companion, a student worktext, has graphic organizers and other tools, such as Vocabulary Builder and Think-Write Boxes, that allow for differentiated instruction.

Differentiated instruction engages students where they are.

> "Differentiated instruction does not change what is taught; it changes how it is taught."
>
> —Basia Hall

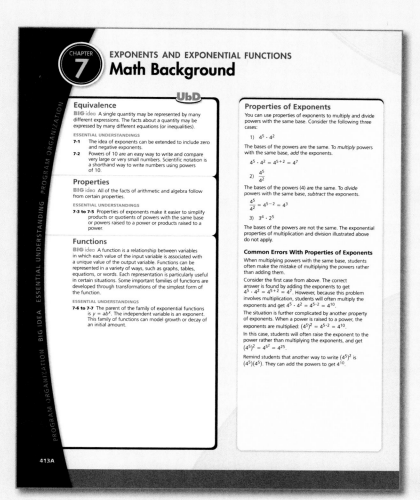

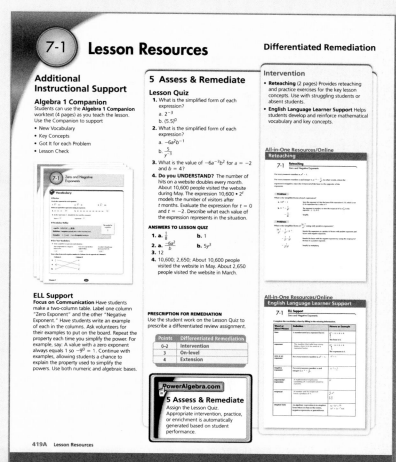

Math Background provides ongoing professional development in key content for each chapter and lesson, enabling teachers to adapt and respond to the needs of each individual learner.

Lesson Resources provide a detailed blueprint for instruction, assessment, and remediation that includes prescriptions for all levels of students from intervention to extension.

Assessment

Effective and useful assessments are frequent and varied. The program includes formative assessment, such as Got It?, that allows teachers to evaluate students' understanding of concepts and informs instruction. The summative assessments at the end of each lesson and chapter are more structured and give students valuable practice for the Algebra 1 End-of-Course exam.

Frequent, varied assessments allow accurate measurement of student learning from start to finish.

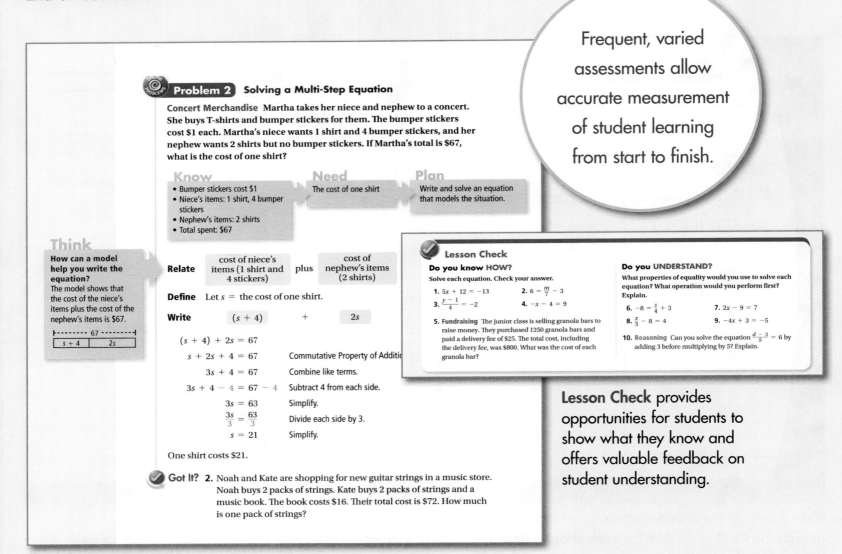

Problem 2 Solving a Multi-Step Equation

Concert Merchandise Martha takes her niece and nephew to a concert. She buys T-shirts and bumper stickers for them. The bumper stickers cost $1 each. Martha's niece wants 1 shirt and 4 bumper stickers, and her nephew wants 2 shirts but no bumper stickers. If Martha's total is $67, what is the cost of one shirt?

Know
• Bumper stickers cost $1
• Niece's items: 1 shirt, 4 bumper stickers
• Nephew's items: 2 shirts
• Total spent: $67

Need
The cost of one shirt

Plan
Write and solve an equation that models the situation.

Think

How can a model help you write the equation?
The model shows that the cost of the niece's items plus the cost of the nephew's items is $67.

67
s + 4   2s

Relate cost of niece's items (1 shirt and 4 stickers) plus cost of nephew's items (2 shirts)

Define Let s = the cost of one shirt.

Write $(s + 4)$ + $2s$

$(s + 4) + 2s = 67$

$s + 2s + 4 = 67$ Commutative Property of Addition

$3s + 4 = 67$ Combine like terms.

$3s + 4 - 4 = 67 - 4$ Subtract 4 from each side.

$3s = 63$ Simplify.

$\frac{3s}{3} = \frac{63}{3}$ Divide each side by 3.

$s = 21$ Simplify.

One shirt costs $21.

Got It? 2. Noah and Kate are shopping for new guitar strings in a music store. Noah buys 2 packs of strings. Kate buys 2 packs of strings and a music book. The book costs $16. Their total cost is $72. How much is one pack of strings?

Lesson Check

Do you know HOW?
Solve each equation. Check your answer.

1. $5x + 12 = -13$ 2. $6 = \frac{m}{7} - 3$
3. $\frac{y-1}{4} = -2$ 4. $-x - 4 = 9$

5. **Fundraising** The junior class is selling granola bars to raise money. They purchased 1250 granola bars and paid a delivery fee of $25. The total cost, including the delivery fee, was $800. What was the cost of each granola bar?

Do you UNDERSTAND?
What properties of equality would you use to solve each equation? What operation would you perform first? Explain.

6. $-8 = \frac{s}{4} + 3$ 7. $2x - 9 = 7$
8. $\frac{x}{3} - 8 = 4$ 9. $-4x + 3 = -5$

10. **Reasoning** Can you solve the equation $\frac{d-3}{5} = 6$ by adding 3 before multiplying by 5? Explain.

Lesson Check provides opportunities for students to show what they know and offers valuable feedback on student understanding.

Got It? checkpoints after each problem in the lesson constantly monitor student understanding. These quick assessments keep instruction on track for all students and allow teachers to make informed instructional decisions.

"The key to education is to be fair and consistent. The same is true for assessment. Fair, consistent, quality assessment is the only way to ensure that students are learning what you are teaching."

—*Bill Handlin*

Success ✪ Tracker™

The Success Tracker online assessment system provides instant analysis of student performance. Success Tracker includes built-in diagnostic and benchmark tests, diagnoses student mastery, prescribes automatically assigned remediation for every standard not mastered, and reports on student and class progress.

MathXL® for School

MathXL® for School is a powerful online homework, tutorial, and assessment system for *Prentice Hall Algebra 1*. It provides students with a personalized, interactive learning environment where they can learn at their own pace. MathXL for School assigns students homework problems, automatically grades their work, and then provides immediate feedback and tutorial assistance to ensure mastery before high-stakes tests.

MathXL® for School
Go to PowerAlgebra.com

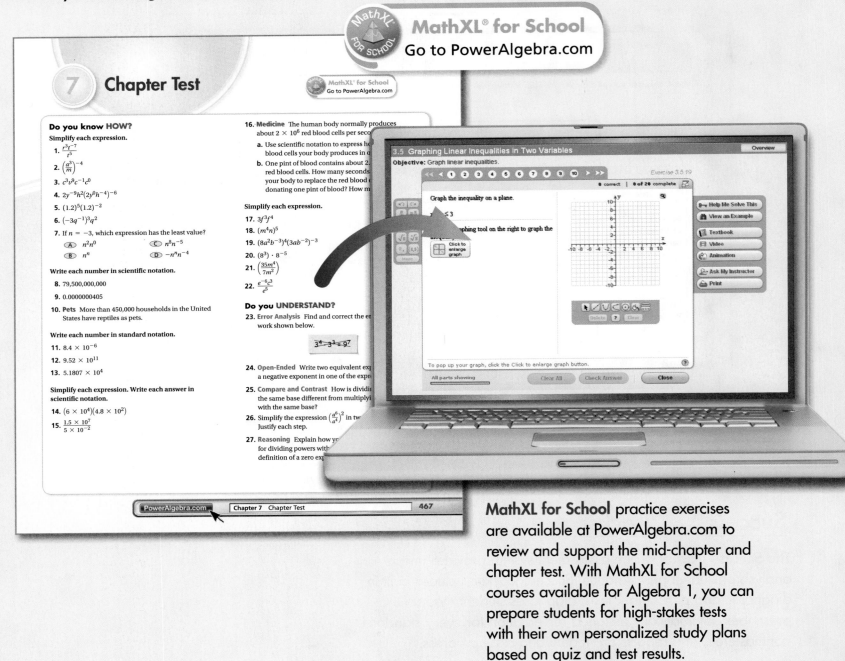

MathXL for School practice exercises are available at PowerAlgebra.com to review and support the mid-chapter and chapter test. With MathXL for School courses available for Algebra 1, you can prepare students for high-stakes tests with their own personalized study plans based on quiz and test results.

Success for All Students

Success in mathematics is essential for students facing rigorous coursework in college, career challenges, and global competitiveness. But success can no longer be determined solely by a student's performance on a math assessment. Students need to develop the thinking and reasoning habits that will empower them to reach full potential in their lives at school and in their career paths. While only some students will pursue further math education or careers in math and science, all students will benefit from learning to analyze problems independently and solve them in different applications. They will need those abilities to lead successful lives as citizens and leaders of the 21st century.

Engage Students

- Blended environment of print and digital motivates students.
- Different approaches make learning accessible to more students.
- Visual approach makes math more interesting.

Teach for Understanding

- Comprehensive coverage ensures strong grasp of algebra (or geometry) skills.
- Stepped-out instruction reduces cognitive load.
- Emphasis on math reasoning helps students make sense of math.

Promote Mastery

- Ongoing formative assessment cements skills.
- Teacher and students ask and answer questions to reinforce understanding.
- Development of math reasoning results in transferability of skills.

SUCCESS
School • Career • Life

Indiana Academic Standards for
Algebra 1

The following chart shows where each Indiana Algebra 1 Content Standard is presented in Pearson's *Prentice Hall Algebra 1* text.

Standards		Where to Find
1	**Relations and Functions.**	
A1.1.1	Determine whether a relation represented by a table, graph, words or equation is a function or not a function and translate among tables, graphs, words and equations.	Lessons: 4-2, 4-3, 4-4, 4-5, 4-6 Concept Byte: p. 260
A1.1.2	Identify the domain and range of relations represented by tables, graphs, words, and equations.	Lessons: 4-6, 9-1, 10-5
2	**The student will use relations and functions to model number relationships.**	
A1.2.1	Translate among various representations of linear functions including tables, graphs, words and equations.	Lessons: 1-8, 1-9, 4-2, 4-4, 4-5, 4-6, 5-2, 5-3, 5-4, 5-5 Concept Byte: p. 59
A1.2.2	Graph linear equations and show that they have constant rates of change.	Lesson: 5-1, 5-3, 5-4, 5-5, 5-6 Concept Byte: p. 305
A1.2.3	Determine the slope, x-intercept, and y-intercept of a line given its graph, its equation, or two points on the line and determine the equation of a line given sufficient information.	Lessons: 5-1, 5-2, 5-3, 5-4, 5-5, 5-6 Concept Byte: p. 305
A1.2.4	Write, interpret, and translate among equivalent forms of equations for linear functions (slope-intercept, point-slope, and standard), recognizing that equivalent forms reveal more or less information about a given situation.	Lessons: 5-1, 5-2, 5-3, 5-4, 5-5
A1.2.5	Solve problems that can be modeled using linear equations and inequalities, interpret the solutions, and determine whether the solutions are reasonable.	Lessons: 2-1, 2-2, 2-3, 2-4, 2-5, 3-1, 3-2, 3-3, 3-4, 3-6, 4-2, 4-4, 4-5, 4-6, 5-2, 5-3, 5-5, 6-5
A1.2.6	Graph a linear inequality in two variables.	Lesson: 6-5
3	**Pairs of Linear Functions and Inequalities**	
A1.3.1	Understand the relationship between a solution of a pair of linear equations in two variables and the graphs of the corresponding lines and solve pairs of linear equations in two variables by graphing, substitution or elimination.	Lessons: 6-1, 6-2, 6-3, 6-4 Concept Byte: pp. 366, 367, 381
A1.3.2	Graph the solution set for a pair of linear inequalities in two variables with and without technology and use the graph to find the solution set.	Lesson: 6-6 Concept Byte: p. 402
A1.3.3	Solve problems that can be modeled using pairs of linear equations in two variables, interpret the solutions, and determine whether the solutions are reasonable.	Lessons: 6-1, 6-2, 6-3, 6-4
4	**Polynomials**	
A1.4.1	Use the laws of exponents for variables with exponents and multiply, divide, and find powers of variables with exponents.	Lessons: 7-1, 7-3, 7-4, 7-5 Concept Byte: p. 432
A1.4.2	Add, subtract and multiply polynomials and divide polynomials by monomials.	Lessons: 8-1, 8-2, 8-3, 8-4, 11-3 Concept Bytes: pp. 485, 665
A1.4.3	Factor common terms from polynomials and factor quadratic expressions.	Lessons: 8-2, 8-5, 8-6, 8-7, 8-8 Concept Byte: p. 499
5	**Quadratic Equations and Functions**	
A1.5.1	Graph quadratic functions.	Lessons: 9-1, 9-2,
A1.5.2	Solve quadratic equations in the real number system with real number solutions by factoring, by completing the square, and by using the quadratic formula.	Lessons: 9-3, 9-4, 9-5, 9-6 Concept Byte: p. 554
A1.5.3	Solve problems that can be modeled using quadratic equations, interpret the solutions, and determine whether the solutions are reasonable.	Lessons: 9-1, 9-3, 9-4, 9-5, 9-6, 9-7

Standards		Where to Find
A1.5.4	Analyze and describe the relationships among the solutions of a quadratic equation, the zeros of a quadratic function, the x-intercepts of the graph of a quadratic function, and the factors of a quadratic expression.	Lessons: 9-3, 9-4
A1.5.5	Sketch and interpret linear and non-linear graphs representing given situations and identify independent and dependent variables.	Lessons: 4-1, 4-2, 4-3, 9-1, 9-7
6	**Rational and Radical Expressions and Equations**	
A1.6.1	Add, subtract, multiply, divide, reduce, and evaluate rational expressions with polynomial denominators. Simplify rational expressions with linear and quadratic denominators, including denominators with negative exponents.	Lessons: 7-1, 7-5, 11-1, 11-2, 11-3, 11-4
A1.6.2	Solve equations involving rational and common irrational expressions.	Lessons: 2-5, 11-5, 11-7
A1.6.3	Simplify radical expressions involving square roots.	Lessons: 10-2, 10-3
A1.6.4	Solve equations that contain radical expressions on only one side of the equation and identify extraneous roots when they occur.	Lessons: 10-4, 10-5
7	**Data Analysis**	
A1.7.1	Organize and display data using appropriate methods to detect patterns and departures from patterns. Summarize the data using measures of center (mean, median) and spread (range, percentiles, variance, standard deviation). Compare data sets using graphs and summary statistics.	Lessons: 5-7, 12-1, 12-2, 12-3, 12-4 Concept Byte: p. 733
A1.7.2	Distinguish between random and non-random sampling methods, identify possible sources of bias in sampling, describe how such bias can be controlled and reduced, evaluate the characteristics of a good survey and well-designed experiment, design simple experiments or investigations to collect data to answer questions of interest, and make inferences from sample results.	Lesson: 12-5 Concept Bytes: pp. 740, 748
A1.7.3	Evaluate reports based on data published in the media by considering the source of the data, the design of the study, the way the data are analyzed and displayed and whether the report confuses correlation with causation.	Lesson: 12-5 Concept Bytes: pp. 740, 748

Indiana Algebra 1 Leveled Pacing Chart

This Leveled Pacing Chart is provided as a guide to help you customize your course and to provide for differentiated instruction.

The suggested number of days for each chapter is based on a traditional 45-minute class period and on a 90-minute block period. The total of 160 days of instruction leaves time for assessments, projects, assemblies, preparing for your state test, or other special days that vary from school to school.

Chapter 1 Foundations for Algebra		Traditional 12		Block 6
1-1 Variables and Expressions		○	○	○
1-2 Order of Operations and Evaluating Expressions		○	○	○
1-3 Real Numbers and the Number Line		○	○	○
1-4 Properties of Real Numbers		○	○	○
1-5 Adding and Subtracting Real Numbers		○	○	○
Concept Byte: Always, Sometimes, or Never			○	○
1-6 Multiplying and Dividing Real Numbers		○	○	○
Concept Byte: Closure				○
1-7 The Distributive Property		○	○	○
1-8 An Introduction to Functions	A1.2.1	✓	✓	✓
Concept Byte: Using Tables to Solve Equations	A1.2.1	✓	✓	✓
Review: Graphing in the Coordinate Plane		○	○	○
1-9 Patterns, Equations, and Graphs	A1.2.1	✓	✓	✓
Chapter 2 Solving Equations		**Traditional 12**		**Block 6**
Concept Byte: Modeling One-Step Equations		○	○	○
2-1 Solving One-Step Equations	A1.2.5	✓	✓	✓
2-2 Solving Two-Step Equations	A1.2.5	✓	✓	✓
2-3 Solving Multi-Step Equations	A1.2.5	✓	✓	✓
Concept Byte: Modeling Equations With Variables on Both Sides		✓		
2-4 Solving Equations With Variables on Both Sides	A1.2.5	✓	✓	✓
2-5 Literal Equations and Formulas	A1.2.5, A1.6.2	✓	✓	✓
Concept Byte: Finding Perimeter, Area, and Volume		✓	✓	✓
2-6 Ratios, Rates, and Conversions		✓	✓	✓
2-7 Solving Proportions		✓	✓	✓
2-8 Proportions and Similar Figures		✓	✓	✓
2-9 Percents		○	○	○
2-10 Change Expressed as a Percent		○	○	○
Chapter 3 Solving Inequalities		**Traditional 20**		**Block 10**
3-1 Inequalities and Their Graphs	A1.2.5	✓	✓	✓
3-2 Solving Inequalities Using Addition or Subtraction	A1.2.5	✓	✓	✓

	SC Academic Standards	Basic	Average	Advanced
3-3 Solving Inequalities Using Multiplication or Division	A1.2.5	✓	✓	✓
Concept Byte: More Algebraic Properties		❑	❑	❑
Concept Byte: Modeling Multi-Step Inequalities		✓		
3-4 Solving Multi-Step Inequalities	A1.2.5	✓	✓	✓
3-5 Working With Sets		❑	❑	❑
3-6 Compound Inequalities	A1.2.5	✓	✓	✓
3-7 Absolute Value Equations and Inequalities				o
3-8 Unions and Intersections of Sets		❑	❑	❑
Chapter 4 An Introduction to Functions		**Traditional 12**	**Block**	**6**
4-1 Using Graphs to Relate Two Quantities	A1.5.5	✓	✓	✓
4-2 Patterns and Linear Functions	A1.1.1, A1.2.1, A1.2.5, A1.5.5	✓	✓	✓
4-3 Patterns and Nonlinear Functions	A1.1.1, A1.5.5	✓	✓	✓
4-4 Graphing a Function Rule	A1.1.1, A1.2.1, A1.2.5	✓	✓	✓
Concept Byte: Graphing Functions and Solving Equations	A1.1.1	✓	✓	✓
4-5 Writing a Function Rule	A1.1.1, A1.2.1, A1.2.5	✓	✓	✓
4-6 Formalizing Relations and Functions	A1.1.1, A1.1.2, A1.2.5	✓	✓	✓
4-7 Sequences and Functions		❑	❑	❑
Chapter 5 Linear Functions		**Traditional 18**	**Block**	**9**
5-1 Rate of Change and Slope	A1.2.2, A1.2.3, A1.2.4	✓	✓	✓
5-2 Direct Variation	A1.2.1, A1.2.3, A1.2.4, A1.2.5	✓	✓	✓
Concept Byte: Investigating $y = mx + b$	A1.2.2, A1.2.3	✓	✓	✓
5-3 Slope-Intercept Form	A1.2.1, A1.2.2, A1.2.3, A1.2.4, A1.2.5	✓	✓	✓
5-4 Point-Slope Form	A1.2.1, A1.2.2, A1.2.3, A1.2.4	✓	✓	✓
5-5 Standard Form	A1.2.1, A1.2.2, A1.2.3, A1.2.4, A1.2.5	✓	✓	✓
5-6 Parallel and Perpendicular Lines	A1.2.2, A1.2.3	✓	✓	✓
5-7 Scatter Plots and Trend Lines	A1.7.1	✓	✓	✓
Concept Byte: Collecting Linear Data		○	○	○
5-8 Graphing Absolute Value Functions		❑	❑	❑
Concept Byte: Characteristics of Absolute Value Graphs		❑	❑	❑
Chapter 6 Systems of Equations and Inequalities		**Traditional 12**	**Block**	**6**
6-1 Solving Systems by Graphing	A1.3.1, A1.3.3	✓	✓	✓
Concept Byte: Solving Systems Using Tables and Graphs	A1.3.1	✓	✓	✓
Concept Byte: Solving Systems Using Algebra Tiles	A1.3.1	✓	✓	✓
6-2 Solving Systems Using Substitution	A1.3.1, A1.3.3	✓	✓	✓
6-3 Solving Systems Using Elimination	A1.3.1, A1.3.3	✓	✓	✓
Concept Byte: Matrices and Solving Systems	A1.3.1	✓	✓	✓
6-4 Applications of Linear Systems	A1.3.1, A1.3.3	✓	✓	✓
6-5 Linear Inequalities	A1.2.5, A1.2.6	✓	✓	✓
6-6 Systems of Linear Inequalities	A1.3.2	✓	✓	✓
Concept Byte: Graphing Linear Inequalities	A1.3.2	✓	✓	✓

	SC Academic Standards	Basic	Average	Advanced
Chapter 7 Exponents and Exponential Functions		**Traditional 12**		**Block 6**
7-1 Zero and Negative Exponents	A1.4.1, A1.6.1	✓	✓	✓
7-2 Scientific Notation		✓	✓	✓
7-3 Multiplication Powers With the Same Base	A1.4.1	✓	✓	✓
Concept Byte: Powers of Powers and Powers of Products	A1.4.1	✓	✓	✓
7-4 More Multiplication Properties of Exponents	A1.4.1	✓	✓	✓
7-5 Division Properties of Exponents	A1.4.1, A1.6.1	✓	✓	✓
7-6 Exponential Functions		❑	❑	❑
Concept Byte: Geometric Sequence		❑	❑	❑
7-7 Exponential Growth and Decay			❑	❑
Chapter 8 Polynomials and Factoring		**Traditional 12**		**Block 6**
8-1 Adding and Subtracting Polynomials	A1.4.2	✓	✓	✓
8-2 Multiplying and Factoring	A1.4.2, A1.4.3	✓	✓	✓
Concept Byte: Using Models to Multiply	A1.4.2	✓	✓	✓
8-3 Multiplying Binomials	A1.4.2	✓	✓	✓
8-4 Multiplying Special Cases	A1.4.2	✓	✓	✓
Concept Byte: Using Models to Factor	A1.4.3	✓	✓	✓
8-5 Factoring $x^2 + bx + c$	A1.4.3	✓	✓	✓
8-6 Factoring $ax^2 + bx + c$	A1.4.3	✓	✓	✓
8-7 Factoring Special Cases	A1.4.3	✓	✓	✓
8-8 Factoring by Grouping	A1.4.3	✓	✓	✓
Chapter 9 Quadratic Functions and Equations		**Traditional 20**		**Block 10**
9-1 Quadratic Graphs and Their Properties	A1.1.2, A1.5.1, A1.5.3, A1.5.5	✓	✓	✓
9-2 Quadratic Functions	A1.5.1	✓	✓	✓
Concept Byte: Collecting Quadratic Data		❑	❑	❑
9-3 Solving Quadratic Equations	A1.5.2, A1.5.3, A1.5.4	✓	✓	✓
Concept Byte: Finding Roots	A1.5.2	✓	✓	✓
9-4 Factoring to Solve Quadratic Equations	A1.5.2, A1.5.3, A1.5.4	✓	✓	✓
9-5 Completing the Square	A1.5.2, A1.5.3	✓	✓	✓
9-6 The Quadratic Formula and the Discriminant	A1.5.2, A1.5.3	✓	✓	✓
9-7 Linear, Quadratic, and Exponential Models	A1.5.3, A1.5.5	✓	✓	✓
Concept Byte: Performing Regressions		❑	❑	❑
9-8 Systems of Linear and Quadratic Equations		❑	❑	❑
Chapter 10 Radical Expressions and Equations		**Traditional 10**		**Block 5**
10-1 The Pythagorean Theorem		❑	❑	❑
Concept Byte: Distance and Midpoint Formulas		❑	❑	❑
10-2 Simplifying Radicals	A1.6.3	✓	✓	✓
10-3 Operations with Radical Expressions	A1.6.3	✓	✓	✓
10-4 Solving Radical Equations	A1.6.4	✓	✓	✓

	SC Academic Standards	Basic	Average	Advanced
10-5 Graphing Square Root Functions	A1.1.2, A1.6.4	✓	✓	✓
Concept Byte: Right Triangle Ratios		❑	❑	❑
10-6 Trigonometric Ratios		❑	❑	❑
Chapter 11 Rational Expressions and Functions			**Traditional 10 Block 5**	
11-1 Simplifying Rational Expressions	A1.6.1	✓	✓	✓
11-2 Multiplying and Dividing Rational Expressions	A1.6.1	✓	✓	✓
Concept Byte: Dividing Polynomials Using Algebra Tiles	A1.4.2	✓	✓	✓
11-3 Dividing Polynomials	A1.4.2, A1.6.1	✓	✓	✓
11-4 Adding and Subtracting Rational Expressions	A1.6.1	✓	✓	✓
11-5 Solving Rational Equations	A1.6.2	✓	✓	✓
11-6 Inverse Variation		❑	❑	❑
11-7 Graphing Rational Functions	A1.6.2	✓	✓	✓
Concept Byte: Graphing Rational Functions		❑	❑	❑
Chapter 12 Rational Expressions and Functions			**Traditional 10 Block 5**	
12-1 Organizing Data Using Matrices	A1.7.1	✓	✓	✓
12-2 Frequency and Histograms	A1.7.1	✓	✓	✓
12-3 Measures of Central Tendency and Dispersion	A1.7.1	✓	✓	✓
Concept Byte: Standard Deviation	A1.7.1	✓	✓	✓
12-4 Box-and-Whisker Plots	A1.7.1	✓	✓	✓
Concept Byte: Designing Your Own Survey	A1.7.2, A1.7.3	✓	✓	✓
12-5 Samples and Surveys	A1.7.2, A1.7.3	✓	✓	✓
Concept Byte: Misleading Graphs and Statistics	A1.7.2, A1.7.3	✓	✓	✓
12-6 Permutations and Combinations		❑	❑	❑
12-7 Theoretical and Experimental Probability		❑	❑	❑
Concept Byte: Conducting Simulations		❑	❑	❑
12-8 Probability of Compound Events		❑	❑	❑
Concept Byte: Conditional Probability		❑	❑	❑

BIGideas

These Big Ideas are the organizing ideas for the study of important areas of mathematics: algebra, geometry, and statistics.

Stay connected! These Big Ideas will help you understand how the math you study in high school fits together.

Algebra

Properties
- In the transition from arithmetic to algebra, attention shifts from arithmetic operations (addition, subtraction, multiplication, and division) to use of the *properties* of these operations.
- All of the facts of arithmetic and algebra follow from certain properties.

Variable
- Quantities are used to form expressions, equations, and inequalities.
- An expression refers to a quantity but does not make a statement about it. An equation (or an inequality) is a statement about the quantities it mentions.
- Using variables in place of numbers in equations (or inequalities) allows the statement of relationships among numbers that are unknown or unspecified.

Equivalence
- A single quantity may be represented by many different expressions.
- The facts about a quantity may be expressed by many different equations (or inequalities).

Solving Equations & Inequalities
- Solving an equation is the process of rewriting the equation to make what it says about its variable(s) as simple as possible.
- Properties of numbers and equality can be used to transform an equation (or inequality) into equivalent, simpler equations (or inequalities) in order to find solutions.
- Useful information about equations and inequalities (including solutions) can be found by analyzing graphs or tables.
- The numbers and types of solutions vary predictably, based on the type of equation.

Proportionality
- Two quantities are *proportional* if they have the same ratio in each instance where they are measured together.
- Two quantities are *inversely proportional* if they have the same product in each instance where they are measured together.

Function
- A function is a relationship between variables in which each value of the input variable is associated with a unique value of the output variable.
- Functions can be represented in a variety of ways, such as graphs, tables, equations, or words. Each representation is particularly useful in certain situations.
- Some important families of functions are developed through transformations of the simplest form of the function.
- New functions can be made from other functions by applying arithmetic operations or by applying one function to the output of another.

Modeling
- Many real-world mathematical problems can be represented algebraically. These representations can lead to algebraic solutions.
- A function that models a real-world situation can be used to make estimates or predictions about future occurrences.

xx

Statistics and Probability

Data Collection and Analysis

- Sampling techniques are used to gather data from real-world situations. If the data are representative of the larger population, inferences can be made about that population.
- Biased sampling techniques yield data unlikely to be representative of the larger population.
- Sets of numerical data are described using measures of central tendency and dispersion.

Data Representation

- The most appropriate data representations depend on the type of data—quantitative or qualitative, and univariate or bivariate.
- Line plots, box plots, and histograms are different ways to show distribution of data over a possible range of values.

Probability

- Probability expresses the likelihood that a particular event will occur.
- Data can be used to calculate an experimental probability, and mathematical properties can be used to determine a theoretical probability.
- Either experimental or theoretical probability can be used to make predictions or decisions about future events.
- Various counting methods can be used to develop theoretical probabilities.

Geometry

Visualization

- Visualization can help you connect properties of real objects with two-dimensional drawings of these objects.

Transformations

- Transformations are mathematical functions that model relationships with figures.
- Transformations may be described geometrically or by coordinates.
- Symmetries of figures may be defined and classified by transformations.

Measurement

- Some attributes of geometric figures, such as length, area, volume, and angle measure, are measurable. Units are used to describe these attributes.

Reasoning & Proof

- Definitions establish meanings and remove possible misunderstanding.
- Other truths are more complex and difficult to see. It is often possible to verify complex truths by reasoning from simpler ones using deductive reasoning.

Similarity

- Two geometric figures are similar when corresponding lengths are proportional and corresponding angles are congruent.
- Areas of similar figures are proportional to the squares of their corresponding lengths.
- Volumes of similar figures are proportional to the cubes of their corresponding lengths.

Coordinate Geometry

- A coordinate system on a line is a number line on which points are labeled, corresponding to the real numbers.
- A coordinate system in a plane is formed by two perpendicular number lines, called the x- and y-axes, and the quadrants they form. The coordinate plane can be used to graph many functions.
- It is possible to verify some complex truths using deductive reasoning in combination with the distance, midpoint, and slope formulas.

1 Foundations for Algebra

IN Standards

Chapter 1

A1.2.1 Translate among various representations of linear functions including tables, graphs, words and equations.

Chapter 2

A1.2.5 Solve problems that can be modeled using linear equations and inequalities, interpret the solutions, and determine whether the solutions are reasonable.

A1.6.2 Solve equations involving rational and common irrational expressions.

2 Solving Equations

Visual See It!

My Math Video 3
Solve It! 53
Connecting BIG IDEAS 68

Reasoning Try It!

Essential Understanding 109
Think-Write 41
Know → Need → Plan 95

Practice Do It!

Practice by Example 34
Think About a Plan 21
Error Analysis/Reasoning 99

3

Solving Inequalities

IN Standards

Chapter 3

A1.2.5 Solve problems that can be modeled using linear equations and inequalities, interpret the solutions, and determine whether the solutions are reasonable.

Chapter 4

A1.1.1 Determine whether a relation represented by a table, graph, words or equation is a function or not a function and translate among tables, graphs, words and equations.

A1.1.2 Identify the domain and range of relations represented by tables, graphs, words, and equations.

A1.5.5 Sketch and interpret linear and non-linear graphs representing given situations and identify independent and dependent variables.

4 An Introduction to Functions

Visual See It!

My Math Video 163
Solve It! 171
Connecting BIG IDEAS 222

Reasoning Try It!

Essential Understanding 253
Think-Write 172
Know → Need → Plan 242

Practice Do It!

Practice by Example 190
Think About a Plan 169
Error Analysis/Reasoning 212

5

Linear Functions

IN Standards

Chapter 5

A1.2.2 Graph linear equations and show that they have constant rates of change.

A1.2.3 Determine the slope, x-intercept, and y-intercept of a line given its graph, its equation, or two points on the line and determine the equation of a line given sufficient information.

A1.2.4 Write, interpret, and translate among equivalent forms of equations for linear functions (slope-intercept, point-slope, and standard), recognizing that equivalent forms reveal more or less information about a given situation.

Chapter 6

A1.2.6 Graph a linear inequality in two variables.

A1.3.1 Understand the relationship between a solution of a pair of linear equations in two variables and the graphs of the corresponding lines and solve pairs of linear equations in two variables by graphing, substitution or elimination.

A1.3.2 Graph the solution set for a pair of linear inequalities in two variables with and without technology and use the graph to find the solution set.

A1.3.3 Solve problems that can be modeled using pairs of linear equations in two variables, interpret the solutions, and determine whether the solutions are reasonable.

6

Systems of Equations and Inequalities

Visual See It!

My Math Video 357
Solve It! 390
Connecting BIG IDEAS 349

Reasoning Try It!

Essential Understanding 313
Think-Write 294
Know → Need → Plan 369

Practice Do It!

Practice by Example 386
Think About a Plan 378
Error Analysis/Reasoning 364

7

Exponents and Exponential Functions

IN Standards

Chapter 7

A1.4.1 Use the laws of exponents for variables with exponents and multiply, divide, and find powers of variables with exponents.

A1.6.1 Add, subtract, multiply, divide, reduce, and evaluate rational expressions with polynomial denominators. Simplify rational expressions with linear and quadratic denominators, including denominators with negative exponents.

Chapter 8

A1.4.2 Add, subtract and multiply polynomials and divide polynomials by monomials.

A1.4.3 Factor common terms from polynomials and factor quadratic expressions.

8 Polynomials and Factoring

Visual See It!

Reasoning Try It!

Practice Do It!

9

Quadratic Functions and Equations

IN Standards

Chapter 9

A1.5.1 Graph quadratic functions.

A1.5.2 Solve quadratic equations in the real number system with real number solutions by factoring, by completing the square, and by using the quadratic formula.

A1.5.3 Solve problems that can be modeled using quadratic equations, interpret the solutions, and determine whether the solutions are reasonable.

A1.5.4 Analyze and describe the relationships among the solutions of a quadratic equation, the zeros of a quadratic function, the x-intercepts of the graph of a quadratic function, and the factors of a quadratic expression.

Chapter 10

A1.1.2 Identify the domain and range of relations represented by tables, graphs, words, and equations.

A1.6.3 Simplify radical expressions involving square roots.

A1.6.4 Solve equations that contain radical expressions on only one side of the equation and identify extraneous roots when they occur.

10 Radical Expressions and Equations

Use this Indiana chapter to review and practice for the Algebra 1 End-of-Course Assessment.

IN **INDIANA** *Standards Review and Practice*

11

Rational Expressions and Functions

IN Standards

Chapter 11

A1.4.2 Add, subtract and multiply polynomials and divide polynomials by monomials.

A1.6.1 Add, subtract, multiply, divide, reduce, and evaluate rational expressions with polynomial denominators. Simplify rational expressions with linear and quadratic denominators, including denominators with negative exponents.

A1.6.2 Solve equations involving rational and common irrational expressions.

Chapter 12

A1.7.1 Organize and display data using appropriate methods to detect patterns and departures from patterns. Summarize the data using measures of center (mean, median) and spread (range, percentiles, variance, standard deviation). Compare data sets using graphs and summary statistics.

A1.7.2 Distinguish between random and non-random sampling methods, identify possible sources of bias in sampling, describe how such bias can be controlled and reduced, evaluate the characteristics of a good survey and well-designed experiment, design simple experiments or investigations to collect data to answer questions of interest, and make inferences from sample results.

12

Data Analysis and Probability

Visual **See It!**

My Math Video
Solve It!
Connecting BIG IDEAS

Reasoning **Try It!**

Essential Understanding
Think-Write
Know → Need → Plan

Practice **Do It!**

Practice by Example
Think About a Plan
Error Analysis/Reasoning

Answers

1. D

2. I

3. C

4. G

5. D

6. G

7. D

8. H

Entry-Level Assessment

Multiple Choice

Read each question. Then write the letter of the correct answer on your paper.

1. Sophia had $50 she put into a savings account. If she saves $15 per week for one year, how much will she have saved altogether?

   A $50

   B $65

   C $780

   D $830

2. Which set below is the domain of $\{(2, -3), (-1, 0), (0, 4), (-1, 5), (4, -2)\}$?

   F $\{-3, 0, 4, 5, -2\}$

   G $\{-3, 4, 5, -2\}$

   H $\{2, -1, 4\}$

   I $\{2, -1, 0, 4\}$

3. Which ordered pair is the solution of the system of equations graphed below?

   A $(4, 1)$

   B $(1, 4)$

   C $(4, 2)$

   D $(2, 4)$

4. The Martins keep goats and chickens on their farm. If there are 23 animals with a total of 74 legs, how many of each type of animal are there?

   F 14 chickens, 9 goats

   G 19 chickens, 4 goats

   H 9 chickens, 14 goats

   I 4 chickens, 19 goats

5. Which equation represents the phrase "six more than twice a number is 72"?

   A $6 + x = 72$

   B $2x = 6 + 72$

   C $2 + 6x = 72$

   D $6 + 2x = 72$

6. Which of the following graphs best represents a person walking slowly and then speeding up?

   F

   H

   G

   I

7. The graph below shows the time it takes Sam to get from his car to the mall door.

   Walking From Car to Mall

   Which of the following best describes the x-intercept?

   A Sam's car was parked 24 ft from the mall door.

   B After 24 s, Sam reached the mall door.

   C Sam's car was parked 8 ft from the mall door.

   D After 8 s, Sam reached the mall door.

8. What is 23.7×10^4 written in standard notation?

   F 0.00237

   G 0.0237

   H 237,000

   I 2,370,000

xxxiv

9. What equation do you get when you solve
$2x + 3y = 12$ for y?

Ⓐ $y = -\frac{2}{3}x + 4$

Ⓑ $y = -\frac{2}{3}x + 12$

Ⓒ $y = -2x + 12$

Ⓓ $y = 12 - 2x$

10. The formula for the circumference of a circle is
$C = 2\pi r$. What is the formula solved for r?

Ⓕ $r = C \cdot 2\pi$ Ⓗ $r = 2\pi$

Ⓖ $r = \frac{C}{2\pi}$ Ⓘ $r = \frac{C\pi}{2}$

11. Which table of values was used to make the
following graph?

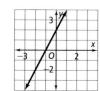

Ⓐ

x	-3	-1	0	1
y	-2	-1	2	4

Ⓑ
x	-3	-2	0	1
y	4	2	2	4

Ⓒ

x	-3	-2	0	1
y	-4	0	2	4

Ⓓ

x	-3	-2	0	1
y	-3	-2	2	4

12. A jewelry store marks up the price of a topaz ring
215%. The store paid $70 for the ring. For how much is
the store selling the ring?

Ⓕ $91.50 Ⓗ $161.50

Ⓖ $150.50 Ⓘ $220.50

13. What is the solution of $-3p + 4 < 22$?

Ⓐ $p < -6$ Ⓒ $p < 18$

Ⓑ $p > -6$ Ⓓ $p > 18$

14. Which of the graphs below show the solution of
$-5 + x > 8$?

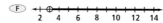

Ⓕ ├─○─┼─┼─┼─┼─┼─┼
  2 4 6 8 10 12 14

Ⓖ ├─┼─○─┼─┼─┼─┼─┼┼
  2 4 6 8 10 12 14

Ⓗ ├─┼─┼─┼─┼─┼─┼─○─┼
  2 4 6 8 10 12 14

Ⓘ ├─┼─┼─┼─┼─┼─┼─○─┼
  2 4 6 8 10 12 14

15. Between which two whole numbers does $\sqrt{85}$ fall?

Ⓐ 8 and 9 Ⓒ 41 and 42

Ⓑ 9 and 10 Ⓓ 42 and 43

16. What is the simplified form of $\frac{6 + 3^2}{(2^3)(3)}$?

Ⓕ $\frac{1}{3}$ Ⓗ $\frac{5}{8}$

Ⓖ $\frac{1}{2}$ Ⓘ $\frac{5}{6}$

17. Which of the following expressions is equivalent to $\frac{4^3}{4^6}$?

Ⓐ $\frac{1}{4^3}$ Ⓒ 4^2

Ⓑ $\frac{1}{4^2}$ Ⓓ 4^3

18. What is 40,500,000 written in scientific notation?

Ⓕ 4.05×10^7 Ⓗ 4.05×10^{-6}

Ⓖ 4.05×10^6 Ⓘ 4.05×10^{-7}

19. There are $3\frac{3}{4}$ c of flour, $1\frac{1}{2}$ c of sugar, $\frac{2}{3}$ c of brown sugar,
and $\frac{1}{4}$ c of oil in a cake mix. How many cups of
ingredients are there in all?

Ⓐ $4\frac{1}{2}$ c Ⓒ $5\frac{1}{2}$ c

Ⓑ $5\frac{1}{6}$ c Ⓓ $6\frac{1}{6}$ c

9. A

10. G

11. C

12. G

13. A

14. H

15. B

16. I

17. A

18. G

19. D

Answers

20. H
21. A
22. H
23. D
24. H
25. B
26. H
27. C
28. H
29. A

---

20. Cathy ran for 30 min at a rate of 5.5 mi/h. Then she ran for 15 min at a rate of 6 mi/h. How many miles did she run in all?

- Ⓕ 2.75 mi
- Ⓗ 4.25 mi
- Ⓖ 4.375 mi
- Ⓘ 5.75 mi

21. A 6-ft-tall man casts a shadow that is 9 ft long. At the same time, a tree nearby casts a 48 ft shadow. How tall is the tree?

- Ⓐ 32 ft
- Ⓒ 45 ft
- Ⓑ 36 ft
- Ⓓ 72 ft

22. Triangle *ABC* is similar to triangle *DEF*. What is *x*?

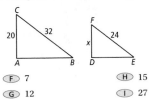

- Ⓕ 7
- Ⓗ 15
- Ⓖ 12
- Ⓘ 27

23. Which side lengths given below can form a right triangle?

- Ⓐ 12, 13, 17
- Ⓑ 3.2, 5.6, 6.4
- Ⓒ 14, 20, 24
- Ⓓ 10, 24, 26

24. The formula $F = \frac{9}{5}C + 32$ converts temperatures in degrees Celsius *C* to temperatures in degrees Fahrenheit *F*. What is 35°C in degrees Fahrenheit?

- Ⓕ 20°F
- Ⓗ 95°F
- Ⓖ 67°F
- Ⓘ 120°F

25. A bowling ball is traveling at 15 mi/h when it hits the pins. How fast is the bowling ball traveling in feet per second? (*Hint:* 1 mi = 5280 ft)

- Ⓐ 11 ft/s
- Ⓑ 88 ft/s
- Ⓒ 22 ft/s
- Ⓓ 1320 ft/s

26. What is the median of the tree height data displayed in the box-and-whisker plot below?

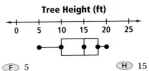

Tree Height (ft)

- Ⓕ 5
- Ⓗ 15
- Ⓖ 10
- Ⓘ 20

27. Helena tracked the number of hours she spent working on a science experiment each day in the scatter plot below.

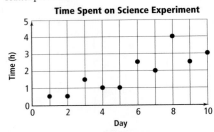

Time Spent on Science Experiment

Between which two days was there the greatest increase in the number of hours Helena spent working on her science experiment?

- Ⓐ Day 2 and 3
- Ⓑ Day 7 and 8
- Ⓒ Day 5 and 6
- Ⓓ Day 9 and 10

28. Your grades on four exams are 78, 85, 97, and 92. What grade do you need on the next exam to have an average of 90 on the five exams?

- Ⓕ 71
- Ⓗ 98
- Ⓖ 92
- Ⓘ 100

29. The number of points scored by a basketball team during the first 8 games of the season are shown below.

65 58 72 74 82 67 75 71

How much will their average game score increase by if the team scores 93 points in the next game?

- Ⓐ 2.5
- Ⓒ 11.6
- Ⓑ 10.5
- Ⓓ 19.5

Get Ready!

Skills Handbook, page 787

◆ Factors

Find the greatest common factor of each set of numbers.

1. 12, 18   **2.** 25, 35   **3.** 13, 20   **4.** 40, 80, 100

Skills Handbook, page 787

◆ Least Common Multiple

Find the least common multiple of each set of numbers.

5. 5, 15   **6.** 11, 44   **7.** 8, 9   **8.** 10, 15, 25

Skills Handbook, page 788

◆ Using Estimation

Estimate each sum or difference.

9. $956 - 542$ **10.** $1.259 + 5.312 + 1.7$ **11.** $\$14.32 + \$1.65 + \$278.05$

Skills Handbook, page 789

◆ Simplifying Fractions

Write in simplest form.

12. $\frac{12}{15}$ **13.** $\frac{20}{28}$ **14.** $\frac{8}{56}$ **15.** $\frac{48}{52}$

Skills Handbook, page 790

◆ Fractions and Decimals

Write each fraction as a decimal.

16. $\frac{7}{10}$ **17.** $\frac{3}{5}$ **18.** $\frac{13}{20}$ **19.** $\frac{93}{100}$ **20.** $\frac{7}{15}$

Skills Handbook, page 791

◆ Adding and Subtracting Fractions

Find the sum or difference.

21. $\frac{4}{7} + \frac{3}{14}$ **22.** $6\frac{2}{3} + 3\frac{4}{5}$ **23.** $\frac{9}{10} - \frac{4}{5}$ **24.** $8\frac{3}{4} - 4\frac{5}{6}$

Looking Ahead Vocabulary

25. Several expressions may have the same meaning. For actors, the English *expression* "break a leg" means "good luck." In math, what is another *expression* for $5 \cdot 7$?

26. A beginning guitarist learns to play using *simplified* guitar music. What does it mean to write a *simplified* math expression as shown at the right?

$$5 \cdot 7 \div 5 = 7$$

27. A study *evaluates* the performance of a hybrid bus to determine its value. What does it mean to *evaluate* an expression in math?

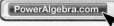

Answers

Get Ready!

1. 6   **2.** 5   **3.** 1

4. 20   **5.** 15   **6.** 44

7. 72   **8.** 150   **9.** 400

10. 8   **11.** $294   **12.** $\frac{4}{5}$

13. $\frac{5}{7}$ **14.** $\frac{1}{7}$ **15.** $\frac{12}{13}$

16. 0.7   **17.** 0.6   **18.** 0.65

19. 0.93   **20.** $0.4\overline{6}$ **21.** $\frac{11}{14}$

22. $10\frac{7}{15}$ **23.** $\frac{1}{10}$ **24.** $3\frac{11}{12}$

25. Answers may vary. Sample: $20 + 15$

26. Answers may vary. Sample: A simplified expression is one that is briefer or easier to work with than the original expression.

27. Answers may vary. Sample: To evaluate an expression means to find its numeric value for given values of the variables.

Get Ready!

Assign this diagnostic assessment to determine if students have the prerequisite skills for Chapter 1.

Lesson	Skill
Skills Handbook, page 787	Factors
Skills Handbook, page 787	Least Common Multiple
Skills Handbook, page 788	Using Estimation
Skills Handbook, page 789	Simplifying Fractions
Skills Handbook, page 790	Fractions and Decimals
Skills Handbook, page 791	Adding and Subtracting Fractions

To remediate students, select from these resources (available for every lesson).
- Online Problems (PowerAlgebra.com)
- Reteaching (All-in-One Teaching Resources)
- Practice (All-in-One Teaching Resources)

Why Students Need These Skills

FACTORS

A strong understanding of factors is necessary when operating with fractions.

LEAST COMMON MULTIPLE

The least common multiple is used when adding and subtracting fractions.

USING ESTIMATION

Estimation strategies allow students to check whether their calculations are reasonable.

SIMPLIFYING FRACTIONS

Fractions written in simplest form have smaller numbers in their numerators and denominators, which are better when comparing values and converting fractions to decimals.

FRACTIONS AND DECIMALS

Many real-world application problems involve fractions and decimals. Being proficient in the basic operations means that students can perform these operations on all real numbers.

ADDING AND SUBTRACTING FRACTIONS

Learning to add and subtract fractions prepares students for computing with real numbers.

Looking Ahead Vocabulary

EXPRESSION Ask students to name other examples of different expressions that mean the same thing.

SIMPLIFIED Show students two expressions, one which is simplified and one which is not.

EVALUATE Define the mathematical meaning of *evaluate* and compare it to the mathematical meaning of *simplify*.

Chapter 1 Overview

UbD Understanding by Design

Chapter 1 introduces students to variables and expressions and explores real-number operations. Students will develop the answers to the Essential Questions posed on the opposite page as they learn the concepts and skills bulleted below.

BIG idea Variable

ESSENTIAL QUESTION How can you represent quantities, patterns, and relationships?
- Students will learn to write and evaluate expressions with unknown values.

BIG idea Properties

ESSENTIAL QUESTION How are properties related to algebra?
- Properties are used to simplify expressions.

Indiana Academic Standard

A1.2.1 Translate among various representations of linear functions including tables, graphs, words and equations.

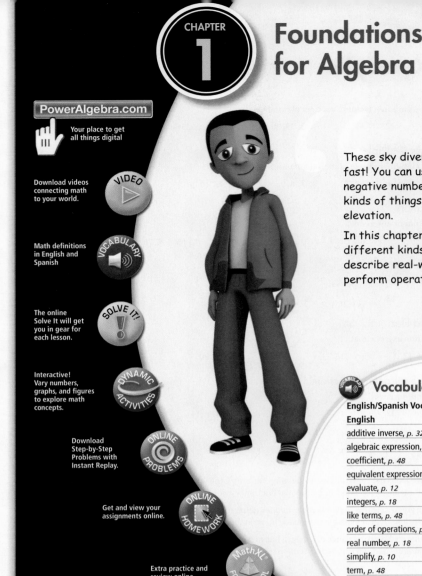

PowerAlgebra.com

Your place to get all things digital

Download videos connecting math to your world.

VIDEO

Math definitions in English and Spanish

VOCABULARY

The online Solve It will get you in gear for each lesson.

SOLVE IT!

Interactive! Vary numbers, graphs, and figures to explore math concepts.

DYNAMIC ACTIVITIES

Download Step-by-Step Problems with Instant Replay.

ONLINE PROBLEMS

Get and view your assignments online.

ONLINE HOMEWORK

Extra practice and review online

MathXL FOR SCHOOL

These sky divers are falling very fast! You can use positive and negative numbers to describe all kinds of things, like changes in elevation.

In this chapter, you'll learn to use different kinds of numbers to describe real-world situations and perform operations.

Vocabulary

English/Spanish Vocabulary Audio Online:

English	Spanish
additive inverse, *p. 32*	inverso aditivo
algebraic expression, *p. 4*	expresión algebraica
coefficient, *p. 48*	coeficiente
equivalent expressions, *p. 23*	ecuaciones equivalentes
evaluate, *p. 12*	evaluar
integers, *p. 18*	números enteros
like terms, *p. 48*	términos semejantes
order of operations, *p. 11*	orden de las operaciones
real number, *p. 18*	número real
simplify, *p. 10*	simplificar
term, *p. 48*	término
variable, *p. 4*	variable

PowerAlgebra.com

Chapter 1 Overview

Use these online assets to engage your students. These include support for the Solve It and step-by-step solutions for Problems.

 Show the student-produced video demonstrating relevant and engaging applications of the new concepts in the chapter.

 Find online definitions for new terms in English and Spanish.

 Start each lesson with an attention-getting Problem. View the Problem online with helpful hints.

My Math Video

My Math Video

FACILITATE Like skydiving, algebra is an adventure. Students can apply the tools they learn in algebra to a wide range of real-world problems, from economics and business to physics and biology. As students progress they will not only learn strategies for solving equations, but also general problem-solving techniques. Like the skydiver, students will gain a broader perspective on the world.

Q What must a person do before skydiving? **[Divers must complete training for the jump.]**

Q What would you want to know before you go skydiving? **[Answers may vary. Samples: the speed of your fall, when to open the parachute, how to land]**

Q Algebra involves using variables to represent real numbers. What do you already know before you begin to study Algebra? **[Answers may vary. Samples: definition of real numbers, how to work with real numbers, and properties of real numbers]**

EXTENSION

Set the stage for studying the Order of Operations. Place students in groups and provide each group a numerical expression that uses several operations. Have each group member begin simplifying the expression at a different operation. When they are finished, compare answers and discuss the origin of discrepancies. Be sure that students come to the conclusion that a set of rules is necessary for everyone to get the same answer.

BIG ideas

- **Variable**
  Essential Question How can you represent quantities, patterns, and relationships?

- **Properties**
  Essential Question How are properties related to algebra?

Chapter Preview

PowerAlgebra.com | Chapter 1 Foundations for Algebra | 3

 Increase students' depth of knowledge with interactive online activities.

 Show Problems from each lesson solved step by step. Instant replay allows students to go at their own pace when studying online.

 Assign homework to individual students or to an entire class.

 Prepare students for the Mid-Chapter Quiz and Chapter Test with online practice and review.

FOUNDATIONS FOR ALGEBRA
Math Background

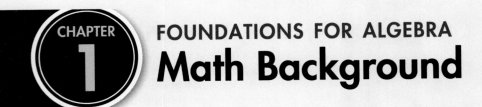

Variable

BIG idea Quantities are used to form expressions, equations and inequalities. An expression refers to a quantity but does not make a statement about it. An equation (or an inequality) is a statement about the quantities it mentions. Using variables in place of numbers in equations (or inequalities) allows the statement of relationships among numbers that are unknown or unspecified.

ESSENTIAL UNDERSTANDINGS

1-1 Algebra uses symbols to represent quantities that are unknown or that vary. Mathematical phrases and real-world relationships can be represented using symbols and operations.

1-8 Equations are used to represent the relationship between two quantities that have the same value.

1-9 Sometimes the value of one quantity can be found if the value of another is known. The relationship between the quantities can be represented in different ways, including tables, equations, and graphs.

Properties

BIG idea In the transition from arithmetic to algebra, attention shifts from arithmetic operations (addition, subtraction, multiplication, and division) to use of the properties of these operations. All of the facts of arithmetic and algebra follow from certain properties.

ESSENTIAL UNDERSTANDINGS

1-2 Powers can be used to shorten the representation of repeated multiplication, such as $2 \times 2 \times 2 \times 2 \times 2 \times 2$.
When simplifying an expression operations must be performed in the correct order.

1-3 The definition of a square root can be used to find the exact square roots of some nonnegative numbers. The square roots of other nonnegative numbers can be approximated.
Numbers can be classified by their characteristics. Some types of numbers can be represented on the number line.

1-4 Relationships that are always true for real numbers are called properties, which are rules used to rewrite and compare expressions.

1-5 Any real numbers can be added or subtracted using a number line model or using rules involving absolute value.

1-6 The rules for multiplying real numbers are related to the properties of real numbers and the definitions of operations.

1-7 The distributive property can be used to simplify the product of a number and a sum or difference.
An algebraic expression can be simplified by combining the parts of the expression that are alike.

Order of Operations

It may seem reasonable to evaluate the expression $3 \times 4 - 2$ in two ways:

1) $3 \times 4 - 2 = 12 - 2 = 10$

2) $3 \times 4 - 2 = 3 \times 2 = 6$

In option (1), you first multiply and then subtract. In (2), you first subtract and then multiply. To avoid this sort of ambiguity, mathematicians have agreed upon an **order of operations** that ensures every expression has a unique value.

First perform any operation(s) inside grouping symbols, such as parentheses ( ) and brackets [ ]. A fraction bar also acts as a grouping symbol. For example, to evaluate $(3 + 2)^2 \times 6 - 2$, first add inside the parentheses to get $5^2 \times 6 - 2$.

Next, simplify powers. For $5^2 \times 6 - 2$, you get $25 \times 6 - 2$.

Then, multiply and divide from left to right. So, $25 \times 6 - 2 = 150 - 2$.

Finally, add and subtract from left to right: $150 - 2 = 148$.

There are several mnemonics to help students remember the order of operations. The most famous is "Please Excuse My Dear Aunt Sally," or PEMDAS:

Parentheses

Exponentiation

Multiplication/**D**ivision

Addition/**S**ubtraction

Notice that the first step in the order of operations, to perform any operations inside the grouping symbols, is *recursive*. That is, the first step in the order of operations tells you to first perform the order of operations inside any parentheses. *Recursion*, or defining something in terms of itself, is used throughout mathematics and computer science.

Common Errors With Order of Operations

Students might think the rule for multiplication and division tells you to do multiplication and then division, or the rule for addition and subtraction tells you to do addition and then subtraction. Students need to learn that multiplication and division are on the same level and should be applied from left to right. Addition and subtraction are on the same level and should also be applied from left to right, but only after any multiplication and division in the problem.

Properties of Real Numbers

Students may take the properties of real numbers for granted. It seems clear, for example, that $3 + 5 = 5 + 3$, and that the sum of two real numbers is a real number. Point out to students that some sets of mathematical objects do not obey these rules.

For example, the set of real-valued functions is not commutative. In other words, it matters in what order functions are applied to a number. For example, let $f(x) = |x|$ and $g(x) = -x$. If we first apply g to a real number a, and then apply f, the result is again a:

$$f(g(a)) = |-a| = a$$

However, if we first apply f and then g, we get $-a$:

$$g(f(a)) = -|a| = -a$$

You can summarize this by saying that the set of real-valued functions is not commutative.

A more familiar mathematical example is that the set of integers is not closed under division. A non-mathematical example is that putting on shoes and putting on socks are not commutative actions. Can students think of other examples from math or everyday life that do not follow these rules?

On the other hand, the set of real numbers is not the only set that has these properties. For example, the set of all even integers is closed under addition and multiplication. It may be helpful for students to think of other sets that have these properties.

One way to motivate negative, rational, and real numbers, is with algebraic equations that would not have solutions without these sets of numbers. Without negative numbers, you cannot solve

$$x + 11 = 3.$$

You need rational numbers to solve the equation

$$\frac{2}{x} = 3.$$

Real numbers are necessary in order to solve

$$x^2 = 2.$$

Later, students will learn that yet another set of numbers, complex numbers, is needed to solve equations such as

$$x^2 = -2.$$

Common Errors With Real Numbers

Some students have difficulty understanding the relationships among the various sets of numbers. The diagram on page 18 may help students visualize these relationships.

Equations

The fundamental building blocks of an English sentence are its subject and its predicate. For example, the sentence

The ball is red

is made up of the subject *The ball* and the predicate *is red*. By itself, *The ball* cannot be true or false, but *The ball is red* may be true or it may be false (the ball may be lime green).

Equations are the mathematical equivalent of sentences. The subjects of an equation are mathematical expressions, while the predicate is the equals sign.

By themselves, expressions such as $3 + 6$ and $11 - 2$ are like *The ball* above, they do not have truth values. However, if they are connected with an equals sign then the result is a true equation

$$3 + 6 = 11 - 2.$$

Some equations are neither true nor false. For example, $x + 6 = 11 - 2$ is true if $x = 3$ and false otherwise. Such an equation is called an *open sentence*. To solve an open sentence is to find values of the variable that makes the original equation true.

Other equations are true for every value of the variable. Consider

$$2x = x + x.$$

Clearly, this equation is true no matter what x equals. Such equations are called *identities*.

If you add, subtract, or multiply any value to both sides of a true equation, the equation remains true. If you divide both sides of a true equation by a nonzero number, the equation remains true.

Common Errors With Equations

Substituting negative numbers for variables can lead to confusion for students.

One possibility is that they will write the negative number, see the negative sign, and do subtraction instead of multiplication. For example, when substituting -2 into the expression $-3x + 7$ might yield $-3 - 2 + 7$, as opposed to the correct substitution $-3(-2) + 7$.

Another possibility is that they will not remember how to multiply two negatives or simply ignore one of the negative signs.

FOUNDATION FOR ALGEBRA
Pacing and Assignment Guide

Lesson	Teaching Day(s)	TRADITIONAL Basic	Average	Advanced	BLOCK Block
1-1	1	Problems 1-5 Exs. 9–40, 45–49, 56–66	Problems 1-5 Exs. 9–39 odd, 41–52, 56–66	Problems 1-5 Exs. 9–39 odd, 41–66	**Day 1** Problems 1-5 Exs. 9–39 odd, 41–52, 56–66
1-2	1	Problems 1-4 Exs. 9–35, 41–47, 55, 61–80	Problems 1-4 Exs. 9–35 odd, 36–55, 61–80	Problems 1-4 Exs. 9–35 odd, 36–80	Problems 1-4 Exs. 9–35 odd, 36–55, 61–80
1-3	1	Problems 1-3 Exs. 9–50, 51–56, 58, 60, 62–67, 72–85	Problems 1-5 Exs. 9–49 odd, 51–68, 72–85	Problems 1-5 Exs. 9–49 odd, 51–85	**Day 2** Problems 1-5 Exs. 9–49 odd, 51–68, 72–85
1-4	1	Problems 1-4 Exs. 7–35 all, 36–46 even, 47–48, 58–68	Problems 1-4 Exs. 7–35 odd, 36–55, 58–68	Problems 1-4 Exs. 7–35 odd, 36–68	Problems 1-4 Exs. 7–35 odd, 36–55, 58–68
1-5	1	Problems 1-4 Exs. 10–43, 47–61, 70–85	Problems 1-4 Exs. 11–43 odd, 44–63, 70–85	Problems 1-4 Exs. 11–43 odd, 44–85	**Day 3** Problems 1-4 Exs. 11–43 odd, 44–63, 70–85
1-6	1	Problems 1-4 Exs. 8–50 all, 54–64 even, 70–78	Problems 1-4 Exs. 11–43 odd, 44–65, 70–78	Problems 1-4 Exs. 11–43 odd, 44–78	Problems 1-4 Exs. 11–43 odd, 44–65, 70–78
1-7	1	Problems 1-3 Exs. 9–40	Problems 1-5 Exs. 9–63 odd, 65–83, 91–100	Problems 1-5 Exs. 9–63 odd, 65–100	**Day 4** Problems 1-5 Exs. 9–63 odd, 65–83, 91–100
	2	Problems 4-5 Exs. 41–64, 66, 68–76, 91–100			
1-8	1	Problems 1-3 Exs. 7–28, 50	Problems 1-3 Exs. 7–27 odd, 50, 64	Problems 1-6 Exs. 7–47 odd, 49–86	Problems 1-3 Exs. 7–27 odd, 50, 64
	2	Problems 4-6 Exs. 29–48 all, 52–62 even, 63, 67–86	Problems 4-6 Exs. 29–47 odd, 49, 51–63, 67–86		**Day 5** Problems 4-6 Exs. 29–47 odd, 49, 51–63, 67–86
1-9	1	Problems 1-3 Exs. 8–25 all, 26–34 even, 35–38, 42–60	Problems 1-3 Exs. 9–25 odd, 26–39, 42–60	Problems 1-3 Exs. 9–25 odd, 26–60	Problems 1-3 Exs. 9–25 odd, 26–39, 42–60
Review	1	Chapter 1 Review	Chapter 1 Review	Chapter 1 Review	**Day 6** Chapter 1 Review
Assess	1	Chapter 1 Test	Chapter 1 Test	Chapter 1 Test	Chapter 1 Test
Total		**13 Days**	**12 Days**	**11 Days**	**6 Days**

Note: Pacing does not include Concept Bytes and other feature pages.

Resources

	For the Chapter	1-1	1-2	1-3	1-4	1-5	1-6	1-7	1-8	1-9
Planning										
Teacher Center Online Planner & Grade Book	I	I	I	I	I	I	I	I	I	I
Interactive Learning & Guided Instruction										
My Math Video	I									
Solve It!		I TM	I TM	I TM	I TM	I TM	I TM	I TM	I TM	I TM
Student Companion (SP)*		P M	P M	P M	P M	P M	P M	P M	P M	P M
Vocabulary Support		I P M	I P M	I P M	I P M	I P M	I P M	I P M	I P M	I P M
Got It? Support		I P	I P	I P	I P	I P	I P	I P	I P	I P
Dynamic Activity	I	I	I	I		I		I		
Online Problems	I	I	I	I	I	I	I	I	I	I
Additional Problems		M	M	M	M	M	M	M	M	M
English Language Learner Support (TR)		E P M	E P M	E P M	E P M	E P M	E P M	E P M	E P M	E P M
Activities, Games, and Puzzles		E M	E M	E M	E M	E M	E M	E M	E M	E M
Teaching With TI Technology With CD-ROM							✓ P			
TI-Nspire™ Support CD-ROM	✓	✓	✓	✓	✓	✓	✓	✓	✓	✓
Lesson Check & Practice										
Student Companion (SP)*		P M	P M	P M	P M	P M	P M	P M	P M	P M
Lesson Check Support		I P	I P	I P	I P	I P	I P	I P	I P	I P
Practice and Problem Solving Workbook (SP)		P	P	P	P	P	P	P	P	P
Think About a Plan (TR)*		E P M	E P M	E P M	E P M	E P M	E P M	E P M	E P M	E P M
Practice Form G (TR)*		E P M	E P M	E P M	E P M	E P M	E P M	E P M	E P M	E P M
Standardized Test Prep (TR)*		P M	P M	P M	P M	P M	P M	P M	P M	P M
Practice Form K (TR)*		E P M	E P M	E P M	E P M	E P M	E P M	E P M	E P M	E P M
Extra Practice	E M									
Find the Errors!	M									
Enrichment (TR)		E P M	E P M	E P M	E P M	E P M	E P M	E P M	E P M	E P M
Answers and Solutions CD-ROM	✓	✓	✓	✓	✓	✓	✓	✓	✓	✓
Assess & Remediate										
ExamView CD-ROM	✓	✓	✓	✓	✓	✓	✓	✓	✓	✓
Lesson Quiz		I TM	I TM	I TM	I TM	I TM	I TM	I TM	I TM	I TM
Quizzes and Tests Form G (TR)*	E P M				E P M					E P M
Quizzes and Tests Form K (TR)*	E P M				E P M					E P M
Reteaching (TR)*		E P M	E P M	E P M	E P M	E P M	E P M	E P M	E P M	E P M
Performance Tasks (TR)*	P M									
Cumulative Review (TR)*	P M									
Progress Monitoring Assessments	I P M									

(TR) Available in All-In-One Teaching Resources   * Spanish available

1 Interactive Learning

Solve It!

PURPOSE To distinguish between variable and constant mathematical quantities that occur in real-world situations

PROCESS Students may consider factors that affect each quantity.

FACILITATE

Q What are some reasons why the amount of time it takes to fly from Philadelphia to San Francisco might vary? **[Answers may vary. Samples: type of plane, the plane's speed, the weather, the route traveled, the volume of air traffic, wind speed]**

ANSWER See Solve It in Answers on next page.
CONNECT THE MATH In the Solve It students identify constant and variable quantities. In this lesson students represent constant and variable quantities algebraically.

2 Guided Instruction

Problem 1

Q In 1A, what does the phrase "more than" mean? **[added to]**

Q In 1B, how does the value described in the word phrase compare to 58? **[It is less than 58.]**

Got It?   ERROR PREVENTION

Encourage students to make a model like the ones shown.

1-1   Variables and Expressions

Indiana Academic Standard
Prepares for A1.4.2 Add, subtract and multiply polynomials and divide polynomials by monomials.

Objective   To write algebraic expressions

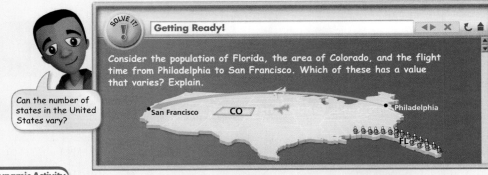

Can the number of states in the United States vary?

Getting Ready!

Consider the population of Florida, the area of Colorado, and the flight time from Philadelphia to San Francisco. Which of these has a value that varies? Explain.

Dynamic Activity Using Variable Expressions

Lesson Vocabulary
• quantity
• variable
• algebraic expression
• numerical expression

A mathematical **quantity** is anything that can be measured or counted. Some quantities remain constant. Others change, or vary, and are called *variable quantities*.

Essential Understanding Algebra uses symbols to represent quantities that are unknown or that vary. You can represent mathematical phrases and real-world relationships using symbols and operations.

A **variable** is a symbol, usually a letter, that represents the value(s) of a variable quantity. An **algebraic expression** is a mathematical phrase that includes one or more variables. A **numerical expression** is a mathematical phrase involving numbers and operation symbols, but no variables.

Plan

How can a diagram help you write an algebraic expression?
Models like the ones shown can help you to visualize the relationships described by the word phrases.

Problem 1   Writing Expressions With Addition and Subtraction

What is an algebraic expression for the word phrase?

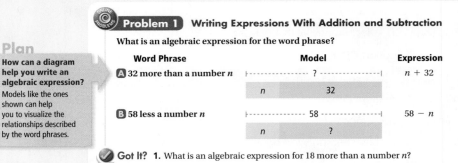

Word Phrase	Model	Expression
A 32 more than a number n	? / n / 32	$n + 32$
B 58 less a number n	58 / n / ?	$58 - n$

Got It? 1. What is an algebraic expression for 18 more than a number n?

1-1   Preparing to Teach

BIG idea   Variable   UbD

ESSENTIAL UNDERSTANDINGS
• Algebra uses symbols to represent quantities that are unknown or that vary.
• Mathematical phrases and real-world relationships can be represented using symbols and operations.

Math Background

Algebra is a language that is comprised of symbols and letters. The symbols represent operations and numbers. The letters represent unknown quantities or quantities that vary. When symbols are combined into a mathematical phrase, the phrase is an expression, such as $15 + 23$. The expression $15 + 23$ always equals 38.

When variables are combined with symbols, the phrase is an algebraic expression, such as $x + 23$. The expression $x + 23$ equals different values, depending on the number assigned to x. Students are probably familiar with the concept of unknown

quantities, but may not be familiar with the term *variables*. In early grades, students used an empty box or other shapes to represent an unknown value, such as $8 + \square = 12$.

In this chapter, students learn to translate verbal phrases into algebraic expressions and interpret algebraic expressions as word phrases. Students will learn to write algebraic expressions that will be used to generate equations. Later, students manipulate these expressions to solve for the unknown values.

Support Student Learning

Use the **Algebra 1 Companion** to engage and support students during instructions. See Lesson Resources at the end of this lesson for details.

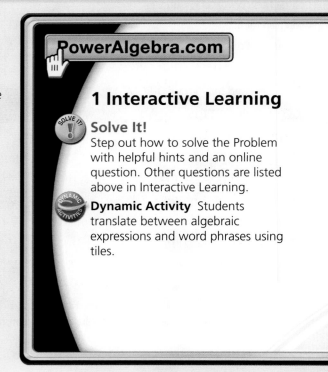

PowerAlgebra.com

1 Interactive Learning

Solve It!
Step out how to solve the Problem with helpful hints and an online question. Other questions are listed above in Interactive Learning.

Dynamic Activity Students translate between algebraic expressions and word phrases using tiles.

Problem 2 Writing Expressions With Multiplication and Division

Think

Is there more than one way to write an algebraic expression with multiplication?
Yes. Multiplication can be represented using a dot or parentheses in addition to an ×.

What is an algebraic expression for the word phrase?

Word Phrase	Model	Expression
A 8 times a number n		$8 \times n, 8 \cdot n, 8n$
B the quotient of a number n and 5		$n \div 5, \frac{n}{5}$

Got It? **2.** What is an algebraic expression for each word phrase in parts (a) and (b)?
  a. 6 times a number n **b.** the quotient of 18 and a number n
  c. Reasoning Do the phrases *6 less a number y* and *6 less than a number y* mean the same thing? Explain.

Problem 3 Writing Expressions With Two Operations

Plan

How can I represent the phrases visually?
Draw a diagram. You can represent the phrase in Problem 2, part (A), as shown below.

What is an algebraic expression for the word phrase?

Word Phrase	Expression
A 3 more than twice a number x	$3 + 2x$
B 9 less than the quotient of 6 and a number x	$\frac{6}{x} - 9$
C the product of 4 and the sum of a number x and 7	$4(x + 7)$

Got It? **3.** What is an algebraic expression for each word phrase?
  a. 8 less than the product of a number x and 4
  b. twice the sum of a number x and 8
  c. the quotient of 5 and the sum of 12 and a number x

In Problems 1, 2, and 3, you were given word phrases and wrote algebraic expressions. You can also translate algebraic expressions into word phrases.

Problem 4 Using Words for an Expression

Think

Is there only one way to write the expression in words?
No. The operation performed on 3 and x can be described by different words like "multiply," "times," and "product."

What word phrase can you use to represent the algebraic expression $3x$?

Expression $3x$ ⟨ A number and a variable side by side indicate a product.
  $3 \cdot x$

Words three times a number x or the product of 3 and a number x

Got It? **4.** What word phrase can you use to represent the algebraic expression?
  a. $x + 8.1$ **b.** $10x + 9$ **c.** $\frac{n}{3}$ **d.** $5x - 1$

Problem 2

Q What operation does the word "times" indicate? **[multiplication]**
Q What does the word "quotient" mean? **[the answer to a division problem]**
Q What notation other than a division symbol can you use for division? **[a fraction bar]**

Got It?
Tell students to select a value to use for n. Then do a computation for each phrase. If $n = 10$, *6 less than a number* is $10 - 6 = 4$ and *6 less a number* is $6 - 10 = -4$.

Problem 3

Q What word or words indicate the operations in each expression? **[3a: more than means +, twice means ×; 3b: less than means −, quotient means ÷; 3c: product means ×, sum means +.]**

Got It?   SYNTHESIZING

Q What operations are in each expression? **[3a: subtraction and multiplication; 3b: multiplication and addition; 3c: division and addition]**

Problem 4

Q Why do you think mathematicians prefer to use efficient notations rather than verbal phrases? **[Answers may vary. Sample: To save time when working long problems or a large quantity of problems.]**

Got It?
Asking students to write out word phrases to represent algebraic expressions helps them appreciate the efficiency of algebraic notation and provides a motivation for learning it.

---

2 Guided Instruction

Each Problem is worked out and supported online.

Problem 1
Writing Expressions With Addition and Subtraction
Animated

Problem 2
Writing Expressions With Multiplication and Division

Problem 3
Writing Expressions With Two Operations
Animated

Problem 4
Using Words for an Expression

Problem 5
Writing a Rule to Describe a Pattern
Animated

Support in Algebra 1 Companion
• Vocabulary
• Key Concepts
• Got It?

Answers

Solve It!
Answers may vary. Sample: The area of Colorado is one number. The flight time from Philadelphia to San Francisco is many different numbers since weather affects flight time. The population in Florida is many numbers since some people only live there in the winter.

Got It?
1. $n + 18$
2. a. $6n$ **b.** $\frac{18}{n}$
  c. No; 6 less a number y means $6 - y$ and 6 less than a number y means $y - 6$.
3. a. $4x - 8$ **b.** $2(x + 8)$ **c.** $\frac{5}{12 + x}$
4. a. the sum of a number x and 8.1
  b. the sum of ten times a number x and 9
  c. the quotient of a number n and 3
  d. five times a number x less 1

Problem 5

> **Q** Which quantity varies and which quantities remain constant in the table? **[The number of levels varies; the height of each level and the starting height remain constant.]**
>
> **Q** What values can the variable n assume? **[0, 1, 2, 3, ….]**

Got It?

> **Q** What is the least value of n that can be used in the algebraic expression? Explain. **[n must be at least 3 in order for a polygon to be defined.]**
>
> **Q** What is the largest value of n? **[There is no limit for how large n can be.]**
>
> **Q** If the number of non-overlapping triangles that can be formed is 24, how many sides does the polygon have? Explain. **[26; the number of triangles formed is the number of sides minus 2, so the number of sides is the number of triangles formed plus 2.]**

You can use words or an algebraic expression to write a mathematical rule that describes a real-life pattern.

Problem 5 Writing a Rule to Describe a Pattern

Hobbies The table below shows how the height above the floor of a house of cards depends on the number of levels. What is a rule for the height? Give the rule in words and as an algebraic expression.

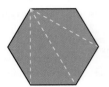

3.5 in.

24 in.

House of Cards

Number of Levels	Height (in.)
2	$(3.5 \cdot 2) + 24$
3	$(3.5 \cdot 3) + 24$
4	$(3.5 \cdot 4) + 24$
n	?

Know

Numerical expressions for the height given several different numbers of levels

Need

A rule for finding the height given a house with any number of levels n

Plan

Look for a pattern in the table. Describe the pattern in words. Then use the words to write an algebraic expression.

Rule in Words Multiply the number of levels by 3.5 and add 24.

Rule as an Algebraic Expression The variable n represents the number of levels in the house of cards.

$$3.5n + 24$$

This expression lets you find the height for any number of levels n.

Got It? 5. Suppose you draw a segment from any one vertex of a regular polygon to the other vertices. A sample for a regular hexagon is shown below. Use the table to find a pattern. What is a rule for the number of nonoverlapping triangles formed? Give the rule in words and as an algebraic expression.

Triangles in Polygons

Number of Sides of Polygon	Number of Triangles
4	$4 - 2$
5	$5 - 2$
6	$6 - 2$
n	■

Additional Problems

1. What is an algebraic expression for each word phrase?

   a. 25 more than a number n

   b. 74 less than a number n

   ANSWER a. $n + 25$

   b. $n - 74$

2. What is an algebraic expression for each word phrase?

   a. 5 times a number n

   b. the quotient of a number n and 7

   ANSWER a. $5n$ **b.** $\frac{n}{7}$

3. What is an algebraic expression for each word phrase?

   a. 4 more than twice a number x

   b. 7 less than the quotient of 8 and a number x

   c. the product of 9 and the sum of a number x and 2

   ANSWER a. $4 + 2x$

   b. $\frac{8}{x} - 7$ **c.** $9(x + 2)$

4. What word phrase can you use to represent the algebraic expression $4x$?

   ANSWER the product of 4 and a number x

5. The table shows how the cost of renting a scooter depends on how long the scooter is rented. What is a rule for the total cost? Give the rule in words and as an algebraic expression.

Hours	Cost
1	$17.50
2	$25.00
3	$32.50
4	$40.00
5	$47.50

   ANSWER Multiply the number of hours by 7.5 and add 10; $7.5n + 10$

Lesson Check

Do you know HOW?

1. Is each expression *algebraic* or *numerical*?

   a. $7 \div 2$ b. $4m + 6$ c. $2(5 - 4)$

2. What is an algebraic expression for each phrase?

   a. the product of 9 and a number t

   b. the difference of a number x and $\frac{1}{2}$

   c. the sum of a number m and 7.1

   d. the quotient of 207 and a number n

Use words to describe each algebraic expression.

3. $6c$ 4. $x - 1$

5. $\frac{t}{2}$ 6. $3t - 4$

Do you UNDERSTAND?

7. **Vocabulary** Explain the difference between numerical expressions and algebraic expressions.

8. **Reasoning** Use the table to decide whether $49n + 0.75$ or $49 + 0.75n$ represents the total cost to rent a truck that you drive n miles.

Truck Rental Fees

Number of Miles	Cost
1	$49 + ($.75 \times 1)$
2	$49 + ($.75 \times 2)$
3	$49 + ($.75 \times 3)$
n	■

Practice and Problem-Solving Exercises

A Practice

Write an algebraic expression for each word phrase.   ◀ See Problems 1–3.

9. 4 more than p

10. y minus 12

11. 12 fewer than n

12. the product of 15 and c

13. the quotient of n and 8

14. the quotient of 17 and k

15. 23 less than x

16. the sum of v and 3

17. a third of a number n

18. a number t divided by 82

19. 2 more than twice a number w

20. the sum of 13 and twice a number h

21. 9 more than the difference of 17 and k

22. 6.7 more than the product of 5 and n

23. 9.85 less than the product of 37 and t

24. 7 minus the quotient of 3 and v

25. 15 plus the quotient of 60 and w

26. the product of 2.1 and the sum of 5 and k

Write a word phrase for each algebraic expression.   ◀ See Problem 4.

27. $q + 5$

28. $3 - t$

29. $\frac{y}{5}$

30. $12x$

31. $14.1 - w$

32. $49 + m$

33. $9n + 1$

34. $62 + 7h$

35. $\frac{z}{8} - 9$

36. $13p + 0.1$

37. $15 - \frac{1.5}{d}$

38. $2(5 - n)$

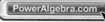

---

3 Lesson Check

Do you know HOW?

- If students have difficulty with Exercise 1, then have them review the definitions of an algebraic expression and a numerical expression.

Do you UNDERSTAND?

- If students have difficulty with Exercise 8, then have them substitute values for n in each expression and compare to those in the table.

Close

> **Q** How is an algebraic expression like a numerical expression? How are they different? **[Answers may vary. Sample: An algebraic expression and a numerical expression can contain numbers and operation signs. An algebraic expression and a numerical expression represent a value; In addition to numbers and operations, an algebraic expression contains a variable, while a numerical expression does not.]**

Answers

Got It? (continued)

5. subtract 2 from the number of sides in the polygon; $n - 2$

Lesson Check

1. a. numerical   b. algebraic

   c. numerical

2. a. $9t$ b. $x - \frac{1}{2}$

   c. $m + 7.1$ d. $\frac{207}{n}$

3. six times a number c

4. one less than a number x

5. the quotient of a number t and 2

6. 4 less than the product of 3 and number t

7. Numerical expressions are mathematical phrases involving only numbers and operations. Algebraic expressions are mathematical phrases that include one or more variables. An algebraic expression includes at least one variable. A numerical expression does not include any variables.

8. $49 + 0.75n$

Practice and Problem-Solving Exercises

9. $p + 4$ 10. $y - 12$ 11. $n - 12$

12. $15c$ 13. $\frac{n}{8}$ 14. $\frac{17}{k}$

15. $x - 23$ 16. $v + 3$ 17. $\frac{1}{3}n$

18. $\frac{t}{82}$ 19. $2w + 2$ 20. $13 + 2h$

21. $(17 - k) + 9$ 22. $5n + 6.7$

23. $37t - 9.85$ 24. $7 - \frac{3}{v}$

25. $15 + \frac{60}{w}$ 26. $2.1(5 + k)$

27. 5 more than a number q

28. 3 less a number t

29. the quotient of y and 5

30. the product of 12 and x

31. 14.1 less a number w

32. the sum of 49 and m

33–38. See next page.

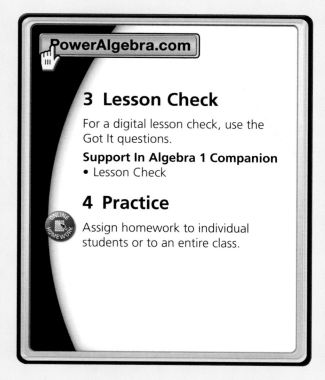

3 Lesson Check

For a digital lesson check, use the Got It questions.

Support In Algebra 1 Companion
- Lesson Check

4 Practice

Assign homework to individual students or to an entire class.

4 Practice

ASSIGNMENT GUIDE

Basic: 9–40 all, 45–49

Average: 9–39 odd, 41–52

Advanced: 9–39 odd, 41–55

Standardized Test Prep: 56–58

Mixed Review: 59–60

Reasoning exercises have blue headings.

Applications exercises have red headings.

EXERCISE 48: Use the Think About a Plan worksheet in the **Practice and Problem Solving Workbook** (also available in the Teaching Resources in print and online) to further support students' development in becoming independent learners.

HOMEWORK QUICK CHECK

To check students' understanding of key skills and concepts, go over Exercises 21, 39, 45, 46, and 48.

Write a rule in words and as an algebraic expression to model the relationship in each table.   ◀ See Problem 5.

39. Sightseeing While on vacation, you rent a bicycle. You pay $9 for each hour you use it. It costs $5 to rent a helmet while you use the bicycle.

Bike Rental

Number of Hours	Rental Cost
1	($9 × 1) + $5
2	($9 × 2) + $5
3	($9 × 3) + $5
n	■

40. Sales At a shoe store, a salesperson earns a weekly salary of $150. A salesperson is also paid $2.00 for each pair of shoes he or she sells during the week.

Shoe Sales

Pairs of Shoes Sold	Total Earned
5	$150 + ($2 × 5)
10	$150 + ($2 × 10)
15	$150 + ($2 × 15)
n	■

B Apply   Write an algebraic expression for each word phrase.

41. 8 minus the product of 9 and r

42. the sum of 15 and x, plus 7

43. 4 less than three sevenths of y

44. the quotient of 12 and the product of 5 and t

45. Error Analysis A student writes the word phrase "the quotient of n and 5" to describe the expression $\frac{5}{n}$. Describe and correct the student's error.

46. Think About a Plan The table at the right shows the number of bagels a shop gives you per "baker's dozen." Write an algebraic expression that gives the rule for finding the number of bagels in any number b of baker's dozens.
- What is the pattern of increase in the number of bagels?
- What operation can you perform on b to find the number of bagels?

Bagels

Baker's Dozens	Number of Bagels
1	13
2	26
3	39
b	■

47. Tickets You and some friends are going to a museum. Each ticket costs $4.50. Write an algebraic expression that gives the rule for finding the cost of any number t of tickets.

48. Volunteering Serena and Tyler are wrapping gift boxes at the same pace. Serena starts first, as shown in the diagram. Write an algebraic expression that represents the number of boxes Tyler will have wrapped when Serena has wrapped x boxes.

Answers

Practice and Problem-Solving Exercises (continued)

33. one more than the product of 9 and a number n

34. the sum of 62 and the product of 7 and a number h

35. the quotient of z and 8 less 9

36. the sum of 13 times a number p and 0.1

37. the difference of 15 and the quotient of 1.5 and d

38. twice the difference of 5 and a number n

39. 5 more than the product of 9 and a number n; $9n + 5$

40. the sum of 150 and 2 times a number n; $150 + 2n$

41. $8 - 9r$

42. $(15 + x) + 7$

43. $\frac{3}{7}y - 4$

44. $\frac{12}{5t}$

45. It should be "The quotient of 5 and n."

46. $13b$

47. $4.50t$

48. $x - 2$

49. Multiple Choice Which expression gives the value in dollars of *d* dimes?

Ⓐ 0.10*d*   Ⓑ 0.10 + *d*   Ⓒ $\frac{0.10}{d}$ Ⓓ 10*d*

Open-Ended Describe a real-world situation that each expression might model. Tell what each variable represents.

50. 5*t*   **51.** *b* + 3   **52.** $\frac{40}{h}$

Ⓒ **Challenge**

53. Reasoning You write $(5 - 2) \div n$ to represent the phrase *2 less than 5 divided by a number n.* Your friend writes $(5 \div n) - 2$. Are these both reasonable interpretations? Can verbal descriptions lack precision? Explain.

Write two different expressions that could each represent the given diagram.

54.

x	1	1	1	1
x	1	1	1	1
x	1	1	1	1

55.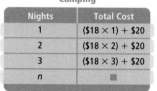

Standardized Test Prep

SAT/ACT

56. What is an algebraic expression for *2 less than the product of 3 and a number x*?

Ⓐ 3*x* − 2   Ⓑ (3 − 2)*x*   Ⓒ 3 − 2*x*   Ⓓ 2 − 3*x*

57. Which word phrase can you use to represent the algebraic expression $n \div 8$?

Ⓕ the product of a number *n* and 8   Ⓗ the difference of a number *n* and 8

Ⓖ the quotient of a number *n* and 8   Ⓘ the quotient of 8 and a number *n*

58. A state park charges an entrance fee plus $18 for each night of camping. The table shows this relationship. Which algebraic expression describes the total cost of camping for *n* nights?

Ⓐ 20*n* + 18   Ⓒ 18*n* + 20*n*

Ⓑ 18*n* + 20   Ⓓ 18*n* − 20

Camping

Nights	Total Cost
1	($18 × 1) + $20
2	($18 × 2) + $20
3	($18 × 3) + $20
n	■

Mixed Review

Find each sum or difference. Write each answer in simplest form. ◀ See p. 791.

59. $\frac{1}{4} + \frac{1}{2}$ **60.** $\frac{9}{14} - \frac{2}{7}$ **61.** $\frac{2}{5} + \frac{3}{10}$ **62.** $\frac{5}{6} - \frac{2}{3}$

Get Ready! **To prepare for Lesson 1-2, do Exercises 63–66.**

Find the greatest common factor of each pair of numbers. ◀ See p. 787.

63. 3 and 6   **64.** 12 and 15   **65.** 7 and 11   **66.** 8 and 12

49. A

50. Check students' work.

51. Check students' work.

52. Check students' work.

53. Answers may vary. Sample: Yes; sometimes you cannot be sure from a verbal description what order is intended for the operations.

54. 3*x* + 12 or 12 + 3*x* or 3(*x* + 4)

55. 2*x* + 6 or 6 + 2*x*

56. A   **57.** G   **58.** B

59. $\frac{3}{4}$ **60.** $\frac{5}{14}$ **61.** $\frac{7}{10}$

62. $\frac{1}{6}$ **63.** 3   **64.** 3

65. 1   **66.** 4

Lesson Resources

Additional Instructional Support

Algebra 1 Companion

Students can use the **Algebra 1 Companion** worktext (4 pages) as you teach the lesson. Use the Companion to support

- New Vocabulary
- Key Concepts
- Got It for each Problem
- Lesson Check

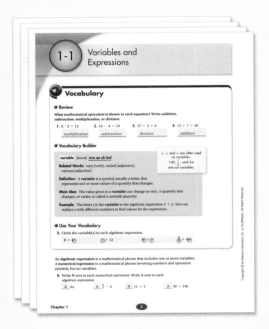

ELL Support

Use Graphic Organizers Tell students to make a 3-column KWL table. The columns are labeled "Know", "Want to Know", and "Learned". In the first column, have students write a declarative sentence about each of the following words: number, quantity, variable, expression, and algebra. In the second column, have them write a question about each word. After the lesson, ask students to write what they have learned about each word in the third column.

Give the students this example to help them get started:
K: 3, 4, and 5 are numbers.
W: What is the biggest number?

After the lesson, give the students this example to help them get started on the "Learned" column:
L: An unknown number can be shown by a letter.

5 Assess & Remediate

Lesson Quiz

1. What is an algebraic expression for each word phrase?
  a. 16 more than a number n
  b. 22 less than a number n
  c. 3 times a number n
  d. the quotient of a number n and 12

2. What is an algebraic expression for each word phrase?
  a. 11 more than twice a number x
  b. 2 less than the quotient of 5 and a number x
  c. the product of 4 and the sum of a number x and 8

3. What word phrase can you use to represent the algebraic expression $7x$?

4. Do you UNDERSTAND? The table shows how the cost of hiring a plumber depends on how long the work takes. What is a rule for the total cost? Give the rule in words and as an algebraic expression.

Hours	Cost
1	$65
2	$90
3	$115
4	$140
5	$165

ANSWERS TO LESSON QUIZ

1. a. $n + 16$, **b.** $n - 22$, **c.** $3n$, **d.** $\frac{n}{12}$

2. a. $11 + 2x$, **b.** $\frac{5}{x} - 2$, **c.** $4(x + 8)$

3. the product of 7 and a number x

4. Multiply the number of hours by 25 and add 40; $25x + 40$

PRESCRIPTION FOR REMEDIATION

Use the student work on the Lesson Quiz to prescribe a differentiated review assignment.

Points	Differentiated Remediation
0–2	Intervention
3	On-level
4	Extension

5 Assess & Remediate

Assign the Lesson Quiz. Appropriate intervention, practice, or enrichment is automatically generated based on student performance.

Intervention

- **Reteaching** (2 pages) Provides reteaching and practice exercises for the key lesson concepts. Use with struggling students or absent students.

- **English Language Learner Support** Helps students develop and reinforce mathematical vocabulary and key concepts.

All-in-One Resources/Online

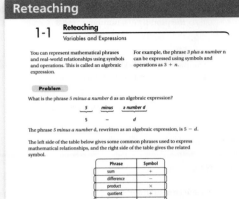

All-in-One Resources/Online

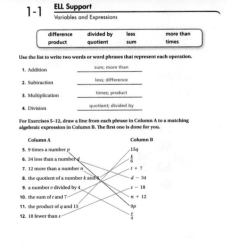

Differentiated Remediation *continued*

On-Level

- **Practice** (2 pages) Provides extra practice for each lesson. For simpler practice exercises, use the Form K Practice pages found in the All-in-One Teaching Resources and online.

- **Think About a Plan** Helps students develop specific problem-solving skills and strategies by providing scaffolded guiding questions.

- **Standardized Test Prep** Focuses on all major exercises, all major question types, and helps students prepare for the high-stakes assessments.

Extension

- **Enrichment** Provides students with interesting problems and activities that extend the concepts of the lesson.

- **Activities, Games, and Puzzles** Worksheets that can be used for concepts development, enrichment, and for fun!

Practice and Problem Solving WKBK/ All-in-One Resources/Online
Practice page 1

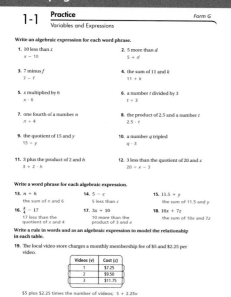

Practice and Problem Solving WKBK/ All-in-One Resources/Online
Practice page 2

1-1 Practice (continued) — Form G
Variables and Expressions

20. Dorothy gets paid to walk her neighbor's dog. For every week that she walks the dog, she earns $10.

Weeks (w)	Pay (p)
4	$40.00
5	$50.00
6	$60.00

$10 times the number of weeks; 10w

Write an algebraic expression for each word phrase.

21. 8 minus the quotient of 15 and y $8 - 15 \div y$

22. a number q tripled plus z doubled $3q + 2z$

23. the product of 8 and z plus the product of 6.5 and y $8z + 6.5y$

24. the quotient of 5 plus d and 12 minus w $\frac{5+d}{12-w}$

25. **Error Analysis** A student writes $5y \cdot 3$ to model the relationship *the sum of 5y and 3.* Explain the error.
The word "sum" indicates that addition should be used and not multiplication. The student has used the multiplication symbol instead of the +.

26. **Error Analysis** A student writes *the difference between 15 and the product of 5 and y* to describe the expression $5y - 15$. Explain the error.
The number 15 should be first and the expression should be written $15 - 5y$.

27. Jake is trying to mail a package to his grandmother. He already has s stamps on the package. The postal worker tells him that he's going to have to double the number of stamps on the package and then add 3 more. Write an algebraic expression that represents the number of stamps that Jake will have to put on the package.
$2s + 3$

All-in-One Resources/Online
Enrichment

1-1 Enrichment
Variables and Expressions

An equation is used to set an expression and a constant, or two expressions, equal to each other.

Write the phrase *a number h plus 3 is equal to 8* as an equation.

a number h	plus 3	is equal to 8
h	+3	=8

The phrase *a number h plus 3 is equal to 8*, written as an algebraic equation, is $h + 3 = 8$.

Write an algebraic equation for each word phrase.

1. The sum of 10 and a number y is equal to 18. $10 + y = 18$

2. 15 less than a number g is equal to 45. $g - 15 = 45$

3. The product of 25 and a number f is 5. $25 \times f = 5$

4. The quotient of 49 and x is 7. $49 \div x = 7$

5. The sum of t and 2 is equal to 5 less than t. $t + 2 = t - 5$

6. The quotient of 6 + n and 3 − f is 11. $\frac{6+n}{3-f} = 11$

Write an algebraic equation to model the relationship expressed.

7. Jane tried to fly her kite but discovered that the kite string was too short. If she doubles the length of the string, it will be 28 feet long.
$2 \times l = 28$

8. Raul is saving money to buy a car. He decides to withdraw $50 from his savings account for books. The amount left in his account after the withdrawal is $200.
$b - 50 = 200$

Practice and Problem Solving WKBK/ All-in-One Resources/Online
Think About a Plan

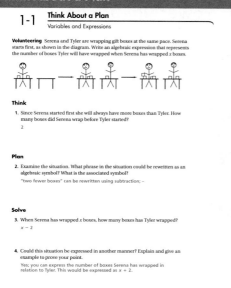

Practice and Problem Solving WKBK/ All-in-One Resources/Online
Standardized Test Prep

1-1 Standardized Test Prep
Variables and Expressions

Multiple Choice

For Exercises 1–7, choose the correct letter.

1. The word *minus* corresponds to which symbol? B
   A. + B. − C. · D. ×

2. The phrase *product* corresponds to which symbol? F
   F. × G. + H. − I. ÷

3. The word *plus* corresponds to which symbol? B
   A. − B. + C. < D. ÷

4. What is an algebraic expression for the word phrase *10 more than a number f*? I
   F. $10 - f$ G. $\frac{10}{f}$ H. $10 \times f$ I. $f + 10$

5. What is an algebraic expression for the word phrase *the product of 11 and a number s*? B
   A. $\frac{11}{s}$ B. $11 \times s$ C. $11 + s$ D. $11 - s$

6. Hannah and Tim collect stamps. Tim is bringing his stamps to Hannah's house so that they can compare. Hannah has 60 stamps. Which expression represents the total number of stamps that they will have if t represents the number of stamps Tim has? H
   F. $60 \times t$ G. $\frac{60}{t}$ H. $60 + t$ I. $60 - t$

7. Hershel's bakery sells donuts by the box. There are d donuts in each box. Beverly is going to buy 10 boxes for a class field trip. Which expression represents the total number of donuts that Beverly is going to get for her field trip? A
   A. $10 \times d$ B. $10 \div d$ C. $10 - d$ D. $10 + d$

Short Response

8. There are 200 people interested in playing in a basketball league. The leaders of the league are going to divide all of the people into n teams. What algebraic expression represents the number of players on each team? $200 \div n$
   [2] Question answered correctly.
   [1] Answer is incomplete.
   [0] Answer is wrong.

Online Teacher Resource Center
Activities, Games, and Puzzles

1-1 Game: Matching Expressions
Variables and Expressions

This is a game for two players. Cut out the *algebraic expressions* from the top table, mix them up, and place them in a stack with the expressions face down. Then cut out the *verbal expressions* from the bottom table and arrange them face down on your desk in 4 rows and 5 columns.

Player 1 picks the top card from the *algebraic expressions* stack. He or she then turns over a card from the *verbal expressions* arrangement. If the *algebraic expression* matches the *verbal expression*, the player keeps both cards. If there is no match, then the player places the *algebraic expression* at the bottom of the stack and places the *verbal expression* in the same location as it originally was.

Players take turns trying to find correct matches. The player with the most matches wins. The key is to try to remember the locations of the *verbal expressions*.

$\frac{w}{17}$	$\frac{3}{a} - 10$	$2(t - 15)$	$\frac{5}{8} \cdot b$	$8 + \frac{d}{15}$
$4(x + 5)$	$5j + 20$	$6z$	$2 + \frac{7}{k}$	$\frac{9}{14(g + 5)}$
$\frac{10}{3 + h}$	$\frac{y}{6}$	$p - 5$	$\frac{g}{8} - 5$	$11q - 8$
$12m$	$11 + \frac{u}{8}$	$15(r - 8)$	$17f$	$4 - \frac{5}{c}$

the sum of 2 and the quotient of 7 and a number	the product of 4 and the sum of a number and 5	the quotient of 10 and the sum of 3 and a number	8 less than the product of 11 and a number	the product of 6 and a number
5 less than a number	the product of 14 and a number	9 divided by the product of 14 and 5 more than a number	the product of a number and the quotient of 5 and 8	12 times a number
the difference of 4 and the quotient of 5 and a number	the product of 2 and the difference of a number and 15	11 more than the quotient of a number and 8	20 more than the product of 5 and a number	the quotient of a number and 17
8 plus the quotient of a number and 15	the product of 15 and the difference of a number and 8	the quotient of a number and 6	10 less than the quotient of 3 and a number	5 less than one-ninth of a number

Row 1: $2 + \frac{7}{a}$; $4(x + 5)$; $\frac{10}{3 + h}$; $11q - 8$; $6z$ Row 2: $p - 5$; $17f$; $\frac{9}{14(g + 5)}$; $\frac{g}{8} - 5$; $12m$

Row 3: $4 - \frac{5}{c}$; $2(t - 15)$; $11 + \frac{u}{8}$; $5j + 20$; $\frac{w}{17}$ Row 4: $8 + \frac{d}{15}$; $15(r - 8)$; $\frac{y}{6}$; $\frac{3}{a} - 10$; $\frac{5}{8} \cdot b$

1 Interactive Learning

Solve It!

PURPOSE To use a real-world situation to introduce the concept of repeated multiplication and provide motivation for learning exponential notation

PROCESS Students may make a chart, write expressions involving repeated multiplication, or write and evaluate exponential expressions.

FACILITATE

Q What operation would you use to represent "twice the previous day's amount"? Explain. **[multiplication by 2; twice indicates multiplication by 2.]**

Q Under option 2, how many times will the amount of money awarded per day be doubled? **[5 times]**

Q What is the amount of money awarded on the 6th day under option 2? **[$32]**

ANSWER See Solve It in Answers on next page.
CONNECT THE MATH In the Solve It, students use repeated multiplication by 2 to calculate prize 2. In this lesson, students will learn to express this as a power.

2 Guided Instruction

Problem 1

Q How many different products do you calculate when determining the simplified form of $(0.2)^5$? **[4]**

Got It?

Show students that the process for determining the simplified form of the expression in 1b can be visualized two ways:

$$\frac{2}{3} \cdot \frac{2}{3} \cdot \frac{2}{3} = \frac{4}{9} \cdot \frac{2}{3} = \frac{8}{27} \text{ or } \frac{2 \cdot 2 \cdot 2}{3 \cdot 3 \cdot 3} = \frac{4 \cdot 2}{9 \cdot 3} = \frac{8}{27}$$

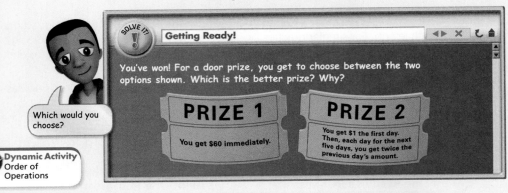

1-2 Order of Operations and Evaluating Expressions

Indiana Academic Standard
Prepares for A1.4.2 Add, subtract and multiply polynomials and divide polynomials by monomials.

Objectives To simplify expressions involving exponents
To use the order of operations to evaluate expressions

Getting Ready!

You've won! For a door prize, you get to choose between the two options shown. Which is the better prize? Why?

Which would you choose?

PRIZE 1
You get $60 immediately.

PRIZE 2
You get $1 the first day. Then, each day for the next five days, you get twice the previous day's amount.

Dynamic Activity Order of Operations

Lesson Vocabulary
• power
• exponent
• base
• simplify
• evaluate

Essential Understanding You can use *powers* to shorten how you represent repeated multiplication, such as $2 \times 2 \times 2 \times 2 \times 2 \times 2$.

A **power** has two parts, a *base* and an *exponent*. The **exponent** tells you how many times to use the **base** as a factor. You read the power 2^3 as "two to the third power" or "two cubed." You read 5^2 as "five to the second power" or "five squared."

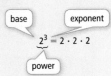

$$2^3 = 2 \cdot 2 \cdot 2$$

You **simplify** a numerical expression when you replace it with its single numerical value. For example, the simplest form of $2 \cdot 8$ is 16. To simplify a power, you replace it with its simplest name.

Think
What does the exponent indicate?
It shows the number of times you use the base as a factor.

Problem 1 Simplifying Powers

What is the simplified form of the expression?

A 10^7

$10^7 = 10 \cdot 10 \cdot 10 \cdot 10 \cdot 10 \cdot 10 \cdot 10$
$= 10,000,000$

B $(0.2)^5$

$(0.2)^5 = 0.2 \cdot 0.2 \cdot 0.2 \cdot 0.2 \cdot 0.2$
$= 0.00032$

Got It? 1. What is the simplified form of each expression?

a. 3^4

b. $\left(\frac{2}{3}\right)^3$

c. $(0.5)^3$

BIG idea Properties **UbD**

ESSENTIAL UNDERSTANDINGS

• Powers can be used to shorten the representation of repeated multiplication, such as $2 \times 2 \times 2 \times 2 \times 2 \times 2$.

• When simplifying an expression operations must be performed in the correct order.

Math Background

Many times, real-world situations must be modeled with more than one operation. Therefore, students must learn how to evaluate expressions that contain multiple operations and variables. To be consistent, students must follow the order of operations when evaluating mathematical expressions.

Consider the expression $5 + 2 \times 3$. Without an agreement on the order of operations, one

simplification of the expression may yield $5 + 2 = 7$ and $7 \times 3 = 21$, while another would yield the correct simplification of $2 \times 3 = 6$ and $5 + 6 = 11$.

In order for the value of a numerical expression to be unique, a rule is needed so that everyone performs calculations in the same order. The order of operations provides rules that must be followed when simplifying expressions.

Support Student Learning

Use the **Algebra I Companion** to engage and support students during instruction. See Lesson Resources at the end of this lesson for details.

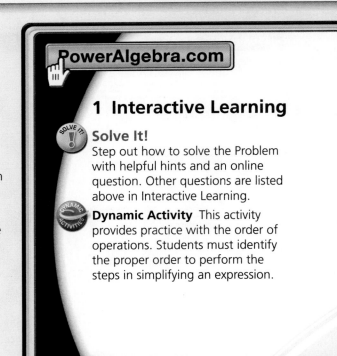

PowerAlgebra.com

1 Interactive Learning

Solve It!
Step out how to solve the Problem with helpful hints and an online question. Other questions are listed above in Interactive Learning.

Dynamic Activity This activity provides practice with the order of operations. Students must identify the proper order to perform the steps in simplifying an expression.

Essential Understanding When simplifying an expression, you need to perform operations in the correct order.

You might think about simplifying the expression $2 + 3 \times 5$ in two ways:

Add first.	Multiply first.
$2 + 3 \times 5 = 5 \times 5 = 25$ ✗	$2 + 3 \times 5 = 2 + 15 = 17$ ✔

Both results may seem sensible, but only the second result is considered correct. This is because the second way uses the order of operations that mathematicians have agreed to follow. Always use the following order of operations:

Key Concept Order of Operations

1. Perform any operation(s) inside grouping symbols, such as parentheses ( ) and brackets [ ]. A fraction bar also acts as a grouping symbol.
2. Simplify powers.
3. Multiply and divide from left to right.
4. Add and subtract from left to right.

 Problem 2 Simplifying a Numerical Expression

Think

How do you simplify an expression that contains a fraction?
You start by simplifying the numerator and denominator. Then you divide the numerator by the denominator.

What is the simplified form of each expression?

A $(6 - 2)^3 \div 2$

$$(6 - 2)^3 \div 2 = 4^3 \div 2 \quad \text{Subtract inside parentheses.}$$
$$= 64 \div 2 \quad \text{Simplify the power.}$$
$$= 32 \quad \text{Divide.}$$

 B $\dfrac{2^4 - 1}{5}$

$$\dfrac{2^4 - 1}{5} = \dfrac{16 - 1}{5} \quad \text{Simplify the power.}$$
$$= \dfrac{15}{5} \quad \text{Subtract.}$$
$$= 3 \quad \text{Divide.}$$

Got It? **2.** What is the simplified form of each expression?
    a. $5 \cdot 7 - 4^2 \div 2$
    b. $12 - 25 \div 5$
    c.  $\dfrac{4 + 3^4}{7 - 2}$
    d. Reasoning How does a fraction bar act as a grouping symbol? Explain.

---

2 Guided Instruction

Each Problem is worked out and supported online.

Problem 1
Simplifying Powers

Alternative Problem 1
Simplifying Powers
Animated

Problem 2
Simplifying a Numerical Expression
Animated

Alternative Problem 2
Simplifying a Numerical Expression

Problem 3
Evaluating Algebraic Expressions

Problem 4
Evaluating a Real-World Expression
Animated

Support in Algebra 1 Companion
• Vocabulary
• Key Concepts
• Got It?

Take Note   **ERROR PREVENTION**

Students sometimes mistakenly conclude that all multiplication should be performed prior to all division and that all addition should be performed prior to all subtraction. Remind students that multiplication and division are performed from left to right as is addition and subtraction. Provide an example such as $6 - 4 + 2 = 4$ to illustrate this point.

Problem 2

Q Suppose the parentheses were removed from 2A. What expression would you have after your first step? **[$6 - 8 \div 2$]**

Q In 2B, how does the fraction bar serve in terms of the order of operations? **[It is a grouping symbol.]**

Got It?

Q How could you write the expression in 2b using grouping symbols to show which operation to perform first? **[$12 - (25 \div 5)$]**

Answers

Solve It!

Answers may vary. Prize 2 is the better prize if you want more money. However, if you want the money right away, Prize 1 is better.

Got It?

1. a. 81
  b. $\frac{8}{27}$
  c. 0.125

2. a. 27
  b. 7
  c. 17
  d. A fraction bar acts as a grouping symbol since you simplify the numerator and denominator before you divide.

Problem 3

Q How could you include grouping symbols in part (a) so that it would not change the value of the expression? $[x^2 + x - (12 \div y^2)]$

Q What operation is indicated by the algebraic expression xy? **[multiplication]**

Q Why is multiplication performed prior to simplifying the power in part (b)? **[Multiplication is performed first because it is inside the parentheses.]**

Got It?

Q In 3a and 3b, after making the substitutions, what operation is performed first? **[powers]**

Q In 3a and 3b, what operation is performed last? **[subtraction]**

Q In 3c, what two operations are needed to simplify the expression after the substitution? **[powers, multiplication]**

Problem 4

Q What operation is indicated by the expression "$\frac{2}{5}$ of wages"? **[multiplication of wages by $\frac{2}{5}$]**

Q What simpler expression is equivalent to the expression $w - \frac{2}{5}w$? **[$\frac{3}{5}w$]**

You **evaluate** an algebraic expression by replacing each variable with a given number. Then simplify the expression using the order of operations.

Problem 3 Evaluating Algebraic Expressions

What is the value of the expression for $x = 5$ and $y = 2$?

A $x^2 + x - 12 \div y^2$

$x^2 + x - 12 \div y^2 = 5^2 + 5 - 12 \div 2^2$ Substitute 5 for x and 2 for y.

$= 25 + 5 - 12 \div 4$ Simplify powers.

$= 25 + 5 - 3$ Divide.

$= 27$ Add and subtract from left to right.

B $(xy)^2$

$(xy)^2 = (5 \cdot 2)^2$ Substitute 5 for x and 2 for y.

$= 10^2$ Multiply inside parentheses.

$= 100$ Simplify the power.

Got It? 3. What is the value of each expression when $a = 3$ and $b = 4$ in parts (a)-(b)?
  a. $3b - a^2$ **b.** $2b^2 - 7a$
  c. Reasoning Find the value of xy^2 for $x = 5$ and $y = 2$. Compare your results to $(xy)^2$ in Problem 3. What can you conclude?

Problem 4 Evaluating a Real-World Expression

Banking What is an expression for the spending money you have left after depositing $\frac{2}{5}$ of your wages in savings? Evaluate the expression for weekly wages of $40, $50, $75, and $100.

Know
- Savings equals $\frac{2}{5}$ of wages.
- Various weekly wages

Need
- Expression for spending money
- Amount of spending money for various weekly wages

Plan
Write an algebraic expression and evaluate it for each amount of weekly wages. Use a table to organize your results.

Relate spending money equals
    wages   minus $\frac{2}{5}$ of   wages

Define Let w = your wages.

Write w $-$ $\frac{2}{5}$ $\cdot$ w

The expression $w - \frac{2}{5} \cdot w$ represents the amount of money you have left after depositing $\frac{2}{5}$ of your wages in savings.

Spending Money

Wages (w)	$w - \frac{2}{5}w$	Total Spending Money ($)
40	$40 - \frac{2}{5}(40)$	24
50	$50 - \frac{2}{5}(50)$	30
75	$75 - \frac{2}{5}(75)$	45
100	$100 - \frac{2}{5}(100)$	60

Plan
How is this Problem like ones you've seen before?
You begin by substituting numbers for the variables. After substituting, you have numerical expressions just like the ones in Problem 2.

Think
How can a model help you write the expression?
This model shows that spending money equals your wages w minus the amount you save: $\frac{2}{5}w$.

|-------- w --------|
| $\frac{2}{5}w$ | ? |

Additional Problems

1. What is the simplified form of each expression?

  a. 10^5

  b. $(0.2)^4$

  ANSWER a. 100,000
            b. 0.0016

2. What is the simplified form of each expression?

  a. $(9 - 3)^2 \div 4$

  b. $2^5 + (11 + 14) \div 5$

  ANSWER a. 9   **b.** 37

3. What is the value of each expression for $x = 3$ and $y = 4$?

  a. $x^2 + 2x + 16 \div y^2$

  b. $(x + y)^2$

  ANSWER a. 16   **b.** 49

4. What is an expression for the spending money you have left after depositing $\frac{1}{4}$ of your wages in savings? Evaluate the expression for weekly wages of $40, $60, $80, and $100.

  ANSWER $\frac{3}{4}w$; $30, $45, $60, $75

Answers

Got It? (continued)

  3. a. 3

    b. 11

    c. 20; $(xy)^2 \neq xy^2$

Got It? 4. The shipping cost for an order at an online store is $\frac{1}{10}$ the cost of the items you order. What is an expression for the total cost of a given order? What are the total costs for orders of $43, $79, $95, and $103?

Lesson Check

Do you know HOW?

What is the simplified form of each expression?

1. 5^2 2. 2^3 3. $\left(\frac{3}{4}\right)^2$

Evaluate each expression for $x = 3$ and $y = 4$.

4. $x^2 + 2(x + y)$

5. $(xy)^3$

6. $4x^2 - 3xy$

Do you UNDERSTAND?

7. **Vocabulary** Identify the exponent and the base in 4^3.

8. **Error Analysis** A student simplifies an expression as shown below. Find the error and simplify the expression correctly.

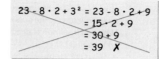

Practice and Problem-Solving Exercises

A Practice   **Simplify each expression.**   ⬅ **See Problems 1 and 2.**

9. 3^5 10. 4^3 11. 2^4 12. 10^8

13. $\left(\frac{2}{3}\right)^3$ 14. $\left(\frac{1}{2}\right)^4$ 15. $(0.4)^6$ 16. 7^4

17. $20 - 2 \cdot 3^2$ 18. $6 + 4 \div 2 + 3$ 19. $(6^2 - 3^3) \div 2$ 20. $5 \cdot 2^2 \div 2 + 8$

21. $80 - (4 - 1)^3$ 22. $52 + 8^2 - 3(4 - 2)^3$ 23. $\frac{6^4 \div 3^2}{9}$ 24. $\frac{2 \cdot 7 + 4}{9 \div 3}$

Evaluate each expression for $s = 4$ and $t = 8$.   ⬅ **See Problem 3.**

25. $(s + t)^3$ 26. $s^4 + t^2 + s \div 2$ 27. $(st)^2$

28. $3st^2 \div st + 6$ 29. $(t - s)^5$ 30. $(2s)^2 t$

31. $2st^2 - s^2$ 32. $2s^2 - t^3 \div 16$ 33. $\frac{(3s)^3 t + t}{s}$

34. Write an expression for the amount of change you will get when you pay for a purchase p with a $20 bill. Make a table to find the amounts of change you will get for purchases of $11.59, $17.50, $19.00, and $20.00.   ⬅ **See Problem 4.**

35. An object's momentum is defined as the product of its mass m and velocity v. Write an expression for the momentum of an object. Make a table to find the momentums of a vehicle with a mass of 1000 kg moving at a velocity of 15 m/s, 20 m/s, and 25 m/s.

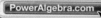

PowerAlgebra.com | **Lesson 1-2** Order of Operations and Evaluating Expressions | 13

Got It? (continued)

4. $c + \frac{1}{10}c$; $47.30, $86.90, $104.50, $113.30

Lesson Check

1. 25
2. 8
3. $\frac{9}{16}$
4. 23
5. 1728
6. 0
7. exponent 3; base 4
8. The student subtracted before multiplying;
$23 - 8 \cdot 2 + 3^2 = 23 - 8 \cdot 2 + 9$
$= 23 - 16 + 9 = 7 + 9 = 16$

Practice and Problem-Solving Exercises

9. 243   10. 64
11. 16   12. 100,000,000
13. $\frac{8}{27}$ 14. $\frac{1}{16}$
15. 0.004096   16. 2401
17. 2   18. 11
19. 4.5   20. 18
21. 53   22. 92
23. 16   24. 6
25. 1728   26. 322
27. 1024   28. 30
29. 1024   30. 512
31. 496   32. 0
33. 3458
34. $20 - p$; $8.41, $2.50, $1.00, $0.00
35. mv; 15,000, 20,000, 25,000

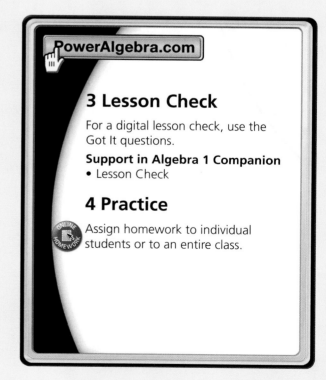

3 Lesson Check

Do you know HOW?

• If students have difficulty with Exercise 6, then have them review Problem 3.

Do you UNDERSTAND?

• If students have difficulty with Exercise 8, then have them show each step of the simplification process rather than performing multiple steps mentally.

Close

Q What is the order of operations? [**Perform operations inside grouping symbols, simplify powers, multiply and divide from left to right, add and subtract from left to right.**]

PowerAlgebra.com

3 Lesson Check

For a digital lesson check, use the Got It questions.

Support in Algebra 1 Companion
• Lesson Check

4 Practice

Assign homework to individual students or to an entire class.

4 Practice

ASSIGNMENT GUIDE

Basic: 9–35 all, 41–47, 55

Average: 9–35 odd, 36–55

Advanced: 9–35 odd, 36–60

Standardized Test Prep: 61–64

Mixed Review: 65–80

Reasoning exercises have blue headings.

Applications exercises have red headings.

EXERCISE 44: Use the Think About a Plan worksheet in the **Practice and Problem Solving Workbook** (also available in the Teaching Resources in print and online) to further support students' development in becoming independent learners.

HOMEWORK QUICK CHECK

To check students' understanding of key skills and concepts, go over Exercises 23, 27, 43, 44, and 55.

 Apply

36. Geometry The expression $\pi r^2 h$ represents the volume of a cylinder with radius r and height h.
  a. What is the volume, to the nearest tenth of a cubic inch, of the juice can at the right? Use 3.14 for π.
  b. Reasoning About how many cubic inches, to the nearest tenth of a cubic inch, does a fluid ounce of juice fill?

$r = 1.2$ in.
CONCENTRATED ORANGE JUICE
12 fl oz
$h = 5.3$ in.

Simplify each expression.

37. $2[(8 - 4)^5 \div 8]$

38. $3[(4 - 2)^5 - 20]$

39. $10 - (2^3 + 4) \div 3 - 1$

40. $\dfrac{22 + 1^3 + (3^4 - 7^2)}{2^3}$

41. $3[42 - 2(10^2 - 9^2)]$

42. $\dfrac{2[8 + (67 - 2^6)^3]}{9}$

43. Think About a Plan The snack bar at your school has added sushi to its menu. The ingredients for one roll include sushi rice, seaweed sheets, cucumbers, cream cheese, and 3 oz of smoked salmon. One roll can be cut into 8 servings. Write an expression for the amount of salmon needed to make s servings of sushi. How much salmon is needed to make 16 servings? 24 servings? 80 servings? 100 servings?
  • What operations are needed in your calculations?
  • Use a table to help you organize your results. What will you use for the column headings in your table?

44. Salary You earn $10 for each hour you work at a canoe rental shop. Write an expression for your salary for working the number of hours h. Make a table to find how much you earn for working 10 h, 20 h, 30 h, and 40 h.

Evaluate each expression for the given values of the variables.

45. $3(s - t)^2; s = 4, t = 1$

46. $2x - y^2; x = 7, y = 3.5$

47. $3m^2 - n; m = 2, n = 6$

48. $(2a + 2b)^2; a = 3, b = 4$

49. $2p^2 + (2q)^2; p = 4, q = 3$

50. $(4c - d + 0.2)^2 - 10c; c = 3.1, d = 4.6$

51. $\dfrac{3g + 6}{h}; g = 5, h = 7$

52. $\dfrac{2w + 3v}{v^2}; v = 6, w = 1$

53. Writing Consider the expression $(1 + 5)^2 - (18 \div 3)$. Can you perform the operations in different orders and still get the correct answer? Explain.

54. A student wrote the expressions shown and claimed they were equal for all values of x and y.
  a. Evaluate each expression for $x = 1$ and $y = 0$.
  b. Evaluate each expression for $x = 1$ and $y = 2$.
  c. Open-Ended Choose another pair of values for x and y. Evaluate each expression for those values.
  d. Writing Is the student's claim correct? Justify your answer.

$(x + y)^2$
$x^2 + y^2$

55. Find the value of $14 + 5 \cdot 3 - 3^2$. Then change two operation signs so that the value of the expression is 8.

Answers

Practice and Problem-Solving Exercises (continued)

36. a. 24.0 in.^{3}
  b. 2.0 in.^{3}

37. 256

38. 36

39. 5

40. $\dfrac{55}{8}$

41. 12

42. $\dfrac{70}{9}$

43. $\dfrac{3}{8} s$; 6 oz; 9 oz; 30 oz; 37.5 oz

44. $10h$; $100, $200, $300, $400

45. 27

46. 1.75

47. 6

48. 196

49. 68

50. 33

51. 3

52. $\dfrac{5}{9}$

53. Yes; you can simplify the expression in the first set of parentheses first, or you can simplify the expression in the second set of parentheses first.

54. a. 1; 1
  b. 9; 5
  c. Check students' work.
  d. No; they are only equal for some values of x and y.

55. 20; $14 - 5 \cdot 3 + 3^2$

Use grouping symbols to make each equation true.

56. $9 + 3 - 2 + 4 = 6$

57. $16 - 4 \div 2 + 3 = 9$

58. $4^2 - 5 \cdot 2 + 1 = 1$

59. $3 \cdot 4 + 5 - 6 + 7 = 28$

60. a. Geometry A cone has a slant height ℓ of 11 cm and a radius r of 3 cm. Use the expression $\pi r(\ell + r)$ to find the surface area of the cone. Use 3.14 for π. Round to the nearest tenth of a square centimeter.

    b. Reasoning Does the surface area of the cone double if the radius doubles? If the slant height doubles? Explain.

Standardized Test Prep

SAT/ACT

61. What is the simplified form of $4 + 10 \div 4 + 6$?

Ⓐ 1.4   Ⓑ 9.5   Ⓒ 12.5   Ⓓ 24

62. What is the value of $(2a)^2 b - 2c^2$ for $a = 2$, $b = 4$, and $c = 3$?

Ⓕ 14   Ⓖ 28   Ⓗ 32   Ⓘ 46

63. A shirt is on sale for $25 at the local department store. The sales tax equals $\frac{1}{25}$ of the shirt's price. What is the total cost of the shirt including sales tax?

Ⓐ $17   Ⓑ $26   Ⓒ $27   Ⓓ $33

64. You can find the distance in feet that an object falls in t seconds using the expression $16t^2$. If you drop a ball from a tall building, how far does the ball fall in 3 s?

Ⓕ 16 ft   Ⓖ 48 ft   Ⓗ 96 ft   Ⓘ 144 ft

Mixed Review

Write an algebraic expression for each word phrase.   ◀ See Lesson 1-1.

65. 4 more than p

66. 5 minus the product of y and 3

67. the quotient of m and 10

68. 3 times the difference of 7 and d

Tell whether each number is *prime* or *composite*.   ◀ See p. 786.

69. 17   **70.** 33   **71.** 43   **72.** 91

Get Ready! To prepare for Lesson 1-3, do Exercises 73–80.

Write each fraction as a decimal and each decimal as a fraction.   ◀ See p. 790.

73. $\frac{3}{5}$ **74.** $\frac{7}{8}$ **75.** $\frac{2}{3}$ **76.** $\frac{4}{7}$

77. 0.7   **78.** 0.07   **79.** 4.25   **80.** 0.425

56. $9 + 3 - (2 + 4) = 6$

57. $(16 - 4) \div 2 + 3 = 9$

58. $4^2 - 5(2 + 1) = 1$

59. $3(4 + 5) - 6 + 7 = 28$

60. a. 131.9 cm^2

    b. No; if the radius doubles, the surface area increases by about 2.4 times; no; if the height doubles, the surface area less than doubles.

61. C

62. I

63. B

64. I

65. $p + 4$

66. $5 - 3y$

67. $\frac{m}{10}$

68. $3(7 - d)$

69. prime

70. composite

71. prime

72. composite

73. 0.6

74. 0.875

75. $0.\overline{6}$

76. $0.\overline{571428}$

77. $\frac{7}{10}$

78. $\frac{7}{100}$

79. $4\frac{1}{4}$ or $\frac{17}{4}$

80. $\frac{17}{40}$

Additional Instructional Support

Algebra 1 Companion

Students can use the **Algebra 1 Companion** worktext (4 pages) as you teach the lesson. Use the Companion to support

- New Vocabulary
- Key Concepts
- Got It for each Problem
- Lesson Check

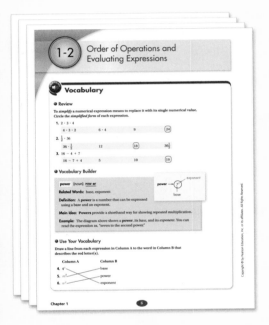

ELL Support

Focus on Language Pair students of different levels of language proficiency. On one side of an index card, have students write the vocabulary words: power, exponent, base, simplify, and evaluate. On the other side of the card, have students write the definition and draw a picture to represent each word. Have each pair of students exchange cards with another pair and compare. Allow students to make new cards combining their ideas.

Students can also use two sets of these word cards (covered on one side) to play a game where they match the word with its definition.

At the end of the activity, each student will have a set of word cards that can be used to review the words, and can be added to throughout the year.

5 Assess & Remediate

Lesson Quiz

1. What is the simplified form of each expression?

  a. 10^8

  b. $(0.2)^5$

2. What is the simplified form of each expression?

  a. $(6 + 3)^2 - 4$

  b. $2^3 + (14 - 4) \div 2$

3. What is the value of $2x + y^2 - xy$ for $x = 1$ and $y = 4$?

4. Do you UNDERSTAND? Raymond spends $\frac{1}{10}$ of his vacation budget on a car rental. Write an expression for how much he has to spend on the rest of his vacation. If he budgets \$650 for the vacation, how much will he have left to spend?

ANSWERS TO LESSON QUIZ

1. a. 100,000,000 **b.** 0.00032

2. a. 77, **b.** 13

3. 14

4. $\frac{9}{10}b$, \$585

PRESCRIPTION FOR REMEDIATION
Use the student work on the Lesson Quiz to prescribe a differentiated review assignment.

Points	Differentiated Remediation
0–2	Intervention
3	On-level
4	Extension

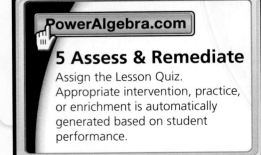

PowerAlgebra.com

5 Assess & Remediate

Assign the Lesson Quiz. Appropriate intervention, practice, or enrichment is automatically generated based on student performance.

Intervention

- **Reteaching** (2 pages) Provides reteaching and practice exercises for the key lesson concepts. Use with struggling students or absent students.

- **English Language Learner Support** Helps students develop and reinforce mathematical vocabulary and key concepts.

All-in-One Resources/Online
Reteaching

Reteaching
1-2 Order of Operations and Evaluating Expressions

Exponents are used to represent repeated multiplication of the same number. For example, $4 \times 4 \times 4 \times 4 \times 4 = 4^5$. The number being multiplied by itself is called the base; in this case, the base is 4. The number that shows how many times the base appears in the product is called the exponent; in this case, the exponent is 5. 4^5 is read *four to the fifth power*.

Problem

How is $6 \times 6 \times 6 \times 6 \times 6 \times 6 \times 6$ written using an exponent?

The number 6 is multiplied by itself 7 times. This means that the base is 6 and the exponent is 7. $6 \times 6 \times 6 \times 6 \times 6 \times 6 \times 6$ written using an exponent is 6^7.

Exercises

Write each repeated multiplication using an exponent.

1. $4 \times 4 \times 4 \times 4 \times 4$

   4^5

2. $2 \times 2 \times 2$

   2^3

3. $1.1 \times 1.1 \times 1.1 \times 1.1 \times 1.1$

   1.1^5

4. $3.4 \times 3.4 \times 3.4 \times 3.4 \times 3.4$

   3.4^5

5. $(-7) \times (-7) \times (-7) \times (-7)$

   $(-7)^4$

6. $11 \times 11 \times 11$

   11^3

Write each expression as repeated multiplication.

7. 4^3 $4 \times 4 \times 4$

8. 5^4 $5 \times 5 \times 5 \times 5$

9. 1.5^2 1.5×1.5

10. $\left(\frac{3}{7}\right)^4$ $\left(\frac{3}{7}\right) \times \left(\frac{3}{7}\right) \times \left(\frac{3}{7}\right) \times \left(\frac{3}{7}\right)$

11. x^7 $x \cdot x \cdot x \cdot x \cdot x \cdot x \cdot x$

12. $(5n)^5$ $5n \times 5n \times 5n \times 5n \times 5n$

13. Trisha wants to determine the volume of a cube with sides of length *s*. Write an expression that represents the volume of the cube. s^3

All-in-One Resources/Online
English Language Learner Support

ELL Support
1-2 Order of Operations and Evaluating Expressions

Complete the vocabulary chart by filling in the missing information.

Word or Word Phrase	Definition	Picture or Example
power	A *power* has two parts, a *base* and an *exponent*.	10^3
exponent	The *exponent* tells you how many times to use the base as an exponent.	10^3
base	The exponent tells you how many times to use the *base* as a factor.	10^3
simplify	To *simplify* is to write an expression in simplest form.	$10^3 = 1,000$
evaluate	You *evaluate* an algebraic expression by replacing each variable with a given number.	Evaluate the expression $(xy)^2$ for $x = 3$ and $y = 4$. $(3 \cdot 4)^2 = 144$

Differentiated Remediation *continued*

On-Level

- **Practice** (2 pages) Provides extra practice for each lesson. For simpler practice exercises, use the Form K Practice pages found in the All-in-One Teaching Resources and online.

- **Think About a Plan** Helps students develop specific problem-solving skills and strategies by providing scaffolded guiding questions.

- **Standardized Test Prep** Focuses on all major exercises, all major question types, and helps students prepare for the high-stakes assessments.

Extension

- **Enrichment** Provides students with interesting problems and activities that extend the concepts of the lesson.

- **Activities, Games, and Puzzles** Worksheets that can be used for concepts development, enrichment, and for fun!

Practice and Problem Solving WKBK/ All-in-One Resources/Online
Practice page 1

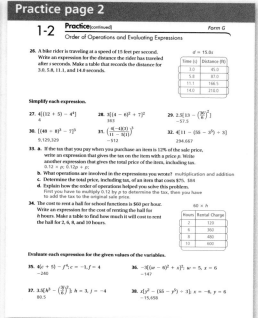

Practice and Problem Solving WKBK/ All-in-One Resources/Online
Practice page 2

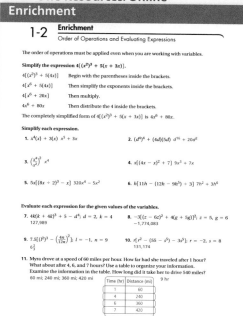

All-in-One Resources/Online
Enrichment

Practice and Problem Solving WKBK/ All-in-One Resources/Online
Think About a Plan

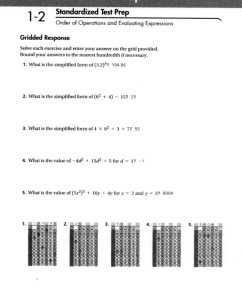

Practice and Problem Solving WKBK/ All-in-One Resources/Online
Standardized Test Prep

Online Teacher Resource Center
Activities, Games, and Puzzles

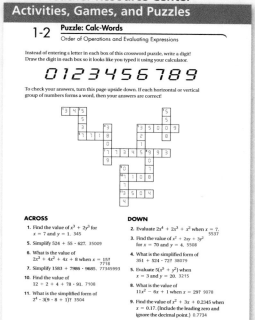

1 Interactive Learning

Solve It!
PURPOSE To introduce the operation of square root as the inverse of the operation of squaring
PROCESS Students may
- make a chart.
- use trial and error.
- find a pattern.

FACILITATE
Q What is the length of the side of the next figure in the pattern? How many square units are in the next figure in the pattern? **[5; 25]**
Q How many square units are in the larger square in the next figure in the pattern? **[25]**
Q Is it possible for a square in this pattern to have exactly 200 square units? Explain. **[No, there is no side length such that $s^2 = 200$.]**

ANSWER See Solve It in Answers on next page.
CONNECT THE MATH In the Solve It, models are shown of the first four perfect squares. Each square represents a perfect square, but also illustrates its square root. This visual model can help students better understand when a number under a radical sign simplifies to an integer and when it does not.

2 Guided Instruction

Take Note
Explain that squaring a number and finding a square root are inverses that "undo" each other.

1-3 Real Numbers and the Number Line

Indiana Academic Standard
Prepares for A1.4.2 Add, subtract and multiply polynomials and divide polynomials by monomials.

Objectives To classify, graph, and compare real numbers
To find and estimate square roots

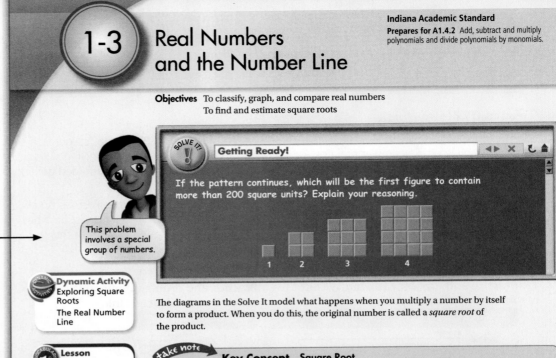

Getting Ready!

If the pattern continues, which will be the first figure to contain more than 200 square units? Explain your reasoning.

1   2   3   4

This problem involves a special group of numbers.

Dynamic Activity
Exploring Square Roots
The Real Number Line

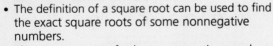

Lesson Vocabulary
- square root
- radicand
- radical
- perfect square
- set
- element of a set
- subset
- rational numbers
- natural numbers
- whole numbers
- integers
- irrational numbers
- real numbers
- inequality

The diagrams in the Solve It model what happens when you multiply a number by itself to form a product. When you do this, the original number is called a *square root* of the product.

take note

Key Concept   Square Root

Algebra A number a is a **square root** of a number b if $a^2 = b$.

Example $7^2 = 49$, so 7 is a square root of 49.

Essential Understanding You can use the definition above to find the exact square roots of some nonnegative numbers. You can approximate the square roots of other nonnegative numbers.

The radical symbol $\sqrt{\ }$ indicates a nonnegative square root, also called a *principal square root*. The expression under the radical symbol is called the **radicand**.

radical symbol $\rightarrow \sqrt{a} \leftarrow$ radicand

Together, the radical symbol and radicand form a **radical**. You will learn about negative square roots in Lesson 1-6.

1-3 Preparing to Teach

BIG idea Properties   **UbD**
ESSENTIAL UNDERSTANDINGS
- The definition of a square root can be used to find the exact square roots of some nonnegative numbers.
- The square roots of other nonnegative numbers can be approximated.
- Numbers can be classified by their characteristics.
- Some types of numbers can be represented on the number line.

Math Background
As students have studied mathematics, the inventory of numbers that they work with has expanded. Students progress through natural numbers, then whole numbers, then positive rational numbers, all the rational numbers, and then finally the entire set of real numbers.

As a number line is examined, it can be seen that each of these subsets of real numbers can be

shown as distinct points on the number line. However, there are numbers that exist between each number that can be shown. For example, there exists infinitely many numbers between 3 and 4. There exists infinitely many numbers between 3 and 3.1. There exists infinitely many numbers between 3 and 3.0000001. Understanding this concept may help to prepare students to comprehend the concept of irrational numbers and will eventually lead to a discussion on imaginary and complex numbers in more advanced courses.

Support Student Learning
Use the **Algebra I Companion** to engage and support students during instruction. See Lesson Resources at the end of this lesson for details.

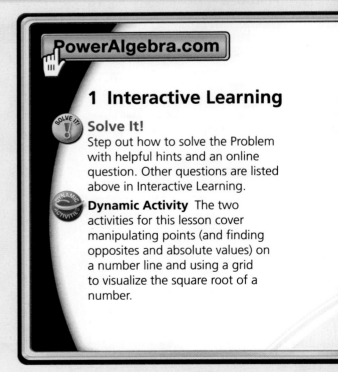

PowerAlgebra.com

1 Interactive Learning

Solve It!
Step out how to solve the Problem with helpful hints and an online question. Other questions are listed above in Interactive Learning.

Dynamic Activity The two activities for this lesson cover manipulating points (and finding opposites and absolute values) on a number line and using a grid to visualize the square root of a number.

Think

How can you find a square root?
Find a number that you can multiply by itself to get a product that is equal to the radicand.

 Problem 1 Simplifying Square Root Expressions

What is the simplified form of each expression?

Ⓐ $\sqrt{81} = 9$ $9^2 = 81$, so 9 is a square root of 81.

Ⓑ $\sqrt{\frac{9}{16}} = \frac{3}{4}$ $\left(\frac{3}{4}\right)^2 = \frac{9}{16}$, so $\frac{3}{4}$ is a square root of $\frac{9}{16}$.

✓ **Got It?** **1.** What is the simplified form of each expression?

a. $\sqrt{64}$ b. $\sqrt{25}$ c. $\sqrt{\frac{1}{36}}$ d. $\sqrt{\frac{81}{121}}$

The square of an integer is called a **perfect square**. For example, 49 is a perfect square because $7^2 = 49$. When a radicand is not a perfect square, you can estimate the square root of the radicand.

 Problem 2 Estimating a Square Root

Biology Lobster eyes are made of tiny square regions. Under a microscope, the surface of the eye looks like graph paper. A scientist measures the area of one of the squares to be 386 square microns. What is the approximate side length of the square to the nearest micron?

386 square microns

Method 1 Estimate $\sqrt{386}$ by finding the two closest perfect squares.

The perfect squares closest to 386 are 361 and 400.
$19^2 = 361$
$20^2 = 400$ $\longleftarrow 386$

Since 386 is closer to 400, $\sqrt{386} \approx 20$, and the side length is about 20 microns.

Method 2 Estimate $\sqrt{386}$ using a calculator.

$\sqrt{386} \approx 19.6$ Use the square root function on your calculator.

The side length of the square is about 20 microns.

✓ **Got It?** **2.** What is the value of $\sqrt{34}$ to the nearest integer?

Plan

How can you get started?
The square root of the area of a square is equal to its side length. So, find $\sqrt{386}$.

Essential Understanding Numbers can be classified by their characteristics. Some types of numbers can be represented on the number line.

You can classify numbers using *sets*. A **set** is a well-defined collection of objects. Each object is called an **element of the set**. A **subset** of a set consists of elements from the given set. You can list the elements of a set within braces { }.

Problem 1

Q How can you describe the relationship between the radicand and its square root? **[The square root multiplied by itself is equal to the radicand.]**

Got It?

Q What do each of the radicands have in common in 1a − 1d? **[For each radicand there is a number that can be multiplied by itself to get the radicand.]**

Problem 2

Q Is there an integer, n, such that $n^2 = 386$? Explain. **[No, because $19^2 = 361$ and $20^2 = 400$.]**

Q If your calculator did not have a square root function, how could you still use your calculator to find an estimate for $\sqrt{386}$? **[You could estimate a number and multiply it by itself until you calculated a product close to 386.]**

Got It?
Emphasize to students that it is not possible to find the exact square root of a number such as 34. Point out that as you round off to more and more decimal places for your estimate, the estimate becomes more accurate.

2 Guided Instruction

 Each Problem is worked out and supported online.

Problem 1
Simplifying Square Root Expressions

Problem 2
Estimating a Square Root
Animated

Problem 3
Classifying Real Numbers

Alternative Problem 3
Classifying Real Numbers
Animated

Problem 4
Comparing Real Numbers

Problem 5
Graphing and Ordering Real Numbers
Animated

Support in Algebra 1 Companion
• Vocabulary
• Key Concepts
• Got It?

Answers

Solve It!
The fifteenth figure is the first figure to contain more than 200 units.

Got It?
1. a. 8
   b. 5
   c. $\frac{1}{6}$
   d. $\frac{9}{11}$
2. about 6

A **rational number** is any number that you can write in the form $\frac{a}{b}$, where a and b are integers and $b \neq 0$. A rational number in decimal form is either a terminating decimal such as 5.45 or a repeating decimal such as $0.41666\ldots$, which you can write as $0.41\overline{6}$. Each graph below shows a subset of the rational numbers on a number line.

Natural numbers $\{1, 2, 3, \ldots\}$

Whole numbers $\{0, 1, 2, 3, \ldots\}$

Integers $\{\ldots -2, -1, 0, 1, 2, 3, \ldots\}$

An **irrational number** cannot be represented as the quotient of two integers. In decimal form, irrational numbers do not terminate or repeat. Here are some examples.

$$0.1010010001\ldots \qquad \pi = 3.14159265\ldots$$

Some square roots are rational numbers and some are irrational numbers. If a whole number is not a perfect square, its square root is irrational.

Rational $\sqrt{4} = 2$ $\qquad\qquad\qquad\sqrt{25} = 5$

Irrational $\sqrt{3} = 1.73205080\ldots$ $\qquad \sqrt{10} = 3.16227766\ldots$

Rational numbers and irrational numbers form the set of **real numbers.**

Problem 3

Q What subsets of numbers are eliminated when you take note of the negative sign in part (b)? **[natural numbers and whole numbers]**

Q Is every number that contains a radicand classified as an irrational number? Explain and give an example. **[No, if the number under the radicand is a perfect square, then the number is an integer or a rational number; for example, $\sqrt{\frac{1}{16}} = \frac{1}{4}$.]**

Got It? ERROR PREVENTION
If students give only one subset for each question, then they most likely do not understand the concept that real numbers can belong to more than one subset of the real numbers.

Take Note VISUAL LEARNERS
Even though students might be unfamiliar with Venn diagrams, take time to point out the "nesting" nature of this diagram. Let students know that the shapes in the diagrams represent boundaries for the various subsets of numbers. Point out that only the subsets of rational numbers and irrational numbers do not have an overlap.

Think

What clues can you use to classify real numbers?
Look for negative signs, fractions, decimals that do or do not terminate or repeat, and radicands that are not perfect squares.

Problem 3 **Classifying Real Numbers**

To which subsets of the real numbers does each number belong?

Ⓐ **15** natural numbers, whole numbers, integers, rational numbers

Ⓑ **−1.4583** rational numbers (since −1.4583 is a terminating decimal)

Ⓒ $\sqrt{57}$ irrational numbers (since 57 is not a perfect square)

Got It? **3.** To which subsets of the real numbers does each number belong?
 a. $\sqrt{9}$ b. $\frac{3}{10}$ c. −0.45 d. $\sqrt{12}$

take note

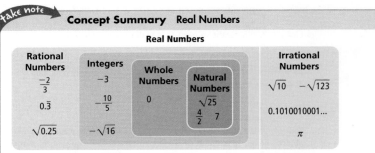

Concept Summary **Real Numbers**

Real Numbers

Rational Numbers				Irrational Numbers
$\frac{-2}{3}$ $0.\overline{3}$ $\sqrt{0.25}$	Integers −3 $-\frac{10}{5}$ $-\sqrt{16}$	Whole Numbers 0	Natural Numbers $\sqrt{25}$ $\frac{4}{2}$ 7	$\sqrt{10}$ $-\sqrt{123}$ 0.1010010001... π

Additional Problems

1. What is the simplified form of each expression?

 a. $\sqrt{25}$

 b. $\sqrt{\frac{4}{81}}$

 ANSWER a. 5, **b.** $\frac{2}{9}$

2. What is the approximate side length of a square that has an area of 220 square inches?

 ANSWER about 15 inches

3. To which subsets of the real numbers does each number belong?

 a. 12

 b. −5.01479

 c. $\sqrt{21}$

 ANSWER a. natural, whole, integer, rational; **b.** rational; **c.** irrational

4. What is an inequality that compares the numbers $\sqrt{34}$ and $5\frac{4}{5}$?

 ANSWER $\sqrt{34} > 5\frac{4}{5}$

5. What is the order of $\sqrt{9}$, 0.3, $-\frac{1}{4}$, $\sqrt{3}$, and −4.25 from least to greatest?

 ANSWER −4.25, $-\frac{1}{4}$, 0.3, $\sqrt{3}$, $\sqrt{9}$

An **inequality** is a mathematical sentence that compares the values of two expressions using an inequality symbol. The symbols are:

$<$, less than $\le$, less than or equal to
$>$, greater than $\ge$, greater than or equal to

 Problem 4 **Comparing Real Numbers**

Plan

How can you compare numbers?
Write the numbers in the same form, such as decimal form.

What is an inequality that compares the numbers $\sqrt{17}$ and $4\frac{1}{3}$?

$\sqrt{17} = 4.12310\ldots$ Write the square root as a decimal.

$4\frac{1}{3} = 4.\overline{3}$ Write the fraction as a decimal.

$\sqrt{17} < 4\frac{1}{3}$ Compare using an inequality symbol.

Got It? 4. a. What is an inequality that compares the numbers $\sqrt{129}$ and 11.52?

   b. Reasoning In Problem 4, is there another inequality you can write that compares the two numbers? Explain.

You can graph and order all real numbers using a number line.

Problem 5 **Graphing and Ordering Real Numbers**

Multiple Choice What is the order of $\sqrt{4}$, 0.4, $-\frac{2}{3}$, $\sqrt{2}$, and -1.5 from least to greatest?

Ⓐ $-\frac{2}{3}$, 0.4, -1.5, $\sqrt{2}$, $\sqrt{4}$ Ⓒ -1.5, $-\frac{2}{3}$, 0.4, $\sqrt{2}$, $\sqrt{4}$

Ⓑ -1.5, $\sqrt{2}$, 0.4, $\sqrt{4}$, $-\frac{2}{3}$ Ⓓ $\sqrt{4}$, $\sqrt{2}$, 0.4, $-\frac{2}{3}$, -1.5

Know	Need	Plan
Five real numbers	Order of numbers from least to greatest	Graph the numbers on a number line.

Think

Why is it useful to rewrite numbers in decimal form?
It allows you to compare numbers whose values are close, like $\frac{1}{4}$ and 0.26.

First, write the numbers that are not in decimal form as decimals: $\sqrt{4} = 2$, $-\frac{2}{3} \approx -0.67$, and $\sqrt{2} \approx 1.41$. Then graph all five numbers on the number line to order the numbers, and read the graph from left to right.

$-1.5 \quad -\frac{2}{3} \quad 0.4 \ \sqrt{2}\ \sqrt{4}$

(number line from -2 to 3)

From least to greatest, the numbers are -1.5, $-\frac{2}{3}$, 0.4, $\sqrt{2}$, and $\sqrt{4}$. The correct answer is C.

Got It? 5. Graph 3.5, -2.1, $\sqrt{9}$, $-\frac{7}{2}$, and $\sqrt{5}$ on a number line. What is the order of the numbers from least to greatest?

Problem 4

Q Without changing the position of the numbers in the final line, can you use another inequality symbol? **[Yes, you can also write $\sqrt{17} \le 4\frac{1}{3}$.]**

Got It?

Q How could you use the process of squaring, instead of taking the square root, to determine the relationship of the two numbers? **[You could compare 11.52^2 to 129.]**

Problem 5

Q What is the most convenient form for the numbers to be written in so that they can be compared? **[decimal form]**

Q Which numbers will be to the left of zero on the number line? **[-1.5, $-\frac{2}{3}$]**

Q Which of the numbers is not part of the same subset of the real numbers as the other four numbers? **[$\sqrt{2}$]**

Got It?   **VISUAL LEARNERS**

As a preview of absolute value, point out that although 3.5 and $-\frac{7}{2}$ are the same distance from zero on the number line, numbers to the left of zero are less than numbers to the right of zero.

Answers

Got It? (continued)

3. a. rational numbers, natural numbers, whole numbers, integers
  b. rational numbers
  c. rational numbers
  d. irrational numbers

4. a. $\sqrt{129} < 11.52$

  b. Yes $4\frac{1}{3} > \sqrt{17}$ also compares the two numbers.

5.   (number line from -4 to 4)

  $-\frac{7}{2}$, -2.1, $\sqrt{5}$, $\sqrt{9}$, 3.5

3 Lesson Check

Do you know HOW?
- If students have difficulty with Exercise 3, then have them convert $\frac{47}{10}$ from fraction to decimal form.

Do you UNDERSTAND?
- If students have difficulty with Exercise 8, then have them review Problem 3.

Close

Q Because 15 is a natural number, does that automatically mean that 15 is also a whole number? Explain. **[Yes; Every natural number is also a whole number.]**

Lesson Check

Do you know HOW?

Name the subset(s) of the real numbers to which each number belongs.

1. $\sqrt{11}$
2. -7
3. Order $\frac{47}{10}$, 4.1, -5, and $\sqrt{16}$ from least to greatest.
4. A square card has an area of 15 in.^{2}. What is the approximate side length of the card?

Do you UNDERSTAND?

5. **Vocabulary** What are the two subsets of the real numbers that form the set of real numbers?

6. **Vocabulary** Give an example of a rational number that is not an integer.

Reasoning Tell whether each square root is *rational* or *irrational*. Explain.

7. $\sqrt{100}$
8. $\sqrt{0.29}$

Practice and Problem-Solving Exercises

A Practice

Simplify each expression.   ◀ See Problem 1.

9. $\sqrt{36}$ 10. $\sqrt{169}$ 11. $\sqrt{16}$ 12. $\sqrt{900}$ 13. $\sqrt{\frac{36}{49}}$

14. $\sqrt{\frac{25}{81}}$ 15. $\sqrt{\frac{1}{9}}$ 16. $\sqrt{\frac{121}{16}}$ 17. $\sqrt{1.96}$ 18. $\sqrt{0.25}$

Estimate the square root. Round to the nearest integer.   ◀ See Problem 2.

19. $\sqrt{17}$ 20. $\sqrt{35}$ 21. $\sqrt{242}$ 22. $\sqrt{61}$ 23. $\sqrt{320}$

Find the approximate side length of each square figure to the nearest whole unit.

24. a mural with an area of 18 m^2

25. a game board with an area of 160 in.^{2}

26. a helicopter launching pad with an area of 3000 ft^2

Name the subset(s) of the real numbers to which each number belongs   ◀ See Problem 3.

27. $\frac{2}{3}$ 28. 13 29. -1 30. $-\frac{19}{100}$ 31. π

32. -2.38 33. $\frac{17}{4573}$ 34. $\sqrt{144}$ 35. $\sqrt{113}$ 36. $\frac{59}{2}$

Compare the numbers in each exercise using an inequality symbol.   ◀ See Problem 4.

37. $5\frac{2}{3}, \sqrt{29}$ 38. $-3.1, -\frac{16}{5}$ 39. $\frac{4}{3}, \sqrt{2}$ 40. $9.6, \sqrt{96}$

41. $-\frac{7}{11}, -0.63$ 42. $\sqrt{115}, 10.72104\ldots$ 43. $-\frac{22}{25}, -0.\overline{8}$ 44. $\sqrt{184}, 15.56987\ldots$

Order the numbers in each exercise from least to greatest.   ◀ See Problem 5.

45. $\frac{1}{2}, -2, \sqrt{5}, -\frac{7}{4}, 2.4$ 46. $-3, \sqrt{31}, \sqrt{11}, 5.5, -\frac{60}{11}$ 47. $-6, \sqrt{20}, 4.3, -\frac{59}{9}$

48. $\frac{10}{3}, 3, \sqrt{8}, 2.9, \sqrt{7}$ 49. $-\frac{13}{6}, -2.1, -\frac{26}{13}, -\frac{9}{4}$ 50. $-\frac{1}{6}, -0.3, \sqrt{1}, -\frac{2}{13}, \frac{7}{8}$

Answers

Lesson Check
1. irrational numbers
2. rational numbers, integers
3. $-5, \sqrt{16}, 4.1, \frac{47}{10}$
4. about 4 in.
5. rational numbers and irrational numbers
6. Answers may vary. Sample: 0.5
7. Rational; its value is 10 which can be written as a ratio of two integers, $\frac{10}{1}$.
8. Irrational; $\sqrt{0.29}$ is a non-repeating, non-terminating number.

Practice and Problem-Solving Exercises
9. 6 10. 13 11. 4 12. 30
13. $\frac{6}{7}$ 14. $\frac{5}{9}$ 15. $\frac{1}{3}$ 16. $\frac{11}{4}$
17. 1.4 18. 0.5

19. about 4 20. about 6
21. about 16 22. about 8
23. about 18 24. about 4 m
25. about 13 in. 26. about 55 ft
27. rational numbers
28. rational numbers, whole numbers, natural numbers, integers
29. rational numbers, integers
30. rational numbers
31. irrational numbers
32. rational numbers
33. rational numbers
34. rational numbers, whole numbers, natural numbers, integers
35. irrational numbers
36. rational numbers

51. Think About a Plan A stage designer paid $4 per square foot for flooring to be used in a square room. If the designer spent $600 on the flooring, about how long is a side of the room? Round to the nearest foot.
- How is the area of a square related to its side length?
- How can you estimate the length of a side of a square?

Tell whether each statement is *true* or *false*. Explain.

52. All negative numbers are integers.

53. All integers are rational numbers.

54. All square roots are irrational numbers.

55. No positive number is an integer.

56. Reasoning A restaurant owner is going to panel a square portion of the restaurant's ceiling. The portion to be paneled has an area of 185 ft². The owner plans to use square tin ceiling panels with a side length of 2 ft. What is the first step in finding out whether the owner will be able to use a whole number of panels?

Show that each number is rational by writing it in the form $\frac{a}{b}$, where a and b are integers.

57. 417 **58.** 0.37 **59.** 2.01 **60.** 2.1 **61.** 3.06

62. Error Analysis A student says that $\sqrt{7}$ is a rational number because you can write $\sqrt{7}$ as the quotient $\frac{\sqrt{7}}{1}$. Is the student correct? Explain.

63. Construction A contractor is tiling a square patio that has the area shown at the right. What is the approximate side length of the patio? Round to the nearest foot.

A = 136 ft²

64. Open-Ended You are tutoring a younger student. How would you explain rational numbers, irrational numbers, and how they are different?

65. Geometry The irrational number π, equal to 3.14159..., is the ratio of a circle's circumference to its diameter. In the sixth century, the mathematician Brahmagupta estimated the value of π to be $\sqrt{10}$. In the thirteenth century, the mathematician Fibonacci estimated the value of π to be $\frac{864}{275}$. Which is the better estimate? Explain.

66. Home Improvement If you lean a ladder against a wall, the length of the ladder should be $\sqrt{(x)^2 + (4x)^2}$ ft to be considered safe. The distance x is how far the ladder's base is from the wall. Estimate the desired length of the ladder when the base is positioned 5 ft from the wall. Round your answer to the nearest tenth.

67. Writing Is there a greatest integer on the real number line? A least fraction? Explain.

68. Reasoning Choose three intervals on the real number line that contain both rational and irrational numbers. Do you think that any given interval on the real number line contains both rational and irrational numbers? Explain.

4 Practice

ASSIGNMENT GUIDE

Basic: 9–50 all, 51–56, 58, 60, 62–67

Average: 9–49 odd, 51–68

Advanced: 9–49 odd, 51–71

Standardized Test Prep: 72–74

Mixed Review: 75–85

Reasoning exercises have blue headings.

Applications exercises have red headings.

EXERCISE 63: Use the Think About a Plan worksheet in the **Practice and Problem Solving Workbook** (also available in the Teaching Resources in print and online) to further support students' development in becoming independent learners.

HOMEWORK QUICK CHECK

To check students' understanding of key skills and concepts, go over Exercises 13, 45, 51, 56, and 63.

---

37. $5\frac{2}{3} > \sqrt{29}$ **38.** $-3.1 > \frac{-16}{5}$

39. $\frac{4}{3} < \sqrt{2}$ **40.** $9.6 < \sqrt{96}$

41. $-\frac{7}{11} < -0.63$

42. $\sqrt{115} > 10.72104...$

43. $-\frac{22}{25} < -0.\overline{8}$

44. $\sqrt{184} < 15.56987...$

45. $-2, -\frac{7}{4}, \frac{1}{2}, \sqrt{5}, 2.4$

46. $-\frac{60}{11}, -3, \sqrt{11}, 5.5, \sqrt{31}$

47. $-\frac{59}{9}, -6, 4.3, \sqrt{20}$

48. $\sqrt{7}, \sqrt{8}, 2.9, 3, \frac{10}{3}$

49. $-\frac{9}{4}, -\frac{13}{6}, -2.1, -\frac{26}{13}$

50. $-0.3, -\frac{1}{6}, -\frac{2}{13}, \frac{7}{8}, \sqrt{1}$

51. about 12 ft

52–55. Explanations may vary.

52. False; $-\frac{1}{2}$ is not an integer.

53. True; any integer can be expressed as a rational number.

54. False; $\sqrt{4} = 2$ which is a rational number.

55. False; 2 is a positive number and an integer.

56. Find the square root 185.

57. $\frac{417}{1}$

58. $\frac{37}{100}$

59. $\frac{201}{100}$

60. $\frac{21}{10}$

61. $\frac{306}{100}$

62. No; a rational number must be written as the ratio of two integers and $\sqrt{7}$ is not an integer.

63. about 12 ft

64. Check students' work.

65. $\frac{864}{275}$; its value 3.14181... is closer to the value of π than $\sqrt{10}$, which is 3.16227...

66. 20.6 ft

67. No; no; the real number line extends indefinitely in both the positive direction and the negative direction.

68. Yes; check students' work.

Answers

Practice and Problem-Solving Exercises
(continued)

69. 228 ft; 457 ft; 685 ft; 4109 ft

70. It is true for products involving two numbers greater than 0 and less than 1.

71. a. 4

   b. 10

   c. 7

   d. 13

72. B

73. I

74. C

75. 16

76. 78

77. 512

78. $14 + x$

79. $4(y + 1)$

80. $\frac{3880}{z}$

81. $\frac{19}{3}t$

82. 18

83. 72

84. 442

85. 9

Challenge

69. Antennas Guy wires are attached to an antenna tower at the heights h shown at the right. Use the expression $\sqrt{h^2 + (0.55h)^2}$ to estimate the wire length for each height. If three wires are attached at each height, what is the minimum total amount of wire needed?

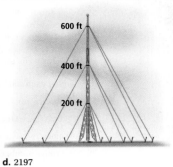

70. Reasoning Sometimes the product of two positive numbers is less than either number. Describe the numbers for which this is true.

71. Cube Roots The number a is the *cube root* of a number b if $a^3 = b$. For example, the cube root of 8 is 2 because $2^3 = 8$. Find the cube root of each number.

   a. 64   **b.** 1000   **c.** 343   **d.** 2197

Standardized Test Prep

SAT/ACT

72. A square picture has an area of 225 in.^{2}. What is the side length of the picture?

   Ⓐ 5 in.   Ⓑ 15 in.   Ⓒ 25 in.   Ⓓ 225 in.

73. To simplify the expression $9 \cdot (33 - 5^2) \div 2$, what do you do first?

   Ⓕ Divide by 2.   Ⓖ Subtract 5.   Ⓗ Multiply by 9.   Ⓘ Square 5.

74. The table at the right shows the number of pages you can read per minute. Which algebraic expression gives a rule for finding the number of pages read in any number of minutes m?

   Ⓐ m Ⓒ $2m$

   Ⓑ $m + 2$ Ⓓ $\frac{m}{2}$

Reading

Minutes	Pages Read
1	2
2	4
3	6
m	■

Mixed Review

Evaluate each expression for the given values of the variables.   ◀ See Lesson 1-2.

75. $(r - t)^2$; $r = 11$, $t = 7$ **76.** $3m^2 + n$; $m = 5$, $n = 3$ **77.** $(2x)^2y$; $x = 4$, $y = 8$

Write an algebraic expression for each word phrase.   ◀ See Lesson 1-1.

78. the sum of 14 and x **79.** 4 multiplied by the sum of y and 1

80. 3880 divided by z **81.** the product of t and the quotient of 19 and 3

Get Ready!   To prepare for Lesson 1-4, do Exercises 82–85.

Simplify each expression.   ◀ See Lesson 1-2.

82. $4 + 7 \cdot 2$ **83.** $(7 + 1)9$ **84.** $2 + 22 \cdot 20$ **85.** $6 + 18 \div 6$

Additional Instructional Support

Algebra 1 Companion

Students can use the **Algebra 1 Companion** worktext (4 pages) as you teach the lesson. Use the Companion to support

- New Vocabulary
- Key Concepts
- Got It for each Problem
- Lesson Check

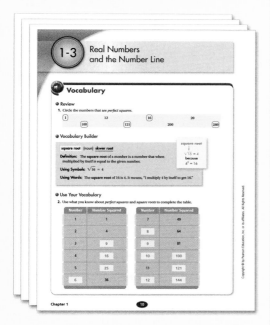

ELL Support

Connect to Prior Knowledge Have a volunteer draw a number line on the board. Ask the students to write a real number on a sticky note. Demonstrate placing one of the sticky notes on the number line. Explain your reasoning. For example, "The square root of 28 ($\sqrt{28}$) is between $\sqrt{25}$ which equals 5, and $\sqrt{36}$ which equals 6. However, 28 is closer to 25 than to 36, so $\sqrt{28}$ is closer to 5 than to 6." Ask the students to form small groups and discuss where their numbers belong on the number line. Say, "Be prepared to explain your reason for placing the number where you do." Then have students place their sticky note on the number line and explain their reasoning. Allow other members of the group to give the student support, as needed.

5 Assess & Remediate

Lesson Quiz

1. Simplify $\sqrt{\frac{25}{36}}$.
2. **Do you UNDERSTAND?** Rachael's patio has an area of 290 square feet. If the patio is shaped like a square, what is the approximate side length?
3. To which subsets of the real numbers does the number 14 belong?
4. Write an inequality to compare the numbers $7\frac{1}{8}$ and $\sqrt{50}$.
5. Order the numbers 2, $-\frac{1}{2}$, $\sqrt{16}$, $\sqrt{5}$, and 4.05 from least to greatest.

ANSWERS TO LESSON QUIZ

1. $\frac{5}{6}$
2. about 17 feet
3. natural, whole, integer, rational
4. $7\frac{1}{8} > \sqrt{50}$
5. $-\frac{1}{2}$, 2, $\sqrt{5}$, $\sqrt{16}$, 4.05

PRESCRIPTION FOR REMEDIATION
Use the student work on the Lesson Quiz to prescribe a differentiated review assignment.

Points	Differentiated Remediation
0–2	Intervention
3–4	On-level
5	Extension

PowerAlgebra.com

5 Assess & Remediate

Assign the Lesson Quiz. Appropriate intervention, practice, or enrichment is automatically generated based on student performance.

Intervention

- **Reteaching** (2 pages) Provides reteaching and practice exercises for the key lesson concepts. Use with struggling students or absent students.
- **English Language Learner Support** Helps students develop and reinforce mathematical vocabulary and key concepts.

All-in-One Resources/Online
Reteaching

1-3 Reteaching
Real Numbers and the Number Line

A number that is the product of some other number with itself, or a number to the second power, such as $9 = 3 \times 3 = 3^2$, is called a perfect square. A number that is raised to the second power is called the square root of the product. In this case, 3 is the square root of 9. This is written in symbols as $\sqrt{9} = 3$. Sometimes square roots are whole numbers, but in other cases, they can be estimated.

Problem

What is an estimate for the square root of 150?

There is no whole number that can be multiplied by itself to give the product of 150.

$10 \times 10 = 100$
$11 \times 11 = 121$
$12 \times 12 = 144$
$13 \times 13 = 169$

You cannot find the exact value of $\sqrt{150}$, but you can estimate it by comparing 150 to perfect squares that are close to 150.

150 is between 144 and 169, so $\sqrt{150}$ is between $\sqrt{144}$ and $\sqrt{169}$.

$\sqrt{144} < \sqrt{150} < \sqrt{169}$
$12 < \sqrt{150} < 13$

The square root of 150 is between 12 and 13. Because 150 is closer to 144 than it is to 169, we can estimate that the square root of 150 is slightly greater than 12.

Exercises

Find the square root of each number. If the number is not a perfect square, estimate the square root to the nearest integer.

1. 100 10
2. 49 7
3. 9 3
4. 25 5
5. 81 9
6. 169 13
7. 15 4
8. 24 5
9. 40 6

10. A square mat has an area of 225 cm². What is the length of each side of the mat? 15 cm

All-in-One Resources/Online
English Language Learner Support

1-3 ELL Support
Real Numbers and the Number Line

Concept List

inequalities	integers	irrational numbers
natural numbers	perfect square	radical
radicand	square root	whole numbers

Choose the concept from the list above that best represents the item in each box.

1. $\sqrt{64}$	2. π, $\sqrt{3}$	3. $\{0, 1, 2, 3, \ldots\}$
radicand	irrational numbers	whole numbers
4. $\sqrt{1.44} = 1.2$	5. $\longrightarrow \sqrt{64}$	6. $8^2 = 64$
square root	radical	perfect square
7. $\{\ldots, -2, -1, 0, 1, 2, 3, \ldots\}$	8. $\{1, 2, 3, \ldots\}$	9. $<, >, \leq, \geq$
integers	natural numbers	inequalities

Differentiated Remediation *continued*

On-Level

- **Practice** (2 pages) Provides extra practice for each lesson. For simpler practice exercises, use the Form K Practice pages found in the All-in-One Teaching Resources and online.

- **Think About a Plan** Helps students develop specific problem-solving skills and strategies by providing scaffolded guiding questions.

- **Standardized Test Prep** Focuses on all major exercises, all major question types, and helps students prepare for the high-stakes assessments.

Extension

- **Enrichment** Provides students with interesting problems and activities that extend the concepts of the lesson.

- **Activities, Games, and Puzzles** Worksheets that can be used for concepts development, enrichment, and for fun!

Practice and Problem Solving WKBK/ All-in-One Resources/Online
Practice page 1

1-3 Practice — Form G
Real Numbers and the Number Line

Simplify each expression.

1. $\sqrt{4}$ 2
2. $\sqrt{36}$ 6
3. $\sqrt{25}$ 5
4. $\sqrt{81}$ 9
5. $\sqrt{121}$ 11
6. $\sqrt{169}$ 13
7. $\sqrt{625}$ 25
8. $\sqrt{225}$ 15
9. $\sqrt{\frac{64}{9}}$ $\frac{8}{3}$
10. $\sqrt{\frac{25}{81}}$ $\frac{5}{9}$
11. $\sqrt{\frac{225}{169}}$ $\frac{15}{13}$
12. $\sqrt{\frac{1}{625}}$ $\frac{1}{25}$
13. $\sqrt{0.64}$ 0.8
14. $\sqrt{0.81}$ 0.9
15. $\sqrt{6.25}$ 2.5

Estimate the square root. Round to the nearest integer.

16. $\sqrt{10}$ 3
17. $\sqrt{15}$ 4
18. $\sqrt{38}$ 6
19. $\sqrt{50}$ 7
20. $\sqrt{16.8}$ 4
21. $\sqrt{37.5}$ 6
22. $\sqrt{67.5}$ 8
23. $\sqrt{81.49}$ 9
24. $\sqrt{121.86}$ 11

Find the approximate side length of each square figure to the nearest whole unit.

25. a rug with an area of 64 ft² 8 ft
26. an exercise mat that is 6.25 m² 2.5 m
27. a plate that is 49 cm² 7 cm

Practice and Problem Solving WKBK/ All-in-One Resources/Online
Practice page 2

1-3 Practice (continued) — Form G
Real Numbers and the Number Line

Name the subset(s) of the real numbers to which each number belongs.

28. $\frac{12}{18}$ rational
29. −5 rational; integer
30. π irrational
31. $\sqrt{2}$ irrational
32. 5564 rational; integer; whole; natural
33. $\sqrt{13}$ irrational
34. $-\frac{4}{5}$ rational
35. $\sqrt{61}$ irrational

Compare the numbers in each exercise using an inequality symbol.

36. $\sqrt{25}$, $\sqrt{64}$ $\sqrt{25} < \sqrt{64}$
37. $\frac{4}{5}$, $\sqrt{1.3}$ $\frac{4}{5} < \sqrt{1.3}$
38. π, $\frac{19}{6}$ $\pi < \frac{19}{6}$
39. $\sqrt{81}$, $-\sqrt{121}$ $\sqrt{81} > -\sqrt{121}$
40. $\frac{27}{17}$, 1.7781356 $\frac{27}{17} < 1.7781356$
41. $-\frac{14}{15}$, $\sqrt{0.8711}$ $-\frac{14}{15} < \sqrt{0.8711}$

Order the numbers from least to greatest.

42. 1.875, $\sqrt{64}$, $-\sqrt{121}$ $-\sqrt{121}$, 1.875, $\sqrt{64}$,
43. $\sqrt{0.8711}$, $\frac{4}{5}$, $\sqrt{1.3}$ $\frac{4}{5}$, $\sqrt{0.8711}$, $\sqrt{1.3}$
44. 8.775, $\sqrt{67.4698}$, $\frac{64.56}{8.477}$ $\frac{64.56}{8.477}$, $\sqrt{67.4698}$, 8.775
45. $-\frac{14}{15}$, 5.587, $\sqrt{81}$ $-\frac{14}{15}$, 5.587, $\sqrt{81}$
46. $\frac{100}{22}$, $\sqrt{25}$, $\frac{27}{17}$ $\frac{27}{17}$, $\frac{100}{22}$, $\sqrt{25}$
47. π, $\sqrt{10.5625}$, $\frac{15}{5.8}$ $\frac{15}{5.8}$, π, $\sqrt{10.5625}$

48. Marsha, Josh, and Tyler are comparing how fast they can type. Marsha types 125 words in 7.5 minutes. Josh types 65 words in 3 minutes. Tyler types 400 words in 28 minutes. Order the students according to who can type the fastest.
Josh, Marsha, Tyler

All-in-One Resources/Online
Enrichment

1-3 Enrichment
Real Numbers and the Number Line

You can find the square root of a variable in the same way that you can find the square root of a number.

$\sqrt{x^2} = x$ because $x \cdot x = x^2$

The same rules hold true for the square roots of expressions as well.

$\sqrt{(x + 1)^2} = (x + 1)$ because $(x + 1)(x + 1) = (x + 1)^2$

Exercises

Simplify each expression.

1. $\sqrt{64}$ 8
2. $\sqrt{121}$ 11
3. $\sqrt{x^4}$ x^2
4. $\sqrt{y^{12}}$ y^6
5. $\sqrt{x^4y^8}$ x^2y^4
6. $\sqrt{\left(\frac{x^4}{x^2}\right)}$ x
7. $\sqrt{(x + 1)^2}$ $x + 1$
8. $\sqrt{(45x + 89)^2}$ $45x + 89$
9. $\sqrt{(-23x^4 + 81)^8}$ $(-23x^4 + 81)^4$
10. $\sqrt{(11g + 81)^6(25h - 16)^4}$ $(11g + 81)^3(25h - 16)^2$
11. $\sqrt{\sqrt{x^8}}$ x^2

12. The formula for finding the area of a circle is $A = \pi r^2$. You are building a target for practicing archery. The area of the target is 706.5 cm². Use 3.14 as an approximation for π and determine the radius of the target.
15

Practice and Problem Solving WKBK/ All-in-One Resources/Online
Think About a Plan

1-3 Think About a Plan
Real Numbers and the Number Line

Home Improvement If you lean a ladder against a wall, the length of the ladder should be $\sqrt{(x)^2 + (4x)^2}$ ft to be considered safe. The distance x is how far the ladder's base is from the wall. Estimate the desired length of the ladder when the base is positioned 5 ft from the wall. Round your answer to the nearest tenth.

Think

1. What does x represent in the given expression? What value is given for x?
the distance from the base of the ladder to the wall; 5 ft

Plan

2. What is the expression when the given value is substituted for x?
$\sqrt{5^2 + (20)^2}$

3. How do you simplify the expression under the square root symbol?
Square each of 5 and 20, then add the results.

4. What is the value of the expression under the square root symbol? Is this number a perfect square?
425; no

Solve

5. What is an estimate for the desired length of the ladder? Round your answer to the nearest tenth.
20.6 ft

Practice and Problem Solving WKBK/ All-in-One Resources/Online
Standardized Test Prep

1-3 Standardized Test Prep
Real Numbers and the Number Line

Multiple Choice

For Exercises 1-6, choose the correct letter.

1. To which subset of the real numbers does −18 not belong? A
   A. irrational   B. rational   C. integer   D. negative integers

2. To which subset of the real numbers does $\sqrt{2}$ belong? F
   F. irrational   G. rational   H. integer   I. whole

3. You can tell that π is an irrational number because it has a what? D
   A. non-repeating decimal   C. repeating decimal
   B. non-terminating decimal   D. non-repeating and a non-terminating decimal

4. What is $\sqrt{324}$? G
   F. 15   G. 18   H. 19   I. 24

5. What is $\sqrt{196}$? A
   A. −14   B. 0   C. 4   D. 19

6. What is $\sqrt{36x^6y^4}$? G
   F. $6x^3y^4$ G. $6x^3y^2$ H. $18x^3y^2$ I. $24x^6y^4$

Short Response

7. Why is 8.8 classified as a rational number?
8.8 can be classified as a rational number because it can be rewritten as the fraction $\frac{88}{10}$.
[2] Question answered correctly.
[1] Answer is incomplete.
[0] Answer is wrong.

Online Teacher Resource Center
Activities, Games, and Puzzles

1-3 Activity: Inequality Ski Trail
Real Numbers and the Number Line

In this activity, you will ski down the trail shown below. You can work with a partner and then discuss your results as a class when everyone has finished.

Begin by filling in the 18 boxes with the 18 numbers below. You can place the numbers anywhere you want. Use each number once. After filling in the numbers, determine the path to take by identifying the symbol (<, =, >) that correctly relates the two numbers. Place the correct symbol in the circle. If the symbol is <, take the left path down the trail. If the symbol is =, take the middle path. If the symbol is >, take the right path.

After you have completed the trail, find the time it took you to ski down. The times (in seconds) are shown next to each of the paths. Compare your time with your partner's and other classmates. Check students' work.

−0.4	$-\frac{7}{8}$	0.32	$-\frac{1}{2}$	0.75	$\frac{5}{12}$	0.09	−0.1	$\frac{3}{4}$
−0.9	$\frac{2}{3}$	−0.5	$\frac{1}{9}$	$\frac{2}{5}$	0.2	0.6	0.625	$\frac{1}{2}$

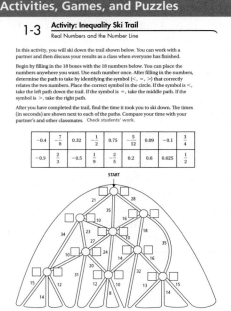

1-4 Properties of Real Numbers

Indiana Academic Standard
Prepares for A1.4.2 Add, subtract and multiply polynomials and divide polynomials by monomials.

Objective To identify and use properties of real numbers

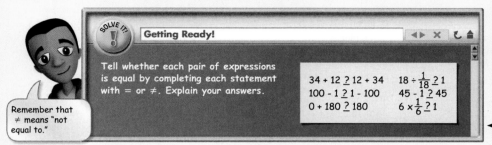

SOLVE IT!

Getting Ready!

Tell whether each pair of expressions is equal by completing each statement with = or ≠. Explain your answers.

$34 + 12 \, \underline{?} \, 12 + 34$ $18 \div \frac{1}{18} \, \underline{?} \, 1$
$100 - 1 \, \underline{?} \, 1 - 100$ $45 - 1 \, \underline{?} \, 45$
$0 + 180 \, \underline{?} \, 180$ $6 \times \frac{1}{6} \, \underline{?} \, 1$

Remember that ≠ means "not equal to."

Lesson Vocabulary
• equivalent expressions
• deductive reasoning
• counterexample

The Solve It illustrates numerical relationships that are always true for real numbers.

Essential Understanding Relationships that are always true for real numbers are called *properties*, which are rules used to rewrite and compare expressions.

Two algebraic expressions are **equivalent expressions** if they have the same value for all values of the variable(s). The following properties show expressions that are equivalent for all real numbers.

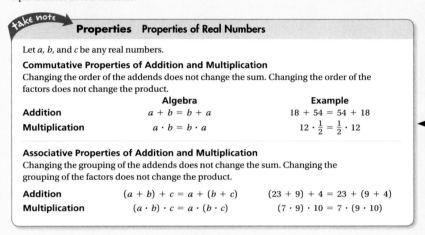

take note

Properties   Properties of Real Numbers

Let a, b, and c be any real numbers.

Commutative Properties of Addition and Multiplication
Changing the order of the addends does not change the sum. Changing the order of the factors does not change the product.

	Algebra	Example
Addition	$a + b = b + a$	$18 + 54 = 54 + 18$
Multiplication	$a \cdot b = b \cdot a$	$12 \cdot \frac{1}{2} = \frac{1}{2} \cdot 12$

Associative Properties of Addition and Multiplication
Changing the grouping of the addends does not change the sum. Changing the grouping of the factors does not change the product.

| **Addition** | $(a + b) + c = a + (b + c)$ | $(23 + 9) + 4 = 23 + (9 + 4)$ |
| **Multiplication** | $(a \cdot b) \cdot c = a \cdot (b \cdot c)$ | $(7 \cdot 9) \cdot 10 = 7 \cdot (9 \cdot 10)$ |

1 Interactive Learning

Solve It!
PURPOSE To use numerical expressions to illustrate properties of real numbers
PROCESS Students may use mathematical reasoning, trial and error, or apply previous knowledge of properties of real numbers.

FACILITATE
Q Which expressions include operations with reciprocals? **[$18 \div \frac{1}{18}$ and $6 \times \frac{1}{6}$]**
Q Which of the expressions with reciprocals equal 1? Explain. **[$6 \times \frac{1}{6}$; $\frac{6}{6}$ simplifies to 1; the other expression equals 18^2.]**

ANSWER See Solve It in Answers on next page.
CONNECT THE MATH In the Solve It, students use the properties of real numbers to evaluate particular expressions. In this lesson, students will learn the general form of these properties and how they apply to all real numbers.

2 Guided Instruction

Take Note

Q How can the everyday usage of the words *commute* and *associate* help you remember the mathematical meaning of the words *commutative* and *associative*? **[Commuting means you travel from point A to point B or from point B to point A. The distance is the same no matter which direction you are traveling. When you are an associate of a person, you are in a group with that person.]**

1-4 Preparing to Teach

BIG idea Properties   **UbD**
ESSENTIAL UNDERSTANDINGS
• Relationships that are always true for real numbers are called properties, which are rules used to rewrite and compare expressions.
• Important properties include the commutative, associative and identity properties, the zero property of multiplication and the multiplication property of −1.

Math Background
The process for solving any equation in one variable is to create a series of equivalent equations until the variable is isolated and has a coefficient of 1. Equivalent equations and inequalities are created by applying the properties of real numbers introduced in this lesson as well as properties that

will be introduced in subsequent lessons. Students should know the formal names for the properties so that they become familiar with the vocabulary used when discussing algebra and justifying operations. A strong knowledge and understanding of properties will help students in later chapters and in higher-level mathematics as they begin to prove theorems. They will learn to use logic and reasoning which will help them in writing algebraic or geometric proofs.

Support Student Learning
Use the **Algebra I Companion** to engage and support students during instruction. See Lesson Resources at the end of this lesson for details.

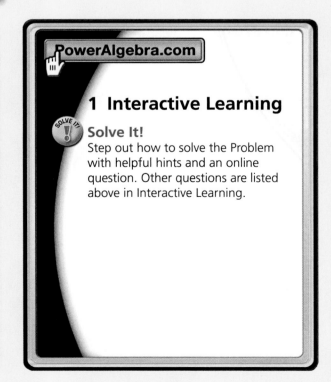

PowerAlgebra.com

1 Interactive Learning

SOLVE IT!

Solve It!
Step out how to solve the Problem with helpful hints and an online question. Other questions are listed above in Interactive Learning.

Problem 1

> **Q** What expression equivalent to $(y + 2.5) + 28$ illustrates the Commutative Property of Addition?
> **[28 + (y + 2.5) and (2.5 + y) + 28]**

Got It?   ERROR PREVENTION
If students identify the expression in 1b as an example of the Associative Property of Addition, caution them that parentheses in a problem are not always an indication of the associative property.

Problem 2

> **Q** Why are both the Commutative and the Associative Properties of Addition used in this problem? **[In order to put 7.75 and 1.25 in the same grouping symbols, the order of the addends must first be changed.]**

Got It?
Encourage students to write down a numerical expression that models the situation.

Properties   Properties of Real Numbers

Let *a* be any real number.

Identity Properties of Addition and Multiplication
The sum of any real number and 0 is the original number. The product of any real number and 1 is the original number.

	Algebra	Example
Addition	$a + 0 = a$	$5\frac{3}{4} + 0 = 5\frac{3}{4}$
Multiplication	$a \cdot 1 = a$	$67 \cdot 1 = 67$

Zero Property of Multiplication
The product of *a* and 0 is 0. $a \cdot 0 = 0$ $18 \cdot 0 = 0$

Multiplication Property of −1
The product of −1 and *a* is −*a*. $-1 \cdot a = -a$ $-1 \cdot 9 = -9$

 Problem 1   **Identifying Properties**

What property is illustrated by each statement?

A $42 \cdot 0 = 0$ Zero Property of Multiplication

B $(y + 2.5) + 28 = y + (2.5 + 28)$ Associative Property of Addition

C $10x + 0 = 10x$ Identity Property of Addition

✓ **Got It? 1.** What property is illustrated by each statement?
  a. $4x \cdot 1 = 4x$ **b.** $x + (\sqrt{y} + z) = x + (z + \sqrt{y})$

Think
What math symbols give you clues about the properties? Parentheses, operation symbols, and the numbers 0 and 1 may indicate certain properties.

You can use properties to help you solve some problems using mental math.

 Problem 2   **Using Properties for Mental Calculations**

Movies A movie ticket costs $7.75. A drink costs $2.40. Popcorn costs $1.25. What is the total cost for a ticket, a drink, and popcorn? Use mental math.

$(7.75 + 2.40) + 1.25 = (2.40 + 7.75) + 1.25$ Commutative Property of Addition
$= 2.40 + (7.75 + 1.25)$ Associative Property of Addition
$= 2.40 + 9$ Simplify inside parentheses.
$= 11.40$ Add.

The total cost is $11.40.

Plan
How can you make the addition easier? Look for numbers having decimal parts you can add easily, such as 0.75 and 0.25.

✓ **Got It? 2.** A can holds 3 tennis balls. A box holds 4 cans. A case holds 6 boxes. How many tennis balls are in 10 cases? Use mental math.

Answers

Solve It!
$34 + 12 = 12 + 34$; $100 − 1 \neq 1 − 100$;
$0 + 180 = 180$; $18 \div \frac{1}{18} \neq 1$; $45 − 1 \neq 45$;
$6 \times \frac{1}{6} = 1$

Got It?
1. a. Identity Prop. of Mult.
   b. Commutative Prop. of Add.
2. 720 tennis balls

PowerAlgebra.com

2 Guided Instruction
Each Problem is worked out and supported online.

Problem 1
Identifying Properties

Problem 2
Using Properties for Mental Calculations
                                    Animated

Problem 3
Writing Equivalent Expressions
                                    Animated

Problem 4
Using Deductive Reasoning and Counterexamples
                                    Animated

Support in Algebra 1 Companion
• Vocabulary
• Key Concepts
• Got It?

Problem 3 Writing Equivalent Expressions

Simplify each expression.

A $5(3n)$

Know	Need	Plan
An expression	Groups of numbers that can be simplified	Use properties to group or reorder parts of the expression.

$5(3n) = (5 \cdot 3)n$ Associative Property of Multiplication

$\qquad\quad = 15n$ Simplify.

B $(4 + 7b) + 8$

$(4 + 7b) + 8 = (7b + 4) + 8$ Commutative Property of Addition

$\qquad\qquad\quad = 7b + (4 + 8)$ Associative Property of Addition

$\qquad\qquad\quad = 7b + 12$ Simplify.

C $\dfrac{6xy}{y}$

$\dfrac{6xy}{y} = \dfrac{6x \cdot y}{1 \cdot y}$ Rewrite denominator using Identity Property of Multiplication.

$\qquad = \dfrac{6x}{1} \cdot \dfrac{y}{y}$ Use rule for multiplying fractions: $\dfrac{a}{b} \cdot \dfrac{c}{d} = \dfrac{ac}{bd}$.

$\qquad = 6x \cdot 1$ $x \div 1 = x$ and $y \div y = 1$.

$\qquad = 6x$ Identity Property of Multiplication

 Got It? 3. Simplify each expression.

     a. $2.1(4.5x)$ **b.** $6 + (4h + 3)$ **c.** $\dfrac{8m}{12mn}$

In Problem 3, reasoning and properties were used to show that two expressions are equivalent. This is an example of *deductive reasoning*. **Deductive reasoning** is the process of reasoning logically from given facts to a conclusion.

To show that a statement is *not* true, find an example for which it is not true. An example showing that a statement is false is a **counterexample.** You need only one counterexample to prove that a statement is false.

 Problem 4 Using Deductive Reasoning and Counterexamples

Is the statement *true* or *false*? If it is false, give a counterexample.

A For all real numbers a and b, $a \cdot b = b + a$.

     False. $5 \cdot 3 \neq 3 + 5$ is a counterexample.

B For all real numbers a, b, and c, $(a + b) + c = b + (a + c)$.

     True. Use properties of real numbers to show that the expressions are equivalent.

$\quad (a + b) + c = (b + a) + c$ Commutative Property of Addition

$\qquad\qquad\quad = b + (a + c)$ Associative Property of Addition

Plan

Look for a counterexample to show the statement is false. If you don't find one, try to use properties to show that it is true.

 **PowerAlgebra.com**   Lesson 1-4   Properties of Real Numbers   25

Problem 3

Q What mathematical operations are indicated by the expression $5(3n)$? Explain. **[Multiplication is indicated by the parentheses. $3n$ means 3 is multiplied by n.]**

Q Why is $7b + 12$ not equal to $19b$ in the simplified form of the expression in 3B? **[The expression $19b$ means that a number b is multiplied by 19, which is not equivalent to multiplying a number by 7 and then adding 12.]**

Got It?   **ERROR PREVENTION**

If students give an answer of $\frac{8}{12n}$ for the expression in 3c, encourage them to use the Identity Property of Multiplication to reduce the fraction.

Problem 4

Q What is a counterexample for the statement "All algebra students are female?" **[Answers may vary. Sample: Joe is male and is an algebra student.]**

Q Many people think that parentheses in a problem are a clue that the property illustrated is the associative property. What do you look at first to decide which property is illustrated? **[the order of the variables on the left side of the equals sign and the order of the variables on the right side]**

Additional Problems

1. Which property is illustrated by each statement?

   a. $31 \cdot 0 = 0$

   b. $(x + 3) + 6 = x + (3 + 6)$

   c. $5x + 0 = 5x$

   ANSWER a. Zero Property of Multiplication
   b. Associative Property of Addition
   c. Identity Property of Addition

2. A movie ticket costs \$6.75. A drink costs \$1.90. Popcorn costs \$2.25. What is the total cost for a ticket, a drink, and popcorn? Use mental math.

   ANSWER \$10.90

3. What is the simplified form of each expression?

   a. $4(8n)$

   b. $(3 + 5b) + 7$

   c. $\dfrac{8xy}{2x}$

   ANSWER a. $32n$
   b. $10 + 5b$ **c.** $4y$

4. Is the statement *true* or *false*? If false, give a counterexample.

   a. For all real numbers a and b, $a - b = b - a$.

   b. For all real numbers a, b, and c, $a \times b \times c = a \times c \times b$.

   ANSWER a. false; sample: $a = 5$ and $b = 6$ **b.** true

Answers

Got It? (continued)

   3. a. $9.45x$

     b. $9 + 4h$

     c. $\dfrac{2}{3n}$

Got It?

Q Is it possible to find a pair of numbers m and n for which $m(n + 1) = nm + 1$? What can you conclude from this? **[Yes; the statement is true for $m = 1$ and $n = 1$. Just because a statement is true for a few numbers does not mean that it is true for all numbers.]**

3 Lesson Check

Do you know HOW?
• If students have difficulty with Exercise 3, then have them review Problem 2.

Do you UNDERSTAND?
• If students have difficulty with Exercise 6, then have them review the properties of real numbers and describe in their own words what is changed in each row.

Close

Q Is it possible to prove that a statement such as $a + b = b + a$ is true by showing that there are no counterexamples for the statement? Explain. **[No, there are an infinite number of real numbers that could be substituted for a and b, and it is impossible to try them all.]**

 Got It? **4. Reasoning** Is each statement in parts (a) and (b) *true* or *false*? If it is false, give a counterexample. If true, use properties of real numbers to show the expressions are equivalent.
  a. For all real numbers j and k, $j \cdot k = (k + 0) \cdot j$.
  b. For all real numbers m and n, $m(n + 1) = mn + 1$.
  c. Is the statement in part (A) of Problem 4 false for *every* pair of real numbers a and b? Explain.

 Lesson Check

Do you know HOW?
Name the property that each statement illustrates.
  1. $x + 12 = 12 + x$
  2. $5 \cdot (12 \cdot x) = (5 \cdot 12) \cdot x$
  3. You buy a sandwich for $2.95, an apple for $.45, and a bottle of juice for $1.05. What is the total cost?
  4. Simplify $\frac{24cd}{c}$.

Do you UNDERSTAND?
  5. Vocabulary Tell whether the expressions in each pair are equivalent.
    a. $5x \cdot 1$ and $1 + 5x$
    b. $1 + (2t + 1)$ and $2 + 2t$
  6. Justify each step.
$$3 \cdot (10 \cdot 12) = 3 \cdot (12 \cdot 10)$$
$$= (3 \cdot 12) \cdot 10$$
$$= 36 \cdot 10$$
$$= 360$$

Practice and Problem-Solving Exercises

A Practice   Name the property that each statement illustrates.   **See Problem 1.**
  7. $75 + 6 = 6 + 75$ **8.** $\frac{7}{9} \cdot 1 = \frac{7}{9}$ **9.** $h + 0 = h$
  10. $389 \cdot 0 = 0$ **11.** $27 \cdot \pi = \pi \cdot 27$ **12.** $9 \cdot (-1 \cdot x) = 9 \cdot (-x)$

Mental Math Simplify each expression.   **See Problem 2.**
  13. $21 + 6 + 9$ **14.** $10 \cdot 2 \cdot 19 \cdot 5$ **15.** $0.1 + 3.7 + 5.9$
  16. $4 \cdot 5 \cdot 13 \cdot 5$ **17.** $55.3 + 0.2 + 23.8 + 0.7$ **18.** $0.25 \cdot 12 \cdot 4$

19. Fishing Trip The sign at the right shows the costs for a deep-sea fishing trip. How much will the total cost be for 1 adult, 2 children, and 1 senior citizen to go on a fishing trip? Use mental math.

DEEP-SEA FISHING
Adults $33
Children (12 & under) $25
Seniors (65 & up) $27

---

3 Lesson Check

For a digital lesson check, use the Got It questions.

Support in Algebra 1 Companion
• Lesson Check

4 Practice

Assign homework to individual students or to an entire class.

Answers

Got It? (continued)
  4. a. True; Commutative Prop. of Mult. and Identity Prop. of Add.
    b. False; answers may vary. Sample: $4(2 + 1) \neq 4(2) + 1$
    c. No; it is true when a and b are both either 0 or 2.

Lesson Check
  1. Comm. Prop. of Add.
  2. Assoc. Prop. of Mult.
  3. $4.45
  4. $24d$
  5. a. no
     b. yes
  6. Comm. Prop. of Mult.; Assoc. Prop. of Mult.; multiply; multiply

Practice and Problem-Solving Exercises
  7. Comm. Prop. of Add.
  8. Ident. Prop. of Mult.
  9. Ident. Prop. of Add.
  10. Zero Prop. of Mult.
  11. Comm. Prop. of Mult.
  12. Mult. Prop. of -1
  13. 36
  14. 1900
  15. 9.7
  16. 1300
  17. 80
  18. 12
  19. $110

Simplify each expression. Justify each step.

← See Problem 3.

20. $8 + (9t + 4)$ **21.** $9(2x)$ **22.** $(4 + 105x) + 5$ **23.** $(10p)11$

24. $(12 \cdot r) \cdot 13$ **25.** $(2 + 3x) + 9$ **26.** $4 \cdot (x \cdot 6.3)$ **27.** $1.1 + (7d + 0.1)$

28. $\frac{56ab}{b}$ **29.** $\frac{1.5mn}{m}$ **30.** $\frac{13p}{pq}$ **31.** $\frac{33xy}{3x}$

Use deductive reasoning to tell whether each statement is *true* or *false*. If it is false, give a counterexample. If true, use properties of real numbers to show the expressions are equivalent.

← See Problem 4.

32. For all real numbers r, s, and t, $(r \cdot s) \cdot t = t \cdot (s \cdot r)$.

33. For all real numbers p and q, $p \div q = q \div p$.

34. For all real numbers x, $x + 0 = 0$.

35. For all real numbers a and b, $-a \cdot b = a \cdot (-b)$.

Ⓑ Apply

36. Error Analysis Your friend shows you the problem at the right. He says that the Associative Property allows you to change the order in which you complete two operations. Is your friend correct? Explain.

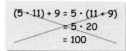

$$(5 \cdot 11) + 9 = 5 \cdot (11 + 9)$$
$$= 5 \cdot 20$$
$$= 100$$

37. Travel It is 258 mi from Tulsa, Oklahoma, to Dallas, Texas. It is 239 mi from Dallas, Texas, to Houston, Texas.
 a. What is the total distance of a trip from Tulsa to Dallas to Houston?
 b. What is the total distance of a trip from Houston to Dallas to Tulsa?
 c. Explain how you can tell whether the distances described in parts (a) and (b) are equal by using reasoning.

Tell whether the expressions in each pair are equivalent.

38. $2 + h + 4$ and $2 \cdot h \cdot 4$ **39.** $9y \cdot 0$ and 1 **40.** $3x$ and $3x \cdot 1$

41. $m(1 - 1)$ and 0 **42.** $(9 - 7) + \pi$ and 2π **43.** $(3 + 7) + m$ and $m + 10$

44. $\frac{63ab}{7a}$ and $9ab$ **45.** $\frac{11x}{(2 + 5 - 7)}$ and $11x$ **46.** $\frac{7t}{4 - 8 + \sqrt{9}}$ and $7t$

47. Think About a Plan Hannah makes a list of possible gifts for Mary, Jared, and Michael. She has two plans and can spend a total of $75 for all gifts. Which plan(s) can Hannah afford?
 • What property can you use to make it easier to find the total cost of different gifts?
 • What number do you compare to the total cost of each plan to decide whether it is affordable?

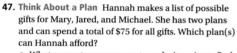
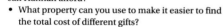

Same Gifts
DVD $22

Different Gifts
Mary:
Sweater $29.26
Jared:
Book $23.99
Michael:
Cactus $23.74

48. Writing Suppose you are mixing red and blue paint in a bucket. Do you think the final color of the mixed paint will be the same whether you add the blue paint or the red paint to the bucket first? Relate your answer to a property of real numbers.

20–31. Steps may vary. Check students' work. Answers given.

20. $9t + 12$

21. $18x$

22. $9 + 105x$

23. $110p$

24. $156r$

25. $11 + 3x$

26. $25.2x$

27. $1.2 + 7d$

28. $56a$

29. $1.5n$

30. $\frac{13}{q}$

31. $11y$

32. True; Commutative Prop. of Mult.

33. False; answers may vary. Sample: $8 \div 4 \neq 4 \div 8$

34. False; answers may vary. Sample: $5 + 0 \neq 0$

35. True; Mult. Prop. of -1

36. No, that prop. applies only when both operations are add. or mult.

37. a. 497 mi
 b. 497 mi
 c. Check students' work. The Commutative Property of Addition applies to this situation.

38. no

39. no

40. yes

41. yes

42. no

43. yes

44. no

45. no

46. no

47. Hannah can only afford to give all her friends the same gift.

48. Yes; blue + red = red + blue; since both make purple, just as with the Comm. Prop. of Add., $a + b = b + a$.

4 Practice

ASSIGNMENT GUIDE

Basic: 7–35 all, 36–46 even, 47–48

Average: 7–35 odd, 36–55

Advanced: 7–35 odd, 36–57

Standardized Test Prep: 58–61

Mixed Review: 62–68

Reasoning exercises have blue headings.

Applications exercises have red headings.

EXERCISE 37: Use the Think About a Plan worksheet in the **Practice and Problem Solving Workbook** (also available in the Teaching Resources in print and online) to further support students' development in becoming independent learners.

HOMEWORK QUICK CHECK

To check students' understanding of key skills and concepts, go over Exercises 11, 15, 37, 47, and 48.

Answers

Practice and Problem-Solving Exercises
(continued)

49–51. Steps may vary. Check students' work.

49. 390

50. $x + 7$

51. 0

52–55. Examples may vary.

52. no; $a - b \neq b - a$

53. no; $(a - b) - c \neq a - (b - c)$

54. no; $a \div b \neq b \div a$

55. no; $(a \div b) \div c \neq a \div (b \div c)$

56. 6 ways; $a + b + c, a + c + b, b + a + c,$ $b + c + a, c + a + b, c + b + a$

57. $(b + c)a = a(b + c)$ and $ba + ca = ab + ac$ by the Comm. Prop. of Mult.

58. D

59. H

60. B

61. F

62. $-6, 1.6, \sqrt{6}, 6^3$

63. $-17, 1.4, \frac{8}{5}, 10^2$

64. $-4.5, 1.75, \sqrt{4}, 14^1$

65. 14

66. 1

67. 1.1

68. $\frac{1}{18}$

Simplify each expression. Justify each step.

49. $25 \cdot 3.9 \cdot 4$ **50.** $(4.4 \div 4.4)(x + 7)$ **51.** $(7^6 - 6^5)(8 - 8)$

Reasoning Answer each question. Use examples to justify your answers.

52. Is subtraction commutative?   **53.** Is subtraction associative?

54. Is division commutative?   **55.** Is division associative?

Ⓒ **Challenge**

56. Patterns The Commutative Property of Addition lets you rewrite addition expressions. How many different ways can you write $a + b + c$? Show each way.

57. Reasoning Suppose you know that $a(b + c) = ab + ac$ is true for all real numbers a, b, and c. Use the properties of real numbers to prove that $(b + c)a = ba + ca$ is true for all real numbers a, b, and c.

Standardized Test Prep

SAT/ACT

58. What is the simplified form of $(1.2 + 0) + 4.6 + 3.8$?
- Ⓐ 1.2
- Ⓑ 8.0
- Ⓒ 8.4
- Ⓓ 9.6

59. Which expression is equal to $3 \cdot 3 \cdot 8 \cdot 8 \cdot 3$?
- Ⓕ $3 \cdot 8$
- Ⓖ 3^8
- Ⓗ $3^3 \cdot 8^2$
- Ⓘ $3 \cdot 3 + 2 \cdot 8$

60. There are four points plotted on the number line below.

Which expression represents the greatest amount?
- Ⓐ $M \div L$
- Ⓑ $M - L$
- Ⓒ $J + K$
- Ⓓ $L - K$

61. Lane 1 at your local track is 0.25 mi long. You live 0.5 mi away from the track. Which of the following results in the shortest jog?
- Ⓕ jogging 6 times around the track in Lane 1
- Ⓖ jogging to the track and then 5 times around the track in Lane 1
- Ⓗ jogging to the track, 3 times around the track in Lane 1, and then home
- Ⓘ jogging 8 times around the track in Lane 1

Mixed Review

Order the numbers in each exercise from least to greatest.   ◀ See Lesson 1-3.

62. $-6, 6^3, 1.6, \sqrt{6}$ **63.** $\frac{8}{5}, 1.4, -17, 10^2$ **64.** $1.75, -4.5, \sqrt{4}, 14^1$

Get Ready! To prepare for Lesson 1-5, do Exercises 65–68.

Find each sum or difference.   ◀ See p. 791.

65. $3 + 11$ **66.** $\frac{3}{8} + \frac{5}{8}$ **67.** $9.7 - 8.6$ **68.** $\frac{5}{9} - \frac{5}{10}$

Additional Instructional Support

Algebra 1 Companion

Students can use the **Algebra 1 Companion** worktext (4 pages) as you teach the lesson. Use the Companion to support

- New Vocabulary
- Key Concepts
- Got It for each Problem
- Lesson Check

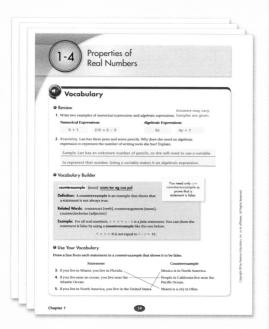

ELL Support

Use Role Playing Have students write first whole numbers, then integers, rational numbers, and irrational numbers on different pieces of paper. Collect these papers, mix them up, and pass one out to each student. Have a volunteer stand in a designated area and draw a card from a set of index cards with the name of one of the subsets of numbers: "whole numbers, rational numbers, integers, irrational numbers, real numbers, . . ." Students whose number is a member of the set called should gather around the volunteer. Students should verify one another's numbers that belong in the set, or in the complement of the set. Continue with more volunteers calling subsets. Sometimes there will be a subset within a set. When students can do the task easily, pass out new numbers and repeat.

5 Assess & Remediate

Lesson Quiz

1. What property of real numbers lets you multiply a number by 1 and have a product equal to the original number?
2. Use mental math to find $14 + 37 + 26$.
3. Simplify each expression.
   a. $-5(2x)$
   b. $\frac{15xy}{3x}$
4. **Do you UNDERSTAND?** Gina says that for all real numbers a and b, $ab = ba$. Is this statement true or false? If false, give a counterexample.

ANSWERS TO LESSON QUIZ

1. Identity Property of Multiplication
2. 77
3. a. $-10x$ b. $5y$
4. true

PRESCRIPTION FOR REMEDIATION
Use the student work on the Lesson Quiz to prescribe a differentiated review assignment.

Points	Differentiated Remediation
0–2	Intervention
3	On-level
4	Extension

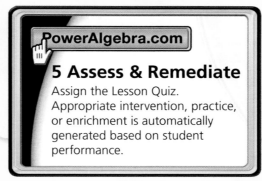

PowerAlgebra.com

5 Assess & Remediate

Assign the Lesson Quiz. Appropriate intervention, practice, or enrichment is automatically generated based on student performance.

Intervention

- **Reteaching** (2 pages) Provides reteaching and practice exercises for the key lesson concepts. Use with struggling students or absent students.
- **English Language Learner Support** Helps students develop and reinforce mathematical vocabulary and key concepts.

All-in-One Resources/Online
Reteaching

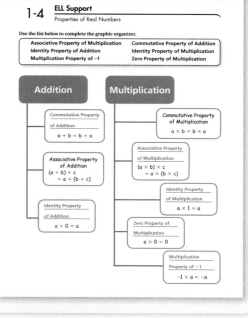

All-in-One Resources/Online
English Language Learner Support

Differentiated Remediation *continued*

On-Level

- **Practice** (2 pages) Provides extra practice for each lesson. For simpler practice exercises, use the Form K Practice pages found in the All-in-One Teaching Resources and online.
- **Think About a Plan** Helps students develop specific problem-solving skills and strategies by providing scaffolded guiding questions.
- **Standardized Test Prep** Focuses on all major exercises, all major question types, and helps students prepare for the high-stakes assessments.

Practice and Problem Solving WKBK/ All-in-One Resources/Online

Practice page 1

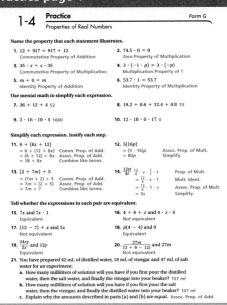

1-4 Practice *Form G*

Properties of Real Numbers

Name the property that each statement illustrates.

1. $12 + 917 = 917 + 12$ Commutative Property of Addition
2. $74.5 \cdot 0 = 0$ Zero Property of Multiplication
3. $35 \cdot x = x \cdot 35$ Commutative Property of Multiplication
4. $3 \cdot (-1 \cdot p) = 3 \cdot (-p)$ Multiplication Property of 1
5. $m + 0 = m$ Identity Property of Addition
6. $53.7 \cdot 1 = 53.7$ Identity Property of Multiplication

Use mental math to simplify each expression.

7. $36 + 12 + 4$ 52
8. $19.2 + 0.6 + 12.4 + 0.8$ 33
9. $2 \cdot 16 \cdot 10 \cdot 5$ 1600
10. $12 \cdot 18 \cdot 0 \cdot 17$ 0

Simplify each expression. Justify each step.

11. $6 + (8x + 12)$
$= 6 + (12 + 8x)$ Comm. Prop. of Add.
$= (6 + 12) + 8x$ Assoc. Prop. of Add.
$= 18 + 8x$ Combine like terms.

12. $5(16p)$
$= (5 \cdot 16)p$ Assoc. Prop. of Mult.
$= 80p$ Simplify.

13. $(2 + 7m) + 5$
$= (7m + 2) + 5$ Comm. Prop. of Add.
$= 7m + (2 + 5)$ Assoc. Prop. of Add.
$= 7m + 7$ Combine like terms.

14. $\frac{12st}{4t}$ $\frac{12}{4} \cdot s \cdot \frac{1}{t} \cdot t$ Prop. of Mult.
$= \frac{12}{4} \cdot s \cdot 1$ Mult. Ident.
$= \frac{12}{4} \cdot 1 \cdot s$ Assoc. Prop. of Mult.
$= 3s$ Simplify.

Tell whether the expressions in each pair are equivalent.

15. $7x$ and $7x \cdot 1$ Equivalent
16. $4 + 6 + x$ and $4 \cdot x \cdot 6$ Not equivalent
17. $(12 - 7) + x$ and $5x$ Not equivalent
18. $p(4 - 4)$ and 0 Equivalent
19. $\frac{24xy}{2x}$ and $12y$ Equivalent
20. $\frac{27m}{(3 + 9 - 12)}$ and $27m$ Not equivalent
21. You have prepared 42 mL of distilled water, 18 mL of vinegar and 47 mL of salt water for an experiment.
    a. How many milliliters of solution will you have if you first pour the distilled water, then the salt water, and finally the vinegar into your beaker? 107 ml
    b. How many milliliters of solution will you have if you first pour the salt water, then the vinegar, and finally the distilled water into your beaker? 107 ml
    c. Explain why the amounts described in parts (a) and (b) are equal. Assoc. Prop. of Add.

Practice and Problem Solving WKBK/ All-in-One Resources/Online

Practice page 2

1-4 Practice (continued) *Form G*

Properties of Real Numbers

Use deductive reasoning to tell whether each statement is *true* or *false*. If it is false, give a counterexample.

22. For all real numbers a and b, $a - b = -b + a$. true
23. For all real numbers p, q and r, $p - q - r = p - r - q$. true
24. For all real numbers x, y and z, $(x + y) + z = z + (x + y)$. true
25. For all real numbers m and n, $\frac{m}{m} \cdot n = \frac{n}{n} \cdot m$. false; $\frac{5}{5} \times 3 \neq \frac{3}{3} \times 5$
26. **Writing** Explain why the commutative and associative properties don't hold true for subtraction and division but the identity properties do.
Examples: $5 - 0 = 5$; $5 \div 1 = 5$; Counterexamples: $5 - 3 \neq 3 - 5$; $(5 - 3) - 2 \neq 5 - (3 - 2)$; $6 \div 3 \neq 3 \div 6$; $(24 \div 6) \div 2 \neq 24 \div (6 \div 2)$
27. **Reasoning** A recipe for brownies calls for mixing one cup of sugar with two cups of flour and 4 ounces of chocolate. They are all to be mixed in a bowl before baking. Will the brownies taste different if you add the ingredients in different orders? Relate your answer to a property of real numbers.
no; Like the Comm. Prop. of Add., the order doesn't matter. Like the Assoc. Prop. of Add., it doesn't matter if the flour and sugar are added and then the chocolate, or if the sugar and chocolate are added and then the flour or any other combination.

Simplify each expression. Justify each step.

28. $(6^7)(5^3 + 2)(2 - 2)$ 0
29. $(m - 16)(-7 \div -7)$ $m - 16$
30. **Open-Ended** Provide examples to show the following.
    a. The associative property of addition holds true for negative integers.
    b. The commutative property of multiplication holds true for non-integers.
    c. The multiplicative property of negative one holds true regardless of the sign of the number on which the operation is performed.
    d. The commutative property of multiplication holds true if one of the factors is zero.

    Answers may vary. Samples:
    a. $[-3 + (-4)] + (-1) = -7 + (-1) = -8$; $-3 + [-4 + (-1)] = -3 + (-5) = -8$
    b. $\left(\frac{1}{2} \cdot \frac{2}{3}\right) \cdot \frac{3}{4} = \frac{1}{4}$; $\frac{1}{2} \cdot \left(\frac{2}{3} \cdot \frac{3}{4}\right) = \frac{1}{4}$
    c. $-1 \cdot 5 =$ the opposite of $5 = -5$; $-1 \cdot -5 =$ the opposite of $-5 = 5$
    d. $3 \cdot 0 = 0 \cdot 3 = 0$

Practice and Problem Solving WKBK/ All-in-One Resources/Online

Think About a Plan

1-4 Think About a Plan

Properties of Real Numbers

Travel It is 235 mi from Tulsa to Dallas. It is 390 mi from Dallas to Houston.

a. What is the total distance of a trip from Tulsa to Dallas to Houston?
b. What is the total distance from Houston to Dallas to Tulsa?
c. Explain how you can tell whether the distances described in parts (a) and (b) are equal by using reasoning.

Think

1. What operation(s) will you use to solve the problem?
Addition
2. Which of the properties of real numbers involve the operations identified in part (a)?
Commutative Property of Addition, Associative Property of Addition, Additive Identity

Plan

3. Write expressions that can be simplified to solve parts (a) and (b).
A. $235 + 390$ B. $390 + 235$
4. How are the two expressions similar? How are those similarities related to the situation as described?
The numbers are the same. Distances between cities are the same, regardless of which direction I am going in.
5. How are the expressions different? How are those differences related to the situation as described?
The numbers are added in different order. The first has you going in one direction, the second has you returning the other direction.

Solve

6. Find the total distances asked for in parts (a) and (b). What do you notice about the answers?
625 miles, 625 miles; They are the same.
7. Which of the properties of real numbers best explains your results?
Commutative property of addition
8. Discuss how that property explains your results.
The property tells us that the order of the addends does not affect the sum.

Practice and Problem Solving WKBK/ All-in-One Resources/Online

Standardized Test Prep

1-4 Standardized Test Prep

Properties of Real Numbers

Multiple Choice

For Exercises 1–5, choose the correct letter.

1. Which of the following statements is *not* always true? B
A. $a + (-b) = -b + a$
B. $a - (-b) = (-b) - a$
C. $(a + b) + (-c) = a + [b + (-c)]$
D. $-(-a) = a$
2. Which pair of expressions are equivalent? I
F. $18m \cdot 0$ and 1
G. $6 + r + 11$ and $6 \cdot r \cdot 11$
H. $(12 - 5) + \pi$ and 7π
I. $x(3 - 3)$ and 0
3. What property is illustrated by the equation $(8 + 2) + 7 = (2 + 8) + 7$? A
A. Commutative Property of Addition
B. Associative Property of Addition
C. Distributive Property
D. Identity Property of Addition
4. Which expression is equivalent to $-a \cdot b$? F
F. $a \cdot (-b)$ G. $b - a$ H. $(-a)(-b)$ I. $-a + b$
5. Which is an example of an identity property? B
A. $a \cdot 0 = 0$ B. $x \cdot 1 = x$ C. $(-1)x = -x$ D. $a + b = b + a$

Short Response

6. The fact that changing the grouping of addends does not change the sum is the basis of what property of real numbers?
Assoc. Prop. of Add.
[2] Question answered correctly.
[1] Answer is incomplete.
[0] Answer is wrong.

Extension

- **Enrichment** Provides students with interesting problems and activities that extend the concepts of the lesson.
- **Activities, Games, and Puzzles** Worksheets that can be used for concepts development, enrichment, and for fun!

All-in-One Resources/Online

Enrichment

1-4 Enrichment

Properties of Real Numbers

Which of the properties of real numbers are illustrated by the following situations? Explain your reasoning.

1. One team scores 3 runs in the first inning and 2 runs in the fourth inning. The other team scores 2 runs in the first inning and 3 runs in the fourth. In the fifth inning, the score is tied.
Commutative Property of Addition
2. Your friend gets a job making $9.50 per hour. One week she takes a vacation and does not work. She makes no money that week.
Zero Property of Multiplication
3. In putting together a mixture of fertilizer, a gardener mixes nitrogen and phosphorus before adding potassium. The next day the gardener mixes phosphorus and potassium before adding nitrogen. The two mixtures are exactly the same.
Associative Property of Addition
4. A restaurant received two orders from the apartment managers of two different apartment buildings. The first apartment manager said he was ordering 3 meals each for the occupants of 4 different apartments. The second said he was ordering 4 meals each for the occupants of 3 different apartments. The apartment managers ordered the same number of meals.
Commutative Property of Multiplication
5. The owner of a theater checked how much money was in the box office 10 minutes before a show began. No tickets were purchased in the last 10 minutes, so the owner was not surprised that the final amount of money was the same as when when he previously checked.
Additive Identity
6. Usually, when Marty makes pancakes for his kids, he changes the amount of each ingredient depending on how many servings he is making. Since he was making the exact number of servings the recipe called for, he was able to use the numbers published in the cook book.
Multiplicative Identity

Online Teacher Resource Center

Activities, Games, and Puzzles

1-4 Game: You've Got My Property

Properties of Real Numbers

This is a game for two players. The top table lists 24 equations, and the bottom table lists eight properties three different times. The object of the game is to match each equation with the property it describes.

Decide which player goes first. Player 1 starts by matching any equation with its property. After each match, use a pencil to cross out both the equation and the property. A player can match as many as three equations with their properties in a single turn. Players check each other's matches after each one is given. An incorrect answer results in the other player taking over, and the equation and property are still in play. The winner of the game is the player who crosses off the last match. The strategy is to match just enough equations and properties so that you will be able to select the last one! Check students' work.

$9 + \sqrt{w} = \sqrt{w} + 9$	$(f \cdot g) \cdot h = f \cdot (g \cdot h)$	$a \cdot 0 = 0$	$-1 \cdot s = -s$
$(5q) \cdot (4p) = (4p) \cdot (5q)$	$-1 \cdot (49b) = -(49b)$	$(2x + 3y) + 5z = 2x + (3y + 5z)$	$k + 0 = k$
$2\sqrt{j} + 0 = 2\sqrt{j}$	$c + d = d + c$	$14 \cdot 1 = 14$	$(5 \cdot 9) \cdot 3 = 5 \cdot (9 \cdot 3)$
$(19 + 5) + 7 = 19 + (5 + 7)$	$(3x) \cdot 1 = 3x$	$u \cdot v = v \cdot u$	$28 \cdot 0 = 0$
$n \cdot 1 = n$	$1\frac{7}{8} \cdot 0 = 0$	$36 + 0 = 36$	$(m + n) + p = m + (n + p)$
$(5r \cdot s) \cdot t = 5r \cdot (s \cdot t)$	$8 + 13 = 13 + 8$	$-1 \cdot \sqrt{7} = -\sqrt{7}$	$6(8) = 8(6)$

Commutative Property of Addition	Associative Property of Addition	Identity Property of Addition	Zero Property of Multiplication
Commutative Prop. of Multiplication	Associative Prop. of Multiplication	Identity Property of Multiplication	Multiplicative Property of −1
Commutative Property of Addition	Associative Property of Addition	Identity Property of Addition	Zero Property of Multiplication
Commutative Prop. of Multiplication	Associative Prop. of Multiplication	Identity Property of Multiplication	Multiplicative Property of −1
Commutative Property of Addition	Associative Property of Addition	Identity Property of Addition	Zero Property of Multiplication
Commutative Prop. of Multiplication	Associative Prop. of Multiplication	Identity Property of Multiplication	Multiplicative Property of −1

Do you know HOW?

Write an algebraic expression for each phrase.

1. a number n divided by 4

2. 2 less than the product of 5 and n

3. The table shows how the total cost of a field trip depends on the number of students. What is a rule for the total cost of the tickets? Give the rule in words and as an algebraic expression.

Field Trip

Number of Students	Total Cost
20	$(12 \cdot 20) + 150$
40	$(12 \cdot 40) + 150$
60	$(12 \cdot 60) + 150$

4. The sign shows the costs associated with a whitewater rafting trip. Write an expression to determine the cost of 3 children and 1 adult renting equipment for a whitewater rafting trip that lasts h hours.

Whitewater Tours

Adult Ticket	$53
Child Ticket	$32
Equipment Rental	$5 per hour

Simplify each expression.

5. $24 \div (3 + 2^2)$

6. $\sqrt{144}$

Evaluate each expression for the given values of the variables.

7. $3x \cdot 2 \div y; x = 3$ and $y = 6$

8. $(4a)^3 \div (b - 2); a = 2$ and $b = 4$

9. Name the subset(s) of real numbers to which each number belongs. Then order the numbers from least to greatest.
$\sqrt{105}, -4, \frac{4}{3}$

10. Estimate $\sqrt{14}$ to the nearest integer.

11. What property is shown in the following equation?
$$(5 + 8) + 11 = 5 + (8 + 11)$$

12. Use the table below. Find the total cost of 2 salads, 1 sandwich, and 2 drinks. Use mental math.

Lunch Menu

Salad	$6.25
Sandwich	$5.50
Drink	$2.75

Do you UNDERSTAND?

13. What word phrases represent the expressions $-2 + 3x$ and $3x + (-2)$? Are the two expressions equivalent? Explain.

14. Use grouping symbols to make the following equation true.
$$4^2 + 2 \cdot 3 = 54$$

15. Choose the correct word to complete the following sentence: A natural number is (*always, sometimes, never*) a whole number.

16. How many natural numbers are in the set of numbers from -10 to 10 inclusive? Explain.

17. What is the simplified form of $\frac{3abc}{abc}$, when $abc \neq 0$? Explain using the properties of real numbers.

18. Reasoning Are the associative properties true for all integers? Explain.

19. Use the Commutative Property of Multiplication to rewrite the expression $(x \cdot y) \cdot z$ in two different ways.

Answers

Mid-Chapter Quiz

1. $\frac{n}{4}$

2. $5n - 2$

3. 150 more than the product of 12 and the number of students n; $12n + 150$

4. $3 \cdot 32 + 53 + 5h = 149 + 5h$

5. $\frac{24}{7}$

6. 12

7. 3

8. 256

9. irrational numbers; rational numbers and integers; rational numbers; $-4, \frac{4}{3}, \sqrt{105}$

10. about 4

11. Assoc. Prop. of Add.

12. $23.50

13. the sum of -2 and the product of 3 and x; the sum of the product of 3 and x, and -2; yes; by the Comm. Prop. of Add.

14. $(4^2 + 2) \cdot 3 = 54$

15. always

16. 10; the natural numbers are whole numbers starting with 1.

17. 3; check students' work.

18. Yes; $(a + b) + c = a + (b + c)$; and $(ab)c = a(bc)$ for all real numbers and integers are real numbers.

19. $(y \cdot x) \cdot z; z \cdot (x \cdot y)$

1 Interactive Learning

Solve It!

PURPOSE To model a real-world situation by adding and subtracting real numbers

PROCESS Students may use rules for adding numbers with the same sign or use rules for subtracting numbers with the same sign.

FACILITATE

Q If you attempted to purchase headphones on 9/9, prior to Aunt Sue's deposit on the gift card, what would happen? **[You would not have enough money on the gift card.]**

Q How much would you need on the card in order to buy the headphones? **[$11]**

ANSWER See Solve It in Answers on next page.

CONNECT THE MATH In this lesson students will explore adding integers on a number line, and will learn rules for adding integers using absolute value.

2 Guided Instruction

Problem 1

Q Can the order of the addends be reversed in parts A–D? Explain. **[Yes, by the Commutative Property of Addition.]**

Got It?

Q Where will you be on the number line with respect to zero after completing this sum? Explain. **[Left of zero, because you begin 8 units to the left of zero and will only move 4 units to the right.]**

1-5 Adding and Subtracting Real Numbers

Indiana Academic Standard
Prepares for A1.4.2 Add, subtract and multiply polynomials and divide polynomials by monomials.

Objective To find sums and differences of real numbers

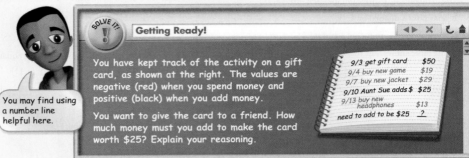

Getting Ready!

You have kept track of the activity on a gift card, as shown at the right. The values are negative (red) when you spend money and positive (black) when you add money.

You want to give the card to a friend. How much money must you add to make the card worth $25? Explain your reasoning.

9/3 get gift card	$50
9/4 buy new game	$19
9/7 buy new jacket	$29
9/10 Aunt Sue adds $	$25
9/13 buy new headphones	$13
need to add to be $25	?

You may find using a number line helpful here.

Essential Understanding You can add or subtract any real numbers using a number line model. You can also add or subtract real numbers using rules involving absolute value.

Lesson Vocabulary
• absolute value
• opposites
• additive inverses

Think

How do you know which direction to move along the number line?
If the number added is positive, move to the right. If the number added is negative, move to the left.

Problem 1 Using Number Line Models

What is each sum? Use a number line.

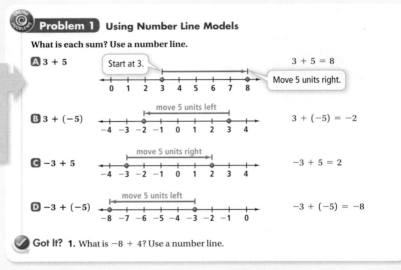

A $3 + 5$ Start at 3.   Move 5 units right. $3 + 5 = 8$

B $3 + (-5)$ move 5 units left $3 + (-5) = -2$

C $-3 + 5$ move 5 units right $-3 + 5 = 2$

D $-3 + (-5)$ move 5 units left $-3 + (-5) = -8$

Got It? 1. What is $-8 + 4$? Use a number line.

1-5 Preparing to Teach

BIG idea Properties   **UbD**

ESSENTIAL UNDERSTANDINGS

• Any real numbers can be added or subtracted using a number line model or using rules involving absolute value.

• Subtracting a real number is equivalent to adding its opposite: $a - b = a + (-b)$

Math Background

Addition and subtraction are inverse operations. To model the concept of "inverse operations", students can use a number line by beginning at zero and moving to a location on that number line. If the location is right of zero, the number is positive. If it is left of zero, the number is negative.

Subtraction is not commutative, so there is no commutative property of subtraction. However, the properties of real numbers can be used in conjunction with signed numbers; subtraction can be thought of as adding the opposite of a number.

Subtracting a number b is the same as adding the opposite of the number, $-b$. Once students understand that every subtraction problem can be rewritten as an addition problem, they can understand why there is no need for separate rules for subtracting with real numbers.

Support Student Learning

Use the **Algebra I Companion** to engage and support students during instruction. See Lesson Resources at the end of this lesson for details.

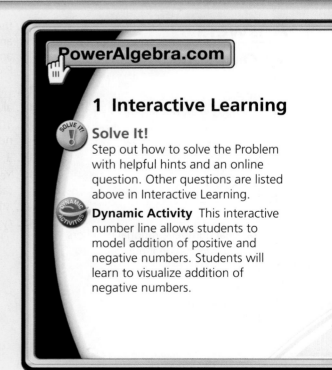

PowerAlgebra.com

1 Interactive Learning

Solve It!
Step out how to solve the Problem with helpful hints and an online question. Other questions are listed above in Interactive Learning.

Dynamic Activity This interactive number line allows students to model addition of positive and negative numbers. Students will learn to visualize addition of negative numbers.

The **absolute value** of a number is its distance from 0 on a number line. Absolute value is always nonnegative since distance is always nonnegative.

For example, the absolute value of 4 is 4 and the absolute value of −4 is 4. You can write this as $|4| = 4$ and $|-4| = 4$.

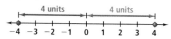

You can use absolute value when you find the sums of real numbers.

Dynamic Activity
Adding Real Numbers

Key Concept Adding Real Numbers

Adding Numbers With the Same Sign
To add two numbers with the same sign, add their absolute values. The sum has the same sign as the addends.

Examples $3 + 4 = 7$ $-3 + (-4) = -7$

Adding Numbers With Different Signs
To add two numbers with different signs, subtract their absolute values. The sum has the same sign as the addend with the greater absolute value.

Examples $-3 + 4 = 1$ $3 + (-4) = -1$

Plan

What is the first step in finding each sum?
Identify whether the addends have the same sign or different signs. Then choose the appropriate rule to use.

 Problem 2 Adding Real Numbers

What is each sum?

Ⓐ $-12 + 7$

$-12 + 7 = -5$ The difference of the absolute values is 5. The negative addend has the greater absolute value. The sum is negative.

Ⓑ $-18 + (-2)$

$-18 + (-2) = -20$ The addends have the same sign (negative), so add their absolute values. The sum is negative.

Ⓒ $-4.8 + 9.5$

$-4.8 + 9.5 = 4.7$ The difference of the absolute values is 4.7. The positive addend has the greater absolute value. The sum is positive.

Ⓓ $\frac{3}{4} + \left(-\frac{5}{6}\right)$

$\frac{3}{4} + \left(-\frac{5}{6}\right) = \frac{9}{12} + \left(-\frac{10}{12}\right)$ Find the least common denominator.

$= -\frac{1}{12}$ The difference of the absolute values is $\frac{1}{12}$. The negative addend has the greater absolute value. The sum is negative.

 **Got It? 2.** What is each sum?

  a. $-16 + (-8)$ **b.** $-11 + 9$ **c.** $9 + (-11)$ **d.** $-6 + (-2)$

Reinforce the rules for adding signed numbers with examples on a number line. For instance, point out that when you begin left of zero and you move left from that position by adding a negative number, you will remain left of zero.

Problem 2

Q Will the sum for part (a) be positive or negative? Explain. **[The sum will be negative because the absolute value of −12 is greater than the absolute value of 7.]**

Q How could you use a number line to check your answer for part (b)? **[Start at −18 on the number line and move to the left 2 units.]**

Got It?   SYNTHESIZING

Q Which problems represent equivalent numerical expressions? Explain. **[−11 + 9 and 9 + (−11) are equivalent by the Commutative Property of Addition.]**

---

2 Guided Instruction

 Each Problem is worked out and supported online.

Problem 1
Using Number Line Models
Animated

Problem 2
Adding Real Numbers
Animated

Problem 3
Subtracting Real Numbers

Problem 4
Adding and Subtracting Real Numbers
Animated

Support in Algebra 1 Companion
• Vocabulary
• Key Concepts
• Got It?

Answers

Solve It!
You must add $11 to make the card to be worth $25.

Got It?
1. -4
2. a. -24
  b. -2
  c. -2
  d. -8

Take Note

Q How are the absolute values of two additive inverses related to each other? [**Additive inverses have equivalent absolute values.**]

Take Note

Point out that there is not a Commutative Property of Subtraction. Further, only rules for adding real numbers have been presented. Rather than learning a new set of rules and exceptions to those rules, students need only to remember that subtracting a number b from another yields the same result as adding the opposite of that number, $-b$. Thus, the rules for adding real numbers can be used as well as the properties involving addition.

Problem 3

Q On a number line, how is subtraction of a positive number related to addition of a negative number? [**Both subtraction of a positive and addition of a negative require a move to the left on the number line.**]

Got It?   ERROR PREVENTION

Q Does $a - b = b - a$ for all real number values of a and b? Explain. [**No, because there is not a commutative property for subtraction.**]

Two numbers that are the same distance from 0 on a number line but lie in opposite directions are **opposites**.

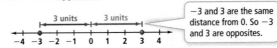

−3 and 3 are the same distance from 0. So −3 and 3 are opposites.

A number and its opposite are called **additive inverses**. To find the sum of a number and its opposite, you can use the **Inverse Property of Addition**.

take note

Property   Inverse Property of Addition

For every real number a, there is an additive inverse $-a$ such that
$a + (-a) = -a + a = 0$.

Examples $14 + (-14) = 0$ $-14 + 14 = 0$

You can use opposites (additive inverses) to subtract real numbers. To see how, look at the number line below, which models $3 - 5$ and $3 + (-5)$.

Start at 3 and move 5 units left.

$3 - 5$ and $3 + (-5)$ are equivalent expressions, illustrating the rule below.

take note

Key Concept   Subtracting Real Numbers

To subtract a real number, add its opposite: $a - b = a + (-b)$.

Examples $3 - 5 = 3 + (-5) = -2$ $3 - (-5) = 3 + 5 = 8$

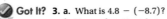

Problem 3   Subtracting Real Numbers

Think
Why rewrite subtraction as addition?
You can simplify expressions using the rules for adding real numbers that you learned earlier in this lesson.

What is each difference?

A $-8 - (-13) = -8 + 13$ The opposite of -13 is 13. So add 13.
        $= 5$ Use rules for addition.

B $3.5 - 12.4 = 3.5 + (-12.4)$ The opposite of 12.4 is -12.4. So add -12.4.
        $= -8.9$ Use rules for addition.

C $9 - 9 = 9 + (-9)$ The opposite of 9 is -9. So add -9.
        $= 0$ Inverse Property of Addition

Got It? 3. a. What is $4.8 - (-8.7)$?
        b. Reasoning For what values of a and b does $a - b = b - a$?

Additional Problems

1. What is each sum? Use a number line.
  a. $4 + 7$
  b. $4 + (-7)$
  c. $-4 + 7$
  ANSWER a. 11,   **b.** −3,
  c. 3

2. What is each sum?
  a. $-14 + 9$
  b. $-15 + (-4)$
  c. $-3.6 + 10.8$
  ANSWER a. −5,   **b.** −19,
  c. 7.2

3. What is each difference?
  a. $-6 - (-12)$
  b. $2.1 - 9.6$
  c. $5 - 5$
  ANSWER a. 6,   **b.** −7.5,
  c. 0

4. A reef explorer dives 20 feet to photograph brain coral and then rises 7 feet to travel over a ridge before diving 31 feet to survey the base of the reef. Then the diver rises 18 feet to see an underwater cavern. What is the location of the cavern in relation to sea level?
  ANSWER −26 feet

Answers

Got It? (continued)
  3. a. 13.5
      b. any value where $a = b$

All of the addition properties of real numbers that you learned in Lesson 1-4 apply to both positive and negative numbers. You can use these properties to reorder and simplify expressions.

 Problem 4 Adding and Subtracting Real Numbers

Scuba Diving A reef explorer dives 25 ft to photograph brain coral and then rises 16 ft to travel over a ridge before diving 47 ft to survey the base of the reef. Then the diver rises 29 ft to see an underwater cavern. What is the location of the cavern in relation to sea level?

Know	Need	Plan
Distance and direction for each change in location	Location in relation to sea level after changes	Represent the diver's trip with an expression. Reorder the values to make calculations easier.

Think

How do you represent the problem with an expression?
Start your expression with zero to represent sea level. Subtract for dives, and add for rises.

$$0 - 25 + 16 - 47 + 29$$ 　　　　Write an expression.

$$= 0 + (-25) + 16 + (-47) + 29$$ 　Use rule for subtracting real numbers.

$$= 0 + 16 + 29 + (-25) + (-47)$$ 　Commutative Property of Addition

$$= 0 + (16 + 29) + [(-25) + (-47)]$$ 　Group addends with the same sign.

$$= 0 + 45 + (-72)$$ 　Add inside grouping symbols.

$$= 45 + (-72)$$ 　Identity Property of Addition

$$= -27$$ 　Use rule for adding numbers with different signs.

The cavern is at −27 ft in relation to sea level.

 Got It? 4. A robot submarine dives 803 ft to the ocean floor. It rises 215 ft as the water gets shallower. Then the submarine dives 2619 ft into a deep crevice. Next, it rises 734 ft to photograph a crack in the wall of the crevice. What is the location of the crack in relation to sea level?

 Lesson Check

Do you know HOW?
Use a number line to find each sum.
1. $-5 + 2$　　　　2. $-2 + (-1)$

Find each sum or difference.
3. $-12 + 9$　　　4. $-4 + (-3)$
5. $-3 - (-5)$　　　6. $1.5 - 8.5$

Do you UNDERSTAND?
7. **Vocabulary** What is the sum of a number and its opposite?
8. **Compare and Contrast** How is subtraction related to addition?
9. **Error Analysis** Your friend says that since $-a$ is the opposite of a, the opposite of a number is always negative. Describe and correct the error.

Problem 4

Q Can you determine if the final location will be above or below sea level by reading the problem? Explain. **[Yes, the diver will still be under the water, so the answer will be negative.]**

Q Is it necessary to reorder the addends in order to simplify the expression? Explain. **[No, you can also simplify the expression by completing the addition and subtraction from left to right.]**

Got It?　　　　　　　　**VISUAL LEARNERS**
Use a vertical number line with the water line marked at zero to help students visualize the submarine's activities.

3 Lesson Check

Do you know HOW?
• If students have difficulty with Exercise 5, then have them review Problem 3.

Do you UNDERSTAND?
• If students have difficulty with Exercise 9, then have them think about the operation of subtracting a known number such as −4.

Close

Q On a number line, how is subtraction of a negative number related to addition of a positive number? **[Both subtraction of a negative and addition of a positive require a move to the right on the number line.]**

Got It? (continued)
4. −2473 ft, or 2473 feet below sea level

Lesson Check
1. −3
2. −3
3. −3
4. −7
5. 2
6. −7
7. 0
8. Subtracting is the same as adding the opposite.
9. The opposite of a number is the number that is added to it to equal 0. If a number is positive, its opposite is negative. However, if a number is negative, its opposite is positive.

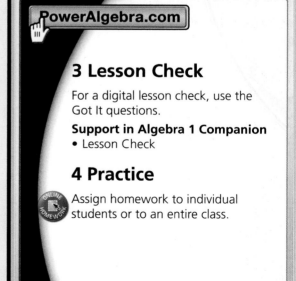

PowerAlgebra.com

3 Lesson Check
For a digital lesson check, use the Got It questions.
Support in Algebra 1 Companion
• Lesson Check

4 Practice
Assign homework to individual students or to an entire class.

4 Practice

ASSIGNMENT GUIDE

Basic: 10–43 all, 47–61

Average: 11–43 odd, 44–63

Advanced: 11–43 odd, 44–69

Standardized Test Prep: 70–74

Mixed Review: 75–85

Reasoning exercises have blue headings.

Applications exercises have red headings.

EXERCISE 61: Use the Think About a Plan worksheet in the **Practice and Problem Solving Workbook** (also available in the Teaching Resources in print and online) to further support students' development in becoming independent learners.

HOMEWORK QUICK CHECK

To check students' understanding of key skills and concepts, go over Exercises 19, 35, 47, 52, and 61.

Practice and Problem-Solving Exercises

A Practice

Use a number line to find each sum. ◀ See Problem 1.

10. $2 + 5$ **11.** $-3 + 8$ **12.** $4 + (-3)$ **13.** $1 + (-6)$

14. $-6 + 9$ **15.** $-4 + 7$ **16.** $-6 + (-8)$ **17.** $-9 + (-3)$

Find each sum. ◀ See Problem 2.

18. $11 + 9$ **19.** $17 + (-28)$ **20.** $12 + (-9)$ **21.** $-2 + 7$

22. $-14 + (-10)$ **23.** $-9 + (-2)$ **24.** $3.2 + 1.4$ **25.** $5.1 + (-0.7)$

26. $-2.2 + (-3.8)$ **27.** $\frac{1}{2} + \left(-\frac{7}{2}\right)$ **28.** $-\frac{2}{3} + \left(-\frac{3}{5}\right)$ **29.** $\frac{7}{9} + \left(-\frac{5}{12}\right)$

Find each difference. ◀ See Problem 3.

30. $5 - 15$ **31.** $-13 - 7$ **32.** $-19 - 7$ **33.** $36 - (-12)$

34. $-29 - (-11)$ **35.** $-7 - (-5)$ **36.** $8.5 - 7.6$ **37.** $-2.5 - 17.8$

38. $-2.9 - (-7.5)$ **39.** $3.5 - 1.9$ **40.** $\frac{1}{8} - \frac{3}{4}$ **41.** $\frac{7}{16} - \left(-\frac{1}{2}\right)$

42. Bird Watching An eagle starts flying at an elevation of 42 ft. Elevation is the distance above sea level. The diagram below shows the elevation changes during the eagle's flight. Write an expression representing the eagle's flight. What is the elevation at the brook? ◀ See Problem 4.

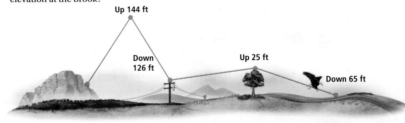

43. Stock Market A stock's starting price per share is $51.47 at the beginning of the week. During the week, the price changes by gaining $1.22, then losing $3.47, then losing $2.11, then losing $.98, and finally gaining $2.41. What is the ending stock price?

B Apply

Evaluate each expression for $a = -2$, $b = -4.1$, and $c = 5$.

44. $a - b + c$ **45.** $-c + b - a$ **46.** $-a + (-c)$

47. Error Analysis Describe and correct the error in finding the difference shown at the right.

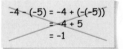

48. Writing Without calculating, tell which is greater, the sum of -135 and 257 or the sum of 135 and -257. Explain your reasoning.

Answers

Practice and Problem-Solving Exercises

10. 7;
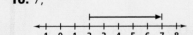

11. 5;
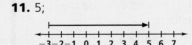

12. 1;
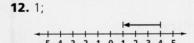

13. -5;
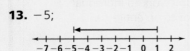

14. 3;

15. 3;

16. -14;

17. -12;

18. 20 **19.** -11 **20.** 3 **21.** 5

22. -24 **23.** -11 **24.** 4.6 **25.** 4.4

26. -6 **27.** -3 **28.** $-\frac{19}{15}$ **29.** $\frac{13}{36}$

30. -10 **31.** -20 **32.** -26 **33.** 48

34. -18 **35.** -2 **36.** 0.9

37. -20.3

38. 4.6

39. 1.6

40. $-\frac{5}{8}$

41. $\frac{15}{16}$

42. $42 + 144 - 126 + 25 - 65$; 20 ft

43. $48.54

44. 7.1

45. -7.1

46. -3

47. The sum of -4 and 5 is $+1$, not -1; $-4 - (-5) = -4 + 5 = 1$

48. The sum of -135 and 257; the absolute value of the positive number is greater, so the answer will be positive.

Simplify each expression.

49. $1 - \frac{1}{2} - \frac{1}{3} - \frac{1}{4}$ **50.** $7 + (2^2 - 3^2)$ **51.** $-2.1 - [2.3 - (3.5 - (-1.9))]$

52. Think About a Plan In golf, the expected number of strokes is called "par." When the number of strokes taken is more than par, your score is positive. When the number of strokes is less than par, your score is negative. The lowest score wins.

Golf Scorecard		
Par	Number of Strokes	Score
4	6	+2
4	3	−1
3	3	0
5	3	−2

The scorecard shows par and one golfer's score for the first four holes played on a nine-hole golf course. The golfer's scores on the remaining five holes are $-1, 0, -1, +1, 0$. Par for the nine holes is 36. What is the golfer's total number of strokes for the nine holes?
- Can you solve the problem by adding the strokes taken on each hole?
- How is the sum of the golfer's scores related to the total number of strokes taken?

Reasoning Use reasoning to determine whether the value of each expression is *positive* or *negative*. Do not calculate the exact answers.

53. $-225 + 318$ **54.** $-\frac{7}{8} + \frac{1}{3}$ **55.** $34.5 + 12.9 - 50$

56. Temperature Scales The Kelvin temperature scale is related to the degrees Celsius (°C) temperature scale by the formula $x = 273 + y$, where x is the number of kelvins and y is the temperature in degrees Celsius. What is each temperature in kelvins?
 a. -22°C   b. 0°C   c. -32°C

57. Writing Explain how you can tell without calculating whether the sum of a positive number and a negative number will be positive, negative, or zero.

Decide whether each statement is true or false. Explain your reasoning.

58. The sum of a positive number and a negative number is always negative.

59. The difference of two numbers is always less than the sum of those two numbers.

60. A number minus its opposite is twice the number.

61. Meteorology Weather forecasters use a barometer to measure air pressure and make weather predictions. Suppose a standard mercury barometer reads 29.8 in. The mercury rises 0.02 in. and then falls 0.09 in. The mercury falls again 0.18 in. before rising 0.07 in. What is the final reading on the barometer?

62. Multiple Choice Which expression is equivalent to $x - y$?
  Ⓐ $y - x$ Ⓑ $x - (-y)$ Ⓒ $x + (-y)$ Ⓓ $y + (-x)$

63. Chemistry Atoms contain particles called protons and electrons. Each proton has a charge of $+1$ and each electron has a charge of -1. A certain sulfur ion has 18 electrons and 16 protons. The charge on an ion is the sum of the charges of its protons and electrons. What is the sulfur ion's charge?

49. $-\frac{1}{12}$
50. 2
51. 1
52. 34 strokes
53. positive
54. negative
55. negative
56. a. 251 K
  b. 273 K
  c. 241 K
57. Find the absolute value of each number. The sign of the number with the larger absolute value will be the sign of the sum. If the absolute values are equal, the sum is 0.

58. False; the sign of the number with the larger absolute value will be the sign of the sum.
59. False; if both numbers are negative, the difference is larger than the sum.
60. True; $x - (-x) = x + x = 2x$
61. 29.62 in.
62. C
63. −2

Answers

Practice and Problem-Solving Exercises
(continued)

64. No; check students' work. Sample: This is not true when $x = -4$ and $y = 3$.

65. Sometimes; only true when $m = 0$, the result will be $-m = m$.

66. 0

67. $\frac{w}{10}$

68. $\frac{2d}{5}$

69. a. Yes; check students' work. Sample:
$|3 - 1| = |2| = 2$ and $|1 - 3| = |-2| = 2$

   b. No; check students' work. Sample:
$|3 + (-6)| = |-3| = 3$ but
$|3| + |-6| = 3 + 6 = 9$

70. B

71. H

72. B

73. F

74. C

75. yes

76. no

77. yes

78. rational numbers

79. rational numbers

80. rational numbers, whole numbers, natural numbers, and integers

81. rational numbers

82. irrational numbers

83. 18.75

84. 17

85. 318

Challenge

64. Reasoning If $|x| > |y|$, does $|x - y| = |x| - |y|$? Justify your answer.

65. Reasoning A student wrote the equation $-|m| = |-m|$. Is the equation *always*, *sometimes*, or *never* true? Explain.

Simplify each expression.

66. $\frac{c}{4} - \frac{c}{4}$

67. $\frac{w}{5} + \left(-\frac{w}{10}\right)$

68. $\frac{d}{5} - \left(-\frac{d}{5}\right)$

69. Reasoning Answer each question. Justify your answers.
   a. Is $|a - b|$ always equal to $|b - a|$?
   b. Is $|a + b|$ always equal to $|a| + |b|$?

Standardized Test Prep

SAT/ACT

70. What is the value of $-b - a$ when $a = -4$ and $b = 7$?
   Ⓐ -11 Ⓑ -3 Ⓒ 3 Ⓓ 11

71. Which expression is equivalent to $19 - 41$?
   Ⓕ $|19 - 41|$ Ⓖ $|19 + 41|$ Ⓗ $-|19 - 41|$ Ⓘ $-|19 + 41|$

72. Which equation illustrates the Identity Property of Multiplication?
   Ⓐ $x \cdot 0 = 0$ Ⓑ $x \cdot 1 = x$ Ⓒ $x(yz) = (xy)z$ Ⓓ $x \cdot y = y \cdot x$

73. What is an algebraic expression for the perimeter of the triangle?
   Ⓕ $8 + x$ Ⓗ 8
   Ⓖ $4x$ Ⓘ $4 + x$

74. Which point on the number line below is the best estimate for $\sqrt{8}$?

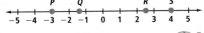

   Ⓐ P Ⓑ Q Ⓒ R Ⓓ S

Mixed Review

Tell whether the expressions in each pair are equivalent.   ◀ See Lesson 1-4.

75. $\frac{3}{4} \cdot d \cdot 4$ and $3d$ **76.** $(2.1 \cdot h) \cdot 3$ and $6.3 + h$ **77.** $(6 + b) + a$ and $6 + (a + b)$

Name the subset(s) of real numbers to which each number belongs.   ◀ See Lesson 1-3.

78. $\frac{1}{3}$ **79.** -5.333 **80.** $\sqrt{16}$ **81.** 82.0371 **82.** $\sqrt{21}$

Get Ready! **To prepare for Lesson 1-6, do Exercises 83–85.**

Evaluate each expression for $a = 2$, $h = 5$, and $w = 8$.   ◀ See Lesson 1-2.

83. $4h - 5a \div w$ **84.** $a^2w - h^2 + 2h$ **85.** $(w^2h - a^2) + 12 \div 3a$

1-5 Lesson Resources

Differentiated Remediation
Available in editable format online.

Additional Instructional Support

Algebra 1 Companion

Students can use the **Algebra 1 Companion** worktext (4 pages) as you teach the lesson. Use the Companion to support

- New Vocabulary
- Key Concepts
- Got It for each Problem
- Lesson Check

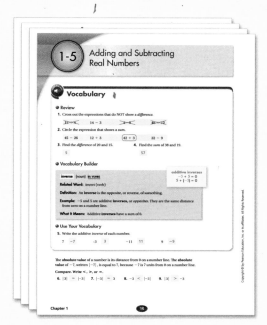

ELL Support

Assess Understanding Have a volunteer draw a number line on the board. Model, while using gestures and talking aloud, how to use the number line to add real numbers. Select volunteers to write the sentences "If a number is positive, move to the right." and "If a number is negative, move to the left." on the board. Ask students to draw a number line on paper. Model finding a sum and a difference on the board. Cue the two volunteers to read the sentences that they wrote at appropriate times.

Now give students a problem to solve in small groups. Call a group to the board to demonstrate how they found their solution. Allow the volunteers who wrote the sentences to help by repeating their sentences when needed.

5 Assess & Remediate

Lesson Quiz

1. Find each sum.
   a. $4 + (-12)$
   b. $-4 + 12$
2. What is the sum: $-13 + 7$?
3. Find each difference.
   a. $11 - (-4)$
   b. $2.4 - 3.1$
4. **Do you UNDERSTAND?** An elevator begins on the ground floor. It travels up 14 floors and then down 6 floors. After this the elevator travels up 3 floors, up 7 floors, and down 12 floors. On what floor does the elevator stop?

ANSWERS TO LESSON QUIZ

1. a. -8, b. 8
2. -6
3. a. 15, b. -0.7
4. 6th floor

PRESCRIPTION FOR REMEDIATION
Use the student work on the Lesson Quiz to prescribe a differentiated review assignment.

Points	Differentiated Remediation
0–2	Intervention
3	On-level
4	Extension

PowerAlgebra.com

5 Assess & Remediate
Assign the Lesson Quiz. Appropriate intervention, practice, or enrichment is automatically generated based on student performance.

Intervention

- **Reteaching** (2 pages) Provides reteaching and practice exercises for the key lesson concepts. Use with struggling students or absent students.
- **English Language Learner Support** Helps students develop and reinforce mathematical vocabulary and key concepts.

All-in-One Resources/Online
Reteaching

1-5 Reteaching
Adding and Subtracting Real Numbers

You can add real numbers using a number line or using the following rules.

Rule 1: To add two numbers with the same sign, add their absolute values. The sum has the same sign as the addends.

Problem
What is the sum of -7 and -4?

Use a number line.

Start at zero.
Move 7 spaces to the left to represent -7.
Move another 4 spaces to the left to represent -4.

The sum is -11.

Use the rule.

$-7 + (-4)$	The addends are both negative.
$|-7| + |-4|$	Add the absolute values of the addends.
$7 + 4 = 11$	$|-7| = 7$ and $|-4| = 4$.
$-7 + (-4) = -11$	The sum has the same sign as the addends.

Rule 2: To add two numbers with different signs, subtract their absolute values. The sum has the same sign as the addend with the greater absolute value.

Problem
What is the sum of -6 and 9?

Use the rule.

$9 + (-6)$	The addends have different signs.
$|9| - |-6|$	Subtract the absolute values of the addends.
$9 - 6 = 3$	$|9| = 9$ and $|-6| = 6$.
$9 + (-6) = 3$	The positive addend has the greater absolute value.

All-in-One Resources/Online
English Language Learner Support

1-5 ELL Support
Adding and Subtracting Real Numbers

Problem
A diver dives 50 ft and then rises 12 ft to look at a fish. Then he dives down 7 ft to look at some coral. Next, he rises 20 ft to take a photograph. What is his location in relation to sea level? Justify your steps. Then check your answer.

$0 - 50 + 12 - 7 + 20$	Write an expression.
$= 0 + (-50) + 12 + (-7) + 20$	Rule for subtracting real numbers
$= 0 + 12 + 20 + (-50) + (-7)$	Commutative Property of Addition
$= 0 + (12 + 20) + [(-50) + (-7)]$	Group addends with the same sign and add.
$= 32 + (-57)$	Identity Property of Addition
$= -25$	Rule for adding numbers with different signs

Exercises

A roller coaster rises 50 ft, falls 20 ft, rises 70 ft and falls 60 ft. What is the final location of the roller coaster in relation to its starting elevation? Justify your steps. Then check your answer.

$0 + 50 - 20 + 70 - 60$	Write an expression.
$= 0 + 50 + (-20) + 70 + (-60)$	Rule for subtracting real numbers
$= 0 + 50 + 70 + (-20) + (-60)$	Commutative Property of Addition
$= 0 + (50 + 70) + [(-20) + (-60)]$	Group addends with the same sign.
$= 0 + 120 + (-80)$	Add inside grouping symbols.
$= 120 + (-80)$	Identity Property of Addition
$= 40$	Rule for adding numbers with different signs

A stock price per share was $45.00 last week. The price changed by gaining $4, losing $6, losing $5, and gaining $7. What was the ending stock price? Justify your steps. Then check your answer.

$45 + 4 - 6 - 5 + 7$	Write an expression.
$= 45 + 4 + (-6) + (-5) + 7$	Rule for subtracting real numbers
$= 45 + 4 + 7 + (-6) + (-5)$	Commutative Property of Addition
$= (45 + 4 + 7) + [(-6) + (-5)]$	Group addends with the same sign.
$= (56) + (-11)$	Add inside grouping symbols.
$= 45$	Rule for adding numbers with different signs

Differentiated Remediation *continued*

On-Level

- **Practice** (2 pages) Provides extra practice for each lesson. For simpler practice exercises, use the Form K Practice pages found in the All-in-One Teaching Resources and online.

- **Think About a Plan** Helps students develop specific problem-solving skills and strategies by providing scaffolded guiding questions.

- **Standardized Test Prep** Focuses on all major exercises, all major question types, and helps students prepare for the high-stakes assessments.

Extension

- **Enrichment** Provides students with interesting problems and activities that extend the concepts of the lesson.

- **Activities, Games, and Puzzles** Worksheets that can be used for concepts development, enrichment, and for fun!

Practice and Problem Solving WKBK/ All-in-One Resources/Online
Practice page 1

1-5 Practice *Form G*
Adding and Subtracting Real Numbers

Use a number line to find each sum.

1. $4 + 8$ 12
2. $-7 + 8$ 1
3. $9 + (-4)$ 5

4. $-6 + (-2)$ -8
5. $-6 + 3$ -3
6. $5 + (-10)$ -5

7. $-7 + (-7)$ -14
8. $9 + (-9)$ 0
9. $-8 + 0$ -8

Find each sum.

10. $22 + (-14)$ 8
11. $-36 + (-13)$ -49
12. $-15 + 17$ 2

13. $45 + 77$ 122
14. $19 + (-30)$ -11
15. $-18 + (-18)$ -36

16. $-1.5 + 6.1$ 4.6
17. $-2.2 + (-16.7)$ -18.9
18. $5.3 + (-7.4)$ -2.1

19. $-\frac{1}{9} + \left(-\frac{5}{9}\right)$ $-\frac{2}{3}$
20. $\frac{3}{4} + \left(-\frac{3}{8}\right)$ $\frac{3}{8}$
21. $-\frac{1}{5} + \frac{7}{10}$ $\frac{1}{2}$

22. **Writing** Explain how you would use a number line to find $6 + (-8)$.
Answers may vary. Sample: Start at 0. Move 6 spaces to the right and then 8 spaces to the left. The answer is -2.

23. **Open-Ended** Write an addition equation with a positive addend and a negative addend and a resulting sum of -8.
Answers may vary. Sample: $-10 + 2 = -8$

24. The Bears football team lost 7 yards and then gained 12 yards. What is the result of the two plays?
a gain of 5 yd

Practice and Problem Solving WKBK/ All-in-One Resources/Online
Practice page 2

1-5 Practice *(continued)* *Form G*
Adding and Subtracting Real Numbers

Find each difference.

25. $7 - 14$ -7
26. $-8 - 12$ -20
27. $-5 - (-16)$ 11

28. $33 - (-14)$ 47
29. $62 - 71$ -9
30. $-25 - (-25)$ 0

31. $1.7 - (-3.8)$ 5.5
32. $-4.5 - 5.8$ -10.3
33. $-3.7 - (-4.2)$ 0.5

34. $-\frac{7}{8} - \left(-\frac{1}{8}\right)$ $-\frac{3}{4}$
35. $\frac{3}{2} - \frac{1}{2}$ 1
36. $\frac{4}{9} - \left(-\frac{2}{3}\right)$ $1\frac{1}{9}$

Evaluate each expression for $m = -4$, $n = 5$, and $p = 1.5$.

37. $m - p$ -5.5
38. $-m + n - p$ 7.5
39. $n + m - p$ -0.5

40. At 4:00 A.M., the temperature was $-9°F$. At noon, the temperature was $18°F$. What was the change in temperature?
27 degrees

41. A teacher had $57.72 in his checking account. He made a deposit of $209.54. Then he wrote a check for $72.00 and another check for $27.50. What is the new balance in his checking account?
$167.76

42. A scuba diver went down 20 feet below the surface of the water. Then she dove down 3 more feet. Later, she rose 7 feet. What integer describes her depth?
-16

43. **Reasoning** Without doing the calculations determine whether $-47 - (-33)$ or $-47 + (-33)$ is greater. Explain your reasoning.
$-47 - (-33)$ is greater; $-47 - (-33)$ is the same as $-47 + 33$ which is greater than $-47 + (-33)$.

All-in-One Resources/Online
Enrichment

1-5 Enrichment
Adding and Subtracting Real Numbers

A number square is a square where the numbers in any row, column, or diagonal have the same sum. Notice that in the square at the right, the sum of each row, each column, and each diagonal is 15.

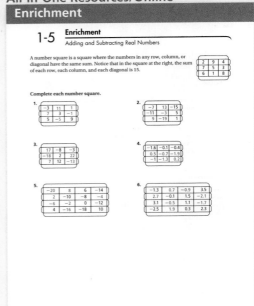

Complete each number square.

Practice and Problem Solving WKBK/ All-in-One Resources/Online
Think About a Plan

1-5 Think About a Plan
Adding and Subtracting Real Numbers

Meteorology Weather forecasters use a barometer to measure air pressure and make weather predictions. Suppose a standard mercury barometer reads 29.8 in. The mercury rises 0.02 in. and then falls 0.09 in. The mercury falls again 0.18 in. before rising 0.07 in. What is the final reading on the barometer?

Think

1. What operation does "rise" suggest? _addition_

2. What operation does "fall" suggest? _subtraction_

Plan

3. Write either *plus* or *minus* in each box so that the following represents the problem.

29.8 plus 0.02 minus 0.09 minus 0.18 plus 0.07

4. Write an expression to represent the problem.
$29.8 + 0.02 - 0.09 - 0.18 + 0.07$

Solve

5. What is the value of the expression you wrote in Exercise 4? _29.62_

6. What is the final reading on the barometer? _29.62 in._

Practice and Problem Solving WKBK/ All-in-One Resources/Online
Standardized Test Prep

1-5 Standardized Test Prep
Adding and Subtracting Real Numbers

Multiple Choice

For Exercises 1–5, choose the correct letter.

1. Which expression is equivalent to $17 + (-15)$? C
   A. $-17 + 15$
   B. $-17 - 15$
   C. $17 - 15$
   D. $17 + 15$

2. Which number could be placed in the square to make the equation true? F
   $-5 - \square = 14$
   F. -19
   G. -9
   H. 9
   I. 19

3. Which expression has the greatest value? B
   A. $-14 - (-5)$
   B. $-5 - (-14)$
   C. $-14 - 5$
   D. $-5 - 14$

4. The wheel was invented about 2500 BC. The gasoline automobile was invented in AD 1885. How many years passed between the invention of the wheel and the invention of the automobile? G
   F. 1615 years
   G. 4385 years
   H. 1725 years
   I. 5385 years

5. If $r = -18$, $s = 27$, and $t = -15$, what is the value of $r - s - t$? B
   A. -60
   B. -30
   C. -6
   D. 6

Short Response

6. In golf, there is a number of strokes assigned to each hole, called the par for that hole. If you get the ball in the hole in fewer strokes than par, you are under par for the hole. If it takes you more strokes than the par, you are over par for the hole. On the first 9 holes of golf, Avery had a par, 1 over par, 1 under par, another par, 1 under par, 1 over par, 3 over par, 2 under par, and 1 under par.
   a. What addition expression would represent all 9 holes?
   $0 + 1 + (-2) + 0 + (-1) + 1 + 3 + (-2) + (-1)$
   b. What is Avery's score relative to par?
   -1
   [2] Both parts answered correctly.
   [1] One part answered correctly.
   [0] Neither part answered correctly.

Online Teacher Resource Center
Activities, Games, and Puzzles

1-5 Puzzle: That's Sum Puzzle!
Adding and Subtracting Real Numbers

Puzzle 1

Use the numbers {19, 25, 34, 47, 78, 94} to fill in the blank squares in the table below. Each number can only be used once. Arrange the numbers so that the sum of the numbers in the first row is 295, and the sum of the numbers in the second row is 120. The differences down each column must equal 28, 36, 42, and 69, from left to right.

					Sums
Row 1	47	78	76	94	295
Row 2	19	42	34	25	120
Differences	28	36	42	69	

Puzzle 2

Use the fractions $\left\{\frac{1}{6}, \frac{7}{30}, \frac{1}{3}, \frac{2}{5}, \frac{3}{5}, \frac{2}{3}\right\}$ to fill in the blank squares in the table below. Each fraction can be used only once. Arrange the fractions so that the sum of the fractions in the first row is 2, and the sum of the fractions in the second row is 1. In addition, the differences down each column must equal $\frac{1}{15}$, $\frac{17}{30}$, $\frac{1}{10}$, and $\frac{4}{15}$, from left to right.

					Sums
Row 1	$\frac{7}{30}$	$\frac{2}{3}$	$\frac{1}{2}$	$\frac{3}{5}$	2
Row 2	$\frac{1}{6}$	$\frac{1}{10}$	$\frac{2}{5}$	$\frac{1}{3}$	1
Differences	$\frac{1}{15}$	$\frac{17}{30}$	$\frac{1}{10}$	$\frac{4}{15}$	

Concept Byte

Use With Lesson 1-5

ACTIVITY

Always, Sometimes, or Never

A statement can be always, sometimes, or never true. For each activity, work with a group of 4 students. Take turns predicting each answer. If the predictor gives a correct answer, he or she scores 1 point. Otherwise, the person who proves the predictor incorrect scores 1 point. Whoever has the most points at the end of an activity wins.

Activity 1

Is each description *always*, *sometimes*, or *never* true about the members of your group?

1. takes an algebra class

2. lives in your state

3. plays a musical instrument

4. is less than 25 years old

5. speaks more than one language

6. is taller than 5 m

Activity 2

Suppose each member of your group takes one of the four cards at the right. Will a group member chosen at random *always*, *sometimes*, or *never* have a number that fits each description?

7. greater than 2

8. greater than 25

9. even

10. irrational number

11. prime number

12. rational number

Activity 3

Each member of your group substitutes any integer for x in each statement. Will a group member chosen at random *always*, *sometimes*, or *never* have a true statement?

13. $x - 2$ is greater than x.

14. $|x|$ is less than x.

15. $7 + x = x + 7$

16. $13 - x = x - 13$

17. $x + 0 = x$

18. $-4 + (3 + x) = x + (-4 + 3)$

19. $x \div 5$ is less than x.

20. $x \cdot 0 = 0$

21. $x + 9$ is less than x.

22. $|x|$ is greater than x.

Guided Instruction

PURPOSE To examine statements that are always, sometimes, or never true

PROCESS Students will

- classify always, sometimes, or never true.
- find counterexamples from statements to prove a statement is not always true or never true.

DISCUSS Have each student make up three situations about themselves. One should be always true. One should be sometimes true. One should be never true. Challenge volunteers to decide if fellow classmates' statements are always, sometimes, or never true.

Activity 1

In this activity students focus on how well they know their classmates when deciding whether a statement is always, sometimes, or never true.

> **Q** How can you prove a statement is not always true? **[Find one counterexample.]**
>
> **Q** Which of the six exercises will always be true for every member in the class? **[takes an algebra class]**

Activity 2

In this activity students focus on number classifications and values when deciding whether a statement is always, sometimes, or never true.

> **Q** When the statement is always true, what percent of the cards in the set will fit the description? **[100%]**
>
> **Q** When the statement is never true, what percent of the cards in the set will fit the description? **[0%]**

Activity 3

In this activity students focus on algebraic expressions, inequalities, and equations when deciding whether a statement is always, sometimes, or never true.

> **Q** When substituting integers for x, what integers should be used? **[Always try to use at least one positive integer, one negative integer, and zero.]**

Answers

Activity 1
1. always
2. sometimes
3. sometimes
4. always
5. sometimes
6. never

Activity 2
7. always
8. never
9. sometimes
10. never
11. sometimes
12. always

Activity 3
13. never
14. never
15. always
16. sometimes
17. always
18. always
19. sometimes
20. always
21. never
22. sometimes

1 Interactive Learning

Solve It!

PURPOSE To derive the rules for multiplying real numbers by using inductive reasoning

PROCESS Students may continue the pattern or use the fact that multiplication is repeated addition to complete the tables.

FACILITATE

Q If you add more rows to the table, both above and below what is given, how can you describe the pattern of the products in the second column? **[Multiplying −2 by factors greater than 3 results in negative products, and multiplying −2 by factors less than −3 results in positive products.]**

Q What property is used to determine the products −2 · 0 and 2 · 0? **[Zero Property of Multiplication]**

ANSWER See Solve It in Answers on next page.

CONNECT THE MATH Discuss with students how they can use the multiplication tables to determine the answers to these questions:

1. What is the sign of a negative number divided by a positive number? **[negative]**
2. What is the sign of a negative number divided by a negative number? **[positive]**
3. What is the sign of a positive number divided by a negative number? **[negative]**

1-6 Multiplying and Dividing Real Numbers

Indiana Academic Standard
Prepares for A1.4.2 Add, subtract and multiply polynomials and divide polynomials by monomials.

Objective To find products and quotients of real numbers

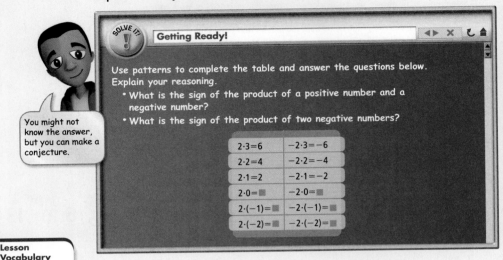

You might not know the answer, but you can make a conjecture.

Lesson Vocabulary
• multiplicative inverse
• reciprocal

The patterns in the Solve It suggest rules for multiplying real numbers.

Essential Understanding The rules for multiplying real numbers are related to the properties of real numbers and the definitions of operations.

You know that the product of two positive numbers is positive. For example, $3(5) = 15$. You can think about the product of a positive number and a negative number in terms of groups of numbers. For example, $3(−5)$ means 3 groups of $−5$. So, $3(−5) = (−5) + (−5) + (−5)$, or $3(−5) = −15$.

You can also derive the product of two negative numbers, such as $−3(−5)$.

$3(−5) = −15$	Start with the product $3(−5) = −15$.
$−[3(−5)] = −(−15)$	The opposites of two equal numbers are equal.
$−1[3(−5)] = −(−15)$	Multiplication Property of $−1$
$[−1(3)](−5) = −(−15)$	Associative Property of Multiplication
$−3(−5) = −(−15)$	Multiplication Property of $−1$
$−3(−5) = 15$	The opposite of $−15$ is 15.

These discussions illustrate the following rules for multiplying real numbers.

BIG idea Properties **UbD**
ESSENTIAL UNDERSTANDINGS
• The rules for multiplying real numbers are related to the properties of real numbers and the definitions of operations.
• The product or quotient of two real numbers with different signs is negative.
• The product or quotient of two real numbers with the same sign is positive.

Math Background

Multiplication and division have an inverse relationship. Just as addition can undo subtraction, multiplication can undo division and vise versa.

The value of $\frac{a}{b}$ is a number c such that $c \cdot b = a$. Students may already know that division by zero is undefined. To see why, consider the following cases.

Assume that a and b are nonzero and $\frac{a}{0} = b$. Then $a = 0 \cdot b = 0$. This is a contradiction because a cannot be both zero and nonzero.

What if $a = 0$? Then assume there is a number b such that $\frac{0}{0} = b$. Then $0 = 0 \cdot b$, which is true for all real numbers b. The problem now is that b is not unique.

Support Student Learning

Use the **Algebra 1 Companion** to engage and support students during instructions. See Lesson Resources at the end of this lesson for details.

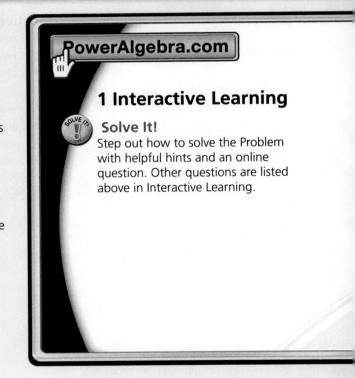

PowerAlgebra.com

1 Interactive Learning

Solve It!
Step out how to solve the Problem with helpful hints and an online question. Other questions are listed above in Interactive Learning.

Key Concept   Multiplying Real Numbers

Words The product of two real numbers with *different* signs is *negative*.

Examples $2(-3) = -6$ $-2 \cdot 3 = -6$

Model $2(-3) = -6$

Words The product of two real numbers with the *same* sign is *positive*.

Examples $2 \cdot 3 = 6$ $-2(-3) = 6$

Model $2 \cdot 3 = 6$

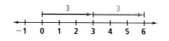

Plan

What is your first step in finding a product of real numbers?
Identify the signs of the factors. Then determine the sign of the product.

Problem 1   Multiplying Real Numbers

What is each product?

A $12(-8) = -96$ The product of two numbers with different signs is negative.

B $24(0.5) = 12$ The product of two numbers with the same sign is positive.

C $-\frac{3}{4} \cdot \frac{1}{2} = -\frac{3}{8}$ The product of two numbers with different signs is negative.

D $(-3)^2 = (-3)(-3) = 9$ The product of two numbers with the same sign is positive.

Got It? 1. What is each product?

  a. $6(-15)$ **b.** $12(0.2)$ **c.** $-\frac{7}{10}\left(\frac{3}{5}\right)$ **d.** $(-4)^2$

Notice that $(-3)^2 = 9$ in part (d) of Problem 1. Recall from Lesson 1-3 that a is a square root of b if $a^2 = b$. So, -3 is a square root of 9. A negative square root is represented by $-\sqrt{}$. Every positive real number has a positive and a negative square root. The symbol $\pm$ in front of the radical indicates both square roots.

Think

How can you find a negative square root?
Look for a negative number that you can multiply by itself to get a product that is equal to the radicand.

Problem 2   Simplifying Square Root Expressions

What is the simplified form of each expression?

A $-\sqrt{25} = -5$ $(-5)^2 = 25$, so $-\sqrt{25} = -5$.

B $\pm\sqrt{\frac{4}{49}} = \pm\frac{2}{7}$ $\left(\frac{2}{7}\right)^2 = \frac{4}{49}$ and $\left(-\frac{2}{7}\right)^2 = \frac{4}{49}$, so $\pm\sqrt{\frac{4}{49}} = \pm\frac{2}{7}$.

Got It? 2. What is the simplified form of each expression?

  a. $\sqrt{64}$ **b.** $\pm\sqrt{16}$ **c.** $-\sqrt{121}$ **d.** $\pm\sqrt{\frac{1}{36}}$

---

2 Guided Instruction

Take Note   VISUAL LEARNERS

Help students remember the rules for multiplying real numbers by displaying a graphic organizer such as the following:

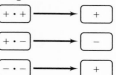

Problem 1

Q Is the product of $(-12)(8)$ the same as the product of $(12)(-8)$? Explain. **[Yes, the products are the same. A positive number times a negative number is negative. So both expressions are negative.]**

Got It?

Q Which two products are negative numbers? **[a and c]**
Q Which two products are positive numbers? **[b and d]**

Problem 2

Q How are the positive and negative square roots of a number related? **[They are additive inverses.]**

Got It?

Q Is it possible to simplify a square root expression that has a negative radicand? Explain. **[No, you cannot get a negative product when squaring a real number.]**

---

2 Guided Instruction

Each Problem is worked out and supported online.

Problem 1
Multiplying Real Numbers
Animated

Problem 2
Simplifying Square Root Expressions
Animated

Problem 3
Dividing Real Numbers
Animated

Problem 4
Dividing Fractions

Support in Algebra 1 Companion
• Vocabulary
• Key Concepts
• Got It?

Answers

Solve It!

$2 \cdot 3 = 6$	$-2 \cdot 3 = -6$
$2 \cdot 2 = 4$	$-2 \cdot 2 = -4$
$2 \cdot 1 = 2$	$-2 \cdot 1 = -2$
$2 \cdot 0 = 0$	$-2 \cdot 0 = 0$
$2(-1) = -2$	$-2(-1) = 2$
$2(-2) = -4$	$-2(-2) = 4$

The sign of the product of a positive and a negative number is negative. The product of two negative numbers is positive.

Got It?

  1. a. -90 **b.** 2.4 **c.** $-\frac{21}{50}$ **d.** 16
  2. a. 8 **b.** ±4 **c.** -11 **d.** $\pm\frac{1}{6}$

Take Note

Using a real-world example to discuss division by zero can help students understand a concept that is often confusing. Relate that while 0 apples can be divided up among 6 children (each child gets 0 apples), 6 apples cannot be divided up among 0 children (there is no one to receive the apples).

Problem 3

Q What is the expected change in elevation for the skydiver 3 minutes after opening the parachute? **[−2700 feet]**

Got It?   ERROR PREVENTION

Q Will the change in account balance be represented by a positive number or a negative number? **[negative]**

Take Note

Remind students of the Inverse Property of Addition introduced in Lesson 1-5. Ask students to compare and contrast the Inverse Properties of Multiplication and Addition.

Essential Understanding Rules for dividing real numbers are related to the rules for multiplying real numbers.

For any real numbers a, b, and c where $a \neq 0$, if $a \cdot b = c$, then $b = c \div a$. For instance, $-8(-2) = 16$, so $-2 = 16 \div (-8)$. Similarly $-8(2) = -16$, so $2 = -16 \div (-8)$. These examples illustrate the following rules.

Key Concept   Dividing Real Numbers

Words The quotient of two real numbers with *different* signs is *negative*.
Examples $-20 \div 5 = -4$ $20 \div (-5) = -4$

Words The quotient of two real numbers with the *same* sign is *positive*.
Examples $20 \div 5 = 4$ $-20 \div (-5) = 4$

Division Involving 0

Words The quotient of 0 and any nonzero real number is 0. The quotient of any real number and 0 is undefined.

Examples $0 \div 8 = 0$ $8 \div 0$ is undefined.

Problem 3   Dividing Real Numbers

Sky Diving A sky diver's elevation changes by -3600 ft in 4 min after the parachute opens. What is the average change in the sky diver's elevation each minute?

$-3600 \div 4 = -900$ The numbers have different signs, so the quotient is negative.

The sky diver's average change in elevation is -900 ft per minute.

Think

How is dividing similar to multiplying?
You find the sign of a quotient using the signs of the numbers you're dividing, just as you find the sign of a product using the signs of the factors.

Got It? 3. You make five withdrawals of equal amounts from your bank account. The total amount you withdraw is $360. What is the change in your account balance each time you make a withdrawal?

The Inverse Property of Multiplication describes the relationship between a number and its multiplicative inverse.

Property   Inverse Property of Multiplication

Words For every nonzero real number a, there is a **multiplicative inverse** $\frac{1}{a}$ such that $a\left(\frac{1}{a}\right) = 1$.

Examples The multiplicative inverse of -4 is $-\frac{1}{4}$ because $-4\left(-\frac{1}{4}\right) = 1$.

Additional Problems

1. What is each product?
  a. $9(-7)$
  b. $32(0.5)$
  c. $-\frac{1}{2} \times \frac{5}{6}$
  d $(-5)^2$
  ANSWER a. -63, **b.** 16,
  c. $\frac{-5}{12}$, **d.** 25

2. What is the simplified form of each expression?
  a. $-\sqrt{49}$
  b. $\pm\sqrt{\frac{4}{9}}$
  ANSWER a. -7, **b.** $\pm\frac{2}{3}$

3. The elevation of a hot air balloon changes by -3750 ft in 5 min after opening the parachute. What is the change in the hot air balloon's elevation each minute?
  ANSWER -750 feet each minute

4. What is the value of $\frac{x}{y}$ when $x = \frac{1}{2}$ and $y = -\frac{2}{3}$?
  A. $\frac{1}{4}$
  B. $-\frac{4}{3}$
  C. $-\frac{3}{2}$
  D. $-\frac{3}{4}$
  ANSWER D

Answers

Got It? (continued)
  3. $-\$72$

The **reciprocal** of a nonzero real number of the form $\frac{a}{b}$ is $\frac{b}{a}$. The product of a number and its reciprocal is 1, so the reciprocal of a number is its multiplicative inverse. This suggests a rule for dividing fractions.

Here's Why It Works Let $a, b, c,$ and d be nonzero integers.

$$\frac{a}{b} \div \frac{c}{d} = \frac{\frac{a}{b}}{\frac{c}{d}}$$ Write the expression as a fraction.

$$= \frac{\frac{a}{b} \cdot \frac{d}{c}}{\frac{c}{d} \cdot \frac{d}{c}}$$ Multiply the numerator and denominator by $\frac{d}{c}$. Since this is equivalent to multiplying by 1, it does not change the quotient.

$$= \frac{\frac{a}{b} \cdot \frac{d}{c}}{1}$$ Inverse Property of Multiplication

$$= \frac{a}{b} \cdot \frac{d}{c}$$ Simplify.

This shows that dividing by a fraction is equivalent to multiplying by the reciprocal of the fraction.

Problem 4 Dividing Fractions

Multiple Choice What is the value of $\frac{x}{y}$ when $x = -\frac{3}{4}$ and $y = -\frac{2}{3}$?

Ⓐ $-\frac{9}{8}$ Ⓑ $-\frac{1}{2}$ Ⓒ $\frac{1}{2}$ Ⓓ $\frac{9}{8}$

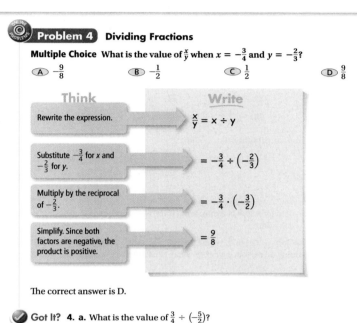

Think

Rewrite the expression.

Substitute $-\frac{3}{4}$ for x and $-\frac{2}{3}$ for y.

Multiply by the reciprocal of $-\frac{2}{3}$.

Simplify. Since both factors are negative, the product is positive.

Write

$$\frac{x}{y} = x \div y$$

$$= -\frac{3}{4} \div \left(-\frac{2}{3}\right)$$

$$= -\frac{3}{4} \cdot \left(-\frac{3}{2}\right)$$

$$= \frac{9}{8}$$

The correct answer is D.

✓ **Got It?** 4. a. What is the value of $\frac{3}{4} \div \left(-\frac{5}{2}\right)$?
  b. **Reasoning** Is $\frac{3}{4} \div \left(-\frac{5}{2}\right)$ equivalent to $-\left(\frac{3}{4} \div \frac{5}{2}\right)$? Explain.

Here's Why It Works
Students can benefit from seeing the algebraic work shown here with real numbers in place of the variables. Let $a = 1$, $b = 2$, $c = 3$ and $d = 4$.

$$\frac{1}{2} \div \frac{3}{4} = \frac{\frac{1}{2}}{\frac{3}{4}}$$

$$= \frac{\frac{1}{2} \cdot \frac{4}{3}}{\frac{3}{4} \cdot \frac{4}{3}} = \frac{\frac{1}{2} \cdot \frac{\cancel{4}^{2}}{3}}{\frac{\cancel{3}}{\cancel{4}} \cdot \frac{\cancel{4}}{\cancel{3}}} = \frac{\frac{2}{3}}{1} = \frac{2}{3}$$

They can compare the result to the calculations with which they should be familiar.

$$\frac{1}{2} \div \frac{3}{4} = \frac{1}{2} \times \frac{4}{3} = \frac{1}{2} \times \frac{\cancel{4}^{2}}{3} = \frac{2}{3}$$

Problem 4

Q What operation is indicated by the expression $\frac{x}{y}$? **[division]**

Q Will the quotient of the two numbers be positive or negative? Explain. **[Positive, the signs of x and y are the same.]**

Q Will you calculate the same quotient if you multiply y by the reciprocal of x rather than multiply x by the reciprocal of y? Explain. **[No, changing the factors will result in a different product.]**

Got It?

Q Can the rule for dividing fractions be used to divide two integers such as -12 and 3? Explain. **[Yes, $-12 \div 3$ is equivalent to $-12 \cdot \frac{1}{3}$.]**

Got It? (continued)

4. a. $-\frac{3}{10}$
  b. Yes; a positive divided by a negative is negative and the opposite of a positive divided by a positive is also negative.

3 Lesson Check

Do you know HOW?
- If students have difficulty with Exercise 4, then have them review Problem 4.

Do you UNDERSTAND?
- If students have difficulty with Exercise 5, then have them review the definition of a reciprocal.

Close

> **Q** Is it possible to square a real number and obtain a negative product? Explain. **[No, the two factors are the same and have the same sign, and will therefore yield a positive product. If the factors are 0, the product will be 0.]**

Lesson Check

Do you know HOW?
Find each product. Simplify, if necessary.

1. $-3(-12)$
2. $\frac{5}{8}\left(-\frac{2}{8}\right)$

Find each quotient. Simplify, if necessary.

3. $-48 \div 3$
4. $-\frac{9}{10} \div \left(-\frac{4}{5}\right)$

Do you UNDERSTAND?

5. **Vocabulary** What is the reciprocal of $-\frac{1}{5}$?

6. **Reasoning** Use a number line to explain why $-15 \div 3 = -5$.

7. **Reasoning** Determine how many real square roots each number has. Explain your answers.
   a. 49
   b. 0

Practice and Problem-Solving Exercises

A Practice · Find each product. Simplify, if necessary. ◆ See Problem 1.

8. $-8(12)$
9. $8(12)$
10. $7(-9)$
11. $5 \cdot 4.1$
12. $-7 \cdot 1.1$
13. $10(-2.5)$
14. $6\left(-\frac{1}{4}\right)$
15. $-\frac{1}{9}\left(-\frac{3}{4}\right)$
16. $-\frac{3}{7} \cdot \frac{9}{10}$
17. $-\frac{2}{11}\left(-\frac{11}{2}\right)$
18. $\left(-\frac{2}{9}\right)^2$
19. $(-1.2)^2$

Simplify each expression. ◆ See Problem 2.

20. $\sqrt{400}$
21. $\sqrt{169}$
22. $-\sqrt{16}$
23. $-\sqrt{900}$
24. $\sqrt{\frac{36}{49}}$
25. $-\sqrt{\frac{25}{81}}$
26. $-\sqrt{\frac{1}{9}}$
27. $\sqrt{\frac{121}{16}}$
28. $\pm\sqrt{1.96}$
29. $\pm\sqrt{0.25}$

Find each quotient. Simplify, if necessary. ◆ See Problem 3.

30. $48 \div 3$
31. $-84 \div 14$
32. $-39 \div (-13)$
33. $\frac{63}{-21}$
34. $-46 \div (-2)$
35. $-8.1 \div 9$
36. $\frac{-121}{11}$
37. $75 \div (-0.3)$

38. **Scuba Diving** A scuba diver's vertical position in relation to the surface of the water changes by -90 ft in 3 min. What is the average change in the diver's vertical position each minute?

39. **Part-Time Job** You earn the same amount each week at your part-time job. The total amount you earn in 4 weeks is $460. How much do you earn per week?

Find each quotient. Simplify, if necessary. ◆ See Problem 4.

40. $20 \div \frac{1}{4}$
41. $-5 \div \left(-\frac{5}{3}\right)$
42. $\frac{9}{10} \div \left(-\frac{4}{5}\right)$
43. $-\frac{12}{13} \div \frac{12}{13}$

Find the value of the expression $\frac{x}{y}$ for the given values of x and y. Write your answer in the simplest form.

44. $x = -\frac{2}{3}; y = -\frac{1}{4}$
45. $x = -\frac{5}{6}; y = \frac{3}{5}$
46. $x = \frac{2}{7}; y = -\frac{20}{21}$
47. $x = \frac{3}{8}; y = \frac{3}{4}$

PowerAlgebra.com

3 Lesson Check

For a digital lesson check, use the Got It questions.

Support In Algebra 1 Companion
- Lesson Check

4 Practice

Assign homework to individual students or to an entire class.

Answers

Lesson Check

1. 36
2. $-\frac{5}{32}$
3. -16
4. $\frac{9}{8}$
5. -5
6.

7. a. 2; a positive number has a positive and negative square root.
   b. 1; $\sqrt{0} = 0$, so there is one square root.

Practice and Problem-Solving Exercises

8. -96
9. 96
10. -63
11. 20.5
12. -7.7
13. -25
14. $-\frac{3}{2}$
15. $\frac{1}{12}$
16. $-\frac{27}{70}$
17. 1
18. $\frac{4}{81}$
19. 1.44
20. 20
21. 13
22. -4
23. -30
24. $\frac{6}{7}$
25. $-\frac{5}{9}$
26. $-\frac{1}{3}$
27. $-\frac{11}{4}$
28. ±1.4
29. ±0.5
30. 16
31. -6
32. 3
33. -3
34. 23
35. -0.9
36. -11
37. -250
38. -30 ft/min
39. $115
40. 80
41. 3
42. $-\frac{9}{8}$
43. -1
44. $\frac{8}{3}$
45. $-\frac{25}{18}$
46. $-\frac{3}{10}$
47. $\frac{1}{2}$

48. **Think About a Plan** A lumberjack cuts 7 pieces of equal length from a log, as shown at the right. What is the change in the log's length after 7 cuts?
  • What operation can you use to find the answer?
  • Will your answer be a positive value or a negative value? How do you know?

$2\frac{1}{4}$ ft

49. **Farmer's Market** A farmer has 120 bushels of beans for sale at a farmer's market. He sells an average of $15\frac{3}{4}$ bushels each day. After 6 days, what is the change in the total number of bushels the farmer has for sale at the farmer's market?

50. **Stocks** The price per share of a stock changed by $-\$4.50$ on each of 5 consecutive days. If the starting price per share was $67.50, what was the ending price?

Open-Ended Write an algebraic expression that uses x, y, and z and simplifies to the given value when $x = -3$, $y = -2$, and $z = -1$. The expression should involve only multiplication or division.

51. -16 **52.** 1   **53.** 12

Evaluate each expression for $m = -5$, $n = \frac{3}{2}$, and $p = -8$.

54. $-7m - 10n$ **55.** $-3mnp$

56. $8n \div (-6p)$ **57.** $2p^2(-n) \div m$

58. **Look for a Pattern** Extend the pattern in the diagram to six factors of -2. What rule describes the sign of the product based on the number of negative factors?

$-2(-2) = 4$
$-2(-2)(-2) = -8$
$-2(-2)(-2)(-2) = 16$

59. **Temperature** The formula $F = \frac{9}{5}C + 32$ changes a temperature reading from the Celsius scale C to the Fahrenheit scale F. What is the temperature measured in degrees Fahrenheit when the Celsius temperature is $-25°C$?

60. **Reasoning** Suppose a and b are integers. Describe what values of a and b make the statement true.
  a. Quotient $\frac{a}{b}$ is positive.   **b.** Quotient $\frac{a}{b}$ is negative.
  c. Quotient $\frac{a}{b}$ is equal to 0.   **d.** Quotient $\frac{a}{b}$ is undefined.

61. **Writing** Explain how to find the quotient of $-1\frac{2}{3}$ and $-2\frac{1}{2}$.

62. **Reasoning** Do you think a negative number raised to an even power will be positive or negative? Explain.

63. **History** The Rhind Papyrus is one of the best-known examples of Egyptian mathematics. One problem solved on the Rhind Papyrus is $100 \div 7\frac{7}{8}$. What is the solution of this problem?

---

4 Practice

ASSIGNMENT GUIDE

Basic: 8–50 all, 54–64 even

Average: 7–47 odd, 48–65

Advanced: 7–47 odd, 48–69

Standardized Test Prep: 70–72

Mixed Review: 73–78

Reasoning exercises have blue headings.

Applications exercises have red headings.

EXERCISE 49: Use the Think About a Plan worksheet in the **Practice and Problem Solving Workbook** (also available in the Teaching Resources in print and online) to further support students' development in becoming independent learners.

HOMEWORK QUICK CHECK

To check students' understanding of key skills and concepts, go over Exercises 15, 35, 48, 49, and 60.

---

48. $15\frac{3}{4}$ ft shorter

49. $-94\frac{1}{2}$ bushels

50. $ 45

51. Check students' work.

52. Check students' work.

53. Check students' work.

54. 20

55. -180

56. $\frac{1}{4}$

57. $38\frac{2}{5}$

58. $-2(-2)(-2)(-2)(-2) = -32;$
$-2(-2)(-2)(-2)(-2)(-2) = 64;$
If the number of negative factors is odd, the product is negative and if the number of negative factors is even, the product is positive.

59. $-13°F$

60. **a.** when the signs of a and b are the same
  b. when the signs of a and b are different
  c. when $a = 0$
  d. when $b = 0$

61. First change $-2\frac{1}{2}$ to the improper fraction $-\frac{5}{2}$. Then multiply $-1\frac{2}{3}$ by the reciprocal of $-\frac{5}{2}$, which is $-\frac{2}{5}$.

62. positive because an even number of negative factors has a positive product

63. $\frac{800}{63}$, or $12\frac{44}{63}$

Answers

Practice and Problem-Solving Exercises
(continued)

64. The reciprocal of the wrong fraction was used; $-\frac{15}{8}$

65. a. If $0 \div x = y$, then $xy = 0$. Since $x \neq 0$, then $y = 0$ by the Zero Property of Multiplication.

    b. Suppose there is a value of y such that $x \div 0 = y$. Then $x = 0 \cdot y$, so $x = 0$. But this is a contradiction, since $x \neq 0$. So there is no value of y such that $x \div 0 = y$.

66. Never; the product is 1, not -1.

67. Always; the quotient is -1.

68. Never; the product and quotient have the same sign.

69. -8

70. C

71. I

72. A

73. 30

74. -10

75. -10

76. Ident. Prop. of Add.

77. Comm. Prop. of Mult.

78. Assoc. Prop. of Mult.

---

64. Error Analysis Describe and correct the error in dividing the fractions at the right.

65. Reasoning You can derive the rule for division involving 0 shown on page 40.
    a. Suppose $0 \div x = y$, where $x \neq 0$. Show that $y = 0$. (*Hint:* If $0 \div x = y$, then $x \cdot y = 0$ by the definition of division.)
    b. If $x \neq 0$, show that there is no value of y such that $x \div 0 = y$. (*Hint:* Suppose there is a value of y such that $x \div 0 = y$. What would this imply about x?)

Challenge

Determine whether each statement is *always*, *sometimes*, or *never* true. Explain your reasoning.

66. The product of a number and its reciprocal is -1.

67. The quotient of a nonzero number and its opposite is -1.

68. If the product of two fractions is negative, then their quotient is positive.

69. Reasoning What is the greatest integer n for which $(-n)^3$ is positive and the value of the expression has a 2 in the ones place?

Standardized Test Prep

SAT/ACT

70. Which expression does NOT have the same value as $-11 + (-11) + (-11)$?
    Ⓐ -33 Ⓑ $3(-11)$ Ⓒ $(-11)^3$ Ⓓ $33 - 66$

71. Miguel measured the area of a piece of carpet and figured out that the approximate error was $3|-0.2|$. What is the decimal form of $3|-0.2|$?
    Ⓕ -0.6 Ⓖ -0.06 Ⓗ 0.06 Ⓘ 0.6

72. What is the perimeter of the triangle shown?
    Ⓐ $6y + 24$ Ⓒ $15y + 15$
    Ⓑ $21y + 9$ Ⓓ $30y$

Mixed Review

Find each difference.   ◀ See Lesson 1-5.

73. $46 - 16$ **74.** $34 - 44$ **75.** $-37 - (-27)$

Get Ready!   **To prepare for Lesson 1-7, do Exercises 76–78.**

Name the property that each statement illustrates.   ◀ See Lesson 1-4.

76. $-x + 0 = -x$ **77.** $13(-11) = -11(13)$ **78.** $-5 \cdot (m \cdot 8) = (-5 \cdot m) \cdot 8$

Additional Instructional Support

Algebra 1 Companion

Students can use the **Algebra 1 Companion** worktext (4 pages) as you teach the lesson. Use the Companion to support

- New Vocabulary
- Key Concepts
- Got It for each Problem
- Lesson Check

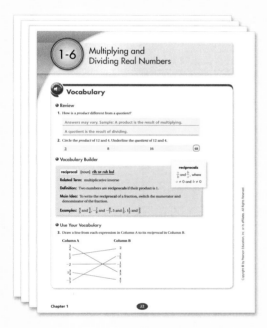

ELL Support

Focus on Language Have students make a vocabulary page for the word inverse. Help them identify similar words, such as verse or invertebrate. Say, "As a noun, inverse means reversed or direct opposite. As a verb, inverse means to turn upside down or to reverse in position. Inverse contains the Latin word, versus, meaning turn." Have students add examples and illustrations to their vocabulary page. Have the students start a personal dictionary by placing their vocabulary page in a loose-leaf notebook. Alternatively, or in addition, students can make vocabulary cards.

Focus on Language Have students work in small groups. Ask students to think of statments that describe events that are always, sometimes, or never true. Have students verify their sentences. Then, assign each student an integer and say, "Write always, sometimes, or never statements about your integer. Use the rules for multiplying and dividing with signed numbers."

5 Assess & Remediate

Lesson Quiz

1. What is each product?
  a. $(-6)(-9)$
  b. $28(-0.25)$
2. What is the simplified form of the expression $-\sqrt{\frac{1}{25}}$?
3. Do you UNDERSTAND? The elevation of an airplane changes by -420 feet in 12 seconds. What is the change in the airplane's elevation each second?
4. What is the value of $\frac{a}{b}$ when $a = -\frac{1}{4}$ and $b = -\frac{5}{6}$?

ANSWERS TO LESSON QUIZ

1. a. 54, **b.** -7
2. $-\frac{1}{5}$
3. -35 feet per second
4. 0.3 or $\frac{3}{10}$

PRESCRIPTION FOR REMEDIATION
Use the student work on the Lesson Quiz to prescribe a differentiated review assignment.

Points	Differentiated Remediation
0–2	Intervention
3	On-level
4	Extension

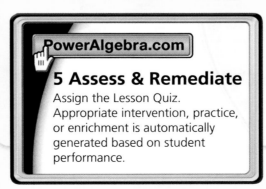

PowerAlgebra.com

5 Assess & Remediate

Assign the Lesson Quiz. Appropriate intervention, practice, or enrichment is automatically generated based on student performance.

Intervention

- **Reteaching** (2 pages) Provides reteaching and practice exercises for the key lesson concepts. Use with struggling students or absent students.
- **English Language Learner Support** Helps students develop and reinforce mathematical vocabulary and key concepts.

All-in-One Resources/Online
Reteaching

All-in-One Resources/Online
English Language Learner Support

Differentiated Remediation *continued*

On-Level

- **Practice** (2 pages) Provides extra practice for each lesson. For simpler practice exercises, use the Form K Practice pages found in the All-in-One Teaching Resources and online.

- **Think About a Plan** Helps students develop specific problem-solving skills and strategies by providing scaffolded guiding questions.

- **Standardized Test Prep** Focuses on all major exercises, all major question types, and helps students prepare for the high-stakes assessments.

Extension

- **Enrichment** Provides students with interesting problems and activities that extend the concepts of the lesson.

- **Activities, Games, and Puzzles** Worksheets that can be used for concepts development, enrichment, and for fun!

Practice and Problem Solving WKBK/All-in-One Resources/Online
Practice page 1

1-6 Practice Form G
Multiplying and Dividing Real Numbers

Find each product. Simplify, if necessary.

1. $-5(-7)$ 35
2. $8(-11)$ -88
3. $9 \cdot 12$ 108

4. $(-9)^2$ 81
5. -3×12 -36
6. $-5(-9)$ 45

7. $-3(2.3)$ -6.9
8. $(-0.6)^2$ 0.36
9. $8(-2.4)$ -19.2

10. $-\frac{3}{4} \cdot \frac{2}{9}$ $-\frac{1}{6}$
11. $-\frac{2}{5}\left(-\frac{5}{8}\right)$ $\frac{1}{4}$
12. $\left(\frac{2}{3}\right)^2$ $\frac{4}{9}$

13. After hiking to the top of a mountain, Raul starts to descend at the rate of 350 feet per hour. What real number represents his vertical change after $1\frac{1}{2}$ hours? -525 ft

14. A dolphin starts at the surface of the water. It dives down at a rate of 3 feet per second. If the water level is zero, what real number describes the dolphin's location after $3\frac{1}{2}$ seconds? $-10\frac{1}{2}$ ft

Simplify each expression.

15. $\sqrt{1600}$ 40
16. $-\sqrt{625}$ -25
17. $\pm\sqrt{10,000}$ ± 100

18. $-\sqrt{0.81}$ -0.9
19. $\pm\sqrt{1.44}$ ± 1.2
20. $\sqrt{0.04}$ 0.2

21. $\pm\sqrt{\frac{4}{9}}$ $\pm\frac{2}{3}$
22. $-\sqrt{\frac{16}{49}}$ $-\frac{4}{7}$
23. $\sqrt{\frac{100}{121}}$ $\frac{10}{11}$

Practice and Problem Solving WKBK/All-in-One Resources/Online
Practice page 2

1-6 Practice (continued) Form G
Multiplying and Dividing Real Numbers

24. **Writing** Explain the differences among $\sqrt{25}$, $-\sqrt{25}$, and $\pm\sqrt{25}$.
There are 2 square roots of 25, 5 and -5. $\sqrt{25}$ represents the positive square root and $-\sqrt{25}$ represents the negative square root, and $\pm\sqrt{25}$ represents both square roots.

25. **Reasoning** Can you name a real number that is represented by $\sqrt{-36}$? Explain.
no; There is no number that can be multiplied by itself and have a negative product.

Find each quotient. Simplify, if necessary.

26. $-51 \div 3$ -17
27. $-250 \div (-25)$ 10
28. $98 \div 2$ 49

29. $84 \div (-4)$ -21
30. $-93 \div (-3)$ 31
31. $\frac{-105}{5}$ -21

32. $14.4 \div (-3)$ -4.8
33. $-1.7 \div (-10)$ 0.17
34. $-8.1 \div 3$ -2.7

35. $17 \div \frac{1}{3}$ 51
36. $-\frac{3}{8} \div \left(-\frac{9}{10}\right)$ $\frac{5}{12}$
37. $-\frac{5}{4} \div \frac{3}{4}$ $-1\frac{2}{3}$

Evaluate each expression for $a = -\frac{1}{2}$, $b = \frac{3}{4}$, and $c = -6$.

38. $-ab$ $\frac{3}{8}$
39. $b \div c$ $-\frac{1}{8}$
40. $\frac{c}{a}$ 12

41. **Writing** Explain how you know that -5 and $\frac{1}{5}$ are multiplicative inverses.
Because $-5 \times \frac{1}{5} = -1$, the two numbers are multiplicative inverses.

42. **Writing** At 6:00 P.M., the temperature was 55°F. At 11:00 P.M. that same evening, the temperature was 40°F. What real number represents the average change in temperature per hour?
$-3°$ F/h

All-in-One Resources/Online
Enrichment

1-6 Enrichment
Multiplying and Dividing Real Numbers

A matrix is a rectangular array of numbers. Some examples of matrices are given at the right.
$$\begin{bmatrix} 5 & 9 \\ 3 & 4 \\ 7 & 0 \end{bmatrix} \quad \begin{bmatrix} -4 & 3 & 0 \\ -8 & 6 & 3 \\ 4 & -1 & 2 \end{bmatrix}$$

You can perform operations using matrices. One operation is called **scalar multiplication**. In scalar multiplication, each number in the matrix is multiplied by the number outside the matrix. The products are listed in another matrix in the same order.

Complete each scalar multiplication.

1. $5\begin{bmatrix} 3 & 10 & 4 \\ 7 & 6 & 11 \end{bmatrix}$ $\begin{bmatrix} 15 & 50 & 20 \\ 35 & 30 & 55 \end{bmatrix}$
2. $-7\begin{bmatrix} 0 & -2 & 4 \\ 10 & -6 & 5 \\ 3 & -7 & 9 \end{bmatrix}$ $\begin{bmatrix} 0 & 14 & -28 \\ -70 & 42 & -35 \\ -21 & 49 & -63 \end{bmatrix}$

3. $10\begin{bmatrix} -3 & 5 & -8 \\ 2 & 10 & -1 \\ 0 & 4 & 4 \end{bmatrix}$ $\begin{bmatrix} -30 & 50 & -80 \\ 20 & 100 & -10 \\ 0 & 40 & 40 \end{bmatrix}$
4. $0\begin{bmatrix} 27 & -84 \\ 16 & -76 \end{bmatrix}$ $\begin{bmatrix} 0 & 0 \\ 0 & 0 \end{bmatrix}$

The matrix at the right compares the prices of 3 different digital cameras at 3 different stores.

	Camera A	Camera B	Camera C
Camera Store	$153.00	$207.00	$255.00
Discount Store	$142.50	$212.00	$251.00
Electronic Store	$192.00	$209.50	$249.50

5. If the sales tax is 6%, each number in the matrix must be multiplied by 1.06 to determine the total cost of each camera. Write a scalar multiplication problem that could be used to determine the total cost of the cameras.
$1.06\begin{bmatrix} \$153.00 & \$207.00 & \$255.00 \\ \$142.00 & \$212.00 & \$251.00 \\ \$192.00 & \$209.00 & \$249.50 \end{bmatrix}$

6. Complete the scalar multiplication you wrote in Exercise 5. $\begin{bmatrix} \$162.18 & \$219.42 & \$270.30 \\ \$151.05 & \$224.72 & \$266.06 \\ \$203.52 & \$222.07 & \$264.47 \end{bmatrix}$

7. Use the matrix you found in Exercise 6 to determine the difference in the total cost if you bought Camera C from the Discount Store rather than the Camera Store. $4.24

8. What is the difference between the greatest total cost and the least total cost for Camera A? $52.47

Practice and Problem Solving WKBK/All-in-One Resources/Online
Think About a Plan

1-6 Think About a Plan
Multiplying and Dividing Real Numbers

Farmer's Market A farmer has 120 bushels of beans for sale at a farmer's market. He sells an average of $15\frac{3}{4}$ bushels each day. After 6 days, what is the change in the total number of bushels the farmer has for sale at the farmer's market?

Understanding the Problem

1. How does the number of bushels the farmer has change each day?
The number of bushels decreases.

2. Should the change be a positive or a negative number? How do you know?
negative: The amount the farmer has is less.

Planning the Solution

3. What expression represents the total number of bushels sold in 6 days?
$6 \cdot \left(-15\frac{3}{4}\right)$

Getting an Answer

4. Evaluate your expression in Exercise 3 to determine the change in the total number of bushels the farmer has for sale at the farmer's market.
$-94\frac{1}{2}$ bushels

5. Is your answer reasonable? Explain.
yes; the change is negative and the absolute value of the change must be less than 120 because the farmer cannot have a negative amount of beans.

Practice and Problem Solving WKBK/All-in-One Resources/Online
Standardized Test Prep

1-6 Standardized Test Prep
Multiplying and Dividing Real Numbers

Multiple Choice

For Exercises 1–5, choose the correct letter.

1. Which expression has a negative value? C
   A. $(-2)^2$
   B. $(-5)(-7)$
   C. $(-3)^3$
   D. $0 \times (-5)$

2. If $x = -\frac{3}{4}$ and $y = \frac{1}{6}$, what is the value of $-2xy$? I
   F. $-\frac{1}{4}$
   G. $-\frac{1}{6}$
   H. $\frac{1}{6}$
   I. $\frac{1}{4}$

3. Which expression has the same value as $-\frac{1}{7} \div \left(-\frac{2}{3}\right)$? A
   A. $\frac{1}{7} \times \frac{3}{2}$
   B. $-\left(\frac{1}{7} \times \frac{3}{2}\right)$
   C. $\frac{7}{1} \times \frac{2}{3}$
   D. $-\left(\frac{7}{1} \times \frac{2}{3}\right)$

4. ABC stock sold for $64.50. Four days later, the same stock sold for $47.10. What is the average change per day? F
   F. $-$4.35
   G. $-$3.48
   H. $3.48
   I. $4.35

5. The formula $C = \frac{5}{9}(F - 32)$ converts a temperature reading from the Fahrenheit scale F to the Celsius scale C. What is the temperature 5°F measured in Celsius? B
   A. $\left(-20\frac{5}{9}\right)°$ C
   B. -15°C
   C. 15°C
   D. $\left(20\frac{5}{9}\right)°$ C

Short Response

6. A clock loses 2 minutes every 6 hours. At 3:00 P.M., the clock is set to the correct time and allowed to run without interference.
   a. What integer would describe the time loss after exactly 3 days? -24 min
   b. What would the clock read at 3:00 P.M. three days later? 2:36 P.M.
   [2] Both parts answered correctly.
   [1] One part answered correctly.
   [0] Neither part answered correctly.

Online Teacher Resource Center
Activities, Games, and Puzzles

1-6 Activity: A Class Divided
Multiplying and Dividing Real Numbers

Your teacher will give you a square with expressions involving multiplication and division. Each expression has a matching equivalent expression. Use mental math to evaluate the expression on your square. Then walk around the class to find the classmate who has the square with the equivalent expression. For example, if your square shows the expression $6 \cdot 4 + 11$, then your expression equals 35 and you will need to find the classmate whose expression also equals 35.

- When you approach a classmate, you are only allowed to read aloud the expression on the classmate's square, and the classmate is only allowed to read aloud the expression on your square. You cannot say anything more.
- When you find the matching square, you and your classmate should return both squares to your teacher to see if you are indeed correct.

$2 \cdot 8$	$6 \cdot 3 + 4$	$4 \cdot 10$	$5 \cdot 5$	$\frac{16}{4}$
$10 \cdot 4$	$2 \cdot 3 + 12$	$-14 \cdot 3$	$(-6)(-6)$	5
$\frac{90}{10}$	$\frac{60}{-2}$	$\frac{14}{-7}$	$-4 \cdot 5 + 10$	$5 \cdot 4 + 4$

$(-4)(-4)$	$(-11)(-2)$	$8 \cdot 5$	$\frac{-75}{-3}$	$\frac{12}{-3}$
$2 \cdot 8$	$6 \cdot 3 + 4$	$4 \cdot 10$	$5 \cdot 5$	$\frac{16}{4}$
$2 \cdot 20$	$9 \cdot 2$	$-6 \cdot 7$	$12 \cdot 3$	$\frac{15}{3}$
$10 \cdot 4$	$2 \cdot 3 + 12$	$-14 \cdot 3$	$(-6)(-6)$	5
$(-3)(-3)$	$-2 \cdot 15$	$4 \cdot 2 - 3$	$-5 \cdot 2$	$8 \cdot 3$
$\frac{90}{10}$	$\frac{60}{-2}$	$\frac{14}{-7}$	$-4 \cdot 5 + 10$	$5 \cdot 4 + 4$

Concept Byte   Closure

Use With Lesson 1-6

ACTIVITY

What does it mean for a set of numbers to be *closed* under the operation of multiplication? Working with a partner, you will learn about closure.

Activity 1

1. Each person makes three cards as shown at the right labeled −1, 0, and 1. On a turn, a player picks any two of the six cards and multiplies the numbers on the cards. The winner is the first person to find a product other than −1, 0, or 1. Has anyone won the game after each person has taken 4 turns? After each person has taken 8 turns? Explain.

Person 1

-1 0 1

Person 2

-1 0 1

It is not possible to win the game in Exercise 1 because the product of any two numbers in the set is a number in the set. This means that the set {−1, 0, 1} is closed under multiplication. When you perform an operation on any two numbers in a set and produce a number in the set, the set is closed under that operation. This property is called closure.

2. Repeat the game in Exercise 1 using addition instead of multiplication. Is the set closed under addition? Explain.

3. Determine whether it is possible to win each game. If so, give an example of a winning result.
   a. Add any two even numbers. Win by finding a result that is not an even number.
   b. Multiply any two negative numbers. Win by finding a product that is not a negative number.
   c. Add, subtract, or multiply any two integers. Win by finding a result that is not an integer.

4. Writing For each game in Exercise 3, determine whether the set of numbers is closed under the operation(s) used in the game. Explain your answers.

Activity 2

5. Determine whether it is possible to win each game. If so, give an example of a winning result.
   a. Find the absolute value of any integer. Win by finding a result that is not an integer.
   b. Square any negative number. Win by finding a result that is not a negative number.
   c. Square any rational number. Win by finding a result that is not a rational number.

6. Reasoning Under what arithmetic operation(s) does the set of whole numbers *not* have closure? Explain.

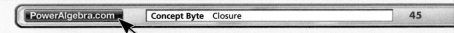

PowerAlgebra.com   Concept Byte Closure   45

Guided Instruction

PURPOSE To build an understanding of a closed set of numbers

PROCESS Students will
• identify if a set of numbers is closed.
• use various operations within a set of numbers.

DISCUSS Students first focus on closure for a small set of numbers, such as three integers. Then larger sets are explored. Review the various types of number sets.

Activity 1
In this activity students decide if a game can be won and if a set of numbers is closed based on the game.

Q If a game is won, is the number set closed? Explain. **[No, it means the number set specified is not closed.]**

Q If an operation changes within the same game, does that change whether the set of numbers is closed or not? Explain. **[Yes, if a set of numbers is closed in an addition game, it does not mean that it will also be closed within the same game for multiplication.]**

Activity 2
In this activity students decide if a game can be won and if a set of numbers is closed based on the game.

Q If a game cannot be won, is the number set closed? **[Yes]**

Answers

Activity 1
1. No; the product will only be −1, 0, or 1.

2. No; 1 + 1 = 2 and 2 is not in the set.

3. a. no
   b. yes
   c. no

4. It is closed in 2a since the sum is always an even number. It is not closed in 2b since the product is *not* a negative number. It is closed in 2c since the result will always be an integer.

Activity 2
5. a. no
   b. yes
   c. no

6. Division; the quotient of two whole numbers could be a fraction.

1 Interactive Learning

Solve It!

PURPOSE To prepare students for using the area model to learn the distributive property

PROCESS Students may count the number of square units shown on the paused screen or may determine that each row has 8 squares and multiply by the number of rows in the final figure.

FACILITATE

Q How many points will you score for each entire row you complete? Explain. **[An entire row fits 8 squares, so one completed row will score 8 points.]**

Q What are two ways you can calculate the area of a rectangle? **[Count the number of square units or multiply the length times the width of the rectangle.]**

ANSWER See Solve It in Answers on next page.

CONNECT THE MATH Multiplication is a more efficient way to solve a repeated addition problem. In this lesson, students will explore how to perform multiplication problems in which one factor is a number and the other is an algebraic expression.

2 Guided Instruction

Take Note   SYNTHESIZING

Point out to students that the first pair of equations involving addition and the last pair of equations involving subtraction are examples of the commutative property. Ask students to verify that this is true.

1-7 The Distributive Property

Indiana Academic Standard
Prepares for A1.4.2 Add, subtract and multiply polynomials and divide polynomials by monomials.

Objective   To use the Distributive Property to simplify expressions

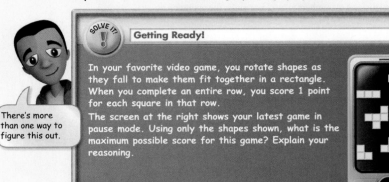

Lesson Vocabulary
• Distributive Property
• term
• constant
• coefficient
• like terms

To solve problems in mathematics, it is often useful to rewrite expressions in simpler forms. The **Distributive Property**, illustrated by the area model below, is another property of real numbers that helps you to simplify expressions.

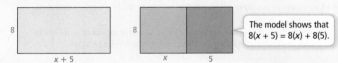

The model shows that $8(x + 5) = 8(x) + 8(5)$.

Essential Understanding You can use the Distributive Property to simplify the product of a number and a sum or difference.

Property   Distributive Property

Let a, b, and c be real numbers.

Algebra	**Examples**
$a(b + c) = ab + ac$	$4(20 + 6) = 4(20) + 4(6)$
$(b + c)a = ba + ca$	$(20 + 6)4 = 20(4) + 6(4)$
$a(b - c) = ab - ac$	$7(30 - 2) = 7(30) - 7(2)$
$(b - c)a = ba - ca$	$(30 - 2)7 = 30(7) - 2(7)$

1-7 Preparing to Teach

BIG ideas **Properties**
                    Variable   **UbD**

ESSENTIAL UNDERSTANDINGS

• The distributive property can be used to simplify the product of a number and a sum or difference.

• An algebraic expression can be simplified by combining the parts of the expression that are alike.

Math Background

Unlike other properties of real numbers, the Distributive Property combines multiplication and addition.

The Distributive Property is:

$a(b + c) = ab + ac$
$a(b - c) = ab - ac$

Multiplication is commutative so the order of the factors can be reversed and the result will be unchanged.

$(b + c)a = ba + ca$
$(b - c)a = ba - ca$

Emphasize the following examples.
$-(2x + 3) = -1(2x + 3)$
$= -1(2x) + (-1)(3)$
$= -2x - 3$
$5(4x - 1) = 5(4x + (-1))$
$= 5(4x) + 5(-1)$
$= 20x - 5$
$-2(-x - 7) = -2(-x + (-7))$
$= -2(-x) + (-2)(-7)$
$= 2x + 14$

The Distributive Property will allow students to find the product of an algebraic expression and a number. Later in algebra, students will use the Distributive Property to find the product of two algebraic expressions as well as to factor some algebraic expressions.

Support Student Learning

Use the **Algebra 1 Companion** to engage and support students during instructions. See Lesson Resources at the end of this lesson for details.

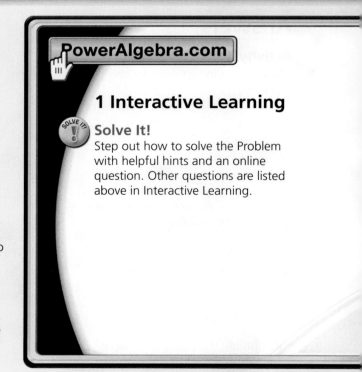

PowerAlgebra.com

1 Interactive Learning

Solve It!
Step out how to solve the Problem with helpful hints and an online question. Other questions are listed above in Interactive Learning.

Think

How do you read expressions like $3(x + 8)$?
Read an expression inside parentheses as "the quantity." Read $3(x + 8)$ as "3 times the quantity x plus 8."

 Problem 1 Simplifying Expressions

What is the simplified form of each expression?

A $3(x + 8)$

$3(x + 8) = 3(x) + 3(8)$ Distributive Property

$\qquad = 3x + 24$ Simplify.

B $(5b - 4)(-7)$

$(5b - 4)(-7) = 5b(-7) - 4(-7)$

$\qquad = -35b + 28$

✓ **Got It?** **1.** What is the simplified form of each expression?

a. $5(x + 7)$ **b.** $12\left(3 - \frac{1}{6}t\right)$ **c.** $(0.4 + 1.1c)3$ **d.** $(2y - 1)(-y)$

Recall that a fraction bar may act as a grouping symbol. A fraction bar indicates division. Any fraction $\frac{a}{b}$ can also be written as $a \cdot \frac{1}{b}$. You can use this fact and the Distributive Property to rewrite some fractions as sums or differences.

Think

How can you get started?
Think of division as multiplying by the reciprocal. So change the division by 5 to multiplication by $\frac{1}{5}$.

 Problem 2 Rewriting Fraction Expressions

What sum or difference is equivalent to $\frac{7x + 2}{5}$?

$\frac{7x + 2}{5} = \frac{1}{5}(7x + 2)$ Write division as multiplication.

$\qquad = \frac{1}{5}(7x) + \frac{1}{5}(2)$ Distributive Property

$\qquad = \frac{7}{5}x + \frac{2}{5}$ Simplify.

✓ **Got It?** **2.** What sum or difference is equivalent to each expression?

a. $\frac{4x - 16}{3}$ **b.** $\frac{11 + 3x}{6}$ **c.** $\frac{15 + 6x}{12}$ **d.** $\frac{4 - 2x}{8}$

The Multiplication Property of -1 states that $-1 \cdot x = -x$. To simplify an expression such as $-(x + 6)$, you can rewrite the expression as $-1(x + 6)$.

Think

What does the negative sign in front of the parentheses mean?
It indicates the opposite of the entire expression inside the parentheses.

 Problem 3 Using the Multiplication Property of -1

Multiple Choice What is the simplified form of $-(2y - 3x)$?

Ⓐ $2y + 3x$ Ⓑ $-2y + (-3x)$ Ⓒ $-2y + 3x$ Ⓓ $2y - 3x$

$-(2y - 3x) = -1(2y - 3x)$ Multiplication Property of -1

$\qquad = (-1)(2y) + (-1)(-3x)$ Distributive Property

$\qquad = -2y + 3x$ Simplify.

The correct choice is C.

✓ **Got It?** **3.** What is the simplified form of each expression?

a. $-(a + 5)$ **b.** $-(-x + 31)$ **c.** $-(4x - 12)$ **d.** $-(6m - 9n)$

---

2 Guided Instruction

 Each Problem is worked out and supported online.

Problem 1
Simplifying Expressions
Animated

Problem 2
Rewriting Fraction Expressions

Problem 3
Using the Multiplication Property of –1

Problem 4
Using the Distributive Property for Mental Math
Animated

Problem 5
Combining Like Terms
Animated

Support in Algebra 1 Companion
• Vocabulary
• Key Concepts
• Got It?

Problem 1

Q What area model can be used to illustrate the product of $3(x + 8)$?

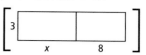

Got It?   **TACTILE LEARNERS**

If students are having difficulty with the distributive property, model a problem using algebra tiles.

Problem 2

Q What operation is equivalent to dividing a number by 5? **[multiplying by $\frac{1}{5}$]**

Q Will the two terms in the sum or difference always have the same denominator as the original expression? Explain. **[No, if the fractions can be simplified, then they will have different denominators.]**

Got It?   **AUDITORY LEARNERS**

Tell students that division is "distributed" to each term in the grouping symbol in these problems.

Problem 3

Q What number is being multiplied by the quantity $(2y - 3x)$ in the expression $-(2y - 3x)$? **[−1]**

Got It?   **ERROR PREVENTION**

Errors could be due to misunderstanding the distributive property or the rules for multiplying real numbers. Ask students to verbalize their processes to help find errors.

Answers

Solve It!
24; all of the squares will be used to form rows.

Got It?

1. a. $5x + 35$

  b. $36 - 2t$

  c. $1.2 + 3.3c$

  d. $-2y^2 + y$

2. a. $\frac{4}{3}x - \frac{16}{3}$

  b. $\frac{11}{6} + \frac{1}{2}x$

  c. $\frac{5}{4} + \frac{1}{2}x$

  d. $\frac{1}{2} - \frac{1}{4}x$

3. a. $-a - 5$

  b. $x - 31$

  c. $-4x + 12$

  d. $-6m + 9n$

Problem 4

Q Prior to doing any calculations, how would you estimate the total cost for the sandwiches? **[Answers may vary. Sample: Round the cost to $5 and multiply by 8.]**

Q When rewriting $4.95, why use 5 − 0.05? **[By using 5 and 0.5, you can use mental math to find each product.]**

Q In terms of money, how can you think of 8 times 0.05? **[8 nickels or $0.40]**

Got It?

Q Is it more convenient to split $7.25 into a sum or a difference? Explain. **[sum, because $0.25 is easier to work with than $0.75]**

Q What is the distributive property expression that represents Julia's weekly transportation costs? **[4(7 + 0.25)]**

Q In terms of money, how can you think of 4 times 0.25? **[4 quarters or $1.00]**

You can use the Distributive Property to make calculations easier to do with mental math. Some numbers can be thought of as simple sums or differences.

 Problem 4 Using the Distributive Property for Mental Math

Eating Out Deli sandwiches cost $4.95 each. What is the total cost of 8 sandwiches? Use mental math.

Know	Need	Plan
• Sandwiches cost $4.95. • You are buying 8 sandwiches.	Total cost of 8 sandwiches	Express $4.95 as a difference and use the Distributive Property.

The total cost is the product of the number of sandwiches you buy, 8, and the cost per sandwich, $4.95.

Think

How can you express decimals as simple sums and differences?

Think of a decimal as the sum or difference of its whole number portion and its decimal portion.

$$8(4.95) = 8(5 − 0.05) \quad \text{Think of 4.95 as 5 − 0.05.}$$
$$= 8(5) − 8(0.05) \quad \text{Distributive Property}$$
$$= 40 − 0.4 \quad \text{Multiply mentally.}$$
$$= 39.6 \quad \text{Subtract mentally.}$$

The total cost for 8 sandwiches is $39.60.

Got It? 4. Julia commutes to work on the train 4 times each week. A round-trip ticket costs $7.25. What is her weekly cost for tickets? Use mental math.

Essential Understanding You can simplify an algebraic expression by combining the parts of the expression that are alike.

In an algebraic expression, a **term** is a number, a variable, or the product of a number and one or more variables. A **constant** is a term that has no variable. A **coefficient** is a numerical factor of a term. Rewrite expressions as sums to identify these parts of an expression.

$6a^2$, $−5ab$, $3b$, and $−12$ are terms.

$$6a^2 − 5ab + 3b − 12 = 6a^2 + (−5ab) + 3b + (−12)$$

coefficients · · · · constant

In the algebraic expression $6a^2 − 5ab + 3b − 12$, the terms have coefficients of 6, −5, and 3. The term −12 is a constant.

Like terms have the same variable factors. To identify like terms, compare the variable factors of the terms, as shown below.

Terms	$7a$ and $−3a$	$4x^2$ and $12x^2$	$6ab$ and $−2a$	xy^2 and x^2y
Variable Factors	a and a	x^2 and x^2	ab and a	xy^2 and x^2y
Like Terms?	yes	yes	no	no

Additional Problems

1. What is the simplified form of each expression?

a. $4(x + 5)$

b. $(4b − 1)(−6)$

ANSWER a. $4x + 20$,

b. $−24b + 6$

2. What sum or difference is equivalent to $\frac{3x + 1}{5}$?

ANSWER $\frac{3x}{5} + \frac{1}{5}$

3. What is the simplified form of $−(3m − 4n)$?

A. $−3m − 4n$

B. $−3m + 4n$

C. $3m + 4n$

D. $3m − 4n$

ANSWER B

4. Deli sandwiches cost $3.95 each. What is the total cost of 6 sandwiches? Use mental math.

ANSWER $23.70

5. What is the simplified form of each expression?

a. $5x^2 + 7x^2$

b. $7x − 5 − 3x + 2y + 1$

ANSWER a. $12x^2$,

b. $4x + 2y − 4$

Answers

Got It? (continued)

4. $29

An algebraic expression in simplest form has no like terms or parentheses.

Not Simplified	Simplified
$2(3x - 5 + 4x)$	$14x - 10$

You can use the Distributive Property to help combine like terms. Think of the Distributive Property as $ba + ca = (b + c)a$.

 Plan

What terms can you combine?
You can combine any terms that have exactly the same variables with exactly the same exponents.

Problem 5 Combining Like Terms

What is the simplified form of each expression?

Ⓐ $8x^2 + 2x^2$

$8x^2 + 2x^2 = (8 + 2)x^2$ Distributive Property

$= 10x^2$ Simplify.

Ⓑ $5x - 3 - 3x + 6y + 4$

$5x - 3 - 3x + 6y + 4 = 5x + (-3) + (-3x) + 6y + 4$ Rewrite as a sum.

$= 5x + (-3x) + 6y + (-3) + 4$ Commutative Property

$= (5 - 3)x + 6y + (-3) + 4$ Distributive Property

$= 2x + 6y + 1$ Simplify.

Got It? 5. What is the simplified form of each expression in parts (a)–(c)?

a. $3y - y$ **b.** $-7mn^4 - 5mn^4$ **c.** $7y^3z - 6yz^3 + y^3z$

d. Reasoning Can you simplify $8x^2 - 2x^4 - 2x + 2 + xy$ further? Explain.

 **Lesson Check**

Do you know HOW?

1. What is the simplified form of each expression? Use the Distributive Property.

  a. $(j + 2)7$

  b. $-8(x - 3)$

  c. $-(4 - c)$

  d. $-(11 + 2b)$

Rewrite each expression as a sum.

2. $-8x^2 + 3xy - 9x - 3$

3. $2ab - 5ab^2 - 9a^2b$

Tell whether the terms are like terms.

4. $3a$ and $-5a$ **5.** $2xy^2$ and $-x^2y$

Do you UNDERSTAND?

6. Vocabulary Does each equation demonstrate the Distributive Property? Explain.

  a. $-2(x + 1) = -2x - 2$

  b. $(s - 4)8 = 8(s - 4)$

  c. $5n - 45 = 5(n - 9)$

  d. $8 + (t + 6) = (8 + t) + 6$

7. Mental Math How can you express 499 to find the product 499×5 using mental math? Explain.

8. Reasoning Is each expression in simplified form? Justify your answer.

  a. $4xy^3 + 5x^3y$

  b. $-(y - 1)$

  c. $5x^2 + 12xy - 3yx$

Problem 5

Q In 5B, which terms should be grouped together using the commutative and associative properties? **[5x and −3x; −3 and 4]**

Q In part (b), why are the 2x and 6y terms not combined together? **[because they do not have the same variable factors]**

Got It?

Q How many terms are in the expression shown in 5d? Are any of the terms like terms? Explain. **[5; No, although some of the terms have the same coefficient and the same variable, none of them have the same variable raised to the same exponent.]**

3 Lesson Check

Do you know HOW?

• If students have difficulty with Exercise 1, then have them change any subtraction to addition. After they have used the Distributive Property, have them change any addition signs that are next to a negative number back into subtraction.

Do you UNDERSTAND?

• If students have difficulty with Exercise 7, then have them think about how to write 499 in terms of 500.

Close

Q What are the two reasons to use the Distributive Property when simplifying an expression? Explain. **[The Distributive Property is used when adding and subtracting like variable terms. The Distributive Property is also used to be able to do more difficult multiplication problems using mental math.]**

---

5. a. $2y$

  b. $-12mn^4$

  c. $8y^3z - 6yz^3$

  d. No; it is already simplified since there are no like terms to combine.

Lesson Check

1. a. $7j + 14$

  b. $-8x + 24$

  c. $-4 + c$

  d. $-11 - 2b$

2. $-8x^2 + 3xy + (-9x) + (-3)$

3. $2ab + (-5ab^2) + (-9a^2b)$

4. yes

5. no

6. a. yes

  b. no; commutative prop. of mult.

  c. yes

  d. no; associative prop. of add.

7. $500 - 1$; answers may vary. Sample: These numbers are easily multiplied by 5, making it possible to use the Distr. Prop. to solve this using mental math.

8. a. yes; no like terms

  b. No; this expression can be simplified by using the Distr. Prop.

  c. No; $12xy$ and $-3yx$ are like terms.

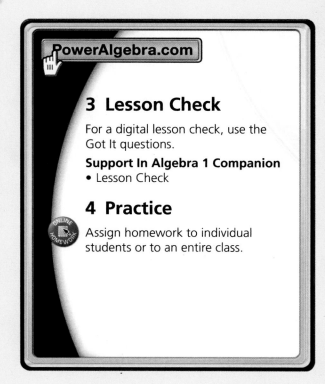

PowerAlgebra.com

3 Lesson Check

For a digital lesson check, use the Got It questions.

Support In Algebra 1 Companion
• Lesson Check

4 Practice

Assign homework to individual students or to an entire class.

4 Practice

ASSIGNMENT GUIDE

Basic: 9–64 all, 66, 68–76

Average: 9–63 odd, 65–83

Advanced: 9–63 odd, 65–90

Standardized Test Prep: 91–94

Mixed Review: 95–100

Reasoning exercises have blue headings.

Applications exercises have red headings.

EXERCISE 68: Use the Think About a Plan worksheet in the **Practice and Problem Solving Workbook** (also available in the Teaching Resources in print and online) to further support students' development in becoming independent learners.

HOMEWORK QUICK CHECK

To check students' understanding of key skills and concepts, go over Exercises 39, 61, 68, 69, and 74.

Practice and Problem-Solving Exercises

A Practice — Use the Distributive Property to simplify each expression.   ◀ See Problem 1.

9. $6(a + 10)$ **10.** $8(4 + x)$ **11.** $(5 + w)5$ **12.** $(2t + 3)11$

13. $10(9 - t)$ **14.** $12(2j - 6)$ **15.** $16(7b + 6)$ **16.** $(1 + 3d)9$

17. $(3 - 8c)1.5$ **18.** $(5w - 15)2.1$ **19.** $\frac{1}{4}(4f - 8)$ **20.** $6\left(\frac{1}{3}h + 1\right)$

21. $(-8z - 10)(-1.5)$ **22.** $0(3.7x - 4.21)$ **23.** $1\left(\frac{3}{11} - \frac{7d}{17}\right)$ **24.** $\frac{1}{2}\left(\frac{1}{2}y - \frac{1}{2}\right)$

Write each fraction as a sum or difference.   ◀ See Problem 2.

25. $\frac{2x + 7}{5}$ **26.** $\frac{17 + 5n}{4}$ **27.** $\frac{8 - 9x}{3}$ **28.** $\frac{4y - 12}{2}$

29. $\frac{25 - 8t}{5}$ **30.** $\frac{18x + 51}{17}$ **31.** $\frac{22 - 2n}{2}$ **32.** $\frac{42w + 14}{7}$

Simplify each expression.   ◀ See Problem 3.

33. $-(20 + d)$ **34.** $-(-5 - 4y)$ **35.** $-(9 - 7c)$ **36.** $-(-x + 15)$

37. $-(18a - 17b)$ **38.** $-(2.1c - 4d)$ **39.** $-(-m + n + 1)$ **40.** $-(x + 3y - 3)$

Use mental math to find each product.   ◀ See Problem 4.

41. 5.1×8 **42.** 3×7.25 **43.** 299×3 **44.** 4×197

45. 3.9×6 **46.** 5×2.7 **47.** 6.15×4 **48.** 6×9.1

49. You buy 50 of your favorite songs from a Web site that charges $.99 for each song. What is the cost of 50 songs? Use mental math.

50. The perimeter of a baseball diamond is about 360 ft. If you take 12 laps around the diamond, what is the total distance you run? Use mental math.

51. One hundred and five students see a play. Each ticket costs $45. What is the total amount the students spend for tickets? Use mental math.

52. Suppose the distance you travel to school is 5 mi. What is the total distance for 197 trips from home to school? Use mental math.

Simplify each expression by combining like terms.   ◀ See Problem 5.

53. $11x + 9x$ **54.** $8y - 7y$ **55.** $5t - 7t$

56. $-n + 4n$ **57.** $5w^2 + 12w^2$ **58.** $2x^2 - 9x^2$

59. $-4y^2 + 9y^2$ **60.** $6c - 4 + 2c - 7$ **61.** $5 - 3x + y + 6$

62. $2n + 1 - 4m - n$ **63.** $-7h + 3h^2 - 4h - 3$ **64.** $10ab + 2ab^2 - 9ab$

B Apply — Write a word phrase for each expression. Then simplify each expression.

65. $3(t - 1)$ **66.** $4(d + 7)$ **67.** $\frac{1}{3}(6x - 1)$

Answers

Practice and Problem-Solving Exercises

9. $6a + 60$ **10.** $32 + 8x$

11. $25 + 5w$ **12.** $22t + 33$

13. $90 - 10t$ **14.** $24j - 72$

15. $112b + 96$ **16.** $9 + 27d$

17. $4.5 - 12c$ **18.** $10.5w - 31.5$

19. $f - 2$ **20.** $2h + 6$

21. $12z + 15$ **22.** 0

23. $\frac{3}{11} - \frac{7d}{17}$ **24.** $\frac{1}{4}y - \frac{1}{4}$

25. $\frac{2}{5}x + \frac{7}{5}$ **26.** $\frac{17}{4} + \frac{5}{4}n$

27. $\frac{8}{3} - 3x$ **28.** $2y - 6$

29. $5 - \frac{8}{5}t$ **30.** $\frac{18}{17}x + 3$

31. $11 - n$ **32.** $6w + 2$

33. $-20 - d$ **34.** $5 + 4y$

35. $-9 + 7c$ **36.** $x - 15$

37. $-18a + 17b$ **38.** $-2.1c + 4d$

39. $m - n - 1$ **40.** $-x - 3y + 3$

41. 40.8   **42.** 21.75

43. 897   **44.** 788

45. 23.4   **46.** 13.5

47. 24.6   **48.** 54.6

49. $49.50   **50.** 4320 ft

51. $4725   **52.** 985 mi

53. $20x$ **54.** y

55. $-2t$ **56.** $3n$

57. $17w^2$ **58.** $-7x^2$

59. $5y^2$ **60.** $8c - 11$

61. $-3x + y + 11$

62. $n - 4m + 1$

63. $3h^2 - 11h - 3$

64. $ab + 2ab^2$

65. the product of 3 and the difference of t and 1; $3t - 3$

66. the product of 4 and the sum of d and 7; $4d + 28$

67. one third the difference of 6 times x and 1; $2x - \frac{1}{3}$

68. Exercise The recommended heart rate for exercise, in beats per minute, is given by the expression $0.8(200 - y)$ where y is a person's age in years. Rewrite this expression using the Distributive Property. What is the recommended heart rate for a 20-year-old person? For a 50-year-old person? Use mental math.

69. Error Analysis Identify and correct the error shown at the right.

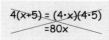

70. Error Analysis A friend uses the Distributive Property to simplify $4(2b - 5)$ and gets $8b - 5$ as the result. Describe and correct the error.

Geometry Write an expression in simplified form for the area of each rectangle.

71.

11

3x + 2

72.

5 + 2y

5

73.

7

5n − 9

74. Think About a Plan You are replacing your regular shower head with a water-saving shower head. These shower heads use the amount of water per minute shown. If you take an 8-min shower, how many gallons of water will you save?
- Which would you use to represent water saved each minute, an expression involving addition or an expression involving subtraction?
- How can you use the Distributive Property to find the total amount of water saved?

New

2.5 gallons per minute

7 gallons per minute

Simplify each expression.

75. $6yz + 2yz - 8yz$

76. $-2ab + ab + 9ab - 3ab$

77. $-9m^3n + 4m^3n + 5mn$

78. $3(-4cd - 5)$

79. $12x^2y - 8x^2y^2 + 11x^2y - 4x^3y^2 - 9xy^2$

80. $a - \frac{a}{4} + \frac{3}{4}a$

81. Reasoning The Distributive Property also applies to division, as shown.

$$\frac{a + b}{c} = \frac{a}{c} + \frac{b}{c}$$

Use the Distributive Property of Division to rewrite $\frac{9 + 12n}{3}$. Then simplify.

82. Lawn Game You play a game where you throw a pair of connected balls at a structure, as shown at the right. When a pair wraps around a bar, you earn the points shown. You toss 3 pairs, and all of them wrap around a bar. Which expression could represent your total score if a pairs of balls wrap around the blue bar?

10 points

20 points

- Ⓐ $30 + 10a$
- Ⓒ $10a + 20(3 - a)$
- Ⓑ $20a + 3 - 10a$
- Ⓓ $30a + 10$

68. $160 - 0.8y$; 144 beats/min; 120 beats/min

69. The sum, not the product, of the terms should be found; $4(x + 5) = 4x + 4 \cdot 5 = 4x + 20$.

70. The 4 was not distributed to both terms inside parentheses; $8b - 20$.

71. $33x + 22$

72. $25 + 10y$

73. $35n - 63$

74. 36 gal

75. 0

76. $5ab$

77. $-5m^3n + 5mn$

78. $-12cd - 15$

79. $23x^2y - 8x^2y^2 - 4x^3y^2 - 9xy^2$

80. $\frac{3}{2}a$

81. $\frac{1}{3}(9 + 12n) = \frac{9}{3} + \frac{12n}{3} = 3 + 4n$

82. A

Answers

Practice and Problem-Solving Exercises
(continued)

83. Answers may vary. Sample: $3(m - 2n - 5)$.

84. Check students' work. Either way will give the correct answer.

85. $45d + 26$

86. $6t + 6$

87. $24 + 2t$

88. $-6r + 37$

89. $-m - 9n + 12$

90. $-18 + 17x + 44y$

91. C

92. H

93. C

94. F

95. -25

96. $\frac{9}{16}$

97. 1.44

98. 10 less than a number x

99. 18 less than the product of 5 and x

100. 12 more than the quotient of 7 and y

---

83. Open-Ended Suppose you used the Distributive Property to get the expression $3m - 6n - 15$. With what expression could you have started?

 Challenge

84. Writing Your friend uses the order of operations to find the value of $11(39 - 3)$. Would you prefer to use the Distributive Property instead? Explain.

Simplify each expression.

85. $5(2d + 1) + 7(5d + 3)$ **86.** $6(4t - 3) + 6(4 - 3t)$ **87.** $9(5 + t) - 7(t + 3)$

88. $4(r + 8) - 5(2r - 1)$ **89.** $-(m + 9n - 12)$ **90.** $-6(3 - 3x - 7y) + 2y - x$

Standardized Test Prep

SAT/ACT

91. What is the simplified form of the expression $2(7c - 1)$?

(A) $14c - 1$ (B) $9c - 3$ (C) $14c - 2$ (D) $9c - 1$

92. You have already traveled 2.3 mi in a canoe. You continue to travel 0.1 mi each minute. The expression $0.1m + 2.3$ gives the distance traveled (in miles) after m minutes. What is your distance traveled after 25 min?

(F) 2.5 mi   (G) 2.55 mi   (H) 4.8 mi   (I) 27.3 mi

93. The table at the right shows the depth several submersible vehicles can reach. Which of the submersibles are capable of diving to 12,500 ft?

(A) *Clelia* and *Pisces* V
(B) *Alvin, Clelia,* and *Pisces* V
(C) *Alvin* and *Mir* I
(D) *Mir* I

Depth of Submersibles

Submersible	Depth (ft)
Alvin	14,764
Clelia	1000
Mir I	20,000
Pisces V	6280

Source: National Oceanic and Atmospheric Administration

94. Which expression gives the value in dollars of n nickels?

(F) $0.05n$ (G) $0.05 + n$ (H) $0.5n$ (I) $5n$

Mixed Review

Find each product.

See Lesson 1-6.

95. -5^2 **96.** $\left(-\frac{3}{4}\right)^2$ **97.** $(-1.2)^2$

Get Ready! To prepare for Lesson 1-8, do Exercises 98–100.

Write a word phrase for each algebraic expression.

See Lesson 1-1.

98. $x - 10$ **99.** $5x - 18$ **100.** $\frac{7}{y} + 12$

Additional Instructional Support

Algebra 1 Companion

Students can use the **Algebra 1 Companion** worktext (4 pages) as you teach the lesson. Use the Companion to support

- New Vocabulary
- Key Concepts
- Got It for each Problem
- Lesson Check

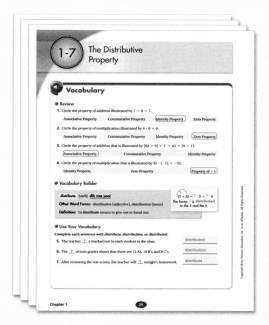

ELL Support

Assess Understanding Have each student fold a sheet of paper in half. The paper, front and back, will have four panels. On three panels, students should write the words True, False, Open, (big enough that you can see it from a distance). On the fourth panel they should write one whole number from 0 to 10. Write the open sentence $3x = 6$ on the board. Have students show you the panel that says Open, or the solution 2 (if they wrote 2 on their paper). Write $7 = 9$ on the board, and have students show you False. Then write $3x + 6 = 3(x + 2)$; students should show you True. Use the following equations to start this activity.

$$2x + 5 = 11 \text{ [Open, 3]}$$
$$14 = 9 \times 2 \text{ [False]}$$
$$5x + 20 = 5(x + 4) \text{ [True]}$$
$$4x - 9 = 19 \text{ [Open, 7]}$$
$$9x + 2 = 7x + 2 + 2x \text{ [True]}$$
$$6x - 2x = 24 \text{ [Open, 6]}$$

Encourage students to come up to the board and write an equation, also.

5 Assess & Remediate

Lesson Quiz

1. Simplify the expression $-3(4x - 1)$.
2. Write $\frac{9y - 2}{11}$ as a sum or difference.
3. Write $-(-2z - 5y)$ in simplified form.
4. **Do you UNDERSTAND?** Bushels of apples cost $7.95 at a farmer's market. How much would 8 bushels of apples cost? Use mental math.
5. Simplify each expression.
   a. $5n^2 - 3n^2$
   b. $8 + 3b - 2c - 4 + 6b$

ANSWERS TO LESSON QUIZ

1. $-12x + 3$
2. $\frac{9y}{11} - \frac{2}{11}$
3. $2z + 5y$
4. $63.60
5. a. $2n^2$, b. $9b - 2c + 4$

PRESCRIPTION FOR REMEDIATION
Use the student work on the Lesson Quiz to prescribe a differentiated review assignment.

Points	Differentiated Remediation
0–2	Intervention
3–4	On-level
5	Extension

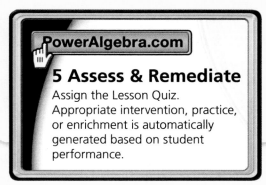

PowerAlgebra.com

5 Assess & Remediate

Assign the Lesson Quiz. Appropriate intervention, practice, or enrichment is automatically generated based on student performance.

Intervention

- **Reteaching** (2 pages) Provides reteaching and practice exercises for the key lesson concepts. Use with struggling students or absent students.
- **English Language Learner Support** Helps students develop and reinforce mathematical vocabulary and key concepts.

All-in-One Resources/Online
Reteaching

1-7 Reteaching
The Distributive Property

The Distributive Property states that the product of a sum and another factor can be rewritten as the sum of two products, each term in the sum multiplied by the other factor. For example, the Distributive Property can be used to rewrite the product $3(x + y)$ as the sum $3x + 3y$. Each term in the sum $x + y$ is multiplied by 3; then the new products are added.

Problem

What is the simplified form of each expression?

a. $4(x + 5)$
   $= 4(x) + 4(5)$ Distributive Property
   $= 4x + 20$ Simplify.

b. $(2x - 3)(-3)$
   $= 2x(-3) - 3(-3)$ Distributive Property
   $= -6x + 9$ Simplify.

The Distributive Property can be used whether the factor being multiplied by a sum or difference is on the left or right.

The Distributive Property is sometimes referred to as the Distributive Property of Multiplication over Addition. It may be helpful to think of this longer name for the property, as it may remind you of the way in which the operations of multiplication and addition are related by the property.

Exercises

Use the Distributive Property to simplify each expression.

1. $6(z + 4)$ 2. $2(-2 - k)$ 3. $(5x + 1)4$ 4. $(7 - 11n)10$
   $6z + 24$ $-4 - 2k$ $20x + 4$ $70 - 110n$

5. $(3 - 8w)4.5$ 6. $(4p + 5)2.6$ 7. $4(y + 4)$ 8. $6(q - 2)$
   $13.5 - 36w$ $10.4p + 13$ $4y + 16$ $6q - 12$

Write each fraction as a sum or difference.

9. $\frac{2m - 5}{9}$ 10. $\frac{8 + 7z}{11}$ 11. $\frac{2f + 15}{9}$ 12. $\frac{12d - 16}{6}$
   $\frac{2m}{9} - \frac{5}{9}$ $\frac{8}{11} + \frac{7z}{11}$ $\frac{2f}{9} + \frac{5}{3}$ $2d - \frac{8}{3}$

Simplify each expression.

13. $-(6 + j)$ 14. $-(-9h - 4)$ 15. $-(-n + 11)$ 16. $-(6 - 8f)$
    $-6 - j$ $9h + 4$ $n - 11$ $-6 + 8f$

All-in-One Resources/Online
English Language Learner Support

1-7 ELL Support
The Distributive Property

Complete the vocabulary chart by filling in the missing information.

Word or Word Phrase	Definition	Picture or Example
coefficient	a numerical factor of a term that contains a variable	$4a^2 - 3ab + 2b - 8$ Coefficients: 4, −3, and 2
constant	a term that has no variable	$4a^2 - 3ab + 2b - 8$ Constant: −8
Distributive Property	For real numbers, a, b, and c the product of a and $(b + c)$ is $ab + bc$	$7(3 + 2) = 7 \cdot 5 = 35$ $7 \cdot 3 + 7 \cdot 2 = 21 + 14 = 35$
like terms	terms that have exactly the same variable factors raised to the same power	$-8x$ and $5x$
term	a number, a variable, or the product of a number and one or more variables	$4a^2 - 3ab + 2b - 8$ Terms: $4a^2$, $-3ab$, $2b$, and −8.

Differentiated Remediation continued

On-Level

- **Practice** (2 pages) Provides extra practice for each lesson. For simpler practice exercises, use the Form K Practice pages found in the All-in-One Teaching Resources and online.

- **Think About a Plan** Helps students develop specific problem-solving skills and strategies by providing scaffolded guiding questions.

- **Standardized Test Prep** Focuses on all major exercises, all major question types, and helps students prepare for the high-stakes assessments.

Extension

- **Enrichment** Provides students with interesting problems and activities that extend the concepts of the lesson.

- **Activities, Games, and Puzzles** Worksheets that can be used for concepts development, enrichment, and for fun!

Practice and Problem Solving WKBK/ All-in-One Resources/Online
Practice page 1

1-7 Practice — Form G
The Distributive Property

Use the Distributive Property to simplify each expression.

1. $3(h - 5)$ 2. $7(-5 + m)$ 3. $(6 + 9v)6$ 4. $(5n + 3)12$
   $3h - 15$ $7m - 35$ $54v + 36$ $60n + 36$

5. $20(8 - a)$ 6. $15(3y - 5)$ 7. $21(2x + 4)$ 8. $(7 + 6w)6$
   $-20a + 160$ $45y - 75$ $42x + 84$ $36w + 42$

9. $(14 - 9p)1.1$ 10. $(2b - 10)3.2$ 11. $\frac{1}{3}(3z + 12)$ 12. $4(\frac{1}{2}t - 5)$
   $-9.9p + 15.4$ $6.4b - 32$ $z + 4$ $2t - 20$

13. $(-5x - 14)(5.1)$ 14. $1(-\frac{1}{7}r - \frac{5}{7})$ 15. $10(6.85j + 7.654)$ 16. $\frac{2}{3}(\frac{3}{2}m - \frac{2}{3})$
    $-25.5x - 71.4$ $-\frac{1}{7}r - \frac{5}{7}$ $68.5j + 76.54$ $\frac{4}{9}m - \frac{4}{9}$

Write each fraction as a sum or difference.

17. $\frac{3m + 5}{7}$ $\frac{3m}{7} + \frac{5}{7}$ 18. $\frac{14 - 6x}{19}$ $\frac{14}{19} - \frac{6x}{19}$ 19. $\frac{3d + 5}{6}$ $\frac{d}{2} + \frac{5}{6}$ 20. $\frac{9p - 6}{3}$ $3p - 2$

21. $\frac{18 + 8z}{6}$ $3 + \frac{4z}{3}$ 22. $\frac{15m - 42}{14}$ $\frac{15m}{14} - 3$ 23. $\frac{56 - 28w}{8}$ $7 - \frac{7w}{2}$ 24. $\frac{81f + 63}{9}$ $9f + 7$

Simplify each expression.

25. $-(14 + x)$ 26. $-(8 - 6t)$ 27. $-(6 + d)$ 28. $-(-r + 1)$
    $-14 - x$ $8 + 6t$ $-6 - d$ $r - 1$

29. $-(4m - 6n)$ 30. $-(5.8a + 4.2b)$ 31. $-(-x + y - 1)$ 32. $-(f + 3g - 7)$
    $-4m + 6n$ $-5.8a - 4.2b$ $x - y + 1$ $-f - 3g + 7$

Use mental math to find each product.

33. 3.2×3 9.6 34. 5×8.2 41 35. 149×2 298 36. 6×397 2382

37. 4.2×5 21 38. 4×10.1 40.4 39. 8.25×4 33 40. 11×4.1 45.1

41. You buy 75 candy bars at a cost of $0.49 each. What is the total cost of 75 candy bars? Use mental math. $36.75

42. The distance around a track is 400 m. If you take 14 laps around the track, what is the total distance you walk? Use mental math. 5600 m

43. There are 32 classmates that are going to the fair. Each ticket costs $19. What is the total amount the classmates spend for tickets? Use mental math. $608

Practice and Problem Solving WKBK/ All-in-One Resources/Online
Practice page 2

1-7 Practice (continued) — Form G
The Distributive Property

Simplify each expression by combining like terms.

44. $4t + 6t$ $10t$ 45. $17y - 15y$ $2y$ 46. $-11b^2 + 4b^2$ $-7b^2$

47. $-2y - 5y - 7y$ 48. $14n^2 - 7n^2$ $7n^2$ 49. $8x^2 - 10x^2$ $-2x^2$

50. $2f + 7g - 6 + 8g$ 51. $8x + 3 - 5x - 9$ 52. $-5k - 6k^2 - 12k + 10$
    $2f + 15g - 6$ $3x - 6$ $-6k^2 - 17k + 10$

Write a word phrase for each expression. Then simplify each expression.

53. $2(n + 1)$ 54. $-5(x - 7)$ 55. $\frac{1}{2}(4m - 8)$
    two times the sum of a   negative five times the   one-half the difference
    number and one; $2n + 2$ difference of a number   of four times a number
                              minus seven; $-5x + 35$ minus eight; $2m - 4$

56. The tax a plumber must charge for a service call is given by the expression $0.06(35 + 25h)$ where h is the number of hours the job takes. Rewrite this expression using the Distributive Property. What is the tax for a 5 hour job and a 20 hour job? Use mental math. $2.1 + 1.5h$; $9.60; $32.10

Geometry Write an expression in simplified form for the area of each rectangle.

57. $5x$ by 4
$20x - 8$

58. $-2n + 17$ by 24
$-48n + 408$

59. 15 by $x - 5$
$15x - 75$

Simplify each expression.

60. $4jk - 7jk + 12jk$ $9jk$ 61. $-17mn + 4mn - mn + 10mn$ $-4mn$

62. $8xy^4 - 7xy^3 - 11xy^4 - 3xy^4 - 7xy^3$ 63. $-2(5ab - 6) - 10ab + 12$
    $3m^2n + 4m^2n^2 - 5m^3n^2 - 5mn^2$

64. $z + \frac{2z}{5} - \frac{4z}{5} \frac{3z}{5}$ 65. $7m^2n + 4m^2n^2 - 4m^2n - 5m^3n^2 - 5mn^2$
                                                         $3m^2n + 4m^2n^2 - 5m^3n^2 - 5mn^2$

66. **Reasoning** Demonstrate why $\frac{12x - 6}{6} \ne 2x - 6$. Show your work.
    $\frac{12x - 6}{6} = \frac{1}{6}(12x - 6) = \frac{1}{6}(12x) - \frac{1}{6}(6) = 2x - 1; 2x - 1 \ne 2x - 6$

Simplify each expression.

67. $4(2h + 1) + 3(4h + 7)$ 68. $5(n - 8) + 6(7 - 2n)$ 69. $7(3 + x) - 4(x + 1)$
    $20h + 25$ $-7n + 2$ $3x + 17$

70. $6(y + 5) - 3(4y + 2)$ 71. $-(a - 3b + 27)$ 72. $-2(5 - 4s + 6t) - 5s + t$
    $-6y + 24$ $-a + 3b - 27$ $3s - 11t - 10$

All-in-One Resources/Online
Enrichment

1-7 Enrichment
The Distributive Property

The Distributive Property can be used more than once in the same expression. In this lesson, you learned that basic multiplication calculations can be completed using mental math.

$3 \cdot 84 = 3(80 + 4) = 3(80) + 3(4) = 240 + 12 = 252$

The same process can be used when both numbers are two-digit numbers. However, the Distributive Property must be used more than once. Look at the following example.

$(49)(26) = (40 + 9)(20 + 6)$ — Rewrite 49 as 40 + 9 and 26 as 20 + 6.
$= (40)(20 + 6) + (9)(20 + 6)$ — (20 + 6) can be distributed into (40 + 9).
$= (40)(20) + (40)(6) + (9)(20) + (9)(6)$ — Distribute 40 and 9 into (20 + 6).
$= 800 + 240 + 180 + 54$ — Multiply.
$= 1274$ — Add.

Exercises

Use the Distributive Property to find each product. Show your work.

1. $(15)(32)$ 2. $(48)(72)$ 3. $(84)(63)$
   480 3456 5292

This same procedure can be utilized for simplifying algebraic expressions. Instead of $(20 + 2)(30 + 1)$, the expression might be $(x + 2)(x + 1)$.

$(x + 2)(x + 1) = (x)(x + 1) + (2)(x + 1)$ — (x + 2) can be distributed into (x + 1).
$= (x)(x) + (x)(1) + (2)(x) + (2)(1)$ — Distribute x and 2 into (x + 1).
$= x^2 + x + 2x + 2$ — Multiply.
$= x^2 + 3x + 2$ — Add.

Exercises

Use the Distributive Property to find each product. Show your work.

4. $(x + 3)(x + 4)$ 5. $(x + 1)(x + 8)$ 6. $(x + 4)(x + 2)$
   $x^2 + 7x + 12$ $x^2 + 9x + 8$ $x^2 + 6x + 8$
7. $(x + 1)^2$ (Hint: Remember that $(x + 1)^2 = (x + 1)(x + 1)$.)
   $x^2 + 2x + 1$

Practice and Problem Solving WKBK/ All-in-One Resources/Online
Think About a Plan

1-7 Think About a Plan
The Distributive Property

Exercise The recommended heart rate for exercise, in beats per minute, is given by the expression $0.8(200 - y)$ where y is a person's age in years. Rewrite this expression using the Distributive Property. What is the recommended heart rate for a 20-year-old person? For a 50-year-old person? Use mental math.

Understanding the Problem

1. What relationship does the given expression represent? What does the variable in the expression represent?
   It gives the recommended heart rate for exercise, in beats per minute, for people of different ages. The variable is the age of the person being evaluated.

2. What does it mean to rewrite the expression using the Distributive Property?
   The 0.8 must be distributed by multiplying it by each term inside the parentheses.

3. What does it mean to use mental math?
   Calculations that can be done mentally without work being shown.

Planning the Solution

4. How do you determine the recommended heart rate for people of different ages?
   You can substitute their ages in for y of the given expression.

Getting an Answer

5. Rewrite the expression using the Distributive Property.
   $160 - 0.8y$

6. What is the recommended heart rate for a 20-year-old person? Show your work.
   144 beats/min

7. What is the recommended heart rate for a 50-year-old person? Show your work.
   120 beats/min

Practice and Problem Solving WKBK/ All-in-One Resources/Online
Standardized Test Prep

1-7 Standardized Test Prep
The Distributive Property

Multiple Choice

For Exercises 1–6, choose the correct letter.

1. What is the simplified form of the expression $6(4x - 7)$? C
   A. $10x - 1$ B. $24x - 7$ C. $24x - 42$ D. $24x + 42$

2. What is the simplified form of the expression $-2(-5x - 8)$? I
   F. $-7x - 10$ G. $10x - 8$ H. $10x - 16$ I. $10x + 16$

3. What is the simplified form of the expression $14mn + 6mn^2 - 8mn - 7m^2n + 5m^2n$? D
   A. $10m^2n^2$
   B. $6mn - 4m^2n$
   C. $6mn + 5m^2n - 1mn^2$
   D. $6mn - 2m^2n + 6mn^2$

4. Concert tickets cost $14.95 each. Which expression represents the total cost of 25 tickets? F
   F. $25(15 - 0.05)$ G. $25(15 + 0.05)$ H. $15(25 - 10.05)$ I. $25(15) - 0.05$

5. Which expression represents 7 times the sum of a number and 8? B
   A. $7n + 8$ B. $7(n + 8)$ C. $8(n + 7)$ D. $n + 56$

6. There are 297 students in a senior class. The cost of the senior trip is $150 per student. Which expression represents the total cost of the senior trip? H
   F. $150(300)$ G. $300(150 - 3)$ H. $150(300 - 3)$ I. $150(300) - 3$

Short Response

7. The profit Samantha's company makes is given by the expression $0.1(1000 + 300m)$ where m is total number of sales. Rewrite this expression using the Distributive Property. What is the profit if her company sells 50 pieces of merchandise? Use mental math.
   $100 + 3m$; $1600
   [2] Both parts answered correctly.
   [1] One part answered correctly.
   [0] Neither part answered correctly.

Online Teacher Resource Center
Activities, Games, and Puzzles

1-7 Game: Algebra Baseball
The Distributive Property

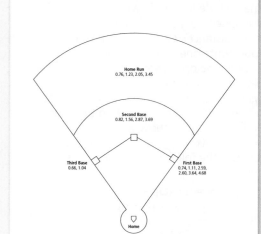

1-8 An Introduction to Equations

Indiana Academic Standard
A1.2.1 Translate among various representations of linear functions including tables, graphs, words and equations.

Objective To solve equations using tables and mental math

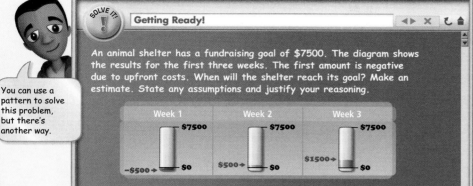

You can use a pattern to solve this problem, but there's another way.

Getting Ready!

An animal shelter has a fundraising goal of $7500. The diagram shows the results for the first three weeks. The first amount is negative due to upfront costs. When will the shelter reach its goal? Make an estimate. State any assumptions and justify your reasoning.

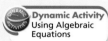
Dynamic Activity Using Algebraic Equations

Lesson Vocabulary
• equation
• open sentence
• solution of an equation

The problem in the Solve It can be modeled by an equation. An **equation** is a mathematical sentence that uses an equal sign (=).

Essential Understanding You can use an equation to represent the relationship between two quantities that have the same value.

An equation is true if the expressions on either side of the equal sign are equal $(1 + 1 = 2, x + x = 2x)$. An equation is false if the expressions on either side of the equal sign are not equal $(1 + 1 = 3, x + x = 3x)$. An equation is an **open sentence** if it contains one or more variables and may be true or false depending on the values of its variables.

Plan

How do you classify an equation?
If an equation contains only numbers, simplify the expressions on either side to determine if they are equal. If there is a variable in the equation, it is open.

Problem 1 Classifying Equations

Is the equation *true*, *false*, or *open*? Explain.

Ⓐ $24 + 18 = 20 + 22$ True, because both expressions equal 42

Ⓑ $7 \cdot 8 = 54$ False, because $7 \cdot 8 = 56$ and $56 \neq 54$

Ⓒ $2x - 14 = 54$ Open, because there is a variable

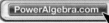 **Got It?** 1. Is the equation *true*, *false*, or *open*? Explain.
   a. $3y + 6 = 5y - 8$ b. $16 - 7 = 4 + 5$ c. $32 \div 8 = 2 \cdot 3$

---

1 Interactive Learning

Solve It!
PURPOSE To utilize non-algebraic solution strategies for solving a linear equation
PROCESS Students may determine the pattern or may model the situation with an equation.

FACILITATE

Q At the end of the third week, what is the total amount the fundraising drive has collected for the shelter? Explain **[$1500; −500 + $500 + $1500]**

Q What is the average amount raised each week during Weeks 2 and 3? Show your work. **[($500 + $1500) ÷ 2 = $1000]**

Q If the fundraising continues at a similar rate, what expression models the total amount raised from Week 1 to Week w? **[$1000w − $500]**

ANSWER See Solve It in Answers on next page.
CONNECT THE MATH In the Solve It, students solve a problem that can be modeled with an equation. In this lesson, students are introduced to equations and modeling.

2 Guided Instruction

Problem 1

Q Can you determine whether an open equation like in part (c) is true or false? Explain. **[No, without knowing the value of the variable, you cannot determine whether the equation is true.]**

Got It?

Q What is a value of *y* that makes the equation in part (a) false? true? **[Answers may vary. Sample: 1; 7]**

1-8 Preparing to Teach

BIG idea Variable   **UbD**
ESSENTIAL UNDERSTANDINGS
• Sometimes the value of one quantity can be found if the value of another is known.
• The relationship between the quantities can be represented in different ways, including tables, equations, and graphs.

Math Background

Equations bring together many important algebraic concepts such as variables, expressions, and the order of operations. Often in the study of algebra, students become mechanical when solving equations and lose sight of the many non-algebraic methods that they know for solving problems. They also lose sight of what it

means for a number(s) to be the solution(s) of an equation. Stressing the importance of these non-algebraic methods like making a table or using a number line will aid students when they need to judge the reasonableness of a solution, solve a word problem, or graph a linear equation.

Support Student Learning

Use the **Algebra 1 Companion** to engage and support students during instructions. See Lesson Resources at the end of this lesson for details.

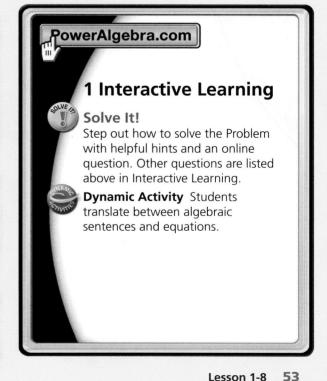

1 Interactive Learning

Solve It!
Step out how to solve the Problem with helpful hints and an online question. Other questions are listed above in Interactive Learning.

Dynamic Activity Students translate between algebraic sentences and equations.

Problem 2

> **Q** Why do you multiply the 6 and 2 prior to adding 12 on the right side of the equation? **[order of operations]**
>
> **Q** What must the expression $2x$ be equal to so that when 12 is added you get 32? Explain. **[20 + 12 = 32, so $2x$ must equal 20.]**

Got It?

> **Q** Is there another value of m that makes the equation true? Explain. **[No, only $\frac{1}{2}$ makes the left side of the equation equal to -5.]**

Problem 3

> **Q** If you are given a width for the court, how do you check to see if the model is accurate? **[You multiply the width by 2.4 and check to see if the answer is 54.]**
>
> **Q** What expression represents multiplying a given width, w, by 2.4? **[2.4w]**

Got It?

> **Q** Is the solution a whole number? Explain. **[No, 14 is not a factor of 49.]**

A **solution of an equation** containing a variable is a value of the variable that makes the equation true.

Problem 2 Identifying Solutions of an Equation

Is $x = 6$ a solution of the equation $32 = 2x + 12$?

$32 = 2x + 12$

$32 \overset{?}{=} 2(6) + 12$ Substitute 6 for x.

$32 \neq 24$ Simplify.

No, $x = 6$ is not a solution of the equation $32 = 2x + 12$.

Got It? 2. Is $m = \frac{1}{2}$ a solution of the equation $6m - 8 = -5$?

Plan

How can you tell if a number is a solution of an equation? Substitute the number for the variable in the equation. Simplify each side to see if you get a true statement.

In real-world problems, the word *is* can indicate equality. You can represent some real-world situations using an equation.

Problem 3 Writing an Equation

Multiple Choice An art student wants to make a model of the Mayan Great Ball Court in Chichén Itzá, Mexico. The length of the court is 2.4 times its width. The length of the student's model is 54 in. What should the width of the model be?

- (A) 2.4 in.
- (B) 11.25 in.
- (C) 22.5 in.
- (D) 129.6 in.

Relate The length is 2.4 times the width

Define Let w = the width of the model.

Write 54 = 2.4 · w

Test each answer choice in the equation to see if it is a solution.

Check A:	Check B:	Check C:	Check D:
$54 = 2.4w$	$54 = 2.4w$	$54 = 2.4w$	$54 = 2.4w$
$54 \overset{?}{=} 2.4(2.4)$	$54 \overset{?}{=} 2.4(11.25)$	$54 \overset{?}{=} 2.4(22.5)$	$54 \overset{?}{=} 2.4(129.6)$
$54 \neq 5.76$	$54 \neq 27$	$54 = 54$ ✔	$54 \neq 311.04$

The correct answer is C.

Got It? 3. The length of the ball court at La Venta is 14 times the height of its walls. Write an equation that can be used to find the height of a model that has a length of 49 cm.

54 in.

w

Satellite view of Chichén Itzá

Plan

Why do you need to test each answer choice? You should test each answer choice in case you made a calculation error. If you get two correct answers, then you know you need to double-check your work.

Answers

Solve It!

The shelter should reach its goal by week 9 because it appears it raises $1000 per week.

Got It?

1. a. open

  b. true

  c. false

2. yes

3. $49 = 14h$

PowerAlgebra.com

2 Guided Instruction

Each Problem is worked out and supported online.

Problem 1
Classifying Equations
Animated

Problem 2
Identifying Solutions of an Equation

Problem 3
Writing an Equation

Problem 4
Using Mental Math to Find Solutions

Problem 5
Using a Table to Find a Solution
Animated

Problem 6
Estimating a Solution
Animated

Support in Algebra 1 Companion
- Vocabulary
- Key Concepts
- Got It?

Problem 4 Using Mental Math to Find Solutions

ONLINE PROBLEMS

Plan

How can you find the solution of an equation?
You can use mental math to find a value that makes the equation true.

What is the solution of each equation? Use mental math.

	Think	Solution	Check
A $x + 8 = 12$	What number plus 8 equals 12?	4	$4 + 8 = 12$ ✔
B $\frac{a}{8} = 9$	What number divided by 8 equals 9?	72	$\frac{72}{8} = 9$ ✔

✅ **Got It? 4.** What is the solution of $12 - y = 3$? Use mental math.

Problem 5 Using a Table to Find a Solution

Think

How can you start?
You can use mental math to quickly check values like 0, 1, and 10. Use these results to choose a reasonable starting value for your table.

What is the solution of $5n + 8 = 48$? Use a table.

Make a table of values. Choose a starting value using mental math. $5(1) + 8 = 13$ and $5(10) + 8 = 58$, so 1 is too low and 10 is too high.

Try $n = 5$ and $n = 6$.

n	$5n + 8$	Value of $5n + 8$
5	$5(5) + 8$	33
6	$5(6) + 8$	38
7	$5(7) + 8$	43
8	$5(8) + 8$	48

The value of $5n + 8$ increases as n increases, so try greater values of n.

When $n = 8$, $5n + 8 = 48$. So the solution is 8.

✅ **Got It? 5. a.** What is the solution of $25 - 3p = 55$? Use a table.
b. What is a good starting value to solve part (a)? Explain your reasoning.

Problem 6 Estimating a Solution

What is an estimate of the solution of $-9x - 5 = 28$? Use a table.

To estimate the solution, find the integer values of x between which the solution must lie. $-9(0) - 5 = -5$ and $-9(1) - 5 = -14$. If you try greater values of x, the value of $-9x - 5$ gets farther from 28.

Think

Can identifying a pattern help you make an estimate?
Yes. Identify how the value of the expression changes as you substitute for the variable. Use the pattern you find to work *toward* the desired value.

Try lesser values, such as $x = -1$ and $x = -2$.

x	$-9x - 5$	Value of $-9x - 5$
-1	$-9(-1) - 5$	4
-2	$-9(-2) - 5$	13
-3	$-9(-3) - 5$	22
-4	$-9(-4) - 5$	31

Now the values of $-9x - 5$ are getting closer to 28.

28 is between 22 and 31, so the solution is between -3 and -4.

✅ **Got It? 6.** What is the solution of $3x + 3 = -22$? Use a table.

Problem 4

Q How do you check to see if a solution to an equation is correct? **[You must substitute the value for the variable and simplify both sides to see if they are equal.]**

Got It?

Q What are the limitations of using mental math to find solutions? **[If the solution is not a whole number, it may be hard to find the solution.]**

Problem 5

Q What is a pattern in the table for the value of n? For the value of $5n + 8$? **[The values of n increase by 1 and the values of $5n + 8$ increase by 5.]**

Got It?

Q What are the limitations of using a table to find solutions? **[You may have to make a large table before you find the answer.]**

Problem 6

Q How can you tell that the value of x must be a negative number by examining the equation? **[The product of x and a negative number is positive, so x must be negative.]**

Got It?

Q How could you use your estimate for the solution to find the actual solution for the equation? **[You could begin trying rational numbers between -8 and -9.]**

Additional Problems

1. Is the equation true, false, or open? Explain.
   a. $17 + 9 = 19 + 6$
   b. $4 \times 11 = 44$
   c. $3x - 1 = 17$
   ANSWER a. false   **b.** true   **c.** open

2. Is $x = 5$ a solution of the equation $16 = 4x - 4$?
   ANSWER yes

3. An art student wants to make a model of a classroom. The length of the classroom is 2.4 times its width. The length of the student's model is 42 in. What should the width of the model be?
   A. 17.5 in.
   B. 20.5 in.
   C. 82.6 in.
   D. 100.8 in.
   ANSWER A

4. What is the solution of each equation? Use mental math.
   a. $x + 7 = 13$
   b. $\frac{x}{6} = 12$
   ANSWER a. 6   **b.** 72

5. What is the solution of $3n + 5 = 26$? Use a table.
   ANSWER 7

6. What is an estimate of the solution of $-6x + 4 = 21$? Use a table.
   ANSWER between -3 and -2

Answers

Got It? (continued)
4. 9
5. a. -10
   b. Answers may vary. Sample: -5, Check students' work.
6. The solution is between -8 and -9.

3 Lesson Check

Do you know HOW?
- If students have difficulty with Exercise 3, then have them review Problem 3.

Do you UNDERSTAND?
- If students have difficulty with Exercise 4, then have them substitute a value for the variable and simplify each side of the equation.

Close

> **Q** How can you verify that an equation is true? **[Verify that the left side of the equation is equal to the right side of the equation.]**

 Lesson Check

Do you know HOW?

1. Is $y = -9$ a solution of $y + 1 = 8$?

2. What is the solution of $x - 3 = 12$? Use mental math.

3. **Reading** You can read 1.5 pages for every page your friend can read. Write an equation that relates the number of pages p that you can read and the number of pages n that your friend can read.

Do you UNDERSTAND?

4. **Vocabulary** Give an example of an equation that is true, an equation that is false, and an open equation.

5. **Open-Ended** Write an open equation using one variable and division.

6. **Compare and Contrast** Use two different methods to find the solution of the equation $x + 4 = 13$. Which method do you prefer? Explain.

 Practice and Problem-Solving Exercises

 Practice Tell whether each equation is *true, false,* or *open.* Explain. ◀ See Problem 1.

7. $85 + (-10) = 95$
8. $225 \div t - 4 = 6.4$
9. $29 - 34 = -5$
10. $-8(-2) - 7 = 14 - 5$
11. $4(-4) \div (-8)6 = -3 + 5(3)$
12. $91 \div (-7) - 5 = 35 \div 7 + 3$
13. $4a - 3b = 21$
14. $14 + 7 + (-1) = 21$
15. $5x + 7 = 17$

Tell whether the given number is a solution of each equation. ◀ See Problem 2.

16. $8x + 5 = 29; 3$
17. $5b + 1 = 16; -3$
18. $6 = 2n - 8; 7$
19. $2 = 10 - 4y; 2$
20. $9a - (-72) = 0; -8$
21. $-6b + 5 = 1; \frac{1}{2}$
22. $7 + 16y = 11; \frac{1}{4}$
23. $14 = \frac{1}{3}x + 5; 27$
24. $\frac{3}{2}t + 2 = 4; \frac{2}{3}$

Write an equation for each sentence. ◀ See Problem 3.

25. The sum of $4x$ and -3 is 8.
26. The product of 9 and the sum of 6 and x is 1.

27. **Training** An athlete trains for 115 min each day for as many days as possible. Write an equation that relates the number of days d that the athlete spends training when the athlete trains for 690 min.

28. **Salary** The manager of a restaurant earns $2.25 more each hour than the host of the restaurant. Write an equation that relates the amount h that the host earns each hour when the manager earns $11.50 each hour.

Use mental math to find the solution of each equation. ◀ See Problem 4.

29. $x - 3 = 10$
30. $4 = 7 - y$
31. $18 + d = 24$
32. $2 - x = -5$
33. $\frac{m}{3} = 4$
34. $\frac{x}{7} = 5$
35. $6t = 36$
36. $20a = 100$
37. $13c = 26$

---

3 Lesson Check

For a digital lesson check, use the Got It questions.

Support in Algebra 1 Companion
- Lesson Check

4 Practice

Assign homework to individual students or to an entire class.

Answers

Lesson Check
1. no
2. 15
3. $p = 1.5n$
4. Check students' work.
5. Answers may vary. Sample: $\frac{x}{3} = 15$
6. 9; check students' work.

Practice and Problem-Solving Exercises

7. false
8. open
9. true
10. true
11. false
12. false
13. open
14. false
15. open
16. yes
17. no
18. yes
19. yes
20. yes
21. no
22. yes
23. yes
24. no
25. $4x + (-3) = 8$
26. $9(6 + x) = 1$
27. $115d = 690$
28. $h + 2.25 = 11.50$
29. 13
30. 3
31. 6
32. 7
33. 12
34. 35
35. 6
36. 5
37. 2

Use a table to find the solution of each equation.   See Problem 5.

38. $2t - 1 = 11$ **39.** $5x + 3 = 23$ **40.** $0 = 4 + 2y$ **41.** $8a - 10 = 38$

42. $12 = 6 - 3b$ **43.** $8 - 5w = -12$ **44.** $-48 = -9 - 13n$ **45.** $\frac{1}{2}x - 5 = -1$

Use a table to find two consecutive integers between which the solution lies. See Problem 6.

46. $6x + 5 = 81$ **47.** $3.3 = 1.5 - 0.4y$ **48.** $-115b + 80 = -489$

 Apply

49. Bicycle Sales In the United States, the number y (in millions) of bicycles sold with wheel sizes of 20 in. or greater can be modeled by the equation $y = 0.3x + 15$, where x is the number of years since 1981. In what year were about 22 million bicycles sold?

50. Error Analysis A student checked whether $d = -2$ is a solution of $-3d + (-4) = 2$, as shown. Describe and correct the student's error.

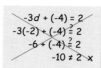

51. Writing What are the differences between an expression and an equation? Does a mathematical expression have a solution? Explain.

52. Basketball A total of 1254 people attend a basketball team's championship game. There are six identical benches in the gymnasium. About how many people would you expect each bench to seat?

Find the solution of each equation using mental math or a table. If the solution lies between two consecutive integers, identify these integers.

53. $x + 4 = -2$ **54.** $4m + 1 = 9$ **55.** $10.5 = 3n - 1$ **56.** $-3 + t = 19$

57. $5a - 4 = -16$ **58.** $9 = 4 + (-y)$ **59.** $1 = -\frac{1}{4}n + 1$ **60.** $17 = 6 + 2x$

61. Open-Ended Give three examples of equations that involve multiplication and subtraction and have a solution of -4.

62. Think About a Plan Polar researchers drill into an ice sheet. The drill is below the surface at the location shown. The drill advances at a rate of 67 m/h. About how many hours will it take the drill to reach a depth of 300 m?
- What equation models this situation?
- What integers do you need?

Ice drill

67 m/h

0 m

−75 m

−300 m

63. Deliveries The equation $25 + 0.25p = c$ gives the cost c in dollars that a store charges to deliver an appliance that weighs p pounds. Use the equation and a table to find the weight of an appliance that costs $55 to deliver.

64. Look for a Pattern Use a table. Evaluate $2x + 2$ for $x = -2, -1, 0, 1, 2,$ and 3. What pattern do you notice in your results? Use this pattern to find the solution of $2x + 2 = 28$. Check your solution.

4 Practice

ASSIGNMENT GUIDE

Basic: 7–48 all, 50–62 even, 63

Average: 7–47 odd, 49–64

Advanced: 7–47 odd, 49–66

Standardized Test Prep: 67–70

Mixed Review: 71–86

Reasoning exercises have blue headings.

Applications exercises have red headings.

EXERCISE 52: Use the Think About a Plan worksheet in the **Practice and Problem Solving Workbook** (also available in the Teaching Resources in print and online) to further support students' development in becoming independent learners.

HOMEWORK QUICK CHECK

To check students' understanding of key skills and concepts, go over Exercises 13, 37, 50, 52, and 62.

38. 6   **39.** 4   **40.** −2   **41.** 6
42. −2   **43.** 4   **44.** 3   **45.** 8
46. between 12 and 13
47. between −5 and −4
48. between 4 and 5
49. 2004
50. The product of two negative numbers is positive; $-3(-2) + (-4) \stackrel{?}{=} 2; 6 + (-4) \stackrel{?}{=} 2;$ $2 = 2$
51. An expression describes the relationship between numbers and variables. An equation shows that two expressions are equal. An expression can be simplified but has no solution.

52. 209 people
53. −6
54. 2
55. between 3 and 4
56. 22
57. between −3 and −2
58. −5
59. 0
60. between 5 and 6
61. Check students' work.
62. between 3 and 4 hours
63. 120 lb
64. −2; 0; 2; 4; 6; 8; the pattern increases by 2 for each following integer; 13

Answers

Practice and Problem-Solving Exercises
(continued)

65. No; they have 8 hours of time to install and they need a little more time than that.
$c = 32h + 272$

66. Answers may vary. Sample: The friend knows an odd number divided by an even number can not be an integer.

67. C
68. G
69. C
70. I
71. $28 + 14y$
72. $-18b - 66$
73. $-16.8 - 4.2t$
74. $-5 + 25x$
75. 10
76. -1
77. -12
78. 7
79. -9
80. -7
81. 2
82. $-7\frac{1}{2}$
83. 2
84. -1
85. 3
86. 0

 Challenge **65. Construction** A construction crew needs to install 550 ft of curbing along a street. The crew can install curbing at a rate of 32 ft/h. Yesterday the crew installed 272 ft of curbing. Today it wants to finish the job in at most 10 h, which includes a 15-min drive to the job, an hour lunch break, and 45 min to break down the equipment. Can the crew achieve its goal? Explain.

66. Reasoning Your friend says that the solution of $15 = 4 + 2t$ is between two consecutive integers, because 15 is an odd number and 4 and 2 are both even numbers. Explain your friend's reasoning.

Standardized Test Prep

SAT/ACT

67. Which equation is false?
Ⓐ $\frac{2}{3} + 1 \cdot \frac{1}{2} = \frac{7}{6}$ Ⓑ $84 - 25 = 59$ Ⓒ $51 - (-57) = -6$ Ⓓ $3(-3) + 3 = -6$

68. Which equation has a solution of 4?
Ⓕ $0 = 8 + 2y$ Ⓖ $5x + 3 = 23$ Ⓗ $8a - 10 = 42$ Ⓘ $2t - 1 = 9$

69. At 7 P.M., the temperature is 6.8°C. Over the next 4 h, the temperature changes by the amounts shown in the table. What is the final temperature?
Ⓐ -12.6°C   Ⓒ 1°C
Ⓑ 3.9°C   Ⓓ 5.8°C

Temperature Changes

Time	Change in Temperature
8 P.M.	-0.4°C
9 P.M.	-1.2°C
10 P.M.	-1.3°C
11 P.M.	-2.9°C

70. Monique has ordered 32 pizzas to serve at the student government picnic. If each person will get $\frac{1}{4}$ of a pizza, how many people will she be able to serve?
Ⓕ 8   Ⓗ 64
Ⓖ 32   Ⓘ 128

Mixed Review

Use the Distributive Property to simplify each expression.   ◀ See Lesson 1-7.

71. $7(4 + 2y)$ **72.** $-6(3b + 11)$ **73.** $(8 + 2t)(-2.1)$ **74.** $(-1 + 5x)5$

Evaluate each expression for $m = 4$, $n = -1$, and $p = -\frac{1}{2}$.   ◀ See Lesson 1-6.

75. $2m - 2n$ **76.** $pm - n$ **77.** $6mp$ **78.** $7m \div (-4n)$

79. $8p - (-5n)$ **80.** $-2m - n$ **81.** $-1.5m \div 6p$ **82.** $3n^2 \cdot (-10p^2)$

Get Ready! **To prepare for Lesson 1-9, do Exercises 83–86.**

Use a table to find the solution of each equation.   ◀ See Lesson 1-8.

83. $4x - 1 = 7$ **84.** $0 = 10 + 10y$ **85.** $5\frac{1}{2} = 7 - \frac{1}{2}b$ **86.** $3t - (-5.4) = 5.4$

Additional Instructional Support

Algebra 1 Companion

Students can use the **Algebra 1 Companion** worktext (4 pages) as you teach the lesson. Use the Companion to support

- New Vocabulary
- Key Concepts
- Got It for each Problem
- Lesson Check

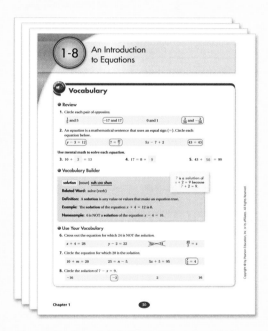

ELL Support

Focus on Language To create a wall display, have students illustrate and define words from the chapter on a $\frac{1}{2}$ sheet of paper. Include words from this chapter such as always, inverse, rational. . . . Allow students to add other words from the chapter that are unfamiliar to them. Students can write information about roots, synonyms, and antonyms on their page. They can include diagrams or other clues that help them understand the meaning. Allow a small group of students to organize how the words are presented. This activity should be updated and repeated for each chapter, or as needed.

Focus on Communication Have students become familiar with using algebra tiles by modeling simple equations such as $3x + 1 = 7$. Have students work in pairs, so they can verbalize the math sentence that they are making the tiles represent. Keep the algebra tiles available for students use in later lessons.

5 Assess & Remediate

Lesson Quiz

1. Is the equation $2x + 5 = 1$ true, false, or open? Explain.
2. Is $n = 6$ a solution of the equation $3n + 5 = 22$?
3. **Do you UNDERSTAND?** Molly is making a scale drawing of her bedroom. The length of the room is 1.2 times the width. If Molly's drawing is 15 inches long, how wide is the drawing?
4. Use mental math to solve the equation $n - 4 = 12$.
5. Solve the equation $4b + 3 = 27$. Use a table.
6. Use a table to estimate the solution of $4x + 5 = 34$.

ANSWERS TO LESSON QUIZ

1. open because there is a variable
2. no
3. 12.5 in.
4. 16
5. 6
6. between 7 and 8

PRESCRIPTION FOR REMEDIATION
Use the student work on the Lesson Quiz to prescribe a differentiated review assignment.

Points	Differentiated Remediation
0–3	Intervention
4–5	On-level
6	Extension

PowerAlgebra.com

5 Assess & Remediate

Assign the Lesson Quiz. Appropriate intervention, practice, or enrichment is automatically generated based on student performance.

Intervention

- **Reteaching** (2 pages) Provides reteaching and practice exercises for the key lesson concepts. Use with struggling students or absent students.
- **English Language Learner Support** Helps students develop and reinforce mathematical vocabulary and key concepts.

All-in-One Resources/Online
Reteaching

All-in-One Resources/Online
English Language Learner Support

Differentiated Remediation *continued*

On-Level

- **Practice** (2 pages) Provides extra practice for each lesson. For simpler practice exercises, use the Form K Practice pages found in the All-in-One Teaching Resources and online.

- **Think About a Plan** Helps students develop specific problem-solving skills and strategies by providing scaffolded guiding questions.

- **Standardized Test Prep** Focuses on all major exercises, all major question types, and helps students prepare for the high-stakes assessments.

Extension

- **Enrichment** Provides students with interesting problems and activities that extend the concepts of the lesson.

- **Activities, Games, and Puzzles** Worksheets that can be used for concepts development, enrichment, and for fun!

Practice and Problem Solving WKBK/ All-in-One Resources/Online
Practice page 1

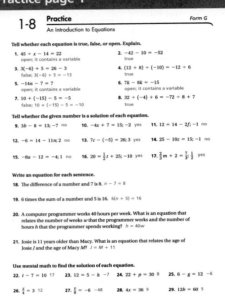

1-8 Practice — Form G
An Introduction to Equations

Tell whether each equation is true, false, or open. Explain.

1. $45 + x - 14 = 22$ — open; it contains a variable
2. $-42 - 10 = -52$ — true
3. $3(-6) + 5 = 26 - 3$ — false; $3(-6) + 5 = -13$
4. $(12 + 8) + (-10) = -12 + 6$ — true
5. $-14n - 7 = 7$ — open; it contains a variable
6. $7k - 8k = -15$ — open; it contains a variable
7. $10 + (-15) - 5 = -5$ — false; $10 + (-15) - 5 = -10$
8. $32 \div (-4) + 6 = -72 + 8 + 7$ — true

Tell whether the given number is a solution of each equation.

9. $3b - 8 = 13; -7$ — no
10. $-4x + 7 = 15; -2$ — yes
11. $12 = 14 - 2j; -1$ — no
12. $-6 = 14 - 11n; 2$ — no
13. $7c - (-5) = 26; 3$ — yes
14. $25 - 10z = 15; -1$ — no
15. $-8a - 12 = -4; 1$ — no
16. $20 = \frac{1}{2}t + 25; -10$ — yes
17. $\frac{2}{3}m + 2 = \frac{1}{2}; \frac{1}{2}$ — yes

Write an equation for each sentence.

18. The difference of a number and 7 is 8. $n - 7 = 8$
19. 6 times the sum of a number and 5 is 16. $6(n + 5) = 16$
20. A computer programmer works 40 hours per week. What is an equation that relates the number of weeks w that the programmer works and the number of hours h that the programmer spends working? $h = 40w$
21. Josie is 11 years older than Macy. What is an equation that relates the age of Josie J and the age of Macy M? $J = M + 11$

Use mental math to find the solution of each equation.

22. $t - 7 = 10$ 17
23. $12 = 5 - h$ -7
24. $22 + p = 30$ 8
25. $6 - g = 12$ -6
26. $\frac{x}{4} = 3$ 12
27. $\frac{r}{8} = -6$ -48
28. $4x = 36$ 9
29. $12b = 60$ 5

Practice and Problem Solving WKBK/ All-in-One Resources/Online
Practice page 2

1-8 Practice (continued) — Form G
An Introduction to Equations

Use a table to find the solution of each equation.

30. $4m - 5 = 11$ 4
31. $-3d + 10 = 43$ -11
32. $2 = 3a + 8$ -2
33. $5h - 13 = 12$ 5
34. $-8 = 3y - 2$ -2
35. $8n + 16 = 24$ 1
36. $35 = 7z - 7$ 6
37. $\frac{1}{4}p + 6 = 8$ 8

Use a table to find two consecutive integers between which the solution lies.

38. $7t - 20 = 33$ — between 7 and 8
39. $7.5 = 3.2 - 2.1n$ — between -2 and -3
40. $37d + 48 = 368$ — between 8 and 9
41. The population of a particular village can be modeled by the equation $y = 110x + 56$, where x is the number of years since 1990. In what year were there 1706 people living in the village? 2005
42. **Open-Ended** Write four equations that all have a solution of -10. The equations should consist of one multiplication, one division, one addition, and one subtraction equation. Answers may vary. Sample: $-2x = 20; \frac{x}{5} = -5; x - 4 = -14; x + 3 = -7$
43. There are 68 members of the marching band. The vans the band uses to travel to games each carry 15 passengers. How many vans does the band need to reserve for each away game? 5 vans

Find the solution of each equation using mental math or a table. If the solution lies between two consecutive integers, identify those integers.

44. $d + 8 = 10$ 2
45. $3p - 14 = 8$ — between 7 and 8
46. $8.3 = 4k - 2.5$ — between 2 and 3
47. $c - 8 = -12$ -4
48. $6y - 13 = -13$ 0
49. $15 = 8 + (-a)$ -7
50. $-3 = -\frac{1}{3}h - 10$ 21
51. $21 = 7x + 8$ — between 1 and 2
52. **Writing** Explain the difference between an expression and an equation.
An equation has two different quantities that are equal to each other and an expression does not. An expression can only be simplified whereas an equation can be solved.

All-in-One Resources/Online
Enrichment

1-8 Enrichment
An Introduction to Equations

The relationships you have examined in this lesson are all called linear — that is, the graph of the relation forms a straight line. Linear relationships are convenient because, once you know the equation or rule, the pattern is predictable.

The relationships shown in the tables are linear. Fill in the missing cells in each table.

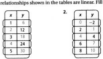

1.

x	y
1	6
2	12
3	18
4	24
5	30

2.

x	y
0	-2
2	1
4	4
6	7
8	10

3.

x	y
1	1
3	5
5	9
7	13
9	17

4. What is the rule or equation for the relationship represented in the table in Exercise 1? $y = 6x$
5. What is the rule or equation for the relationship represented in the table in Exercise 2? $y = \frac{3}{2}x - 2$
6. What is the rule or equation for the relationship represented in the table in Exercise 3? $y = 2x - 1$
7. Make a table of coordinate pairs from the graph shown at the right.

x	y
-1	-2
0	1
1	4

8. What is the rule or equation for the relationship represented in the graph? $y = 3x + 1$
9. What do you notice about the equation and where the line crosses the y-axis on the graph? The line crosses the y-axis at $y = 1$ and there is $+1$ in the equation.

Practice and Problem Solving WKBK/ All-in-One Resources/Online
Think About a Plan

1-8 Think About a Plan
An Introduction to Equations

Deliveries The equation $25 + 0.25p = c$ gives the cost c in dollars that a store charges to deliver an appliance that weighs p pounds. Use the equation and a table to find the weight of an appliance that costs $55 to deliver.

Understanding the Problem

1. What information are you given about the situation? What is the relationship between the delivery charge and the weight of an appliance?
the relationship between cost and weight; $25 + 0.25p = c$

2. What are you being asked to determine?
the weight of an appliance that costs $55 to deliver

Planning the Solution

3. How can you determine the cost to deliver an appliance that weighs 50 pounds?
Substitute 50 for p in the given equation and simplify.

4. Make a table that shows the delivery charge for appliances of various weights. Your table should include the weight of an appliance that produces the desired delivery cost.

Weight (lbs.)	Delivery Charge ($)
10	27.50
60	40
100	50
120	55

Getting an Answer

5. What is the weight of an appliance that costs $55 to deliver?
120 pounds

Practice and Problem Solving WKBK/ All-in-One Resources/Online
Standardized Test Prep

1-8 Standardized Test Prep
An Introduction to Equations

Multiple Choice

For Exercises 1-5, choose the correct letter.

1. Which equation is true? B
   A. $25 - (-18) = 7$
   B. $\frac{1}{3}(-9) - 6 = -9$
   C. $25(-2) + 7 = -39 + 4$
   D. $-19 + 8(-2) = -7(-5)$

2. Which equation has a solution of -6? I
   F. $15x - 20 = 70$
   G. $14 = 6x - 12$
   H. $3x - 8 = -10$
   I. $\frac{1}{2}x - 8 = -11$

3. Which equation has a solution of $\frac{1}{2}$? C
   A. $13x - 12 = 14$
   B. $9x + 15 = 20$
   C. $-6x - 18 = -21$
   D. $-11x = 12x + 12$

4. The money a company received from sales of their product is represented by the equation $y = 45x - 120$, where y is the money in dollars and x is the number of products sold. How many products does the company need to sell in order to receive $3705? G
   F. 42
   G. 85
   H. 105
   I. 166,605

5. Mrs. Decker walks for 30 minutes each day as often as possible. What is an equation that relates the number of days d that Mrs. Decker walks and the number of minutes m that she spends walking? A
   A. $m = 30d$
   B. $d = 30m$
   C. $d = m + 30$
   D. $m = d + 30$

Short Response

6. There are 450 people travelling to watch a playoff football game. Each bus can seat up to 55 people. Write an equation that represents the number of buses it will take to transport the fans. Use a table to find a solution. $55b = f$; 9 buses
[2] Both parts answered correctly.
[1] One part answered correctly.
[0] Neither part answered correctly.

Online Teacher Resource Center
Activities, Games, and Puzzles

1-8 Puzzle: Algebra Connections
An Introduction to Equations

Determine whether the given number is a solution to the equation. Show your work below each problem or on a separate piece of paper.

If the given number is a solution, then circle the problem number in the maze below. For example, you would circle "1" in the maze if 11 is a solution to $-3u + 5 = 28$. Follow the circled numbers as a guide to find the correct path through the maze!

1. $-3u + 5 = 28; 11$ false
2. $4.5 - 0.9y = 2.7; 2$ true
3. $9m - (-7) = 61; 6$ true
4. $\frac{1}{4}z + 7 = 11; 1$ false
5. $10b - (-5) = 75; 7$ true
6. $7x - 5 = 33; 4$ true
7. $5k + 1 = 16; 3$ true
8. $7r - (-35) = 42; -1$ false
9. $\frac{3}{8}t + 2 = 5; 8$ true

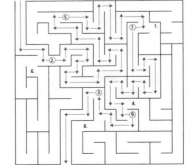

START

Using Tables to Solve Equations

Indiana Academic Standard

A1.2.1 Translate among various representations of linear functions including tables, graphs, words and equations.

You can solve equations by making a table using a graphing calculator.

Activity

A raft floats downriver at 9 mi/h. The distance y the raft travels can be modeled by the equation $y = 9x$, where x is the number of hours. Make a table on a graphing calculator to find how long it takes the raft to travel 153 mi.

Step 1 Enter the equation $y = 9x$ into a graphing calculator.
- Press **y=**. The cursor appears next to Y_1.
- Press 9 **x,t,θ,n** to enter $y = 9x$.

Step 2 Access the table setup feature.
- Press **2nd** **window**.
- TblStart represents the starting value in the table. Enter 1 for TblStart.
- △Tbl represents the change in the value of x as you go from row to row. Enter 1 for △Tbl.

Step 3 Display the table and find the solution.
- Press **2nd** **graph**. Use ▽ to scroll through the table until you find the x-value for which $y = 153$. This x-value is 17. It takes the raft 17 h to travel 153 mi.

```
TABLE SETUP
  Tb1Start = 1
  △Tb1 = 1
Indpnt:   Auto  Ask
Depend:   Auto  Ask
```

```
  X      Y₁
 11      99
 12      108
 13      117
 14      126
 15      135
 16      144
 17      153
Y₁ = 153
```

Exercises

Solve each problem by making a table on a graphing calculator.

1. A town places 560 t of waste in a landfill each month. The amount y of waste in the landfill can be modeled by the equation $y = 560x$, where x is the number of months. How many months will it take to accumulate 11,200 t of waste in the landfill?

2. A coupon gives $15 off a customer's purchase. The total amount y of the customer's purchase can be modeled by $y = x - 15$, where x is the amount of the purchase before the coupon is used. A customer using the coupon pays $17 for a shirt. What was the original price of the shirt?

PowerAlgebra.com | Concept Byte Using Tables to Solve Equations | 59

Guided Instruction

PURPOSE To solve equations by making a table using a graphing calculator

PROCESS Students will
- make a table using a graphing calculator.
- solve equations using the tables they made.

DISCUSS Have students explore the graphing calculator by using basic equations such as $y = 2x$ and $y = -3x$. Make simple changes in settings, and then challenge students to identify how the changes affect the solution.

Activity

In this activity students enter an equation into a graphing calculator and use the table function to find the solution to the equation.

Q If the △ Tbl was entered as 2 instead of 1, how would this change the table? **[It would change both the x- and y-columns. The x-column would increase by 2 instead of 1, which in turn would change the output for the y-column.]**

Q How would this affect the solution to the problem? **[It would make it more difficult because 17 hours would not be displayed on the graphing calculator because the x-column increases by 2. The x-column would only display the even numbers.]**

Answers

Exercises
1. 20 months
2. $32

Guided Instruction

PURPOSE To plot ordered pairs on a coordinate plane

PROCESS Students will
- differentiate between *x*- and *y*-coordinates.
- plot an ordered pair on a coordinate plane.

DISCUSS Before beginning the activity, discuss the components of a coordinate plane. Depending on how your classroom is set up, you may be able to choose the student in the middle of the room to represent the origin. Then have students decide who is sitting on the *x*-axis and *y*-axis and who is in the 1st, 2nd, 3rd, and 4th quadrants.

Activity
In this activity students focus on plotting ordered pairs on a coordinate plane.

> **Q** In what quadrant is an ordered pair with a positive *x*-coordinate and a negative *y*-coordinate? **[Quadrant IV]**
>
> **Q** In what quadrant is an ordered pair with a negative *x*-coordinate and a negative *y*-coordinate? **[Quadrant III]**

ERROR PREVENTION

Students may find this activity easier if they are given two different colored number cubes. One cube should represent positive numbers and the other should represent negative numbers.

Two number lines that intersect at right angles form a **coordinate plane.** The horizontal axis is the **x-axis** and the vertical axis is the **y-axis.** The axes intersect at the **origin** and divide the coordinate plane into four sections called **quadrants.**

An **ordered pair** of numbers names the location of a point in the plane. These numbers are the **coordinates** of the point. Point B has coordinates $(-3, 4)$.

> The first coordinate is the *x*-coordinate. $(-3, 4)$ The second coordinate is the *y*-coordinate.

To reach the point (x, y), you use the *x*-coordinate to tell how far to move right (positive) or left (negative) from the origin. You then use the *y*-coordinate to tell how far to move up (positive) or down (negative).

Activity

Play against a partner using two number cubes and a coordinate grid. One cube represents positive numbers and the other cube represents negative numbers.

- During each turn, a player rolls both cubes and adds the numbers to find an *x*-coordinate. Both cubes are rolled a second time, and the numbers are added to find the *y*-coordinate. The player graphs the resulting ordered pair on the grid.

- The two players take turns, with each player using a different color to graph points. If an ordered pair has already been graphed, the player does not graph a point, and the turn is over.

- Play ends after each player has completed 10 turns. The player with the most points graphed in a quadrant scores 1 for Quadrant I, 2 for Quadrant II, and so on. Points graphed on either axis do not count. If both players graph an equal number of points in a quadrant, both players score 0 for that quadrant.

Exercises

Describe a pair of number cube rolls that would result in a point plotted at the given location.

1. $(-3, 4)$ **2.** $(4, -3)$ **3.** in Quadrant III **4.** the origin

---

Answers

Exercises

1. Answers may vary. Sample: For the sum -3 for the *x*-coordinate, you could roll a 4 on the negative cube and a 1 on the positive cube. For the sum 4 for the *y*-coordinate, you could roll a 1 on the negative cube and a 5 on the positive cube. Check students' work.

2. Answers may vary. Sample: For the sum 4 for the *x*-coordinate, you could roll a 2 on the negative cube and a 6 on the positive cube. For the sum -3 for the *y*-coordinate, you could roll a 5 on the negative cube and a 2 on the positive cube. Check students' work.

3. Answers may vary. The number on the negative cube must be greater than the number on the positive cube. Check students' work.

4. Answers may vary. The number on the negative cube must be the same as the number on the positive cube. Check students' work.

Patterns, Equations, and Graphs

Indiana Academic Standard
A1.2.1 Translate among various representations of linear functions including tables, graphs, words and equations.

Objective To use tables, equations, and graphs to describe relationships

Lesson Vocabulary
• solution of an equation
• inductive reasoning

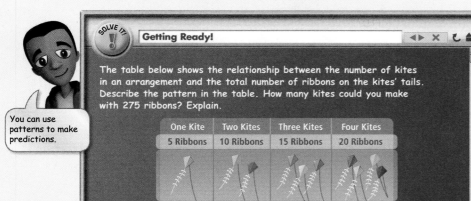

You can use patterns to make predictions.

Getting Ready!

The table below shows the relationship between the number of kites in an arrangement and the total number of ribbons on the kites' tails. Describe the pattern in the table. How many kites could you make with 275 ribbons? Explain.

One Kite	Two Kites	Three Kites	Four Kites
5 Ribbons	10 Ribbons	15 Ribbons	20 Ribbons

In the Solve It, you may have described the pattern using words. You can also use an equation or a graph to describe a pattern.

Essential Understanding Sometimes the value of one quantity can be found if you know the value of another. You can represent the relationship between the quantities in different ways, including tables, equations, and graphs.

You can use an equation with two variables to represent the relationship between two varying quantities. A **solution of an equation** with two variables x and y is any ordered pair (x, y) that makes the equation true.

Plan

How can you tell whether an ordered pair is a solution?
Replace x with the first value in the ordered pair and y with the second value in the ordered pair. Is the resulting equation true?

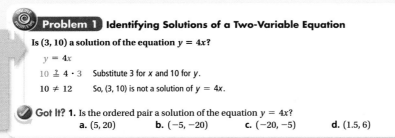

Problem 1 Identifying Solutions of a Two-Variable Equation

Is (3, 10) a solution of the equation $y = 4x$?

$y = 4x$

$10 \stackrel{?}{=} 4 \cdot 3$ Substitute 3 for x and 10 for y.

$10 \neq 12$ So, (3, 10) is not a solution of $y = 4x$.

✓ **Got It?** 1. Is the ordered pair a solution of the equation $y = 4x$?
     a. (5, 20)   **b.** (−5, −20)   **c.** (−20, −5)   **d.** (1.5, 6)

---

1 Interactive Learning

Solve It!

PURPOSE To familiarize students with the patterns that exist in a table of values for a linear equation
PROCESS Students may use patterns in the number of kites and number of ribbons or may make a table of values.

FACILITATE

Q What is the pattern of the total number of ribbons? **[As the number of kites increases by 1, the number of ribbons increases by 5.]**

Q What is the relationship between the number of kites and the total number of ribbons in each arrangement? [The total number of ribbons in each arrangement is 5 times the number of kites in each arrangement.]**

ANSWER See Solve It in Answers on next page.
CONNECT THE MATH While extending the table is a practical solution method for only 6 kites, it is not realistic for a large number of kites. In this lesson, students will formulate equations.

2 Guided Instruction

Problem 1

Q What is a verbal representation of the equation $y = 4x$? **[y is four times the value of x.]**

Got It?

Q How many solutions are there for the equation $y = 4x$? Explain. **[infinite; Every value of x yields a different value for y.]**

1-9 Preparing to Teach

BIG idea Variable   **UbD**
ESSENTIAL UNDERSTANDINGS
• Sometimes the value of one quantity can be found if the value of another is known.
• The relationship between the quantities can be represented in different ways, including tables, equations, and graphs.

Math Background
This lesson teaches variety and flexibility in how to approach math problems. An underlying message that should be learned when studying patterns, equations, and graphs is that *there is more than one way to represent a problem*. Whether the relationship defined by a two-variable equation is demonstrated in using a pattern, a table, or a graph, the relationship remains the same and the only thing that differs is its presentation or appearance.

Introducing the study of two-variable equations will lay a foundation for many of the concepts coming later in the course. The equations in this section are all functions and illustrate the notion of one input paired with one unique output. Making tables for the equations and graphing the equations will prepare students for using tables and graphing when solving systems of equations. Finally, the tables and graphs of the equations introduce students to the characteristics of the graphs of all linear equations in two variables.

Support Student Learning
Use the **Algebra 1 Companion** to engage and support students during instructions. See Lesson Resources at the end of this lesson for details.

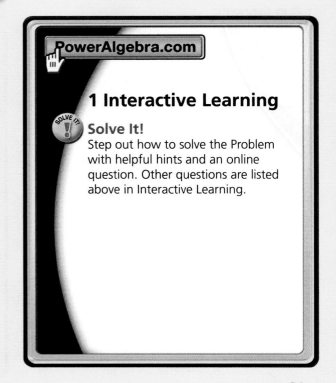

PowerAlgebra.com

1 Interactive Learning

Solve It!
Step out how to solve the Problem with helpful hints and an online question. Other questions are listed above in Interactive Learning.

Problem 2

Q What is a pattern for Carrie's age in the table? **[They increase by 1.]**

Q What is a pattern for Kim's age in the table? **[They increase by 1.]**

Q If x = Kim's age and y = Carrie's age, what equation would represent the data in the table? **[$y = x - 2$]**

Q Where does the graph intersect with the vertical axis? **[(0, 2)]**

Q How many ordered pairs are on the line shown in the graph? Are they all solutions to the equation $y = x + 2$? **[an infinite number; yes]**

Got It?

Q Would the graph still be a straight line if Will were running at a faster pace than Megan? Explain. **[No, because the difference between the laps run would keep increasing.]**

You can represent the same relationship between two variables in several different ways.

Problem 2 Using a Table, an Equation, and a Graph

Ages Both Carrie and her sister Kim were born on October 25, but Kim was born 2 years before Carrie. How can you represent the relationship between Carrie's age and Kim's age in different ways?

Know	Need	Plan
Kim was born 2 years before Carrie.	Different ways to represent the relationship	Use a table, an equation, and a graph.

Step 1 Make a table.

Carrie's and Kim's Ages (years)										
Carrie's Age	1	2	3	4	5	6	7	8	9	10
Kim's Age	3	4	5	6	7	8	9	10	11	12

Step 2 Write an equation.

Let x = Carrie's age. Let y = Kim's age. From the table, you can see that y is always 2 greater than x.

So $y = x + 2$.

Step 3 Draw a graph.

Think

Why does it make sense to connect the points on the graph? A person's age can be any positive real number, and the ages of the girls are always 2 years apart. So every point on the line makes sense in this situation.

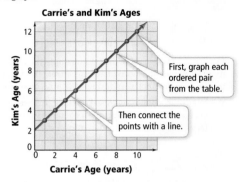

First, graph each ordered pair from the table.

Then connect the points with a line.

Got It? **2. a.** Will runs 6 laps before Megan joins him at the track. They then run together at the same pace. How can you represent the relationship between the number of laps Will runs and the number of laps Megan runs in different ways? Use a table, an equation, and a graph.

 b. **Reasoning** Describe how the graph in Problem 2 above would change if the difference in ages were 5 years instead of 2 years.

Answers

Solve It!

Each kite has 5 ribbons on its tail. The number of ribbons is 5 times the number of kites. With 275 ribbons, you could make 55 kites.

Got It?

1. a. yes **2. a.**
 b. yes
 c. no
 d. yes

Megan's and Will's Laps					
Megan's laps	1	2	3	4	5
Will's laps	7	8	9	10	11

$y = x + 6$;

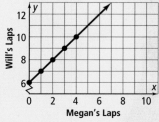

Megan's and Will's Laps

b. The graph would start at (0, 5) instead of (0, 2); y would always be 5 greater than x.

 PowerAlgebra.com

2 Guided Instruction

Each Problem is worked out and supported online.

Problem 1
Identifying Solutions of a Two-Variable Equation
Animated

Problem 2
Using a Table, an Equation, and a Graph
Animated

Problem 3
Extending a Pattern
Animated

Support in Algebra 1 Companion
• Vocabulary
• Key Concepts
• Got It?

Inductive reasoning is the process of reaching a conclusion based on an observed pattern. You can use inductive reasoning to predict values.

 Problem 3 Extending a Pattern

The table shows the relationship between the number of blue tiles and the total number of tiles in each figure. Extend the pattern. What is the total number of tiles in a figure with 8 blue tiles?

 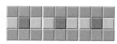

Tiles

Number of Blue Tiles, x	Total Number of Tiles, y
1	9
2	18
3	27
4	36
5	45

Think

Should you connect the points on the graph with a solid line?
No. The number of tiles must be a whole number. Use a dotted line to see the trend.

Method 1 Draw a graph.

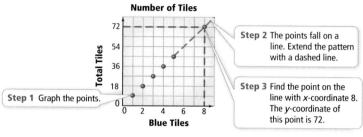

Number of Tiles

Step 1 Graph the points.

Step 2 The points fall on a line. Extend the pattern with a dashed line.

Step 3 Find the point on the line with x-coordinate 8. The y-coordinate of this point is 72.

The total number of tiles is 72.

Method 2 Write an equation.

$y = 9x$ The total number of tiles is 9 times the number of blue tiles.

$= 9(8)$ Substitute 8 for x.

$= 72$ Simplify.

The total number of tiles is 72.

 Got It? **3.** Use the tile figure from Problem 3.
   a. Make a table showing the number of orange tiles and the total number of tiles in each figure. How many tiles in all will be in a figure with 24 orange tiles?
   b. Make a table showing the number of blue tiles and the number of yellow tiles in each figure. How many yellow tiles will be in a figure with 24 blue tiles?

Problem 3

Q What is a pattern for the x-values in the table shown? **[They increase by 1.]**

Q What is a pattern for the y-values in the table shown? **[They increase by 9.]**

Q Why is the graph in Problem 3 steeper than the graph in Problem 2? **[The y-values in Problem 2 are only increasing by 1, whereas the y-values in Problem 3 are increasing by 9.]**

Q How could you use the equation $y = 9x$ to determine the number of red tiles given that the total number of tiles is 108? **[Substitute 108 for y, and use trial and error to determine the correct value for x.]**

Got It?

Elicit from students that writing an equation is the most efficient way to solve these problems and many other problems. Use this efficiency to motivate students to learn to write algebraic equations.

Additional Problems

1. Is (5, 15) a solution of the equation $y = 3x$?

   ANSWER yes

2. You have 4 more left socks than right socks. How can you represent the relationship between the number of left and right socks in three different ways?

   ANSWER x = number of right socks
            y = number of left socks

$y = x + 4$

x	y
8	12
9	13
10	14
11	15
12	16

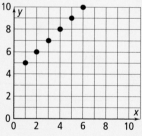

3. The table shows the relationship between the number of chairs and the total number of legs. Extend the pattern. What is the total number of legs on 10 chairs?

x	y
1	4
2	8
3	12
4	16
5	20

   ANSWER 40

Answers

Got It? (continued)

3. a.

Orange tiles	4	8	12	16
Total tiles	9	18	27	36

54 tiles

b.

Blue tiles	1	2	3	4
Yellow tiles	2	4	6	8

48 yellow tiles

3 Lesson Check

Do you know HOW?
- If students have difficulty with Exercise 3, then have them review Problem 2.

Do you UNDERSTAND?
- If students have difficulty with Exercise 7, then have them review Problem 1.

Close

> **Q** What is true of a graph of an equation that is a straight line? **[The difference between the *y*-values remains constant.]**

Lesson Check

Do you know HOW?

1. Is $(2, 4)$ a solution of the equation $y = x - 2$?

2. Is $(-3, -9)$ a solution of the equation $y = 3x$?

3. Drinks at the fair cost $2.50. Use a table, an equation, and a graph to represent the relationship between the number of drinks bought and the cost.

4. **Exercise** On a treadmill, you burn 11 Cal in 1 min, 22 Cal in 2 min, 33 Cal in 3 min, and so on. How many Calories do you burn in 10 min?

Do you UNDERSTAND?

5. **Vocabulary** Describe the difference between inductive reasoning and deductive reasoning.

6. **Compare and Contrast** How is writing an equation to represent a situation involving two variables similar to writing an equation to represent a situation involving only one variable? How are they different?

7. **Reasoning** Which of $(3, 5)$, $(4, 6)$, $(5, 7)$, and $(6, 8)$ are solutions of $y = x + 2$? What is the pattern in the solutions of $y = x + 2$?

Practice and Problem-Solving Exercises

(A) Practice   Tell whether the given equation has the ordered pair as a solution.   **See Problem 1.**

8. $y = x + 6$; $(0, 6)$ 9. $y = 1 - x$; $(2, 1)$ 10. $y = -x + 3$; $(4, 1)$

11. $y = 6x$; $(3, 16)$ 12. $-x = y$; $(-3.1, 3.1)$ 13. $y = -4x$; $(-2, 8)$

14. $y = x + \frac{2}{3}$; $\left(1, \frac{1}{3}\right)$ 15. $y = x - \frac{3}{4}$; $\left(2, 1\frac{1}{4}\right)$ 16. $\frac{x}{5} = y$; $(-10, -2)$

Use a table, an equation, and a graph to represent each relationship.   **See Problem 2.**

17. Ty is 3 years younger than Bea.

18. The number of checkers is 24 times the number of checkerboards.

19. The number of triangles is $\frac{1}{3}$ the number of sides.

20. Gavin makes $8.50 for each lawn he mows.

Use the table to draw a graph and answer the question.   **See Problem 3.**

21. The table shows the height in inches of stacks of tires. Extend the pattern. What is the height of a stack of 7 tires?

Stacks of Tires

Number of Tires, x	Height of Stack, y
1	8
2	16
3	24
4	32

22. The table shows the length in centimeters of a scarf you are knitting. Suppose the pattern continues. How long is the scarf after 8 days?

Knitted Scarf

Number of Days, x	Length of Scarf, y
1	12.5
2	14.5
3	16.5
4	18.5

---

3 Lesson Check

For a digital lesson check, use the Got It questions.

Support in Algebra 1 Companion
- Lesson Check

4 Practice

Assign homework to individual students or to an entire class.

Answers

Lesson Check

1. no   **2.** yes

3.

Drink Cost

Drinks bought	1	2	3	4
Cost ($)	2.50	5	7.50	10

$y = 2.50x$;

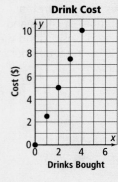

Drink Cost

4. 110 calories

5. With inductive reasoning, conclusions are reached by observing patterns. With deductive reasoning, conclusions are reached by reasoning logically from given facts.

6. Answers may vary. Sample: Both equations contain unknown values. An equation in one-variable represents a situation with one unknown quantity. An equation in 2 variable represents a situation where two variables quantities have a relationship.

7. All; *y* is 2 more than *x*.

Practice and Problem-Solving Exercises

8. yes   **9.** no   **10.** no   **11.** no

12. yes   **13.** yes   **14.** no   **15.** yes

16. yes

Use the table to write an equation and answer the question.

23. The table shows the heights in inches of trees after they have been planted. What is the height of a tree that is 64 in. tall in its pot?

Tree Height

Height in Pot, x	Height Without Pot, y
30	18
36	24
42	30
48	36

24. The table shows amounts earned for pet sitting. How much is earned for a 9-day job?

Pet Sitting

Days, x	Dollars, y
1	17
2	34
3	51
4	68

25. Patterns Make a table and draw a graph to show the relationship between the number of houses and the number of windows. What is the number of windows in 9 houses?

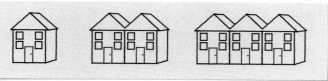

 Apply **Tell whether the given ordered pair is a solution of the equation.**

26. $y = 2x + 7$; $(-2, 3)$

27. $y = -4x - 3$; $(0, 3)$

28. $y = 5x - 8$; $(2, -2)$

29. $y = 9 - 2x$; $(-2, 5)$

30. $-\frac{1}{4}x + 6 = y$; $(2, 4)$

31. $y = 3 - \frac{x}{5}$; $\left(\frac{1}{2}, \frac{1}{10}\right)$

32. $y = 11 - 2x$; $(5, 1)$

33. $1.9x - 4 = y$; $(2, 0.2)$

34. $y = -1.2x - 2.6$; $(3.5, 6.8)$

35. Think About a Plan The table shows how long it takes Kayla to learn new songs. How many hours does Kayla need to practice to learn 9 songs?
- From row to row, how much does the number of hours h increase? How much does the number of songs s increase?
- By how many rows would you need to extend the table to solve the problem?

Kayla's Piano Practice

Hours, h	Songs Learned, s
1.5	1
3.0	2
4.5	3
6.0	4

36. Error Analysis A student reasons that $(4, 1)$ is a solution of $y = 3x + 1$ because $x = 1$ when $y = 4$. Explain and correct the student's error.

37. Air Travel Use the table at the right. How long will the jet take to travel 5390 mi?

Passenger Jet Travel

Hours, h	1	2	3	4
Miles, m	490	980	1470	1960

4 Practice

ASSIGNMENT GUIDE

Basic: 8–25 all, 26–34 even, 35–38

Average: 9–25 odd, 26–39

Advanced: 9–25 odd, 26–41

Standardized Test Prep: 42–45

Mixed Review: 46–60

Reasoning exercises have blue headings.

Applications exercises have red headings.

EXERCISE 37: Use the Think About a Plan worksheet in the **Practice and Problem Solving Workbook** (also available in the Teaching Resources in print and online) to further support students' development in becoming independent learners.

HOMEWORK QUICK CHECK

To check students' understanding of key skills and concepts, go over Exercises 9, 21, 35, 37, and 38.

17.

Bea's and Ty's Ages

Bea's age	4	5	6	7
Ty's age	1	2	3	4

$y = x - 3$;

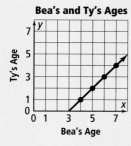

Bea's and Ty's Ages

18.

Checker Boards and Checkers

Checker boards	1	2	3	4
Checkers	24	48	72	96

$y = 24x$;

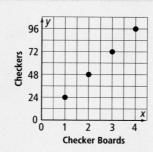

19.

Sides and Triangles

Number of sides	3	6	9	12
Number of triangles	1	2	3	4

$y = \frac{1}{3}x$;

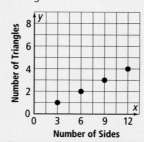

20.

Amount Earned Mowing Lawns				
Lawns mowed	1	2	3	4
Amount earned ($)	8.50	17	25.50	34

$y = 8.50x$;

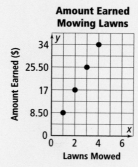

21. 56 in.

22. 26.5 cm

23–37. See next page.

Answers

Practice and Problem-Solving Exercises
(continued)

23. $y = x - 12$; 52 in.

24. $y = 17x$; $153

25.

Number of Houses	1	2	3	4	5
Number of Windows	4	8	12	16	20

36 windows;

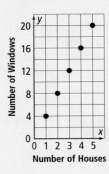

26. yes

27. no

28. no

29. no

30. no

31. no

32. yes

33. no

34. no

35. 13.5 h

36. coordinates are reversed; the student should write (1, 4).

37. 11 h

38. They are both correct because subtracting 6 from x is the same as adding the opposite of 6 to x.

39. Check students' work.

40.

Temperature Change Over Time

Hours	0	.75	1.5	2.25
Temperature (°F)	60	62	64	66

$y = \frac{8}{3}x + 60$

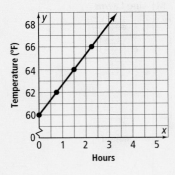

---

38. Reasoning Savannah looks at the table shown and says the equation $y = x - 6$ represents the pattern. Mary says $y = x + (-6)$ represents the pattern. Who is correct? Explain.

x	y
0	−6
1	−5
2	−4
3	−3

39. Open-Ended Think of a real-world pattern. Describe the pattern using words and an equation with two variables. Define the variables.

Ⓒ **Challenge** **40. Temperature** Suppose the temperature starts at 60°F and rises 2°F every 45 min. Use a table, an equation, and a graph to describe the relationship between the amount of time that has passed in hours and the temperature.

41. Use a table, a graph, and an equation to represent the ordered pairs (2, −5.5), (−3, −0.5), (1, −4.5), (0, −3.5), (−3.5, 0), and (−1, −2.5).

Standardized Test Prep

SAT/ACT **42.** Use the graph. What is the total price for 4 bags of seeds?
  - Ⓐ $.50
  - Ⓑ $2.00
  - Ⓒ $4.00
  - Ⓓ $8.00

Seed Cost

43. What is the simplified form of the expression $-5(n - 2)$?
  - Ⓕ $-7n$
  - Ⓖ $-5n - 2$
  - Ⓗ $-5n + 10$
  - Ⓘ $n + 10$

44. If $a = 3$ and $b = -2$, what does $-2b - a$ equal?
  - Ⓐ -9
  - Ⓑ -7
  - Ⓒ -1
  - Ⓓ 1

45. What is the value of -3^4?
  - Ⓕ -81
  - Ⓖ -12
  - Ⓗ 12
  - Ⓘ 81

Mixed Review

Tell whether the given number is a solution of each equation. ◀ See Lesson 1-8.

46. $3x + 7 = 10$; 0   **47.** $80 = 4a$; 20   **48.** $10 = -5t$; -2

Give an example that illustrates each property. ◀ See Lesson 1-4.

49. Commutative Property of Addition   **50.** Associative Property of Multiplication

51. Identity Property of Multiplication   **52.** Zero Property of Addition

Get Ready! To prepare for Lesson 2-1, do Exercises 53–60. ◀ See Lesson 1-5.

Find each sum or difference.

53. $12 + (-3)$ **54.** $-7 + 4$ **55.** $-8 + (-6)$ **56.** $-42 + 15$

57. $32 - (-8)$ **58.** $-18 - 12$ **59.** $-15 - (-14)$ **60.** $-76 - 5$

41.

x	−3.5	−3	−1	0	1	2
y	0	−0.5	−2.5	−3.5	−4.5	−5.5

$y = -x - 3.5$;

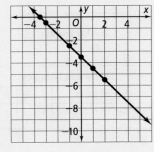

42. B

43. H

44. D

45. F

46. no

47. yes

48. yes

49. Check students' work.

50. Check students' work.

51. Check students' work.

52. Check students' work.

53. 9

54. −3

55. −14

56. −27

57. 40

58. −30

59. −1

60. −81

Lesson Resources

Additional Instructional Support

Algebra 1 Companion

Students can use the **Algebra 1 Companion** worktext (4 pages) as you teach the lesson. Use the Companion to support

- New Vocabulary
- Key Concepts
- Got It for each Problem
- Lesson Check

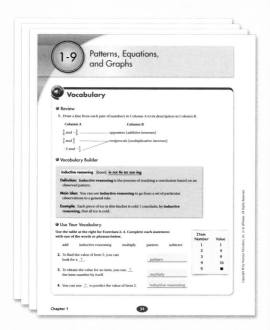

ELL Support

Assess Understanding Demonstrate different types of equations by writing some on the board and using gestures and repetitive language as you think aloud what type of equation it is. Have volunteers write equations on the board. Have the volunteers repeat your language and gestures. When a volunteer writes a non-example, say "Great. This is **NOT** an equation." Explain why it is not an equation. Challenge students by asking them to write their own examples and non-examples.

Focus on Language Ask students to write about tables, equations, and graphs. Have students answer the following questions: "What is an equation?", "How do you graph an equation?", "Why do you graph an equation?", and "Why do you use a table?" Ask for student volunteers to share their work. Display student work for others to appreciate.

5 Assess & Remediate

Lesson Quiz

1. Is $(-3, 7)$ a solution of the equation $y = 4x + 15$?
2. **Do you UNDERSTAND?** Melanie's dog is 3 years older than her cat. Let x represent the age of the cat and y the age of the dog. Express this relationship in an equation, a table, and a graph.
3. The table shows the number of eggs, y, in x cartons. How many eggs are there in 15 cartons?

x	y
1	12
2	24
3	36
4	48
5	60

ANSWERS TO LESSON QUIZ

1. no
2. $y = x + 3$

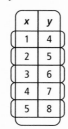

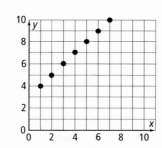

3. 180 eggs

PRESCRIPTION FOR REMEDIATION

Use the student work on the Lesson Quiz to prescribe a differentiated review assignment.

Points	Differentiated Remediation
0–1	Intervention
2	On-level
3	Extension

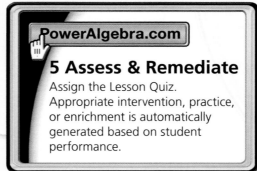

PowerAlgebra.com

5 Assess & Remediate

Assign the Lesson Quiz. Appropriate intervention, practice, or enrichment is automatically generated based on student performance.

Intervention

- **Reteaching** (2 pages) Provides reteaching and practice exercises for the key lesson concepts. Use with struggling students or absent students.
- **English Language Learner Support** Helps students develop and reinforce mathematical vocabulary and key concepts.

All-in-One Resources/Online
Reteaching

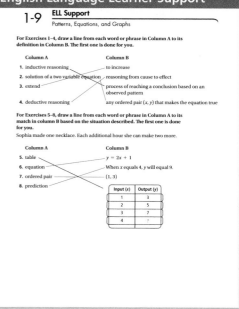

All-in-One Resources/Online
English Language Learner Support

Differentiated Remediation *continued*

On-Level

- **Practice** (2 pages) Provides extra practice for each lesson. For simpler practice exercises, use the Form K Practice pages found in the All-in-One Teaching Resources and online.

- **Think About a Plan** Helps students develop specific problem-solving skills and strategies by providing scaffolded guiding questions.

- **Standardized Test Prep** Focuses on all major exercises, all major question types, and helps students prepare for the high-stakes assessments.

Extension

- **Enrichment** Provides students with interesting problems and activities that extend the concepts of the lesson.

- **Activities, Games, and Puzzles** Worksheets that can be used for concepts development, enrichment, and for fun!

Practice and Problem Solving WKBK/ All-in-One Resources/Online
Practice page 1

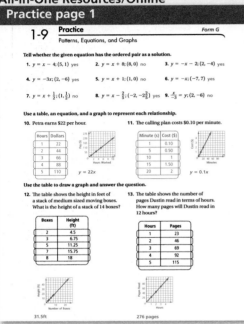

Practice and Problem Solving WKBK/ All-in-One Resources/Online
Practice page 2

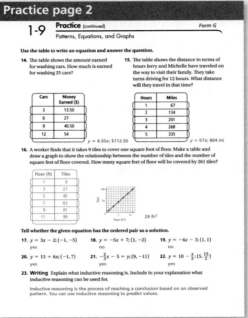

All-in-One Resources/Online
Enrichment

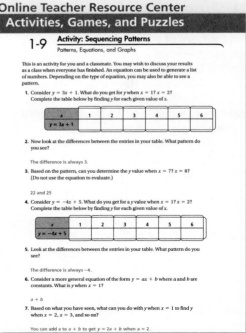

Practice and Problem Solving WKBK/ All-in-One Resources/Online
Think About a Plan

Practice and Problem Solving WKBK/ All-in-One Resources/Online
Standardized Test Prep

Online Teacher Resource Center
Activities, Games, and Puzzles

1 Pull It All Together

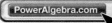
To solve these problems, you will pull together many concepts and skills related to expressions, real-number properties and operations, and equations.

BIG idea Variable

You can use variables to represent quantities that are unknown or vary and to write expressions and equations.

Task 1

Solve. Show all of your work and explain your steps.

A riding-stable manager is planning a nutritional diet for 6 horses. The manager finds the table below in a guide about horse health. The cost of 1000 Calories of horse feed is $.15. What is the cost per day to feed the 6 horses? (*Hint:* First, try writing an expression for the number of daily Calories needed for h horses.)

Calories Needed				
Number of Horses	1	2	3	4
Daily Calories Needed	15,000	30,000	45,000	60,000

Task 2

Use the table at the right to complete each part.

a. Copy the table. Extend the table by writing expressions for y when $x = 5, 6,$ and 7.
b. Simplify each expression for y in your table from part (a). What pattern do you notice in the simplified expressions?
c. Write an equation that relates x and y. Use your equation to find the value of y when $x = 15$.

x	y
1	1
2	1 + 2
3	1 + 2 + 4
4	1 + 2 + 4 + 8

BIG idea Properties

The properties of real numbers describe relationships that are always true. The properties of real numbers are true in both arithmetic and algebra. You can use them to rewrite expressions.

Task 3

Solve. Show all of your work and explain your steps.

You are buying gifts for 10 people. You decide to buy each person either a CD or a DVD. A CD costs $12 and a DVD costs $20.

a. Let c = the number of CDs you decide to buy. What is an expression in terms of c for the number of DVDs you buy?
b. What is an expression in terms of c for the cost of the CDs? For the cost of the DVDs?
c. Write and simplify an expression in terms of c for the *total* cost of all the gifts you buy. What properties of real numbers did you use to simplify the expression?

Performance Task

Pull It All Together

The concepts and skills required to solve these problems are from several lessons within this chapter and from the previous chapter. As students solve these problems, they will demonstrate their reasoning strategies and their growth as independent problem solvers.

The following questions are designed for you to:
• Help support students as they do the Tasks.
• Gauge the amount of support a student needs as he or she progresses to becoming an independent problem solver.

Task 1
• What pattern is in the Number of Horses row in the table?
• What pattern is in the Daily Calories Needed row in the table?
• What is the relationship between the number of horses and the number of daily calories needed?

Task 2
• What is the expression for y when $x = 5$?
• Is it easier to continually extend the table, or to obtain a rule for the pattern? Explain.

Task 3
• How many variables do you need to define?
• What is the coefficient on each variable?

Assess Performance UbD

Analytic Holistic Scoring

Holistic scoring provides feedback to students to help them become autonomous, confident problem solvers. Holistic scoring considers the entire solution to evaluate students' strategies, process, and answers. Use the rubric below to evaluate students' work for Pull It All Together and for Performance Tasks found in the Teaching Resources.

Understanding the Problem

2	complete understanding of the problem
1	part of the problem misunderstood or misinterpreted
0	complete misunderstanding of the problem

Planning a Solution

2	plan could lead to a correct solution if implemented properly
1	partially correct plan based on part of the problem interpreted correctly
0	no attempt or totally inappropriate plan

Getting an Answer

2	correct answer and correct label for the answer
1	copying error; computational error; partial answer for a problem with multiple answers
0	no answer or wrong answer based on an inappropriate plan

Developing Autonomy

2	completed the problem without help
1	needed one or two hints
0	could not work the problem without extensive guidance

SOLUTION OUTLINES

Task 1

First step: Write an expression that represents daily recommended Calorie intake c for h horses. (Answer: $c = 15000h$)

Second step: Find the daily number of Calories needed for 6 horses. (Answer: 90,000 Calories)

Third step: Write an expression that represents the number n of groups of 1000 Calories of feed c the horses need each day. $\left(\text{Answer: } n = \frac{c}{1000}\right)$

Fourth step: Find the number of groups of 1000 Calories of feed 6 horses need each day. (Answer: 90)

Fifth step: Write an expression that represents the cost y of n groups of 1000 Calories of feed. (Answer: $y = 0.15n$)

Sixth step: Find the cost of 90 groups of 1000 Calories of feed. (Answer: $13.50)

Task 2–3. See next page.

Essential Questions

BIG idea **Variable**

ESSENTIAL QUESTION How can you represent quantities, patterns, and relationships?

ANSWER You can use variables to represent quantities and to write algebraic expressions and equations.

BIG ideas **Properties**

ESSENTIAL QUESTION How are properties related to algebra?

ANSWER The properties of real numbers describe relationships that are always true. You can use them to rewrite expressions.

---

① Chapter Review

Connecting **BIG** ideas and Answering the Essential Questions

1 Variable
You can use variables to represent quantities and to write algebraic expressions and equations.

Variables and Expressions (Lesson 1-1)
a number n plus 3 |---- ? ----|
$n + 3$ | n | 3 |

Patterns and Equations (Lessons 1-8 and 1-9)
1 variable: $x + 3 = 5$
2 variables: $y = 2x$

2 Properties
The properties of real numbers describe relationships that are always true. You can use them to rewrite expressions.

Operations With Real Numbers (Lessons 1-2, 1-5, and 1-6)
2^5 $0 \cdot 3$ $2 + (-5)$ $7(-3)$

Properties (Lessons 1-4 and 1-7)
$a \cdot b = b \cdot a$ $(a \cdot b) \cdot c = a \cdot (b \cdot c)$
$a(b + c) = ab + ac$

Chapter Vocabulary

- absolute value (p. 31)
- additive inverse (p. 32)
- algebraic expression (p. 4)
- base (p. 10)
- coefficient (p. 48)
- constant (p. 48)
- counterexample (p. 25)
- deductive reasoning (p. 25)
- Distributive Property (p. 46)
- element of the set (p. 17)
- equation (p. 53)
- equivalent expressions (p. 23)
- evaluate (p. 12)
- exponent (p. 10)
- inductive reasoning (p. 63)
- inequality (p. 19)
- integer (p. 18)
- irrational number (p. 18)
- like terms (p. 48)
- multiplicative inverse (p. 40)
- natural number (p. 18)
- numerical expression (p. 4)
- open sentence (p. 53)
- opposite (p. 32)
- order of operations (p. 11)
- perfect square (p. 17)
- power (p. 10)
- quantity (p. 4)
- radical (p. 16)
- radicand (p. 16)
- rational number (p. 18)
- real number (p. 18)
- reciprocal (p. 41)
- set (p. 17)
- simplify (p. 10)
- solution of an equation (p. 54, 61)
- square root (p. 16)
- subset (p. 17)
- term (p. 48)
- variable (p. 4)
- whole number (p. 18)

Choose the correct term to complete each sentence.

1. Real numbers that you cannot represent as a quotient of two integers are _?_ numbers.

2. The sum of a number and its _?_ equals zero.

3. You can simplify an expression by combining _?_.

4. _?_ is a number's distance from zero on a number line.

5. When you make conclusions based on patterns you observe, you use _?_.

Summative Questions **UbD**

Use the following prompts as you review this chapter with your students. The prompts are designed to help you assess your students' understanding of the Big Ideas they have studied.

- What ways can you represent a pattern?
- What properties can you use to rewrite expressions as equivalent ones?
- What order should you use to simplify numeric expressions?

Pull It All Together (continued)

Task 2

a.

x	y
1	1
2	1 + 2
3	1 + 2 + 4
4	1 + 2 + 4 + 8
5	1 + 2 + 4 + 8 + 16
6	1 + 2 + 4 + 8 + 16 + 32
7	1 + 2 + 4 + 8 + 16 + 32 + 64

b.

x	y
1	1
2	3
3	7
4	15
5	31
6	63
7	127

Answers may vary. Sample: The values of y increase by a higher power of 2 in each row.

c. $y = 2^x - 1$; $y = 32,767$

Task 3

a. $10 - c$

b. $12c$; $20(10 - c)$

c. First step: Write an expression for the total cost of all the gifts. [Answer: $12c + 20(10 - c)$]

Second step: Use the Distributive Property to simplify the second term in the expression. (Answer: $12c + 200 - 20c$)

Third step: Use the Commutative Property of Addition to rewrite the expression so that like terms are next to each other. (Answer: $12c - 20c + 200$)

Fourth step: Combine like terms. (Answer: $-8c + 200$)

1-1 Variables and Expressions

Quick Review

A **variable** is a symbol, usually a letter, that represents values of a variable quantity. For example, *d* often represents distance. An **algebraic expression** is a mathematical phrase that includes one or more variables. A **numerical expression** is a mathematical phrase involving numbers and operation symbols, but no variables.

Example

What is an algebraic expression for the word phrase *3 less than half a number x*?

You can represent "half a number *x*" as $\frac{x}{2}$. Then subtract 3 to get $\frac{x}{2} - 3$.

Exercises

Write an algebraic expression for each word phrase.

6. the product of a number *w* and 737

7. the difference of a number *q* and 8

8. the sum of a number *x* and 84

9. 9 more than the product of 51 and a number *t*

10. 14 less than the quotient of 63 and a number *h*

11. a number *b* less the quotient of a number *k* and 5

Write a word phrase for each algebraic expression.

12. $12 + a$

13. $r - 31$

14. $19t$

15. $b \div 3$

16. $7c - 3$

17. $2 + \frac{x}{8}$

18. $\frac{y}{11} - 6$

19. $21d + 13$

1-2 Order of Operations and Evaluating Expressions

Quick Review

To **evaluate** an algebraic expression, first substitute a given number for each variable. Then simplify the numerical expression using the order of operations.

1. Do operation(s) inside grouping symbols.

2. Simplify powers.

3. Multiply and divide from left to right.

4. Add and subtract from left to right.

Example

A student studies with a tutor for 1 hour each week and studies alone for *h* hours each week. What is an expression for the total hours spent studying each week? Evaluate the expression for *h* = 5.

The expression is $h + 1$. To evaluate the expression for $h = 5$, substitute 5 for *h*: $(5) + 1 = 6$.

Exercises

Simplify each expression.

20. 9^2

21. 5^3

22. $\left(\frac{1}{6}\right)^2$

23. $7^2 \div 5$

24. $(2^4 - 6)^2$

25. $(3^3 - 4) + 5^2$

Evaluate each expression for c = 3 and d = 5.

26. $d^3 \div 15$

27. $(2 + d)^2 - 3^2$

28. $cd^2 + 4$

29. $(3c^2 - 3d)^2 - 21$

30. The expression $6s^2$ represents the surface area of a cube with edges of length *s*.

   a. What is the cube's surface area when $s = 6$?

   b. **Reasoning** Explain how a cube's surface area changes if you divide *s* by 2 in the expression $6s^2$.

31. A race car travels at 205 mi/h. How far does the car travel in 3 h?

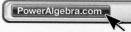

| **Chapter 1** Chapter Review | 69 |

Answers

Chapter Review

1. irrational

2. opposite or additive inverse

3. like terms

4. absolute value

5. inductive reasoning

6. $737w$

7. $q - 8$

8. $x + 84$

9. $51t + 9$

10. $\frac{63}{h} - 14$

11. $b - \frac{k}{5}$

12. the sum of 12 and a number *a*

13. 31 less than a number *r*

14. the product of 19 and a number *t*

15. the quotient of *b* and 3

16. 3 less than the product of 7 and *c*

17. the sum of 2 and the quotient of *x* and 8

18. 6 less than the quotient of *y* and 11

19. 13 more than the product of 21 and *d*

20. 81

21. 125

22. $\frac{1}{36}$

23. 9.8

24. 100

25. 48

26. $8\frac{1}{3}$

27. 40

28. 79

29. 123

30. a. 216

   b. The surface area is reduced to a fourth of its previous value.

31. 615 mi

Answers

Chapter Review (continued)

32. irrational

33. rational

34. irrational

35. rational

36. 10

37. 7

38. 5

39. rational numbers, integers

40. rational numbers

41. irrational numbers

42. rational numbers, whole numbers, natural numbers, integers

43. rational numbers

44. rational numbers

45. $-1\frac{4}{5}$, $-1\frac{2}{3}$, 1.6

46. -0.8, $\frac{7}{9}$, $\sqrt{3}$

47. $9w - 31$

48. -96

49. 0

50. $41 - 4t$

51. 1

52. yes

53. no

54. no

55. no

1-3 Real Numbers and the Number Line

Quick Review

The rational numbers and irrational numbers form the **set** of **real numbers.**

A **rational number** is any number that you can write as $\frac{a}{b}$, where a and b are integers and $b \neq 0$. The rational numbers include all positive and negative integers, as well as fractions, mixed numbers, and terminating and repeating decimals.

Irrational numbers cannot be represented as the quotient of two integers. They include the square roots of all positive integers that are not perfect squares.

Example

Is the number rational or irrational?

Ⓐ -5.422 rational

Ⓑ $\sqrt{7}$ irrational

Exercises

Tell whether each number is rational or irrational.

32. π **33.** $-\frac{1}{2}$

34. $\sqrt{\frac{2}{3}}$ **35.** $0.\overline{57}$

Estimate each square root. Round to the nearest integer.

36. $\sqrt{99}$ **37.** $\sqrt{48}$ **38.** $\sqrt{30}$

Name the subset(s) of the real numbers to which each number belongs.

39. -17 **40.** $\frac{13}{62}$ **41.** $\sqrt{94}$

42. $\sqrt{100}$ **43.** 4.288 **44.** $1\frac{2}{3}$

Order the numbers in each exercise from least to greatest.

45. $-1\frac{2}{3}$, 1.6, $-1\frac{4}{5}$ **46.** $\frac{7}{9}$, -0.8, $\sqrt{3}$

1-4 Properties of Real Numbers

Quick Review

You can use properties such as the ones below to simplify and evaluate expressions.

Commutative Properties	$-2 + 7 = 7 + (-2)$
	$3 \times 4 = 4 \times 3$
Associative Properties	$2 \times (14 \times 3) = (2 \times 14) \times 3$
	$3 + (12 + 2) = (3 + 12) + 2$
Identity Properties	$-6 + 0 = -6$
	$21 \times 1 = 21$
Zero Property of Multiplication	$-7 \times 0 = 0$
Multiplication Property of -1	$6 \cdot (-1) = -6$

Example

Use an identity property to simplify $-\frac{7ab}{a}$.

$-\frac{7ab}{a} = -7b \cdot \frac{a}{a} = -7b \cdot 1 = -7b$

Exercises

Simplify each expression. Justify each step.

47. $-8 + 9w + (-23)$

48. $\frac{6}{5} \cdot (-10 \cdot 8)$

49. $\left(\frac{4}{3} \cdot 0\right) \cdot (-20)$

50. $53 + (-12) + (-4t)$

51. $\frac{6 + 3}{9}$

Tell whether the expressions in each pair are equivalent.

52. $(5 - 2)c$ and $c \cdot 3$

53. $41 + z + 9$ and $41 \cdot z \cdot 9$

54. $\frac{81xy}{3x}$ and $9xy$

55. $\frac{11t}{(5 + 7 - 11)}$ and t

1-5 and 1-6 Operations With Real Numbers

Quick Review

To add numbers with different signs, find the difference of their **absolute values**. Then use the sign of the addend with the greater absolute value.

$$3 + (-4) = -(4 - 3) = -1$$

To subtract, add the opposite.

$$9 - (-5) = 9 + 5 = 14$$

The product or quotient of two numbers with the same sign is positive: $5 \cdot 5 = 25$ $(-5) \cdot (-5) = 25$

The product or quotient of two numbers with different signs is negative: $6 \cdot (-6) = -36$ $-36 \div 6 = -6$

Example

Cave explorers descend to a site that has an elevation of -1.3 mi. (Negative elevation means below sea level.) The explorers descend another 0.6 mi before they stop to rest. What is the elevation at their resting point?

$$-1.3 + (-0.6) = -1.9$$

The elevation at their resting point is -1.9 mi.

Exercises

Find each sum. Use a number line.

56. $1 + 4$ **57.** $3 + (-8)$ **58.** $-2 + (-7)$

Simplify each expression.

59. $-5.6 + 7.4$ **60.** -12^2

61. $-5(-8)$ **62.** $4.5 \div (-1.5)$

63. $-13 + (-6)$ **64.** $-9 - (-12)$

65. $(-2)(-2)(-2)$ **66.** $-54 \div (-0.9)$

Evaluate each expression for $p = 5$ and $q = -3$.

67. $-3q + 7$ **68.** $-(4q)$

69. $q - 8$ **70.** $5p - 6$

71. $-(2p)^2$ **72.** $7q - 7p$

73. $(pq)^2$ **74.** $2q \div 4p$

1-7 The Distributive Property

Quick Review

Terms with exactly the same variable factors are **like terms**. You can combine like terms and use the Distributive Property to simplify expressions.

Distributive Property $a(b + c) = ab + ac$

$a(b - c) = ab - ac$

Example

Simplify $7t + (3 - 4t)$.

$7t + (3 - 4t) = 7t + (-4t + 3)$	Commutative Property
$= (7t + (-4t)) + 3$	Associative Property
$= (7 + (-4))t + 3$	Distributive Property
$= 3t + 3$	Simplify.

Exercises

Simplify each expression.

75. $5(2x - 3)$ **76.** $-2(7 - a)$

77. $(-j + 8)\frac{1}{2}$ **78.** $3v^2 - 2v^2$

79. $2(3y - 3)$ **80.** $(6y - 1)\frac{1}{4}$

81. $(24 - 24y)\frac{1}{4}$ **82.** $6y - 3 - 5y$

83. $\frac{1}{3}y + 6 - \frac{2}{3}y$ **84.** $-ab^2 - ab^2$

85. Music All 95 members of the jazz club pay \$30 each to go see a jazz performance. What is the total cost of tickets? Use mental math.

86. Reasoning Are $8x^2y$ and $-5yx^2$ like terms? Explain.

56. 5

57. -5

58. -9

59. 1.8

60. -144

61. 40

62. -3

63. -19

64. 3

65. -8

66. 60

67. 16

68. 12

69. -11

70. 19

71. -100

72. -56

73. 225

74. $-\frac{3}{10}$

75. $10x - 15$

76. $-14 + 2a$

77. $-\frac{1}{2}j + 4$

78. v^2

79. $6y - 6$

80. $\frac{3}{2}y - \frac{1}{4}$

81. $6 - 6y$

82. $y - 3$

83. $-\frac{1}{3}y + 6t$

84. $-2ab^2$

85. \$2850

86. Yes; the variable parts of the terms are the same.

Answers

Chapter Review (continued)

87. yes
88. no
89. no
90. yes
91. 10
92. between 12 and 13
93. between 2 and 3
94. between 3 and 4
95. yes
96. no
97. no
98. no
99. y is 5 more than the product of 10 and x; $y = 10x + 5$;

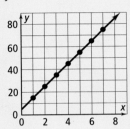

55, 65, 75

1-8 An Introduction to Equations

Quick Review

An **equation** can be true or false, or it can be an **open sentence** with a variable. A **solution** of an equation is the value (or values) of the variable that makes the equation true.

Example

Is $c = 6$ a solution of the equation $25 = 3c - 2$?

$25 = 3c - 2$

$25 \overset{?}{=} 3 \cdot 6 - 2$ Substitute 6 for c.

$25 \neq 16$ Simplify.

No, $c = 6$ is not a solution of the equation $25 = 3c - 2$.

Exercises

Tell whether the given number is a solution of each equation.

87. $17 = 37 + 4f; f = -5$ **88.** $-3a^2 = 27; a = 3$

89. $3b - 9 = 21; b = -10$ **90.** $-2b + 4 = 3; b = \frac{1}{2}$

Use a table to find or estimate the solution of each equation.

91. $x + (-2) = 8$ **92.** $3m - 13 = 24$

93. $4t - 2 = 9$ **94.** $6b - 3 = 17$

1-9 Patterns, Equations, and Graphs

Quick Review

You can represent the relationship between two varying quantities in different ways, including tables, equations, and graphs. A **solution of an equation** with two variables is an **ordered pair** (x, y) that makes the equation true.

Example

Bo makes $15 more per week than Sue. How can you represent this with an equation and a table?

First write an equation. Let $b = $ Bo's earnings and $s = $ Sue's earnings. Bo makes $15 more than Sue, so $b = s + 15$. You can use the equation to make a table for $s = 25, 50, 75,$ and 100.

Sue's Earnings (s)	25	50	75	100
Bo's Earnings (b)	40	65	90	115

Exercises

Tell whether the given ordered pair is a solution of each equation.

95. $3x + 5 = y; (1, 8)$

96. $y = -2(x + 3); (-6, 0)$

97. $y = (x - 1.2)(-3); (0, 1.2)$

98. $10 - 5x = y; (-4, 10)$

99. Describe the pattern in the table using words, an equation, and a graph. Extend the pattern for $x = 5, 6,$ and 7.

x	y
1	15
2	25
3	35
4	45

 **Chapter Test**

Do you know HOW?

1. Write an algebraic expression for the phrase *the quotient of n and 6.*

2. Write a word phrase for $-12t + 2$.

3. Evaluate the expression $-(pq)^2 \div (-8)$ for $p = 2$ and $q = 4$.

4. **Dance** The table shows how the total cost of dance classes at a studio depends on the number of classes you take. Write a rule in words and as an algebraic expression to model the relationship.

Dance Classes

Number of Classes	Total Cost
1	$(1 \times 15) + 20$
2	$(2 \times 15) + 20$
3	$(3 \times 15) + 20$

Simplify each expression.

5. $-20 - (-5) \cdot (-2^2)$

6. $\left(-\frac{1}{4}\right)^3$

7. $-\frac{7ab}{a}, a \neq 0$

8. $-|-25|$

9. $\sqrt{\frac{16}{25}}$

10. Is each statement true or false? If false, give a counterexample.

   a. For all real numbers a and b, $a \cdot b$ is equivalent to $b \cdot a$.

   b. For all real numbers a and b, $a(b \cdot c) = ab \cdot ac$.

11. Is the ordered pair $(2, -5)$ a solution to the equation $4 + 3x = -2y$? Show your work.

12. Order the numbers $-\frac{7}{8}, \frac{7}{4}, -1\frac{4}{5},$ and $-\frac{13}{16}$ from least to greatest.

13. **Soccer** There are t teams in a soccer league. Each team has 11 players. Make a table, write an equation, and draw a graph to describe the total number of players p in the league. How many players are on 17 teams?

Simplify each expression.

14. $5x^2 - x^2$

15. $12 \div \left(-\frac{3}{4}\right)$

16. $-(-2 + 6t)$

17. $-3[b - (-7)]$

18. Name the subset(s) of the real numbers to which each number belongs.

   a. -2.324 **b.** $\sqrt{46}$

19. Identify each property.

   a. $a(b + c) = ab + ac$

   b. $(a + b) + c = a + (b + c)$

Do you UNDERSTAND?

20. Is the set of positive integers the same as the set of nonnegative integers? Explain.

21. **Error Analysis** Find and correct the error in the work shown at the right.

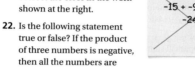

22. Is the following statement true or false? If the product of three numbers is negative, then all the numbers are negative. If false, give a counterexample.

23. **Reasoning** You notice that $10°C = 50°F$, $20°C = 68°F$, and $30°C = 86°F$. Use inductive reasoning to predict the value in degrees Fahrenheit of $40°C$.

24. **Reasoning** When is the absolute value of a difference equal to the difference of the absolute values? Explain.

18. **a.** rational numbers
   b. irrational numbers

19. **a.** Distr. Prop.
   b. Assoc. Prop. of Add.

20. No; positive integers do not include 0, but nonnegative integers do.

21. division was performed before addition;
$-3 \cdot 5 - 9 \div 4 + 3^2 = -15 - 9 \div 4 + 9 = -15 - 2.25 + 9 = -8.25$

22. false; $-2 \cdot 3 \cdot 4 = -24$

23. 104°F

24. Sample; They will be equal if $a > b > 0$, $a < b < 0$, or $a = b$.

Answers

Chapter Test

1. $\frac{n}{6}$

2. two more than the product of -12 and t

3. 8

4. 20 more than the product of 15 and the number of classes c; $15c + 20$

5. -40 6. $-\frac{1}{64}$ 7. $-7b$

8. -25 9. $\frac{4}{5}$

10. **a.** true

   b. false; Answers may vary. Sample:
$3(2 \cdot 5) = 3(10) = 30$ and
$3(2) \cdot 3(5) = 6 \cdot 15 = 90$

11. yes; $4 + 3(2) = -2(-5)$, $4 + 6 = 10$

12. $-1\frac{4}{5}, -\frac{7}{8}, -\frac{13}{16}, \frac{7}{4}$

13.

Players in Soccer League				
Number of teams	1	2	3	4
Players in league	11	22	33	44

$p = 11t$;

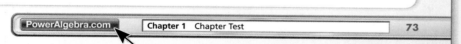

Players in Soccer League

187 players

14. $4x^2$ 15. -16

16. $2 - 6t$ 17. $-3b - 21$

MathXL for School
Prepare students for the Mid-Chapter Quiz and Chapter Test with online practice and review.

Item Number	Lesson
1	1-6
2	1-8
3	1-6
4	1-1
5	1-2
6	1-9
7	1-4
8	1-8
9	1-7
10	1-5
11	1-6
12	1-9
13	1-5
14	1-6
15	1-3
16	1-6
17	1-2
18	1-9
19	1-7
20	1-9
21	1-2
22	1-2
23	1-2
24	1-3
25	1-6
26	1-5
27	1-5

1 Cumulative Test Prep

TIPS FOR SUCCESS

Some test questions ask you to enter a numerical answer on a grid. In this textbook, you will record answers on a grid like the one shown below.

What is the value of $\frac{1}{2} + \frac{3}{4}$?

Solution

$\frac{1}{2} + \frac{3}{4} = \frac{2}{4} + \frac{3}{4} = \frac{5}{4} = 1\frac{1}{4}$

Record the answer as $\frac{5}{4}$ or 1.25.

Do not record the answer as $1\frac{1}{4}$ because the test-scoring computer will read it as $\frac{11}{4}$.

TIP 2

You do not have to simplify a fraction unless the question asks for simplest form or the fraction does not fit on the grid.

Think It Through

You can add the fractions as shown in the solution on the left, or you can convert the fractions to decimals and add.

$\frac{1}{2} + \frac{3}{4} = 0.5 + 0.75 = 1.25$

Record the decimal answer on the grid.

TIP 1

An answer may be either a fraction or a decimal. If an answer is a mixed number, rewrite it as an improper fraction or as a decimal.

Vocabulary Builder

As you solve test items, you must understand the meanings of mathematical terms. Select the correct term to complete each sentence.

A. An algebraic (*expression, equation*) is a mathematical sentence with an equal sign.

B. A (*coefficient, constant*) is a numerical factor of a term.

C. The (*exponent, base*) of a power tells how many times a number is used as a factor.

D. To (*simplify, evaluate*) an algebraic expression, you substitute a given number for each variable.

E. A(n) (*rational, irrational*) number is any number that you can write in the form $\frac{a}{b}$, where a and b are integers, and $b \neq 0$.

Multiple Choice

Read each question. Then write the letter of the correct answer on your paper.

1. If $x = -2$, $y = 3$, and $z = 4$, which expression has the greatest value?

Ⓐ $z(x - y)$ Ⓒ $z(x - y)^3 + x$

Ⓑ $z(x - y)^2 - x$ Ⓓ $\frac{z}{x} - xy$

2. What is the solution of the equation $7d + 7 = 14$?

Ⓕ -3 Ⓗ 1

Ⓖ -1 Ⓘ 3

3. What is the value of the expression $8(-9) - 6(-3)$?

Ⓐ -90 Ⓒ 54

Ⓑ -54 Ⓓ 90

Answers

Cumulative Test Prep

A. equation

B. coefficient

C. exponent

D. evaluate

E. rational

1. B

2. H

3. B

4. What is the order of the numbers $\sqrt{10}$, 3.3, $\frac{8}{3}$, and $\sqrt{9}$ from least to greatest?

Ⓕ $\sqrt{10}$, 3.3, $\frac{8}{3}$, $\sqrt{9}$

Ⓖ $\frac{8}{3}$, $\sqrt{9}$, 3.3, $\sqrt{10}$

Ⓗ 3.3, $\sqrt{10}$, $\sqrt{9}$, $\frac{8}{3}$

Ⓘ $\frac{8}{3}$, $\sqrt{9}$, $\sqrt{10}$, 3.3

5. You ship an 8-lb care package to your friend at college. It will cost you $.85 per pound, plus a flat fee of $12, to ship the package. How much will you pay to ship the package?

Ⓐ $6.92   Ⓒ $12.85

Ⓑ $10.20   Ⓓ $18.80

6. Which ordered pair is NOT a solution of the equation $y = x - 3$?

Ⓕ $(-4, -7)$ Ⓗ $(0, -3)$

Ⓖ $(12, 9)$ Ⓘ $(-8, 11)$

7. Which property does the equation $4 + x + 7 = 4 + 7 + x$ illustrate?

Ⓐ Identity Property of Addition

Ⓑ Distributive Property

Ⓒ Commutative Property of Addition

Ⓓ Associative Property of Addition

8. Bill has a $10 coupon for a party store. He needs to buy some balloons for a birthday party. If each balloon costs $2 and Bill uses his coupon, what is an equation that gives the total price y of his purchase?

Ⓕ $y = 2x$

Ⓖ $y = 2x - 10$

Ⓗ $y = 2x + 10$

Ⓘ $y = 10 - 2x$

9. Which expression is equivalent to $2.5(k - 3.4)$?

Ⓐ $k - 0.9$ Ⓒ $2.5k - 3.4$

Ⓑ $k - 5.9$ Ⓓ $2.5k - 8.5$

10. What is the value of $2 + |x + 4|$ for $x = -5$?

Ⓕ -7 Ⓗ 3

Ⓖ 1   Ⓘ 11

11. You own 100 shares of Stock A and 30 shares of Stock B. On Monday, Stock A decreased by $.40 per share and Stock B increased by $.25 per share. What was the total change in value of your shares?

Ⓐ $-$32.50   Ⓒ $-$.15

Ⓑ $-$21.20   Ⓓ $12

12. The table shows the relationship between the number of laps x you swim in a pool and the distance y, in meters, that you swim. Which equation describes the pattern in the table?

Laps, x	2	4	5	8
Distance (m), y	100	200	250	400

Ⓕ $y = 50x$ Ⓗ $y = x + 50$

Ⓖ $y = 100x$ Ⓘ $y = x + 100$

13. Which expression does NOT equal 9?

Ⓐ $|-4 - 5|$ Ⓒ $-|9|$

Ⓑ $|-9|$ Ⓓ $|9|$

14. A store is having a sale on cases of juice. The first two cases of juice cost $8 each. Any additional cases of juice cost $6 each. What is the cost of buying 9 cases of juice?

Ⓕ $54   Ⓗ $58

Ⓖ $68   Ⓘ $72

15. Which statement about real numbers is true?

Real Numbers

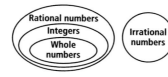

Ⓐ Every rational number is an integer.

Ⓑ Every real number is a rational number.

Ⓒ Every integer is a rational number.

Ⓓ Every irrational number is an integer.

4. I
5. D
6. I
7. C
8. G
9. D
10. H
11. A
12. F
13. C
14. H
15. C

Answers

Cumulative Test Prep (continued)

16. F
17. B
18. F
19. D
20. H
21. C
22. H
23. B
24. 53.75
25. 11.97
26. $\frac{7}{10}$
27. 577

---

16. Chris spends $3 per square foot on carpet for a square room. If he spends about $430 on carpet, what is the approximate length, in feet, of a side of the room?

F 12 ft   H 72 ft
G 36 ft   I 215 ft

17. To make 12 muffins, you need $1\frac{1}{4}$ cups of milk. You want to make 36 muffins, and you have $2\frac{1}{3}$ cups of milk. How many cups of milk do you still need?

A $1\frac{1}{2}$ cups   C $2\frac{1}{3}$ cups
B $1\frac{5}{12}$ cups   D $3\frac{3}{4}$ cups

18. A blank CD can hold 80 min of music. You have m minutes of music to burn onto the CD. Which expression models the amount of time t that is left on the CD?

F $t = 80 - m$ H $t = 80 + m$
G $t = m - 80$ I $t = 80m$

19. Which expression is equivalent to $3(2n + 1) + 4(n - 2)$?

A $10n + 1$ C $10n - 7$
B $10n - 1$ D $10n - 5$

20. A clock originally costs x dollars. After you apply a $3 discount, the clock costs y dollars. Which graph models this situation?

F   H

G   I

21. The expression 2^5 represents the number of cells in a petri dish after a single cell has gone through several stages of cell division. How many cells are in the petri dish after cell division?

A 10   C 32
B 16   D 64

22. To order movie tickets online, John has to pay $10 per ticket plus a $2 handling fee. If John buys three tickets, how much money will he spend?

F $12   H $32
G $30   I $36

23. What is the value of $(7 - 3)^2 + 3(8)$?

A 32   C 64
B 40   D 152

GRIDDED RESPONSE

Record your answers in a grid.

24. Marlee orders a window blind. She measures the window's length at three locations and displays her results in the table below. The length of the blind should be the same as the greatest length measured. What should be the length, in inches, of the blind?

Location	Left side	Center	Right side
Length (in.)	$53\frac{1}{2}$	$53\frac{3}{4}$	$53\frac{3}{8}$

25. Cole has $15 to spend on notebooks. Each notebook costs $3.99. What is the greatest amount, in dollars, that Cole can spend on notebooks?

26. What is the value of $-\frac{1}{5} + \frac{9}{10}$?

27. Tom auditions for a music school. For his piano audition, he will select two pieces from the table below. He can play for no more than 10 min.

Piano Piece	Time
Prelude	4 min, 13 s
Étude	5 min, 24 s
Waltz	4 min, 52 s

What is the greatest amount of time, in seconds, that he can play for his audition?

Get Ready!

◆ **Describing a Pattern**

Describe the relationship shown in each table below using words and using an equation.

1.

Number of Lawns Mowed	Money Earned
1	$7.50
2	$15.00
3	$22.50
4	$30.00

2.

Number of Hours	Pages Read
1	30
2	60
3	90
4	120

◆ **Adding and Subtracting Real Numbers**

Simplify each expression.

3. $6 + (-3)$ **4.** $-4 - 6$ **5.** $-5 - (-13)$ **6.** $-7 + (-1)$

7. $-4.51 + 11.65$ **8.** $8.5 - (-7.9)$ **9.** $\frac{3}{10} - \frac{3}{4}$ **10.** $\frac{1}{5} + \left(-\frac{2}{3}\right)$

◆ **Multiplying and Dividing Real Numbers**

Simplify each expression.

11. $-85 \div (-5)$ **12.** $7\left(-\frac{6}{14}\right)$ **13.** $4^2(-6)^2$ **14.** $22 \div (-8)$

◆ **Combining Like Terms**

Simplify each expression.

15. $14k^2 - (-2k^2)$ **16.** $4xy + 9xy$ **17.** $6t + 2 - 4t$ **18.** $9x - 4 + 3x$

 Looking Ahead Vocabulary

19. If you say that two shirts are *similar*, what does that mean about the shirts? What would you expect *similar* to mean if you are talking about two similar triangles?

20. A model ship is a type of *scale model*. What is the relationship of a model ship to the actual ship that it models?

Get Ready!

Assign this diagnostic assessment to determine if students have the prerequisite skills for Chapter 2.

Lesson	Skill
1-4	Describing a Pattern
1-5	Adding and Subtracting Real Numbers
1-6	Multiplying and Dividing Real Numbers
1-7	Combining Like Terms

To remediate students, select from these resources (available for every lesson).
• Online Problems (PowerAlgebra.com)
• Reteaching (All-in-One Teaching Resources)
• Practice (All-in-One Teaching Resources)

Why Students Need These Skills

DESCRIBING A PATTERN
The visual and verbal representation of data reinforces students' understanding of its representation through an equation.

ADDING AND SUBTRACTING REAL NUMBERS
The addition and subtraction of real numbers is essential to the application of the Addition and Subtraction Properties of Equality.

MULTIPLYING AND DIVIDING REAL NUMBERS
The multiplication and division of real numbers is essential to the application of the Multiplication and Subtraction Properties of Equality.

COMBINING LIKE TERMS
Students will need to identify and combine like terms when solving multi-step equations, and equations with variables on both sides.

Looking Ahead Vocabulary

SIMILAR Ask students how two people may be similar, and how they may be different. Then ask how two triangles might be similar.

SCALE MODEL Have students suggest other examples of scale models, such as an architecture model, or a globe.

Answers

Get Ready!

1. Answers may vary. Sample: For each lawn mowed, $7.50 is earned; $y = 7.50x$.

2. Answers may vary. Sample: 30 pages are read each hour; $y = 30x$.

3. 3

4. -10

5. 8

6. -8

7. 7.14

8. 16.4

9. $-\frac{9}{20}$

10. $-\frac{7}{15}$

11. 17

12. -3

13. 576

14. -2.75

15. $16k^2$

16. $13xy$

17. $2t + 2$

18. $12x - 4$

19. Answers may vary. Sample: The shirts might look the same but be different sizes or different colors; the triangles will be the same shape but different sizes.

20. Answers may vary. Sample: The model ship is the same shape but just a smaller size than the actual ship.

Chapter 2 Overview

UbD Understanding by Design

Chapter 2 connects and extends the Big Ideas introduced in the last chapter to solving equations and proportions. In this chapter, students will develop the answers to the Essential Questions posed on the opposite page as they learn the concepts and skills bulleted below.

BIG idea Proportionality

ESSENTIAL QUESTION What kinds of relationships can proportions represent?
- Students will calculate unit rates.
- Students will use proportions to solve problems involving percents, measurements in similar figures, and indirect measurement.
- Students will use scale drawings such as maps.

BIG idea Equivalence

ESSENTIAL QUESTION Can equations that appear to be different be equivalent?
- Students will find equivalent equations using inverse operations and simplification.

BIG idea Solving Equations & Inequalities

ESSENTIAL QUESTION How can you solve equations?
- Students will solve equations using addition, subtraction, multiplication, or division.
- Students will use the Distributive Property to simplify expressions and solve equations.
- Students will use the Multiplication Property of Equality and the Cross Products Property to solve proportions.

Indiana Academic Standards

A1.2.5 Solve problems that can be modeled using linear equations and inequalities, interpret the solutions, and determine whether the solutions are reasonable.

A1.6.2 Solve equations involving rational and common irrational expressions.

CHAPTER 2

Solving Equations

PowerAlgebra.com

Your place to get all things digital

VIDEO Download videos connecting math to your world.

VOCABULARY Math definitions in English and Spanish

SOLVE IT! The online Solve It will get you in gear for each lesson.

DYNAMIC ACTIVITIES Interactive! Vary numbers, graphs, and figures to explore math concepts.

ONLINE PROBLEMS Download Step-by-Step Problems with Instant Replay.

ONLINE HOMEWORK Get and view your assignments online.

MathXL FOR SCHOOL Extra practice and review online

Have you ever seen a board game as big as this one? A ratio relates the dimensions of each oversized game piece to the dimensions of a normal-sized game piece.

You'll find out how ratios and models are related using proportions in this chapter.

Vocabulary

English/Spanish Vocabulary Audio Online:

English	Spanish
conversion factor, p. 119	factor de conversión
cross products, p. 125	productos cruzados
equivalent equations, p. 81	ecuaciones equivalentes
formula, p. 110	fórmula
inverse operations, p. 82	operaciones inversas
literal equation, p. 109	ecuación literal
percent change, p. 144	cambio porcentual
proportion, p. 124	proporción
rate, p. 118	tasa
ratio, p. 118	razón
scale, p. 132	escala
unit analysis, p. 119	análisis de unidades

PowerAlgebra.com

Chapter 2 Overview

Use these online assets to engage your students. There is support for the Solve It and step-by-step solutions for Problems.

 Show the student-produced video demonstrating relevant and engaging applications of the new concepts in the chapter.

 Find online definitions for new terms in English and Spanish.

 Start each lesson with an attention-getting Problem. View the Problem online with helpful hints.

My Math Video

ZIEHEN SIE
RÜBERGEHE
EHAN

00:04:04 | VIDEO ▶

BIGideas

1 Equivalence
Essential Question Can equations that appear to be different be equivalent?

2 Solving Equations and Inequalities
Essential Question How can you solve equations?

3 Proportionality
Essential Question What kinds of relationships can proportions represent?

Chapter Preview

PowerAlgebra.com | Chapter 2 Solving Equations | 79

My Math Video

FACILITATE Use this photo to discuss the concept of enlarging and reducing figures. In this chapter, students will learn how to solve equations. They will use them to find values of proportional measurements. Dilations, such as this scale model, provide real-world examples of proportionality.

Q How does the board game in the picture compare to the board in a regular game? **[The board in the picture appears to be an enlarged version of the regular board that is sized so that people can walk from square to square.]**

Q How do you think the board was made? **[Answers may vary. Sample: The makers decided how much bigger they wanted the board and they enlarged everything in the game by that amount.]**

Q How could you determine the amount by which the game was enlarged? **[Compare the lengths of the original board and the enlarged board. The percent increase can be found using these dimensions.]**

EXTENSION
Have students estimate the length of the board in the picture. Students can use the length of a standard board to determine the relationship between the two boards. Introduce the concept of scale factor. If you have a board game available, have students calculate the measurements of pieces in an enlarged set based on measurements they take of an original boxed game set.

ERROR PREVENTION
Be sure that students compare the larger measurement to the smaller measurement, not the other way around. Stress the difference between an enlargement factor and a reduction factor.

 Increase students' depth of knowledge with interactive online activities.

 Show Problems from each lesson solved step by step. Instant replay allows students to go at their own pace when studying online.

 Assign homework to individual students or to an entire class.

 Prepare students for the Mid-Chapter Quiz and Chapter Test with online practice and review.

Equivalence

BIG idea Any algebraic equation can be represented using symbols in an infinite number of ways, where each representation has the same solution.

ESSENTIAL UNDERSTANDINGS

2-1 through 2-5 Equivalent equations are equations that have the same solution(s). In these lessons, students learn to use the properties of equality and inverse operations to find equivalent equations.

Solving Equations & Inequalities

BIG idea Properties of numbers and equality can transform an equation into equivalent simpler equations. This process is used to find solutions.

ESSENTIAL UNDERSTANDINGS

2-1 through 2-5 Equations can describe, explain, and predict various aspects of the real world. In these lessons, students solve one-step, two-step, and multi-step linear equations, as well as equations with variables on both sides.

Proportionality

BIG idea Proportionality involves a relationship in which the ratio of two quantities remains constant as the corresponding values of the quantities change. In a proportional relationship there are an infinite number of ratios equal to this constant ratio.

ESSENTIAL UNDERSTANDINGS

2-6 Ratios and rates can be used to compare quantities and make conversions.

2-7 If two ratios are equal and a quantity in one of the ratios is unknown, the unknown quantity can be found by writing and solving a proportion.

2-8 Proportional reasoning can be used to find missing side lengths in similar figures.

2-9 to 2-10 Percents represent another application of proportions. The percent proportion can be used to solve for any one of the missing components and to solve percent increase and percent decrease problems.

Creating Equivalent Equations

Solving equations involves writing equivalent equations. Each step in solving an equation uses properties, identities, or inverse operations. Each new equation is a simpler version of the previous one.

Common Errors With Solving Equations

Some students have difficulty determining the number of solutions. The following graphing technique improves visualization. By graphing each side of the original equation on the same coordinate plane, students see if there is one solution, infinite solutions, or no solutions.

Example A: One Solution

$$2(2x - 1) = -2(x - 2)$$

Graph: $y = 2(2x - 1)$ and

$$y = -2(x - 2)$$

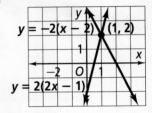

The intersection of these two lines is the solution.

Example B: Infinite Solutions

When the variable is eliminated from an equation and a true statement results, such as $8 = 8$, then the equation has an infinite number of solutions. Any value can be substituted for the variable, and a true statement results.

$$4x - 2 = 2(2x - 1)$$

Graph: $y = 4x - 2$ and

$$y = 2(2x - 1)$$

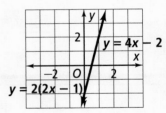

The graphs of these equations lie on top of each other. They have an infinite number of points in common.

Example C: No Solution

When the variable is eliminated from an equation and a false statement results, then the equation does not have a solution.

$$-2x + 3 = -5x - 1 - 7x$$

Graph: $y = -2x + 3$ and

$$y = 5x - 1 - 7x$$

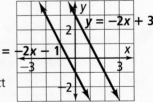

These equations never intersect because the lines are parallel.

Solving Proportions

When solving proportions, students have choices. They can multiply both sides of the equation by the least common multiple (LCM) or use the Cross Products Property.

Least Common Multiple

$$\frac{12}{9} = \frac{8}{x}$$

$$(9x)\frac{12}{9} = \frac{8}{x}(9x)$$

$$12x = 72$$

$$x = 6$$

Cross Products Property

$$\frac{12}{9} = \frac{8}{x}$$

$$12x = 72$$

$$x = 6$$

Students tend to prefer the cross products property, especially if a variable is in the denominator.

Common Errors When Solving Proportions

Students may try to use the Cross Products Property any time they encounter two fractions, such as $\frac{3}{4} \times \frac{5}{6}$. They may overlook the fact that the expression is not an equation.

When solving proportions, students must also recognize the multiplicative nature of the equation. Using the Cross Products Property when a constant is added to one side of the equation is not appropriate as an initial first step.

For example:

$$\frac{5}{8} + 3 = \frac{x}{6}$$

In this example, students must simplify the left-hand side of the equation before using cross products.

$$\frac{29}{8} = \frac{x}{6}$$

$$174 = 8x$$

$$21.75 = x$$

Another correct technique is multiplying each term of the original equation by the LCM, 24.

$$\frac{5}{8} + 3 = \frac{x}{6}$$

$$(24)\frac{5}{8} + 3(24) = \frac{x}{6}(24)$$

$$15 + 72 = 4x$$

$$87 = 4x$$

$$21.75 = x$$

The ability to recognize proportionality enables students to solve a vast array of problems involving rates, scale factors, similar figures, percents, and percent of change.

Working With Percents as Proportions

Students can create proportions to solve problems involving percents. The definition of percent means "out of 100," so 15% is the ratio $\frac{15}{100}$. The other side of the proportion is represented by $\frac{part}{base}$. A diagram can help students visualize a problem.

2.1 is what percent of 14?

$$\frac{2.1}{14} = \frac{p}{100}$$ Write a proportion.

$$14p = 210$$
$$p = 15$$ Use cross products.

2.1 is 15% of 14.   Divide 21 by 14 to find p.

A sale is offering 15% off the original price. Monique wants to buy a camera and she knows that she can save $75 by buying during the sale. What is the original price of the camera?

The proportion to represent this situation is $\frac{15}{100} = \frac{75}{x}$. The full price of the camera is unknown, so it is represented by x. The format of this proportion can be used regardless of the part of the problem a question asks you to find.

Common Errors When Solving Equations

Some students may believe that the value representing the base always follows the word "of." These students might also say that the value representing the part follows the word "is." These are both true in the following example:

18 is what percent of 42?

Care needs to be taken as using keywords this way can be misleading. For example: I bought a painting at an auction for $8000. Several years later I sold the painting back to the dealer for 25% less than what I had paid for it. What was the price I got for the painting from the dealer?

In this example, the words "of" and "is" are not used. Students need to depend on the context of the problem to establish the correct proportion.

SOLVING EQUATIONS
Pacing and Assignment Guide

		TRADITIONAL			BLOCK
Lesson	Teaching Days	Basic	Average	Advanced	Block
2-1	1	Problems 1-6 Exs. 10–54, all, 56–70 even, 71, 73, 79–88	Problems 1-6 Exs. 11–51 odd, 52–76, 79–88	Problems 1-6 Exs. 11–51 odd, 52–88	**Day 1** Problems 1-6 Exs. 11–51 odd, 52–76, 79–88
2-2	1	Problems 1-2 Exs. 11–25 all, 54, 56, 66–78	Problems 1-4 Exs. 11–37 odd, 38–60, 66–78	Problems 1-4 Exs. 11–37 odd, 38–78	Problems 1-4 Exs. 11–37 odd, 38–60, 66–78
	2	Problems 3-4 Exs. 26–37 all, 38–52 even, 59			
2-3	1	Problems 1-3 Exs. 10–29 all, 54, 61, 69–80	Problems 1-3 Exs. 11–29 odd, 54, 61–63, 65, 69–80	Problems 1-5 Exs. 11–43 odd, 45–80	**Day 2** Problems 1-5 Exs. 11–43 odd, 45–65, 69–80
	2	Problems 4-5 Exs. 30–44 all, 46–52 even, 55–59, 61	Problems 4-5 Exs. 31–43 odd, 45–53, 55–60, 64		
2-4	1	Problems 1-2 Exs. 10–20 all, 43, 44, 46	Problems 1-2 Exs. 11–19 odd, 43–46	Problems 1-4 Exs. 11–31 odd, 33–66	**Day 3** Problems 1-4 Exs. 11–31 odd, 33–49, 57–66
	2	Problems 3-4 Exs. 21–32 all, 34–42 even, 44, 57–66	Problems 3-4 Exs. 21–31 odd, 33–42, 47–49, 57–66		
2-5	1	Problems 1-4 Exs. 11–35 all, 36–42 even, 43, 45–47, 51–66	Problems 1-4 Exs. 11–35 odd, 36–48, 51–66	Problems 1-4 Exs. 11–35 odd, 36–66	**Day 4** Problems 1-4 Exs. 11–35 odd, 36–48, 51–66
2-6	1	Problems 1-4 Exs. 9–24 all, 26–34 even, 35–39, 42, 45–57	Problems 1-4 Exs. 9–23 odd, 25–42, 45–57	Problems 1-4 Exs. 9–23 odd, 25–57	Problems 1-4 Exs. 9–23 odd, 25–42, 45–57
2-7	1	Problems 1-4 Exs. 10–41 all, 42–50 even, 51–53, 60–73	Problems 1-4 Exs. 11–41 odd, 42–54, 60–73	Problems 1-4 Exs. 11–41 odd, 42–73	**Day 5** Problems 1-4 Exs. 11–41 odd, 42–54, 60–73
2-8	1	Problems 1-4 Exs. 6–25, 31–43	Problems 1-4 Exs. 7–17 odd, 19–28, 31–43	Problems 1-4 Exs. 7–17 odd, 19–43	Problems 1-4 Exs. 7–17 odd, 19–28, 31–43
2-9	1	Problems 1-2 Exs. 9–22 all, 45, 47	Problems 1-2 Exs. 9–21 odd, 45, 47–48, 51	Problems 1-5 Exs. 9–29 odd, 31–62	**Day 6** Problems 1-5 Exs. 9–29 odd, 31–51, 54–62
	2	Problems 3-5 Exs. 23–30 all, 32–36 even, 37, 38, 40–44 even, 48–49, 54–62	Problems 3-5 Exs. 23–29 odd, 31–44, 46, 49–50, 54–62		
2-10	1	Problems 1-2 Exs. 7–17 all, 36	Problems 1-2 Exs. 7–17 odd, 35, 36	Problems 1-5 Exs. 7–23 odd, 25–51	**Day 7** Problems 1-5 Exs. 7–23 odd, 25–39, 42–51
	2	Problems 3-5 Exs. 18–24 all, 26–32 even, 34–35, 37–39, 42–51	Problems 3-5 Exs. 19–23 odd, 25–34, 37–39, 42–51		
Review	1	Chapter 2 Review	Chapter 2 Review	Chapter 2 Review	**Day 8** Chapter 2 Review
Assess	1	Chapter 2 Test	Chapter 2 Test	Chapter 2 Test	Chapter 2 Test
Total		**17 Days**	**16 Days**	**12 Days**	**8 Days**

Note: Pacing does not include Concept Bytes and other feature pages.

Resources

	For the Chapter	2-1	2-2	2-3	2-4	2-5	2-6	2-7	2-8	2-9	2-10
Planning											
Teacher Center Online Planner & Grade Book	I	I	I	I	I	I	I	I	I	I	I
Interactive Learning & Guided Instruction											
My Math Video	I										
Solve It!		I TM	I TM	I TM	I TM	I TM	I TM	I TM	I TM	I TM	I TM
Student Companion (SP)*		P M	P M	P M	P M	P M	P M	P M	P M	P M	P M
Vocabulary Support		I P M	I P M	I P M	I P M	I P M	I P M	I P M	I P M	I P M	I P M
Got It? Support		I P	I P	I P	I P	I P	I P	I P	I P	I P	I P
Dynamic Activity		I	I		I	I				I	
Online Problems		I	I	I	I	I	I	I	I	I	I
Additional Problems		M	M	M	M	M	M	M	M	M	M
English Language Learner Support (TR)		E P M	E P M	E P M	E P M	E P M	E P M	E P M	E P M	E P M	E P M
Activities, Games, and Puzzles		E M	E M	E M	E M	E M	E M	E M	E M	E M	E M
Teaching With TI Technology With CD-ROM			✓ P		✓ P	✓ P	✓ P				
TI-Nspire™ Support CD-ROM		✓	✓	✓	✓	✓	✓	✓	✓	✓	✓
Lesson Check & Practice											
Student Companion (SP)*		P M	P M	P M	P M	P M	P M	P M	P M	P M	P M
Lesson Check Support		I P	I P	I P	I P	I P	I P	I P	I P	I P	I P
Practice and Problem Solving Workbook (SP)		P	P	P	P	P	P	P	P	P	P
*Think About a Plan (TR)**		E P M	E P M	E P M	E P M	E P M	E P M	E P M	E P M	E P M	E P M
*Practice Form G (TR)**		E P M	E P M	E P M	E P M	E P M	E P M	E P M	E P M	E P M	E P M
*Standardized Test Prep (TR)**		P M	P M	P M	P M	P M	P M	P M	P M	P M	P M
Practice *Form K* (TR)*		E P M	E P M	E P M	E P M	E P M	E P M	E P M	E P M	E P M	E P M
Extra Practice	E M										
Find the Errors!	M										
Enrichment (TR)		E P M	E P M	E P M	E P M	E P M	E P M	E P M	E P M	E P M	E P M
Answers and Solutions CD-ROM	✓	✓	✓	✓	✓	✓	✓	✓	✓	✓	✓
Assess & Remediate											
ExamView CD-ROM	✓	✓	✓	✓	✓	✓	✓	✓	✓	✓	✓
Lesson Quiz		I TM	I TM	I TM	I TM	I TM	I TM	I TM	I TM	I TM	I TM
Quizzes and Tests *Form G* (TR)*	E P M					E P M					E P M
Quizzes and Tests *Form K* (TR)*	E P M					E P M					E P M
Reteaching (TR)*		E P M	E P M	E P M	E P M	E P M	E P M	E P M	E P M	E P M	E P M
Performance Tasks (TR)*	P M										
Cumulative Review (TR)*	P M										
Progress Monitoring Assessments	I P M										

(TR) Available in All-In-One Teaching Resources   * Spanish available

Guided Instruction

PURPOSE To use algebra tiles to model and solve single-variable, one-step equations

PROCESS Students will
- model an equation using algebra tiles.
- use algebra tiles to apply properties of equality and inverse operations.

DISCUSS Students have solved one-step equations using strategies such as work backward, or guess and check. Now, have them reason algebraically. Algebra tiles help students focus on balancing the equation and performing inverse operations.

Q Why are there two red tiles and a variable tile on the left side of the equation? **[The variable tile corresponds to x, and the two red tiles correspond to –2.]**

Q Why do you add two yellow tiles to both sides of the equation? **[Adding two yellow tiles forms a zero pair with each of the red tiles on the left side of the equation. Adding two yellow tiles to the right side of the equation maintains balance.]**

Q How can you check your answer? **[Replace the variable tile in the original equation with six yellow tiles. Then, remove two zero pairs. The result is an equation with four yellow tiles on each side. The answer checks.]**

TACTILE LEARNERS

Before assigning Exercises 3–10, discuss and compare maintaining equivalent expressions with balancing a scale. Use a set of scales and different weights to model equivalence and properties of equality. Have students solve different equations using the scales.

 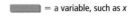

Concept Byte

Use With Lesson 2-1

ACTIVITY

Modeling One-Step Equations

Algebra tiles can help you understand how to solve one-step equations in one variable. You can use the algebra tiles shown below to model equations. Notice that the yellow tile is positive and the red tile is negative. Together, they form a zero pair, which represents 0.

Unit tiles	Variable tiles
☐ = +1 ■ = −1	▬ = a variable, such as x
■ + ☐ = 0	

Activity

Model and solve $x - 2 = 4$.

Equation	Algebra tiles	Step
$x - 2 = 4$		Model the equation using tiles.
$x - 2 + 2 = 4 + 2$		The green tile represents x. To get the green tile by itself on one side of the equation, add two yellow tiles to each side. Remember, a yellow tile and a red tile form a zero pair. Remove all zero pairs.
$x = 6$		The green tile equals six yellow tiles. This represents $x = 6$. The solution of $x - 2 = 4$ is 6.

Exercises

Write the equation modeled by the algebra tiles.

1.

2.

Use algebra tiles to model and solve each equation.

3. $x - 3 = 2$	**4.** $x - 4 = 7$	**5.** $x + 1 = 5$	**6.** $x + 4 = 7$
7. $1 + x = -3$	**8.** $5 + x = -3$	**9.** $x - 4 = -3$	**10.** $-4 + x = -8$

Answers

Exercises

1. $x + 3 = 5$

2. $2x = 4$

3. 5

4. 11

5. 4

6. 3

7. −4

8. −8

9. 1

10. −4

2-1 Solving One-Step Equations

Indiana Academic Standard
A1.2.5 Solve problems that can be modeled using linear equations and inequalities, interpret the solutions, and determine whether the solutions are reasonable.

Objective To solve one-step equations in one variable

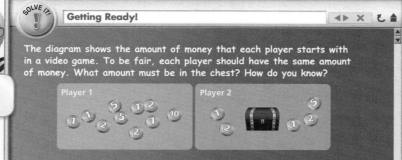

Getting Ready!

The diagram shows the amount of money that each player starts with in a video game. To be fair, each player should have the same amount of money. What amount must be in the chest? How do you know?

Player 1

Player 2

In a fair game, all players start out equal.

Dynamic Activity
One-Step Equations

Lesson Vocabulary
• equivalent equations
• Addition Property of Equality
• Subtraction Property of Equality
• isolate
• inverse operations
• Multiplication Property of Equality
• Division Property of Equality

In the Solve It, you may have used reasoning to find the amount of money in the chest. In this lesson, you will learn to solve problems like the one above by using equations.

Essential Understanding **Equivalent equations** are equations that have the same solution(s). You can find the solution of a one-step equation using the properties of equality and inverse operations to write a simpler equivalent equation.

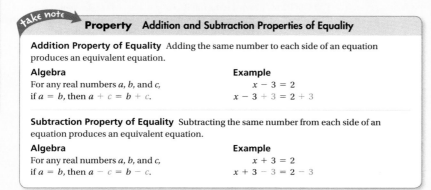

take note

Property **Addition and Subtraction Properties of Equality**

Addition Property of Equality Adding the same number to each side of an equation produces an equivalent equation.

Algebra	**Example**
For any real numbers a, b, and c,	$x - 3 = 2$
if $a = b$, then $a + c = b + c$.	$x - 3 + 3 = 2 + 3$

Subtraction Property of Equality Subtracting the same number from each side of an equation produces an equivalent equation.

Algebra	**Example**
For any real numbers a, b, and c,	$x + 3 = 2$
if $a = b$, then $a - c = b - c$.	$x + 3 - 3 = 2 - 3$

2-1 Preparing to Teach

BIG ideas **Equivalence** **UbD**
Solving Equations & Inequalities

ESSENTIAL UNDERSTANDINGS
• Equivalent equations are equations that have the same solution(s).
• The solution of a one-step equation can be found using the properties of equality and inverse operations to write a simpler equation.

Math Background

Inverse operations and properties of equality help solve equations. As students isolate variables, they must use inverse operations. For example, $x + 3 = 15$ shows addition of 3 to the variable x. To solve, students will

"undo" the addition by subtracting 3 from each side of the equation. In this lesson, students will use inverse operations to solve for the variable in one-step equations. When discussing the Division Property of Equality, remind students that zero does not have a reciprocal. Division by zero is undefined.

Support Student Learning

Use the **Algebra I Companion** to engage and support students during instructions. See Lesson Resources at the end of this lesson for details.

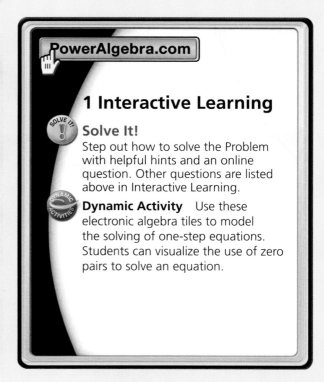

PowerAlgebra.com

1 Interactive Learning

Solve It!
Step out how to solve the Problem with helpful hints and an online question. Other questions are listed above in Interactive Learning.

Dynamic Activity Use these electronic algebra tiles to model the solving of one-step equations. Students can visualize the use of zero pairs to solve an equation.

1 Interactive Learning

Solve It!
PURPOSE To develop the algebraic reasoning skills needed to solve one-step equations by considering a game situation
PROCESS Students may
• mentally determine the amount of money that must be in the chest to make the game fair.
• draw a sketch and cross out money (and chest as necessary) from each side.

FACILITATE
Q What operation can you use to find the answer? Explain. **[Subtraction; the chest contains the difference between the coins Player 1 has and the coins Player 2 has.]**

ANSWERS See Solve It in Answers on next page.
CONNECT THE MATH To maintain equality, students remove the same amount of money from each player. In this lesson, students learn that the same amount must always be taken away from or added to both sides of an equation to maintain equality.

2 Guided Instruction

Take Note
Connect the words of each property to the algebraic representation and to each example.

Problem 1   ERROR PREVENTION

If you use the form below, connect this to the Subtraction Property of Equality shown in Problem 1.

$$x + 13 = 27$$
$$\underline{-13 = -13}$$
$$x = 14$$

The format here emphasizes that subtracting the same amount from both sides maintains equality.

Got It?

Q What will happen if we add 2 to each side of the equation? **[The resulting equivalent equation will be $y + 4 = -4$. Adding 2 to both sides does not help isolate the variable. Addition is not the inverse operation of $+2$.]**

Problem 2

Point out that the variable is on the right side in this equation.

Q Should you add 7 or add 3 to each side? Explain. **[Add 3, since 3 is subtracted from the variable.]**

Q Could you rewrite the original equation as $b - 3 = -7$ and then solve? **[Yes, since the solution to both equations is -4, they are equivalent.]**

Got It?

Q How can you tell what to add or subtract to solve each equation? **[If something is added to the variable, subtract that amount from each side. If something is subtracted, add that amount to each side.]**

To solve an equation, you must **isolate** the variable. You do this by getting the variable with a coefficient of 1 alone on one side of the equation.

You can isolate a variable using the properties of equality and inverse operations. An **inverse operation** undoes another operation. For example, subtraction is the inverse of addition. When you solve an equation, each inverse operation you perform should produce a simpler equivalent equation.

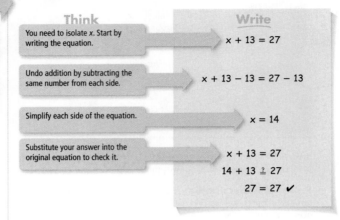

Problem 1 Solving an Equation Using Subtraction

What is the solution of $x + 13 = 27$?

Plan
How can you visualize the equation?
You can draw a *diagram*. Use a model like the one below to help you visualize an equation. A model for the equation $x + 13 = 27$ is

◄------- 27 -------►
x	13

Think

You need to isolate x. Start by writing the equation.

Undo addition by subtracting the same number from each side.

Simplify each side of the equation.

Substitute your answer into the original equation to check it.

Write

$x + 13 = 27$

$x + 13 - 13 = 27 - 13$

$x = 14$

$x + 13 = 27$
$14 + 13 \overset{?}{=} 27$
$27 = 27$ ✔

Got It? **1. a.** What is the solution of $y + 2 = -6$? Check your answer.
     b. Reasoning In Problem 1, why does subtracting 13 from both sides of the original equation result in an equivalent equation?

Problem 2 Solving an Equation Using Addition

What is the solution of $-7 = b - 3$?

$$-7 = b - 3$$
$$-7 + 3 = b - 3 + 3 \quad \text{Add 3 to each side.}$$
$$-4 = b \quad\quad\quad\quad \text{Simplify.}$$

Plan
How can you get started?
Undo operations. Add 3 to each side to undo subtraction.

Got It? **2.** What is the solution of each equation? Check your answer.
     a. $m - 8 = -14$ **b.** $\frac{1}{2} = y - \frac{3}{2}$

Answers

Solve It!

19; explanations may vary.

Got It?

1. a. -8

  b. The Subtr. Prop. of Eq. states that subtracting the same number from each side of an equation produces another equation that is equivalent.

2. a. -6

  b. 2

 PowerAlgebra.com

2 Guided Instruction

Each Problem is worked out and supported online.

Problem 1
Solving an Equation Using Subtraction

Problem 2
Solving an Equation Using Addition

Alternative Problem 2
Solving an Equation Using Addition

Problem 3
Solving an Equation Using Division
Animated

Alternative Problem 3
Solving an Equation Using Division
Animated

Problem 4
Solving an Equation Using Multiplication

Problem 5
Solving Equations Using Reciprocals

Problem 6
Using a One-Step Equation as a Model   *Animated*

Support in Algebra 1 Companion
• Vocabulary
• Key Concepts
• Got It?

You can use the multiplication and division properties of equality to solve equations. Division is the inverse of multiplication.

Property Multiplication and Division Properties of Equality

Multiplication Property of Equality Multiplying each side of an equation by the same nonzero number produces an equivalent equation.

Algebra

For any real numbers a, b, and c,
if $a = b$, then $a \cdot c = b \cdot c$.

Example

$$\frac{x}{3} = 2$$

$$\frac{x}{3} \cdot 3 = 2 \cdot 3$$

Division Property of Equality Dividing each side of an equation by the same nonzero number produces an equivalent equation.

Algebra

For any real numbers a, b, and c, such
that $c \neq 0$, if $a = b$, then $\frac{a}{c} = \frac{b}{c}$.

Example

$$5x = 20$$

$$\frac{5x}{5} = \frac{20}{5}$$

Plan

How can a model help you solve the equation?
The model tells you that you must divide 6.4 by 4 in order to solve the equation $4x = 6.4$.

Problem 3 Solving an Equation Using Division   GRIDDED RESPONSE

What is the solution of $4x = 6.4$?

$$4x = 6.4$$

$$\frac{4x}{4} = \frac{6.4}{4} \quad \text{Divide each side by 4.}$$

$$x = 1.6 \quad \text{Simplify.}$$

✓ **Got It?** **3.** What is the solution of each equation? Check your answer.
   a. $10 = 15x$ **b.** $-3.2z = 14$

Plan

How can a model help you solve the equation?
The model tells you that you must multiply -9 by 4 in order to solve the equation $\frac{x}{4} = -9$.

Problem 4 Solving an Equation Using Multiplication

What is the solution of $\frac{x}{4} = -9$?

$$\frac{x}{4} = -9$$

$$\frac{x}{4} \cdot 4 = -9 \cdot 4 \quad \text{Multiply each side by 4.}$$

$$x = -36 \quad \text{Simplify.}$$

✓ **Got It?** **4.** What is the solution of each equation? Check your answer.
   a. $19 = \frac{r}{3}$ **b.** $\frac{x}{-9} = 8$

Take Note
Discuss why the Division Property of Equality applies only to division by a nonzero number.

Q How do you simplify the equation $5x = 20$? **[Divide each side by 5.]**

Q How do you know that $5x = 20$ and $x = 4$ are equivalent equations? **[They each have 4 as their solution.]**

Problem 3
Students use the Division Property of Equality to solve a one-step equation. Remind students that $4x$ is 4 times x.

Got It?

Q In 3a, could you solve by multiplying both sides by $\frac{1}{15}$? **[Yes; multiplying by $\frac{1}{15}$ is the same as dividing by 15.]**

Problem 4
Students use the Multiplication Property of Equality to solve a one-step equation.

Q What operation can you use to undo division? **[multiplication]**

Q Are $\frac{x}{15}$ and $\frac{1}{15}x$ equivalent expressions? Explain. **[Yes; write x as $\frac{x}{1}$ and multiply: $\frac{1}{15}\left(\frac{x}{1}\right) = \frac{x}{15}$.]**

Got It?   ERROR PREVENTION

Q What number do you need to multiply by? **[the number that divides the variable]**

Q In 4b, does multiplying both sides by 9 give the same result? **[No; the result is $-x = 72$. An extra step (multiplication or division by -1) is required to get the final solution of -72.]**

Additional Problems

1. What is the solution of $15 + s = 42$?

ANSWER 27

2. What is the solution of $-12 + x = 17$?

ANSWER 29

3. What is the solution of $2x = \frac{3}{5}$?

ANSWER $\frac{3}{10}$

4. What is the solution of $\frac{x}{5} = -12$?

ANSWER -60

5. What is the solution of $\frac{5}{2}x = 15$?

ANSWER 6

6. Rob is driving at 40 miles per hour. Stacey is driving $\frac{3}{2}$ times as fast. How fast is Stacey driving?

ANSWER 60 mi/h

Answers

Got It? (continued)

3. a. $\frac{2}{3}$
   b. -4.375
4. a. 57
   b. -72

Problem 5

Q Will the product of a number and its reciprocal always equal 1? Why or why not? **[Yes; if $\frac{x}{y}$ is the original number, then $\frac{x}{y} \times \frac{y}{x} = \frac{xy}{yx} = 1$.]**

Got It?

Q In 5a, what is the reciprocal of $\frac{3}{4}$? How can you use it to solve the equation? **[The reciprocal is $\frac{4}{3}$. To solve the equation, multiply both sides by $\frac{4}{3}$.]**

Q In 5b, how can you determine if two equations are equivalent? Find and compare the solutions for both equations. **[If they are the same, the equations are equivalent.]**

Problem 6

Students must determine what information is relevant, and translate phrases such as "about half of" into algebraic expressions.

Q If the length of the macaw is ℓ, what is the length of the toucan? **[$\frac{2}{3}\ell$]**

Q What is the equation relating ℓ with the length of the toucan? **[$24 = \frac{2}{3}\ell$]**

Ask students to think of situations where other words or phrases might indicate multiplication. Words or phrases may include: by, per hour, everyday.

Got It?

Q What will the variable represent? **[number of months allowed to purchase the DVDs using the gift certificate]**

Q What is the cost per month to rent the DVDs? **[$5]**

Q What equation will model this problem? **[$5x = 30$]**

When the coefficient of the variable in an equation is a fraction, you can use the reciprocal of the fraction to solve the equation.

Problem 5 Solving Equations Using Reciprocals

What is the solution of $\frac{4}{5}m = 28$?

$$\frac{4}{5}m = 28$$

$$\frac{5}{4}\left(\frac{4}{5}m\right) = \frac{5}{4}(28) \quad \text{Multiply each side by } \frac{5}{4}, \text{ the reciprocal of } \frac{4}{5}.$$

$$m = 35 \quad \text{Simplify.}$$

Think
Why multiply by the reciprocal?
You want the coefficient of m to be 1. The product of a number and its reciprocal is 1, so multiply by the reciprocal.

Got It? **5. a.** What is the solution of $12 = \frac{3}{4}x$? Check your answer.
b. Reasoning Are the equations $m = 18$ and $\frac{2}{3}m = 12$ equivalent? How do you know?

Problem 6 Using a One-Step Equation as a Model

Biology Toucans and blue-and-yellow macaws are both tropical birds. The length of an average toucan is about two thirds of the length of an average blue-and-yellow macaw. Toucans are about 24 in. long. What is the length of an average blue-and-yellow macaw?

Relate | length of toucan | is $\frac{2}{3}$ of | length of blue-and-yellow macaw |

Define Let ℓ = the length of an average blue-and-yellow macaw.

Think
How else can you solve this problem?
You can work backward. The toucan's length is $\frac{2}{3}$ the macaw's length, so the macaw's length is $\frac{3}{2}$ the toucan's length. You can multiply the length of the toucan by $\frac{3}{2}$.

Write $\quad 24 \quad = \frac{2}{3} \cdot \quad \ell$

$$24 = \frac{2}{3}\ell$$

$$\frac{3}{2}(24) = \frac{3}{2}\left(\frac{2}{3}\ell\right) \quad \text{Multiply each side by } \frac{3}{2}.$$

$$36 = \ell \quad \text{Simplify.}$$

An average blue-and-yellow macaw is 36 in. long.

Check $\quad 24 = \frac{2}{3}\ell$

$$24 \stackrel{?}{=} \frac{2}{3}(36) \quad \text{Substitute 36 for } \ell.$$

$$24 = 24 \quad \text{Simplify. The solution checks.}$$

Got It? **6.** An online DVD rental company offers gift certificates that you can use to purchase rental plans. You have a gift certificate for $30. The plan you select costs $5 per month. How many months can you purchase with the gift certificate?

Answers

Got It? (continued)

5. a. 16

b. Yes; multiplying each side of the second equation by the reciprocal of $\frac{2}{3}$ produces the first equation.

6. 6 months

Lesson Check

Do you know HOW?

Solve each equation. Check your answer.

1. $x + 7 = 3$

2. $9 = m - 4$

3. $5y = 24$

4. **Books** You have already read 117 pages of a book. You are one third of the way through the book. Write and solve an equation to find the number of pages in the book.

Do you UNDERSTAND?

Vocabulary Which property of equality would you use to solve each equation? Why?

5. $3 + x = -34$

6. $2x = 5$

7. $x - 4 = 9$

8. $\frac{x}{7} = 9$

9. **Reasoning** Write a one-step equation. Then write two equations that are equivalent to your equation. How can you prove that all three equations are equivalent?

 Practice and Problem-Solving Exercises

 Practice

Solve each equation using addition or subtraction. Check your answer.   **See Problems 1 and 2.**

10. $6 = x + 2$

11. $27 + n = 46$

12. $23 = v + 5$

13. $4 = q + 13$

14. $f + 9 = 20$

15. $-5 + a = 21$

16. $-17 = 3 + k$

17. $5.5 = -2 + d$

18. $c + 4 = -9$

19. $67 = w - 65$

20. $23 = b - 19$

21. $g - 3.5 = 10$

22. $y - 19 = 37$

23. $q - 11 = -9$

24. $-2.5 = p + 7.1$

25. $j - 3 = -7$

Solve each equation using multiplication or division. Check your answer.   **See Problems 3 and 4.**

26. $-8n = -64$

27. $-7y = 28$

28. $5b = 145$

29. $6a = 0.96$

30. $-96 = 4c$

31. $11 = 2.2t$

32. $17.5 = 5s$

33. $7r = -\frac{7}{2}$

34. $\frac{m}{7} = 12$

35. $35 = \frac{j}{5}$

36. $\frac{k}{7} = 13$

37. $-39 = \frac{q}{3}$

38. $14 = \frac{z}{2}$

39. $\frac{q}{-9} = -9$

40. $-13 = \frac{m}{-5}$

41. $\frac{k}{4} = -\frac{17}{2}$

Solve each equation. Check your answer.   **See Problem 5.**

42. $\frac{2}{3}q = 18$

43. $\frac{3}{4}x = 9$

44. $\frac{5}{8}y = -1$

45. $\frac{3}{5}m = -15$

46. $\frac{1}{5}x = \frac{2}{7}$

47. $36 = \frac{4}{9}d$

48. $-6 = \frac{3}{7}n$

49. $\frac{3}{8}p = 9$

Define a variable and write an equation for each situation. Then solve.   **See Problem 6.**

50. **Music** You have a rack that can hold 30 CDs. You can fit 7 more CDs on the rack before the rack is full. How many CDs are in the rack?

51. **Population** In a 3-year period, a city's population decreased by 7525 to about 581,600. What was the city's population at the beginning of the 3-year period?

3 Lesson Check

Do you know HOW?

- If students have difficulty with Exercise 4, then compare the key phrase "one third of" with the phrase "two thirds of" from Problem 6. This should help them conclude that "one third of" can be written algebraically as "$\frac{1}{3}n$," where n is the number of pages in the book.

Do you UNDERSTAND?

- For Exercise 9, it is important that students understand that applying the properties of equality and inverse operations to any equation transforms it into an equivalent equation.

Close

Q When solving a one-step equation, how do you know which operation to use in order to isolate the variable? [**Determine what operation is being performed on the variable, then use the opposite operation to isolate the variable. If a number is added to the variable, then subtract that number from both sides. If a number is subtracted from the variable, then add that number to both sides. If the variable is multiplied by a number, then divide both sides by that number. If the variable is divided by a number, then multiply both sides by that number.**]

Answers

Lesson Check

1. -4

2. 13

3. $4\frac{4}{5}$

4. $\frac{1}{3}b = 117$; 351 pages

5. Subtr. Prop. of Eq.

6. Div. Prop. of Eq.

7. Add. Prop. of Eq.

8. Mult. Prop. of Eq.

9. Check students' work.

Practice and Problem-Solving Exercises

10. 4

11. 19

12. 18

13. -9

14. 11

15. 26

16. -20

17. 7.5

18. -13

19. 132

20. 42

21. 13.5

22. 56

23. 2

24. -9.6

25. -4

26. 8

27. -4

28. 29

29. 0.16

30. -24

31. 5

32. 3.5

33. $-\frac{1}{2}$

34. 84

35. 175

36. 91

37. -117

38. 28

39. 81

40. 65

41. -34

42. 27

43. 12

44. $-1\frac{3}{5}$

45. -25

46. $1\frac{3}{7}$

47. 81

48. -14

49. 24

50. c = number of CDs already on rack; $c + 7 = 30$; 23

51. p = city's population at start of three-year period; $p - 7525 = 581,600$; 589,125

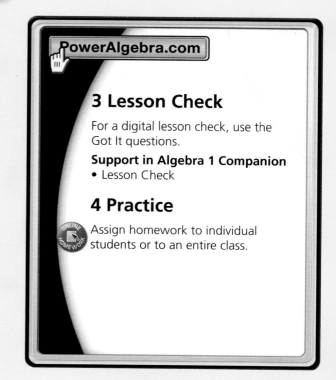

PowerAlgebra.com

3 Lesson Check

For a digital lesson check, use the Got It questions.

Support in Algebra 1 Companion
- Lesson Check

4 Practice

Assign homework to individual students or to an entire class.

4 Practice

ASSIGNMENT GUIDE

Basic: 10–54 all, 56–70 even, 71, 73

Average: 11–51 odd, 52–76

Advanced: 11–51 odd, 52–78

Standardized Test Prep: 79–81

Mixed Review: 82–88

Reasoning exercises have blue headings.

Applications exercises have red headings.

EXERCISE 73: Use the Think About a Plan worksheet in the **Practice and Problem Solving Workbook** (also available in the Teaching Resources in print and online) to further support students' development in becoming independent learners.

HOMEWORK QUICK CHECK

To check students' understanding of key skills and concepts, go over Exercises 23, 37, 52, 53, and 73.

 Apply

52. Writing If a one-step equation includes addition, should you expect to solve it by using addition? Why or why not?

53. Think About a Plan Costumes for a play at a community theater cost $1500, which is one third of the total budget. What is the total budget for the play?
- How can the model at the right help you solve the problem?
- How does the model tell you which operation to use in the equation?

⊢-------- ? --------⊣		
1500	1500	1500

54. Entertainment On a quiz show, a contestant was penalized 250 points for an incorrect answer, leaving the contestant with 1050 points. How many points did the contestant have before the penalty?

Solve each equation. Check your answer.

55. $\frac{2}{7} = \frac{1}{3} + a$

56. $23 = 7x$

57. $z - 4\frac{2}{3} = 2\frac{2}{3}$

58. $\frac{2}{3}g = -4\frac{1}{2}$

59. $6\frac{1}{4} = \frac{r}{5}$

60. $h + 2.8 = -3.7$

61. $\frac{3}{2}f = \frac{1}{2}$

62. $-4 = \frac{2}{9}d$

63. $1.6m = 1.28$

64. $4d = -2.4$

65. $4\frac{1}{4} = 1\frac{3}{4} + p$

66. $-5.3 + z = 8.9$

67. $-2\frac{1}{2} = \frac{t}{10}$

68. $5b = 8.5$

69. $\frac{3}{5}n = -\frac{3}{10}$

70. Picnics At a party of 102 people, 17 lb of potato salad is served.
a. Write and solve an equation to find how many people each pound of potato salad serves.
b. Write and solve an equation to find the average number of pounds of potato salad that each person is served. Round your answer to the nearest hundredth.

71. Error Analysis Describe and correct the error in solving the equation at the right.

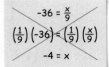

72. U.S. History Between 1788 and 2008, the U.S. Constitution was amended 27 times. How many years have passed on average between one amendment and the next, to the nearest tenth of a year?

73. Volleyball In volleyball, players serve the ball to the opposing team. If the opposing team fails to hit the ball, the service is called an ace. A player's ace average is the number of aces served divided by the number of games played. A certain player has an ace average of 0.3 and has played in 70 games this season. How many aces has the player served?

74. Open-Ended Write a problem that you can model with a one-step equation. Write the equation and solve the problem.

75. Language According to one count, the letter *e* makes up one eighth of a typical document written in English. A document contains 2800 letters. About how many letters in the document are *not e*?

Answers

Practice and Problem-Solving Exercises (continued)

52. Answers may vary. Sample: Normally you would use subtraction. You could use addition by adding to each side of the equation the additive inverse of the term you would have subtracted.

53. $4500

54. 1300 pts

55. $-\frac{1}{21}$

56. $3\frac{2}{7}$

57. $7\frac{1}{3}$

58. $-6\frac{3}{4}$

59. $31\frac{1}{4}$

60. -6.5

61. $\frac{1}{3}$

62. -18

63. 0.8

64. -0.6

65. $2\frac{1}{2}$

66. 14.2

67. -25

68. 1.7

69. $-\frac{1}{2}$

70. a. $17p = 102; 6$
b. $102p = 17; 0.17$

71. Each side of the equation should be multiplied by 9 not $\frac{1}{9}$; $(9)(-36) = (9)\left(\frac{x}{9}\right)$, so $x = -324$.

72. 8.1 yr

73. 21 aces

74. Check students' work.

75. 2450 letters

76. Typography A point is a unit of length that can be used to measure the distance between two lines of text. Font sizes are often stated in points. Capital letters measure two thirds of the stated point size, as shown in the diagram for a font size of 48 points. There are 72 points in 1 inch. What point size produces capital letters that are $\frac{1}{2}$ in. tall?

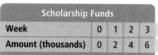

© Challenge **77. Reasoning** In a school's musical, a choir member sang in the backup chorus for half the songs in the show, which was 12 songs. A student concludes that one half of 12 is 6, so there were 6 songs in the show. Write an equation that would help the student understand the correct number of songs in the musical.

78. Cooking Uncooked rice has about $\frac{4}{13}$ the weight of cooked rice. You want to make 6.5 lb of rice for a recipe. How many pounds of uncooked rice do you need?

Standardized Test Prep

SAT/ACT **79.** Luis helped raise money for his school by jogging in the school jog-a-thon. The total amount of money he raised can be represented by the expression $1.75m$, where m is the number of miles he jogged. If Luis raised a total of $21, how many miles did he jog?

(A) 12   (B) 19.25   (C) 22.75   (D) 36.75

80. What operation should you use to solve $14 + c = 39$?

(F) squaring   (G) subtraction   (H) multiplication   (I) division

81. Sonya is checking orders at the fabric store where she works. Some of the orders are in decimals and some are in fractions. Which of the following statements is *not* true?

(A) $\frac{10}{4} = 2.5$ (B) $1.3 = 1\frac{1}{3}$ (C) $0.03 = \frac{3}{100}$ (D) $\frac{6}{5} = 1.2$

Mixed Review

82. If the pattern shown in the table continues, what amount will have been raised by Week 5?

Scholarship Funds				
Week	0	1	2	3
Amount (thousands)	0	2	4	6

See Lesson 1-9.

Simplify each expression. Justify each step. *See Lesson 1-4.*

83. $4(13x)$ **84.** $2.2 + (3.8 - x)$ **85.** $(m + 4.5) - 0.5$

Get Ready! To prepare for Lesson 2-2, do Exercises 86–88.

Simplify each expression. *See Lesson 1-2.*

86. $2[2 - (2 - 3) - 2]$ **87.** $\left(\frac{1}{2} + \frac{1}{3}\right)^2$ **88.** $-1 + 2 \cdot 3 - 4$

76. 54 points   **77.** $\frac{1}{2}s = 12$ **84.** $6 - x$ **85.** $m + 4$
78. 2 lb   **79.** A   **86.** 2   **87.** $\frac{25}{36}$
80. G   **81.** B   **88.** 1
82. 10,000   **83.** $52x$

Additional Instructional Support

Algebra 1 Companion

Students can use the **Algebra 1 Companion** worktext (4 pages) as you teach the lesson. Use the Companion to support

- New Vocabulary
- Key Concepts
- Got It for each Problem
- Lesson Check

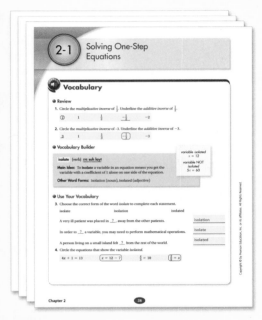

ELL Support

Use Graphic Organizers Have students fold a sheet of paper twice to form four equal sections. As students label each section with a property of equality, discuss their meanings. Write the equations $x - 4 = 5$, $x + 4 = 5$, $4x = 5$, $\frac{x}{4} = 5$ on the board. Invite volunteers to classify each equation according to the property of equality that is necessary to solve it. Then have students suggest additional equations, and record the equations in the appropriate sections of their papers.

Use Manipulatives In small groups, use algebra tiles to demonstrate $x + 18 = 33$. Talk through the manipulation of the tiles as you are doing it. Then, have students talk through the same equation. Provide other equations for students to use. Talk through $x + 5 = -3$, using negative tiles.

5 Assess & Remediate

Lesson Quiz

1. What is the solution of $x + 11 = -14$?
2. What is the solution of $-6 + a = 22$?
3. What is the solution of $3x = \frac{6}{7}$?
4. What is the solution of $\frac{x}{5} = -12$?
5. What is the solution of $\frac{2}{3}x = 12$?
6. **Do you UNDERSTAND?** The average home size in the United States in 1970 was 1,400 square feet. The average size was about $\frac{5}{3}$ times as great in 2004. What was the average home size in 2004?

ANSWERS TO LESSON QUIZ

1. -25
2. 28
3. $\frac{2}{7}$
4. -60
5. 18
6. about 2333 square feet

PRESCRIPTION FOR REMEDIATION
Use the student work on the Lesson Quiz to prescribe a differentiated review assignment.

Points	Differentiated Remediation
0–3	Intervention
4–5	On-level
6	Extension

PowerAlgebra.com

5 Assess & Remediate

Assign the Lesson Quiz. Appropriate intervention, practice, or enrichment is automatically generated based on student performance.

Intervention

- **Reteaching** (2 pages) Provides reteaching and practice exercises for the key lesson concepts. Use with struggling students or absent students.
- **English Language Learner Support** Helps students develop and reinforce mathematical vocabulary and key concepts.

All-in-One Resources/Online
Reteaching

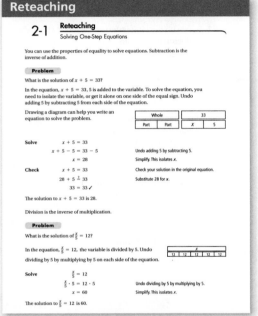

All-in-One Resources/Online
English Language Learner Support

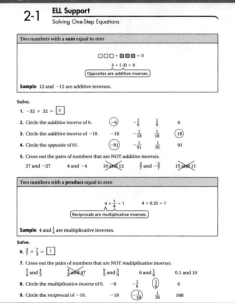

Differentiated Remediation *continued*

On-Level

- **Practice** (2 pages) Provides extra practice for each lesson. For simpler practice exercises, use the Form K Practice pages found in the All-in-One Teaching Resources and online.

- **Think About a Plan** Helps students develop specific problem-solving skills and strategies by providing scaffolded guiding questions.

- **Standardized Test Prep** Focuses on all major exercises, all major question types, and helps students prepare for the high-stakes assessments.

Extension

- **Enrichment** Provides students with interesting problems and activities that extend the concepts of the lesson.

- **Activities, Games, and Puzzles** Worksheets that can be used for concepts development, enrichment, and for fun!

Practice and Problem Solving WKBK/ All-in-One Resources/Online
Practice page 1

2-1 Practice — Form G
Solving One-Step Equations

Solve each equation using addition or subtraction. Check your answer.

1. $8 = a - 2$ 10
2. $x + 7 = 11$ 4
3. $r - 2 = -6$ −4
4. $-18 = m + 12$ −30
5. $f + 10 = -10$ −20
6. $-1 = n + 5$ −6

Solve each equation using multiplication or division. Check your answer.

7. $-3p = -48$ 16
8. $-98 = 7t$ −14
9. $-4.4 = -4y$ 1.1
10. $2.8c = 4.2$ 1.5
11. $\frac{k}{6} = 8$ 48
12. $16 = \frac{w}{8}$ 128
13. $-9 = \frac{y}{-3}$ 27
14. $\frac{h}{10} = \frac{-22}{5}$ −44

Solve each equation. Check your answer.

15. $\frac{3}{5}n = 12$ 20
16. $-4 = \frac{2}{3}b$ −6
17. $\frac{5}{8}x = -15$ −24
18. $\frac{1}{4}z = \frac{2}{5}$ $\frac{8}{5}$

19. Jeremy mowed several lawns to earn money for camp. After he paid $17 for gas, he had $75 leftover to pay towards camp. Write and solve an equation to find how much money Jeremy earned mowing lawns. $m - 17 = 75;$ $92

Practice and Problem Solving WKBK/ All-in-One Resources/Online
Practice page 2

2-1 Practice (continued) — Form G
Solving One-Step Equations

Define a variable and write an equation for each situation. Then solve.

20. Susan's cell phone plan allows her to use 950 minutes per month with no additional charge. She has 188 minutes left for this month. How many minutes has she already used this month? $n + 188 = 950;$ 762 minutes

21. In the fifth year of operation, the profit of a company was 3 times the profit it earned in the first year of operation. If its profit was $114,000 in the fifth year of operation, what was the profit in the first year? $3p = 114,000;$ $38,000

Solve each equation. Check your answer.

22. $-9x = 48$ $-5\frac{1}{3}$
23. $-\frac{7}{8} = \frac{2}{3} + n$ $-\frac{37}{24}$
24. $a + 1\frac{1}{4} = 2\frac{7}{10}$ $1\frac{9}{20}$
25. $-7t = 5.6$ −0.8
26. $2.3 = -7.9 + y$ 10.2
27. $\frac{2}{3}p = \frac{8}{5}$ $\frac{8}{5}$
28. $\frac{x}{8} = -\frac{3}{4}$ −6
29. $\frac{m}{8} = 8\frac{1}{3}$ $66\frac{2}{3}$

30. A community center is serving a free meal to senior citizens. The center plans to feed 700 people in 4 hours.
   a. Write and solve an equation to find the average number of people the center is planning to feed each hour. $4a = 700;$ 175
   b. During the first hour and a half, the center fed 270 people. Write and solve an equation to find the number of people that remain to be fed. $700 = n + 270;$ 430 people

---

All-in-One Resources/Online
Enrichment

2-1 Enrichment
Solving One-Step Equations

Equivalent equations are equations that have the same solution(s). For example, the equations $\frac{x}{3} = 6$ and $x - 12 = 12$ are equivalent because the solution of each is $x = 18$. Every equation has many equivalent equations.

There are four different forms of equations representing the four different operations mentioned in the lesson. If a and b represent constants, the different forms can be represented by the following equations:

1) $x + a = b$
2) $ax = b$
3) $x - a = b$
4) $\frac{x}{a} = b$

Determine which equations in the following exercises are equivalent, justify your answer. If they are not, explain.

1. $-2x = 14$ $x - 8 = -15$ $\frac{x}{7} = -1$ $-19 = x - 12$
   all equations are equivalent; for all, $x = -7$
2. $y - 8 = 12$ $\frac{y}{2} = 2$ $2y = 40$ $-22 = y - 42$
   first, third, and fourth equations are equivalent; $y = 20$ except for the second equation where $y = 4$
3. $-6n = -12$ $n + 8 = 6$ $-4 = n - 2$ $\frac{n}{2} = 1$
   first and fourth equations are equivalent ($n = 2$); second and third equations are equivalent ($n = -2$);

For each of the following equations, find three equivalent equations in the three other forms that are different from the original equation. For example, $x + 3 = 5, 3x = 6,$ and $\frac{x}{2} = 1$ are equivalent because $x = 2$ is the solution of each equation.

4. $x + 6 = -5$
   Answers may vary. Sample: The solution of the given equation is $x = -11$, so $20 + x = 9, 3x = -33$, and $x + 2 = -9$ are equivalent.
5. $8x = -24$
   Answers may vary. Sample: The solution of $8x = -24$, is −3, so $10 + x = 7, 15 - x = 18$, and $5x = -15$ are equivalent.
6. $\frac{x}{3} = -9$
   Answers may vary. Sample: The solution $\frac{x}{3} = -9$ is −27, so $x + 30 = 3, 4x = -108,$ and $x - 6 = -33$ are equivalent.
7. $14 = x - 18$
   Answers may vary. Sample: The solution of $14 = x - 18$, is 32. So, $x - 10 = 22, \frac{x}{8} = 4,$ and $x + 15 = 47$ are equivalent.

Practice and Problem Solving WKBK/ All-in-One Resources/Online
Think About a Plan

2-1 Think About a Plan
Solving One-Step Equations

Volleyball In volleyball, players serve the ball to the opposing team. If the opposing team fails to hit the ball, the service is called an ace. A player's ace average is the number of aces served divided by the number of games played. A certain player has an ace average of 0.3 and has played in 70 games this season. How many aces has the player served?

Understanding the Problem

1. What values are you given?
   a player's ace average, 0.3, and the number of games the player played, 70

Planning the Solution

2. Write an expression, using words, to represent the relationship between ace average, number of aces, and the number of games played.

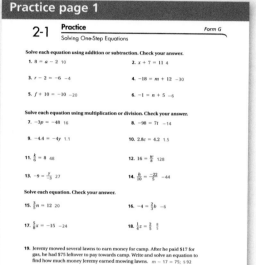

   Ace Average = $\dfrac{\text{number of aces served}}{\text{number of games played}}$

3. Use the expression to write an equation, where A = number of aces.

   $0.3 = \dfrac{A}{70}$

Getting an Answer

4. Solve the equation you wrote in Step 3.
   21

5. Explain what this solution represents.
   the number of aces served

6. Is your answer reasonable? Explain.
   yes; $\frac{21}{70}$ is a little less than $\frac{1}{3}$ or about 0.3

Practice and Problem Solving WKBK/ All-in-One Resources/Online
Standardized Test Prep

2-1 Standardized Test Prep
Solving One-Step Equations

Multiple Choice

For Exercises 1–6, choose the correct letter.

1. What is the solution of $-3 = x + 5$? B
   A. −15   B. −8   C. 2   D. 8

2. What operation should you use to solve $-6x = -24$? I
   F. addition   G. subtraction   H. multiplication   I. division

3. Which of the following solutions is true for $\frac{x}{3} = \frac{1}{4}$? C
   A. $-2\frac{3}{4}$ B. $\frac{1}{12}$ C. $\frac{3}{4}$ D. $3\frac{1}{4}$

4. There are 37 more cats c than dogs d in an animal shelter. If there are 78 cats at the shelter, which equation represents the relationship between the number of cats and dogs? F
   F. $d + 37 = 78$ G. $d - 37 = 78$ H. $c + 37 = 78$ I. $c - 37 = 78$

5. Which property of equality should you use to solve $6x = 48$? D
   A. Addition Property of Equality
   B. Subtraction Property of Equality
   C. Multiplication Property of Equality
   D. Division Property of Equality

6. Shelly completed 10 problems of her homework in study hall. This is $\frac{2}{5}$ of the total assignment. How many problems does she have left to complete? G
   F. 20   G. 25   H. 30   I. 35

Short Response

7. A high school marching band has 55 male members. It is determined that five-eighths of the band members are male.
   a. What equation represents the total number of members in the band? $\frac{5}{8}n = 55;$
   b. How many members are in the band? 88 band members
   [2] Both parts answered correctly.
   [1] One part answered correctly.
   [0] Neither part answered correctly.

Online Teacher Resource Center
Activities, Games, and Puzzles

2-1 Game: Algebra 1-Step
Solving One-Step Equations

This is a game for three or more players. Your teacher will provide you with a blank scoring card.

- Players use the scoring card to place the integers from −12 to 12 in the twenty-four squares in any arrangement they choose. A sample is shown. Each integer is used once; do not use 0.
- A student or the teacher can serve as the game's caller.
- The caller randomly announces one of the exercise numbers to the left of an equation below. Players solve the equation called. If the solution is one of the numbers on his or her scoring card, then the player marks an X in the appropriate box. The equation is then crossed out.
- The first player to have Xs in all boxes in any row, column, or diagonal wins the game. The caller checks to be sure the scoring card is indeed correct. See Teacher Instructions page.

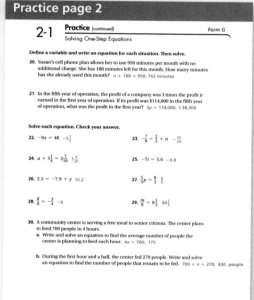

	S	T	E	P
6	−12	−1	1	7
−2	11	−5	12	−3
3	−6		9	2
−7	8	−8	10	−4
5	−11	−9	4	−10

1. $\frac{1}{5}t = 10$
2. $80x = -640$
3. $a + 5 = 9$
4. $b - 7 = -19$
5. $5d = 35$
6. $-4x = -24$
7. $\frac{1}{4}z = -1$
8. $30x = 90$
9. $12 = -\frac{1}{3}t$
10. $8 + n = 13$
11. $10 = g + 17$
12. $10r = -60$
13. $5t = 10$
14. $-\frac{m}{9} = 1$
15. $y + 18 = 28$
16. $y - 17 = -28$
17. $-15x = 90$
18. $100k = 100$
19. $-\frac{a}{5} = \frac{1}{5}$
20. $3p = -9$
21. $8 + w = 20$
22. $u + 12 = 23$
23. $-10x = 100$
24. $j + 19 = 28$
25. $5g = 40$
26. $8x = 104$
27. $2x = -10$
28. $x + 156 = 154$
29. $\frac{1}{10}g = -5$
30. $9 + b = 18$
31. $-\frac{t}{7} = 2$
32. $s - 19 = 24$
33. $-2x = 28$
34. $a + 5 = -10$
35. $27 = y + 20$
36. $-11r = -33$

1 Interactive Learning

Solve It!

PURPOSE To develop the algebraic reasoning skills needed to solve two-step linear equations by working with a concrete model

PROCESS Students may

- guess and check what must be in a chest.
- mentally determine the amount of money that must be in the chest to make the game fair.
- draw a sketch and cross out money (and chest as necessary) from each side.

FACILITATE

Q Compare this Solve It to the Solve It from Lesson 2-1. The Solve It in Lesson 2-1 modeled the equation $30 = x + 11$. How is this Solve It the same? How is it different?

ANSWERS See Solve It in Answers on next page.

CONNECT THE MATH Though the exact amount in the chest is not yet known, students understand that it is a quantity that can be added, subtracted, multiplied, and divided. Similarly, students learn to perform various mathematical operations on unknown quantities represented by a variable. Similarly, unknown quantities represented by the same variable can be added or subtracted from each side of an equation.

2-2 Solving Two-Step Equations

Indiana Academic Standard
A1.2.5 Solve problems that can be modeled using linear equations and inequalities, interpret the solutions, and determine whether the solutions are reasonable.

Objective To solve two-step equations in one variable

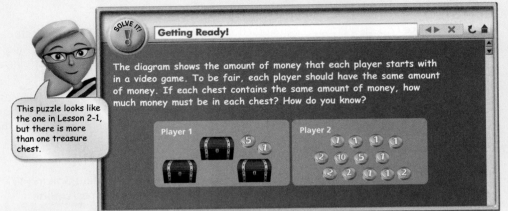

This puzzle looks like the one in Lesson 2-1, but there is more than one treasure chest.

Getting Ready!

The diagram shows the amount of money that each player starts with in a video game. To be fair, each player should have the same amount of money. If each chest contains the same amount of money, how much money must be in each chest? How do you know?

Player 1

Player 2

Dynamic Activity
Solving Two-Step Equations

The problem in the Solve It can be modeled by an equation. The equations in this lesson are different from the equations in Lesson 2-1 because they require two steps to solve.

Essential Understanding To solve two-step equations, you can use the properties of equality and inverse operations to form a series of simpler equivalent equations. You can use the properties of equality repeatedly to isolate the variable.

A two-step equation, like the one shown below, involves two operations.

Multiplication   Addition

$$2x + 3 = 15$$

To solve a two-step equation, identify the operations and undo them using inverse operations. You can undo the operations in the reverse order of the order of operations. For example, to solve $2x + 3 = 15$, you can use subtraction first to undo the addition, and then use division to undo the multiplication.

2-2 Preparing to Teach

BIG ideas Equivalence
Solving Equations & Inequalities

UbD

ESSENTIAL UNDERSTANDINGS

- Equivalent equations are equations that have the same solution(s).
- The solution of a two-step equation can be found using the properties of equality and inverse operations to form a series of simpler equations.
- The properties of equality can be used repeatedly to isolate the variable.

Math Background

There is more than one way to solve two-step equations like $2x + 3 = 15$. You could multiply each side by $\frac{1}{2}$ (obtaining $x + 1\frac{1}{2} = 7\frac{1}{2}$) or you could subtract 3 from each side (obtaining $2x = 12$). Knowing that there are two ways will be

helpful with more complex equations. As a routine approach to solving two-step equations, students can choose to undo operations in the reverse order of the order of operations. In the expression $2x + 3$, x is first multiplied by 2, then 3 is added. Reversing the order means first subtracting 3 from each side of the equation, then dividing each side by 2.

Support Student Learning

Use the **Algebra I Companion** to engage and support students during instructions. See Lesson Resources at the end of this lesson for details.

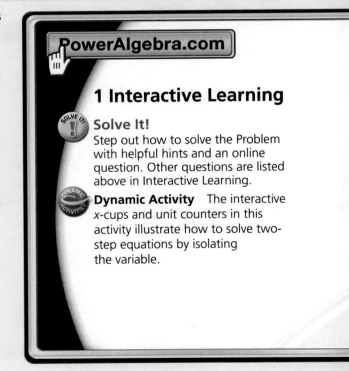

PowerAlgebra.com

1 Interactive Learning

Solve It!
Step out how to solve the Problem with helpful hints and an online question. Other questions are listed above in Interactive Learning.

Dynamic Activity The interactive x-cups and unit counters in this activity illustrate how to solve two-step equations by isolating the variable.

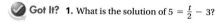 **Problem 1** Solving a Two-Step Equation

 Think

What operations are used in the equation?
The equation uses multiplication and addition. You can undo the addition first, and then the multiplication.

What is the solution of $2x + 3 = 15$?

$$2x + 3 = 15$$
$$2x + 3 - 3 = 15 - 3 \quad \text{Subtract 3 from each side.}$$
$$2x = 12 \quad \text{Simplify.}$$
$$\frac{2x}{2} = \frac{12}{2} \quad \text{Divide each side by 2.}$$
$$x = 6 \quad \text{Simplify.}$$

Check $2x + 3 = 15$
$$2(6) + 3 \overset{?}{=} 15 \quad \text{Substitute 6 for } x.$$
$$15 = 15 \quad \text{Simplify. The solution checks.}$$

✓ **Got It?** **1.** What is the solution of $5 = \frac{t}{2} - 3$?

Problem 2 Using an Equation as a Model

Community Service You are making a bulletin board to advertise community service opportunities in your town. You plan to use half a sheet of construction paper for each ad. You need 5 sheets of construction paper for a title banner. You have 18 sheets of construction paper. How many ads can you make?

Know	Need	Plan
• Paper per ad: $\frac{1}{2}$ sheet • Paper for banner: 5 sheets • Total paper: 18 sheets	The number of ads you can make	Write and solve an equation. Let the variable represent the unknown.

 Think

How can a model help you write the equation?
The model shows that a half of a sheet per ad plus 5 sheets for the title banner is equal to 18 sheets.

18	
$\frac{1}{2}a$	5

Let a = the number of ads you can make.

$$\frac{1}{2}a + 5 = 18$$
$$\frac{1}{2}a + 5 - 5 = 18 - 5 \quad \text{Subtract 5 from each side.}$$
$$\frac{1}{2}a = 13 \quad \text{Simplify.}$$
$$2\left(\frac{1}{2}a\right) = 2(13) \quad \text{Multiply each side by 2.}$$
$$a = 26 \quad \text{Simplify.}$$

You can make 26 community service advertisements for the bulletin board.

✓ **Got It?** **2.** Suppose you used one quarter of a sheet of paper for each ad and four full sheets for the title banner in Problem 2. How many ads could you make?

---

2 Guided Instruction

Problem 1

Q To evaluate the expression $2x + 3$, what operations do you perform, and in what order? **[Multiply by 2, and then add 3.]**

Q To solve $2x + 3 = 15$, how will inverse operations be used? **[The inverse operation of addition will be used to remove the 3 from the side with the variable, so subtract 3. Then the inverse operation of multiplication is used to isolate the variable, so divide by 2.]**

Got It?

Q To evaluate the expression $\frac{t}{2} - 3$, what operations do you perform, and in what order? **[First divide by 2, and then subtract 3.]**

Q To solve $5 = \frac{t}{2} - 3$, what operations should you perform, and in what order? **[First add 3, and then multiply by 2.]**

Problem 2

Q What does $\frac{1}{2}a$ represent in the equation? **[the amount of paper used for the ads]**

Q What does the 5 represent? **[the amount of paper used for the banner]**

Q Why don't you multiply the 5 by a? **[Because the amount of paper used for the banner is constant. It is not affected by how many ads are made.]**

Got It?

Q How does the equation in Problem 2 change? **[The $\frac{1}{2}$ becomes $\frac{1}{4}$; the five becomes four. The eighteen does not change because the amount of paper you have does not change.]**

---

2 Guided Instruction

Each Problem is worked out and supported online.

Problem 1
Solving a Two-Step Equation

Alternative Problem 1
Solving a Two-Step Equation
Animated

Problem 2
Using an Equation as a Model
Animated

Problem 3
Solving With Two Terms in the Numerator
Animated

Problem 4
Using Deductive Reasoning

Support in Algebra 1 Companion
• Vocabulary
• Key Concepts
• Got It?

Answers

Solve It!
8; explanations may vary.

Got It?
1. 16
2. 56 ads

Problem 3   ERROR PREVENTION

Students may not recognize the order of operations. Explain that in $\frac{x-7}{3}$, the fraction bar is a grouping symbol so the expression can be written as $(x-7) \div 3$.

Q To evaluate the expression $(x-7) \div 3$, what operations do you perform, and in what order? **[First subtract 7, and then divide by 3.]**

Q To solve the equation $\frac{x-7}{3} = -12$, what will be the first step? Why? **[Multiply by 3; you perform the opposite operation of the last step used when evaluating the expression.]**

Q What is the last step in solving the equation? Why? **[Add 7; you perform the opposite operation of the first step used when evaluating the expression.]**

Got It?

Q What is the result of rewriting $\frac{x-2}{4}$ as the difference of two fractions? $\left[\frac{x}{4} - \frac{2}{4}\right]$

Q Was the method used in 3a or 3b more efficient? Explain. **[They are the same. If you multiply each side of each equation by 4, the resulting equation is identical.]**

Problem 4

Q What is deductive reasoning? **[the process of reasoning logically from given statements to a conclusion]**

Got It?

Q Which properties of equality should you use to solve the equation? **[Addition and Multiplication Properties of Equality]**

When one side of an equation is a fraction with more than one term in the numerator, you can still undo division by multiplying each side by the denominator.

 Problem 3   **Solving With Two Terms in the Numerator**

Plan

What operation should you perform first?
Multiplication. When you multiply by the denominator of the fraction in the equation, you get a one-step equation. So, multiplying first gets rid of the fraction.

What is the solution of $\frac{x-7}{3} = -12$?

$$\frac{x-7}{3} = -12$$

$$3\left(\frac{x-7}{3}\right) = 3(-12) \qquad \text{Multiply each side by 3.}$$

$$x - 7 = -36 \qquad \text{Simplify.}$$

$$x - 7 + 7 = -36 + 7 \qquad \text{Add 7 to each side.}$$

$$x = -29 \qquad \text{Simplify.}$$

 Got It? 3. a. What is the solution of $6 = \frac{x-2}{4}$?

     b. Reasoning Write the right side of the equation in part (a) as the difference of two fractions. Solve the equation. Did you find the equation in part (a) or the rewritten equation easier to solve? Why?

When you use deductive reasoning, you must state your steps and your reason for each step using properties, definitions, or rules. In Problem 4, you are asked to provide the reasons for each step of the problem using deductive reasoning.

 Problem 4   **Using Deductive Reasoning**

What is the solution of $-t + 8 = 3$? Justify each step.

Steps	Reasons
$-t + 8 = 3$	Original equation
$-t + 8 - 8 = 3 - 8$	Subtraction Property of Equality
$-t = -5$	Use subtraction to simplify.
$-1t = -5$	Multiplicative Property of -1
$\frac{-1t}{-1} = \frac{-5}{-1}$	Division Property of Equality
$t = 5$	Use division to simplify.

Think

Why isn't $-t = -5$ the solution?
When you solve for a variable, the coefficient must be 1, not -1.

 Got It? 4. What is the solution of $\frac{x}{3} - 5 = 4$? Justify each step.

Additional Problems

1. What is the solution of $2x + 11 = 51$?

   ANSWER 20

2. A train is 100 miles away from a station. It is approaching the station at 40 miles per hour. How long will it take for the train to arrive?

   ANSWER 2.5 h

3. What is the solution of $\frac{x+5}{6} = 15$?

   ANSWER 85

4. What is the solution of $10 + 2x = 20$? Justify each step.

   ANSWER The steps are:

   (1) $10 + 2x = 20$
   (2) $10 - 10 + 2x = 20 - 10$
   (3) $2x = 10$
   (4) $\frac{2x}{2} = \frac{10}{2}$
   (5) $x = 5$

   The reasons are:

   (1) original equation
   (2) Subtraction Property of Equality
   (3) Simplify.
   (4) Division Property of Equality
   (5) Simplify.

Answers

Got It? (continued)

3. a. 26

   b. $6 = \frac{x}{4} - \frac{2}{4}$; 26; Answers may vary. Sample: The equation in 3a is easier because it uses fewer fractions.

4. $\frac{x}{3} - 5 + 5 = 4 + 5$ Add. Prop. of Eq.

   $\frac{x}{3} = 9$ Use addition to simplify.

   $\frac{x}{3} \cdot 3 = 9 \cdot 3$ Mult. Prop. of Eq.

   $x = 27$

   Use multiplication to simplify.

Lesson Check

Do you know HOW?

Solve each equation. Check your answer.

1. $5x + 12 = -13$ **2.** $6 = \frac{m}{7} - 3$

3. $\frac{y-1}{4} = -2$ **4.** $-x - 4 = 9$

5. Fundraising The junior class is selling granola bars to raise money. They purchased 1250 granola bars and paid a delivery fee of $25. The total cost, including the delivery fee, was $800. What was the cost of each granola bar?

Do you UNDERSTAND?

What properties of equality would you use to solve each equation? What operation would you perform first? Explain.

6. $-8 = \frac{s}{4} + 3$ **7.** $2x - 9 = 7$

8. $\frac{x}{3} - 8 = 4$ **9.** $-4x + 3 = -5$

10. Reasoning Can you solve the equation $\frac{d-3}{5} = 6$ by adding 3 before multiplying by 5? Explain.

Practice and Problem-Solving Exercises

 Practice

Solve each equation. Check your answer.   ← **See Problem 1.**

11. $2 + \frac{a}{4} = -1$ **12.** $3n - 4 = 11$ **13.** $-1 = 7 + 8x$ **14.** $\frac{y}{5} + 2 = -8$

15. $4b + 6 = -2$ **16.** $10 = \frac{x}{4} - 8$ **17.** $10 + \frac{h}{3} = 1$ **18.** $-14 = -5 + 3c$

19. $26 = \frac{m}{6} + 5$ **20.** $\frac{a}{5} - 18 = 2$ **21.** $-5x - 2 = 13$ **22.** $14 = -2k + 3$

Define a variable and write an equation for each situation. Then solve.   ← **See Problem 2.**

23. Maximum Capacity A delivery person uses a service elevator to bring boxes of books up to an office. The delivery person weighs 160 lb and each box of books weighs 50 lb. The maximum capacity of the elevator is 1000 lb. How many boxes of books can the delivery person bring up at one time?

24. Shopping You have $16 and a coupon for a $5 discount at a local supermarket. A bottle of olive oil costs $7. How many bottles of olive oil can you buy?

25. Rentals Two college friends rent an apartment. They have to pay the landlord two months' rent and a $500 security deposit when they sign the lease. The total amount they pay the landlord is $2800. What is the rent for one month?

Solve each equation. Check your answer.   ← **See Problem 3.**

26. $\frac{y-4}{2} = 10$ **27.** $7 = \frac{x-8}{3}$ **28.** $\frac{z+10}{9} = 2$ **29.** $4 = \frac{a+10}{2}$

30. $7\frac{1}{2} = \frac{x+3}{2}$ **31.** $\frac{b+3}{5} = -1$ **32.** $-2 = \frac{d-7}{7}$ **33.** $\frac{g-3}{3} = \frac{5}{3}$

Solve each equation. Justify each step.   ← **See Problem 4.**

34. $14 - b = 19$ **35.** $20 - 3h = 2$ **36.** $3 - \frac{x}{2} = 6$ **37.** $-1 = 4 + \frac{x}{3}$

Answers

Lesson Check

1. -5 **2.** 63 **3.** -7

4. -13 **5.** $.62

6. Subtr. Prop. of Eq. and Mult. Prop. of Eq.; subtr.

7. Add. Prop. of Eq. and Div. Prop. of Eq.; add.

8. Add. Prop. of Eq. and Mult. Prop. of Eq.; add.

9. Subtr. Prop. of Eq. and Div. Prop. of Eq.; subtr.

10. Answers may vary. Sample: No, you must either multiply both sides by 5 first or write the left side as the difference of two fractions and then add $\frac{3}{5}$ to both sides.

Practice and Problem-Solving Exercises

11. -12 **12.** 5 **13.** -1

14. -50 **15.** -2 **16.** 72

17. -27 **18.** -3 **19.** 126

20. 100 **21.** -3 **22.** -5.5

23. 16 boxes   **24.** 3 bottles

25. $1150   **26.** 24 **27.** 29

28. 8 **29.** -2 **30.** 12 **31.** -8

32. -7 **33.** 8 **34.** -5 **35.** 6

36. -6 **37.** -15

---

3 Lesson Check

Do you know HOW?

- If students have difficulty translating Exercise 5 into an equation, then refer to Problem 2 and review the Know, Need, Plan method.

Do you UNDERSTAND?

- If students have difficulty with Exercise 10, then refer to the Error Prevention that accompanies Problem 3. If students add first, they must rewrite the problem as $\frac{d}{5} - \frac{3}{5} = 6$. This shows that $\frac{3}{5}$, and not 3, is added.

Close

> **Q** How can you determine a good first step in solving a two-step equation? **[Determine what operations are being performed in the original equation, and in what order. Once you have determined the operation that is performed last, apply the inverse of that operation to both sides of the equation.]**

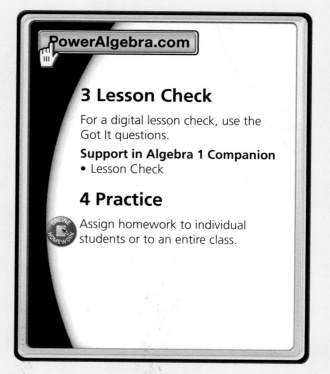

PowerAlgebra.com

3 Lesson Check

For a digital lesson check, use the Got It questions.

Support in Algebra 1 Companion
- Lesson Check

4 Practice

Assign homework to individual students or to an entire class.

4 Practice

ASSIGNMENT GUIDE

Basic: 11–37 all, 38–56 even, 59

Average: 11–37 odd, 38–60

Advanced: 11–37 odd, 38–65

Standardized Test Prep: 66–68

Mixed Review: 69–78

Reasoning exercises have blue headings.

Applications exercises have red headings.

EXERCISE 59: Use the Think About a Plan worksheet in the **Practice and Problem Solving Workbook** (also available in the Teaching Resources in print and online) to further support students' development in becoming independent learners.

HOMEWORK QUICK CHECK

To check students' understanding of key skills and concepts, go over Exercises 17, 25, 51, 56, and 59.

 Apply

Solve each equation. Check your answer.

38. $\frac{2+y}{3} = -1$ **39.** $-24 = -10t + 3$ **40.** $10 = 0.3x - 9.1$

41. $\frac{1}{2} = \frac{1}{2}c - 2$ **42.** $\frac{x-3}{3} = -4\frac{1}{2}$ **43.** $9.4 = -d + 5.6$

44. $\frac{d+17}{2} = 5\frac{1}{3}$ **45.** $2.4 + 10m = 6.89$ **46.** $\frac{1}{5}t - 3 = -17$

Solve each equation. Justify each step.

47. $15 = 9 - 3p$ **48.** $4 - 5k = -16$ **49.** $9 + \frac{c}{-5} = -5$ **50.** $\frac{q}{-3} + 12 = 2$

51. Error Analysis Describe and correct the error in finding the solution of the equation at the right.

52. Writing Without solving the equation $-3x + 5 = 44$, tell whether the value of x is positive or negative. How do you know?

53. a. Solve the equation $2x - 1 = 7$ by undoing subtraction first.
  b. Solve the equation in part (a) by undoing multiplication first. Do you get the same answer you got in part (a)?
  c. Reasoning Which method from parts (a) and (b) do you prefer? Explain.

Geometry In each triangle, the measure of $\angle A$ equals the measure of $\angle B$. Find the value of x.

54.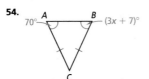

55.

56. Think About a Plan A Web site allows musicians to post their songs online. Then people using the Web site can buy any of the posted songs. Suppose each musician must pay a one-time fee of $5 to use the Web site. Each musician earns $.09 every time a particular song of his or hers is downloaded. If a musician earned $365 for a particular song, how many times was the song downloaded?
  • How can the model at the right help you solve the problem?
  • How does the model tell you which operations to use in the equation?

⊢-------- 365 --------⊣

| 0.09x | −5 |

57. Open-Ended Write a real-world problem that you can model with the two-step equation $8b + 6 = 38$. Then solve the problem.

58. Home Improvement A contractor is adding a back porch on to a house. The porch needs to hold 20 people and furniture that weighs 250 lb. The contractor calculates that the porch needs to hold 3750 lb to meet that specification. What value did the contractor use for the weight of a person?

Answers

Practice and Problem-Solving Exercises
(continued)

38. −5   **39.** 2.7

40. $63.\overline{6}$ **41.** 5

42. $-10\frac{1}{2}$ **43.** −3.8

44. $-6\frac{1}{3}$ **45.** 0.449

46. −70

47. $15 - 9 = 9 - 3p - 9$ Subt. Prop. of Eq.
  $6 = -3p$ Use subtraction to simplify.
  $\frac{6}{-3} = \frac{-3p}{-3}$ Div. Prop of Eq.
  $-2 = p$ Use division to simplify.

48. $4 - 5k - 4 = -16 - 4$ Sub. Prop. of Eq.
  $-5k = -20$ Use subtraction to simplify.
  $\frac{-5k}{-5} = \frac{-20}{-5}$ Div. Prop. of Eq.
  $k = 4$ Use division to simplify.

49. $9 + \frac{c}{-5} - 9 = -5 - 9$ Sub. Prop. of Eq.
  $\frac{c}{-5} = -14$ Use subtraction to simplify.
  $\frac{c}{-5} \cdot -5 = -14 \cdot -5$ Mult. Prop. of Eq.
  $c = 70$ Use multiplication to simplify.

50. $\frac{q}{-3} + 12 - 12 = 2 - 12$ Sub. Prop. of Eq.
  $\frac{q}{-3} = -10$ Use subtraction to simplify.
  $\frac{q}{-3} \cdot -3 = -10 \cdot -3$ Mult. Prop. of Eq.
  $q = 30$ Use multiplication to simplify.

51. 4 should be added to each side;
  $2x - 4 + 4 = 8 + 4$, so $2x = 12$ and $x = 6$.

52. Negative; x must be negative in order for $-3x + 5$ to equal 44.

53. a. 4
  b. yes
  c. Answers may vary. Sample: The method in part (a) is easier because it doesn't involve fractions.

54. 21

55. 10.5

56. 4112 times

57. Check students' work; 4.

58. 175 lb

59. Earth Science The air temperature beneath Earth's surface increases by about 10°C per kilometer. The surface temperature and the air temperature at the bottom of a mine are shown. How many kilometers below Earth's surface is the bottom of the mine?

60. Car-Sharing Program Members of a car-sharing program pay a fee of $50 per month plus $7.65 for every hour they use a car. A member's bill was $149.45 last month. How many hours did the customer use a car last month?

Surface: 18°C

Bottom of mine: 38°C
Not drawn to scale

© Challenge **61. Word Processing** You format a document in three columns of equal width. The document is 8.5 in. wide. You want left and right margins of 1 in. each. Between the columns there is a "gutter" that is one eighth as wide as each column. What is the width of each column?

Tell whether each equation has a solution. If so, find the solution. If not, explain why not.

62. $2x - 0 = 0$ **63.** $0(-2x) = 4$ **64.** $\frac{x-2}{2} = 0$ **65.** $\frac{x-2}{0} = 2$

Standardized Test Prep

SAT/ACT   GRIDDED RESPONSE

66. William's age w and Jamie's age j are related by the equation $w = 2j - 12$. When William is 36.5 years old, how old is Jamie?

67. Dominique paints faces at an annual carnival. Her goal this year is to earn $100. She spends $15 on supplies and will work for 2.5 h. How much will she need to earn in dollars per hour in order to reach her goal?

68. The cost of a gallon of milk m is $.50 more than five times the cost of a gallon of water w. If a gallon of milk costs $3.75, what is the cost of a gallon of water?

Mixed Review

Solve each equation.   ◀ See Lesson 2-1.

69. $-5x = -25$ **70.** $7 = 3.2 + y$ **71.** $\frac{y}{4} = 36$ **72.** $z - 2 = 4.5$

Tell whether each statement is *true* or *false*. If it is false, give a counterexample.   ◀ See Lesson 1-4.

73. The difference of the absolute value of two numbers is the same as the difference of the two numbers themselves.

74. Adding 1 to a number always increases its absolute value.

Get Ready! **To prepare for Lesson 2-3, do Exercises 75–78.**

Simplify each expression.   ◀ See Lesson 1-7.

75. $7(5 - t)$ **76.** $-2(-2x + 5)$ **77.** $-3(2 - b)$ **78.** $5(2 - 5n)$

---

59. about 2 km   **60.** 13 h   **70.** 3.8   **71.** 144
61. 2 in.   **62.** yes; 0   **72.** 6.5
63. No; the left side of the equation is 0   **73.** false; sample: $|-5| - |2| \neq -5 - 2$
  and the right side of the equation is 4.   **74.** false; sample: $-4 + 1 = -3$,
64. yes; 2 $|-4| = 4$ and $|-3| = 3$
65. No; division by 0 is not allowed.   **75.** $35 - 7t$ **76.** $4x - 10$
66. 24.25 yr   **67.** 46   **77.** $-6 + 3b$ **78.** $10 - 25n$
68. $.65   **69.** 5

Lesson Resources

Additional Instructional Support

Algebra 1 Companion

Students can use the **Algebra 1 Companion** worktext (4 pages) as you teach the lesson. Use the Companion to support

- New Vocabulary
- Key Concepts
- Got It for each Problem
- Lesson Check

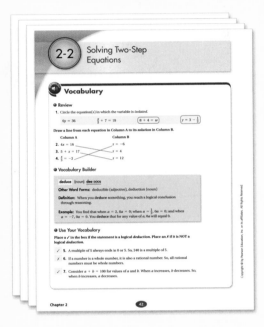

ELL Support

Focus on Communication Divide the class into pairs. Write the following equations on the board: $3x + 5 = 11$, $\frac{x}{4} + 2 = 10$, $\frac{x}{2} - 7 = 19$, and $5x - 3 = 11$. Have pairs practice using the properties of equality. Assign one person in each pair to work on the equations that use the Subtraction Property of Equality first and their partner to work on the equations that use the Addition Property of Equality first. Then have students finish solving the equation using the Multiplication (or Division) Property of Equality. After students have finished, have partners switch papers and explain their work.

5 Assess & Remediate

Lesson Quiz

1. What is the solution of $5b + 6 = 21$?
2. **Do you UNDERSTAND?** A tank currently holds 5 gallons of water. It is being filled at the rate of $\frac{1}{4}$ gallon per minute. How long will it take for the tank to hold 9 gallons of water?
3. What is the solution of $\frac{x + 2}{5} = 12$?
4. What is the solution of $8 + a = 13$? Justify each step.

ANSWERS TO LESSON QUIZ

1. 3
2. 16 min
3. 58
4. The steps are:
   (1) $8 + a = 13$
   (2) $8 - 8 + a = 13 - 8$
   (3) $a = 5$
   The reasons are:
   (1) Original equation
   (2) Subtraction Property of Equality
   (3) Simplify.

PRESCRIPTION FOR REMEDIATION
Use the student work on the Lesson Quiz to prescribe a differentiated review assignment.

Points	Differentiated Remediation
0–2	Intervention
3	On-level
4	Extension

PowerAlgebra.com

5 Assess & Remediate
Assign the Lesson Quiz. Appropriate intervention, practice, or enrichment is automatically generated based on student performance.

Intervention

- **Reteaching** (2 pages) Provides reteaching and practice exercises for the key lesson concepts. Use with struggling students or absent students.
- **English Language Learner Support** Helps students develop and reinforce mathematical vocabulary and key concepts.

All-in-One Resources/Online
Reteaching

2-2 Reteaching
Solving Two-Step Equations

Properties of equality and inverse operations can be used to solve equations that involve more than one step to solve. To solve a two-step equation, identify the operations and undo them using inverse operations. Undo the operations in the reverse order of the order of operations.

Problem
What is the solution of $5x - 8 = 32$?

$5x - 8 + 8 = 32 + 8$	To get the variable term alone on the left side, add 8 to each side.
$5x = 40$	Simplify.
$\frac{5x}{5} = \frac{40}{5}$	Divide each side by 5 since x is being multiplied by 5 on the left side. This isolates x.
$x = 8$	Simplify.

Check $5x - 8 = 32$ Check your solution in the original equation.
$5(8) - 8 = 32$ Substitute 8 for x.
$32 = 32$ ✓ Simplify.

To solve $-16 = \frac{x}{3} + 5$, you can use subtraction first to undo the addition, and then use multiplication to undo the division.

Problem
What is the solution of $-16 = \frac{x}{3} + 5$?

$-16 - 5 = \frac{x}{3} + 5 - 5$	To get the variable term alone on the right, subtract 5 from each side.
$-21 = \frac{x}{3}$	Simplify.
$3(-21) = 3\left(\frac{x}{3}\right)$	Since x is being divided by 3, multiply each side by 3 to undo the division. This isolates x.
$-63 = x$	Simplify.

All-in-One Resources/Online
English Language Learner Support

2-2 ELL Support
Solving Two-Step Equations

Use the chart below to review vocabulary. These vocabulary words will help you complete this page.

Related Words	Explanations	Examples
solution suh loo shun	The value that makes an equation true. A method for answering a problem	A solution to $x + 2 = 5$ is 3 because $3 + 2 = 5$.
solve sahlv	To work out a correct answer to a problem	She was able to solve the hardest problem on the test.
solving SAHL ving	Finding an answer to a problem	He spent an hour solving his homework problems.

Use the vocabulary above to fill in the blanks. The first one is done for you.

The teacher wants all her students to get the correct __solution__ to the problem on the test.

1. The purpose of the test was to __solve__ ten problems.
2. __Solving__ the easiest problem only took a minute.

Circle the correct answer.

3. What is the solution of the equation $2x - 35 = 15$?   10   15   20   **25**
4. Which answer solves the equation $5y + 25 = 50$?   **5**   10   25   50

Fill-in—the—blank

A package of flashcards tests addition, subtraction, multiplication, and division. There are 12 cards for each operation. Derek found a deck that has 46 cards. How many cards are missing from the deck?

Know
5. There are __12__ cards for each operation.
6. There are __4__ operations in a deck of flash cards.
7. How many cards did Derek find? __46__

Need
8. How many cards are in a full deck? __12__ × __4__ = __48__

Plan
9. To find the number of missing cards, you will need to __subtract the number of cards Derek found from the number of cards in a full deck.__

Differentiated Remediation *continued*

On-Level

- **Practice** (2 pages) Provides extra practice for each lesson. For simpler practice exercises, use the Form K Practice pages found in the All-in-One Teaching Resources and online.

- **Think About a Plan** Helps students develop specific problem-solving skills and strategies by providing scaffolded guiding questions.

- **Standardized Test Prep** Focuses on all major exercises, all major question types, and helps students prepare for the high-stakes assessments.

Extension

- **Enrichment** Provides students with interesting problems and activities that extend the concepts of the lesson.

- **Activities, Games, and Puzzles** Worksheets that can be used for concepts development, enrichment, and for fun!

Practice and Problem Solving WKBK/ All-in-One Resources/Online
Practice page 1

2-2 Practice Form G
Solving Two-Step Equations

Solve each equation. Check your answer.

1. $6 + 3b = -18$ -8 2. $-3 + 5x = 12$ 3

3. $7n + 12 = -23$ -5 4. $\frac{t}{6} - 3 = 8$ 66

5. $-12 = 8 + \frac{f}{2}$ -40 6. $13 = 8 - 5d$ -1

7. $\frac{k}{4} + 6 = -2$ -32 8. $-22 = -8 + 7y$ -2

9. $16 - 3p = 34$ -6 10. $15 + \frac{q}{6} = -21$ -216

11. $-19 + \frac{c}{3} = 8$ 81 12. $-18 - 11r = 26$ -4

13. $-9 = \frac{y}{-3} - 6$ 9 14. $14 + \frac{m}{10} = 24$ 100

Define a variable and write an equation for each situation. Then solve.

15. Chip earns a base salary of $500 per month as a salesman. In addition to the salary, he earns $90 per product that he sells. If his goal is to earn $5000 per month, how many products does he need to sell?
$500 + 90n = 5000$; 50 products

16. A pizza shop charges $9 for a large cheese pizza. Additional toppings cost $1.25 per topping. Heather paid $15.25 for her large pizza. How many toppings did she order?
$9 + 1.25n = 15.25$; 5 toppings

Practice and Problem Solving WKBK/ All-in-One Resources/Online
Practice page 2

2-2 Practice *(continued)* Form G
Solving Two-Step Equations

Solve each equation. Check your answer.

17. $\frac{z + 6}{3} = 8$ 18 18. $\frac{n - 7}{2} = -11$ -15

19. $\frac{l + 18}{-4} = 8$ -50 20. $\frac{1}{3}a - 6 = -15$ -27

21. $\frac{1}{4} = \frac{1}{4}h + 4$ -15 22. $6.42 - 10d = 2.5$ 0.392

23. The selling price of a television in a retail store is $66 less than 3 times the wholesale price. If the selling price of a television is $899, write and solve an equation to find the wholesale price of the television.
$3w - 66 = 899$; $321.67

24. The fare for a taxicab is $5 per trip plus $0.50 per mile. The fare for the trip from the airport to the convention center was $11.50. Write and solve an equation to find how many miles the trip is from the airport to the convention center.
$5 + 0.50m = 11.50$; 13 miles

25. An online movie club offers a membership for $5 per month. Members can rent movies for $1.50 per rental. A member was billed $15.50 one month. Write and solve an equation to find how many movies the member rented.
$5 + 1.50n = 15.50$; 7 movies

26. **Writing** Describe, using words, how to solve the equation $6 - 4x = 18$. List any properties utilized in the solution.
$6 - 4x = 18$
$6 - 4x = 18 - 6$ Subtract 6 from both sides. (Subt. Prop. of Equal.)
$-4x = 12$ Simplify.
$\frac{-4x}{-4} = \frac{12}{-4}$ Divide both sides by -4. (Div. Prop. of Equal.)
$x = -3$ Simplify.

27. **a.** Solve $-8 = \frac{x + 2}{4}$ -34
b. Write the right side of the equation in part (a) as the sum of two fractions. Solve the equation. -34
c. Did you find the equation in part (a) or the rewritten equation easier to solve? Why? Answers may vary. Sample: the original equation; It's easier to subtract whole numbers than a whole number and a fraction.

All-in-One Resources/Online
Enrichment

2-2 Enrichment
Solving Two-Step Equations

Equations are used in geometry. One example is the relationship between the angles that are formed by intersecting lines. The measures of the pairs of opposite angles are equal. The measures of two adjacent angles add up to 180°.

Use the drawing shown to answer the following questions.

1. $m\angle 1 = 30$ and $m\angle 2 = 4x$. What is the value of x? 37.5

2. $m\angle 3 = 5x$ and $m\angle 4 = 75$. What is the value of x? 21

3. $m\angle 4 = 45$ and $m\angle 2 = 9x$. What is the value of x? 5

The formula for the perimeter of a rectangle is $P = 2l + 2w$, where l is the length and w is the width of the rectangle.

4. The width of a rectangle is 12 ft. The perimeter of the rectangle is 42 ft. What is the length of the rectangle? 9 ft.

5. The perimeter of a rectangle is 158.5 cm. The length of the rectangle is 42.5 cm. What is the width of the rectangle? 36.75 cm

Another geometric application for 2-step equations involves the measures of the interior angles of a polygon. Regardless of the number of sides, n, a polygon has, the sum of the measures of the interior angles is $180n - 360$ degrees.

For example, the sum of the measures of the angles of a rectangle is $180(4) - 360 = 360°$.

The sum of the measures of the interior angles of various polygons are given. Set up an equation and solve to find the number of sides of each polygon.

6. 1080° 8 sides   7. 1440° 10 sides   8. 2340° 15 sides

9. 180° 3 sides   10. 3600° 22 sides   11. 540° 5 sides

Practice and Problem Solving WKBK/ All-in-One Resources/Online
Think About a Plan

2-2 Think About a Plan
Solving Two-Step Equations

Earth Science The temperature beneath Earth's surface increases by 10°C per kilometer. The surface temperature and the temperature at the bottom of a mine are shown. How many kilometers below Earth's surface is the bottom of the mine?

Surface: 18°C
Bottom of mine: 38°C

Understanding the Problem

1. What happens to the temperature as the distance below Earth's surface increases?
The temperature increases 10°C per km.

2. What do you need to determine?
how far below Earth's surface the mine is

3. What is the change in temperature from Earth's surface to the bottom of the mine?
The temperature increases 20°C.

Planning the Solution

4. Write an expression for how much the temperature increases x kilometers below the surface.
$10x$

5. Write an equation that relates the change in temperature, from 18°C at Earth's surface to 38°C at the bottom of the mine, to the expression for how much the temperature increases x kilometers below the surface.
$38 - 18 = 10x$

Getting an Answer

6. Solve the equation.
$x = 2$

7. Is your answer reasonable? Explain.
yes; an increase of 20°C

Practice and Problem Solving WKBK/ All-in-One Resources/Online
Standardized Test Prep

2-2 Standardized Test Prep
Solving Two-Step Equations

Gridded Response

Solve each exercise and enter your answer on the grid provided.

1. What is the solution of $-28 = 22 - 5x$? 10

2. What is the solution of $\frac{m}{4} - 3 = 7$? 40

3. The amount of money that Pamela p has and Julie j has are related by the equation $3p + 5 = j$. If Julie has $83, how much money does Pamela have? $26

4. An ice cream sundae costs $1.75 plus an additional $0.35 for each topping. If the total cost is $2.80, how many toppings did the sundae have? 3

5. The cost of a gallon of gasoline g is $3.25 less than 2 times the cost of a gallon of diesel d. If a gallon of gasoline costs $3.95, what is the cost of a gallon of diesel? $3.60

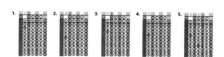
1.   2.   3.   4.   5.

Online Teacher Resource Center
Activities, Games, and Puzzles

2-2 Game: Equation Challenge
Solving Two-Step Equations

This is a game for three or more players. A student or the teacher can serve as the host.

The host calls out a combination from the table at the left below and a combination from the table at the right below. For example, the call "A3 T2" gives the following equation.

$$4x + 5 = 6$$

Each player writes the equation, solves it, and records the solution using the score sheet below.

At the end of Round 6, the host polls the players to agree upon the correct solutions for each round. A correct solution earns 3 points, while an incorrect solution earns no points. Check students' work.

	1	2	3
A	$2x + 5$	$-3x + 1$	$4x + 5$
B	$-3x + 4$	$10x + 1$	$-9x + 2$
C	$-x - 3$	$6x - 5$	$-2x + 7$
D	$3x + 7$	$11x + 3$	$-2x + 1$
E	$-x - 3$	$6x - 4$	$-2x + 5$

	1	2	3
P	-7	-6	-5
Q	-4	-3	-2
R	-1	0	1
S	2	3	4
T	5	6	7

My Score Sheet	Round 1	Round 2	Round 3	Round 4	Round 5	Round 6
Equation						
Solution						
Points						

My total: ☐

Wait—the game is not over! You can boost your score by correctly solving $10^6 x + 10^5 = 10^6$. The correct solution is worth 10 points. _____ 0.9

1 Interactive Learning

Solve It!

PURPOSE To model a real-life situation using linear equations

PROCESS Students may choose various numbers of tickets and find the total, or write an equation.

FACILITATE
Point out that the total cost is Cost of tickets + Total processing fee + Service charge.

> **Q** If t is the number of tickets purchased, what is the cost of the tickets and the processing fee? What is the total cost? **[$9t + t$; $9t + t + 5$]**
>
> **Q** If the total cost is equal to the amount of money you have to spend, how can you express this relationship in terms of an equation? **[$9t + t + 5 = 45$]**

ANSWERS See Solve It in Answers on next page.
CONNECT THE MATH Discuss how this problem can be solved using estimation and by trying and testing specific values. Point out that writing and solving an equation can answer problems like this.

2 Guided Instruction

Problem 1
Students must combine like terms to solve a linear equation.

> **Q** What is meant by "like terms?" **[See Math Background.]**

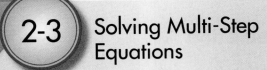

2-3 Solving Multi-Step Equations

Indiana Academic Standard
A1.2.5 Solve problems that can be modeled using linear equations and inequalities, interpret the solutions, and determine whether the solutions are reasonable.

Objective To solve multi-step equations in one variable

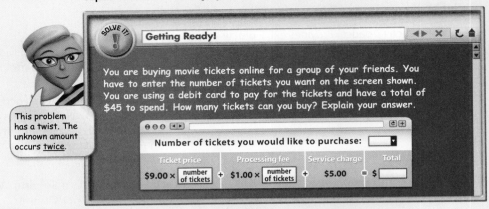

SOLVE IT!

Getting Ready!

You are buying movie tickets online for a group of your friends. You have to enter the number of tickets you want on the screen shown. You are using a debit card to pay for the tickets and have a total of $45 to spend. How many tickets can you buy? Explain your answer.

This problem has a twist. The unknown amount occurs twice.

Number of tickets you would like to purchase: ▯

Ticket price	Processing fee	Service charge	Total
$9.00 × number of tickets	+ $1.00 × number of tickets	+ $5.00	= $

In this lesson, you will learn to write and solve multi-step equations.

Essential Understanding To solve multi-step equations, you form a series of simpler equivalent equations. To do this, use the properties of equality, inverse operations, and properties of real numbers. You use the properties until you isolate the variable.

Think
How is this equation different from equations you've seen before?
The variable occurs in *two* terms. You can simplify the equation by grouping like terms and combining them.

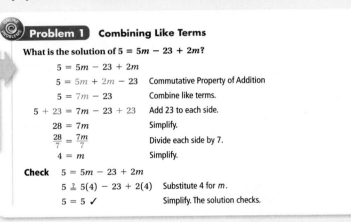

Problem 1 Combining Like Terms

What is the solution of $5 = 5m - 23 + 2m$?

$$5 = 5m - 23 + 2m$$
$$5 = 5m + 2m - 23 \quad \text{Commutative Property of Addition}$$
$$5 = 7m - 23 \quad \text{Combine like terms.}$$
$$5 + 23 = 7m - 23 + 23 \quad \text{Add 23 to each side.}$$
$$28 = 7m \quad \text{Simplify.}$$
$$\frac{28}{7} = \frac{7m}{7} \quad \text{Divide each side by 7.}$$
$$4 = m \quad \text{Simplify.}$$

Check $5 = 5m - 23 + 2m$
$$5 \overset{?}{=} 5(4) - 23 + 2(4) \quad \text{Substitute 4 for } m.$$
$$5 = 5 \checkmark \quad \text{Simplify. The solution checks.}$$

BIG ideas Equivalence   **UbD**
Solving Equations &
Inequalities

ESSENTIAL UNDERSTANDINGS
- Equivalent equations are equations that have the same solution(s).
- The solution of a multi-step equation can be found using the properties of equality and real numbers and inverse operations to form a series of simpler equations.
- The properties of equality and real numbers can be used repeatedly to isolate the variable.

Math Background
Each step leading to the solution of an equation produces a simpler equivalent equation. As equations become more complex, students may need to simplify either side of the equation by

combining like terms. Students need to be able to identify like terms as terms that have the same variables raised to the same powers. For example, $12xy^5$ and $-5xy^5$ are like terms, but $12xy^3$ and $-5xy^5$ are not. This should make it clear to students that it is not the coefficients, but the variables and their respective exponents, which must be the same.

Support Student Learning
Use the **Algebra I Companion** to engage and support students during instruction. See Lesson Resources at the end of this lesson for details.

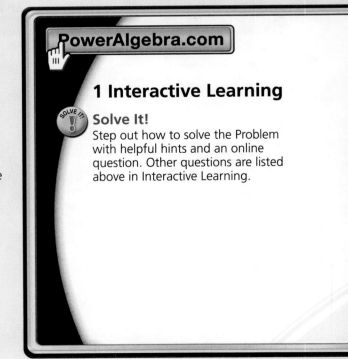

PowerAlgebra.com

1 Interactive Learning

SOLVE IT!

Solve It!
Step out how to solve the Problem with helpful hints and an online question. Other questions are listed above in Interactive Learning.

Got It? **1.** What is the solution of each equation? Check each answer.

    a. $11m - 8 - 6m = 22$ **b.** $-2y + 5 + 5y = 14$

 Problem 2   **Solving a Multi-Step Equation**

Concert Merchandise Martha takes her niece and nephew to a concert. She buys T-shirts and bumper stickers for them. The bumper stickers cost $1 each. Martha's niece wants 1 shirt and 4 bumper stickers, and her nephew wants 2 shirts but no bumper stickers. If Martha's total is $67, what is the cost of one shirt?

Know
- Bumper stickers cost $1
- Niece's items: 1 shirt, 4 bumper stickers
- Nephew's items: 2 shirts
- Total spent: $67

Need
The cost of one shirt

Plan
Write and solve an equation that models the situation.

Think

How can a model help you write the equation?
The model shows that the cost of the niece's items plus the cost of the nephew's items is $67.

67	
s + 4	2s

Relate   cost of niece's items (1 shirt and 4 stickers)   **plus**   cost of nephew's items (2 shirts)   **is**   total Martha spent

Define   Let $s =$ the cost of one shirt.

Write $(s + 4)$ $+$ $2s$ $=$ 67

$(s + 4) + 2s = 67$

$s + 2s + 4 = 67$	Commutative Property of Addition
$3s + 4 = 67$	Combine like terms.
$3s + 4 - 4 = 67 - 4$	Subtract 4 from each side.
$3s = 63$	Simplify.
$\frac{3s}{3} = \frac{63}{3}$	Divide each side by 3.
$s = 21$	Simplify.

One shirt costs $21.

 Got It? **2.** Noah and Kate are shopping for new guitar strings in a music store. Noah buys 2 packs of strings. Kate buys 2 packs of strings and a music book. The book costs $16. Their total cost is $72. How much is one pack of strings?

Q Which terms are like terms? How do you know? **[11m and −6m; −2y and 5y; they contain the same variable raised to the same power.]**

Problem 2

Q Is there another way to group the costs? Explain. **[Yes; group the costs by item.]**

Q What does the equation look like if it is grouped this way? **[Cost of shirts + Cost of bumper stickers = Total cost]**

Q If *s* is the cost of a shirt, how do you write the equation? **[3s + 4 = 67]**

Q Does it matter which way you group the costs? **[No; you end up with the same equation. This method just combines like terms at the beginning.]**

Got It?

Q If *p* is the cost of a pack of strings, what model shows the cost of Noah's items plus the cost of Kate's items?

2p	2p + 16

Q What does your model look like if you group the costs by item?

4p	16

2 Guided Instruction

 Each Problem is worked out and supported online.

Problem 1
Combining Like Terms

Problem 2
Solving a Multi-Step Equation
                    Animated

Problem 3
Solving an Equation Using the Distributive Property

Problem 4
Solving an Equation That Contains Fractions
                    Animated

Problem 5
Solving an Equation That Contains Decimals

Alternative Problem 5
Solving an Equation That Contains Decimals
                    Animated

Support in Algebra 1 Companion
- Vocabulary
- Key Concepts
- Got It?

Answers

Solve It!

4 tickets; explanations may vary.

Got It?
  1. a. 6
     b. 3
  2. $14

Problem 3   ERROR PREVENTION

Students use the Distributive Property to remove grouping symbols and simplify an equation. As students distribute the -8, they often neglect to apply the negative sign to both terms in parentheses. They mistakenly conclude that $-8(2x - 1) = -16x - 8$.

> **Q** How is the Distributive Property different from and how is it similar to the properties of equality? **[The Distributive Property only affects one side of an equation, whereas the properties of equality affect both sides. Each property results in an equivalent equation.]**

Got It?

> **Q** In 3b, why does using the Division Property of Equality as the first step make this problem easier to solve than using the Distributive Property? **[Sample: The Division Property of Equality results in smaller numbers.]**

Problem 4   ERROR PREVENTION

When using Method 2, students need to remember to multiply **each term** by the least common multiple. Doing so maintains the balance of the equation.

> **Q** In Method 1, why don't you rewrite the right side of the equation when you rewrite the left side? **[By rewriting the fractions with a common denominator, the value of the left side of the equation did not change.]**
>
> **Q** Do you prefer Method 1 or 2? Explain. **[Sample: Method 2 results in larger numbers, but it does not require working with as many fractions.]**

Think

How can you make the equation easier to solve?
Remove the grouping symbols by using the Distributive Property.

 Problem 3   **Solving an Equation Using the Distributive Property**

What is the solution of $-8(2x - 1) = 36$?

$$-8(2x - 1) = 36$$

$-16x + 8 = 36$ Distributive Property

$-16x + 8 - 8 = 36 - 8$ Subtract 8 from each side.

$-16x = 28$ Simplify.

$\dfrac{-16x}{-16} = \dfrac{28}{-16}$ Divide each side by -16.

$x = -\dfrac{7}{4}$ Simplify.

✓ **Got It?**   **3. a.** What is the solution of $18 = 3(2x - 6)$? Check your answer.
    b. Reasoning Can you solve the equation in part (a) by using the Division Property of Equality instead of the Distributive Property? Explain.

You can use different methods to solve equations that contain fractions.

Plan

How do you get started?
You can either combine like terms by writing the fractions with a common denominator, or you can clear the fractions from the equation.

 Problem 4   **Solving an Equation That Contains Fractions**

What is the solution of $\frac{3x}{4} - \frac{x}{3} = 10$?

Method 1   Write the like terms using a common denominator and solve.

$\frac{3}{4}x - \frac{1}{3}x = 10$ Rewrite the fractions.

$\frac{9}{12}x - \frac{4}{12}x = 10$ Write the fractions using a common denominator, 12.

$\frac{5}{12}x = 10$ Combine like terms.

$\frac{12}{5}\left(\frac{5}{12}x\right) = \frac{12}{5}(10)$ Multiply each side by $\frac{12}{5}$, the reciprocal of $\frac{5}{12}$.

$x = 24$ Simplify.

Method 2   Clear the fractions from the equation.

$12\left(\frac{3x}{4} - \frac{x}{3}\right) = 12(10)$ Multiply each side by a common denominator, 12.

$12\left(\frac{3x}{4}\right) - 12\left(\frac{x}{3}\right) = 12(10)$ Distributive Property

$9x - 4x = 120$ Multiply.

$5x = 120$ Combine like terms.

$x = 24$ Divide each side by 5 and simplify.

Additional Problems

1. What is the solution of $8x + 5 - 6x = 25$?

ANSWER 10

2. Jason bought 5 movie tickets and a bag of popcorn. Jeremy bought 2 movie tickets. They spent $54 total. If the popcorn cost $5, how much did each movie ticket cost?

ANSWER $7

3. What is the solution of $12(3 - x) = 60$?

ANSWER -2

4. What is the solution of $\frac{3x}{4} - \frac{x}{8} = 5$?

ANSWER 8

5. What is the solution of $2.3 - 0.05x = 4.80$?

ANSWER -50

Answers

Got It? (continued)

3. a. 6

    b. Yes; divide both sides of the equation by 3 first.

Got It? 4. What is the solution of each equation? Why did you choose the method you used to solve each equation?

a. $\frac{2b}{5} + \frac{3b}{4} = 3$ 　　　　　　　　**b.** $\frac{1}{9} = \frac{5}{6} - \frac{m}{3}$

You can clear decimals from an equation by multiplying by a power of 10. First, find the greatest number of digits to the right of any decimal point, and then multiply by 10 raised to that power.

 Problem 5 **Solving an Equation That Contains Decimals**

What is the solution of $3.5 - 0.02x = 1.24$?

Plan

The equation contains tenths (3.5) and hundredths (0.02 and 1.24). The greatest number of digits to the right of any decimal point is 2. So, multiply each side of the equation by 10^2, or 100, to clear the decimals.

 Think
When you multiply a decimal by 10^n, where n is a positive integer, you can move the decimal point n places to the right. For example, $100(3.5) = 350$.

$3.5 - 0.02x = 1.24$	
$100(3.5 - 0.02x) = 100(1.24)$	Multiply each side by 10^2, or 100.
$350 - 2x = 124$	Distributive Property
$350 - 2x - 350 = 124 - 350$	Subtract 350 from each side.
$-2x = -226$	Simplify.
$\frac{-2x}{-2} = \frac{-226}{-2}$	Divide each side by -2.
$x = 113$	Simplify.

 Got It? 5. What is the solution of $0.5x - 2.325 = 3.95$? Check your answer.

Lesson Check

Do you know HOW?

Solve each equation. Check your answer.

1. $7p + 8p - 12 = 59$ 　　　**2.** $-2(3x + 9) = 24$

3. $\frac{2m}{7} + \frac{3m}{14} = 1$ 　　　**4.** $1.2 = 2.4 - 0.6x$

5. Gardening There is a 12-ft fence on one side of a rectangular garden. The gardener has 44 ft of fencing to enclose the other three sides. What is the length of the garden's longer dimension?

Do you UNDERSTAND?

Explain how you would solve each equation.

6. $1.3 + 0.5x = -3.41$

7. $7(3x - 4) = 49$

8. $-\frac{2}{9}x - 4 = \frac{7}{18}$

9. Reasoning Ben solves the equation $-24 = 5(g + 3)$ by first dividing each side by 5. Amelia solves the equation by using the Distributive Property. Whose method do you prefer? Explain.

Problem 5
Students multiply both sides by the lowest power of ten that clears all decimals from the equation. Review multiplication by powers of 10.

Q What is the pattern?

$8 \times 10 =$	$0.23 \times 10 =$
$0.8 \times 10 =$	$2.3 \times 10 =$
$0.8 \times 100 =$	$23 \times 10 =$

[When multiplying by 10^n, the decimal place shifts n places to the right.]

Q Why was 100 selected to multiply through the equation? **[Both 0.02 and 1.24 have two decimal places, so you multiply by $10^2 = 100$.]**

Got It?

Q What number clears the decimal values? **[10^3]**

3 Lesson Check

Do you know HOW?
• Encourage students to draw a diagram of the situation in Exercise 5, if needed.

Do you UNDERSTAND?
• Explain that efficiency in this context means using the fewest number of operations and/or avoiding numbers that are difficult to work with.

Close

Q There is often more than one method for solving multi-step equations. How can you decide which method to use? **[Samples: Efficiency and clearing fractions are possible considerations.]**

Got It? (continued)

4. a. $2\frac{14}{23}$; check students' work.

　b. $2\frac{1}{6}$; check students' work.

5. 12.55

Lesson Check

1. $4\frac{11}{15}$

2. -7

3. 2

4. 2

5. 16 ft

6. Answers may vary. Sample: Subtract 1.3 from each side, and then divide each side by 0.5.

7. Answers may vary. Sample: Apply the Distr. Prop., and then add 28 to each side and divide each side by 21.

8. Answers may vary. Sample: Multiply each side by the common denominator 18 to clear the fractions. Add 72 to each side and then divide by −4.

9. Answers may vary. Sample: Amelia's method: it does not involve working with fractions until the end.

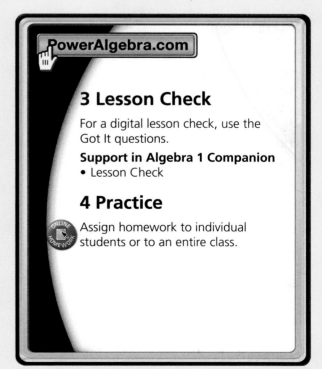

PowerAlgebra.com

3 Lesson Check

For a digital lesson check, use the Got It questions.

Support in Algebra 1 Companion
• Lesson Check

4 Practice

Assign homework to individual students or to an entire class.

4 Practice

ASSIGNMENT GUIDE

Basic: 10–44 all, 46–54 even, 55–59, 61

Average: 11–43 odd, 45–65

Advanced: 11–43 odd, 45–68

Standardized Test Prep: 69–71

Mixed Review: 72–80

Reasoning exercises have blue headings.

Applications exercises have red headings.

EXERCISE 55: Use the Think About a Plan worksheet in the **Practice and Problem Solving Workbook** (also available in the Teaching Resources in print and online) to further support students' development in becoming independent learners.

HOMEWORK QUICK CHECK

To check students' understanding of key skills and concepts, go over Exercises 19, 35, 54, 55, and 58.

Practice and Problem-Solving Exercises

A Practice   Solve each equation. Check your answer.   ◀ **See Problem 1.**

10. $7 - y - y = -1$ **11.** $72 + 4 - 14d = 36$ **12.** $13 = 5 + 3b - 13$

13. $6p - 2 - 3p = 16$ **14.** $x + 2 + x = 22$ **15.** $b - 9 + 6b = 30$

16. $9t - 6 - 6t = 6$ **17.** $17 = p - 3 - 3p$ **18.** $-23 = -2a - 10 + a$

Write an equation to model each situation. Then solve the equation.   ◀ **See Problem 2.**

19. **Employment** You have a part-time job. You work for 3 h on Friday and 6 h on Saturday. You also receive an allowance of $20 per week. You earn $92 per week. How much do you earn per hour at your part-time job?

20. **Travel** A family buys airline tickets online. Each ticket costs $167. The family buys travel insurance with each ticket that costs $19 per ticket. The Web site charges a fee of $16 for the entire purchase. The family is charged a total of $1132. How many tickets did the family buy?

Solve each equation. Check your answer.   ◀ **See Problem 3.**

21. $64 = 8(r + 2)$ **22.** $5(2x - 3) = 15$ **23.** $5(2 + 4z) = 85$

24. $2(8 + 4c) = 32$ **25.** $7(f - 1) = 45$ **26.** $15 = -2(2t - 1)$

27. $26 = 6(5 - 4f)$ **28.** $n + 5(n - 1) = 7$ **29.** $-4(r + 6) = -63$

Solve each equation. Choose the method you prefer to use. Check your answer.   ◀ **See Problem 4.**

30. $\frac{b}{13} - \frac{3b}{13} = \frac{8}{13}$ **31.** $5y - \frac{3}{5} = \frac{4}{5}$ **32.** $\frac{n}{5} - \frac{3n}{10} = \frac{1}{5}$

33. $\frac{2}{3} + \frac{3m}{5} = \frac{31}{15}$ **34.** $\frac{n}{2} - \frac{2n}{16} = \frac{3}{8}$ **35.** $\frac{b}{3} + \frac{1}{8} = 19$

36. $\frac{1}{4} + \frac{4x}{5} = \frac{11}{20}$ **37.** $\frac{11z}{16} + \frac{7z}{8} = \frac{5}{16}$ **38.** $\frac{x}{3} - \frac{7x}{12} = \frac{2}{3}$

Solve each equation. Check your answer.   ◀ **See Problem 5.**

39. $1.06g - 3 = 0.71$ **40.** $0.11k + 1.5 = 2.49$

41. $1.025v + 2.458 = 7.583$ **42.** $1.12 + 1.25g = 8.62$

43. $25.24 = 5g + 3.89$ **44.** $0.25n + 0.1n = 9.8$

B Apply   Solve each equation.

45. $6 + \frac{v}{-8} = \frac{4}{7}$ **46.** $\frac{2}{3}(c - 18) = 7$ **47.** $3d + d - 7 = \frac{25}{4}$

48. $0.25(d - 12) = 4$ **49.** $8n - (2n - 3) = 12$ **50.** $\frac{2}{3} + n + 6 = \frac{3}{4}$

51. $0.5d - 3d + 5 = 0$ **52.** $-(w + 5) = -14$ **53.** $\frac{a}{20} + \frac{4}{15} = \frac{9}{15}$

Answers

Practice and Problem-Solving Exercises

10. 4   **11.** $2\frac{6}{7}$

12. 7   **13.** 6

14. 10   **15.** $5\frac{4}{7}$

16. 4   **17.** -10

18. 13

19. $3x + 6x + 20 = 92$; $8 per h

20. $167t + 19t + 16 = 1132$; 6 tickets

21. 6   **22.** 3

23. 3.75 or $3\frac{3}{4}$ **24.** 2

25. $7\frac{3}{7}$ **26.** -3.25 or $-3\frac{1}{4}$

27. $\frac{1}{6}$ **28.** 2

29. 9.75 or $9\frac{3}{4}$ **30.** -4

31. $\frac{7}{25}$ **32.** -2

33. $2\frac{1}{3}$ **34.** 1

35. $56\frac{5}{8}$ **36.** $\frac{3}{8}$

37. $\frac{1}{5}$ **38.** $-2\frac{2}{3}$

39. 3.5   **40.** 9

41. 5   **42.** 6

43. 4.27   **44.** 28

45. $43\frac{3}{7}$ **46.** $28\frac{1}{2}$

47. $3\frac{5}{16}$ **48.** 28

49. 1.5 or $1\frac{1}{2}$ **50.** $-5\frac{11}{12}$

51. 2   **52.** 9

53. $6\frac{2}{3}$

54. Think About a Plan Jillian and Tyson are shopping for knitting supplies. Jillian wants 3 balls of yarn and 1 set of knitting needles. Tyson wants 1 ball of yarn and 2 sets of knitting needles. Each ball of yarn costs $6.25. If their total cost is $34.60, what is the cost of 1 set of knitting needles?

- How can the model at the right help you solve the problem?
- How does the model tell you which operations to use in the equation?

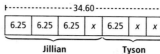

55. Online Video Games Angie and Kenny play online video games. Angie buys 1 software package and 3 months of game play. Kenny buys 1 software package and 2 months of game play. Each software package costs $20. If their total cost is $115, what is the cost of one month of game play?

56. Error Analysis Describe and correct the error in solving the equation at the right.

$$\frac{3x}{8} - 1 = \frac{5}{8}$$
$$8\left(\frac{3x}{8} - 1\right) = 8\left(\frac{5}{8}\right)$$
$$3x - 1 = 5$$
$$3x = 6$$
$$x = 2$$

57. Reasoning Suppose you want to solve $-4m + 5 + 6m = -3$. What would you do as your first step? Explain.

58. Writing Describe two ways in which you can solve $-\frac{1}{2}(5x - 9) = 17$.

59. Bowling Three friends go bowling. The cost per person per game is $5.30. The cost to rent shoes is $2.50 per person. Their total cost is $55.20. How many games did they play?

60. Moving Expenses A college student is moving into a campus dormitory. The student rents a moving truck for $19.95 plus $.99 per mile. Before returning the truck, the student fills the tank with gasoline, which costs $65.32. The total cost is $144.67. How many miles did the student drive the truck?

Geometry Find the value of *x*. (*Hint*: The sum of the angle measures of a quadrilateral is 360°.)

61.

62.

63.

64. Dining Out You are ordering a meal and have $15 to spend. The restaurant charges 6% sales tax. You plan to leave a 15% tip. The equation $c = x + 0.06x + 0.15x$ gives the total cost c of your meal, where x is the cost before tax and tip. What is the maximum amount you can spend before tax and tip?

65. Savings You have $85 in your bank account. Each week you plan to deposit $8 from your allowance and $15 from your paycheck. The equation $b = 85 + (15 + 8)w$ gives the amount b in your bank account after w weeks. How many weeks from now will you have $175 in your bank account?

54. $3.20   **55.** $15

56. The 8 should be distributed to all terms;
$8\left(\frac{3x}{8} - 1\right) = 8\left(\frac{5}{8}\right)$ gives $3x - 8 = 5$
and
$3x = 13$ so $x = 4\frac{1}{3}$.

57. Answers may vary. Sample: Combine the like terms on the left side of the equation.

58. Answers may vary. Sample: Distribute $-\frac{1}{2}$ on the left side of the equation or multiply both sides of the equation by the reciprocal of $-\frac{1}{2}$.

59. 3 games   **60.** 60 mi
61. 25   **62.** 26
63. 20   **64.** $12.40
65. 4 weeks

Answers

Practice and Problem-Solving Exercises
(continued)

66. 14, 15, 16

67. 4 c

68. a. $\frac{1}{6}; \frac{1}{3}$

  b. $\frac{d}{6}; \frac{d}{3}$

  c. $\frac{1}{6} + \frac{1}{3} = \frac{1}{2}; \frac{d}{6} + \frac{d}{3} = \frac{d}{2}$

  d. $\frac{d}{6} + \frac{d}{3} = 1$; 2 days

69. B

70. H

71. B

72. -5

73. 7

74. 4

75. Inv. Prop. of Add.

76. Assoc. Prop. of Mult.

77. Mult. Prop. of Zero

78. $3y$

79. $-3y$

80. 0

 Challenge

66. Open-Ended Find three consecutive integers with a sum of 45. Show your work.

67. Cooking A cook buys two identical bags of rice and uses some of the rice in each bag so that one bag is half full and the other is one-third full. The cook combines them into one bag, which then contains $3\frac{1}{3}$ cups of rice. How much rice was in a full bag?

68. Painting Tim can paint a house in 6 days. Tara can paint the same house in 3 days.
  a. What fraction of the house can Tim paint in one day? What fraction of the house can Tara paint in one day?
  b. What fraction of the house can Tim paint in d days? What fraction of the house can Tara paint in d days?
  c. What fraction of the house can Tim and Tara together paint in one day? What fraction of the house can Tim and Tara together paint in d days?
  d. Write and solve an equation to find the number of days it will take Tim and Tara to paint the whole house working together.

Standardized Test Prep

SAT/ACT

69. When a number is increased by 3 and that number is doubled, the result is -8. What was the original number?

  ⒜ -14 ⒝ -7 ⒞ -5.5 ⒟ -1

70. What is the value of the expression $-3r + 6 + r$ when $r = -2$?

  ⒡ -2 ⒢ 0   ⒣ 10   ⒤ 12

71. Roy's car gets an average gas mileage of 29 mi/gal. Roy starts his trip with the amount of gas shown. About how many gallons of gas are left at the end of his trip?

  ⒜ 6 gal   ⒞ 8 gal
  ⒝ 7 gal   ⒟ 9 gal

Mixed Review

Solve each equation.   ◀ See Lesson 2-2.

72. $3y + 5 = -10$ **73.** $4x - 5 = 23$ **74.** $-3a + 21 = 9$

Name the property that each statement illustrates.   ◀ See Lesson 1-4.

75. $4 + (-4) = 0$ **76.** $(5 \cdot 6) \cdot 2 = 5 \cdot (6 \cdot 2)$ **77.** $7 \cdot 0 = 0$

Get Ready! To prepare for Lesson 2-4, do Exercises 78–80.

Simplify each expression.   ◀ See Lesson 1-7.

78. $7y - 4y$ **79.** $4y - 7y$ **80.** $7y - 7y$

Additional Instructional Support

Algebra 1 Companion

Students can use the **Algebra 1 Companion** worktext (4 pages) as you teach the lesson. Use the Companion to support

- New Vocabulary
- Key Concepts
- Got It for each Problem
- Lesson Check

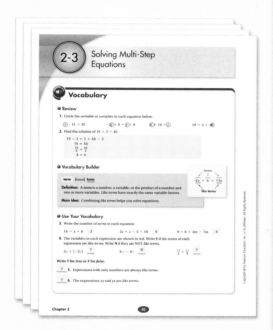

ELL Support

Focus on Language Have one pair of students sit with another pair. This is a good opportunity for peer-mentoring, wherein students who are more proficient can guide students who may still need help. Encourage students to ask each other questions, such as: What can you do to form a simpler equation? What do you need to undo first? Why did you use division for this multiplication problem? How can you make the fractions easier to work with?

Assess Understanding Zvi and Ari went shopping. Notebooks cost $2 each. Zvi buys 4 notebooks and 1 flash drive, and Ari buys 3 notebooks and two of the same flash drive that Zvi has. Together they spent $65. Draw a picture to model the cost of 1 flash drive.

5 Assess & Remediate

Lesson Quiz

1. What is the solution of
   $7x + 14 - 3x = 30$?

2. **Do you UNDERSTAND?** Lisa buys a dozen apples and two oranges. Jeremy buys six apples. Oranges cost $1 each, and they spent $9 total. How could you define variables to find the cost of the apples and oranges?

3. What is the solution of $6(3 - 2x) = 54$?

4. What is the solution of $\frac{2x}{5} - \frac{x}{2} = 40$?

5. What is the solution of
   $1.4 - 0.04x = 5.20$?

ANSWERS TO LESSON QUIZ

1. 4

2. Answers may vary. Sample: Define $a =$ the cost of apples and $x =$ the cost of oranges.

3. -3

4. -400

5. -95

PRESCRIPTION FOR REMEDIATION
Use the student work on the Lesson Quiz to prescribe a differentiated review assignment.

Points	Differentiated Remediation
0–2	Intervention
3–4	On-level
5	Extension

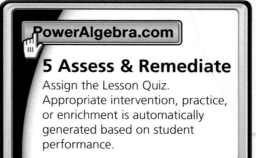

PowerAlgebra.com

5 Assess & Remediate

Assign the Lesson Quiz. Appropriate intervention, practice, or enrichment is automatically generated based on student performance.

Intervention

- **Reteaching** (2 pages) Provides reteaching and practice exercises for the key lesson concepts. Use with struggling students or absent students.

- **English Language Learner Support** Helps students develop and reinforce mathematical vocabulary and key concepts.

All-in-One Resources/Online
Reteaching

2-3 Reteaching
Solving Multi-Step Equations

To solve multi-step equations, use properties of equality, inverse operations, the Distributive Property, and properties of real numbers to isolate the variable. Like terms on either side of the equation should be combined first.

Problem
a) What is the solution of $-3y + 8 + 13y = -52$?

$-3y + 13y + 8 = -52$	Group the terms with y together so that the like terms are grouped together.
$10y + 8 = -52$	Add the coefficients to combine like terms.
$10y + 8 - 8 = -52 - 8$	To get the variable term by itself on the left side, subtract 8 from each side.
$10y = -60$	Simplify.
$\frac{10y}{10} = \frac{-60}{10}$	Divide each side by 10 since y is being multiplied by 10 on the left side. This isolates y.
$y = -6$	Simplify.

b) What is the solution of $-2(3n - 4) = -10$?

$-6n + 8 = -10$	Distribute the −2 into the parentheses by multiplying each term inside by −2.
$-6n + 8 - 8 = -10 - 8$	To get the variable term by itself on the left side, subtract 8 from each side.
$-6n = -18$	Simplify.
$\frac{-6n}{-6} = \frac{-18}{-6}$	Divide each side by −6 since n is being multiplied by −6 on the left side. This isolates n.
$n = 3$	Simplify.

Solve each equation. Check your answer.

1. $4 - 6h - 8h = 60$ −4
2. $-32 = -7n - 12 + 3n$ 5
3. $14 + 12 = -15x + 2x$ −2
4. $8(-3d + 2) = 88$ −3
5. $-22 = -(x - 4)$ 26
6. $35 = -5(2k + 5)$ −6
7. $3m + 6 - 2m = -22$ −28
8. $4(3r + 2) - 3r = -10$ −2
9. $-18 = 15 - 3(6z + 5)$ 1
10. $-5 + 2(10b - 2) = 31$ 2
11. $7 = 5x + 3(x - 2) + 5$ 1
12. $-18 = 3(-z + 6) + 2z$ 36
13. **Reasoning** Solve the equation $14 = 7(2x - 4)$ using two different methods. Show your work. Which method do you prefer? Explain. 3; The first way of solving is better because there are fewer steps.

All-in-One Resources/Online
English Language Learner Support

2-3 ELL Support
Solving Multi-Step Equations

Problem
What is the solution of the multi-step equation $3x + 7 + 6x = 34$? Justify your steps. Then check your solution.

$3x + 7 + 6x = 34$	Write the original equation.
$3x + 6x + 7 = 34$	Commutative Property of Addition
$9x + 7 = 34$	Combine like terms.
$9x + \boxed{7 - 7} = 34 - 7$	Subtract 7 from each side. Subtraction Property of Equality
$9x = 27$	Simplify.
$\frac{9x}{9} = \frac{27}{9}$	Divide each side by 9. Division Property of Equality
$x = 3$	Simplify.

Check	$3x + 7 + 6x = 34$	Copy the original equation.
	$3(3) + 7 + 6(3) = 34$	Substitute 3 for x.
	$9 + 7 + 18 = 34$	Simplify.
	$34 = 34$ ✓	

Exercise
What is the solution to the multi-step equation $4d - 2 + 3d = 61$? Justify your steps. Then check your solution.

$4d - 2 + 3d = 61$	Write the original equation.
$4d + 3d - 2 = 61$	Commutative Property of Addition
$7d - 2 = 61$	Combine like terms.
$7d - 2 + 2 = 61 + 2$	Add 2 to each side. Addition Property of Equality
$7d = 63$	Simplify.
$\frac{7d}{7} = \frac{63}{7}$	Divide each side by 7. Division Property of Equality
$d = 9$	Simplify.

Check	$4d - 2 + 3d = 61$	Copy the original equation.
	$4(9) - 2 + 3(9) = 61$	Substitute 9 for d.
	$\boxed{36} - 2 + \boxed{27} = 61$	Simplify.
	$\boxed{61} = 61$ ✓	

Differentiated Remediation *continued*

On-Level

- **Practice** (2 pages) Provides extra practice for each lesson. For simpler practice exercises, use the Form K Practice pages found in the All-in-One Teaching Resources and online.

- **Think About a Plan** Helps students develop specific problem-solving skills and strategies by providing scaffolded guiding questions.

- **Standardized Test Prep** Focuses on all major exercises, all major question types, and helps students prepare for the high-stakes assessments.

Extension

- **Enrichment** Provides students with interesting problems and activities that extend the concepts of the lesson.

- **Activities, Games, and Puzzles** Worksheets that can be used for concepts development, enrichment, and for fun!

Practice and Problem Solving WKBK/ All-in-One Resources/Online
Practice page 1

2-3 Practice *Form G*
Solving Multi-Step Equations

Solve each equation. Check your answer.

1. $19 - h - h = -13$ 2. $14 + 6a - 8 = 18$ 3. $25 = 7 + 3k - 12$
   16   2   10

4. $5n - 16 - 8n = -10$ 5. $-34 = v + 42 - 5v$ 6. $x - 1 + 5x = 23$
   -2   19   4

7. $42j + 18 - 19j = -28$ 8. $-49 = 6c - 13 - 4c$ 9. $-28 + 15 - 22z = 31$
   -2   -18   -2

Write an equation to model each situation. Then solve the equation.

10. General admission tickets to the fair cost $3.50 per person. Ride passes cost an additional $5.50 per person. Parking costs $6 for the family. The total costs for ride passes and parking was $51. How many people in the family attended the fair? $3.50p + 5.50p + 6 = 51$; 5 people

11. Five times a number decreased by 18 minus 4 times the same number is −36. What is the number? $5n - 18 - 4n = -36$; −18

Solve each equation. Check your answer.

12. $6(3m + 5) = 66$ 13. $3(4y - 8) = 12$ 14. $-5(x - 3) = -25$
   2   3   8

15. $42 = 3(2 - 3h)$ 16. $-10 = 5(2w - 4)$ 17. $(3p - 4) = 31$
   -4   1 $11\frac{2}{3}$

18. $-3 = -3(2t - 1)$ 19. $x - 2(x + 10) = 12$ 20. $-15 = 5(3q - 10) - 5q$
   1   -32   3.5

21. Angela ate at the same restaurant four times. Each time she ordered a salad and left a $5 tip. She spent a total of $54. Write and solve to find the cost of each salad. $4c + 4 \times 5 = 54$; $8.50

Practice and Problem Solving WKBK/ All-in-One Resources/Online
Practice page 2

2-3 Practice (continued) *Form G*
Solving Multi-Step Equations

Solve each equation. Choose the method you prefer to use. Check your answer.

22. $\frac{a}{7} + \frac{a}{7} = \frac{2}{7}$ 23. $6v - \frac{5}{8} = \frac{7}{8}$ 24. $\frac{t}{6} - 9 = \frac{5}{6}$
   -3 $\frac{1}{4}$ 59

25. $\frac{c}{6} - \frac{1}{2} = \frac{3}{4}$ 26. $\frac{g}{6} + \frac{g}{6} = 6$ 27. $\frac{b}{9} - \frac{1}{2} = \frac{5}{18}$
   $3\frac{3}{4}$ $25\frac{5}{6}$ 7

28. $0.52y + 2.5 = 5.1$ 29. $4n + 0.24 = 15.76$ 30. $2.45 - 3.1t = 21.05$
   5   3.88   -6

31. $-4.2 = 9.1x + 23.1$ 32. $11.3 - 7.2f = -3.82$ 33. $14.2 = -6.8 + 4.2d$
   -3   2.1   5

34. **Reasoning** Suppose you want to solve $-5 = 6x + 3 + 7x$. What would you do as your first step? Explain.
Combine the like terms 6x and 7x by first grouping them and then adding their coefficients.

35. **Writing** Describe two different ways to solve $-10 = \frac{1}{4}(8y - 12)$.
Multiply both sides of the equation by 4 or distribute the $\frac{1}{4}$. Then isolate the variable using the addition property of equality and then the division property of equality.

Solve each equation. Round to the nearest hundredth if necessary.

36. $5 + \frac{2q}{3} = \frac{5}{11}$ 37. $\frac{3}{5}(p - 3) = -4$ 38. $11m - (6m - 5) = 25$
   6.83   -3.67   4

39. The sum of three integers is 228. The second integer is 1 more than the first, and the third integer is 2 more than the first. Write an equation to determine the integers. Solve your equation. Show your work.
$i + i + 1 + i + 2 = 228$; 75, 76, 77

40. Can you solve the equation $\frac{2}{3}(4x - 5) = 8$ by using the Division Property of Equality? Explain.
yes; divide both sides of the equation by $\frac{2}{3}$, which is the same as multiplying both sides of the equation by $\frac{3}{2}$.

Practice and Problem Solving WKBK/ All-in-One Resources/Online
Think About a Plan

2-3 Think About a Plan
Solving Multi-Step Equations

Online Video Games Angie and Kenny play online video games. Angie buys 1 software package and 3 months of game play. Kenny buys 1 software package and 2 months of game play. Each software package costs $20. If their total cost is $115, what is the cost of one month of game play?

Know

1. What values are you given?
the number of software packages Angie and Kenny buy, the number of months they play, the cost of one software package, the total cost

Need

2. What do you need to find?
the cost of one month of play

Plan

3. What equation can you use to solve the problem?
$20 + 3c + 20 + 2c = 115$

4. Solve the equation. Show your work and justify each step.

$20 + 20 + 3c + 2c = 115$	Comm. Prop. of Add.
$40 + 5c = 115$	Combine like terms.
$40 - 40 + 5c = 115 - 40$	Subtract 40 from each side. (Subt. Prop. of Equal.)
$5c = 75$	Simplify.
$\frac{5c}{5} = \frac{75}{5}$	Divide both sides by 5. (Div. Prop. of Equal.)
$c = 15$	Simplify.

5. Check your answer.
$20 + 3(15) + 20 + 2(15) \stackrel{?}{=} 115$
$20 + 45 + 20 + 30 \stackrel{?}{=} 115$
$115 = 115$ ✓

6. Is your answer reasonable? Explain.
yes; 5 months of play accounts for $75 of the total cost, so $15 is reasonable

---

Practice and Problem Solving WKBK/ All-in-One Resources/Online
Standardized Test Prep

2-3 Standardized Test Prep
Solving Multi-Step Equations

Multiple Choice

For Exercises 1–5, choose the correct letter.

1. What is the solution of $-17 = -2n + 13 - 8n$?   C
   A. −3   B. $-\frac{3}{2}$ C. 3   D. 5

2. What is the solution of $-4(-3m - 2) = 32$?   G
   F. −2   G. 2   H. 4   I. 6

3. What is the solution of $\frac{c}{5} + \frac{3}{5} = -\frac{1}{15}$?   A
   A. −2   B. $\frac{8}{3}$ C. 2   D. $\frac{16}{3}$

4. When the sum of a number and 7 is multiplied by 4, the result is 16. What is the original number?   G
   F. −12   G. −3   H. 3   I. 11

5. A merchant is selling wind chimes from a booth at a flea market. He rents his space for $125 per day. The profit from each wind chime sold is $12. His goal is to make $3500 in a five day work week. Which equation represents how many chimes he needs to sell in a week to meet his goal?   A
   A. $12c - 625 = 3500$
   B. $5(12c) - 125 = 3500$
   C. $5(12c + 125) = 3500$
   D. $5(12c - 125) = 3500$

Short Response

6. Four friends are planning to play 18 holes of golf. Two of them need to rent clubs at $5 per set. Cart rental is $10. The total cost of the golf outing, including green fees, is $92. $2(5) + 10 + g = 92$; $72
   a. Write an equation to represent the total cost of the golf outing per player.
   b. How much did the friends pay in green fees?
   [2] Both parts answered correctly.
   [1] One part answered correctly.
   [0] Neither part answered correctly.

All-in-One Resources/Online
Enrichment

2-3 Enrichment
Solving Multi-Step Equations

Consecutive integers are simply integers that follow each other in order. For example, 1, 2, and 3, are consecutive integers. Algebraically, these consecutive integers can be represented as follows:

   $1 \rightarrow N$
   $2 \rightarrow N + 1$
   $3 \rightarrow N + 2$

Therefore, the sum of three consecutive integers is written as

$N + (N + 1) + (N + 2)$

So, consecutive even integers would be represented by N, $N + 2$, and $N + 4$, where N must be an even integer. Consecutive odd integers would also be represented by N, $N + 2$, and $N + 4$, where N must be an odd integer.

1. Find three consecutive even integers whose sum is 48.
   14, 16, and 18

2. Find three consecutive odd integers whose sum is 141.
   45, 47, and 49

3. Find three consecutive even integers whose sum is −240.
   −82, −80, −78

4. Find three consecutive odd integers whose sum is −465.
   −157, −155, and −153

5. Find three consecutive integers whose sum is 300.
   99, 100, and 101

6. Find three consecutive integers whose sum of the first and the third is −88.
   −45, −44, and −43

7. Find three consecutive integers for which 3 times the sum of the first and the third integers is −342.
   −58, −57, and −56

8. Find three consecutive integers for which −4 times the sum of the first and the third integers is 192.
   −26, −24, and −22

Online Teacher Resource Center
Activities, Games, and Puzzles

2-3 Activity: Actors and Equations
Solving Multi-Step Equations

This is an activity for the entire class. Beforehand, the students and/or teacher will need to make cards showing the following:

$($ x $+$ $-$ $)$ $=$ and 0

The sketch below shows actors (students) lined up in a row. Some actors are holding cards, and some are not. Together, they model the equation $2(x + 1) = 4$.

Students from the audience must choose operations to perform to solve the equation. In doing so, actors may be directed to leave the stage, come onto the stage, or move to another position on the stage. After instructions are given and stage movements take place, a small group of actors will be left to reveal the solution.

- **Actors:** Line up in a row to illustrate $2(x + 1) = 4$. You may need feedback from the audience in order to do so.
- **Audience:** Solve the equation by giving instructions to the actors. Be sure to use the Distributive Property.
   Write the solution to the equation here: [1]

Now let's try a different approach.

- **Actors:** Line up in a row to illustrate $2(x + 1) = 4$.
- **Audience:** Solve the equation by giving instructions to the actors. Instead of applying the Distributive Property, use a different method to solve.
   Write the solution to the equation here: [1]

Summarize what you learned about solving two-step equations in the space below.

Answers may vary. Sample: I learned that a two-step equation can be solved in two different ways. The first step can involve applying the Distributive Property, or the first step can involve division.

Concept Byte

Use With Lesson 2-4

ACTIVITY

Modeling Equations With Variables on Both Sides

Algebra tiles can help you understand how to solve equations with variables on both sides.

Activity

Model and solve $3b - 4 = b + 2$.

Equation	Algebra tiles	Step
$3b - 4 = b + 2$		Model the equation using tiles.
$3b - 4 - b = b + 2 - b$ $2b - 4 = 2$		Remove one green tile from each side of the equation so that all remaining green tiles are on one side.
$2b - 4 + 4 = 2 + 4$ $2b = 6$		Add four yellow tiles to each side of the equation to form zero pairs that can be removed.
$\frac{2b}{2} = \frac{6}{2}$		Notice that two green tiles equal six yellow tiles. You can divide the tiles on each side of the equation into two identical groups, as shown.
$b = 3$		So, one green tile equals three yellow tiles. The solution of $3b - 4 = b + 2$ is $b = 3$. You can substitute 3 for b to check.

Exercises

Write the equation modeled by the algebra tiles.

1.

2.

Use algebra tiles to model and solve each equation.

3. $3x - 5 = x + 3$ **4.** $6x - 4 = 3x + 2$ **5.** $5x - 3 = 3x + 1$ **6.** $4x + 4 = 1 + x$

Guided Instruction

PURPOSE To use algebra tiles to model and solve equations with variables on both sides

PROCESS Students may
- model an equation with variables on both sides using algebra tiles.
- use algebra tiles to apply properties of equality and inverse operations.

DISCUSS The goal is for students to solve equations through algebraic reasoning. The tiles help students focus on balancing the equation and performing inverse operations.

Q Which tiles correspond to the term $3b$? **[the three green tiles]**

Q How are zero pairs related to inverse operations? **[Forming zero pairs is equivalent to using addition and subtraction as inverse operations.]**

Q What property of equality corresponds to dividing each side of the equation into two identical groups? **[Division Property of Equality]**

Q How can you check to make sure your answer is correct? **[Replace each green tile in the original model with three yellow tiles. You then have nine yellow tiles and four red tiles on the left side, and five yellow tiles on the right side. After forming zero pairs, you have five yellow tiles on each side. The answer checks.]**

Activity

In this Activity students use algebra tiles to model and solve an equation with variables on both sides with the aid of inverse operations and properties of equality.

VISUAL LEARNERS

Before assigning Exercises 3–6, provide students with unlined paper as a workspace for the tiles. Have them fold the paper in half and then open the paper. The resulting crease in the paper represents the equal sign. The two sides of the paper represent the two sides of the equation.

Answers

Exercises

1. $4x - 3 = 2x + 1$

2. $5x + 2 = 2x + 5$

3. 4

4. 2

5. 2

6. -1

1 Interactive Learning

Solve It!

PURPOSE To model a real-world situation that requires an equation with variables on both sides

PROCESS Students may
• build a chart.
• use an equation.

FACILITATE

Students may have difficulty translating the word problem into an equation.

Q If x represents the number of years, how do you express the towns' population? **[The population of Town A increases by $100x$ after x years. The total population of Town A is $3225 + 100x$ after x years. For Town B, the population is $3300 + 75x$.]**

Q What equation indicates that the populations are equal? **[$3225 + 100x = 3300 + 75x$]**

ANSWERS See Solve It in Answers on next page.

CONNECT THE MATH In the Solve It, two quantities, the populations of Towns A and B, respectively, are both dependent on the same variable, time. If the quantities can be modeled with algebraic expressions, then it may be possible to discover for what value of the variable the quantities are equal.

2 Guided Instruction

Problem 1

Q You could subtract $5x$ or $2x$. Which is easier? **[$2x$; the resulting variable coefficient is positive.]**

2-4 Solving Equations With Variables on Both Sides

Indiana Academic Standard
A1.2.5 Solve problems that can be modeled using linear equations and inequalities, interpret the solutions, and determine whether the solutions are reasonable.

Objectives To solve equations with variables on both sides
To identify equations that are identities or have no solution

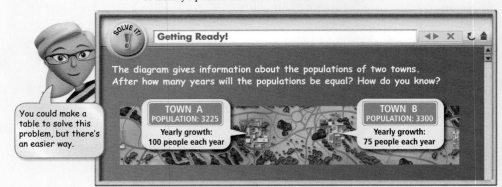

SOLVE IT

Getting Ready!

The diagram gives information about the populations of two towns. After how many years will the populations be equal? How do you know?

You could make a table to solve this problem, but there's an easier way.

TOWN A
POPULATION: 3225
Yearly growth:
100 people each year

TOWN B
POPULATION: 3300
Yearly growth:
75 people each year

Lesson Vocabulary
• identity

The problem in the Solve It can be modeled by an equation that has variables on *both* sides.

Essential Understanding To solve equations with variables on both sides, you can use the properties of equality and inverse operations to write a series of simpler equivalent equations.

Plan

How do you get started?
There are variable terms on both sides of the equation. Decide which variable term to add or subtract to get the variable on one side only.

Problem 1 Solving an Equation With Variables on Both Sides

What is the solution of $5x + 2 = 2x + 14$?

$$5x + 2 = 2x + 14$$
$$5x + 2 - 2x = 2x + 14 - 2x \quad \text{Subtract } 2x \text{ from each side.}$$
$$3x + 2 = 14 \quad \text{Simplify.}$$
$$3x + 2 - 2 = 14 - 2 \quad \text{Subtract 2 from each side.}$$
$$3x = 12 \quad \text{Simplify.}$$
$$\frac{3x}{3} = \frac{12}{3} \quad \text{Divide each side by 3.}$$
$$x = 4 \quad \text{Simplify.}$$

Check $5x + 2 = 2x + 14$
$$5(4) + 2 \stackrel{?}{=} 2(4) + 14 \quad \text{Substitute 4 for } x.$$
$$22 = 22 \checkmark \quad \text{Simplify. The solution checks.}$$

BIG ideas **Equivalence**
Solving Equations & Inequalities

UbD

ESSENTIAL UNDERSTANDINGS

• Equivalent equations are equations that have the same solution(s).
• The solution of an equation with variables on both sides can be found using the properties of equality and inverse operations to form a series of simpler equations.
• The properties of equality can be used repeatedly to isolate the variable.

Math Background

Discuss with students that as equations become more complex, it will be helpful to find solutions that are as efficient as possible. In some cases, efficiency may entail minimizing the number of steps in the solution. In other cases, the most efficient solution may involve the simplest numbers.

Support Student Learning

Use the **Algebra I Companion** to engage and support students during instruction. See Lesson Resources at the end of this lesson for details.

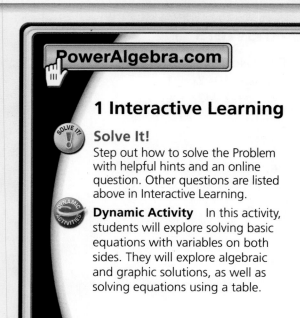

PowerAlgebra.com

1 Interactive Learning

Solve It!

Step out how to solve the Problem with helpful hints and an online question. Other questions are listed above in Interactive Learning.

Dynamic Activity In this activity, students will explore solving basic equations with variables on both sides. They will explore algebraic and graphic solutions, as well as solving equations using a table.

 Dynamic Activity
Solving Equations

 Got It? **1. a.** What is the solution of $7k + 2 = 4k - 10$?

b. Reasoning Solve the equation in Problem 1 by subtracting $5x$ from each side instead of $2x$. Compare and contrast your solution with the solution in Problem 1.

Problem 2 **Using an Equation With Variables on Both Sides**

Graphic Design It takes a graphic designer 1.5 h to make one page of a Web site. Using new software, the designer could complete each page in 1.25 h, but it takes 8 h to learn the software. How many Web pages would the designer have to make in order to save time using the new software?

Know	Need	Plan
• Current design time: 1.5 h per page • Time with new software: 1.25 h per page • Time to learn software: 8 h	The number of pages the designer needs to make for the new software to save time	Write and solve an equation that models the situation.

Think

How can a model help you write the equation?
The model shows that the current design time is equal to the new design time plus the 8 h needed to learn the new software.

1.5p	
1.25p	8

Relate $\underset{\text{design time}}{\text{current}}$ = $\underset{\text{new software}}{\text{design time with}}$ + $\underset{\text{software}}{\text{time to learn}}$

Define Let p = the number of pages the designer needs to make.

Write $\quad 1.5p \quad = \quad 1.25p \quad + \quad 8$

$$1.5p = 1.25p + 8$$

$1.5p - 1.25p = 1.25p + 8 - 1.25p$ Subtract $1.25p$ from each side.

$0.25p = 8$ Simplify.

$\dfrac{0.25p}{0.25} = \dfrac{8}{0.25}$ Divide each side by 0.25.

$p = 32$ Simplify.

It will take the designer the same amount of time to make 32 Web pages using either software. The designer must make 33 pages or more in order to save time using the new software.

 Got It? **2.** An office manager spent $650 on a new energy-saving copier that will reduce the monthly electric bill for the office from $112 to $88. In how many months will the copier pay for itself?

---

2 Guided Instruction

Each Problem is worked out and supported online.

Problem 1
Solving an Equation With Variables on Both Sides

Problem 2
Using an Equation With Variables on Both Sides
Animated

Problem 3
Solving an Equation With Grouping Symbols
Animated

Problem 4
Identities and Equations With No Solution

Alternative Problem 4
Identities and Equations With No Solution
Animated

Support in Algebra 1 Companion
• Vocabulary
• Key Concepts
• Got It?

Got It?

In 1b, discuss using multiple strategies for solving equations with variables on both sides. Some strategies may be easier than others. In this case, students would have to work with a negative coefficient.

Problem 2   **ERROR PREVENTION**

To show why this equation makes sense, have students calculate the time required to make 1, 2, and 3 pages.

Number of Pages	Hours With Old Software	Hours With New Software
1	1.5	9.25
2	3	10.5
3	4.5	11.75

If students find the difference between the times, they will see that it decreases as the number of pages increases. They need to find the number of pages required for a difference of zero.

Q How many hours does it take to make p pages with the old software? **[1.5p]**

Q What expression describes the number of hours it takes to make p pages with the new number software? **[time per page + time to learn new software, or 1.25p + 8]**

Got It?

Q How can you interpret the answer, 27.083, in the Got It? **[Since the answer is 27.083, it takes more that 27 months. The final payment occurs in the 28th month.]**

Answers

Solve It!

3 yr; explanations may vary.

Got It?

1. a. -4

    b. The answer is the same, -4.

2. about 27 months

Problem 3
Students use the Distributive Property to solve an equation with variables on both sides.

Q The book suggests using the Distributive Property to remove the parentheses. Are there other options? **[You can use the Division Property of Equality, but you end up with fractions.]**

Got It?
Point out that once students have applied the Distributive Property, the equations can be solved as in Problem 1.

Problem 4
Students solve an equation with infinitely many solutions, and an equation with no solutions.

Q What is the difference between an identity and other linear equations? **[An identity is true for every value of the variable. Other linear equations are either true for one or for no values of the variable.]**

Q How do you know if the equation has an infinite number of solutions or no solution? **[If, in the process of solving the equation, the variable disappears, then one of these situations is occurring. If you end up with a true statement, such as 12 = 12, then the equation is an identity. Otherwise, there is no solution.]**

Got It?   ERROR INTERVENTION
In 4b, if students state that the solution is $\frac{-10}{4}$ or $\frac{-5}{2}$, then they have not distributed the -1 throughout the parentheses.

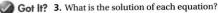

Plan

How do you get started?
There are parentheses on both sides of the equation. So, remove the parentheses using the Distributive Property.

Problem 3   Solving an Equation With Grouping Symbols

What is the solution of $2(5x - 1) = 3(x + 11)$?

$$2(5x - 1) = 3(x + 11)$$

$10x - 2 = 3x + 33$	Distributive Property
$10x - 2 - 3x = 3x + 33 - 3x$	Subtract $3x$ from each side.
$7x - 2 = 33$	Simplify.
$7x - 2 + 2 = 33 + 2$	Add 2 to each side.
$7x = 35$	Simplify.
$\frac{7x}{7} = \frac{35}{7}$	Divide each side by 7.
$x = 5$	Simplify.

Got It? 3. What is the solution of each equation?

    a. $4(2y + 1) = 2(y - 13)$ **b.** $7(4 - a) = 3(a - 4)$

An equation that is true for every possible value of the variable is an **identity**. For example, $x + 1 = x + 1$ is an identity. An equation has no solution if there is no value of the variable that makes the equation true. The equation $x + 1 = x + 2$ has no solution.

Problem 4   Identities and Equations With No Solution

Think

How can you tell how many solutions an equation has?
If you eliminate the variable in the process of solving, the equation is either an identity with infinitely many solutions or an equation with no solution.

What is the solution of each equation?

Ⓐ $10x + 12 = 2(5x + 6)$

$$10x + 12 = 2(5x + 6)$$

$10x + 12 = 10x + 12$ Distributive Property

Because $10x + 12 = 10x + 12$ is always true, there are infinitely many solutions of the equation. The original equation is an identity.

Ⓑ $9m - 4 = -3m + 5 + 12m$

$$9m - 4 = -3m + 5 + 12m$$

$9m - 4 = 9m + 5$	Combine like terms.
$9m - 4 - 9m = 9m + 5 - 9m$	Subtract $9m$ from each side.
$-4 = 5$ ✗	Simplify.

Because $-4 \neq 5$, the original equation has no solution.

Got It? 4. What is the solution of each equation?

    a. $3(4b - 2) = -6 + 12b$ **b.** $2x + 7 = -1(3 - 2x)$

Additional Problems

1. What is the solution of $5s + 13 = 2s + 22$?

    ANSWER 3

2. Lorelle pays someone $35 to clear her driveway when it snows. She wants to buy an electric snow blower for $689 so that she can clear her own driveway. If the area Lorelle lives in has an average of 5.2 snowfalls each season, how many seasons will it take her to break even on what she spent for the snow blower?

    ANSWER Almost 4 seasons

3. What is the solution of $2(3x + 1) = 4(x - 5)$?

    ANSWER -11

4. What is the solution of the equation $t + 8 = -t + 6 + 2t$?

    ANSWER The equation has no solution.

Answers

Got It? (continued)

3. a. -5

    b. 4

4. a. infinitely many solutions

    b. no solution

When you solve an equation, you use reasoning to select properties of equality that produce simpler equivalent equations until you find a solution. The steps below provide a general guideline for solving equations.

Concept Summary   Solving Equations

Step 1   Use the Distributive Property to remove any grouping symbols. Use properties of equality to clear decimals and fractions.

Step 2   Combine like terms on each side of the equation.

Step 3   Use the properties of equality to get the variable terms on one side of the equation and the constants on the other.

Step 4   Use the properties of equality to solve for the variable.

Step 5   Check your solution in the original equation.

Lesson Check

Do you know HOW?

Solve each equation. Check your answer.

1. $3x + 4 = 5x - 10$ **2.** $5(y - 4) = 7(2y + 1)$

3. $2a + 3 = \frac{1}{2}(6 + 4a)$ **4.** $4x - 5 = 2(2x + 1)$

5. Printing Pristine Printing will print business cards for $.10 each plus a setup charge of $15. The Printing Place offers business cards for $.15 each with a setup charge of $10. What number of business cards costs the same from either printer?

Do you UNDERSTAND?

Vocabulary Match each equation with the appropriate number of solutions.

6. $3y - 5 = y + 2y - 9$ **A.** infinitely many

7. $2y + 4 = 2(y + 2)$ **B.** one solution

8. $2y - 4 = 3y - 5$ **C.** no solution

9. Writing A student solved an equation and found that the variable was eliminated in the process of solving the equation. How would the student know whether the equation is an identity or an equation with no solution?

Practice and Problem-Solving Exercises

A Practice   Solve each equation. Check your answer.   ◀ See Problem 1.

10. $5x - 1 = x + 15$ **11.** $4p + 2 = 3p - 7$ **12.** $6m - 2 = 2m + 6$

13. $3 + 5q = 9 + 4q$ **14.** $8 - 2y = 3y - 2$ **15.** $3n - 5 = 7n + 11$

16. $2b + 4 = -18 - 9b$ **17.** $-3c - 12 = -5 + c$ **18.** $-n - 24 = 5 - n$

Answers

Lesson Check

1. 7

2. −3

3. infinitely many solutions

4. no solution

5. 100 business cards

6. C

7. A

8. B

9. If the numeric values are the same on both sides, it is an identity. If they are different, there is no solution.

Practice and Problem-Solving Exercises

10. 4

11. −9

12. 2

13. 6

14. 2

15. −4

16. −2

17. $-1\frac{3}{4}$

18. no solution

Take Note

It may be helpful for students to solve an equation that involves each step. For example:

$$5(x + 4) = x + 2x + 6$$
$$5x + 20 = x + 2x + 6 \qquad \text{Step 1}$$
$$5x + 20 = 3x + 6 \qquad \text{Step 2}$$
$$2x = -14 \qquad \text{Step 3}$$
$$x = -7 \qquad \text{Step 4}$$
$$5(-7 + 4) = -7 + 2(-7) + 6$$
$$5(-3) = -7 - 14 + 6$$
$$-15 = -15 \qquad \text{Step 5}$$

3 Lesson Check

Do you know HOW?

• It may help students to refer to Problem 2 when solving Exercise 5. Use Know, Need, Plan to generate the equation as seen in Problem 2.

Do you UNDERSTAND?

• It may help students to refer to Problem 4 when solving Exercise 9. The difference between 4a and 4b is that the last equation in 4a is true, while the last equation in 4b is false. This is how the student can tell whether the equation is an identity, or whether it has no solution.

Close

Q In the Take Note, do any steps apply only to solving equations with variables on both sides of the equation? **[No; each step could be used when solving equations with variables on both or on only one side of the equation.]**

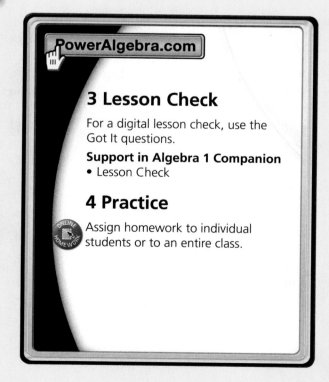

PowerAlgebra.com

3 Lesson Check

For a digital lesson check, use the Got It questions.

Support in Algebra 1 Companion
• Lesson Check

4 Practice

Assign homework to individual students or to an entire class.

4 Practice

ASSIGNMENT GUIDE

Basic: 10–32 all, 34–42 even, 43, 44, 46

Average: 11–31 odd, 33–49

Advanced: 11–31 odd, 33–56

Standardized Test Prep: 57–59

Mixed Review: 60–66

Reasoning exercises have blue headings.

Applications exercises have red headings.

EXERCISE 44: Use the Think About a Plan worksheet in the **Practice and Problem Solving Workbook** (also available in the Teaching Resources in print and online) to further support students' development in becoming independent learners.

HOMEWORK QUICK CHECK

To check students' understanding of key skills and concepts, go over Exercises 19, 29, 42, 44, and 46.

Write and solve an equation for each situation. Check your solution. ◀ See Problem 2.

19. **Architecture** An architect is designing a rectangular greenhouse. Along one wall is a 7-ft storage area and 5 sections for different kinds of plants. On the opposite wall is a 4-ft storage area and 6 sections for plants. All of the sections for plants are of equal length. What is the length of each wall?

20. **Business** A hairdresser is deciding where to open her own studio. If the hairdresser chooses Location A, she will pay $1200 per month in rent and will charge $45 per haircut. If she chooses Location B, she will pay $1800 per month in rent and will charge $60 per haircut. How many haircuts would she have to give in one month to make the same profit at either location?

Solve each equation. Check your answer. ◀ See Problem 3.

21. $3(q - 5) = 2(q + 5)$

22. $8 - (3 + b) = b - 9$

23. $7(6 - 2a) = 5(-3a + 1)$

24. $(g + 4) - 3g = 1 + g$

25. $2r - (5 - r) = 13 + 2r$

26. $5g + 4(-5 + 3g) = 1 - g$

Determine whether each equation is an *identity* or whether it has *no solution*. ◀ See Problem 4.

27. $2(a - 4) = 4a - (2a + 4)$

28. $5y + 2 = \frac{1}{2}(10y + 4)$

29. $k - 3k = 6k + 5 - 8k$

30. $2(2k - 1) = 4(k - 2)$

31. $-6a + 3 = -3(2a - 1)$

32. $4 - d = -(d - 4)$

Ⓑ Apply **Solve each equation. If the equation is an identity, write *identity*. If it has no solution, write *no solution*.**

33. $3.2 - 4d = 2.3d + 3$

34. $3d + 4 = 2 + 3d - \frac{1}{2}$

35. $2.25(4x - 4) = -2 + 10x + 12$

36. $3a + 1 = -3.6(a - 1)$

37. $\frac{1}{2}h + \frac{1}{3}(h - 6) = \frac{5}{6}h + 2$

38. $0.5b + 4 = 2(b + 2)$

39. $-2(-c - 12) = -2c - 12$

40. $3(m + 1.5) = 1.5(2m + 3)$

41. **Travel** Suppose a family drives at an average rate of 60 mi/h on the way to visit relatives and then at an average rate of 40 mi/h on the way back. The return trip takes 1 h longer than the trip there.
   a. Let d be the distance in miles the family traveled to visit their relatives. How many hours did it take to drive there?
   b. In terms of d, how many hours did it take to make the return trip?
   c. Write and solve an equation to determine the distance the family drove to see their relatives. What was the average rate for the entire trip?

Answers

Practice and Problem-Solving Exercises (continued)

19. 22 ft

20. 40 haircuts

21. 25

22. 7

23. −37

24. 1

25. 18

26. $1\frac{1}{6}$

27. no solution

28. identity

29. no solution

30. no solution

31. identity

32. identity

33. $\frac{2}{63}$

34. no solution

35. −19

36. $\frac{13}{33}$

37. no solution

38. 0

39. −9

40. identity

41. a. $\frac{d}{60}$

   b. $\frac{d}{40}$

   c. $\frac{d}{60} + 1 = \frac{d}{40}$; 120 mi; 48 mi/h

42. Think About a Plan Each morning, a deli worker has to make several pies and peel a bucket of potatoes. On Monday, it took the worker 2 h to make the pies and an average of 1.5 min to peel each potato. On Tuesday, the worker finished the work in the same amount of time, but it took 2.5 h to make the pies and an average of 1 min to peel each potato. About how many potatoes are in a bucket?

- What quantities do you know and how are they related to each other?
- How can you use the known and unknown quantities to write an equation for this situation?

43. Error Analysis Describe and correct the error in finding the solution of the equation $2x = 6x$.

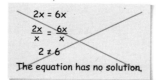

$$2x = 6x$$
$$\frac{2x}{x} = \frac{6x}{x}$$
$$2 \neq 6$$

The equation has no solution.

44. Skiing A skier is trying to decide whether or not to buy a season ski pass. A daily pass costs $67. A season ski pass costs $350. The skier would have to rent skis with either pass for $25 per day. How many days would the skier have to go skiing in order to make the season pass less expensive than daily passes?

45. Health Clubs One health club charges a $50 sign-up fee and $65 per month. Another club charges a $90 sign-up fee and $45 per month. For what number of months is the cost of the clubs equal?

46. Geometry The perimeters of the triangles shown are equal. Find the side lengths of each triangle.

47. Business A small juice company spends $1200 per day on business expenses plus $1.10 per bottle of juice they make. They charge $2.50 for each bottle of juice they produce. How many bottles of juice must the company sell in one day in order to equal its daily costs?

48. Spreadsheet You set up a spreadsheet to solve $7(x + 1) = 3(x - 1)$.

a. Does your spreadsheet show the solution of the equation?

b. Between which two values of x is the solution of the equation? How do you know?

c. For what spreadsheet values of x is $7(x + 1)$ less than $3(x - 1)$?

	A	B	C
1	x	$7(x + 1)$	$3(x - 1)$
2	−5	−28	−18
3	−3	−14	−12
4	−1	0	−6
5	1	14	0
6	3	28	6

42. 60 potatoes

43. Subtraction should be used to isolate the variable, not division by the variable. $2x = 6x$, so $0 = 4x$, and $x = 0$.

44. 6 days

45. 2 months

46. $AB = 16$, $BC = 15$, $AC = 12$; $PQ = 12$, $QR = 12$, $PR = 19$

47. about 857 bottles

48. a. no

b. Between −1 and −3; answers may vary. Sample: $7(x + 1)$ is less than $3(x - 1)$ when $x = -3$, but is greater than $3(x - 1)$ when $x = -1$.

c. all values −3 or less

Answers

Practice and Problem-Solving Exercises
(continued)

49. a. always true

   b. sometimes true

   c. sometimes true

50. Check students' work.

51. Check students' work.

52. Check students' work.

53. Check students' work.

54. Check students' work.

55. Check students' work.

56. 0, 1, 2

57. B

58. G

59. A

60. 5

61. −6

62. 1

63. 0.9 m

64. 22

65. 9

66. 11.2

---

49. Reasoning Determine whether each statement is *always*, *sometimes*, or *never* true.

   a. An equation of the form $ax + 1 = ax$ has no solution.

   b. An equation in one variable has at least one solution.

   c. An equation of the form $\frac{x}{a} = \frac{x}{b}$ has infinitely many solutions.

 Challenge   **Open-Ended** Write an equation with a variable on both sides such that you get each solution.

50. $x = 5$ **51.** $x = 0$ **52.** x can be any number.

53. No values of x are solutions.   **54.** x is a negative number.   **55.** x is a fraction.

56. Suppose you have three consecutive integers. The greatest of the three integers is twice as great as the sum of the first two. What are the integers?

Standardized Test Prep

SAT/ACT

57. What is the solution of $-2(3x - 4) = -2x + 2$?

   Ⓐ $-\frac{2}{3}$ Ⓑ $\frac{3}{2}$ Ⓒ 2   Ⓓ 24

58. Two times a number plus three equals one half of the number plus 12. What is the number?

   Ⓕ 3.6   Ⓖ 6   Ⓗ 8   Ⓘ 10

59. Josie's goal is to run 30 mi each week. This week she has already run the distances shown in the table. She wants to have one day of rest and to spread out the remaining miles evenly over the rest of the week. Which equation can she use to find how many miles m per day she must run?

Miles per Day						
M	T	W	T	F	S	S
4	4.5	3.5	■	■	■	■

   Ⓐ $4 + 4.5 + 3.5 + 3m = 30$ Ⓒ $30 - (4 + 4.5 + 3.5) = m$

   Ⓑ $4 + 4.5 + 3.5 + 4m = 30$ Ⓓ $4 + 4.5 + 3.5 + m = 30$

Mixed Review

Solve each equation.   ◀ See Lesson 2-3.

60. $-2a + 5a - 4 = 11$ **61.** $6 = -3(x + 4)$ **62.** $3\left(c + \frac{1}{3}\right) = 4$

63. A carpenter is filling in an open entranceway with a door and two side panels of the same width. The entranceway is 3 m wide. The door will be 1.2 m wide. How wide should the carpenter make the panels on either side of the door so that the two panels and the door will fill the entranceway exactly?   ◀ See Lesson 2-2.

Get Ready!   **To prepare for Lesson 2-5, do Exercises 64–66.**

Evaluate each expression for the given values of the variables.   ◀ See Lesson 1-2.

64. $n + 2m$; $m = 12, n = -2$ **65.** $3b \div c$; $b = 12, c = 4$ **66.** xy^2; $x = 2.8, y = 2$

Additional Instructional Support

Algebra 1 Companion

Students can use the **Algebra 1 Companion** worktext (4 pages) as you teach the lesson. Use the Companion to support

- New Vocabulary
- Key Concepts
- Got It for each Problem
- Lesson Check

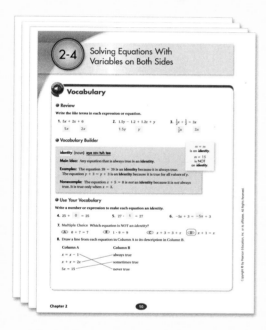

ELL Support

Use Manipulatives Write $6x + 4 = 8x - 10$ at the top of the board. Ask students what they are solving for in the equation. Use one color of sticky notes with X's on them under the equation, a different color for the positive ones, and a third color for the negative ones. Remind students that they have to do the same thing to both sides of the equation. Have them subtract 6 X's from each side. Ask students if they recognize this problem as one they can already solve. Continue using the properties of equality and inverse operations to adjust the sticky notes until they show that $x = 7$.

5 Assess & Remediate

Lesson Quiz

1. What is the solution of $10m + 8 = 7m + 17$?

2. Tony is $\frac{1}{2}$ mile ahead of Laura on a jogging path. If Tony is running at 5 miles per hour, and Laura is running at 7 miles per hour, how long will it take Laura to catch up with Tony?

3. What is the solution of $3(4a + 2) = 2(a - 2)$?

4. **Do you UNDERSTAND?** Why does the equation $3x + 7 = -3x + 2 + 6x$ have no solution?

ANSWERS TO LESSON QUIZ

1. 3

2. $\frac{1}{4}$ of an hour, or 15 minutes

3. -1

4. Answers may vary. Sample: The variable cancels out and leaves a false statement.

PRESCRIPTION FOR REMEDIATION

Use the student work on the Lesson Quiz to prescribe a differentiated review assignment.

Points	Differentiated Remediation
0–2	Intervention
3	On-level
4	Extension

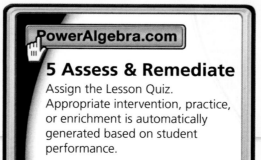

PowerAlgebra.com

5 Assess & Remediate

Assign the Lesson Quiz. Appropriate intervention, practice, or enrichment is automatically generated based on student performance.

Intervention

- **Reteaching** (2 pages) Provides reteaching and practice exercises for the key lesson concepts. Use with struggling students or absent students.

- **English Language Learner Support** Helps students develop and reinforce mathematical vocabulary and key concepts.

All-in-One Resources/Online
Reteaching

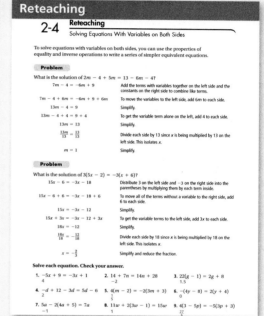

All-in-One Resources/Online
English Language Learner Support

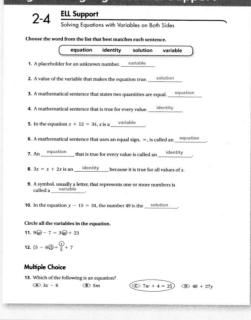

Differentiated Remediation *continued*

On-Level

- **Practice** (2 pages) Provides extra practice for each lesson. For simpler practice exercises, use the Form K Practice pages found in the All-in-One Teaching Resources and online.

- **Think About a Plan** Helps students develop specific problem-solving skills and strategies by providing scaffolded guiding questions.

- **Standardized Test Prep** Focuses on all major exercises, all major question types, and helps students prepare for the high-stakes assessments.

Extension

- **Enrichment** Provides students with interesting problems and activities that extend the concepts of the lesson.

- **Activities, Games, and Puzzles** Worksheets that can be used for concepts development, enrichment, and for fun!

Practice and Problem Solving WKBK/ All-in-One Resources/Online
Practice page 1

2-4 Practice *Form G*
Solving Equations With Variables on Both Sides

Solve each equation. Check your answer.

1. $3n + 2 = -2n - 8$
  -2
2. $8b - 7 = 7b - 2$
  5
3. $-12 + 5k = 15 - 4k$
  3
4. $-q - 11 = 2q + 4$
  -5
5. $4t + 9 = -8t - 13$
  $-1\frac{5}{6}$
6. $22p + 11 = 4p - 7$
  -1
7. $17 - 9y = -3 + 16y$
  $\frac{4}{5}$
8. $15m + 22 = -7m + 18$
  $-\frac{2}{11}$
9. $3x + 7 = 14 + 3x$
  no solution

Write and solve an equation for each situation. Check your solution.

10. Shirley is going to have the exterior of her home painted. Tim's Painting charges $250 plus $14 per hour. Colorful Paints charges $22 per hour. How many hours would the job need to take for Tim's Painting to be the better deal? $250 + 14h = 22h$; more than $31\frac{1}{4}$ h

11. Tracey is looking at two different travel agencies to plan her vacation. ABC Travel offers a plane ticket for $295 and a rental car for $39 per day. M & N Travel offers a plane ticket for $350 and a rental car for $33 per day. What is the minimum number of days that Shirley's vacation should be for M & N Travel to have the better deal? $295 + 39d = 350 + 33d$; $d = 9\frac{1}{6}$; less than 10 days

Solve each equation. Check your answer.

12. $7(h + 3) = 6(h - 3)$
  -39
13. $-(5a + 6) = 2(3a + 8)$
  -2
14. $-2(2f - 4) = -4(-f + 2)$
  2
15. $3w - 6 + 2w = -2 + w$
  1
16. $-8x - (3x + 6) = 4 - x$
  -1
17. $14 + 3n = 8n - 3(n - 4)$
  1

Determine whether each equation is an *identity* or whether it has no solution.

18. $4(3m + 4) = 2(6m + 8)$
  an identity
19. $5x + 2x - 3 = -3x + 10x$
  no solution
20. $-(3z + 4) = 6z - 3(3z + 2)$
  no solution
21. $-2(j - 3) = -2j + 6$
  an identity

Practice and Problem Solving WKBK/ All-in-One Resources/Online
Practice page 2

2-4 Practice (continued) *Form G*
Solving Equations With Variables on Both Sides

Solve each equation. If the equation is an identity, write *identity*. If it has no solution, write *no solution*.

22. $6.8 - 4.2b = 5.6b - 3$
  5
23. $\frac{1}{3} + \frac{2}{3}m = \frac{3}{2}m - \frac{2}{3}$
  no solution
24. $-2(5.25 + 6.2x) = 4(-3.1x + 2.68)$
  no solution
25. $\frac{1}{2}r + 6 = 3 - 2r$
  $-\frac{6}{5}$
26. $0.5t + 0.25(t + 16) = 4 + 0.75t$
  an identity
27. $2.5(2z + 5) = 5(z + 2.5)$
  an identity
28. $-6(-p + 8) = -6p + 12$
  5
29. $\frac{3}{8}f + \frac{1}{2} = 6(\frac{1}{16}f - 3)$
  no solution

30. Three times the sum of a number and 4 is 8 less than one-half the number. Write and solve an equation to find the number.
  -8

31. A square and a rectangle have the same perimeters. The length of a side of the square is $4x - 1$. The length of the rectangle is $2x + 1$ and the width is $x + 2$. Write and solve an equation to find x.
  1

32. A movie club charges a one-time membership fee of $25 which allows members to purchase movies for $7 each. Another club does not charge a membership fee and sells movies for $12 each. How many movies must a member purchase for the cost of the two clubs to be equal?
  $25 + 7n = 12n$; 5 movies

33. **Writing** Describe the difference between an equation that is defined as an identity and an equation that has no solution. Provide an example of each and explain why each example is an identity or has no solution.
  Because $4x - 2 = 4x - 4 + 2$ is always true, the equation has infinitely many solutions and so it is an identity. Because $3y + 10 = 3y + 15$ is never true, the equation has no solution.

Practice and Problem Solving WKBK/ All-in-One Resources/Online
Think About a Plan

2-4 Think About a Plan
Solving Equations With Variables on Both Sides

Skiing A skier is trying to decide whether or not to buy a season ski pass. A daily pass costs $67. A season ski pass costs $350. The skier would have to rent skis with either pass for $25 per day. How many days would the skier have to go skiing in order to make the season pass less expensive than daily passes?

Understanding the Problem

1. What do you know about the costs associated with buying a daily pass?
  the costs of a daily pass and a daily ski rental

2. What do you know about the costs associated with buying a season pass?
  the costs of a season pass and a daily ski rental

Planning the Solution

3. Write an expression using words to represent the cost of a daily pass. Write the algebraic expression.
  Let d = number of days you ski. $67d + 25d$

4. Write an expression using words to represent the cost of a season pass. Write the algebraic expression.
  Let d = the number of days you ski. $350 + 25d$

5. How can you compare the cost of a daily pass with the cost of a season pass algebraically? What is the equation?
  write an equation to find when the costs are the same; $67d + 25d = 350 + 25d$

Getting an Answer

6. Solve the equation you wrote in Step 5. Show your work.
  $5\frac{15}{67}$

7. Explain what this solution means.
  The season pass is less if the person goes skiing 6 times or more.

Practice and Problem Solving WKBK/ All-in-One Resources/Online
Standardized Test Prep

2-4 Standardized Test Prep
Solving Equations With Variables on Both Sides

Multiple Choice

For Exercises 1-5, choose the correct letter.

1. What is the solution of $-8x - 5 + 3x = 7 + 4x - 9$? B
  A. -3 B. $-\frac{1}{3}$ C. $\frac{1}{3}$ D. 3

2. What is the solution of $-(-5 - 6x) = 4(5x + 3)$? G
  F. -2 G. $-\frac{1}{2}$ H. $\frac{1}{2}$ I. 2

3. What is the solution of $2n - 3(4n + 5) = -6(n - 3) - 1$? A
  A. -8 B. -6 C. $-\frac{1}{2}$ D. 4

4. Negative one times the sum of twice a number and 3 is equal to two times the difference of -4 times the number and 3. What is the number? H
  F. -4 G. -2 H. $\frac{1}{2}$ I. 2

5. Jacob is saving for a new bicycle which costs $175. He has already saved $35. His goal is to have enough money saved in six weeks to pay for the bicycle. Which equation represents how much money he needs to save each week to meet his goal? A
  A. $35 + 6d = 175$
  B. $35 + 12d = 175$
  C. $6(35 + 2d) = 175$
  D. $2(35 + 6d) = 175$

Short Response

6. Admission for a water park is $17.50 per day. A season pass costs $125. A locker rental costs $3.50 per day.
  a. What is an equation that represents the relationship between the cost of a daily pass and the cost of a season pass? $17.50d \approx 125$
  b. How many days would you have to go to the water park for the season pass to save you money?
  Because $d \approx 7.1$, you would have to go to the water park at least 8 days.
  [2] Both parts answered correctly.
  [1] One part answered correctly.
  [0] Neither part answered correctly.

All-in-One Resources/Online
Enrichment

2-4 Enrichment
Solving Equations With Variables on Both Sides

The circumference and area of a circle are determined by the formulas $C = 2\pi r$ and $A = \pi r^2$. An increase of 1 unit in the radius causes predictable increases in the circumference and area.

Start with a circle of radius 1 unit. Then $C = 2\pi$ units and $A = \pi$ square units. Increasing the radius by 1 unit, meaning $r = 2$, leads to $C = 4\pi$ units and $A = 4\pi$ square units. Increasing the radius 1 unit again, meaning $r = 3$, leads to $C = 6\pi$ and $A = 9\pi$. You may notice a pattern emerging.

Even if the radius is not known, knowing by how much the radius changes makes it possible to compare the circumference and area of the new circle to the circumference and area of the old circle.

For a circle with radius x, $C = 2\pi x$ and $A = \pi x^2$.
If the radius is increased by 1 unit to $x + 1$, $C = 2\pi(x + 1)$ or $2\pi x + 2\pi$, and $A = \pi(x + 1)^2$ or $\pi(x^2 + 2x + 1)$.

1. The circumference of a circle is 8π cm. The radius is increased, and the circumference of the new circle is 16π cm. By how much was the radius of the original circle increased?
  radius increased by 4 cm

2. One circle has a radius 1 unit greater than another circle. The area of the larger circle is 9π square units greater than the area of the smaller circle. What are the radius and area of each circle?
  radii are 4 and 5; areas are 16π and 25π sq units

3. If the radius is increased by 1 unit, the area of the circle is increased by 16π square units. What is the radius of the original circle?
  7.5

4. By how many units must the radius of a circle be increased to increase its circumference by 22π units?
  11

5. The circumference of a circle is 4 times the circumference of a circle with a radius 1 unit less. What is the radius of each circle?
  radii $\frac{4}{3}$ and $\frac{1}{3}$

Online Teacher Resource Center
Activities, Games, and Puzzles

2-4 Puzzle: Breaking the Code
Solving Equations With Variables on Both Sides

Solve each equation. Write the solution in the blocks in the three columns to the right of the equation. Then use the code below to translate the numbers in the *shaded* boxes to letters. The first one has been done for you. You will see a secret message when you read from the top to the bottom of the column.

$A \to 1$ $B \to 2$ $C \to 3$ $\ldots$ $X \to 24$ $Y \to 25$ $Z \to 26$

Equation	Number	Number	Letter
$2x = 3x - 8$	8		H
$-n = 2n - 3$	1		A
$-x + 5 = -4x + 71$	2	2	V
$11m - 10 = 9m$	5		E
$3x + 1 = 2x + 2$	1		A
$5x + 4 = 2x + 46$	1	4	N
$-3t = 3t - 54$	9		I
$12x - 33 = x$	3		C
$25a + 125 = 50a$	5		E
$14w + 56 = 28w$	4		D
$13b - 39 = 11b - 37$	1		A
$125 + 13x = 21x - 75$	2	5	Y
$6 + 6h = 7h$	6		F
$-2x + 12 = 2x - 48$	1	5	O
$5c - 10 = 2c + 26$	1	2	L
$-4x - 13 = -6x + 9$	1	1	K
$4x + 10 = -6x + 200$	1	9	S

2-5 Literal Equations and Formulas

Indiana Academic Standards

A1.2.5 Solve problems that can be modeled using linear equations and inequalities, interpret the solutions, and determine whether the solutions are reasonable.

A1.6.2 Solve equations involving rational and common irrational expressions.

Objective   To rewrite and use literal equations and formulas

SOLVE IT!

Getting Ready! ◀▶ ✕ ↻ ⬆

You are ordering pizzas and sandwiches. You have a budget of $80. How many sandwiches can you buy if you buy 4 pizzas? 5 pizzas? Explain your answer.

MENU
Pizza $10
Sandwich $5

Hey—there are <u>two</u> variable quantities here!

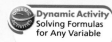

Dynamic Activity
Solving Formulas for Any Variable

Lesson Vocabulary
• literal equation
• formula

In this lesson, you will learn to solve problems using equations in more than one variable. A **literal equation** is an equation that involves two or more variables.

Essential Understanding When you work with literal equations, you can use the methods you have learned in this chapter to isolate any particular variable.

Think

Why should you rewrite the equation?
If you rewrite the equation, you have to isolate *y* only once. Then substitute for *x*. If you substitute for *x* first, you must isolate *y* twice (once for each *x*-value).

Problem 1 Rewriting a Literal Equation

The equation $10x + 5y = 80$, where *x* is the number of pizzas and *y* is the number of sandwiches, models the problem in the Solve It. How many sandwiches can you buy if you buy 3 pizzas? 6 pizzas?

Step 1   Solve the equation $10x + 5y = 80$ for *y*.

$$10x + 5y = 80$$
$$10x + 5y - 10x = 80 - 10x \quad \text{Subtract } 10x \text{ from each side.}$$
$$5y = 80 - 10x \quad \text{Simplify.}$$
$$\frac{5y}{5} = \frac{80 - 10x}{5} \quad \text{Divide each side by 5.}$$
$$y = 16 - 2x \quad \text{Simplify.}$$

Step 2   Use the rewritten equation to find *y* when $x = 3$ and when $x = 6$.

$$y = 16 - 2x \qquad\qquad y = 16 - 2x$$
$$y = 16 - 2(3) \quad \text{Substitute for } x. \quad y = 16 - 2(6)$$
$$y = 10 \qquad \text{Simplify.} \qquad y = 4$$

If you buy 3 pizzas, you can buy 10 sandwiches. If you buy 6 pizzas, you can buy 4 sandwiches.

1 Interactive Learning

Solve It!

PURPOSE To see how literal equations can be used to model real-world situations
PROCESS Students may
• build a chart.
• use the number of pizzas required to calculate the money remaining for sandwiches.
• use an equation.

FACILITATE

Q What is the relationship between the number of pizzas and the number of sandwiches you can buy? **[As the number of pizzas increases, the number of sandwiches decreases.]**

ANSWER See Solve it in Answers on next page.
CONNECT THE MATH In this Solve It, the amount of money spent depends on two variables, the number of pizzas and the number of sandwiches. In this lesson, students will learn to use algebra to model situations with multiple variables.

2 Guided Instruction

Problem 1
Once a value for one variable has been given, the equation is a one-variable linear equation.

Q How does knowing how to solve a one-variable linear equation help you solve a literal equation? **[Solving the literal equation involves the same steps as solving a one-variable, linear equation.]**

2-5 Preparing to Teach

BIG ideas **Equivalence**   **UbD**
Solving Equations & Inequalities

ESSENTIAL UNDERSTANDINGS
• A literal equation is an equation that involves two or more variables.
• The solution of a literal equation can be found using the properties of equality and inverse operations to form a series of simpler equations.
• The properties of equality can be used repeatedly to isolate any particular variable.

Math Background
When solving literal equations, students can use the same properties of equality and inverse operations that they have used throughout this chapter. Students can treat all variables that they are not solving for as constants. This skill is particularly useful in working with math and science formulas. For example, the uniform motion formula $d = rt$ (distance = rate × time) can be solve for *r*, yielding a specific formula for speed (rate = distance/time).

Support Student Learning
Use the **Algebra I Companion** to engage and support students during instruction. See Lesson Resources at the end of this lesson for details.

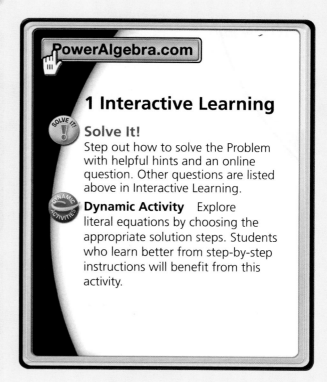

PowerAlgebra.com

1 Interactive Learning

SOLVE IT!
Solve It!
Step out how to solve the Problem with helpful hints and an online question. Other questions are listed above in Interactive Learning.

Dynamic Activity Explore literal equations by choosing the appropriate solution steps. Students who learn better from step-by-step instructions will benefit from this activity.

Got It?

In 1b, students may prefer to substitute each value for x separately and then solve. While this may be easier on a case-by-case basis, it is more efficient to solve for y without substituting a value for x. Then y can be found for any value of x without having to solve the equation again.

Problem 2

To solve this problem, students need to realize that the Distributive Property can be used not only to distribute a variable across terms, but also to factor an expression. For example, students can use the Distributive Property to write $2(x - 3)$ as $2x - 6$. Or, given $2x - 6$, they can write $2(x - 3)$. Provide students with a few problems to factor before attempting Problem 2.

Q Factor each of the following expressions:

$-3x - 9 = \_(x + 3)$ **[$-3(x + 3)$]**

$2xy + 6y = \_(x + 3)$ **[$2y(x + 3)$]**

$9x - 18 = \_(x - 2)$ **[$9(x - 2)$]**

$ax - bx = \_(\_ - \_)$ **[$x(a - b)$]**

Q How can you use this work to solve $ax - bx = c$? **[Factor $ax - bx$ as $x(a - b)$, then divide by $a - b$.]**

Q Describe the operations performed on the left side of the equation. In what order are they performed? **[First b is subtracted from a, then the result is multiplied by x.]**

Q What should you do to isolate x? What is the result? **[Divide by $(a - b)$. The result is $x = \frac{c}{a - b}$.]**

Got It?

Emphasize that students can treat variables like constants, so they can solve this equation just like the two-step equations they have already seen.

 Got It? **1. a.** Solve the equation $4 = 2m - 5n$ for m. What are the values of m when $n = -2, 0$, and 2?

     b. Reasoning Solve Problem 1 by substituting $x = 3$ and $x = 6$ into the equation $10x + 5y = 80$ and then solving for y in each case. Do you prefer this method or the method shown in Problem 1? Explain.

When you rewrite literal equations, you may have to divide by a variable or variable expression. When you do so in this lesson, assume that the variable or variable expression is not equal to zero because division by zero is not defined.

Problem 2   Rewriting a Literal Equation With Only Variables

Think

How can you solve a literal equation for a variable?
When a literal equation contains only variables, treat the variables you are *not* solving for as constants.

What equation do you get when you solve $ax - bx = c$ for x?

$$ax - bx = c$$

$$x(a - b) = c \qquad \text{Distributive Property}$$

$$\frac{x(a - b)}{a - b} = \frac{c}{a - b} \qquad \text{Divide each side by } a - b, \text{ where } a - b \neq 0.$$

$$x = \frac{c}{a - b} \qquad \text{Simplify.}$$

 Got It? **2.** What equation do you get when you solve $-t = r + px$ for x?

A **formula** is an equation that states a relationship among quantities. Formulas are special types of literal equations. Some common formulas are given below. Notice that some of the formulas use the same variables, but the definitions of the variables are different.

Formula Name	Formula	Definitions of Variables
Perimeter of a rectangle	$P = 2\ell + 2w$	P = perimeter, ℓ = length, w = width
Circumference of a circle	$C = 2\pi r$	C = circumference, r = radius
Area of a rectangle	$A = \ell w$	A = area, ℓ = length, w = width
Area of a triangle	$A = \frac{1}{2}bh$	A = area, b = base, h = height
Area of a circle	$A = \pi r^2$	A = area, r = radius
Distance traveled	$d = rt$	d = distance, r = rate, t = time
Temperature	$C = \frac{5}{9}(F - 32)$	C = degrees Celsius, F = degrees Fahrenheit

---

Answers

Got It?

1. a. $\frac{4 + 5n}{2}$; -3; 2, 7

     b. $y = 10$; $y = 4$; check students' work.

2. $x = \frac{-t - r}{p}$

 PowerAlgebra.com

2 Guided Instruction

Each Problem is worked out and supported online.

Problem 1
Rewriting a Literal Equation

Problem 3
Rewriting a Geometric Formula

Problem 2
Rewriting a Literal Equation With Only Variables
Animated

Problem 4
Rewriting a Formula
Animated

Alternative Problem 2
Rewriting a Literal Equation With Only Variables
Animated

Support in Algebra 1 Companion
• Vocabulary
• Key Concepts
• Got It?

Problem 3 Rewriting a Geometric Formula

What is the radius of a circle with circumference 64 ft? Round to the nearest tenth. Use 3.14 for π.

$C = 2\pi r$ Write the appropriate formula.

$\dfrac{C}{2\pi} = \dfrac{2\pi r}{2\pi}$ Divide each side by 2π.

$\dfrac{C}{2\pi} = r$ Simplify.

$\dfrac{64}{2\pi} = r$ Substitute 64 for C.

$10.2 \approx r$ Simplify. Use 3.14 for π.

The radius of the circle is about 10.2 ft.

✓ **Got It?** **3.** What is the height of a triangle that has an area of 24 in.^{2} and a base with a length of 8 in.?

 Problem 4 Rewriting a Formula

Biology The monarch butterfly is the only butterfly that migrates annually north and south. The distance that a particular group of monarch butterflies travels is shown. It takes a typical butterfly about 120 days to travel one way. What is the average rate at which a butterfly travels in miles per day? Round to the nearest mile per day.

$d = rt$ Write the appropriate formula.

$\dfrac{d}{t} = \dfrac{rt}{t}$ Divide each side by t.

$\dfrac{d}{t} = r$ Simplify.

$\dfrac{1700}{120} = r$ Substitute 1700 for d and 120 for t.

$14 \approx r$ Simplify.

The butterflies travel at an average rate of about 14 mi per day.

Indiana
1700 miles
Mexico

✓ **Got It?** **4.** Pacific gray whales migrate annually from the waters near Alaska to the waters near Baja California, Mexico, and back. The whales travel a distance of about 5000 mi each way at an average rate of 91 mi per day. About how many days does it take the whales to migrate one way?

Think
How do you know which formula to use?
Read the information given in the problem. This problem gives you a measure of time and a distance. You need to find the rate, so use $d = rt$.

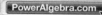
Problem 3
Students have worked with this formula before.

Q What does "circumference" mean? **[the distance around the circle]**

Q The formula $C = 2\pi r$ relates circumference and radius. Which variable do you need to solve for? Which property of equality should you use? **[r; Division Property of Equality]**

Got It?

Q What formula is needed to solve this problem? **[$A = \frac{1}{2}bh$]**

Q What does the b stand for? What does the h stand for? **[length of the base and height]**

Q What is the variable that you are solving for? **[h]**

Problem 4
Students must determine the appropriate literal equation to model a word problem.

Q Which formula involves what you know and what you are looking for? **[d = rt]**

Q How is the solution to this formula similar to the solution to the formula from Problem 3? **[Both solutions use the Division Property of Equality.]**

Got It?

Q What do you know? **[The distance is 5000 miles and the average rate is 91 mi/day.]**

Q What do you want to find out? **[the number of days it takes the whales to migrate one way]**

Q What formula can you use? **[d = rt]**

Q What variable do you need to solve for? **[t]**

Additional Problems

1. Solve the equation $3x + y = 10$ for y. What does y equal if $x = 1$? If $x = 3$?

ANSWER
$y = 10 - 3x$; $y = 7$; $y = 1$

2. What equation do you get when you solve the equation $\dfrac{a}{x} - \dfrac{b}{x} = c$ for x?

ANSWER $x = \dfrac{a}{c} - \dfrac{b}{c}$

3. What is the length of a rectangle with area 98 square inches and base 14 inches?

ANSWER 7 in.

4. Karen walks 3 miles per hour and covers 12 miles. For how long did she walk?

ANSWER 4 h

Answers

Got It? (continued)
3. 6 in.
4. about 55 days

3 Lesson Check

Do you know HOW?
- In Exercise 5, encourage students to draw a diagram of the garden so that they include all four sides.
- Use the Know, Need, Plan procedure to write an equation, if needed.

Do you UNDERSTAND?
- In Exercise 10, students may want to refer to the Take Note from Lesson 2-4 to better understand what is meant by the process of solving an equation.

Close

> **Q** What situations can best be modeled by literal equations? [**Literal equations can be used to model situations where one variable depends on other variables. For example, the distance a runner travels depends on how fast and for how long she runs, so $d = rt$.**]

 Lesson Check

Do you know HOW?
Solve each equation for the given variable.

1. $-2x + 5y = 12$ for y 2. $a - 2b = -10$ for b

3. $mx + 2nx = p$ for x 4. $C = \frac{5}{9}(F - 32)$ for F

5. **Gardening** Jonah is planting a rectangular garden. The perimeter of the garden is 120 yd, and the width is 20 yd. What is the length of the garden?

Do you UNDERSTAND?
Vocabulary Classify each equation below as a formula, a literal equation, or both.

6. $c = 2d$ 7. $y = 2x - 1$

8. $A = \frac{1}{2}bh$ 9. $P = 2\ell + 2w$

10. **Compare and Contrast** How is the process of rewriting literal equations similar to the process of solving equations in one variable? How is it different?

  Practice and Problem-Solving Exercises

A **Practice**   Solve each equation for y. Then find the value of y for each value of x.   ◀ See Problem 1.

11. $y + 2x = 5; x = -1, 0, 3$ 12. $2y + 4x = 8; x = -2, 1, 3$

13. $3x - 5y = 9; x = -1, 0, 1$ 14. $4x = 3y - 7; x = 4, 5, 6$

15. $5x = -4y + 4; x = 1, 2, 3$ 16. $2y + 7x = 4; x = 5, 10, 15$

17. $x - 4y = -4; x = -2, 4, 6$ 18. $6x = 7 - 4y; x = -2, -1, 0$

Solve each equation for x.   ◀ See Problem 2.

19. $mx + nx = p$ 20. $ax - x = c$ 21. $\frac{rx + sx}{t} = 1$

22. $y = \frac{x - v}{b}$ 23. $S = C + xC$ 24. $\frac{x}{a} = \frac{y}{b}$

25. $A = Bxt + C$ 26. $4(x - b) = x$ 27. $\frac{x + 2}{y - 1} = 2$

Solve each problem. Round to the nearest tenth, if necessary. Use 3.14 for π.   ◀ See Problem 3.

28. What is the radius of a circle with circumference 22 m?

29. What is the length of a rectangle with width 10 in. and area 45 in.²?

30. A triangle has height 4 ft and area 32 ft². What is the length of its base?

31. A rectangle has perimeter 84 cm and length 35 cm. What is its width?

32. **Parks** A public park is in the shape of a triangle. The side of the park that forms the base of the triangle is 200 yd long, and the area of the park is 7500 yd². What is the length of the side of the park that forms the height of the triangle?

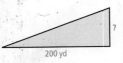
200 yd

 PowerAlgebra.com

3 Lesson Check
For a digital lesson check, use the Got It questions.

Support in Algebra 1 Companion
- Lesson Check

4 Practice
Assign homework to individual students or to an entire class.

Answers

Lesson Check

1. $y = \frac{2x + 12}{5}$ 2. $b = \frac{a + 10}{2}$

3. $x = \frac{p}{m + 2n}$ 4. $F = \frac{9}{5}C + 32$

5. 40 yd

6. literal equation   7. literal equation

8. both   9. both

10. Answers may vary. Sample: They are the same in each case since you are isolating a variable by using inverse operations. They are different because, in an equation in one variable, to isolate the variable, inverse operations are used on numbers only. In a literal equation, inverse operations are used on variables as well as numbers.

Practice and Problem-Solving Exercises

11. $y = -2x + 5$; 7; 5; -1

12. $y = -2x + 4$; 8; 2; -2

13. $y = \frac{3x - 9}{5}$; $-\frac{12}{5}$; $-\frac{9}{5}$; $-\frac{6}{5}$

14. $y = \frac{4x + 7}{3}$; $\frac{23}{3}$; 9; $\frac{31}{3}$

15. $y = -\frac{5x - 4}{4}$; $-\frac{1}{4}$; $-\frac{3}{2}$; $-\frac{11}{4}$

16. $y = \frac{-7x + 4}{2}$; $-\frac{31}{2}$; -33; $-\frac{101}{2}$

17. $y = \frac{x + 4}{4}$; $\frac{1}{2}$; 2; $\frac{5}{2}$

18. $y = -\frac{6x - 7}{4}$; $4\frac{3}{4}$; $3\frac{1}{4}$; $1\frac{3}{4}$

19. $x = \frac{p}{m + n}$ 20. $x = \frac{c}{a - 1}$

21. $x = \frac{t}{r + s}$ 22. $x = by + v$

23. $x = \frac{S - C}{C}$ 24. $x = \frac{ay}{b}$

25. $x = \frac{A - C}{Bt}$ 26. $x = \frac{4b}{3}$

27. $x = 2y - 4$ 28. 3.5 m

29. 4.5 in.   30. 16 ft

Solve each problem. Round to the nearest tenth, if necessary.

33. **Travel** A vehicle travels on a highway at a rate of 65 mi/h. How long does it take the vehicle to travel 25 mi?

34. **Baseball** You can use the formula $a = \frac{h}{n}$ to find the batting average a of a batter who has h hits in n times at bat. Solve the formula for h. If a batter has a batting average of .290 and has been at bat 300 times, how many hits does the batter have?

35. **Construction** Bricklayers use the formula $n = 7\ell h$ to estimate the number n of bricks needed to build a wall of length ℓ and height h, where ℓ and h are in feet. Solve the formula for h. Estimate the height of a wall 28 ft long that requires 1568 bricks.

 Apply

Solve each equation for the given variable.

36. $2m - nx = x + 4$ for x

37. $\frac{x}{a} - 1 = \frac{y}{b}$ for x

38. $ax + 2xy = 14$ for y

39. $V = \frac{1}{3}\pi r^2 h$ for h

40. $A = \left(\frac{f + g}{2}\right)h$ for g

41. $2(x + a) = 4b$ for a

42. **Think About a Plan** The interior angles of a polygon are the angles formed inside a polygon by two adjacent sides. The sum S of the measures of the interior angles of a polygon with n sides can be found using the formula $S = 180(n - 2)$. The sum of a polygon's interior angle measures is 1260°. How many sides does the polygon have?
   • What information are you given in the problem?
   • What variable do you need to solve for in the formula?

43. **Weather** Polar stratospheric clouds are colorful clouds that form when temperatures fall below −78°C. What is this temperature in degrees Fahrenheit?

44. **Science** The energy E of a moving object is called its *kinetic energy*. It is calculated using the formula $E = \frac{1}{2}mv^2$, where m is the object's mass in kilograms and v is its speed in meters per second. The units of kinetic energy are $\frac{kilograms \cdot meters^2}{second^2}$, abbreviated as $kg \cdot m^2/s^2$.
   a. Solve the given formula for m.
   b. What is the mass of an object moving at 10 m/s with a kinetic energy of 2500 kg · m²/s²?

Polar stratospheric clouds

45. **Error Analysis** Describe and correct the error made in solving the literal equation at the right for n.

46. **Geometry** The formula for the volume of a cylinder is $V = \pi r^2 h$, where r is the cylinder's radius and h is its height. Solve the equation for h. What is the height of a cylinder with volume 502.4 cm³ and radius 4 cm? Use 3.14 for π.

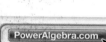
$2m = -6n + 3$
$2m + 3 = -6n$
$\frac{2m + 3}{-6} = n$

47. **Density** The density of an object is calculated using the formula $D = \frac{m}{V}$, where m is the object's mass and V is its volume. Gold has a density of 19.3 g/cm³. What is the volume of an amount of gold that has a mass of 96.5 g?

PowerAlgebra.com   Lesson 2-5 Literal Equations and Formulas   113

---

4 Practice

ASSIGNMENT GUIDE

Basic: 11–35 all, 36–42 even, 43, 45–47

Average: 11–35 odd, 36–48

Advanced: 11–35 odd, 36–50

Standardized Test Prep: 51–53

Mixed Review: 54–66

Reasoning exercises have blue headings.

Applications exercises have red headings.

EXERCISE 47: Use the Think About a Plan worksheet in the **Practice and Problem Solving Workbook** (also available in the Teaching Resources in print and online) to further support students' development in becoming independent learners.

HOMEWORK QUICK CHECK

To check students' understanding of key skills and concepts, go over Exercises 23, 31, 42, 46, and 47.

---

31. 7 cm
32. 75 yd
33. 0.4 h
34. $h = an$; 87 hits
35. $h = \frac{n}{7\ell}$; 8 ft
36. $x = \frac{2m - 4}{1 + n}$
37. $x = \frac{ay}{b} + a$
38. $y = \frac{-ax + 14}{2x}$
39. $h = \frac{3V}{\pi r^2}$
40. $g = \frac{2A}{h} - f$
41. $a = 2b - x$
42. 9 sides
43. −108.4°F
44. **a.** $m = \frac{2E}{v^2}$
    b. 50 kg

45. 3 was added to the left side of the equation instead of subtracted; $2m - 3 = -6n$, $\frac{2m - 3}{-6} = n$.
46. $h = \frac{V}{\pi r^2}$; 10 cm
47. 5 cm³

Answers

Practice and Problem-Solving Exercises
(continued)

48. Check students' work.

49. a. $A = 2s^2 + 4sh$

    b. $h = \dfrac{A - 2s^2}{4s}$; 14 cm

    c. $A = 6s^2$

50. a. 5.7

    b. $b = 2m - a$

    c. -1.9

51. 6

52. 6.5

53. 92 chirps

54. 5

55. 3

56. -4

57. 3

58. identity

59. no solution

60. 147

61. -40

62. 567

63. 100

64. 3

65. $\dfrac{8}{5}$

66. $\dfrac{7}{45}$

---

48. Open-Ended Write an equation in three variables. Solve the equation for each variable. Show all your steps.

 Challenge

49. Surface Area A rectangular prism with height h and with square bases with side length s is shown.
  a. Write a formula for the surface area A of the prism.
  b. Rewrite the formula to find h in terms of A and s. If s is 10 cm and A is 760 cm^2, what is the height of the prism?
  c. Writing Suppose h is equal to s. Write a formula for A in terms of s only.

50. Midpoints Suppose a segment on a number line has endpoints with coordinates a and b. The coordinate of the segment's midpoint m is given by the formula $m = \dfrac{a + b}{2}$.
  a. Find the midpoint of a segment with endpoints at 9.3 and 2.1.
  b. Rewrite the given formula to find b in terms of a and m.
  c. The midpoint of a segment is at 3.5. One endpoint is at 8.9. Find the other endpoint.

Standardized Test Prep

GRIDDED RESPONSE

 SAT/ACT

51. What is the value of the expression $-\frac{3}{4}m + 15$ when $m = 12$?

52. What is the solution of $9p + 6 - 3p = 45$?

53. The formula $F = \frac{n}{4} + 37$ relates the number of chirps n a cricket makes in 1 min to the outside temperature F in degrees Fahrenheit. How many chirps can you expect a cricket to make in 1 min when the outside temperature is 60°F?

Mixed Review

Solve each equation. If the equation is an *identity*, write *identity*. If it has no solution, write *no solution*.

◀ See Lesson 2-4.

54. $3x - 3 = x + 7$
                    55. $2b - 10 = -3b + 5$

56. $4 + 12a = -2(6 - 4a)$
      57. $2(y - 4) = -4y + 10$

58. $4c - 10 = 2(2c - 5)$
      59. $5 + 4p = 2(2p + 1)$

Evaluate each expression for $b = 3$ and $c = 7$.

◀ See Lesson 1-2.

60. bc^2
        61. $b^2 - c^2$
        62. $(3b)^2c$
        63. $(b + c)^2$

Get Ready! To prepare for Lesson 2-6, do Exercises 64–66.

Simplify each product.

◀ See p. 792.

64. $\frac{35}{25} \times \frac{30}{14}$
             65. $\frac{99}{108} \times \frac{96}{55}$
             66. $\frac{21}{81} \times \frac{63}{105}$

Lesson Resources

Additional Instructional Support

Algebra 1 Companion

Students can use the **Algebra 1 Companion** worktext (4 pages) as you teach the lesson. Use the Companion to support

- New Vocabulary
- Key Concepts
- Got It for each Problem
- Lesson Check

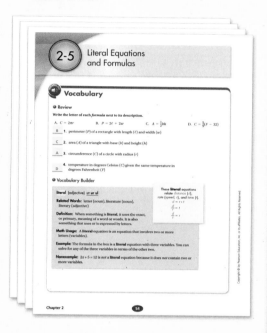

ELL Support

Assess Understanding Write the word *circumference* on the board and have students repeat the term as you say it aloud. Ask: What is circumference? [distance around a circle] Draw a circle on the board. Trace the circle with your finger as you say: The circumference of a circle is the total distance around the outside, or the edge of the circle. Use your finger to trace a circle on your desk. Have students trace the circumference of real objects, such as cans, CDs, or cups.

5 Assess & Remediate

Lesson Quiz

1. Solve the equation $6x + 3y = 15$ for y. What does y equal if $x = 2$? If $x = 5$?
2. What equation do you get when you solve the equation $qx + rx = s$ for x?
3. **Do you UNDERSTAND?** What is the height of a triangle with area 40 square inches and base 20 inches?
4. If it is 40 degrees Celsius, what is the temperature in Fahrenheit?

ANSWERS TO LESSON QUIZ

1. $y = 5 - 2x$; $y = 1$; $y = -5$
2. $x = \dfrac{s}{q + r}$
3. 4 in.
4. 104 degrees

PRESCRIPTION FOR REMEDIATION

Use the student work on the Lesson Quiz to prescribe a differentiated review assignment.

Points	Differentiated Remediation
0–2	Intervention
3	On-level
4	Extension

PowerAlgebra.com

5 Assess & Remediate

Assign the Lesson Quiz. Appropriate intervention, practice, or enrichment is automatically generated based on student performance.

Intervention

- **Reteaching** (2 pages) Provides reteaching and practice exercises for the key lesson concepts. Use with struggling students or absent students.
- **English Language Learner Support** Helps students develop and reinforce mathematical vocabulary and key concepts.

All-in-One Resources/Online
Reteaching

2-5 **Reteaching**
Literal Equations and Formulas

All-in-One Resources/Online
English Language Learner Support

2-5 **ELL Support**
Literal Equations and Formulas

Differentiated Remediation *continued*

On-Level

- **Practice** (2 pages) Provides extra practice for each lesson. For simpler practice exercises, use the Form K Practice pages found in the All-in-One Teaching Resources and online.

- **Think About a Plan** Helps students develop specific problem-solving skills and strategies by providing scaffolded guiding questions.

- **Standardized Test Prep** Focuses on all major exercises, all major question types, and helps students prepare for the high-stakes assessments.

Extension

- **Enrichment** Provides students with interesting problems and activities that extend the concepts of the lesson.

- **Activities, Games, and Puzzles** Worksheets that can be used for concepts development, enrichment, and for fun!

Practice and Problem Solving WKBK/ All-in-One Resources/Online
Practice page 1

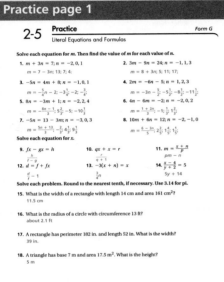

2-5 Practice — Form G
Literal Equations and Formulas

Solve each equation for *m*. Then find the value of *m* for each value of *n*.

1. $m + 3n = 7; n = -2, 0, 1$
   $m = 7 - 3n; 13; 7; 4;$

2. $3m - 9n = 24; n = -1, 1, 3$
   $m = 8 + 3n; 5; 11; 17;$

3. $-5n = 4m + 8; n = -1, 0, 1$
   $m = -\frac{5}{4}n - 2; -\frac{3}{4}; -2; -\frac{3}{4};$

4. $2m = -6n - 5; n = 1, 2, 3$
   $m = -3n - \frac{5}{2}; -5\frac{1}{2}; -8\frac{1}{2}; -11\frac{1}{2};$

5. $8n = -3m + 1; n = -2, 2, 4$
   $m = -\frac{8n-1}{3}; 5\frac{2}{3}; -5; -10\frac{1}{3}$

6. $m - 6m = -2; n = -2, 0, 2$
   $m = \frac{1+2n}{3}; -1; \frac{1}{3}; 1\frac{2}{3};$

7. $-5n = 13 - 3m; n = -3, 0, 3$
   $m = \frac{5n + 13}{3}; -\frac{2}{3}; 4\frac{1}{3}; 9\frac{1}{3}$

8. $10m + 6n = 12; n = -2, -1, 0$
   $m = \frac{6 - 3n}{5}; 2\frac{2}{5}; 1\frac{4}{5}; 1\frac{1}{5};$

Solve each equation for *x*.

9. $fx - gx = h$
   $\frac{h}{f-g}$

10. $qx + x = r$
    $\frac{r}{q+1}$

11. $m = \frac{x+n}{p}$
    $pm - n$

12. $d = f + fx$
    $\frac{d}{f} - 1$

13. $-3(x + n) = x$
    $\frac{3n}{2}$

14. $\frac{x-4}{y+2} = 5$
    $5y + 14$

Solve each problem. Round to the nearest tenth, if necessary. Use 3.14 for pi.

15. What is the width of a rectangle with length 14 cm and area 161 cm²?
    11.5 cm

16. What is the radius of a circle with circumference 13 ft?
    about 2.1 ft

17. A rectangle has perimeter 182 in. and length 52 in. What is the width?
    39 in.

18. A triangle has base 7 m and area 17.5 m². What is the height?
    5 m

Practice and Problem Solving WKBK/ All-in-One Resources/Online
Practice page 2

2-5 Practice *(continued)* — Form G
Literal Equations and Formulas

Solve each problem. Round to the nearest tenth, if necessary.

19. To find the average number of points per game a player scores, use the formula Points Per Game = $\frac{\text{Total Points}}{\text{Games}}$. Find the number of games a player has played if she has scored a total of 221 points and is averaging 17 points per game. 13 games

20. Joan drives 333.5 miles before she has to buy gas. Her car gets 29 miles per gallon. How many gallons of gas did the car start out with? 11.5 gal

21. Stan is purchasing sub-flooring for a kitchen he is remodeling. The area of the floor is 180 ft² and the width of the kitchen is 12 ft. What is the length of the sub-floor? 15 ft

Solve each equation for the given variable.

22. $4k + mn = n - 3; n$
    $\frac{-4k - 3}{m - 1}$

23. $\frac{c}{6} + 2 = \frac{f}{8}; c$
    $6\left(\frac{f}{8} - 2\right)$

24. $3ab - 2bc = 12; c$
    $-\frac{6}{b} + \frac{3a}{2}$

25. $z = \left(\frac{x+y}{3}\right)w; y$
    $\frac{3z}{w} - x$

26. $-3(m - 2n) = 5m; m$
    $\frac{3n}{4}$

27. $A = \frac{1}{2}bcd + bc; d$
    $\frac{2(A - bc)}{bc}$

28. A room with width *w*, length *l*, and height *h* with four walls needs to be painted.
    a. Write a formula for the area that needs to be painted not accounting for doors or windows. $A = 2lh + 2wh$
    b. Rewrite the formula to find *h* in terms of *A*, *l*, and *w*. $\frac{A}{2l + 2w}$
    c. If *l* is 18 ft, *w* is 14 ft and *A* is 512 ft², what is the height of the room? 8 ft
    d. **Reasoning** Suppose *l* is equal to *w*. Write a formula for *A* in terms of *w* and *h*. $A = 4wh$

Practice and Problem Solving WKBK/ All-in-One Resources/Online
Think About a Plan

2-5 Think About a Plan
Literal Equations and Formulas

Density The density of an object is calculated using the formula $D = \frac{m}{V}$, where *m* is the object's mass and *V* is its volume. Gold has a density of 19.3 g/cm³. What is the volume of an amount of gold that has a mass of 96.5 g?

KNOW

1. What is the formula you are given for the density of an object?
   $D = \frac{m}{V}$

2. What values are you given in the problem?
   the density of gold is 19.3 $\frac{g}{cm^3}$; the mass of a certain amount of gold is 96.5 g.

NEED

3. What measurement are you asked to determine?
   the volume of the gold

4. Solve $D = \frac{m}{V}$ for the variable *V*. Show your work.
   $V = \frac{m}{D}$

PLAN

5. Write your new formula. Substitute the values you are given into the formula.
   $V = \frac{96.5}{19.3}$

6. What is the volume of 96.5 g of gold?
   5 cm³

7. In what units is your answer? Do these units make sense? Explain.
   cm³; yes; $\frac{g}{\frac{g}{cm^3}} = cm^3$

All-in-One Resources/Online
Enrichment

2-5 Enrichment
Literal Equations and Formulas

Celsius (used in other countries) and Fahrenheit (used in the U.S.) are the two most commonly used scales for measuring temperature. Water freezes at 0°C and at 32°F. The boiling point of water is 100°C and 212°F.

To convert temperature from Celsius to Fahrenheit, you can use the formula $\frac{9}{5}C + 32 = F$, where *C* is degrees Celsius and *F* is degrees Fahrenheit.

1. Solve the above formula for *C* to find a formula you can use to convert degrees Fahrenheit to Celsius. $C = \frac{5}{9}(F - 32)$

Use the formulas above for Exercises 2–6.

2. Convert 45°C to F.
   113°F

3. Convert 45°F to C.
   7.2°C

4. Convert 20°C to F.
   −6.7°C

5. Convert 110°C to F.
   230°F

6. Sherry lives in Baltimore and is pen pals with Lynn who lives in England. Lynn tells Sherry that the average temperature for the past week in May was 25°C. Sherry asked Lynn if she still needed her winter coat. What was Lynn's reply? Explain.
   The temperature is 77°F, so Lynn didn't need her winter coat.

7. The formula for the volume of a pyramid is $V = \frac{Bh}{3}$ where *B* is the area of the base and *h* is the height of the pyramid. Solve for *h*.
   $\frac{3V}{B} = h$

8. Use the formula you found in question 7 to determine the height of a pyramid whose volume is 5 cm³ and the area of the base is 3 cm².
   5 cm

Practice and Problem Solving WKBK/ All-in-One Resources/Online
Standardized Test Prep

2-5 Standardized Test Prep
Literal Equations and Formulas

Multiple Choice

For Exercises 1–5, choose the correct letter.

1. What is the value of the expression $-2(3x - 2) + x + 9$ when $x = -3$? C
   A. −16   B. −2   C. 28   D. 34

2. What is the value of the expression $6m + m - 4(-2m + 1 - m)$ when $m = -8$? F
   F. −156   G. −92   H. −44   I. 36

3. What is the solution of $2d = \frac{a - b}{b - c}$ when you solve for *a*? D
   A. $2d - b + c + b$
   B. $\frac{2d + b}{b - c}$
   C. $\frac{2d}{b - c} + b$
   D. $2d(b - c) + b$

4. A triangle has area 49.5 cm². If the base of the triangle is 9 cm, what is the height of the triangle? G
   F. 5.5 cm   G. 11 cm   H. 222.75 cm   I. 445.5 cm

5. A circle has circumference 10.99 yd. What is the radius of the circle? Round to the nearest tenth if necessary. (Use 3.14 for π.) A
   A. 1.8 yd   B. 3.5 yd   C. 7 yd   D. 34.5 yd

Short Response

6. The formula for the circumference of a circle is $C = 2\pi r$, where *r* is the radius of the circle.
   a. What is the formula when solved for *r*? $r = \frac{C}{2\pi}$
   b. What is the radius of a circle with a circumference of 37.7 m? Round to the nearest tenth if necessary. 6 m
   [2] Both parts answered correctly.
   [1] One part answered correctly.
   [0] Neither part answered correctly.

Online Teacher Resource Center
Activities, Games, and Puzzles

2-5 Activity: Advertising Formulas
Literal Equations and Formulas

You will need poster paper and markers or colored pencils for this activity. You may work by yourself or in small groups.

We may not think about it, but there are literal equations and formulas all around us. For example, the sample poster shown at the right involves hourly wages. Notice that the formula at the top is solved for *w* while the formula at the bottom has been rewritten solved for *h*.

Sara earns $8 per hour.
$w = 8h$
dollars / hours
Calculate Sara's wages given the number of hours she works.
$h = \frac{w}{8}$
Find how many hours Sara needs to work to earn a given number of dollars.

Your job is to make a similar poster that
1. gives a simple formula,
2. describes how the formula can be used in real life, and
3. shows how a new formula can be rewritten from the original one.

Here are some ideas to help you get started.

Food Prices: a formula to calculate cost based on unit price

Age: a formula to determine your age *y* years in the future

Cycling: a formula to determine how far a cyclist can bike at a given speed

Gardening: a formula to determine the area of a garden in the corner of a backyard

Field Trips: a formula to determine how many buses are needed to transport a certain number of students given a seating capacity

Numbers: a formula to determine the *n*th positive multiple of 7

Sports: a formula for points scored by touchdowns and field goals

Describe the plan for your poster in the space below. Then, go ahead and make your poster. Your teacher may ask you to share it with the rest of the class, and then display it afterwards. Check students' work.

You can use formulas to find the perimeters and areas of shapes called *composite figures*. Composite figures are composed of two or more simpler shapes.

Example 1

The composite figure at the right is made up of a rectangle and half of a circle. What are the perimeter and area of the figure? Use 3.14 for π.

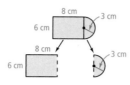

Step 1 The perimeter P is the sum of the lengths of the exterior sides of the rectangle, plus half the circumference of the circle. To find the perimeter, add these measures.

$$P = 8 + 6 + 8 + \left(\frac{1}{2} \cdot 2\pi(3)\right)$$
$$\approx 8 + 6 + 8 + \left(\frac{1}{2} \cdot 2(3.14)(3)\right)$$
$$= 31.42 \text{ cm}$$

Step 2 The total area A is the sum of the area A_r of the rectangle and the area A_h of the half circle. Use the appropriate formula to find the area of each shape. Then add to find the total area.

$$A_r = \ell w \qquad\qquad A_h = \frac{1}{2}\pi r^2$$
$$= 6 \cdot 8 \qquad\qquad \approx \frac{1}{2}(3.14)(3)^2$$
$$= 48 \text{ cm}^2 \qquad\qquad = 14.13 \text{ cm}^2$$

$$A = A_r + A_h = 48 + 14.13 = 62.13 \text{ cm}^2$$

The perimeter is 31.42 cm. The area is 61.13 cm².

A rectangular prism with length ℓ, width w, and height h and a cylinder with radius r and height h are shown at the right.

For each figure, the surface area S.A. is the sum of the area of the two bases and the lateral area.

Prism: S.A. = area of bases + lateral area

Cylinder: S.A. = area of bases + lateral area

$$= 2\ell w + 2\ell h + 2wh \qquad\qquad = 2\pi r^2 + 2\pi rh$$

The volume V of each figure is the area of the base times the height.

Prism: V = area of base × **height**

Cylinder: V = area of base × **height**

$$= \ell wh \qquad\qquad = \pi r^2 h$$

Guided Instruction

PURPOSE To use formulas to find the perimeter, area, and volume of composite figures

PROCESS Students will
- identify geometric shapes in composite figures.
- identify the required dimension in a given formula.
- answer questions with the correct unit measure.
- substitute known values to solve for variables.

DISCUSS Models that can be measured provide an opportunity to relate formulas to real-world objects. Distribute two- and three-dimensional models of figures, such as circles, spheres, rectangles, and prisms.

Q What are some two-dimensional measurements you can find for each shape? **[Samples: area, surface area, lateral area]**

Q What is a three-dimensional measurement you can find? **[volume]**

Example 1
This Example calculates the area and perimeter of a figure composed of a rectangle and a half circle.

Q If you did not know the formula for area, how could you approximate the area? **[Sample: Trace the shape on cm-square graph paper and count the approximate number of squares.]**

Q What is the difference between lateral area and base area? **[The bases are identical shapes that are parallel to each other. The lateral area is found on the sides of the figure when it is placed on a base.]**

Q To paint the figures, would the amount of paint needed be found by using surface area or volume measurements? **[surface area]**

Q If you wanted to store paint inside the figures, what measurement would tell you the amount of paint they would hold? **[volume]**

TACTILE LEARNING

Provide students with a container of rulers, tape, scissors, construction paper or clay. Have students model a three-dimensional unit of measurement. For example, students might make a clay cube or a box made from paper and tape.

Guided Instruction

Example 2

In this Example, students calculate the surface area and volume of a rectangular prism and a cylinder.

Q What is the figure on the left? On the right? **[rectangular prism; cylinder]**

Q What identifies each figure? **[All sides of the rectangular prism are rectangles; the cylinder has a circular base and top.]**

Q What is the length, width, and height of the prism? **[4 in., 3 in., 5 in.]**

Q What is the radius and length of the cylinder? **[3 cm, 8 cm]**

ERROR PREVENTION

In Exercises 1–3, students apply the principle that the area of a figure is the sum of the areas of its non-overlapping parts. You may need to review that the area of a triangle is $A = \frac{1}{2} bh$.

Example 2

What are the surface area and volume of each figure? Use 3.14 for π.

Prism
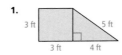

Cylinder

Step 1 To find the surface area of each figure, use the appropriate formula. Substitute. Then calculate.

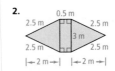

S.A. $= 2\ell w + 2\ell h + 2wh$
$= 2(4 \cdot 3) + 2(4 \cdot 5) + 2(3 \cdot 5)$
$= 94 \text{ in.}^2$

The surface area is 94 in.^{2}.

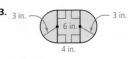

S.A. $= 2\pi r^2 + 2\pi rh$
$\approx 2(3.14)(3)^2 + 2(3.14)(3)(8)$
$= 207.24 \text{ cm}^2$

The surface area is about 207 cm^2.

Step 2 To find the volume of each figure, use the appropriate formula. Substitute. Then multiply.

$V = \ell wh$
$= 4(3)(5)$
$= 60 \text{ in.}^3$

The volume is 60 in.^{3}.

$V = \pi r^2 h$
$\approx 3.14(3)^2(8)$
$= 226.08 \text{ cm}^3$

The volume is about 226 cm^3.

Exercises

Find the area and perimeter of each composite figure. Use 3.14 for π. Round your answer to the nearest tenth.

1.
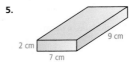
3 ft, 5 ft, 3 ft, 4 ft

2.
0.5 m
2.5 m, 2.5 m
3 m
2.5 m, 2.5 m
|←2 m→| |←2 m→|

3. 3 in., 6 in., 3 in.
4 in.

Find the surface area and volume of each figure. Use 3.14 for π. Round your answer to the nearest tenth.

4. 6 yd

20 yd

5.
9 cm
2 cm
7 cm

6.
11 mm
11 mm
11 mm

Answers

Exercises

1. 15 ft^2; 18 ft

2. 7.5 m^2; 11 m

3. 52.3 in.^{2}; 26.8 in.

4. 979.7 yd^2; 2260.8 yd^3

5. 190 cm^2; 126 cm^3

6. 726 mm^2; 1331 mm^3

MathXL® for School
Go to PowerAlgebra.com

Do you know HOW?

Solve each equation. Check your answer.

1. $38 = 2a + 54$

2. $t + 18.1 = 23.9$

3. $18.9 = 2.1x$

4. $\frac{1}{2}(b - 3) = \frac{5}{2}$

Solve each equation. Justify your steps.

5. $9 - 3r = 14$

6. $3 = \frac{1}{2}b + 11$

Solve each equation. If the equation is an identity, write *identity*. If it has no solution, write *no solution*.

7. $8(h - 1) = 6h + 4 + 2h$

8. $\frac{1}{7}(14 - 7p) - 2 = -2\left(\frac{1}{2}p + 3\right) + 6$

9. $\frac{c + 3}{5} = 15$

10. $\frac{2}{3}(x - 4) = \frac{1}{3}(2x - 6)$

11. $1.7m = 10.2$

12. $2 + \frac{1}{3}t = 1 + \frac{1}{4}t$

13. Geometry The formula for the area of a triangle is $A = \frac{1}{2}bh$. Solve the formula for h. A triangle has a base of 7 cm and an area of 28 cm². What is its height?

14. Menus A new pizza shop is going to print new menus. Each menu costs $.50 to produce. The owners have a total budget of $2500 for the new menus. How many menus can the pizza shop print?

15. Guitars You paid $600 for a new guitar. Your guitar cost $40 more than twice the cost of your friend's guitar. How much did your friend's guitar cost?

Define a variable and write an equation to model each situation. Then solve.

16. Concerts Concert tickets cost $25 each. A college student ordered some tickets online. There was a service charge of $3 per ticket. The total came to $252. How many tickets did the student order?

17. Gyms Membership for the Alpine rock-climbing gym costs $25 per month plus a $125 sign-up fee. Membership for Rocco's rock-climbing gym costs $30 per month plus a $50 sign-up fee.

   a. After how many months will the memberships cost the same?

   b. If you only wanted a one-year membership, which gym would you join?

Do you UNDERSTAND?

18. Vocabulary Complete: You can use subtraction to undo addition. Subtraction is called the ? of addition.

19. Reasoning The equation $\frac{5}{x} = \frac{2}{x} + \frac{3}{x}$ is true for all values of x where $x \neq 0$. Is the equation an identity?

20. Writing Would you solve the equation $10 = 4(y - 1)$ by using the Distributive Property or by dividing each side by 4? Explain.

21. Reasoning In the process of solving an equation, a student noticed that the variable was eliminated. The student concluded that the equation must be an identity. Is the student correct? Explain.

22. Reasoning You are solving the equation $0.02x - 0.004 = 0.028$. Your first step is to multiply both sides by 1000 to clear the decimals. Your classmate starts by dividing both sides by 0.02. Is there any disadvantage to your classmate's method? Explain.

Answers

Mid-Chapter Quiz

1. -8

2. 5.8

3. 9

4. 8

5. $-1\frac{2}{3}$

6. -16

7. no solution

8. identity

9. 72

10. no solution

11. 6

12. -12

13. $h = \frac{2A}{b}$; 8 cm

14. 5000 menus

15. $280

16. Let $t =$ number of tickets ordered; $25t + 3t = 252$; 9 tickets.

17. a. Let $m =$ number of months when memberships cost the same; $25m + 125 = 30m + 50$; 15 months.

   b. Rocco's

18. inverse

19. No; an identity is true for *all* values of a variable with no exceptions.

20. Check students' work.

21. No; the equation could be an identity or have no solution.

22. Dividing by decimals is harder and more prone to error.

PowerAlgebra.com

MathXL for School
Prepare students for the Mid-Chapter Quiz and Chapter Test with online practice and review.

1 Interactive Learning

Solve It!

PURPOSE To see the value of computing a unit rate to make comparisons in real-life situations
PROCESS Students may construct a table of values, use ratios, compare times for similar distances, or find unit rates.

FACILITATE

Q If you assume that Athlete A maintains the same speed, how long would he take to run 1600 m instead of 800 m? How does this information help? **[232 s; it shows Athlete A runs farther than Athlete B in less time.]**

Q What other methods find the faster runner? **[Sample: Divide an athlete's distance by their time to calculate speed. The faster runner has the greater speed.]**

Q Could you divide the number of seconds for each athlete by the number of meters they run? How would this be helpful? **[Yes; the result will be in seconds per meter, so in this case the lesser value (fewer seconds per meter) represents the faster runner.]**

ANSWER See Solve it in Answers on next page.
CONNECT THE MATH Since the rates are quite different in this situation, an approximate answer can be found by doubling the distance and time of athlete A. However, this does not always work. In this lesson, students learn to calculate a unit rate, a method that always works.

Problem 1

Q Why are the ratios simplified? **[It is easier to compare them with the unit rate.]**

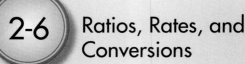

Objectives To find ratios and rates
To convert units and rates

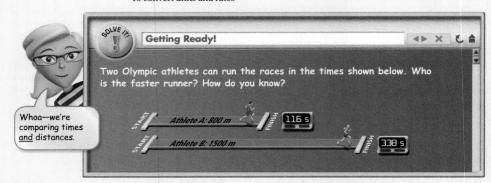

Getting Ready!

Two Olympic athletes can run the races in the times shown below. Who is the faster runner? How do you know?

Whoa—we're comparing times and distances.

Athlete A: 800 m — FINISH — 116 s

Athlete B: 1500 m — FINISH — 338 s

Lesson Vocabulary
• ratio
• rate
• unit rate
• conversion factor
• unit analysis

A **ratio** compares two numbers by division. The ratio of two numbers a and b, where $b \neq 0$, can be written in three ways: $\frac{a}{b}$, $a : b$, and a to b. For every a units of one quantity, you have b units of another quantity.

You can also think of a ratio as a multiplicative relationship. For example, if the ratio of the number of boys to the number of girls in a class is $2 : 1$, then the number of boys is *two times* the number of girls.

A ratio that compares quantities measured in different units is called a **rate**. A rate with a denominator of 1 unit is a **unit rate**. In the Solve It, you can express each athlete's speed as the number of meters traveled per 1 second of time. This is an example of a unit rate.

Essential Understanding You can write ratios and find unit rates to compare quantities. You can also convert units and rates to solve problems.

Think
How can estimation help you?
Use estimation to *solve a simpler problem.* You can use the given information to estimate the unit rates. The estimates can help you find the solution.

Problem 1 Comparing Unit Rates

Shopping You are shopping for T-shirts. Which store offers the best deal?
Store A: $25 for 2 shirts   Store B: $45 for 4 shirts   Store C: $30 for 3 shirts

Write each price as a ratio. Then write the ratio as a unit rate to compare.

Store A	Store B	Store C
$\frac{\$25}{2 \text{ shirts}} = \frac{\$12.50}{1 \text{ shirt}}$	$\frac{\$45}{4 \text{ shirts}} = \frac{\$11.25}{1 \text{ shirt}}$	$\frac{\$30}{3 \text{ shirts}} = \frac{\$10}{1 \text{ shirt}}$

Store C has the best deal because its unit rate is the lowest.

BIG idea Proportionality **UbD**
ESSENTIAL UNDERSTANDINGS
• Ratios and unit rates can be used to compare quantities.
• Units and rates can be converted to solve problems.

Math Background

There are several ways to express a relationship of two numbers as a ratio. Consider a class of 25 students that has 11 boys. The ratio of boys to the total number of students is $\frac{11}{25}$, while $\frac{11}{14}$ is the ratio of the number of boys to the number of girls. Other possible ratios include: $\frac{\text{students}}{\text{boys}} \rightarrow \frac{25}{11}$, $\frac{\text{girls}}{\text{boys}} \rightarrow \frac{14}{11}$, or $\frac{\text{girls}}{\text{students}} \rightarrow \frac{14}{25}$. Students should consider which ratio is most efficient for the task at hand.

Because ratios are not always written as fractions, you can choose to not call the numbers numerators and denominators. To prevent confusion, you may refer to them, instead, as the first term and the second term.

Support Student Learning

Use the **Algebra I Companion** to engage and support students during instruction. See Lesson Resources at the end of this lesson for details.

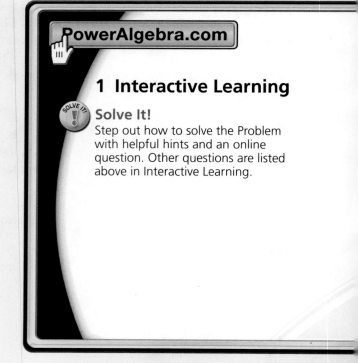

PowerAlgebra.com

1 Interactive Learning

Solve It!
Step out how to solve the Problem with helpful hints and an online question. Other questions are listed above in Interactive Learning.

Got It? **1.** If Store B lowers its price to $42 for 4 shirts, does the solution to Problem 1 change? Explain.

To convert from one unit to another, such as feet to inches, you multiply the original unit by a *conversion factor* that produces the desired unit. A **conversion factor** is a ratio of two equivalent measures in different units. A conversion factor is always equal to 1, such as $\frac{1\,\text{ft}}{12\,\text{in.}}$. See the table on page 723 for some common equivalent units of measure.

 Problem 2 **Converting Units**

What is the given amount converted to the given units?

Choose and multiply by the appropriate conversion factor. The appropriate factor will allow you to divide out the common units and simplify.

Plan

How do you choose the conversion factor?
Write a conversion factor that has the desired units in the numerator and the original units in the denominator.

A 330 min; hours

$330\,\text{min} \cdot \frac{1\,\text{h}}{60\,\text{min}}$ ← Choose a conversion factor. →

$= 330\,\cancel{\text{min}} \cdot \frac{1\,\text{h}}{60\,\cancel{\text{min}}}$ ← Divide out common units. →

$= 5.5\,\text{h}$ ← Simplify. →

B 15 kg; grams

$15\,\text{kg} \cdot \frac{1000\,\text{g}}{1\,\text{kg}}$

$= 15\,\cancel{\text{kg}} \cdot \frac{1000\,\text{g}}{1\,\cancel{\text{kg}}}$

$= 15{,}000\,\text{g}$

C 5 ft 3 in.; inches

$5\,\text{ft}\ 3\,\text{in.} = 5\,\text{ft} + 3\,\text{in.}$

$\qquad = 5\,\cancel{\text{ft}} \cdot \frac{12\,\text{in.}}{1\,\cancel{\text{ft}}} + 3\,\text{in.}$

$\qquad = 60\,\text{in.} + 3\,\text{in.} = 63\,\text{in.}$

 Got It? **2.** What is 1250 cm converted to meters?

In Problem 2, notice that the units for each quantity are included in the calculations to help determine the units for the answers. This process is called **unit analysis**, or *dimensional analysis*.

 Problem 3 **Converting Units Between Systems**

Architecture The CN Tower in Toronto, Canada, is about 1815 ft tall. About how many meters tall is the tower? Use the fact that 1 m ≈ 3.28 ft.

Plan

How can you convert units?
Write the conversion factor so that the original units divide out and leave only the desired units.

Multiply by the appropriate conversion factor and divide out common units.

$1815\,\text{ft} \cdot \frac{1\,\text{m}}{3.28\,\text{ft}} = 1815\,\cancel{\text{ft}} \cdot \frac{1\,\text{m}}{3.28\,\cancel{\text{ft}}} \approx 553\,\text{m}$

The CN Tower is about 553 m tall.

Check Round 1815 to 1800 and 3.28 to 3. Then divide 1800 by 3. $1800 \div 3 = 600$, and 600 is about 553. So, 553 m is a reasonable answer.

---

2 Guided Instruction

Got It?

Q Can you make a quick estimate to answer this question? Explain. **[Yes; the lowest price of $10/shirt would make 4 shirts at store C cost $40. Since the new price is $42, the shirts are still more expensive.]**

Problem 2   ERROR PREVENTION

Students practice setting up conversion factors and converting units. A common error is writing the conversion factor "upside down." Discuss the following:

Q What factor changes miles to feet? $\left[\frac{5280\,\text{ft}}{1\,\text{mi}}\right]$

Q What factor changes feet to miles? $\left[\frac{1\,\text{mi}}{5280\,\text{ft}}\right]$

Got It?

Q What is the conversion factor that will help change centimeters to meters? $\left[\frac{1\,\text{m}}{100\,\text{cm}}\right]$

Problem 3
This problem shows how to convert units from one system to another.

Q What does it mean to "divide out common units"? **[Any value or unit, divided by itself is 1, so $\frac{\text{ft}}{\text{ft}} = 1$.]**

---

2 Guided Instruction

 Each Problem is worked out and supported online.

Problem 1
Comparing Unit Rates
Animated

Problem 2
Converting Units
Animated

Problem 3
Converting Units Between Systems

Problem 4
Converting Rates
Animated

Support in Algebra 1 Companion
• Vocabulary
• Key Concepts
• Got It?

Answers

Solve It!
Athlete A; explanations may vary.

Got It?
1. No; Store C is still the lowest.
2. 12.5 m

Got It?

Q What conversion factor can you use in 3a? $\left[\frac{1\text{ m}}{3.28\text{ ft}}\right]$

Q What is the conversion rate in 3b?
[1 dollar = 0.63 euros]

Q What is the expression that converts \$325 to euros? $\left[325\text{ dollars} \times \frac{0.63\text{ euros}}{1\text{ dollar}}\right]$

Problem 4
Converting rates provides another application of unit analysis.

Q What is this problem asking for? [speed in miles per hour]

Q What are you given? [yards per second]

Q How many conversion factors are used in this example? Explain. [2; one to convert seconds to hours and one to convert yards to miles]

Q Have you changed the actual amount? Explain. [No; the amount is just expressed using different units.]

Got It?

Q What conversion factor will cancel the seconds unit? $\left[\frac{60\text{ sec}}{1\text{ min}}\text{ or }\frac{3600\text{ sec}}{1\text{ hr}}\right]$

Q If you know the units in $\frac{\text{ft}}{\text{min}}$, what conversion factor is needed to get $\frac{\text{ft}}{\text{hr}}$? $\left[\frac{60\text{ min}}{1\text{ hr}}\right]$

Q What is the final equation?
$\left[x = \frac{100\text{ ft}}{3.1\text{ sec}} \times \frac{60\text{ sec}}{1\text{ min}} \times \frac{60\text{ min}}{1\text{ hr}} \times \frac{1\text{ mi}}{5280\text{ ft}}\right]$

 Got It? 3. a. A building is 1450 ft tall. How many meters tall is the building? Use the fact that 1 m ≈ 3.28 ft.

b. Monetary exchange rates change from day to day. On a particular day, the exchange rate for dollars to euros was about 1 dollar = 0.63 euro. About how many euros could you get for \$325 on that day?

You can also convert rates. For example, you can convert a speed in miles per hour to feet per second. Because rates compare measures in two different units, you must multiply by two conversion factors to change both of the units.

 Problem 4 Converting Rates

A student ran the 50-yd dash in 5.8 s. At what speed did the student run in miles per hour? Round your answer to the nearest tenth.

Know	Need	Plan
The running speed in yards per second	The running speed in miles per hour	Write the speed as a ratio. Choose conversion factors so that the original units (yards and seconds) divide out, leaving you with the units you need (miles and hours).

$\frac{50\text{ yd}}{5.8\text{ s}} \cdot \frac{1\text{ mi}}{1760\text{ yd}} \cdot \frac{3600\text{ s}}{1\text{ h}}$ Use appropriate conversion factors.

This conversion factor cancels yards and leaves miles.

This conversion factor cancels seconds and leaves hours.

$= \frac{50\text{ yd}}{5.8\text{ s}} \cdot \frac{1\text{ mi}}{1760\text{ yd}} \cdot \frac{3600\text{ s}}{1\text{ h}}$ Divide common units.

$= \frac{180,000\text{ mi}}{10,208\text{ h}} \approx 17.6\text{ mi/h}$ Simplify.

The student ran at a speed of about 17.6 mi/h.

Got It? 4. a. An athlete ran a sprint of 100 ft in 3.1 s. At what speed was the athlete running in miles per hour? Round to the nearest mile per hour.

b. Reasoning In Problem 4, one student multiplied by the conversion factors $\frac{1\text{ mi}}{1760\text{ yd}}$, $\frac{60\text{ s}}{1\text{ min}}$, and $\frac{60\text{ min}}{1\text{ h}}$ to find the speed. Can this method work? Why or why not?

Additional Problems

1. You are shopping for sweaters. Store A sells 2 sweaters for \$60 and Store B sells 3 sweaters for \$80. Which store offers the best deal? Explain.

   ANSWER Store B. The sweaters in Store A cost \$30, while those in Store B cost \$26.67.

2. What is 155 cm converted to meters?

   ANSWER 1.55 m

3. The Space Needle in Seattle, Washington, is 605 ft tall. About how many meters tall is the building? Use the fact that 1 m ≈ 3.28 ft.

   ANSWER about 184.5 m

4. A student ran 100 yd in 12 s. At what speed did the student run in miles per hour?

   ANSWER 17 mi/h

Answers

Got It? (continued)

3. **a.** about 442 m
   b. about 205 euros

4. **a.** about 22 mi/h
   b. Yes; $\frac{60\text{ s}}{1\text{ min}} \cdot \frac{60\text{ min}}{1\text{ h}}$ is the same as $\frac{3600\text{ s}}{1\text{ h}}$.

Lesson Check

Do you know HOW?

1. Which is the better buy, 6 bagels for $3.29 or 8 bagels for $4.15?

2. What is 7 lb 4 oz converted to ounces?

3. Which is longer, 12 m or 13 yd?

4. A car is traveling at 55 mi/h. What is the car's speed in feet per second?

Do you UNDERSTAND?

Vocabulary Tell whether each rate is a unit rate.

5. 20 mi every 3 h

6. 2 dollars per day

7. **Reasoning** Does multiplying by a conversion factor change the amount of what is being measured? How do you know?

8. **Reasoning** If you convert pounds to ounces, will the number of ounces be greater or less than the number of pounds? Explain.

Practice and Problem-Solving Exercises

A Practice

9. **Running** Trisha ran 10 km in 2.5 h. Jason ran 7.5 km in 2 h. Olga ran 9.5 km in 2.25 h. Who had the fastest average speed? ◀ See Problem 1.

10. **Population** Bellingham, Washington, had an area of 25.4 mi² and a population of 74,547 during one year. Bakersfield, California, had an area of 113.1 mi² and a population of 295,536 during the same year. Which city had a greater number of people per square mile?

Convert the given amount to the given unit. ◀ See Problems 2 and 3.

11. 63 yd; feet
12. 168 h; days
13. 2.5 lb; ounces
14. 200 cm; meters
15. 4 min; seconds
16. 1500 mL; liters
17. 9 yd; meters
18. 5 kg; pounds
19. 79 dollars; cents
20. 3 qt; liters
21. 89 cm; inches
22. 2 ft; centimeters

23. **Maintenance** The janitor at a school discovered a slow leak in a pipe. The janitor found that it was leaking at a rate of 4 fl oz per minute. How fast was the pipe leaking in gallons per hour? ◀ See Problem 4.

24. **Shopping** Mr. Swanson bought a package of 10 disposable razors for $6.30. He found that each razor lasted for 1 week. What was the cost per day?

B Apply

Copy and complete each statement.

25. 7 ft 3 in. = ■ in.
26. 2.2 kg = ■ lb
27. 2.5 h = ■ min
28. 2 qt/min = ■ gal/s
29. 75 cents/h = ■ dollars/day
30. 60 ft/s = ■ km/h

3 Lesson Check

Do you know HOW?   ERROR INTERVENTION

- If students are having difficulty converting units, revisit Problems 2 and 3 or Additional Problems 2 and 3.

Do you UNDERSTAND?

- Review the definition of a unit rate.
- Students may think that multiplying by a conversion factor changes the actual amount. Review the definition of conversion factor to assure understanding.

Close

> **Q** How can you tell whether the number of units will be lesser or greater when you are converting from one unit to another?
>
> [Number of Greater sized units ⟶ More Smaller sized units
>
> Number of Smaller sized units ⟶ Fewer Greater sized units]
>
> **Q** What type of problems does unit analysis help you solve? **[those that require a conversion factor]**

Answers

Lesson Check

1. 8 bagels for $4.15
2. 116 oz
3. 12 m
4. $80\frac{2}{3}$ ft/s
5. not a unit rate
6. unit rate
7. No; a conversion factor is a ratio of two equivalent measures in different units and is always equal to 1.
8. Greater; to convert you multiply by 16.

Practice and Problem-Solving Exercises

9. Olga
10. Bellingham, WA
11. 189 ft
12. 7 d
13. 40 oz
14. 2 m
15. 240 s
16. 1.5 L
17. about 8.2 m
18. about 11 lb
19. 7900 cents
20. about 2.8 L
21. about 35 in.
22. about 61 cm
23. 1.875 gal/h
24. $.09 a day
25. 87
26. about 4.8
27. 150
28. $\frac{1}{120}$
29. 18
30. about 65.8

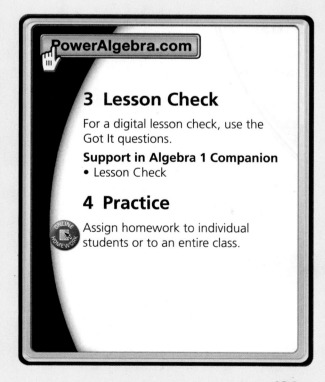

PowerAlgebra.com

3 Lesson Check

For a digital lesson check, use the Got It questions.

Support in Algebra 1 Companion
- Lesson Check

4 Practice

Assign homework to individual students or to an entire class.

4 Practice

ASSIGNMENT GUIDE

Basic: 9–24 all, 26–34 even, 35–39, 42

Average: 9–23 odd, 25–42

Advanced: 9–23 odd, 25–44

Standardized Test Prep: 45–47

Mixed Review: 48–57

Reasoning exercises have blue headings.

Applications exercises have red headings.

EXERCISE 42: Use the Think About a Plan worksheet in the **Practice and Problem Solving Workbook** (also available in the Teaching Resources in print and online) to further support students' development in becoming independent learners.

HOMEWORK QUICK CHECK

To check students' understanding of key skills and concepts, go over Exercises 17, 23, 30, 34, and 42.

Choose a Method Choose paper and pencil, mental math, or a calculator to tell which measurement is greater.

31. 640 ft; 0.5 mi   **32.** 63 in.; 125 cm   **33.** 75 g; 5 oz

34. Think About a Plan A college student is considering a subscription to a social-networking Internet site that advertises its cost as "only 87 cents per day." What is the cost of membership in dollars per year?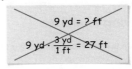
  • How many conversion factors will you need to use to solve the problem?
  • How do you choose the appropriate conversion factors?

35. Recipes Recipe A makes 5 dinner rolls using 1 c of flour. Recipe B makes 24 rolls using $7\frac{1}{2}$ c of flour. Recipe C makes 45 rolls using 10 c of flour. Which recipe requires the most flour per roll?

36. Error Analysis Find the mistake in the conversion below. Explain the mistake and convert the units correctly.

37. Writing Suppose you want to convert kilometers to miles. Which unit should be in the numerator of the conversion factor? Which unit should be in the denominator? Explain how you know.

38. Reasoning Without performing the conversion, determine whether the number of new units will be greater or less than the number of original units.
  a. 3 min 20 s converted to seconds
  b. 23 cm converted to inches
  c. kilometers per hour converted to miles per hour

39. Exchange Rates The table below shows some exchange rates on a particular day. If a sweater sells for $39.95 in U.S. dollars, what should its price be in rupees and pounds?

U.S. DOLLARS	1.00
INDIAN RUPEES	39.57
ALGERIAN DINARS	64.15
BRITISH POUNDS	.50

40. Estimation Five mi is approximately equal to 8 km. Use mental math to estimate the distance in kilometers to a town that is 30 mi away.

41. Reasoning A carpenter is building an entertainment center. She is calculating the size of the space to leave for the television. She wants to leave about a foot of space on either side of the television. Would measuring the size of the television exactly or estimating the size to the nearest inch be more appropriate? Explain.

Answers

Practice and Problem-Solving Exercises (continued)

31. 0.5 mi

32. 63 in.

33. 5 oz

34. $317.55 per year

35. recipe B

36. The numbers are correct but the units are reversed in the conversion factor; $9 \text{ yd} \cdot \frac{3 \text{ ft}}{1 \text{ yd}} = 27 \text{ ft}$.

37. Miles; kilometers; kilometers cancel out and miles are left.

38. a. greater than
  b. less than
  c. less than

39. 1580.82 INR; 19.98 GBP

40. 48 km

41. Answers may vary. Sample: Estimating the size to the nearest inch is appropriate because the carpenter is leaving an estimated amount on either side of the television, not an exact amount.

42. Reasoning A traveler changed $300 to euros for a trip to Germany, but the trip was canceled. Three months later, the traveler changed the euros back to dollars. Would you expect that the traveler got exactly $300 back? Explain.

Ⓒ **Challenge**

43. Measurement Dietrich draws a line on the blackboard whose length is given by the expression 1 mm + 1 cm + 1 in. + 1 ft + 1 yd + 1 m. What is the length of the line in millimeters?

44. Square Measurements There are 2.54 cm in 1 in.
   a. How many square centimeters are there in 1 in.²? Give your answer to the nearest hundredth of a square centimeter.
   b. How many square inches are there in 129 cm²?

Standardized Test Prep

SAT/ACT

45. Most mammals take 1 breath for every 4 heartbeats. The heart of a large dog beats about 180 times in 1 min. About how many times does the dog take a breath in 1 min?
   Ⓐ 40   Ⓑ 45   Ⓒ 90   Ⓓ 720

46. Which equation best describes the relationship shown in the table?

x	-2	-1	0	1	2
y	-4	-2	0	2	4

   Ⓕ $y = x - 2$ Ⓖ $y = x - 1$ Ⓗ $y = x$ Ⓘ $y = 2x$

47. Which expression is equivalent to $-2(3x - 4) - (-2x + 1)$?
   Ⓐ $-4x - 7$ Ⓑ $-4x - 5$ Ⓒ $-4x + 7$ Ⓓ $-4x + 9$

Mixed Review

48. What is the height of a triangle with an area of 30 cm² and a base length of 12 cm?   ◀ **See Lesson 2-5.**

49. What is the diameter of a circle with a circumference of 47.1 in.? Use 3.14 for π.

Solve each equation. Check your answer.   ◀ **See Lesson 2-3.**

50. $2y + 0.5y + 4.5 = 17$

51. $-\frac{2}{3}x - 8 = -12$

52. $-4.8 = -4(2.4d)$

53. $\frac{3a + 1}{5} = 2$

Get Ready! To prepare for Lesson 2-7, do Exercises 54–57.

Simplify each expression. Justify each step.   ◀ **See Lesson 1-4.**

54. $\frac{27x}{x}$ **55.** $\frac{b}{112b}$ **56.** $\frac{20mn}{n}$ **57.** $\frac{2xy}{7x}$

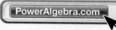

---

42. No; exchange rates vary from day to day.

43. 2255.6 mm

44. a. 6.45 cm²

     b. about 20 in.²

45. B

46. I

47. C

48. 5 cm

49. 15 in.

50. 5

51. 6

52. 0.5

53. 3

54. 27

55. $\frac{1}{112}$

56. 20m

57. $\frac{2y}{7}$

Additional Instructional Support

Algebra 1 Companion

Students can use the **Algebra 1 Companion** worktext (4 pages) as you teach the lesson. Use the Companion to support

- New Vocabulary
- Key Concepts
- Got It for each Problem
- Lesson Check

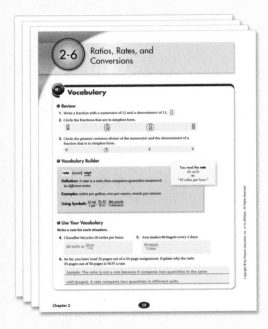

ELL Support

Focus on Communication Draw a rectangle on the board and run your finger around its sides. Ask: What do you call the distance around the rectangle? (perimeter) Now draw another rectangle and shade it in. Ask what do you call the inside of the rectangle? (area) Now hold up a box, or rectangular prism, and ask: What do you call the inside of this? (volume) How are perimeter, area, surface area and volume alike? (They are measures of size in different dimensions.) Ask: How are they different? (They measure the outside length, the surface, and the interior space of figures respectively.)

5 Assess & Remediate

Lesson Quiz

1. Your friend is selling 5 tickets to the next ice hockey game for $80. You can buy 3 tickets online for $50. Which source offers the best price? Explain.
2. What is 3.2 m converted to centimeters?
3. **Do you UNDERSTAND?** If a football field is 100 yd long, how would you find its length in miles?
4. A Queensland toad travels 10 m/day. How far will it travel in 5 hours? Round your answer to the nearest hundredth.

ANSWERS TO LESSON QUIZ

1. your friend; Your friend is selling tickets for $16 each, while the online price is $16.67.
2. 320 cm
3. Answers may vary. Sample: Evaluate $100 \text{ yd} \times \frac{3 \text{ ft}}{1 \text{ yd}} \times \frac{1 \text{ mi}}{5,280 \text{ ft}}$.
4. 2.08 m

PRESCRIPTION FOR REMEDIATION

Use the student work on the Lesson Quiz to prescribe a differentiated review assignment.

Points	Differentiated Remediation
0–2	Intervention
3	On-level
4	Extension

PowerAlgebra.com

5 Assess & Remediate

Assign the Lesson Quiz. Appropriate intervention, practice, or enrichment is automatically generated based on student performance.

Intervention

- **Reteaching** (2 pages) Provides reteaching and practice exercises for the key lesson concepts. Use with struggling students or absent students.
- **English Language Learner Support** Helps students develop and reinforce mathematical vocabulary and key concepts.

All-in-One Resources/Online

Reteaching

2-6 Reteaching
Ratios, Rates, and Conversions

A unit rate is a rate with denominator 1. For example, $\frac{12 \text{ in.}}{1 \text{ ft}}$ is a unit rate. Unit rates can be used to compare quantities and convert units.

Problem

Which is greater, 74 inches or 6 feet?

It is helpful to convert to the same units. Conversion factors, a ratio of two equivalent measures in different units, are used to do conversions.

Multiply the original quantity by the conversion factor(s) so that units cancel out, leaving you with the desired units.

$6 \text{ ft} \times \frac{12 \text{ in.}}{1 \text{ ft}} = 72 \text{ in.}$

Since 72 in. is less than 74 in., 74 in. is greater than 6 ft.

Rates, which involve two different units, can also be converted. Since rates involve two different units, you must multiply by two conversion factors to change both of the units.

Problem

Jared's car gets 26 mi per gal. What is his fuel efficiency in kilometers per liter? You need to convert miles to kilometers and gallons to liters. This will involve multiplying by two conversion factors.

There are 1.6 km in 1 mi. The conversion factor is either $\frac{1.6 \text{ km}}{1 \text{ mi}}$ or $\frac{1 \text{ mi}}{1.6 \text{ km}}$.

Since miles is in the numerator of the original quantity, use $\frac{1.6 \text{ km}}{1 \text{ mi}}$ as the conversion factor so that miles will cancel.

$26 \frac{\text{mi}}{\text{gal}} \times \frac{1.6 \text{ km}}{1 \text{ mi}}$

There are 3.8 L in 1 gal. The conversion factor is either $\frac{3.8 \text{ L}}{1 \text{ gal}}$ or $\frac{1 \text{ gal}}{3.8 \text{ L}}$.

Since gallons is in the denominator of the original quantity, use $\frac{1 \text{ gal}}{3.8 \text{ L}}$ as the conversion factor so that gallons will cancel.

$26 \frac{\text{mi}}{\text{gal}} \times \frac{1.6 \text{ km}}{1 \text{ mi}} \times \frac{1 \text{ gal}}{3.8 \text{ L}} = 10.9 \frac{\text{km}}{\text{L}}$

Jared's vehicle gets 10.9 kilometers per liter.

All-in-One Resources/Online

English Language Learner Support

2-6 ELL Support
Ratios, Rates, and Conversions

Complete the vocabulary chart by filling in the missing information.

Word or Word Phrase	Definition	Picture or Example
ratio	A *ratio* compares two numbers by division, and can be written as $\frac{a}{b}$, a to b, or $a : b$, where b does not equal zero.	4 to 6, 4 : 6, or $\frac{4}{6}$
rate	A *rate* is a *ratio* with two quantities with different units.	1. $\frac{\$10}{2 \text{ tickets}}$
unit rate	2. A *unit rate* is a ratio of two quantities with different units and for which the denominator is 1 unit.	$\frac{7 \text{ miles}}{1 \text{ hour}}$, $\frac{\$6.50}{1 \text{ ticket}}$
conversion factor	A *conversion factor* helps you change a value in one measurement unit to a value in a different measurement unit. A *conversion factor* is a ratio of two equivalent measures in different units.	3. $\frac{2.54 \text{ cm}}{1 \text{ in.}}$
numerator	4. The top number in a fraction is the *numerator*.	$\frac{24}{39}$ ←
denominator	The bottom number in a fraction is the *denominator*.	5. $\frac{1}{3}$

Differentiated Remediation *continued*

On-Level

- **Practice** (2 pages) Provides extra practice for each lesson. For simpler practice exercises, use the Form K Practice pages found in the All-in-One Teaching Resources and online.

- **Think About a Plan** Helps students develop specific problem-solving skills and strategies by providing scaffolded guiding questions.

- **Standardized Test Prep** Focuses on all major exercises, all major question types, and helps students prepare for the high-stakes assessments.

Extension

- **Enrichment** Provides students with interesting problems and activities that extend the concepts of the lesson.

- **Activities, Games, and Puzzles** Worksheets that can be used for concepts development, enrichment, and for fun!

Practice and Problem Solving WKBK/ All-in-One Resources/Online
Practice page 1

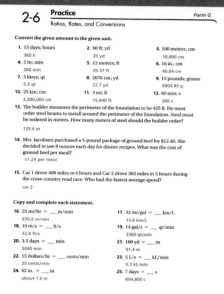

2-6 Practice Form G
Ratios, Rates, and Conversions

Convert the given amount to the given unit.

1. 15 days; hours — 360 h
2. 60 ft; yd — 20 yd
3. 100 meters; cm — 10,000 cm
4. 5 hr; min — 300 min
5. 12 meters; ft — 39.37 ft
6. 16 in.; cm — 40.64 cm
7. 5 liters; qt — 5.3 qt
8. 2076 cm; yd — 22.7 yd
9. 15 pounds; grams — 6803.85 g
10. 25 km; cm — 2,500,000 cm
11. 3 mi; ft — 15,840 ft
12. 60 min; s — 360 s

13. The builder measures the perimeter of the foundation to be 425 ft. He must order steel beams to install around the perimeter of the foundation. Steel must be ordered in meters. How many meters of steel should the builder order? — 129.6 m

14. Mrs. Jacobsen purchased a 5-pound package of ground beef for $12.40. She decided to use 8 ounces each day for dinner recipes. What was the cost of ground beef per meal? — $1.24 per meal

15. Car 1 drove 408 miles in 6 hours and Car 2 drove 365 miles in 5 hours during the cross-country road race. Who had the fastest average speed? — car 2

Copy and complete each statement.

16. 25 mi/hr = ___ m/min — 570.6 m/min
17. 32 mi/gal = ___ km/L — 13.6 km/L
18. 10 m/s = ___ ft/s — 32.8 ft/s
19. 14 gal/s = ___ qt/min — 3360 qt/min
20. 3.5 days = ___ min — 5040 min
21. 100 yd = ___ m — 91.4 m
22. 15 dollars/hr = ___ cents/min — 25 cents/min
23. 5 L/s = ___ kL/min — 0.3 kL/min
24. 62 in. = ___ m — about 1.6 m
25. 7 days = ___ s — 604,800 s

Practice and Problem Solving WKBK/ All-in-One Resources/Online
Practice page 2

2-6 Practice (continued) Form G
Ratios, Rates, and Conversions

26. Which weighs more, 500 pounds or 200 kilograms? — 200 kg

27. Which is longer, 4000 ft or 1 kilometer? — 4000 ft

28. Which is the better buy, 7 pounds for $8.47 or 9 pounds for $11.07? Explain. — $8.47 for 7 lb because it is the lower unit rate

29. A runner is running 10 miles per hour.
   a. What conversion factors should be used to convert 10 mi/hr to ft/s?
   $\frac{5280 \text{ ft}}{1 \text{ mile}} \cdot \frac{1 \text{ hour}}{60 \text{ min}} \cdot \frac{1 \text{ min}}{60 \text{ sec}}$
   b. How many feet per second is the runner running? — about 14.7 ft/s

Determine if each rate is a unit rate. Explain.

30. $1.99 per pound — yes; the rate is $/lb
31. 100 feet per 2 seconds — no; the rate is not ft/s
32. 22 miles per gallon — yes; the rate is mi/gal

Find each unit rate.

33. 4 pounds of green peppers cost $7.56. — $1.89/lb

34. Rahul travelled 348 miles in 6 hours. — 58 mi/h

35. Cheryl assembled 128 chairs in 16 hours. — 8 chairs/h

36. **Writing** Suppose you want to convert feet per second to miles per hour. What conversion factors would you use? How did you determine which unit should go in the numerator and which unit should go in the denominator of the conversion factors? — $\frac{60 \text{ s}}{1 \text{ s}}$ and $\frac{1 \text{ mi}}{1 \text{ hour}}$; the answer is $\frac{\text{miles}}{\text{hour}}$, so miles is the numerator and hours is the denominator

37. The volume of a box is 1344 cubic inches or in.³.
   a. How many cubic inches are in one cubic foot? Justify your answer.
   1 cubic ft = 12 in. × 12 in. × 12 in. = 1728 in.³
   b. What is the volume of the box in cubic feet? Justify your answer.
   1344 in.³ · $\frac{1 \text{ ft}^3}{1728 \text{ in.}^3}$ ≈ 0.78 ft³

All-in-One Resources/Online
Enrichment

2-6 Enrichment
Ratios, Rates, and Conversions

Nutritional information is placed on most food products. This data typically includes the number of calories, and the amount of protein, fat, or carbohydrates per serving. It may also include the amount of vitamins and minerals contained in the food.

Shown below are the nutrition information panels from a can of peanuts and a can of cashews. Both are dry roasted without salt.

Peanuts	Cashews
Serving size .... 3 oz	Serving Size .... 1.5 oz
Servings/container 4	Servings/container 8
Calories 510	Calories 240
Protein .... 21 g	Protein .... .6 g
Carbohydrates ...... 18 g	Carbohydrates ...... 13.5 g
Fat .... 42 g	Fat .... 19.5 g

1. Express the relationship of calories to ounces as a rate for the peanuts and cashews. — peanuts: 170 calories/oz; cashews: 160 calories/oz

2. Express the relationship between grams of protein and ounces as a rate for the peanuts and cashews. — peanuts: 7 g/oz; cashews: 4 g/oz

3. Express the relationship between grams of fat and ounces as a rate for the peanuts and cashews. — peanuts: 14 g/oz; cashews: 13 g/oz

4. Based on your answer to Exercise 1, which product is lower in calories per ounce? How can you tell? — cashews; the unit rate of calories/oz is less than peanuts

5. A friend wants to find products that are low in calories and fat and high in protein. Which would be the better choice for this friend—peanuts or cashews? Why? — cashews; peanuts contain about twice as much fat

6. What factors must be considered when comparing nutrition information labels on different food products? — the serving size, the unit rates

Practice and Problem Solving WKBK/ All-in-One Resources/Online
Think About a Plan

2-6 Think About a Plan
Ratios, Rates, and Conversions

Reasoning A traveler changed $300 to euros for a trip to Germany, but the trip was canceled. Three months later, the traveler changed the euros back to dollars. Would you expect that the traveler got exactly $300 back? Explain.

Know

1. What facts do you know about the situation? — a traveler changed $300 to euros; 3 mo later, the traveler changed the euros back to dollars;

2. What circumstances would affect whether or not the traveler would receive exactly $300 back? — whether or not there is a service charge; what the exchange rate is when the euros were converted back to dollars;

Need

3. What would you need to know to determine the amount of dollars the traveler would receive after three months? — the exchange rate, the service charge

4. How do you convert the amount in euros to dollars? — euros · $\frac{\text{dollars}}{\text{euros}}$

Plan

5. Once you have the information you need to answer the question, explain how you would determine the amount of dollars the traveler would receive in exchange for the euros. — multiply the number of euros by the exchange rate and subtract any service charges

6. Would this process change over time? Explain. — no; The values may change but not the process.

Practice and Problem Solving WKBK/ All-in-One Resources/Online
Standardized Test Prep

2-6 Standardized Test Prep
Ratios, Rates, and Conversions

Multiple Choice

For Exercises 1–6, choose the correct letter.

1. Which of the following rates is a unit rate? C
   A. $\frac{24 \text{ in.}}{1 \text{ yd}}$ B. $\frac{2 \text{ ft}}{8 \text{ ft}}$ C. $\frac{3 \text{ ft}}{1 \text{ yd}}$ D. $\frac{1 \text{ ft}}{12 \text{ in.}}$

2. How many centimeters are in 1 kilometer? I
   F. 0.000001 G. 0.00001 H. 10,000 I. 100,000

3. How many inches are in 3 yd 2 ft? C
   A. 60 B. 72 C. 132 D. 180

4. To convert miles per hour to feet per second, which conversion factor would not be used? I
   F. $\frac{1 \text{ hr}}{60 \text{ min}}$ G. $\frac{1 \text{ min}}{60 \text{ sec}}$ H. $\frac{5280 \text{ ft}}{1 \text{ mi}}$ I. $\frac{1 \text{ mi}}{5280 \text{ ft}}$

5. A healthy, adult cheetah can run 110 feet per second. How fast can a cheetah run in miles per hour? B
   A. 55 B. 75 C. 87 D. 161.3

6. Emmanuel was speaking with a friend from another country. His friend told him that the speed limit on most highways is 100 kilometers per hour in her country. This speed sounded fast to Emmanuel. Approximately what speed is this in miles per hour? F
   F. 62 mph G. 65 mph H. 70 mph I. 100 mph

Short Response

7. Samantha earns $22 per hour as a plumbing apprentice. How much does she earn per minute in cents?
   a. What conversion factors would she use?
   $\frac{100 \text{ cents}}{1 \text{ dollar}} \cdot \frac{1 \text{ h}}{60 \text{ min}}$
   b. What amount does she earn per minute in cents? — about 37 cents/min
   [2] Both parts answered correctly.
   [1] One part answered correctly.
   [0] Neither part answered correctly.

Online Teacher Resource Center
Activities, Games, and Puzzles

2-6 Activity: Everyday Ratios and Rates
Ratios, Rates, and Conversions

This activity should be done in small groups. Each group needs a newspaper. If your newspaper has several sections, you may want to give each group member a separate section to work with.

Read through your newspaper and try to find as many ratios and rates as you can. Read carefully, as a rate or ratio may not appear in the mathematical form you are used to seeing in your textbook. Try and identify more ratios and rates than the other groups in your class! Here are some places where you are likely to find examples of ratios and rates.

- bank advertisements
- car-buying advertisements
- the sports section
- the financial section
- the weather section

The Daily Dispatch
Chock full of ratios and rates!

You will find these in:
- the news section
- the sports section
- the business section
- the weather section
- the entertainment section

To complete the activity, compare your group's findings with those of the other groups. Explain why your information qualifies as a ratio or rate. — Answers may vary. Sample: The information is a ratio because it involves a quotient of two numbers. Sample: The information is a rate because the divison and dividend have different units.

If time permits, have your group answer the following questions.

1. Lisa and her family plan to travel to Italy. Find the current exchange rate for American dollars to Euros (€). How many Euros will they receive for $500? — Answers will vary depending on current exchange rate.

2. At the end of the trip, Lisa's family wants to exchange 200 Euros for American dollars. Find the current exchange rate for Euros to American dollars. How much will they receive for 200 Euros? — Answers will vary depending on current exchange rate.

1 Interactive Learning

Solve It!

PURPOSE To use a concrete model to apply proportional reasoning

PROCESS Students may make a table of red and blue beads, use equivalent ratios, or draw a model.

FACILITATE

Students just learned to use ratios. They now build on this knowledge to set up proportions.

> **Q** What ratios could you write for the given information? **[Sample: red beads to blue beads $\frac{2}{3}$.]**
>
> **Q** What is an equivalent ratio for 30 beads? **[Answers may vary. Sample: $\frac{2}{3} = \frac{20}{30}$]**
>
> **Q** How many beads will be in a 20-in. necklace? **[80 beads]**

ANSWERS See Solve It in Answers on the next page.
CONNECT THE MATH Students can solve this problem in many ways without having a systematic approach. The lesson shows how to write a proportion to solve similar problems.

2 Guided Instruction

Problem 1

This problem introduces fractions in equations that can be solved in one step.

> **Q** Will m be greater or less than 7? Why? **[Greater; twelfths are smaller than eighths, so more of them are needed to maintain equality.]**

Objective To solve and apply proportions

 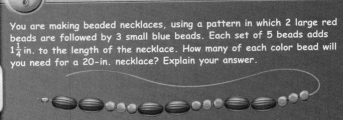

Getting Ready! ◀ ▶ ✕ ↻ ⬛

You are making beaded necklaces, using a pattern in which 2 large red beads are followed by 3 small blue beads. Each set of 5 beads adds $1\frac{1}{4}$ in. to the length of the necklace. How many of each color bead will you need for a 20-in. necklace? Explain your answer.

You've used ratios to compare. This problem involves equal ratios.

In the Solve It, the number of red beads and the number of blue beads are quantities that have a proportional relationship. This means that the ratio of the quantities is constant even though the quantities themselves can change. For example, as you are making the necklace you will have 2 red beads and 3 blue beads, then 4 red beads and 6 blue beads, then 6 red beads and 9 blue beads, and so on. At each stage, the ratio of red beads to blue beads remains constant, 2 : 3.

A proportional relationship can produce an infinite number of equivalent ratios. Any two of these can be used to write a proportion. A **proportion** is an equation that states that two ratios are equal. For example, $\frac{a}{b} = \frac{c}{d}$, where $b \neq 0$ and $d \neq 0$, is a proportion. You read this as "a is to b as c is to d."

Lesson Vocabulary
- proportion
- cross products
- Cross Products Property

Essential Understanding If two ratios are equal and a quantity in one of the ratios is unknown, you can write and solve a proportion to find the unknown quantity.

Think

How is this problem related to problems you've solved before?
Solving this proportion is similar to solving a one-step equation using multiplication. You can simply multiply by 12 to isolate m.

Problem 1   Solving a Proportion Using the Multiplication Property

What is the solution of the proportion $\frac{7}{8} = \frac{m}{12}$?

$$\frac{7}{8} = \frac{m}{12}$$

$$12 \cdot \frac{7}{8} = 12 \cdot \frac{m}{12} \quad \text{Multiply each side by 12.}$$

$$\frac{84}{8} = m \quad \text{Simplify.}$$

$$10.5 = m \quad \text{Divide.}$$

BIG idea Proportionality   **UbD**

ESSENTIAL UNDERSTANDINGS
- A proportion is an equation that states two ratios are equal.
- If two ratios are equal and a quantity in one of the ratios is unknown, the unknown quantity can be found by writing and solving a proportion.

Math Background

Many problems such as this Solve It can be solved using equal ratios as follows:

Red	2	4	6	⋯	26	28	30
Blue	3	6	9	⋯	39	42	n

A short cut to using a table is to write and solve a proportion. Since all ratios in the table are equal, you can write, $\frac{2}{3} = \frac{30}{n}$. This problem can be solved using cross products.

The numbers in this table are all whole numbers. Multiples are used to generate equal ratios. Many problems do not contain numbers related in such convenient ways. In these cases, it is efficient to use the techniques developed in this lesson.

Support Student Learning

Use the **Algebra I Companion** to engage and support students during instruction. See Lesson Resources at the end of this lesson for details.

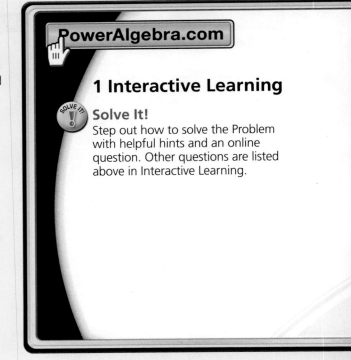

PowerAlgebra.com

1 Interactive Learning

Solve It!

Step out how to solve the Problem with helpful hints and an online question. Other questions are listed above in Interactive Learning.

Got It? **1.** What is the solution of the proportion $\frac{x}{7} = \frac{4}{5}$?

In the proportion $\frac{a}{b} = \frac{c}{d}$, the products ad and bc are called **cross products**. You can use the following property of cross products to solve proportions.

 Property Cross Products Property of a Proportion

Words The cross products of a proportion are equal.

Algebra If $\frac{a}{b} = \frac{c}{d}$, where $b \neq 0$ and $d \neq 0$, then $ad = bc$.

Example $\frac{3}{4} = \frac{9}{12}$, so $3(12) = 4(9)$, or $36 = 36$.

Here's Why It Works You can use the Multiplication Property of Equality to prove the Cross Products Property.

$$\frac{a}{b} = \frac{c}{d} \qquad \text{Assume this equation is true.}$$

$$bd \cdot \frac{a}{b} = bd \cdot \frac{c}{d} \qquad \text{Multiplication Property of Equality}$$

$$\cancel{b}d \cdot \frac{a}{\cancel{b}} = b\cancel{d} \cdot \frac{c}{\cancel{d}} \qquad \text{Divide the common factors.}$$

$$da = bc \qquad \text{Simplify.}$$

$$ad = bc \qquad \text{Commutative Property of Multiplication}$$

For this proportion, a and d are called the *extremes* of the proportion and b and c are called the *means*. Notice that in the Cross Products Property the product of the means equals the product of the extremes.

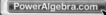 **Problem 2** Solving a Proportion Using the Cross Products Property

Think

Which property should you use?
The Cross Products Property can be easier to use when the variable is in the denominator. If you use the Multiplication Property, you must multiply each side by 3x.

What is the solution of the proportion $\frac{4}{3} = \frac{8}{x}$?

$$\frac{4}{3} = \frac{8}{x}$$

$$4x = 3(8) \qquad \text{Cross Products Property}$$

$$4x = 24 \qquad \text{Multiply.}$$

$$x = 6 \qquad \text{Divide each side by 4 and simplify.}$$

 Got It? **2. a.** What is the solution of the proportion $\frac{y}{3} = \frac{3}{5}$?

b. Reasoning Would you rather use the Cross Products Property or the Multiplication Property of Equality to solve $\frac{3}{5} = \frac{13}{b}$? Explain.

PowerAlgebra.com   Lesson 2-7 Solving Proportions   **125**

---

2 Guided Instruction

Each Problem is worked out and supported online.

Problem 1
Solving a Proportion Using the Multiplication Property
Animated

Problem 2
Solving a Proportion Using the Cross Products Property

Problem 3
Solving a Multi-Step Proportion
Animated

Problem 4
Using a Proportion to Solve a Problem
Animated

Support in Algebra 1 Companion
• Vocabulary
• Key Concepts
• Got It?

Lesson 2-7   **125**

Problem 3

This is the first problem where students see complex expressions in the numerator of ratios. To solve these proportions, students use the Cross Products Property and the Distributive Property.

> **Q** The equation, $1 + \frac{b - 8}{5} = \frac{b + 3}{4}$, looks a lot like Problem 3. Can you use cross products to find the value of b? Explain. **[No; there are two terms on the left side of the equation.]**

Got It?

> **Q** If you use the Multiplication Property to solve this problem, what is the most efficient number to multiply both sides by? Why? **[30; it removes the denominators in one step.]**

Remember that the LCM (least common multiple) should be used to remove denominators.

Problem 4   ERROR PREVENTION

Give students strategies that will help set up the proportion correctly. Consider:

smaller player →   2 gigabytes = 500 songs
larger player   → 80 gigabytes = s songs

> **Q** What other ways can you set up this proportion?
> $$\left[\frac{80 \text{ gigabytes}}{2 \text{ gigabytes}} = \frac{s \text{ songs}}{500 \text{ songs}}, \frac{500 \text{ songs}}{2 \text{ gigabytes}} = \frac{s \text{ songs}}{80 \text{ gigabytes}}\right]$$

Got It?   ERROR PREVENTION

> **Q** What is wrong with the following proportion?
> $\frac{8 \text{ ounces}}{97 \text{ mL}} = \frac{x \text{ mL}}{12 \text{ ounces}}$ **[The relationships have not been maintained.]**

 Problem 3   Solving a Multi-Step Proportion

Think

How is this proportion different from others you've seen?
This proportion looks more complex, but the Cross Products Property is true for *any* proportion. Treat each numerator as a single variable when you cross-multiply.

What is the solution of the proportion $\frac{b - 8}{5} = \frac{b + 3}{4}$?

$$\frac{b - 8}{5} = \frac{b + 3}{4}$$

$4(b - 8) = 5(b + 3)$	Cross Products Property
$4b - 32 = 5b + 15$	Distributive Property
$4b - 32 - 4b = 5b + 15 - 4b$	Subtract $4b$ from each side.
$-32 = b + 15$	Simplify.
$-47 = b$	Subtract 15 from each side and simplify.

 Got It?   **3.** What is the solution of the proportion $\frac{n}{5} = \frac{2n + 4}{6}$?

When you model a real-world situation with a proportion, you must write the proportion carefully. You can write the proportion so that the numerators have the same units and the denominators have the same units.

Correct: $\frac{100 \text{ mi}}{2 \text{ h}} = \frac{x \text{ mi}}{5 \text{ h}}$ **Incorrect:** $\frac{100 \text{ mi}}{2 \text{ h}} = \frac{5 \text{ h}}{x \text{ mi}}$

 **Problem 4**   Using a Proportion to Solve a Problem

Music A portable media player has 2 gigabytes of storage and can hold about 500 songs. A similar but larger media player has 80 gigabytes of storage. About how many songs can the larger media player hold?

Know
- Smaller media player has 2 gigabytes and can hold 500 songs
- Larger media player has 80 gigabytes

Need
The number of songs the larger player can hold

Plan
Write a proportion to model the situation. You can set up the proportion so that the numerators have the same units and the denominators have the same units. Then solve the proportion.

Think

Is there only one way to write a proportion?
No. You can write other proportions to solve the problem. For example, $\frac{2 \text{ gigabytes}}{80 \text{ gigabytes}} = \frac{500 \text{ songs}}{s \text{ songs}}$ also works.

$\frac{2 \text{ gigabytes}}{500 \text{ songs}} = \frac{80 \text{ gigabytes}}{s \text{ songs}}$	Write a proportion.
$2s = 500(80)$	Cross Products Property
$2s = 40,000$	Multiply.
$s = 20,000$	Divide each side by 2 and simplify.

The larger media player can hold 20,000 songs.

 Got It?   **4.** An 8-oz can of orange juice contains about 97 mg of vitamin C. About how many milligrams of vitamin C are there in a 12-oz can of orange juice?

Additional Problems

1. What is the solution of the proportion $\frac{5}{6} = \frac{x}{11}$?

     ANSWER $9\frac{1}{6}$

2. What is the solution of the proportion $\frac{5}{6} = \frac{11}{x}$?

     ANSWER 13.2

3. What is the solution of the proportion $\frac{x - 2}{3} = \frac{x + 3}{5}$?

     ANSWER 9.5

4. Ski socks are on sale at 3 for $40. What is the price of one pair?

     ANSWER $13.33

Answers

Got It? (continued)

   3. −5

   4. 145.5 mg

Lesson Check

Do you know HOW?

Solve each proportion.

1. $\frac{b}{6} = \frac{4}{5}$

2. $\frac{5}{9} = \frac{15}{x}$

3. $\frac{w+3}{4} = \frac{w}{2}$

4. $\frac{3}{x+1} = \frac{1}{2}$

5. **Music** A band went to a recording studio and recorded 4 songs in 3 h. How long would it take the band to record 9 songs if they record at the same rate?

Do you UNDERSTAND?

Vocabulary Use the proportion $\frac{m}{n} = \frac{p}{q}$. Identify the following.

6. the extremes

7. the means

8. the cross products

9. **Reasoning** When solving $\frac{x}{5} = \frac{3}{4}$, Lisa's first step was to write $4x = 5(3)$. Jen's first step was to write $20(\frac{x}{5}) = 20(\frac{3}{4})$. Will both methods work? Explain.

Practice and Problem-Solving Exercises

Ⓐ Practice

Solve each proportion using the Multiplication Property of Equality.   ◀ See Problem 1.

10. $\frac{q}{8} = \frac{4}{5}$

11. $\frac{-3}{4} = \frac{x}{26}$

12. $\frac{3}{4} = \frac{x}{5}$

13. $\frac{m}{7} = \frac{3}{5}$

14. $\frac{3}{16} = \frac{x}{12}$

15. $\frac{9}{2} = \frac{k}{25}$

16. $\frac{x}{120} = \frac{1}{24}$

17. $\frac{2}{15} = \frac{h}{125}$

Solve each proportion using the Cross Products Property.   ◀ See Problem 2.

18. $\frac{3}{v} = \frac{8}{13}$

19. $\frac{15}{a} = \frac{3}{2}$

20. $\frac{3}{8} = \frac{30}{m}$

21. $\frac{2}{7} = \frac{4}{d}$

22. $\frac{-9}{b} = \frac{5}{6}$

23. $\frac{8}{p} = \frac{3}{10}$

24. $\frac{-3}{4} = \frac{m}{22}$

25. $\frac{2}{-5} = \frac{6}{t}$

Solve each proportion using any method.   ◀ See Problem 3.

26. $\frac{a-2}{9} = \frac{2}{3}$

27. $\frac{b+4}{5} = \frac{7}{4}$

28. $\frac{3}{7} = \frac{c+4}{35}$

29. $\frac{2c}{11} = \frac{c-3}{4}$

30. $\frac{7}{k-2} = \frac{5}{8}$

31. $\frac{3}{3b+4} = \frac{2}{b-4}$

32. $\frac{q+2}{5} = \frac{2q-11}{7}$

33. $\frac{c+1}{c-2} = \frac{4}{7}$

34. **Gardening** A gardener is transplanting flowers into a flowerbed. She has been working for an hour and has transplanted 14 flowers. She has 35 more flowers to transplant. If she works at the same rate, how many more hours will it take her?   ◀ See Problem 4.

35. **Florists** A florist is making centerpieces. He uses 2 dozen roses for every 5 centerpieces. How many dozens of roses will he need to make 20 centerpieces?

36. **Picnics** If 5 lb of pasta salad serves 14 people, how much pasta salad should you bring to a picnic with 49 people?

Answers

Lesson Check

1. 4.8
2. 27
3. 3
4. 5
5. 6.75 h
6. m and q
7. n and p
8. mq and np
9. Yes; sample: One method creates an equation using the fact that the cross products are equal, and the other method creates an equivalent equation using the Mult. Prop. of Eq. to clear the denominators.

Practice and Problem-Solving Exercises

10. 6.4
11. −19.5
12. 3.75
13. 4.2
14. 2.25
15. 112.5
16. 5
17. $16\frac{2}{3}$
18. 4.875
19. 10
20. 80
21. 14
22. −10.8
23. $26\frac{2}{3}$
24. −16.5
25. −15
26. 8
27. 4.75
28. 11
29. 11
30. 13.2
31. $-6\frac{2}{3}$
32. 23
33. −5
34. 2.5 h
35. 8 dozen
36. 17.5 lb

---

3 Lesson Check

Do you know HOW?
Students learn to make choices and think independently as they pick the method they will use to solve these problems.

Do you UNDERSTAND?
See page 125 for definitions of vocabulary words.

Close

Q What are the two different methods used to solve proportions? **[the Cross Products Property and the Multiplication Property of Equality]**

Q When are these methods used? **[Answers may vary. Sample: The Mult. Prop. of Eq. is efficient when the LCM is a simple number. The Cross Products Property works better when the LCM is a large number or complicated expression.]**

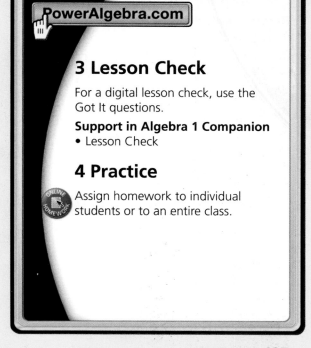

PowerAlgebra.com

3 Lesson Check

For a digital lesson check, use the Got It questions.

Support in Algebra 1 Companion
• Lesson Check

4 Practice

Assign homework to individual students or to an entire class.

4 Practice

Basic: 10–41 all, 42–50 even, 51–53

Average: 11–41 odd, 42–54

Advanced: 11–41 odd, 42–59

Standardized Test Prep: 60–62

Mixed Review: 63–73

Reasoning exercises have blue headings.

Applications exercises have red headings.

EXERCISE 40: Use the Think About a Plan worksheet in the **Practice and Problem Solving Workbook** (also available in the Teaching Resources in print and online) to further support students' development in becoming independent learners.

HOMEWORK QUICK CHECK
To check students' understanding of key skills and concepts, go over Exercises 25, 33, 38, 40, and 51.

 Apply

37. Statistics Approximately 3 people out of every 30 are left-handed. About how many left-handed people would you expect in a group of 140 people?

38. Think About a Plan Maya runs 100 m in 13.4 s. Amy can run 100 m in 14.1 s. If Amy were to finish a 100-m race at the same time as Maya, how much of a head start, in meters, would Amy need?
- What information do you know? What information is unknown?
- What proportion can you write that will help you solve the problem?

39. Electricity The electric bill for Ferguson's Furniture is shown at the right. The cost of electricity per kilowatt-hour and the total charges for one month are given. How many kilowatt-hours of electricity did Ferguson's Furniture use in that month?

⚡ Centerville Electric	
Account Name: Ferguson's Furniture	
Account Number: 34-14567-89	
Cost per kilowatt-hour	$.07
Total charges	$143.32
Previous balance	$.00
Total Amount Due	$143.32

40. Video Downloads A particular computer takes 15 min to download a 45-min TV show. How long will it take the computer to download a 2-h movie?

41. Schedules You want to meet your friend at a park 4 mi away from your house. You are going to bike to the park at an average rate of 10 mi/h. Your friend lives 1.2 mi away from the park and walks at an average rate of 3 mi/h. How many minutes ahead of you should your friend start out so that you meet at the park at the same time?

Solve each proportion. Tell whether you used the Multiplication Property of Equality or the Cross Products Property for your first step. Explain your choice.

42. $\frac{p}{4} = \frac{7}{8}$ **43.** $\frac{m}{4.5} = \frac{2}{5}$ **44.** $\frac{3}{10} = \frac{b}{7}$

45. $\frac{r}{2.1} = \frac{3.6}{2.8}$ **46.** $\frac{9}{14} = \frac{3}{n}$ **47.** $\frac{1.5}{y} = \frac{2.5}{7}$

48. $\frac{b+13}{2} = \frac{-5b}{3}$ **49.** $\frac{3b}{b-4} = \frac{3}{7}$ **50.** $\frac{x+2}{2x-6} = \frac{3}{8}$

51. Error Analysis Describe and correct the error in solving the proportion at the right.

$$\frac{8}{3} = \frac{x+3}{2}$$
$$16 = 3x + 3$$
$$13 = 3x$$
$$\frac{13}{3} = x$$

52. Bakery A bakery sells packages of 10 bagels for $3.69. If the bakery starts selling the bagels in packages of 12, how much would you expect a package of 12 to cost?
- (A) $3.08
- (B) $4.32
- (C) $4.43
- (D) $4.69

53. Open-Ended Write a proportion that contains a variable. Name the extremes, the means, and the cross products. Solve the proportion. Tell whether you used the Multiplication Property of Equality or the Cross Products Property to solve the proportion. Explain your choice.

54. Biology Many trees have concentric rings that can be counted to determine the tree's age. Each ring represents one year's growth. A maple tree with a diameter of 12 in. has 32 rings. If the tree continues to grow at about the same rate, how many rings will the tree have when its diameter is 20 in.?

Answers

Practice and Problem-Solving Exercises
(continued)

37. about 17 people

38. about 5 m

39. $\frac{\$.07}{1\,\text{kw-h}} = \frac{\$143.32}{x\,\text{kw-h}}$; 2047.4 kw-h

40. 40 min

41. at the same time as you

42. 3.5

43. 1.8

44. 2.1

45. 2.7

46. $4\frac{2}{3}$

47. 4.2

48. −3

49. $-\frac{2}{3}$

50. −17

51. 3 was not fully distributed when multiplying 3 and $x + 3$; $16 = 3x + 9$, $7 = 3x$, $x = \frac{7}{3}$.

52. C

53. Check students' work.

54. 53

C **Challenge**   Solve each proportion.

55. $\dfrac{4y - 3}{y^2 + 1} = \dfrac{4}{y}$

56. $\dfrac{w^2 + 3}{2w + 2} = \dfrac{w}{2}$

57. $\dfrac{5x}{x^3 + 5} = \dfrac{5}{x^2 - 7}$

58. Parade Floats A group of high school students is making a parade float by stuffing pieces of tissue paper into a wire frame. They use 150 tissues to fill an area 3 ft long and 2 ft wide. The total area they want to fill is 8 ft long and 7 ft wide. What is the total number of tissues they will need?

59. Insects It takes an insect 15 s to crawl 1 ft. How many hours would it take the insect to crawl 1 mi if the insect crawls at the same rate?

Standardized Test Prep

SAT/ACT

60. A high school soccer team is making trail mix to sell at a fundraiser. The recipe calls for 3 lb of raisins and 2 lb of peanuts. If the team purchases 54 lb of peanuts, how many pounds of raisins will they need?

Ⓐ 27   Ⓑ 36   Ⓒ 81   Ⓓ 162

61. One day during flu season, $\frac{1}{3}$ of the students in a class were out sick, and only 24 students were left. How many students are in the class?

Ⓕ 16   Ⓖ 30   Ⓗ 36   Ⓘ 72

62. An art gallery owner is framing a rectangular painting, as shown. The owner wants the width of the framed painting to be $38\frac{1}{2}$ in. How many wide should each of the vertical sections of the frame be?

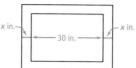

Ⓐ $4\frac{1}{8}$ in.

Ⓒ $4\frac{1}{2}$ in.

Ⓑ $4\frac{1}{4}$ in.

Ⓓ $8\frac{1}{2}$ in.

Mixed Review

Copy and complete each statement.   ◀ See Lesson 2-6.

63. 6 qt = ▉ gal   **64.** 84 in. = ▉ ft   **65.** $2\frac{1}{2}$ yd = ▉ in.   **66.** 3 min 10 s = ▉ s

Solve each equation. If the equation is an identity, write *identity*. If it has no solution, write *no solution*.   ◀ See Lesson 2-4.

67. $3x - (x - 4) = 2x$ **68.** $4 + 6c = 6 - 4c$ **69.** $5a - 2 = 0.5(10a - 4)$

Get Ready!   To prepare for Lesson 2-8, do Exercises 70–73.

Solve each proportion.   ◀ See Lesson 2-7.

70. $\dfrac{x}{12} = \dfrac{7}{30}$ **71.** $\dfrac{y}{12} = \dfrac{8}{45}$ **72.** $\dfrac{w}{15} = \dfrac{12}{27}$ **73.** $\dfrac{n}{9} = \dfrac{n + 1}{24}$

55. $-\dfrac{4}{3}$

56. 3

57. $-\dfrac{5}{7}$

58. 1400 tissues

59. 22 h

60. C

61. H

62. B

63. 1.5

64. 7

65. 90

66. 190

67. no solution

68. $\dfrac{1}{5}$

69. identity

70. $2\dfrac{4}{5}$ or 2.8

71. $2\dfrac{2}{15}$ or $2.1\overline{3}$

72. $6\dfrac{2}{3}$ or $6.\overline{6}$

73. $\dfrac{3}{5}$ or 0.6

Lesson Resources

Additional Instructional Support

Algebra 1 Companion
Students can use the **Algebra 1 Companion** worktext (4 pages) as you teach the lesson. Use the Companion to support
• New Vocabulary
• Key Concepts
• Got It for each Problem
• Lesson Check

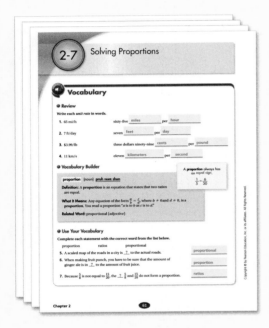

ELL Support
Focus On Language A process in this lesson is called cross multiplication. What other expressions use the word "cross"? (Answers may include *cross-country*, *cross-cultural*, *cross-eyed*, and *cross-legged*.) Ask: Why do you call this cross multiplication? (You multiply across the equal sign.) Reinforce understanding of cross multiplication by providing students with additional pairs of equal ratios and having them determine their cross products.

5 Assess & Remediate

Lesson Quiz
1. What is the solution of the proportion $\frac{2}{3} = \frac{x}{14}$?
2. What is the solution of the proportion $\frac{3}{5} = \frac{13}{x}$?
3. What is the solution of the proportion $\frac{x-1}{2} = \frac{x-4}{5}$?
4. Do you UNDERSTAND? A concession stand at a baseball game sells 3 apples for $2.00. How can you find the cost for 10 apples?

ANSWERS TO LESSON QUIZ
1. 9.3
2. 21.7
3. −1
4. Answers may vary. Sample: Solve the proportion $\frac{3}{2.00} = \frac{10}{x}$.

PRESCRIPTION FOR REMEDIATION
Use the student work on the Lesson Quiz to prescribe a differentiated review assignment.

Points	Differentiated Remediation
0–2	Intervention
3	On-level
4	Extension

PowerAlgebra.com

5 Assess & Remediate
Assign the Lesson Quiz. Appropriate intervention, practice, or enrichment is automatically generated based on student performance.

Intervention

• **Reteaching** (2 pages) Provides reteaching and practice exercises for the key lesson concepts. Use with struggling students or absent students.

• **English Language Learner Support** Helps students develop and reinforce mathematical vocabulary and key concepts.

All-in-One Resources/Online
Reteaching

All-in-One Resources/Online
English Language Learner Support

Differentiated Remediation *continued*

On-Level

- **Practice** (2 pages) Provides extra practice for each lesson. For simpler practice exercises, use the Form K Practice pages found in the All-in-One Teaching Resources and online.

- **Think About a Plan** Helps students develop specific problem-solving skills and strategies by providing scaffolded guiding questions.

- **Standardized Test Prep** Focuses on all major exercises, all major question types, and helps students prepare for the high-stakes assessments.

Extension

- **Enrichment** Provides students with interesting problems and activities that extend the concepts of the lesson.

- **Activities, Games, and Puzzles** Worksheets that can be used for concepts development, enrichment, and for fun!

Practice and Problem Solving WKBK/ All-in-One Resources/Online
Practice page 1

2-7 Practice — Form G
Solving Proportions

Solve each proportion using the Multiplication Property of Equality.

1. $\frac{3}{2} = \frac{n}{6}$ 9

2. $\frac{1}{5} = \frac{t}{3}$ $\frac{3}{5}$

3. $\frac{x}{6} = \frac{10}{9}$ $\frac{10}{3}$

4. $\frac{m}{4} = \frac{6}{5}$ $\frac{24}{5}$

5. $\frac{7}{6} = \frac{b}{2}$ $\frac{7}{3}$

6. $\frac{2}{9} = \frac{j}{18}$ 4

7. $\frac{2}{3} = \frac{5}{4}$ $\frac{55}{12}$

8. $\frac{11}{12} = \frac{w}{15}$ $\frac{55}{12}$

9. $\frac{19}{23} = \frac{c}{23}$ 43.7

Solve each proportion using the Cross Products Property.

10. $\frac{1}{4} = \frac{x}{10}$ $\frac{5}{2}$

11. $\frac{3}{x} = \frac{2}{3}$ $\frac{9}{2}$

12. $\frac{7}{12} = \frac{3}{4}$ 9

13. $\frac{6}{x} = \frac{-3}{4}$ $\frac{25}{3}$

14. $\frac{-3}{4} = \frac{k}{16}$ −12

15. $\frac{-3}{4} = \frac{-6}{5}$ $\frac{-55}{3}$

16. $\frac{15}{24} = \frac{8}{9}$ $\frac{-66}{9}$

17. $\frac{11}{5} = \frac{q}{-6}$

18. $\frac{f}{9} = \frac{6}{-12}$

19. The windows on a building are proportional to the size of the building. The height of each window is 18 in., and the width is 11 in. If the height of the building is 108 ft, what is the width of the building? 66 ft

20. Eric is planning to bake approximately 305 cookies. If 3 pounds of cookie dough make 96 cookies, how many pounds of cookie dough should he make? 9.5 lb

21. On a map, the distance between Sheila's house and Shardae's house is 6.75 inches. According to the scale, 1.5 inches represents 5 miles. How far apart are the houses? 22.5 mi

---

Practice and Problem Solving WKBK/ All-in-One Resources/Online
Think About a Plan

2-7 Think About a Plan
Solving Proportions

Video Downloads A particular computer takes 15 min to download a 45-min TV show. How long will it take the computer to download a 2-hour movie?

Understanding the Problem

1. What facts do you know about the situation?
the time it takes to download a 45-min TV show

2. Are the units given in such a way that the numerators and the denominators of the proportion have the same units? If so, what are the units? If not, which units need to be converted?
no; convert h to min or min to h

Planning the Solution

3. If unit conversions are necessary, use conversion factors to convert the units. Show your work.
$2 \text{ h} \cdot \frac{60 \text{ min}}{1 \text{ h}} = 120 \text{ min}$

4. Write a proportion that can be used to determine the length of time necessary for the computer to download the movie.
$\frac{15 \text{ min}}{45 \text{ min}} = \frac{x \text{ min}}{120 \text{ min}}$

Getting an Answer

5. Solve the proportion you wrote in Step 4 to find how long it will take the computer to download the movie.
40 min

Practice and Problem Solving WKBK/ All-in-One Resources/Online
Practice page 2

2-7 Practice (continued) — Form G
Solving Proportions

Solve each proportion using any method.

22. $\frac{n+4}{-6} = \frac{8}{2}$ −28

23. $\frac{10}{4} = \frac{z-8}{16}$ 48

24. $\frac{3}{i \div 7} = \frac{-59}{5}$

25. $\frac{x-3}{3} = \frac{x+4}{4}$ 24

26. $\frac{3}{n+1} = \frac{4}{n+4}$ 8

27. $\frac{4d+1}{d+9} = \frac{-3}{-2}$ 5

28. Sixty-two students, out of 100 surveyed, chose pizza as their favorite lunch item. If the school has 1250 students, how many students would likely say that pizza is their favorite if the survey is a fair representation of the student body? 775 favor pizza

29. The senior class is taking a trip to an amusement park. They received a special deal where for every 3 tickets they purchased they received one free ticket. 3 tickets cost $53.25. The total purchase of tickets cost $1384.50. How many tickets did they receive? 104 tickets

Solve each proportion.

30. $\frac{x-1}{2} = \frac{x-2}{3}$ 1

31. $\frac{2n+1}{n+2} = \frac{5}{4}$ 2

32. $\frac{3}{2b-1} = \frac{2}{b+2}$ 7

33. **Open-Ended** Give one example of a proportion. Describe the means and the extremes of the proportion. Explain how you know it is a proportion. Give one non-example of a proportion. Explain how you know it is not a proportion.
Answers may vary. Sample:
$\frac{3 \text{ yd}}{2 \text{ dresses}} = \frac{12 \text{ yd}}{8 \text{ dresses}}$; The first and last terms, 3 yd and 8 dresses, are called the extremes; The middle terms, 2 dresses and 12 yd, are the means; non-example: $\frac{3}{2} = \frac{7}{6}$ is not a proportion because $3(6) \neq 2(7)$.

Practice and Problem Solving WKBK/ All-in-One Resources/Online
Standardized Test Prep

2-7 Standardized Test Prep
Solving Proportions

Multiple Choice

For Exercises 1–5, choose the correct letter.

1. What is the solution to the proportion $\frac{3}{5} = \frac{x}{6}$? B
   A. $\frac{10}{3}$ B. 6   C. 10   D. 150

2. What is the solution to the proportion $\frac{x-1}{x} = \frac{2}{3}$? H
   F. −2   G. 0   H. 2   I. 3

3. There are 105 members of the high school marching band. For every 3 boys there are 4 girls. Which proportion represents how many boys are in the marching band? A
   A. $\frac{3}{7} = \frac{b}{105}$ B. $\frac{3}{4} = \frac{b}{105}$ C. $\frac{4}{3} = \frac{b}{105}$ D. $\frac{7}{3} = \frac{b}{105}$

4. A baker is making bread dough. He uses 3 cups of flour for every 8 ounces of water. How many cups of flour will he use if he uses 96 ounces of water? I
   F. 4   G. 12   H. 32   I. 36

5. Mr. Carter offered to stay after school for an extra help session, and $\frac{2}{11}$ of his students stayed for the session. If there were 24 students that stayed for the help session, how many students does Mr. Carter teach throughout the day? C
   A. 100   B. 121   C. 132   D. 144

Extended Response

6. Elisabeth goes on a 5 mile run each Saturday. Her run typically takes her 45 minutes. She wants to increase this distance to 7 miles. Determine the proportion you use to find the time it would take her to run 7 miles. Solve the proportion. What proportion can be used to determine the time it takes for her to run a marathon, which is approximately 26 miles? What is her time?
63 mi; 234 min
[2] All parts answered correctly.
[1] Some parts answered correctly.
[0] No parts answered correctly.

All-in-One Resources/Online
Enrichment

2-7 Enrichment
Solving Proportions

When dealing with right triangles, certain ratios are formed called trigonometric ratios. They are formed by examining various sides in relation to the angles. A commonly used triangle is the 30°-60°-90° triangle shown at the right. The hypotenuse is the side opposite the 90° angle. The other two sides are called sides opposite or adjacent to respective angles in the triangle.

Side a is opposite to angle A and adjacent to angle B. Side b is opposite to angle b and adjacent to angle A.

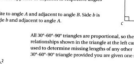

All 30°-60°-90° triangles are proportional, so the relationships shown in the triangle at the left can be used to determine missing lengths of any other 30°-60°-90° triangle provided you are given one side.

Use the relationships shown and proportions to determine the length of the other two sides.

1. about 7.8 units; 4.5 units
2. 5.6 units; about 4.8 units

3.

about 12.7 units; about 25.4 units

4. $2x$; $1.73x$

Online Teacher Resource Center
Activities, Games, and Puzzles

2-7 Game: Climb the Ladder
Solving Proportions

Play Climb the Ladder against a classmate. Decide who will be Player 1 and who will be Player 2.

In this game, players take turns choosing a proportion from the list below and challenging their opponents to solve it. Once a proportion is chosen, it should be crossed out. The game continues until someone climbs to the top, all the proportions have been used, or time runs out.

Use the ladders to keep score. The solution to the selected equation tells the player how many rungs to climb, or how many rungs to go down. A positive solution means "go up," while a negative solution means "go down." *Note:* The rungs are 2 units apart. If a player's score goes below 0, then that play puts the player at 0 and he or she has to begin to climb again.

The player who reaches the top first wins. If time runs out, the player closest to the top wins. Choose your equations wisely in order to limit the number of rungs your opponent can climb!

1. $\frac{x}{3} = \frac{4}{12}$ 1
2. $\frac{1}{a} = \frac{-1}{-2}$ 2
3. $\frac{4}{12} = \frac{2}{6}$ 6
4. $\frac{2}{14} = \frac{-c}{7}$ −1
5. $\frac{x}{100} = \frac{-1}{-50}$ 2
6. $\frac{36}{x} = \frac{3}{2}$ 2
7. $\frac{z}{15} = \frac{9}{45}$ 3
8. $\frac{1}{6} = \frac{-h}{24}$ −4
9. $\frac{x}{49} = \frac{1}{7}$ 7
10. $\frac{12}{12} = \frac{1}{q}$ 1
11. $\frac{64}{32} = \frac{p}{8}$ 8
12. $\frac{-64}{32} = \frac{p}{-8}$ −8
13. $\frac{55}{10} = \frac{11}{-d}$ −2
14. $\frac{z}{2} = \frac{11}{22}$ 1
15. $\frac{12}{60} = \frac{f}{15}$ 3
16. $\frac{-3}{j} = \frac{12}{8}$ −2
17. $\frac{x}{4} = \frac{4}{2}$ −2
18. $\frac{x}{8} = \frac{-12}{18}$ −4
19. $\frac{x}{-5} = \frac{-6}{2}$ 2
20. $\frac{-x}{-20} = \frac{-1}{20}$ −1
21. $\frac{-x}{17} = \frac{8}{-34}$ 4
22. $\frac{16}{-10} = \frac{8}{k}$ −5
23. $\frac{-20}{y} = \frac{-60}{15}$ 5
24. $\frac{12}{-33} = \frac{v}{11}$ −4

Player 1	Player 2
34	34
32	32
30	30
28	28
26	26
24	24
22	22
20	20
18	18
16	16
14	14
12	12
10	10
8	8
6	6
4	4
2	2
0	0

1 Interactive Learning

Solve It!
PURPOSE To bring an understanding of proportions to a problem introducing similarity

PROCESS Students may set up a proportion and solve for the length of the boat model, use equivalent fractions, or create a chart comparing various heights and lengths.

FACILITATE
Q What is the ration of the height of the actual boat to the length of the boat? **[12 : 9 or 4 : 3]**

Q How can you use this information to solve the problem? **[Set up a proportion comparing the ratio of the height and length of the boat to the ratio of the model.]**

ANSWERS See Solve it in Answers on next page.
CONNECT THE MATH Proportions are very useful for modeling real-world situations of similar figures, such as these sailboats. Students practice recently acquired skills in solving proportions as they learn to write them for scale drawings.

2 Guided Instruction

VISUAL LEARNERS

Help students visualize similar triangles. Place a scalene triangle on the overhead projector. Trace the projection of that triangle on the board and label the vertices *ABC*. Then move the projector closer to the board so a new triangle is seen that does not overlap with the first. Trace the new triangle and label the vertices *FGH*. These two triangles are similar. Discuss characteristics of similar triangles such as same shape, different size, equal angles, and proportional sides.

Objectives To find missing lengths in similar figures
To use similar figures when measuring indirectly

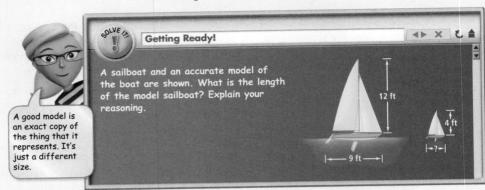

A sailboat and an accurate model of the boat are shown. What is the length of the model sailboat? Explain your reasoning.

A good model is an exact copy of the thing that it represents. It's just a different size.

Lesson Vocabulary
• similar figures
• scale drawing
• scale
• scale model

In the Solve It, the sailboat and its model have the same shape but they are different sizes. **Similar figures** have the same shape but not necessarily the same size.

Essential Understanding You can use proportions to find missing side lengths in similar figures. Such figures can help you measure real-world distances indirectly.

The symbol ~ means "is similar to." In the diagram, $\triangle ABC \sim \triangle FGH$.

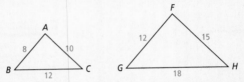

In similar figures, the measures of corresponding angles are equal, and corresponding side lengths are in proportion. The order of the letters when you name similar figures is important because it tells which parts of the figures are corresponding parts. So, because $\triangle ABC \sim \triangle FGH$, the following is true.

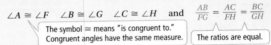

$$\angle A \cong \angle F \quad \angle B \cong \angle G \quad \angle C \cong \angle H \quad \text{and} \quad \frac{AB}{FG} = \frac{AC}{FH} = \frac{BC}{GH}$$

The symbol $\cong$ means "is congruent to." Congruent angles have the same measure. | The ratios are equal.

130 Chapter 2 Solving Equations

BIG idea **Proportionality**
ESSENTIAL UNDERSTANDINGS
• Proportional reasoning can be used to find the missing side lengths in similar figures.
• Such figures can be used to measure real-world distances indirectly.

Math Background
Students who use proportional reasoning understand that ratios represent a relationship. They see that a change in one variable leads to a change in the other variable. Students using proportional reasoning frequently do so with a variety of strategies. They readily discern between situations that involve multiplicative relationships and situations that are based on additive

relationships. Proportional reasoning is an essential skill for future work in mathematics.

Support Student Learning
Use the **Algebra I Companion** to engage and support students during instructions. See Lesson Resources at the end of this lesson for details.

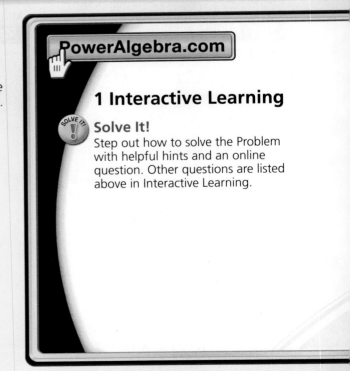

1 Interactive Learning

Solve It!
Step out how to solve the Problem with helpful hints and an online question. Other questions are listed above in Interactive Learning.

Problem 1 Finding the Length of a Side

Multiple Choice In the diagram, $\triangle ABC \sim \triangle DEF$. What is DE?

- (A) 7.5
- (C) 21.3
- (B) 9.5
- (D) 24

Know
- The length of $\overline{AB}$, which corresponds to $\overline{DE}$
- The lengths of two other corresponding sides, $\overline{BC}$ and $\overline{EF}$
- The triangles are similar

Need
The length of $\overline{DE}$

Plan
Write a proportion involving two pairs of corresponding sides: AB and DE, and BC and EF. The length of $\overline{DE}$ is the only unknown, so you can solve for it.

$$\frac{BC}{EF} = \frac{AB}{DE} \qquad \text{Write a proportion.}$$

$$\frac{16}{12} = \frac{10}{DE} \qquad \text{Substitute lengths.}$$

$$16(DE) = 12(10) \qquad \text{Cross Products Property}$$

$$16DE = 120 \qquad \text{Multiply.}$$

$$DE = 7.5 \qquad \text{Divide each side by 16 and simplify.}$$

DE is 7.5. The correct answer is A.

Got It? **1.** Use the figures in Problem 1. What is AC?

You can also use proportions to solve indirect measurement problems like finding a distance using a map. You can use similar figures and proportions to find lengths that you cannot measure directly.

Problem 2 Applying Similarity

Indirect Measurement The sun's rays strike the building and the girl at the same angle, forming the two similar triangles shown. How tall is the building?

$$\frac{\text{girl's shadow}}{\text{building's shadow}} = \frac{\text{girl's height}}{\text{building's height}} \qquad \text{Write a proportion.}$$

$$\frac{3}{15} = \frac{5}{x} \qquad \text{Substitute.}$$

$$3x = 15(5) \qquad \text{Cross Products Property}$$

$$3x = 75 \qquad \text{Multiply.}$$

$$x = 25 \qquad \text{Divide each side by 3.}$$

The building is 25 ft tall.

Think
Is there only one way to write a proportion?
No. You can write different proportions to find the height. For example, the following proportion also works.
$$\frac{\text{building's shadow}}{\text{girl's shadow}} = \frac{\text{building's height}}{\text{girl's height}}$$

x ft

5 ft

3 ft   *15 ft*

Problem 1
This problem illustrates the use of proportions to find missing lengths of similar figures.

Q What is the first step towards solving this problem? **[Answers may vary. Samples: Determine what information you know. Decide what you are asked to find.]**

Q If $\triangle ABC : \triangle DEF$ then what are the corresponding parts?
$$\left[\angle A \cong \angle D, \angle B \cong \angle E, \angle C \cong \angle F \right.$$
$$\left. \frac{AB}{DE}, \frac{BC}{EF}, \frac{AC}{DF} \right]$$

Q What was used to find the missing side length? **[a proportion]**

Got It?

Q What ratio of the side lengths involves the side that you are looking for? **[AB:AC, BC:AC]**

Q Can you use either of these ratios to set up the proportion? **[yes]**

Problem 2
Students will use properties of similar figures to calculate the height of a building.

Q What do you suppose is meant by indirect measurement? **[finding measurements of objects that you cannot measure directly]**

Q Why is the equation in the Think box equivalent to the one used in the problem? **[The cross products are the same.]**

Q When might you need indirect measurements? **[Sample: to find the height of a cliff or width of a lake]**

---

2 Guided Instruction

 Each Problem is worked out and supported online.

Problem 1
Finding the Length of a Side
Animated

Problem 2
Applying Similarity
Animated

Problem 3
Interpreting Scale Drawings
Animated

Problem 4
Using Scale Models

Support in Algebra 1 Companion
- Vocabulary
- Key Concepts
- Got It?

Answers

Solve It!
3 ft; explanations may vary.

Got It?
1. 24

Got It?

> Q Can you draw a sketch of what is happening in this problem? Show it. **[Check students' work.]**
>
> Q What proportion will help you solve this problem? **[Check students' work.]**

ERROR PREVENTION

Lesson 2-6 focused on unit analysis. Students used the units and unit conversions to answer questions. In this lesson, students are using proportions and the concept of equivalent ratios. Note that while units are not included as part of the proportion, consistent placement of unit quantities is necessary to have a correct proportion.

Problem 3

Students use knowledge of similar figures to calculate distance using a map.

> Q Have you ever used a scale on a map? How was the scale helpful? **[Answers may vary. Sample: It helped find the total distance to travel.]**
>
> Q What is this scale telling you? **[1 in. represents 110 mi.]**
>
> Q What is the distance from Jacksonville to Orlando on the map? **[1.25 in.]**
>
> Q How is the proportion set up in this case? **[map distance : actual distance]**

Got It?

> Q What information from the map is needed in this problem? **[1 in. : 110 mi]**

 Got It? 2. A man who is 6 ft tall is standing next to a flagpole. The shadow of the man is 3.5 ft and the shadow of the flagpole is 17.5 ft. What is the height of the flagpole?

A **scale drawing** is a drawing that is similar to an actual object or place. Floor plans, blueprints, and maps are all examples of scale drawings. In a scale drawing, the ratio of any length on the drawing to the actual length is always the same. This ratio is called the **scale** of the drawing.

 Problem 3 Interpreting Scale Drawings

Maps What is the actual distance from Jacksonville to Orlando? Use the ruler to measure the distance from Jacksonville to Orlando on the map below.

Scale
1 in. : 110 mi

Think

What does the scale of the map tell you?
The scale tells you that each inch on the map represents 110 mi of actual distance.

Relate map scale $= \dfrac{\text{map distance}}{\text{actual distance}}$

Define Let $x =$ the total distance from Jacksonville to Orlando.

Write $\dfrac{1}{110} = \dfrac{1.25}{x}$

$1(x) = 110(1.25)$ Cross Products Property

$x = 137.5$ Multiply.

The actual distance from Jacksonville to Orlando is 137.5 mi.

 Got It? 3. a. The distance from Jacksonville to Gainesville on the map is about 0.6 in. What is the actual distance from Jacksonville to Gainesville?

b. Reasoning If you know that the actual distance between two cities is 250 mi and that the cities are 2 in. apart on a map, how can you find the scale of the map?

A **scale model** is a three-dimensional model that is similar to a three-dimensional object. The ratio of a linear measurement of a model to the corresponding linear measurement of the actual object is always the same. This ratio is called the scale of the model.

Additional Problems

1. In the diagram, $\triangle ABC \sim \triangle DEF$. What is DE?

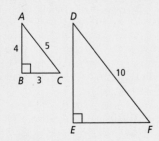

ANSWER 8

2. A student who is 5.25 ft tall is standing next to a tree. The shadow of the student is 20 ft and the shadow of the tree is 80 ft. What is the height of the tree?

ANSWER 21 ft

3. One inch represents 12 mi on a map. If the distance between two buildings is 4 in. on the map, what is the actual distance?

ANSWER 48 mi

4. A model of a new campus building is 5 in. tall. If 1 in. represents 8.5 ft, how tall will the building be?

ANSWER 42.5 ft

Answers

Got It? (continued)

2. 30 ft

3. a. about 66 mi

b. Write and solve the proportion $\frac{2}{250} = \frac{1}{x}$; 1 in. represents 125 mi.

 **Problem 4** Using Scale Models

Science A giant model heart is shown below. The heart is the ideal size for a person who is 170 ft tall. About what size would you expect the heart of a man who is 6 ft tall to be?

 x ft

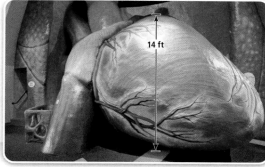

14 ft

6 ft

 Think

Is this problem like ones you have seen?
Yes. Scale model problems are like scale drawing problems, so you can write a proportion like you did to find the height of the building in Problem 2.

$$\frac{\text{height of giant heart}}{\text{height of man's heart}} = \frac{\text{height of giant person}}{\text{height of man}}$$ Write a proportion.

$$\frac{14}{x} = \frac{170}{6}$$ Substitute.

$$14(6) = 170x$$ Cross Products Property

$$0.49 \approx x$$ Divide each side by 170 and simplify.

The size of the man's heart would be about 0.49 ft, or 5.9 in.

 Got It? **4.** A scale model of a building is 6 in. tall. The scale of the model is 1 in. : 50 ft. How tall is the actual building?

Lesson Check

Do you know HOW?

1. Photocopies You use a photocopier to enlarge a drawing of a right triangle with a base of 13 cm and a height of 7 cm. The enlarged triangle has a height of 17.5 cm.
   a. What is the base of the enlarged triangle?
   b. What is the scale of the enlargement?

2. Maps The scale of a map is 1 cm : 75 km. What is the actual distance between two towns that are 3 cm apart on the map?

Do you UNDERSTAND?

3. Vocabulary Suppose $\triangle MNP \sim \triangle RST$. How can you identify corresponding parts?

4. Reasoning Suppose $\triangle ABC \sim \triangle TUV$. Determine whether each pair of measures is equal.
   a. the measures of $\angle A$ and $\angle T$
   b. the perimeters of the two triangles
   c. the ratios of the sides $\frac{BC}{UV}$ and $\frac{AC}{TV}$

5. Reasoning The scale of a map is 1 in. : 100 mi. Is the actual distance between two towns 100 times the map distance between the two towns? Explain.

PowerAlgebra.com   Lesson 2-8   Proportions and Similar Figures   **133**

Problem 4
Students use knowledge of similar figures to solve a scale model problem.

Q What is the height of the model? **[14 ft]**
Q What is the problem asking? **[Find the size of the heart of a man who is 6 ft tall.]**
Q Why is the answer given $0.49 \approx x$? **[The answer is rounded to the nearest hundredth.]**
Q Can you visualize the length 0.49 ft? Is it easier to think about 5.9 in.? **[Answers may vary. Sample: It is easier to think and visualize about inches than parts of a foot.]**

It is helpful to convert answers to units that are easier to think about in the context of the problem.

Got It?

Q What is the scale? **[1 in. : 50 ft]**
Q What do we know? **[model is 6 in. tall]**
Q Do you have all of the information necessary to write a proportion? **[yes]**

3 Lesson Check

Do you know HOW?
• If students have difficulty with the first exercise, let them draw a diagram of the two triangles.

Do you UNDERSTAND?
• In Exercise 3, remember that order of vertices provides a reference for corresponding parts.

Close

Q How do you know when to use a proportion? **[Answers may vary. Sample: I use proportions when making comparisons.]**

Got It? (continued)
4. 300 ft

Lesson Check
1. a. 32.5 cm
   b. 2.5:1
2. 225 km
3. The order of the letters in each triangle tells which parts are corresponding.
4. a. yes
   b. no
   c. yes
5. Answers may vary. Sample: No, it is greater than 100 times since 100 mi is more than 100 times as great as 1 in.

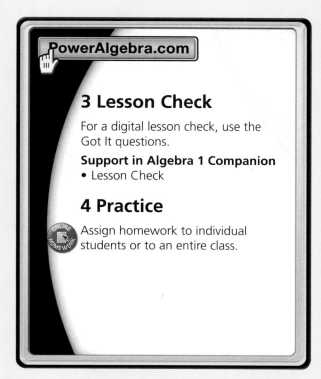

PowerAlgebra.com

3 Lesson Check
For a digital lesson check, use the Got It questions.

Support in Algebra 1 Companion
• Lesson Check

4 Practice
Assign homework to individual students or to an entire class.

Lesson 2-8   **133**

4 Practice

ASSIGNMENT GUIDE

Basic: 6–25

Average: 7–17 odd, 19–28

Advanced: 7–17 odd, 19–30

Standardized Test Prep: 31–34

Mixed Review: 35–43

Reasoning exercises have blue headings.

Applications exercises have red headings.

EXERCISE 25: Use the Think About a Plan worksheet in the **Practice and Problem Solving Workbook** (also available in the Teaching Resources in print and online) to further support students' development in becoming independent learners.

HOMEWORK QUICK CHECK

To check students' understanding of key skills and concepts, go over Exercises 9, 17, 23, 24, and 25.

Practice and Problem-Solving Exercises

A Practice   The figures in each pair are similar. Identify the corresponding sides and angles.   ◀ See Problem 1.

6. $\triangle ABC \sim \triangle DEF$

7. $FGHI \sim KLMN$

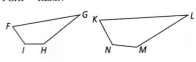
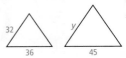

The figures in each pair are similar. Find the missing length.

8.

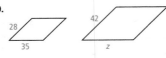

9.

10.

11.

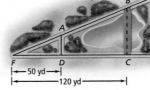

12. Bridges In the diagram of the park, $\triangle ADF \sim \triangle BCF$. The crosswalk at point A is about 20 yd long. A bridge across the pond will be built, from point B to point C. What will the length of the bridge be?   ◀ See Problem 2.

The scale of a map is 1 cm : 15 km. Find the actual distance corresponding to each map distance.   ◀ See Problem 3.

13. 2.5 cm   **14.** 0.2 cm   **15.** 15 cm   **16.** 4.6 cm

17. Movies A professional model-maker is building a giant scale model of a house fly to be used in a science fiction film. An actual fly is about 0.2 in. long with a wingspan of about 0.5 in. The model fly for the movie will be 27 ft long. What will its wingspan be?   ◀ See Problem 4.

18. Maps Abbottsville and Broken Branch are 175 mi apart. On a map, the distance between the two towns is 2.5 in. What is the scale of the map?

Answers

Practice and Problem-Solving Exercises

6. $\angle A \cong \angle D$, $\angle B \cong \angle E$, $\angle C \cong \angle F$, $\frac{AB}{DE} = \frac{AC}{DF} = \frac{BC}{EF}$

7. $\angle F \cong \angle K$, $\angle G \cong \angle L$, $\angle H \cong \angle M$, $\angle I \cong \angle N$, $\frac{FG}{KL} = \frac{GH}{LM} = \frac{HI}{MN} = \frac{FI}{KN}$

8. 12

9. 40

10. 52.5

11. 100

12. about 48 yd

13. 37.5 km

14. 3 km

15. 225 km

16. 69 km

17. 67.5 ft

18. 1 in. : 70 mi

Architecture An architect is using the blueprint below to remodel a laundry room. The side length of each grid square represents 12 in.

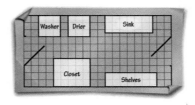

19. Find the actual length and width of the sink.

20. Find the total length and width of the actual room.

21. Will it be possible to wheel a laundry cart that is $3\frac{1}{2}$ ft wide through the room from the doorway at the left to the doorway at the right?

22. Model Rockets A particular model rocket kit uses the scale 1 : 144. The actual rocket is 168 ft tall. How tall will the model rocket be when completed?

23. Error Analysis The two figures at the right are similar. A student uses the proportion $\frac{BC}{CJ} = \frac{GH}{FN}$ to find FN.

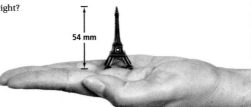

   a. What mistake did the student make?
   b. What proportion should the student have used instead?

24. Think About a Plan An interior designer sketches a design for a rectangular rug. The dimensions of the sketch are 4 in. by 7.5 in. The dimensions of the actual rug will be ten times the dimensions of the drawing, so the scale of the drawing is 1 : 10. How many times the area of the sketch is the area of the actual rug?
   • Which figures in the problem are similar? What are their dimensions?
   • How can proportions help you find the dimensions of the actual rug?

25. Trucks A model of a tractor-trailer is shaped like a rectangular prism and has a width of 2 in., a length of 9 in., and a height of 4 in. The scale of the model is 1 : 34. How many times the volume of the model is the volume of the actual tractor-trailer?

26. Eiffel Tower The height of the Eiffel Tower is 324 m. Which scale was used to make the model of the Eiffel Tower shown at the right?

   Ⓐ 1 mm : 0.9 m

   Ⓑ 1 mm : 6 m

   Ⓒ 1 mm : 30 m

   Ⓓ 1 mm : 324 m

54 mm

27. Writing Are all squares similar? Explain your answer.

28. Reasoning A boat maker wanted to build a canoe 6 ft long and $2\frac{1}{2}$ ft wide but decided that those dimensions were too small. The boat maker wants to add 2 ft to both the length and the width but also wants to keep the canoe the same shape. Explain why this will not work.

19. $6\frac{1}{2}$ ft × $2\frac{1}{2}$ ft

20. 20 ft × 10 ft

21. no

22. $1\frac{1}{6}$ ft or 1 ft 2 in.

23. a. The student used CJ instead of AJ.
   b. $\frac{BC}{AJ} = \frac{GH}{FN}$

24. 100 times

25. 39,304 times

26. B

27. Yes; all squares have sides that are in proportion (the same length), and the measures of corresponding ∠s are equal (90°).

28. Answers may vary. Sample: The ratio of the lengths to the widths will not be in proportion.

Answers

Practice and Problem-Solving Exercises
(continued)

29. Answers may vary. Sample: No; the finished table could have been a parallelogram with different angles than the parallelogram in the sketch. The angle measures were not given.

30. a. 1 : 4.6
   b. 1 : 3.46

31. C

32. F

33. B

34. I

35. 34

36. 4.5

37. −8

38. $-\dfrac{3}{5}$

39. 1.5

40. 8

41. 0.4

42. 0.25

43. 2.9

 Challenge

29. Carpentry A carpenter is building a tabletop from a sketch. The sketch shows a parallelogram with side lengths 2 in. and 3 in. Also, the sketch specifies that the sides of the finished tabletop should be 4 ft and 6 ft. Can the carpenter be certain that the finished tabletop will be a similar parallelogram? Explain.

30. Painting You have a painting that is 30 in. wide and 22.5 in. tall. You would like to reproduce it on a sheet of paper that measures $8\frac{1}{2}$ in. by 11 in., leaving at least a 1-in. margin on all four sides.
   a. What scale should you use if you keep the sheet of paper in the normal upright orientation? Assume that the reproduction will be as large as possible.
   b. What scale should you use if you turn the paper on its side?

Standardized Test Prep

SAT/ACT

31. The scale of a map is 1 in. : 80 mi. If the actual distance between two cities is 350 mi, how far apart will they be on the map?
   Ⓐ $4\frac{1}{4}$ in.   Ⓑ $4\frac{3}{16}$ in.   Ⓒ $4\frac{3}{8}$ in.   Ⓓ $4\frac{1}{2}$ in.

32. The cost c of purchasing r roses from Sandra's Delivery Service is given by the equation $c = 3r + 15$. If Luke has $50 to spend on roses, how many roses can he buy?
   Ⓕ 11   Ⓖ $11\frac{2}{3}$ Ⓗ 12   Ⓘ 13

33. Which property of addition is illustrated by $a + (b + c) = (a + b) + c$?
   Ⓐ Commutative   Ⓑ Associative   Ⓒ Inverse   Ⓓ Identity

34. Tamara and Will set up two booths to sell papayas at the farmer's market. Tamara sold hers for $5 each and Will sold his for $7 each. By noon, Tamara had sold 3 more papayas than Will and together they had earned a total of $147. How many papayas did they sell altogether?
   Ⓕ 8   Ⓖ 11   Ⓗ 14   Ⓘ 25

Mixed Review

Solve each proportion.   ◀ See Lesson 2-7.

35. $\dfrac{y}{4} = \dfrac{17}{2}$ **36.** $\dfrac{3}{a} = \dfrac{2}{3}$ **37.** $\dfrac{20}{14} = \dfrac{2-x}{7}$ **38.** $\dfrac{-3}{m} = \dfrac{2}{m+1}$

39. If you add a certain number to 3, the result is the same as if you had multiplied the number by 3. What is the number?   ◀ See Lesson 2-4.

Get Ready!   To prepare for Lesson 2-9, do Exercises 40–43.

Simplify each expression.   ◀ See Lesson 1-2.

40. $4 + 0.5(8)$ **41.** $0.2(5 - 3)$ **42.** $0.1(5) - 0.25$ **43.** $3 - 0.01(10)$

Additional Instructional Support

Algebra 1 Companion

Students can use the **Algebra 1 Companion** worktext (4 pages) as you teach the lesson. Use the Companion to support

- New Vocabulary
- Key Concepts
- Got It for each Problem
- Lesson Check

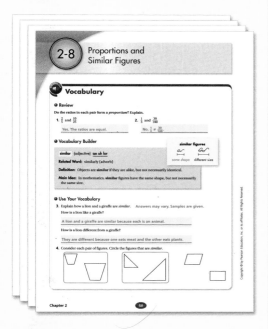

ELL Support

Use Graphic Organizers Write the following problem on the board. Rachelle spends 2 hours out of every 3 studying math. One week, she spent 10 hours studying math. How many hours did she study in all? Then write these questions: What do I know? What do I want to know? Will addition, subtraction, multiplication, or division help me answer the question? Have students write the answers to these questions on a sheet of paper. Then have students follow their steps to determine how many hours Rachelle studies in all. (15 hours)

5 Assess & Remediate

Lesson Quiz

1. In the diagram, $\triangle ABC \sim \triangle DEF$. What is AC?

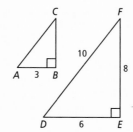

2. A 10–ft tall flagpole stands next to a tree. The shadow of the flagpole is 17 ft and the shadow of the tree is 50 ft. What is the height of the tree?

3. Everglades National Park is 225 mi long. What scale is needed to draw the map 10 in. long?

4. **Do you UNDERSTAND?** A clay model of a new car is 7 in. long. If the car is 21 ft long, how could you find the scale used to make the model?

ANSWERS TO LESSON QUIZ

1. 5
2. about 29.4 ft
3. 1 in. = 22.5 mi
4. Answers may vary. Sample: Solve the proportion $\frac{7 \text{ in.}}{21 \text{ ft}} = \frac{1 \text{ in.}}{x \text{ ft}}$.

PRESCRIPTION FOR REMEDIATION

Use the student work on the Lesson Quiz to prescribe a differentiated review assignment.

Points	Differentiated Remediation
0–2	Intervention
3	On-level
4	Extension

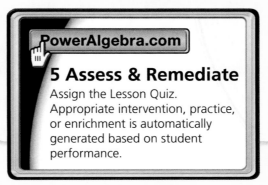

PowerAlgebra.com

5 Assess & Remediate

Assign the Lesson Quiz. Appropriate intervention, practice, or enrichment is automatically generated based on student performance.

Intervention

- **Reteaching** (2 pages) Provides reteaching and practice exercises for the key lesson concepts. Use with struggling students or absent students.

- **English Language Learner Support** Helps students develop and reinforce mathematical vocabulary and key concepts.

All-in-One Resources/Online
Reteaching

All-in-One Resources/Online
English Language Learner Support

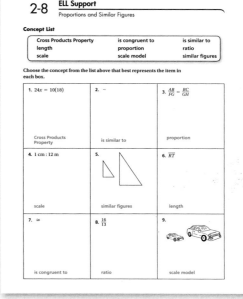

Differentiated Remediation *continued*

On-Level

- **Practice** (2 pages) Provides extra practice for each lesson. For simpler practice exercises, use the Form K Practice pages found in the All-in-One Teaching Resources and online.

- **Think About a Plan** Helps students develop specific problem-solving skills and strategies by providing scaffolded guiding questions.

- **Standardized Test Prep** Focuses on all major exercises, all major question types, and helps students prepare for the high-stakes assessments.

Extension

- **Enrichment** Provides students with interesting problems and activities that extend the concepts of the lesson.

- **Activities, Games, and Puzzles** Worksheets that can be used for concepts development, enrichment, and for fun!

Practice and Problem Solving WKBK/ All-in-One Resources/Online
Practice page 1

Practice and Problem Solving WKBK/ All-in-One Resources/Online
Practice page 2

All-in-One Resources/Online
Enrichment

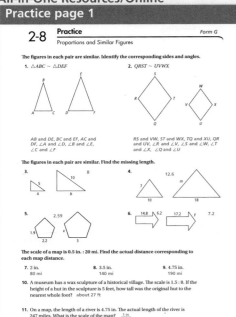

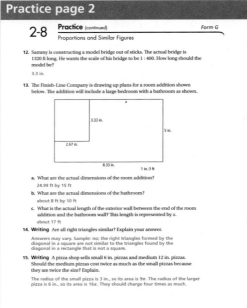

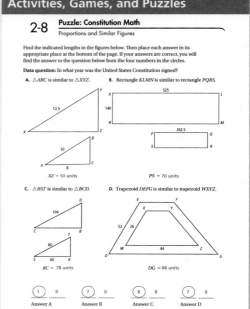

Practice and Problem Solving WKBK/ All-in-One Resources/Online
Think About a Plan

Practice and Problem Solving WKBK/ All-in-One Resources/Online
Standardized Test Prep

Online Teacher Resource Center
Activities, Games, and Puzzles

2-9 Percents

Objectives To solve percent problems using proportions
To solve percent problems using the percent equation

Be careful! You're asked to find who consumed the greater <u>percent</u>, not the greater amount.

Dynamic Activity
Percents and Proportions

SOLVE IT!

Getting Ready!   ◄► ✕ ↻ ⬆

Some recommended daily intakes of vitamins are shown. Carrie consumed 10 mg of niacin today. Her brother consumed 11 mg of niacin. Who consumed the greater percent of their recommended intake? How do you know?

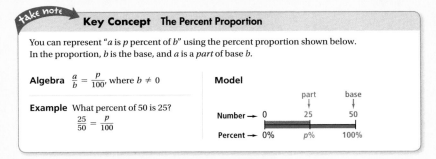

The problem in the Solve It involves percents. Percents are useful because they standardize comparisons to a common base of 100. In this lesson, you will solve percent problems in a variety of ways.

Essential Understanding You can solve problems involving percents using either proportions or the percent equation, which are closely related. If you write a percent as a fraction, you can use a proportion to solve a percent problem.

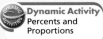

Key Concept   The Percent Proportion

You can represent "a is p percent of b" using the percent proportion shown below. In the proportion, b is the base, and a is a *part* of base b.

Algebra $\frac{a}{b} = \frac{p}{100}$, where $b \neq 0$

Example What percent of 50 is 25?
$\frac{25}{50} = \frac{p}{100}$

Model

part   base
↓   ↓
Number → 0   25   50

Percent → 0% p%   100%

PowerAlgebra.com | Lesson 2-9   Percents | 137

2-9 Preparing to Teach

BIG idea **Proportionality**   **UbD**

ESSENTIAL UNDERSTANDINGS
- Problems involving percents can be solved using either proportions or the percent equation.
- If a percent is written as a fraction, a proportion can be used to solve a percent problem.

Math Background
By using the Percent Proportion Method or the Percent Equation, the students work within the context of the problem. Years ago, percent problems were represented as three different cases: finding the percent of a number, finding the rate given the base and the percent, and finding the

base given the rate and percent. The student determined which case the problem represented and then applied the appropriate algorithm. Students often assumed that there were three different methods and lost sight of the similarities between them. The Percent Proportion Method and the Percent Equation are directly related to the context of the problem and useful regardless of the missing value.

Support Student Learning
Use the **Algebra I Companion** to engage and support students during instruction. See Lesson Resources at the end of this lesson for details.

---

1 Interactive Learning

Solve It!
PURPOSE To use percents as a method of comparison
PROCESS Students may write a fraction for each intake amount over the recommended amount and compare them with common denominators, change them to percents or decimals, or compare them to a recommended fraction such as $\frac{7}{10}$.

FACILITATE

Q What fractions represent each person's intake? [Carrie: $\frac{10}{14}$, brother: $\frac{11}{16}$]

Q How can you compare these fractions to $\frac{7}{10}$? What is the result? [Find $\frac{7}{10}$ of 14 and $\frac{7}{10}$ of 16. Carrie consumes more, her brother less.]

Q How would you convert each fraction to a percent? [Sample: Find the decimal equivalent and multiply by 100.]

Q Is it possible for a person to consume both a greater percent and a lesser amount? Give an example. [Yes; Sample: Carrie could consume 10 mg (less than her brother) but still have the greater percent.]

ANSWER See Solve it in Answers on next page.
CONNECT THE MATH Help students see the connection between fractions and percents in this problem. Since percents provide a standard base of 100, they allow a quick comparison of fractions.

2 Guided Instruction

Take Note
In Lesson 2-1, the word "per" indicated the relationship in a ratio. "Per" in "percent" also indicates a ratio, one with a base of 100.

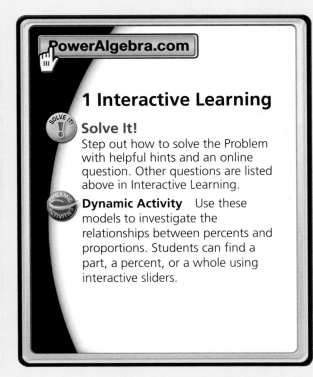

PowerAlgebra.com

1 Interactive Learning

Solve It!
Step out how to solve the Problem with helpful hints and an online question. Other questions are listed above in Interactive Learning.

Dynamic Activity Use these models to investigate the relationships between percents and proportions. Students can find a part, a percent, or a whole using interactive sliders.

Lesson 2-9   137

Problem 1

When writing proportions, students often look for the word "of" and then take the value following the "of" as the base. Encourage students to also try to understand the context of the problem rather than just using this technique. This prepares them to solve problems that do not contain "of."

> **Q** Why is 42 substituted for *a* in the example? **[42 is the part and 56 is the whole.]**

Got It?

> **Q** Which value represents the base? **[90]**
> **Q** Which value represents the part? **[54]**

Take Note

Show students these steps to connect the percent equation with the percent proportion.

$$\frac{a}{b} = \frac{P}{100}$$
$$\frac{a}{b} = p\%$$
$$\frac{a}{b} \cdot b = p\% \cdot b$$
$$a = p\% \cdot b$$

Problem 2

When using the percent equation method method, students must remember to state the decimal value as percent (0.0625 = 6.25%).

> **Q** What do you know? **[a = 2.5 and b = 40]**
> **Q** How do you write 0.0625 as a percent? **[Move the decimal point 2 places to the right.]**

Got It?

> **Q** How do these methods compare? **[Using the percent proportion, the answer is a percent. When using the percent equation, remember to convert the decimal to a percent.]**

Answers

Solve It!
Carrie; explanations may vary.

Got It?
1. 60%
2. 75%; the answers are the same.

Think

How can a model help you visualize the proportion?
Use a model like the one below to visualize any percent problem. A model for the proportion $\frac{42}{56} = \frac{p}{100}$ is

```
0              42  56
|---------------|---|
0%             p% 100%
```

 Problem 1 Finding a Percent Using the Percent Proportion

What percent of 56 is 42?

$\dfrac{a}{b} = \dfrac{p}{100}$	Write the percent proportion.
$\dfrac{42}{56} = \dfrac{p}{100}$	Substitute 42 for *a* and 56 for *b*.
$42(100) = 56p$	Cross Products Property
$4200 = 56p$	Multiply.
$75 = p$	Divide each side by 56.

42 is 75% of 56.

✓ **Got It? 1.** What percent of 90 is 54?

In Problem 1, you used the percent proportion $\frac{a}{b} = \frac{p}{100}$ to find a percent. When you write $\frac{p}{100}$ as $p\%$ and solve for *a*, you get the equation $a = p\% \cdot b$. This equation is called the percent equation. You can use either the percent equation or the percent proportion to solve any percent problem.

 Key Concept The Percent Equation

You can represent "*a* is *p* percent of *b*" using the percent equation shown below. In the equation, *a* is a part of the base *b*.

Algebra $a = p\% \cdot b$, where $b \neq 0$

Model
```
0              25        50
|---------------|---------|
0%             p%       100%
```

Example What percent of 50 is 25?
$$25 = p\% \cdot 50$$

Think

Is this problem related to other problems you've seen?
Yes. This problem is related to Problem 1. Both involve finding a percent, but they use different methods.

 **Problem 2** Finding a Percent Using the Percent Equation

What percent of 40 is 2.5?

$a = p\% \cdot b$	Write the percent equation.
$2.5 = p\% \cdot 40$	Substitute 2.5 for *a* and 40 for *b*.
$0.0625 = p\%$	Divide each side by 40.
$6.25\% = p\%$	Write the decimal as a percent.

2.5 is 6.25% of 40.

✓ **Got It? 2. Reasoning** What percent of 84 is 63? Use the percent equation to solve. Then use the percent proportion. Compare your answers.

 PowerAlgebra.com

2 Guided Instruction

Each Problem is worked out and supported online.

Problem 1
Finding a Percent Using the Percent Proportion

Problem 2
Finding a Percent Using the Percent Equation

Alternative Problem 2
Finding a Percent Using the Percent Equation
Animated

Problem 3
Finding a Part
Animated

Problem 4
Finding a Base
Animated

Problem 5
Using the Simple Interest Formula

Support in Algebra 1 Companion
- Vocabulary
- Key Concepts
- Got It?

Problem 3 Finding a Part

Shopping A dress shirt that normally costs $38.50 is on sale for 30% off. What is the sale price of the shirt?

Step 1 Use the percent equation to find the amount of discount.

$a = p\% \cdot b$ Write the percent equation.

$= 30\% \cdot 38.50$ Substitute 30 for p and 38.50 for b.

$= 0.30 \cdot 38.50$ Write the percent as a decimal.

$= 11.55$ Multiply.

Step 2 Find the sale price.

$\$38.50 - \$11.55 = \$26.95$

The sale price of the shirt is $26.95.

Think

How can a model help you visualize finding a part or base?
Use the model below to help you visualize finding the part in the equation $a = 30\% \cdot 38.50$.

Got It? 3. A family sells a car to a dealership for 60% less than they paid for it. They paid $9000 for the car. For what price did they sell the car?

Think

Will 125% of a number be greater than the number?
Yes. When you multiply a number by a percent greater than 100%, the part will be greater than the base, as shown in the model below.

```
0          b    17.5
|----------|-----|
0%      100% 125%
```

Problem 4 Finding a Base

125% of what number is 17.5?

$a = p\% \cdot b$ Write the percent equation.

$17.5 = 125\% \cdot b$ Substitute 17.5 for a and 125 for p.

$17.5 = 1.25 \cdot b$ Write the percent as a decimal.

$14 = b$ Divide each side by 1.25.

125% of 14 is 17.5.

Got It? 4. 30% of what number is 12.5? Solve the problem using the percent equation. Then solve the problem using the percent proportion.

A common application of percents is simple interest, which is interest you earn on only the principal in an account.

take note

Key Concept Simple Interest Formula

The simple interest formula is given below, where I is the interest, P is the principal, r is the annual interest rate written as a decimal, and t is the time in years.

Algebra $I = Prt$

Example If you invest $50 at a simple interest rate of 3.5% per year for 3 years, the interest you earn is $I = 50(0.035)(3) = \$5.25$.

Problem 3
This problem does not associate the word "of" with the base. Students need to determine the part and the base by the context of the problem.

Q What is known? **[percent, the whole cost]**
Q What do you need to find? **[part: sale price]**
Q Why is Step 2 necessary? **[You need to subtract the discount from the original price.]**

Got It?

Q If 60% represents the discount, what does 40% represent? **[the cost after the discount is applied]**
Q What is an equation that solves this problem in one step? **[x = 0.40(9000)]**

Problem 4
Some students struggle with the concept that the part can be greater than the base. This problem illustrates that possibility by using 125%.

Q How is this problem different from previous problems? **[You are looking for the base.]**
Q Here, the part is greater than the base. Why? **[The percent is greater than 100.]**

Got It?

Q What are differences in the methods? **[One uses a percent written as a decimal in an equation. The other uses a proportion.]**

Take Note
Before introducing this formula, ensure that students understand interest and principal.

Q If you put $1000 into a savings account giving 3% interest each year, how much interest will you have earned at the end of one year? **[$30]**

Additional Problems

1. What percent of 90 is 63?
ANSWER 70%

2. What percent of 90 is 76.5? Use the percent equation.
ANSWER 85%

3. A sweater that normally costs $49.99 is on sale for 25% off. What is the sale price of the sweater?
ANSWER $37.49

4. 77% of what number is 77?
ANSWER 100

5. You deposit $650 in a savings account that earns a simple interest rate of 5% per year. You want to keep the money in the account for 5 years. How much interest will you earn? Check your answer for reasonableness.
ANSWER $162.50

Answers

Got It? (continued)
3. $3600
4. $41\frac{2}{3}$

Q Using the list on this page, what is the fraction equivalent of the sum of 100% and 25%? **[$1\frac{1}{4}$]**

Q What is the fraction equivalent of 75% plus 75%? **[$1\frac{1}{2}$]**

Q If you had $1\frac{1}{2}$ times as many oranges as your friend, what percent of your friend's oranges would you have? if you had twice as many oranges? **[150%, 200%]**

Problem 5

Q What is known? **[principal, rate, time]**

Q In the check for reasonableness, what does $\frac{1}{20}$ represent? **[It is the fraction equivalent of 5%. Since 20 is a factor of 840, it is convenient to use $\frac{1}{20}$.]**

Got It?

Q How is the given information different from Problem 5? **[You know the amount of the interest but not the length of time.]**

Q Do you have everything you need? **[yes]**

Take Note

Q Do you need to memorize these three different types of percent problems? Why? **[No; this summary is shown only for comparison of methods.]**

When you solve problems involving percents, it is helpful to know fraction equivalents for common percents. You can use the fractions to check your answers for reasonableness. Here are some common percents represented as fractions.

$1\% = \frac{1}{100}$ $\quad$ $5\% = \frac{1}{20}$ $\quad$ $10\% = \frac{1}{10}$ $\quad$ $20\% = \frac{1}{5}$ $\quad$ $25\% = \frac{1}{4}$

$33.\overline{3}\% = \frac{1}{3}$ $\quad$ $50\% = \frac{1}{2}$ $\quad$ $66.\overline{6}\% = \frac{2}{3}$ $\quad$ $75\% = \frac{3}{4}$ $\quad$ $100\% = 1$

Problem 5   Using the Simple Interest Formula

Finance You deposited $840 in a savings account that earns a simple interest rate of 4.5% per year. You want to keep the money in the account for 4 years. How much interest will you earn? Check your answer for reasonableness.

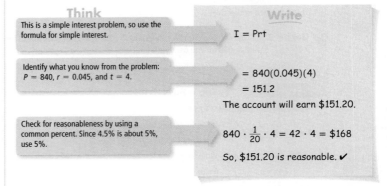

Think

This is a simple interest problem, so use the formula for simple interest.

Identify what you know from the problem: $P = 840$, $r = 0.045$, and $t = 4$.

Check for reasonableness by using a common percent. Since 4.5% is about 5%, use 5%.

Write

$I = Prt$

$= 840(0.045)(4)$

$= 151.2$

The account will earn $151.20.

$840 \cdot \frac{1}{20} \cdot 4 = 42 \cdot 4 = \$168$

So, $151.20 is reasonable. ✔

Got It? **5.** You deposited $125 in a savings account that earns a simple interest rate of 1.75% per year. You earned a total of $8.75 in interest. For how long was your money in the account?

take note

Concept Summary   Solving Percent Problems

Problem Type	Example	Proportion	Equation
Find a percent.	What percent of 6.3 is 3.5?	$\frac{3.5}{6.3} = \frac{p}{100}$	$3.5 = p\% \cdot 6.3$
Find a part.	What is 32% of 125?	$\frac{a}{125} = \frac{32}{100}$	$a = 32\% \cdot 125$
Find a base.	25% of what number is 11?	$\frac{11}{b} = \frac{25}{100}$	$11 = 25\% \cdot b$

Answers

Got It? (continued)

5. 4 yr

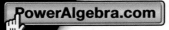

3 Lesson Check

For a digital lesson check, use the Got It questions.

Support in Algebra 1 Companion
• Lesson Check

4 Practice

Assign homework to individual students or to an entire class.

Lesson Check

Do you know HOW?

1. What percent of 70 is 21?

2. What percent of 50 is 60?

3. What is 35% of 80?

4. 75% of what number is 36?

5. **Finance** How much interest will you earn by investing $1200 at a simple interest rate of 2.5% per year for 6 years?

Do you UNDERSTAND?

6. **Vocabulary** Complete: *p*% is equivalent to a fraction with a numerator of *p* and a denominator of __?__ .

7. **Reasoning** You deposited money in a savings account paying 4% simple interest per year. The first year, you earned $75 in interest. How much interest will you earn during the following year?

8. **Open-Ended** Give an example of a percent problem where the part is greater than the base.

Practice and Problem-Solving Exercises

A Practice   Find each percent.   ◀ **See Problems 1 and 2.**

9. What percent of 75 is 15?

10. What percent of 15 is 75?

11. What percent of 16 is 10?

12. What percent of 32 is 40?

13. What percent of 48 is 20?

14. What percent of 88 is 88?

Find each part.   ◀ **See Problem 3.**

15. What is 25% of 144?

16. What is 63% of 150?

17. What is 12.5% of 104?

18. What is 150% of 63?

19. What is 125% of 12.8?

20. What is 1% of 1?

21. **Shopping** A tennis racket normally costs $65. The tennis racket is on sale for 20% off. What is the sale price of the tennis racket?

22. **Hair Care** A beauty salon buys bottles of styling gel for $4.50 per bottle and marks up the price by 40%. For what price does the salon sell each bottle?

Find each base.   ◀ **See Problem 4.**

23. 20% of what number is 80?

24. 80% of what number is 20?

25. 60% of what number is 13.5?

26. 160% of what number is 200?

27. 150% of what number is 34?

28. 1% of what number is 1?

29. **Finance** You deposit $1200 in a savings account that earns simple interest at a rate of 3% per year. How much interest will you have earned after 3 years?   ◀ **See Problem 5.**

30. **Finance** You deposit $150 in a savings account that earns simple interest at a rate of 5.5% per year. How much interest will you have earned after 4 years?

PowerAlgebra.com   Lesson 2-9   Percents   141

---

3 Lesson Check

Do you know HOW?
- Help students who are uncertain about how to write the proportion to make percent representations like those shown in the lesson.

Do you UNDERSTAND?
- Note that an answer to Exercise 8 has already been seen in Problem 4 in the lesson.

Close
This lesson focused on two methods to use when working with percent problems: the Percent Proportion Method and the Percent Equation method.

Q Which method do you prefer? Explain your reasoning. **[Answers may vary. Sample: I prefer the Percent Equation method because I can convert the words directly into a mathematical sentence.]**

Answers

Lesson Check

1. 30%
2. 120%
3. 28
4. 48
5. $180
6. 100
7. $75
8. Answers may vary. Sample: 12 is what percent of 10?

Practice and Problem-Solving Exercises

9. 20%
10. 500%
11. 62.5%
12. 125%
13. $41\frac{2}{3}$%
14. 100%
15. 36
16. 94.5
17. 13
18. 94.5
19. 16
20. 0.01
21. $52
22. $6.30
23. 400
24. 25
25. 22.5
26. 125
27. $22\frac{2}{3}$
28. 100
29. $108
30. $33

4 Practice

ASSIGNMENT GUIDE

Basic: 9–30 all, 32–36 even, 37, 38, 40–44 even, 45, 47–49

Average: 9–29 odd, 31–51

Advanced: 9–29 odd, 31–53

Standardized Test Prep: 54–56

Mixed Review: 57–62

Reasoning exercises have blue headings.

Applications exercises have red headings.

EXERCISE 49: Use the Think About a Plan worksheet in the **Practice and Problem Solving Workbook** (also available in the Teaching Resources in print and online) to further support students' development in becoming independent learners.

HOMEWORK QUICK CHECK

To check students' understanding of key skills and concepts, go over Exercises 13, 25, 45, 48, and 49.

 Apply

Tell whether you are finding a *percent*, a *part*, or a *base*. Then solve.

31. What is 9% of 56? **32.** What percent of 36 is 96? **33.** What is 95% of 150?

34. What is 175% of 64? **35.** What percent of 30 is 400? **36.** 60 is 250% of what number?

37. Geography Water covers approximately 11,800 mi² of Florida, which is about 18% of Florida's area. What is the total area of Florida to the nearest thousand square miles?

38. Finance A student has $1500 to deposit in a savings account. What is the lowest rate that would allow the student to earn $95 in simple interest in a year?

Ⓐ 5.5%
Ⓑ 6.25%
Ⓒ 6.33%
Ⓓ 7%

Solve using mental math.

39. 20% of 80 is __?__. **40.** 120 is 200% of __?__. **41.** 30 is __?__% of 40.

Tell which is greater, A or B. Assume A and B are positive numbers.

42. A is 20% of B. **43.** 150% of A is B. **44.** B is 90% of A.

45. Think About a Plan The United States Mint reported at the end of 2006 that the unit cost of producing and distributing a penny was 1.21¢. What percent of the value of a penny is this cost? What can you conclude about the cost of making pennies?
• How can a model help you to visualize the problem?
• How can you use a proportion or the percent equation to solve the problem?

46. Economics Would you produce an item if the cost of producing and distributing the item is more than 100% of its value? Explain your answer.

47. Error Analysis A student was asked to make up and solve a percent problem, so the student wrote, "What percent of 1.5 is 3?" and solved it as shown at the right. Describe and correct the error in the student's solution.

$$\frac{a}{b} = \frac{p}{100}$$
$$\frac{1.5}{3} = \frac{p}{100}$$
$$150 = 3p$$
$$50 = p$$
3 is 50% of 1.5.

48. Writing Part of a bottle of water has been consumed. Write the steps needed to determine the percent of water that has been consumed.

49. Finance A savings account earns simple interest at a rate of 6% per year. Last year the account earned $10.86 in interest. What was the balance in the account at the beginning of last year?

50. Furniture A furniture store offers a set of furniture for $990. You can also purchase the set on an installment plan for 24 payments of $45 each. If you choose the installment plan, what percent of the original price will you have paid when you finish? Round to the nearest percent.

Answers

Practice and Problem-Solving Exercises
(continued)

31. part; 5.04

32. percent; $266\frac{2}{3}$

33. part; 142.5

34. part; 112

35. percent; $1333\frac{1}{3}$

36. base; 24

37. 66,000 mi²

38. C

39. 16

40. 60

41. 75

42. B

43. B

44. A

45. 121%; it costs more to make a penny than the penny is worth.

46. No; it would cost more to produce the item than you would make from selling it, so you would never make a profit.

47. The values for a and b are reversed; $\frac{3}{1.5} = \frac{p}{100}$, $1.5p = 300$, $p = 200\%$.

48. Answers may vary. Sample: Determine the amount of water that was originally in the bottle. Then determine the amount of water consumed. Find what percent of the original amount of water was consumed.

49. $181

50. about 109%

51. Geometry Each grid square in the figure at the right is the same size. What percent of the figure is red?

 Challenge

52. Shopping Marcia buys a dress that is on sale for 15% off its original price. She uses a store coupon to obtain an additional 10% off the sale price. Marcia pays $91.80 for the dress. What was the original price of the dress?

53. Public Transportation In Mr. Ferreira's class, 80% of the students live more than half a mile from school. Of those students, 80% come to school by public transportation. Of the students using public transportation, 75% take the bus, and 75% of those students buy monthly bus passes. Nine students buy monthly bus passes. How many students are in Mr. Ferreira's class?

Standardized Test Prep

SAT/ACT

54. A rare disease has been discovered that affects 2 out of every 10,000 trees in a forest. What percent of trees are affected?

  (A) 0.0002%   (B) 0.002%   (C) 0.02%   (D) 0.2%

55. One kilometer equals about $\frac{5}{8}$ mi. A European racecar driver is driving at 120 km/h. Approximately what is this speed in miles per hour?

  (F) 75 mi/h   (G) 100 mi/h   (H) 160 mi/h   (I) 192 mi/h

56. What is the solution of $\frac{x}{2} + \frac{x}{3} - 15 = 0$?

  (A) 12   (B) 18   (C) 24   (D) 30

Mixed Review

57. Art A painting 36 cm wide and 22.5 cm tall is going to be reproduced on a postcard. The image on the postcard will be 9 cm tall. How wide will the image be?   ◀ See Lesson 2-8.

58. Cats Alexis's cat eats 3 cans of cat food every 5 days. Alexis is going away for 30 days. A friend has offered to feed her cat. How many cans of cat food must Alexis leave for her cat while she is away?   ◀ See Lesson 2-7.

59. Taxis A taxi charges $1.75 for the first $\frac{1}{8}$ mi and $.30 for each additional $\frac{1}{8}$ mi. Write an equation that gives the cost c of a taxi ride in terms of the number of miles m. How many miles did you travel if a ride costs $7.75?   ◀ See Lesson 2-7.

Get Ready! To prepare for Lesson 2-10, do Exercises 60–62.

Solve each percent problem.   ◀ See Lesson 2-9.

60. What percent of 8 is 100?   **61.** What is 20% of 3?   **62.** 35 is what percent of 20?

PowerAlgebra.com   Lesson 2-9 Percents   143

51. $29\frac{1}{6}\%$
52. $120
53. 25 students
54. C
55. F
56. B
57. 14.4 cm
58. 18 cans
59. $c = 1.75 + 2.4\left(m - \frac{1}{8}\right)$; $2\frac{5}{8}$
60. 1250%
61. 0.6
62. 175%

Additional Instructional Support

Algebra 1 Companion

Students can use the **Algebra 1 Companion** worktext (4 pages) as you teach the lesson. Use the Companion to support

- New Vocabulary
- Key Concepts
- Got It for each Problem
- Lesson Check

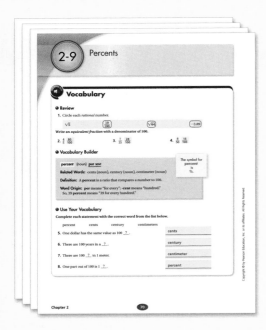

ELL Support

Connect to Prior Knowledge Distribute grid paper with 100 squares. Ask: How many squares are on the grid paper? (100) Ask students to shade 15 squares red, 22 squares blue, and 8 squares green. Remind them that a fraction names part of a whole. A percent is another way to represent part of a whole. A percent is a special kind of ratio in which the first term is compared to 100. If $\frac{15}{100}$ of the paper is shaded red, then you can say 15% of the paper is shaded red. What percent names the part of the paper shaded blue? (22%) What percent names the part of the paper shaded green? (8%)

5 Assess & Remediate

Lesson Quiz

1. What percent of 80 is 52?
2. What percent of 50 is 125? Use the percent equation.
3. $88 tickets to the Miami Dolphins game are offered at a 15% discount. What is the sale price?
4. 125% of what number is 12.5?
5. **Do you UNDERSTAND?** You deposit $900 in a savings account that earns a simple interest rate of 4.5% per year. You calculate you will earn $1215 interest over 3 years. Is your answer reasonable?

ANSWERS TO LESSON QUIZ

1. 65
2. 250
3. $74.80
4. 10
5. Answers may vary. Sample: No; the interest will be much less than the total in the account.

PRESCRIPTION FOR REMEDIATION
Use the student work on the Lesson Quiz to prescribe a differentiated review assignment.

Points	Differentiated Remediation
0–2	Intervention
3–4	On-level
5	Extension

PowerAlgebra.com

5 Assess & Remediate

Assign the Lesson Quiz. Appropriate intervention, practice, or enrichment is automatically generated based on student performance.

Intervention

- **Reteaching** (2 pages) Provides reteaching and practice exercises for the key lesson concepts. Use with struggling students or absent students.
- **English Language Learner Support** Helps students develop and reinforce mathematical vocabulary and key concepts.

All-in-One Resources/Online
Reteaching

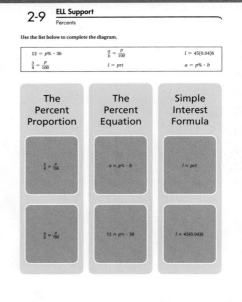

All-in-One Resources/Online
English Language Learner Support

Differentiated Remediation *continued*

On-Level

- **Practice** (2 pages) Provides extra practice for each lesson. For simpler practice exercises, use the Form K Practice pages found in the All-in-One Teaching Resources and online.

- **Think About a Plan** Helps students develop specific problem-solving skills and strategies by providing scaffolded guiding questions.

- **Standardized Test Prep** Focuses on all major exercises, all major question types, and helps students prepare for the high-stakes assessments.

Extension

- **Enrichment** Provides students with interesting problems and activities that extend the concepts of the lesson.

- **Activities, Games, and Puzzles** Worksheets that can be used for concepts development, enrichment, and for fun!

Practice and Problem Solving WKBK/All-in-One Resources/Online
Practice page 1

2-9 Practice — Form G
Percents

Find each percent.

1. What percent of 42 is 28?
$66\frac{2}{3}\%$

2. What percent of 48 is 18?
37.5%

3. What percent of 150 is 350?
$233\frac{1}{3}\%$

4. What percent of 99 is 72?
73%

5. What percent of 15 is 12?
80

6. What percent of 120 is 200?
$166\frac{2}{3}\%$

Find each part.

7. What is 75% of 180?
136

8. What is 40% of 720?
288

9. What is 125% of 62?
77.5

10. What is 50% of 821?
410.5

11. What is 2.75% of 20?
0.55

12. What is 16.5% of 33?
5.445

13. A set of golf clubs that costs $600 are on sale for 40% off the regular price. What is the sale price of the clubs? $360

14. A discount store marks up the merchandise it sells by 55%. If the wholesale price of a particular item is $25, what should the retail price be set at? $38.75

15. A used car lot runs sales at the end of the year to reduce inventory. This year the sale price is 15% less than the regular price. If the regular price of a car is $12,000, what is the sale price of the car? $10,200

Practice and Problem Solving WKBK/All-in-One Resources/Online
Practice page 2

2-9 Practice (continued) — Form G
Percents

Find each base.

16. 60% of what number is 75?
125

17. 115% of what number is 120?
about 104.3

18. 15% of what number is 6.75?
45

19. 5% of what number is 4.1?
82

20. 68% of what number is 64.6?
95

21. 65% of what number is 577.2?
888

22. If you deposit $800 in a savings account that earns simple interest at a rate of 1.5% per year, how much interest will you have earned after 5 years? 760

23. When Marty was born, his parents deposited $5000 in a college savings account that earns simple interest at a rate of 7.25% per year. How much interest will the money have earned after 18 years? $6525

24. You have $10,000 to deposit in a savings account that earns simple interest at a rate of 4.5% per year. How much interest will be in the account after 2 years? $900

Tell whether you are finding a *percent*, a *part*, or a *base*. Then solve.

25. What is 25% of 50?
a part; 12.5

26. What percent of 18 is 63?
a percent; 350%

27. What is 133% of 90?
a part; 119.7

28. What is 44% of 88?
a part; 38.72

29. What percent of 67 is 26.8?
a percent; 40%

30. 42 is 14% of what number?
the base; 300

Practice and Problem Solving WKBK/All-in-One Resources/Online
Think About a Plan

2-9 Think About a Plan
Percents

Finance A savings account earns simple interest at a rate of 6% per year. Last year the account earned $10.86 in interest. What was the balance in the account at the beginning of last year?

Understanding the Problem

1. What is the formula for finding simple interest?
$I = Prt$

2. What values are given in terms of the formula you wrote in Step 1?
interest, rate, time

Planning the Solution

3. Substitute the given values into the formula for simple interest.
$10.81 = P(0.06)(1)$

Getting an Answer

4. Solve for the unknown value.
$181.00

5. Is your answer reasonable? Explain.
yes; 6% of $200 is $12, so 6% of $181.00 would be about $12.

6. What does your solution mean?
There was $181.00 in the account.

Practice and Problem Solving WKBK/All-in-One Resources/Online
Standardized Test Prep

2-9 Standardized Test Prep
Percents

Multiple Choice

For Exercises 1–5, choose the correct letter.

1. What percent of 92 is 23? C
A. 0.25% B. 4% C. 25% D. 400%

2. 60% of a number is 66. Which proportion best represents this relationship? F
F. $\frac{66}{x} = \frac{60}{100}$ G. $\frac{x}{66} = \frac{60}{100}$ H. $\frac{60}{x} = \frac{66}{100}$ I. $\frac{60}{66} = \frac{x}{100}$

3. A store is having a clearance sale where merchandise on the sales racks is reduced by 80% from the original price. If a jacket was originally priced at $76, what is the sale price? A
A. $15.20 B. $24.20 C. $60.80 D. $72.40

4. If you deposit $3000 in a savings account that earns simple interest at a rate of 2.5% per year, how much interest will you have earned after 4 years? G
F. $30 G. $300 H. $3000 I. $30,000

5. Five years ago you deposited a sum of money into a savings account which has earned $150 in interest. The interest rate for the account is 3% simple interest per year. How much money was originally deposited in the account? C
A. $22.50 B. $100 C. $1000 D. $10,000

Short Response

6. There are 3200 students at Martinsville High School. There are 575 students involved in athletics during the spring athletic seasons. What proportion represents the percent of students not involved in athletics during the spring season? What percent of students is not involved in athletics?
$\frac{2625}{3200} = \frac{p}{100}$; about 82%
[2] Both parts answered correctly.
[1] One part answered correctly.
[0] Neither part answered correctly.

All-in-One Resources/Online
Enrichment

2-9 Enrichment
Percents

Compound Interest and Annual Percentage Yield

When money is invested in some types of accounts, such as savings accounts or certificates of deposit, the interest is compounded. This means that interest is paid at intervals, such as monthly, quarterly, or yearly. The interest is added to the account, and interest is then earned on the interest that has already been paid. For every $100 invested in an account paying 6% interest, compounded twice per year, the interest earned is $6.09. This represents a rate of 6.09%, because of the compounding.

The name for the effective percent earned on an account where the interest is compounded is annual percentage yield (APY). It tells what percent of an original investment you will earn in a year.

The equation that expresses this percent is APY $= \left(1 + \frac{i}{n}\right)^n - 1$, where i is the advertised interest rate (written as a decimal) and n is the number of compounding periods per year. The result is the percent, written as a decimal. Using the example above, with $i = 0.06$ and $n = 2$:

APY $= \left(1 + \frac{0.06}{2}\right)^2 - 1$
$= 1.0609 - 1$
$= 0.0609$
$= 6.09\%$

For Exercises 1–4, determine the annual percentage yield (APY).

1. 8% interest rate, 2 compounding periods per year 8.16%

2. 8% interest rate, 4 compounding periods per year 8.24%

3. 8% interest rate, 6 compounding periods per year 8.27%

4. 8% interest rate, 12 compounding periods per year 8.30%

5. What do you notice about the APY as the number of compounding periods increases? the APY increases

6. What is the relationship between the interest rate and the APY when the number of compounding periods is 1? What does this mean?
they are the same; the interest is simple interest

Online Teacher Resource Center
Activities, Games, and Puzzles

2-9 Game: Greater Than or Less Than?
Percents

Twenty-four percent problems are listed below. Players take turns challenging each other by choosing a question that must be answered using mental math. A problem can only be selected once. Two racetracks are provided at the bottom of the page. Players fill in a block for each correct answer. Players must agree on the correct answer. The first player to complete the course wins! If neither player completes the course, then the player who advances the farthest wins.

1. Is 20% of 200 greater than or less than 100? less than
2. Is 25% of 80 greater than or less than10? greater than
3. Is 2% of 1000 greater than or less than 30? less than
4. Is 75% of 8 greater than or less than 5? greater than
5. Is 80% of 20 greater than or less than 10? greater than
6. Is 30% of 70 greater than or less than 15? greater than
7. Is 90% of 120 greater than or less than 110? less than
8. Is 5% of 40 greater than or less than 3? less than
9. Is 150% of 2 greater than or less than 4? less than
10. Is 18% of 18 greater than or less than 9? less than
11. Is 70% of 70 greater than or less than 50? greater than
12. Is 25% of 15 greater than or less than 7? less than
13. Is 43% of 33 greater than or less than 11? greater than
14. Is 55% of 80 greater than or less than 40? greater than
15. Is 20% of 18 greater than or less than 8? less than
16. Is 60% of 45 greater than or less than 22? greater than
17. Is 1% of 180 greater than or less than 2? less than
18. Is 72% of 80 greater than or less than 60? less than
19. Is 30% of 180 greater than or less than 100? greater than
20. Is 95% of 70 greater than or less than 35? greater than
21. Is 10% of 800 greater than or less than 70? greater than
22. Is 66% of 6 greater than or less than 4? less than
23. Is 67% of 15 greater than or less than 10? greater than
24. Is 25% of 800 greater than or less than 100? greater than

Player 1 [ ][ ][ ][ ][ ][ ][ ][ ][ ][ ][ ][ ]
Player 2 [ ][ ][ ][ ][ ][ ][ ][ ][ ][ ][ ][ ]

1 Interactive Learning

Solve It!

PURPOSE To use knowledge of percent change to compare prices of sale items

PROCESS Students may calculate the new sweater price, compare both discounts in dollars, or find the percent discount in each store

FACILITATE

Q How can you find the sale price of each sweater? **[Answers may vary. Sample: Find the discount and subtract it from the original price.]**

Q If the sweaters cost $20, which is the better sale? Why? **[the first store since $5.00 off $20 is 25%]**

ANSWER See Solve It in Answers on next page.

CONNECT THE MATH One discount is given in percent, and the other in dollars. To be compared, one needs to be converted. Converting to and from percent change is the focus of this lesson.

2 Guided Instruction

Take Note

Q What is the denominator of the ratio? **[original amount]**

This is always the case. The original amount represents the whole before any change.

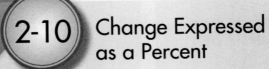

2-10 Change Expressed as a Percent

Objectives To find percent change
To find the relative error in linear and nonlinear measurements

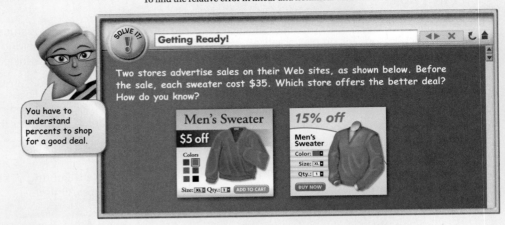

You have to understand percents to shop for a good deal.

Getting Ready!

Two stores advertise sales on their Web sites, as shown below. Before the sale, each sweater cost $35. Which store offers the better deal? How do you know?

In the Solve It, the 15% discount is a percent change in the price of the sweater. A **percent change** expresses an amount of change as a percent of an original amount. In this lesson, you will learn how to calculate a percent change.

Lesson Vocabulary
- percent change
- percent increase
- percent decrease
- relative error
- percent error

Essential Understanding You can find a percent change when you know the original amount and how much it has changed.

If a new amount is greater than the original amount, the percent change is called a **percent increase**. If the new amount is less than the original amount, the percent change is called a **percent decrease**.

Key Concept   Percent Change

Percent change is the ratio of the amount of change to the original amount.

$$\text{percent change, } p\% = \frac{\text{amount of increase or decrease}}{\text{original amount}}$$

- amount of increase = new amount − original amount
- amount of decrease = original amount − new amount

2-10 Preparing to Teach

BIG idea Proportionality   **UbD**

ESSENTIAL UNDERSTANDINGS
- When the original amount and how much it is changed is known, a percent change can be found.
- Relative error is the ratio of the absolute value of the difference of a measured (or estimated) value and an actual value, compared to the actual value.

Math Background

Help students understand that all measurements are approximations and have some degree of error. The accuracy of our instruments determines the

amount of error. If you use a yardstick to measure the width of the section of the sidewalk, you may see that the width is 2 feet 6 inches. If you have a more refined ruler you may measure that width to be 2 feet and 6.4 inches. The more refined the measuring unit, the closer the measure comes to the actual measure.

Support Student Learning

Use the **Algebra I Companion** to engage and support students during instruction. See Lesson Resources at the end of this lesson for details.

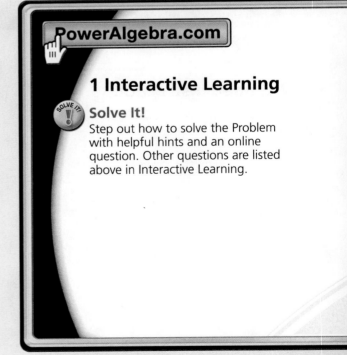

PowerAlgebra.com

1 Interactive Learning

Solve It!

Step out how to solve the Problem with helpful hints and an online question. Other questions are listed above in Interactive Learning.

A common example of finding a percent decrease is finding a percent discount. In this lesson, round your answers to the nearest percent, if necessary.

 Problem 1 Finding a Percent Decrease

Clothing A coat is on sale. The original price of the coat is $82. The sale price is $74.50. What is the discount expressed as a percent change?

Think

Does this problem involve a percent decrease or a percent increase?
The new amount is less than the original amount, so the problem involves a percent decrease.

$$\text{percent change} = \frac{\text{amount of increase or decrease}}{\text{original amount}}$$

$$= \frac{\text{original amount} - \text{new amount}}{\text{original amount}}$$ This is a percent decrease. Write the appropriate ratio.

$$= \frac{82 - 74.50}{82}$$ Substitute.

$$= \frac{7.5}{82}$$ Simplify.

$$\approx 0.09, \text{ or } 9\%$$ Write the result as a percent.

The price of the coat decreased by about 9%.

Got It? **1.** The average monthly precipitation for Chicago, Illinois, peaks in June at 4.1 in. The average monthly precipitation in December is 2.8 in. What is the percent decrease from June to December?

A common example of finding a percent increase is finding a percent markup.

 Problem 2 Finding a Percent Increase

Music A store buys an electric guitar for $295. The store then marks up the price of the guitar to $340. What is the markup expressed as a percent change?

Think

Have you seen a problem like this one?
Yes. Finding percent increase is like finding percent decrease. The difference is in calculating the amount of increase or decrease.

$$\text{percent change} = \frac{\text{amount of increase or decrease}}{\text{original amount}}$$

$$= \frac{\text{new amount} - \text{original amount}}{\text{original amount}}$$ This is a percent increase. Write the appropriate ratio.

$$= \frac{340 - 295}{295}$$ Substitute.

$$= \frac{45}{295}$$ Simplify.

$$\approx 0.15 \text{ or } 15\%$$ Write the result as a percent.

The price of the guitar increased by about 15%.

Got It? **2.** In one year, the toll for passenger cars to use a tunnel rose from $3 to $3.50. What was the percent increase?

Problem 1
Find the percent decrease given the original price and new price.

Q What do you know? **[original price of the coat and the sale price]**

Q How can you tell if this is a percent increase or percent decrease problem? **[If values are going up, it is an increase. In Problem 1, prices are going down, so you are working with percent decrease.]**

Q What does the numerator represent? **[the change, or difference in the two prices]**

Got It?

Q What is the actual decrease in precipitation? Will this amount be the numerator or denominator in the ratio? **[1.3; numerator]**

Q How do you decide what the denominator should be? **[the original amount of 4.1]**

Problem 2
Find the percent increase given the original price and new price.

Q How is this problem different than Problem 1? **[The prices are increasing.]**

Q What are you asked to find? **[the markup expressed as a percent of change]**

Q Do you need any other information? **[Yes, the difference in the two prices.]**

Got It?

Q In another city, the tolls rose from $7.00 to $7.75. Which city had the higher percent of increase? **[the city that increased the tolls $0.50]**

---

2 Guided Instruction

 Each Problem is worked out and supported online.

Problem 1
Finding a Percent Decrease

Alternative Problem 1
Finding a Percent Decrease
Animated

Problem 2
Finding a Percent Increase
Animated

Problem 3
Finding Percent Error

Problem 4
Finding Minimum and Maximum Dimensions
Animated

Problem 5
Finding the Greatest Possible Percent Error

Support in Algebra 1 Companion
• Vocabulary
• Key Concepts
• Got It?

Answers

Solve It!
The store that offers 15% off; explanations may vary.

Got It?
1. about 32%
2. about 17%

Q What statement can you make that compares estimated values to exact values using the word percent? **[Sample: I got 90% of the problems correct that I thought I knew.]**

Take Note

Q What is the connection between the terms "relative error" and "percent error"? **[When relative error is expressed as percent, it is called percent error.]**

When finding percent error, students need to change the decimal to a percent as the last step.

Q Why is the absolute value sign used in this equation? **[You are not concerned whether the estimate is over or under the actual value. The absolute value ensures the result is a positive value after finding the difference.]**

Review absolute value, the distance a number is located from zero on the number line.

ERROR PREVENTION

Note that absolute value bars do not have the same properties as do parentheses. Whereas $-(-3) = +3$, the absolute value result is: $-|-3| = -3$.

Problem 3

Q What do you know? **[the estimated length and width, and the actual length and width]**
Q What are you looking for? **[percent error]**

Got It?

Q What do you know? **[estimate and actual distance]**
Q What equation will solve this problem? **[percent error $= \frac{|5.5 - 4.75|}{4.75}$]**

Essential Understanding You can use percents to compare estimated or measured values to actual or exact values.

 Key Concept **Relative Error**

Relative error is the ratio of the absolute value of the difference of a measured (or estimated) value and an actual value compared to the actual value.

$$\text{relative error} = \frac{|\text{measured or estimated value} - \text{actual value}|}{\text{actual value}}$$

When relative error is expressed as a percent, it is called **percent error.**

 Problem 3 **Finding Percent Error**

Multiple Choice A decorator estimates that a rectangular rug is 5 ft by 8 ft. The rug is actually 4 ft by 8 ft. What is the percent error in the estimated area?

Ⓐ 0.25%   Ⓑ 20%   Ⓒ 25%   Ⓓ 80%

Think

What does the percent error tell you?
The percent error tells how accurate a measurement or estimate is.

$\text{percent error} = \frac{|\text{estimated value} - \text{actual value}|}{\text{actual value}}$ Write the ratio.

$= \frac{|5(8) - 4(8)|}{4(8)}$ Substitute.

$= \frac{|40 - 32|}{32}$ Multiply.

$= \frac{8}{32}$ Simplify.

$= 0.25$, or 25%   Write the result as a percent.

The estimated area is off by 25%. The correct answer is C.

Got It? **3.** You think that the distance between your house and a friend's house is 5.5 mi. The actual distance is 4.75 mi. What is the percent error in your estimation?

In Problem 3, the actual measurements were known. Often you don't know actual measurements, but you know how precise your measurements can be.

Think about the last time you used a ruler. Because the precision of a ruler is limited, you measured to the nearest unit or fraction of a unit, such as centimeters or quarter inches. The most any measurement can be off by is one half of the unit used in measuring.

Additional Problems

1. A popular hybrid car cost $21,500 in 2008. As hybrids became more affordable, the price dropped to $19,780. What is the decrease expressed as a percent change?

ANSWER 8%

2. In 1990 there were 1330 registered alpacas in the United States. By 2008 there were 53,000. What is the increase expressed as a percent change?

ANSWER about 3885%

3. A cube's volume is estimated to be 8 cm³. When measured, each side was 2.1 cm in length. What is the percent error in the estimated volume?

ANSWER about 13.6%

4. A student's height is measured as 144 cm to the nearest centimeter. What are the student's minimum and maximum possible heights?

ANSWER 143.5 cm, 144.5 cm

5. What is the greatest possible percent error in calculating the volume for a cube with a side measured at 2.1 cm?

ANSWER about 7.3%

Answers

Got It? (continued)
3. about 16%

Problem 4 Finding Minimum and Maximum Dimensions

Think

Can a measurement be off by more than one half of the unit that is used?
No, not if you measure correctly. Suppose you measure a length as 8 in. If you were off by 0.5 in. or more, you would have rounded to either 7 in. or 9 in.

Posters You are framing a poster and measure the length of the poster as 18.5 in., to the nearest half inch. What are the minimum and maximum possible lengths of the poster?

You measured to the nearest 0.5 in., so the greatest possible error is 0.25 in.

Minimum length = measured value − possible error = 18.5 − 0.25 = 18.25
Maximum length = measured value + possible error = 18.5 + 0.25 = 18.75

The minimum possible length is 18.25 in. The maximum is 18.75 in.

✓ **Got It? 4.** A student's height is measured as 66 in. to the nearest inch. What are the student's minimum and maximum possible heights?

 Problem 5 Finding the Greatest Possible Percent Error

Crafts The diagram at the right shows the dimensions of a gift box to the nearest inch. What is the greatest possible percent error in calculating the volume of the gift box?

5 in.
12 in.
6 in.

Know
- The dimensions of the gift box to the nearest inch
- The formula for volume: $V = \ell wh$
- The greatest possible error in each dimension is 0.5 in.

Need
The greatest possible percent error in calculating the volume

Plan
Find the minimum and maximum volumes. Find the differences between the possible volumes and the measured volume. Use the greater difference to find the percent error.

Measured volume
$$V = \ell wh$$
$$= (12)(6)(5)$$
$$= 360$$

Minimum volume
$$V = \ell wh$$
$$= (11.5)(5.5)(4.5)$$
$$= 284.625$$

Maximum volume
$$V = \ell wh$$
$$= (12.5)(6.5)(5.5)$$
$$= 446.875$$

Find the differences.

$$|\text{minimum volume} - \text{measured volume}| = |284.625 - 360| = 75.375$$
$$|\text{maximum volume} - \text{measured volume}| = |446.875 - 360| = 86.875$$

Think

Which difference should you use?
The greater difference will result in the greatest possible percent error, so use the difference that has the greatest absolute value.

Use the greater difference to find the greatest possible percent error.

$$\text{greatest possible percent error} = \frac{\text{greater difference in volume}}{\text{measured volume}}$$

$$= \frac{86.875}{360} \quad \text{Substitute.}$$

$$\approx 0.24 \text{ or } 24\% \quad \text{Write the result as a percent.}$$

The greatest possible percent error in the volume, based on measurements to the nearest inch, is about 24%.

Problem 4
Discuss the fact that the greatest possible error in a measurement is one half of the measuring unit. It is helpful to have materials available, such as meter sticks, rulers, or cubic centimeters used in finding volume. It is important for students to realize that measurement errors occur in all measurements, not just linear measures.

Got It?

Q What are the units being used? **[in.]**
Q What is the size of the largest possible error? **[0.5 in.]**
Q If you wanted accuracy of 0.5 mm, what measuring unit should you use? **[1 mm]**

TACTILE LEARNERS
Because no measurement is exact, you always measure to the nearest "something." To illustrate the inaccuracy of measurements, have several students measure the circumference of the same circular object to the nearest millimeter. Instruct students to write the measurement on a piece of paper. Then announce the measurements aloud.

Problem 5
Have students work with partners to study this problem noting the steps taken.

Q Why is the greatest possible error 0.5 in. for each dimension? **[The dimensions are measured to the nearest inch.]**
Q Suppose you measure two cubes. The smaller one measures 18 cm on each side and the larger one measures 45 cm on each side. What is the percent error of the volume of each cube? Round to the nearest percent. **[9%, 3%]**
Q Using the same measuring unit did not yield the same percent error for the two cubes. Why? **[The larger a measure, the smaller the percent error.]**

Got It? (continued)
4. 65.5 in. and 66.5 in.

Got It?

Q What is the new greatest possible error in each dimension? **[0.25 in.]**

Q What is the greater difference in volume? **[41.953]**

Q How do you calculate the greatest possible percent error? How does this answer compare with that from Problem 5? $[\frac{41,953}{360}$; **at 12%, the error is half of 24%.]**

3 Lesson Check

Do you know HOW?

Ask students to solve these problems independently. After trying, have them compare work in small groups. Encourage each group to use the problems illustrated in the lesson as a reference.

• **Running** refer to Problem 1
• **Cars** refer to Problem 2
• **Horses** refer to Problem 4

Do you UNDERSTAND?

• If students have difficulty with Exercise 5, have them inspect a meter stick to find the length of a tenth of a meter.

Close

Have partners choose two numbers and then answer the following:

Q What is the percent of increase between the two numbers? **[Check students' work.]**

Q What is the maximum and minimum area of a rectangle using the two numbers as the dimensions? **[Check students' work.]**

Q What is the percent error using one of the numbers as a measurement? **[Check students' work.]**

 Got It? **5. Reasoning** If the gift box's dimensions in Problem 5 were measured to the nearest half inch, how would the greatest possible error be affected?

 Lesson Check

Do you know HOW?

1. Running Last year, an athlete's average time to run a mile was 6 min 13 s. This year, the athlete's average time is 6 min 5 s. What is the percent decrease?

2. Cars A used-car dealership buys a car for $2800 and then sells it for $4500. What is the percent increase?

3. Horses A veterinarian measures a horse to be 7.5 ft tall at the shoulder to the nearest half foot. What are the minimum and maximum possible heights of the horse?

Do you UNDERSTAND?

4. Vocabulary Determine whether each situation involves a percent increase or a percent decrease.

  a. A hat that originally costs $12 sold for $9.50.

  b. You buy a CD for $10 and sell it for $8.

  c. A store buys glasses wholesale for $2 per glass. The store sells them for $4.50.

5. Reasoning What is the greatest possible error of a measurement taken to the nearest tenth of a meter?

6. Writing How is calculating percent increase different from calculating percent decrease?

 Practice and Problem-Solving Exercises

Practice Tell whether each percent change is an increase or decrease. Then find the percent change. Round to the nearest percent.   See Problems 1 and 2.

7. original amount: 12
new amount: 18

8. original amount: 9
new amount: 6

9. original amount: 15
new amount: 14

10. original amount: 7.5
new amount: 9.5

11. original amount: 40.2
new amount: 38.6

12. original amount: 2008
new amount: 1975

13. original amount: 14,500
new amount: 22,320

14. original amount: 195.50
new amount: 215.25

15. original amount: 1325.60
new amount: 1685.60

16. Employment An employee was hired at a wage of $8 per hour. After a raise, the employee earned $8.75 per hour. What was the percent increase?

17. Climate On June 1, 2007, there were about 18.75 h of daylight in Anchorage, Alaska. On November 1, 2007, there were about 8.5 h of daylight. What was the percent decrease?

Find the percent error in each estimation. Round to the nearest percent. See Problem 3.

18. You estimate that your friend's little brother is about 8 years old. He is actually 6.5 years old.

19. You estimate that your school is about 45 ft tall. Your school is actually 52 ft tall.

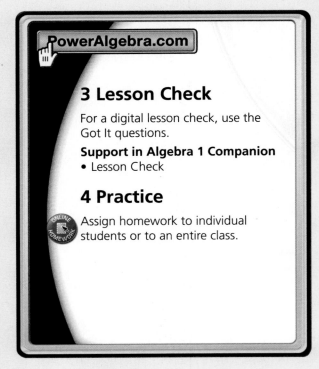

3 Lesson Check

For a digital lesson check, use the Got It questions.

Support in Algebra 1 Companion
• Lesson Check

4 Practice

Assign homework to individual students or to an entire class.

Answers

Got It? (continued)

5. It would be smaller since the measurement of each dimension is closer to the actual value of each dimension.

Lesson Check

1. about 2%
2. about 61%
3. 7.25 ft and 7.75 ft
4. a. percent decrease
  b. percent decrease
  c. percent increase
5. 0.05 m
6. A percent increase involves an increase of the original amount and a percent decrease involves a decrease of the original amount.

Practice and Problem-Solving Exercises

7. increase; 50%
8. decrease; 33%
9. decrease; 7%
10. increase; 27%
11. decrease; 4%
12. decrease; 2%
13. increase; 54%
14. increase; 10%
15. increase; 27%
16. about 9%
17. about 55%
18. about 23%
19. about 13%

A measurement is given. Find the minimum and maximum possible measurements.

 See Problem 4.

20. A doctor measures a patient's weight as 162 lb to the nearest pound.

21. An ostrich egg has a mass of 1.1 kg to the nearest tenth of a kilogram.

22. The length of an onion cell is 0.4 mm to the nearest tenth of a millimeter.

23. Geometry The table below shows the measured dimensions of a prism and the minimum and maximum possible dimensions based on the greatest possible error. What is the greatest possible percent error in finding the volume of the prism?

See Problem 5.

Dimensions	Length	Width	Height
Measured	10	6	4
Minimum	9.5	5.5	3.5
Maximum	10.5	6.5	4.5

24. Geometry The side lengths of the rectangle at the right have been measured to the nearest half of a meter, as shown. What is the greatest possible percent error in finding the area of the rectangle?

7.5 m

18.5 m

 Apply

Find the percent change. Round to the nearest percent.

25. 2 ft to $5\frac{1}{2}$ ft   **26.** 18 lb to $22\frac{1}{4}$ lb   **27.** $140\frac{1}{4}$ g to $80\frac{3}{4}$ g

28. \$8.99 to \$15.99   **29.** \$168.45 to \$234.56   **30.** \$4023.52 to \$982.13

The measured dimensions of a rectangle are given to the nearest whole unit. Find the minimum and maximum possible areas of each rectangle.

31. 7 m by 8 m   **32.** 18 in. by 15 in.   **33.** 24 ft by 22 ft

34. Writing How are percent change and percent error similar?

35. Open-Ended Write a percent change problem that you recently experienced.

36. Think About a Plan In one season, an average of 6500 fans attended each home game played by the basketball team at a college. In the next season, the average number of fans per game increased by about 12%. What was the average number of fans per game for that season?
- What is missing—the new amount or the original amount?
- How can a percent change help you find the missing amount?

37. Error Analysis A student is trying to find the percent of change when an amount increases from 12 to 18, as shown. Describe and correct the student's error.

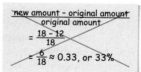

---

20. 161.5 lb; 162.5 lb
21. 1.05 kg; 1.15 kg
22. 0.35 mm; 0.45 mm
23. about 28%
24. about 5%
25. 175% increase
26. 24% increase
27. 42% decrease
28. 78% increase
29. 39% increase
30. 76% decrease

31. 48.75 m²; 63.75 m²
32. 253.75 in.²; 286.75 in.²
33. 505.25 ft²; 551.25 ft²
34. Answers may vary. Sample: They are both the ratio of the amount of a change to an original or actual amount.
35. Check students' work.
36. 7280 fans
37. The original amount is 12, not 18; $\frac{18-12}{12} = \frac{6}{12} = 0.5 = 50\%$.

---

4 Practice

ASSIGNMENT GUIDE

Basic: 7–24 all, 26–32 even, 34–39

Average: 7–23 odd, 25–39

Advanced: 7–23 odd, 25–41

Standardized Test Prep: 42–44

Mixed Review: 45–51

Reasoning exercises have blue headings.

Applications exercises have red headings.

EXERCISE 39: Use the Think About a Plan worksheet in the **Practice and Problem Solving Workbook** (also available in the Teaching Resources in print and online) to further support students' development in becoming independent learners.

HOMEWORK QUICK CHECK

To check students' understanding of key skills and concepts, go over Exercises 11, 23, 26, 34, 36, and 39.

Answers

Practice and Problem-Solving Exercises
(continued)

38. about 4%

39. $12.63

40. 51.25%

41. a. 21%

    b. 21%

    c. 21%; sample: the new length is 1.1 times as great as the original length. $1.1^2 = 1.21$ or 121%, which shows a 21% increase over the original amount of 100%.

42. B

43. I

44. D

45. $66\frac{2}{3}\%$

46. 64.75

47. 21

48–51.

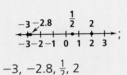

$-3, -2.8, \frac{1}{2}, 2$

---

38. Rounding Error Your science class visits an aquarium. In a report on your class's visit, you sketch one of the fish tanks and round the dimensions as shown in the diagram at the right. You use the rounded dimensions to state that the volume of the tank is approximately $(7)(5)(3) = 105 \text{ m}^3$. What is the percent error in your volume calculation due to rounding?

3.3 m ≈ 3 m

4.6 m ≈ 5 m

7.2 m ≈ 7 m

39. Student Discounts You show your student identification at a local restaurant in order to receive a 5% discount. You spend $12 for your meal at the restaurant. How much would your meal cost without the discount?

Challenge

40. Geometry The height of a cylinder is 2 ft. The diameter of the base is 5 ft. Each dimension is accurate to the nearest foot. What is the greatest possible error in calculating the volume of the cylinder? Use 3.14 for π.

41. a. The sides of a square that measures 4 m by 4 m increased in length by 10%. Find the percent of increase in the area.

    b. The sides of a square that measures 6 m by 6 m increased in length by 10%. Find the percent of increase in the area.

    c. Reasoning Predict the percent of increase in the area of a square that measures 8 m by 8 m if the side lengths increase by 10%. Explain and check your answer.

Standardized Test Prep

SAT/ACT

42. Marcus bought a shirt that was marked $28, but it was on sale for 15% off the marked price. What is the price of the shirt after the discount?

    Ⓐ $4.20   Ⓑ $23.80   Ⓒ $24.80   Ⓓ $32.20

43. What equation do you get when you solve $ax + bx = c$ for x?

    Ⓕ $x = c - ab$ Ⓖ $x = c - a - b$ Ⓗ $x = \frac{c}{a - b}$ Ⓘ $x = \frac{c}{a + b}$

44. A teacher wants to give each student 2 pencils. A store is selling pencils in boxes of 24. If the teacher has a total of 125 students, how many boxes of pencils should he buy?

    Ⓐ 5   Ⓑ 6   Ⓒ 10   Ⓓ 11

Mixed Review

Solve each percent problem.

← See Lesson 2-9.

45. What percent of 12 is 8?   **46.** What is 35% of 185?   **47.** 20% of what number is 4.2?

Get Ready! To prepare for Lesson 3-1, do Exercises 48–51.

Graph the numbers on the same number line. Then order them from least to greatest.

← See Lesson 1-3.

48. -3 **49.** $\frac{1}{2}$ **50.** 2   **51.** -2.8

Additional Instructional Support

Algebra 1 Companion

Students can use the **Algebra 1 Companion** worktext (4 pages) as you teach the lesson. Use the Companion to support

- New Vocabulary
- Key Concepts
- Got It for each Problem
- Lesson Check

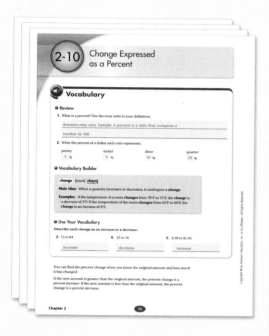

ELL Support

Focus on Language Explore the word *percent*. Ask: What other words sound like percent? (*percentage, percentile*) As an adverb, it means out of each hundred or per hundred. As a noun, it means one part in a hundred. As an adjective, it means paying or demanding interest at a specified amount.

Percent can take either a singular or plural verb. Often the verb is determined by the nearest noun. Twenty percent of the cake is frosted, or twenty percent of the cakes are frosted. When percent is used without a prepositional phrase following it, either a singular or plural verb is correct. Outside the United States, it is sometimes spelled as two words, per cent.

Possible origins and related words are: Latin, per centum; Italian, per cento; and French, pour cent. The percent symbol % comes from the Italian abbreviation of per cento.

5 Assess & Remediate

Lesson Quiz

1. In 1990, the price of a gallon of unleaded gasoline was $1.37. In 1998 it was $1.02 per gallon. What is the decrease expressed as a percent change?

2. In mid-2008, the price of a gallon of unleaded gasoline was $4.02. In 1990 it was only $1.37 per gallon. What is the increase expressed as a percent change?

3. A student's scale recorded his weight as 160 lb. His weight is actually 164 lb. What is the percent error of the scale?

4. **Do you UNDERSTAND?** The heaviest land animal ever recorded (according to the Guinness Book of World Records) was a male African bush elephant. He weighed 13.5 tons measured to the nearest half-ton. How would you find the elephant's minimum and maximum possible weights?

5. What is the greatest possible percent error in calculating the volume of a box measured to the nearest inch with sides of 5 in., 10 in., and 10 in.?

ANSWERS TO LESSON QUIZ

1. 25.5%
2. 193%
3. 2.5%
4. Answers may vary. Sample: Subtract and add 0.25 ton from 13.5 tons.
5. 21%

PRESCRIPTION FOR REMEDIATION
Use the student work on the Lesson Quiz to prescribe a differentiated review assignment.

Points	Differentiated Remediation
0–2	Intervention
3–4	On-level
5	Extension

PowerAlgebra.com

5 Assess & Remediate

Assign the Lesson Quiz. Appropriate intervention, practice, or enrichment is automatically generated based on student performance.

Intervention

- **Reteaching** (2 pages) Provides reteaching and practice exercises for the key lesson concepts. Use with struggling students or absent students.

- **English Language Learner Support** Helps students develop and reinforce mathematical vocabulary and key concepts.

All-in-One Resources/Online
Reteaching

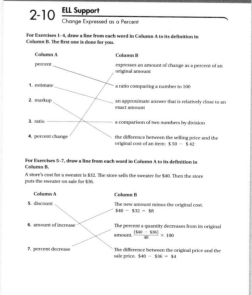

All-in-One Resources/Online
English Language Learner Support

Differentiated Remediation *continued*

On-Level

- **Practice** (2 pages) Provides extra practice for each lesson. For simpler practice exercises, use the Form K Practice pages found in the All-in-One Teaching Resources and online.

- **Think About a Plan** Helps students develop specific problem-solving skills and strategies by providing scaffolded guiding questions.
- **Standardized Test Prep** Focuses on all major exercises, all major question types, and helps students prepare for the high-stakes assessments.

Extension

- **Enrichment** Provides students with interesting problems and activities that extend the concepts of the lesson.
- **Activities, Games, and Puzzles** Worksheets that can be used for concepts development, enrichment, and for fun!

Practice and Problem Solving WKBK/ All-in-One Resources/Online
Practice page 1

2-10 Practice — Form G
Change Expressed as a Percent

Tell whether each percent change is an increase or decrease. Then find the percent change. Round to the nearest percent.

1. Original amount: 10 — New amount: 12 — 20%
2. Original amount: 72 — New amount: 67 — 6.9%
3. Original amount: 36 — New amount: 68 — 89%
4. Original amount: 23 — New amount: 25 — increase; 9%
5. Original amount: 83 — New amount: 41 — decrease; 51%
6. Original amount: 19 — New amount: 30 — increase; 58%
7. Original amount: 38 — New amount: 45 — increase; 18%
8. Original amount: 16 — New amount: 11 — decrease; 31%
9. Original amount: 177 — New amount: 151 — decrease; 15%

10. The price of the truck was advertised as $19,900. After talking with the salesperson, Jack agreed to pay $18,200 for the truck. What is the percent decrease to the nearest percent? 9%

11. The Ragnier's purchased a house for $357,000. They sold their home for $475,000. What was the percent increase to the nearest percent? 33%

12. The original price for a gallon of milk is $4.19. The sale price this week for a gallon of milk is $2.99. What is the percent decrease to the nearest percent? 29%

Find the percent error in each estimation. Round to the nearest percent.

13. You estimate that a building is 20 m tall. It is actually 23 m tall. 13%

14. You estimate the salesman is 45 years old. He is actually 38 years old. 18%

15. You estimate the volume of the storage room is 800 ft³. The room's volume is actually 810 ft³. 1%

Practice and Problem Solving WKBK/ All-in-One Resources/Online
Practice page 2

2-10 Practice (continued) — Form G
Change Expressed as a Percent

A measurement is given. Find the minimum and maximum possible measurements.

16. A nurse measures a newborn baby to be 22 in. long to the nearest in. 21.5 in.; 22.5 in.

17. A bag of apples weighs 4 lbs to the nearest lb. 3.5 lb; 4.5 lb

18. Fencing sections come in lengths of 8 ft to the nearest foot. 7.5 ft; 8.5 ft

Find the percent change. Round to the nearest percent.

19. 16 m to $11\frac{1}{2}$ m 30%
20. 76 ft to $58\frac{1}{2}$ ft 23%
21. $215\frac{1}{2}$ lb to $133\frac{1}{4}$ lb 38%
22. $42.75 to $39.99 6%
23. $315.99 to $499.89 58%
24. $5762.76 to $4999.99 13%

The measured dimensions of a rectangle are given to the nearest whole unit. Find the minimum and maximum possible areas of each rectangle.

25. 4 cm by 7 cm — 22.75 cm²; 33.75 cm²
26. 16 ft by 15 ft — 224.75 ft²; 255.75 ft²
27. 5 m by 12 m — 51.75 m²; 68.75 m²

The measured dimensions of a shape or a solid are given to the nearest whole unit. Find the greatest percent error of each shape or solid.

28. The perimeter of a rectangle with length 127 ft and width 211 ft. 0.3%

29. The area of a rectangle with length 14 in. and width 11 in. 8.3%

30. The volume of a rectangular prism with length 22 cm, width 36 cm, and height 19 cm. 6.4%

All-in-One Resources/Online
Enrichment

2-10 Enrichment
Change Expressed as a Percent

A newspaper advertisement describes an end of the season sale at a store. The ad says you can take an additional 40% off coats that are already marked down 60%.

1. Marco concluded that the ad was presenting a percent change of 100%. What is wrong with Marco's conclusion?
If the change were 100%, the items would be free.

2. Demonstrate how you determine the percent change from the original cost to the final advertised sale price of a coat costing $100. What is the percent change? 76%

3. A bookstore is having a storewide sale where all books are 30% off the list price. There is a clearance shelf where the price is discounted an additional 50% off. What is the percent change of the final discount for books on the clearance shelf? 65%

4. A discount warehouse buys the products it sells and marks up the price by 75%. This weekend the product is being sold for 25% off the regular price. What is the percent change from the wholesale price for this product during the sale? 131%

5. This year there was a 35% increase in attendance for the holiday pageant over last year's attendance. Next year, the committee is planning for a 40% increase in attendance over this year's attendance. What is the percent change from last year's attendance to next year's attendance? 89%

6. The original price of a product is $70. The original price is discounted a certain percentage, but the discount sticker has fallen off. There is a storewide additional 30% off for all merchandise. The price rings up as $36.75 at the register. Write an equation that will determine the percent of the original discount. What is the original discount?
36.75 = 0.7(70 − 70d); 25% or $17.50

Practice and Problem Solving WKBK/ All-in-One Resources/Online
Think About a Plan

2-10 Think About a Plan
Change Expressed as a Percent

Student Discounts You show your student identification at a local restaurant in order to receive a 5% discount. You spend $12 for your meal at the restaurant. How much would your meal cost without the discount?

Understanding the Problem

1. What information are you given in the problem? What are you looking to find?
the percent discount, 5%, and the price after the discount, $12; looking to find the amount the meal would cost without the discount

2. Does this question represent an amount of increase or an amount of decrease? In general, how is the amount of increase or decrease determined?
amount of decrease; divide the change by the original amount

Planning the Solution

3. What formula can you use to determine the solution?
percent = $\frac{\text{decrease}}{\text{original price}}$

4. Substitute values from the problem into your formula using x for the unknown value.
$0.5 = \frac{x}{(12 + x)}$

Getting an Answer

5. Solve for the unknown value.
$0.63

6. Check your answer.
$\frac{0.63}{12.63} = \frac{x}{100}$; 12.63x = 63; x = about 5%

7. Is your answer reasonable? Explain.
yes; The answer is close to a 5% discount.

Practice and Problem Solving WKBK/ All-in-One Resources/Online
Standardized Test Prep

2-10 Standardized Test Prep
Change Expressed as a Percent

Multiple Choice

For Exercises 1–5, choose the correct letter.

1. Sam ran 3.5 miles on Saturday. On Wednesday, he ran 5.2 miles. What was his percent increase to the nearest percent? C
A. 33%   B. 42%   C. 49%   D. 67%

2. A department store purchases sweaters wholesale for $16. The sweaters sell retail for $35. What is the percent increase to the nearest percent? I
F. 19%   G. 46%   H. 54%   I. 119%

3. Josephine measured the room to be 125 ft wide and 225 ft long. What is the maximum possible area of the room? D
A. 700 ft²   B. 27,950.25 ft²   C. 28,125 ft²   D. 28,300.25 ft²

4. You estimate the height of the flagpole to be 16 ft tall. The actual height of the flagpole is 18 ft. Which equation can be used to determine your percent error in the estimated height? G
F. $\frac{16 − 18}{18}$ G. $\left|\frac{16 − 18}{18}\right|$ H. $\left|\frac{16 − 18}{16}\right|$ I. $\frac{16 − 18}{16}$

5. You estimate that a box can hold 1152 in³. The box is actually 10.5 in. long, 10.5 in. wide, and 8 in. tall. What is the percent error in your estimation? Round to the nearest percent. B
A. 23%   B. 31%   C. 42%   D. 77%

Short Response

6. You measure a tub shaped as a rectangular prism to be 3 ft wide, 4 ft long, and 2.5 feet tall to the nearest half foot. What are the minimum and maximum volumes of the tub? What is the greatest possible percent error in calculating the volume of the tub?
7.5 ft³; 47.25 ft³; 57.5%
[2] Both parts answered correctly.
[1] One part answered correctly.
[0] Neither part answered correctly.

Online Teacher Resource Center
Activities, Games, and Puzzles

2-10 Puzzle: Mental-Math Rounds
Change Expressed as a Percent

Round 1

Solve each percent-of-increase or percent-of-decrease problem using mental math. Record a 20% increase as 20 and a 20% decrease as −20. Write your answers to the right of each problem.

from 20 to 25 5   from 40 to 10 −75   from 100 to 110 10
from 30 to 18 −40   from 160 to 400 150   from 220 to 330 50
from 100 to 115 15   from 100 to 85 −15   from 200 to 160 −20

If you answered each problem correctly, all your solutions should be integers.

From your answers above, find a set of three solutions whose sum is 160. There may be more than one solution.
Answer: _____−40, 50, 150; −15, 25, 150_____

Round 2

Solve each percent-of-increase or percent-of-decrease problem using mental math. Follow the same directions as those given in Round 1.

from 200 to 210 5   from 36 to 45 25
from 25 to 10 −60   from 25 to 26 4
from 44 to 33 −25   from 100 to 300 200
from 60 to 3 75   from 8 to 14 75
from 100 to 101 1   from 100 to 170 70
from 100 to 140 40   from 100 to 130 30

From your answers above, find a set of four solutions whose sum is 100. There may be more than one solution.
Answer: Answers may vary. Samples: 5, 25, 30, 40; −25, 25, 30, 70

BIG idea Equivalence

You can represent an equation in many ways. Equivalent representations have the same solution as the original equation.

Task 1

The solution of the equation $\ast\triangle + \heartsuit = \maltese$ is shown. Use mathematical properties to explain your answers in each part below.

a. Explain why you can subtract $\heartsuit$ from each side in Step 2.

b. Write another equation that is equivalent to $\ast\triangle + \heartsuit = \maltese$. Justify your answer.

$\ast\triangle + \heartsuit = \maltese$	
$\ast\triangle + \heartsuit - \heartsuit = \maltese - \heartsuit$	Subtract $\heartsuit$ from each side.
$\ast\triangle = \blacklozenge$	Simplify.
$\dfrac{\ast\triangle}{\ast} = \dfrac{\blacklozenge}{\ast}$	Divide each side by $\ast$.
$\triangle = \bullet$	Simplify.

BIG idea Solving Equations and Inequalities

You can use properties of numbers and equality to transform equations into equivalent, simpler equations and find solutions.

Task 2

Solve using two different methods. Explain which method you prefer to use.

a. $24 = \frac{2}{3}x + 12$

b. $0.5(y + 12) = -2.5y - 8$

c. $\frac{x-3}{5} = \frac{3x}{7}$

BIG idea Proportionality

In a proportional relationship, the ratios of two quantities are equal. You can use this relationship to describe similar figures, scale models, and rates.

Task 3

Solve. Show all your work and explain your steps.

A family rents a truck to move from Buffalo to Chicago. The rental has a base cost of $49.95, plus an additional cost of $1.19 per mile driven. The family also pays for gas, which costs $3.89 per gallon. The truck's average gas mileage is 18 miles per gallon. What is the total cost of the move? (*Hint:* Use the map to estimate the driving distance.)

Scale
1 in. : 96 mi

Performance Task

Pull It All Together

The concepts and skills required to solve these problems are from several lessons within this chapter and from the previous chapter. As students solve these problems, they will demonstrate their reasoning strategies and their growth as independent problem solvers.

The following questions are designed to:
• Help support students as they do the Tasks.
• Gauge the amount of support students need as they become independent problem solvers.

Task 1

Apply properties of equality and inverse operations to write simpler, equivalent equations.
• How can you make the equation simpler?
• How can you clear fractions (or decimals)?
• How do you isolate the variable?

Task 2

Translate words into equations and use ratios and unit rates to solve problems.
• What do you know? What do you need?
• What is an outline of your plan?
• What are the steps in order?

Task 3

Use proportions to solve problems involving percents.
• What do you know? What do you need?
• Does the problem involve a ratio? What is being compared?
• How many steps are there? What are the steps in order?
• What is the proportion you need to write and solve?

Assess
Performance **UbD**

Pull It All Together

See p. 67 for a holistic scoring rubric to gauge a student's progress on Understanding the Problem, Planning a Solution, Getting an Answer, and Assessing Autonomy.

SOLUTION OUTLINES

1. a. Subtraction Property of Equality.

b. Answers may vary. Sample:
$\ast\triangle = \maltese - \heartsuit$

2. a. Subtract 12 from each side and multiply by $\frac{3}{2}$. Or multiply both sides by $\frac{3}{2}$ and subtract 18 from each side. Answer: 18

b. Use the Distributive Property to clear the parentheses, then add 2.5y to each side. Or multiply both sides by 2 to clear the decimals, then use the Distributive Property.

c. Cross-multiply and solve as a proportion. Or multiply by 35 to clear fractions, then solve for x. Answer: $x = -2.625$

3. Find the distance driven by multiplying the measured distance on the map by the scale of the map. Find the gallons of gasoline needed by dividing the distance by the average gas mileage. Find the cost of gas by multiplying the gallons needed by the cost per gallon. Find the cost of the truck rental by multiplying the distance by the cost per mile and adding the base cost. Finally, add the cost of the gasoline and the cost of the truck rental. Answer: about $726.75.

Essential Questions

BIG idea Equivalence
ESSENTIAL QUESTION Can equations that appear to be different be equivalent?
ANSWER You can represent an equation in many ways. Equivalent representations have the same solution as the original solution.

BIG idea Solving Equations & Inequalities
ESSENTIAL QUESTION How can you solve equations?
ANSWER You can use properties of numbers and equations to transform equations into equivalent, simpler equations to find solutions.

BIG idea Proportionality
ESSENTIAL QUESTION What kinds of relationships can proportions represent?
ANSWER In a proportional relationship, the ratios of two quantities are equal. You can use this relationship to describe similar figures, scale models, and rates.

---

2 Chapter Review

Connecting BIG ideas and Answering the Essential Questions

1 Equivalence
You can represent an equation in many ways. Equivalent representations have the same solution as the original equation.

→ **Solving Equations (Lessons 2-1, 2-2, 2-3, 2-4)**
Equivalent equations have the same solution(s). To solve a given equation, form a series of simpler equivalent equations that isolate the variable.

2 Solving Equations and Inequalities
You can use properties of numbers and equality to transform equations into equivalent, simpler equations and find solutions.

→ **Solving Equations (Lessons 2-1, 2-2, 2-3, 2-4)**
Use equations to model real-world situations and find unknown quantities.

→ **Literal Equations and Formulas (Lesson 2-5)**
Formulas represent reliable real-world relationships. Use them to solve problems.

3 Proportionality
In a proportional relationship, the ratios of two quantities are equal. You can use this relationship to describe similar figures, scale models, and rates.

→ **Rates, Proportions, and Similar Figures (Lessons 2-6, 2-7, 2-8)**
Use rates to model ideas like growth, speed, and unit prices. Use proportions to interpret scale drawings.

→ **Percents (Lessons 2-9, 2-10)**
Formulas represent reliable real-world relationships. Use them to solve problems.

Chapter Vocabulary

- Addition Property of Equality (p. 81)
- conversion factor (p. 119)
- cross products (p. 125)
- Cross Products Property (p. 125)
- Division Property of Equality (p. 83)
- equivalent equations (p. 81)
- formula (p. 110)
- identity (p. 104)
- inverse operations (p. 82)
- isolate (p. 82)
- literal equation (p. 109)
- Multiplication Property of Equality (p. 83)
- percent error (p. 146)
- percent change (p. 144)
- percent decrease (p. 144)
- percent increase (p. 144)
- proportion (p. 124)
- rate (p. 118)
- ratio (p. 118)
- relative error (p. 146)
- scale (p. 132)
- scale drawing (p. 132)
- scale model (p. 132)
- similar figures (p. 130)
- Subtraction Property of Equality (p. 81)
- unit analysis (p. 119)
- unit rate (p. 118)

Choose the correct term to complete each sentence.

1. Addition and subtraction are examples of __?__ because they undo each other.

2. An equation that is true for every value of the variable is a(n) __?__.

3. A ratio of two equivalent measures given in different units is a(n) __?__.

4. On a map, information such as "1 in. : 5 mi" is the __?__ of the map.

5. In the proportion $\frac{a}{b} = \frac{c}{d}$, ad and bc are the __?__.

152 **Chapter 2** Solving Equations

Summative Questions

Use the following prompts as you review this chapter with your students. The prompts are designed to help you assess your students' understanding of the Big Ideas they have studied.

- How would you start the solution of $2x - 4 = 3x + 13$? Justify your method. Is there another way?

- Which properties do you need to use to solve the equation $2x - 4 = 3x + 13$? How do you use the properties of equivalence to write an equation that is equivalent to another equation? Give examples.

- If you are making a scale drawing, what do you need to do to make sure that your drawing is accurate?

Answers

Chapter Review

1. inverse operations

2. identity

3. rate

4. scale

5. cross products

2-1 and 2-2 Solving One- and Two-Step Equations

Quick Review
To solve an equation, get the variable by itself on one side of the equation. You can use **properties of equality** and **inverse operations** to isolate the variable. For example, use multiplication to undo its inverse, division.

Example
What is the solution of $\frac{y}{2} + 5 = 8$?

$\frac{y}{2} + 5 - 5 = 8 - 5$ Subtract to undo addition.

$\frac{y}{2} = 3$ Simplify.

$2 \cdot \frac{y}{2} = 3 \cdot 2$ Multiply to undo division.

$y = 6$ Simplify.

Exercises
Solve each equation. Check your answer.

6. $x + 5 = -2$ **7.** $a - 2.5 = 4.5$

8. $3b = 42$ **9.** $\frac{n}{5} = 13$

10. $7x - 2 = 22.5$ **11.** $\frac{y}{4} - 3 = -4$

12. $8 + 3m = -7$ **13.** $-\frac{3d}{4} + 5 = 11$

14. Dining Five friends equally split a restaurant bill that comes to $32.50. How much does each pay?

15. Reasoning Justify each step in solving $4x - 3 = 9$.

$4x - 3 + 3 = 9 + 3$ __?__

$4x = 12$ __?__

$\frac{4x}{4} = \frac{12}{4}$ __?__

$x = 3$ __?__

2-3 Solving Multi-Step Equations

Quick Review
To solve some equations, you may need to combine like terms or use the Distributive Property to clear fractions or decimals.

Example
What is the solution of $12 = 2x + \frac{4}{3} - \frac{2x}{3}$?

$3 \cdot 12 = 3\left(2x + \frac{4}{3} - \frac{2x}{3}\right)$ Multiply by 3.

$36 = 6x + 4 - 2x$ Simplify.

$36 = 4x + 4$ Combine like terms.

$36 - 4 = 4x + 4 - 4$ Subtract 4.

$32 = 4x$ Combine like terms.

$\frac{32}{4} = \frac{4x}{4}$ Divide each side by 4.

$8 = x$ Simplify.

Exercises
Solve each equation. Check your answer.

16. $7(s - 5) = 42$ **17.** $3a + 2 - 5a = -14$

18. $-4b - 5 + 2b = 10$ **19.** $3.4t + 0.08 = 11$

20. $10 = \frac{c}{3} - 4 + \frac{c}{6}$ **21.** $\frac{2x}{7} + \frac{4}{5} = 5$

Write an equation to model each situation. Then solve the equation.

22. Earnings You work for 4 h on Saturday and 8 h on Sunday. You also receive a $50 bonus. You earn $164. How much did you earn per hour?

23. Entertainment Online concert tickets cost $37 each, plus a service charge of $8.50 per ticket. The Web site also charges a transaction fee of $14.99 for the purchase. You paid $242.49. How many tickets did you buy?

6. -7

7. 7

8. 14

9. 65

10. 3.5

11. -4

12. -5

13. -8

14. $6.50

15. Add. Prop. of Eq.; Simplify.; Div. Prop. of Eq.; Simplify.

16. 11

17. 8

18. -7.5

19. $3\frac{18}{85}$

20. 28

21. 14.7

22. $4h + 8h + 50 = 164$; $9.50

23. $37t + 8.50t + 14.99 = 242.49$; 5 tickets

Answers

Chapter Review (continued)

24. -90

25. 7.2

26. identity

27. no solution

28. $8h = 16 + 6h$; 8 ft

29. $\frac{d}{65} = \frac{d}{130} + 3$; 390 mi

30. $x = \frac{-c}{a + b}$

31. $x = -t - r$

32. $x = \frac{m - p}{5}$

33. $x = \frac{pqs}{p + q}$

34. 40 cm

35. 15 mm

36. 16 in.

2-4 Solving Equations With Variables on Both Sides

Quick Review

When an equation has variables on both sides, you can use properties of equality to isolate the variable on one side. An equation has no solution if no value of the variable makes it true. An equation is an **identity** if every value of the variable makes it true.

Example

What is the solution of $3x - 7 = 5x + 19$?

$$3x - 7 - 3x = 5x + 19 - 3x \quad \text{Subtract } 3x.$$
$$-7 = 2x + 19 \quad \text{Simplify.}$$
$$-7 - 19 = 2x + 19 - 19 \quad \text{Subtract 19.}$$
$$-26 = 2x \quad \text{Simplify.}$$
$$\frac{-26}{2} = \frac{2x}{2} \quad \text{Divide each side by 2.}$$
$$-13 = x \quad \text{Simplify.}$$

Exercises

Solve each equation. If the equation is an identity, write *identity*. If it has no solution, write *no solution*.

24. $\frac{2}{3}x + 4 = \frac{3}{5}x - 2$ **25.** $6 - 0.25f = f - 3$

26. $3(h - 4) = -\frac{1}{2}(24 - 6h)$ **27.** $5n = 20(4 + 0.25n)$

28. Architecture Two buildings have the same total height. One building has 8 floors with height h. The other building has a ground floor of 16 ft and 6 other floors with height h. Write and solve an equation to find the height h of these floors.

29. Travel A train makes a trip at 65 mi/h. A plane traveling 130 mi/h makes the same trip in 3 fewer hours. Write and solve an equation to find the distance of the trip.

2-5 Literal Equations and Formulas

Quick Review

A **literal equation** is an equation that involves two or more variables. A **formula** is an equation that states a relationship among quantities. You can use properties of equality to solve a literal equation for one variable in terms of others.

Example

What is the width of a rectangle with area 91 ft^2 and length 7 ft?

$$A = \ell w \quad \text{Write the appropriate formula.}$$
$$\frac{A}{\ell} = w \quad \text{Divide each side by } \ell.$$
$$\frac{91}{7} = w \quad \text{Substitute 91 for } A \text{ and 7 for } \ell.$$
$$13 = w \quad \text{Simplify.}$$

The width of the rectangle is 13 ft.

Exercises

Solve each equation for x.

30. $ax + bx = -c$ **31.** $\frac{x + r}{t} + 1 = 0$

32. $m - 3x = 2x + p$ **33.** $\frac{x}{p} + \frac{x}{q} = s$

Solve each problem. Round to the nearest tenth, if necessary. Use 3.14 for π.

34. What is the width of a rectangle with length 5.5 cm and area 220 cm^2?

35. What is the radius of a circle with circumference 94.2 mm?

36. A triangle has height 15 in. and area 120 in.^{2}. What is the length of its base?

2-6 Ratios, Rates, and Conversions

Quick Review

A ratio between numbers measured in different units is called a **rate**. A **conversion factor** is a ratio of two equivalent measures in different units such as $\frac{1\,h}{60\,min}$, and is always equal to 1. To convert from one unit to another, multiply the original unit by a conversion factor that has the original units in the denominator and the desired units in the numerator.

Example

A painting is 17.5 in. wide. What is its width in centimeters? Recall that 1 in. = 2.54 cm.

$$17.5 \text{ in.} \cdot \frac{2.54 \text{ cm}}{1 \text{ in.}} = 44.45 \text{ cm}$$

The painting is 44.45 cm wide.

Exercises

Convert the given amount to the given unit.

37. $6\frac{1}{2}$ ft; in.

38. 4 lb 7 oz; oz

39. 135 s; min

40. 2.25 mi; yd

41. Production A bread slicer runs 20 h per day for 30 days and slices 144,000 loaves of bread. How many loaves per hour are sliced?

42. Pets A gerbil eats about $\frac{1}{4}$ oz of food per day. About how many pounds of food can a gerbil eat in a year?

43. Sports If a baseball travels at 90 mi/h, how many seconds does it take to travel 60 ft?

2-7 and 2-8 Solving Proportions and Using Similar Figures

Quick Review

The **cross products** of a proportion are equal.

If $\frac{a}{b} = \frac{c}{d}$, where $b \neq 0$ and $d \neq 0$, then $ad = bc$.

If two figures are **similar**, then corresponding angles are congruent and corresponding side lengths are in proportion. You can use proportions to find missing side lengths in similar figures and for indirect measurement.

Example

A tree casts a shadow 10 m long. At the same time, a signpost next to the tree casts a shadow 4 m long. The signpost is 2.5 m tall. How tall is the tree?

$\frac{x}{10} = \frac{2.5}{4}$	Write a proportion.
$4x = 10(2.5)$	Cross Products Property
$4x = 25$	Simplify.
$x = 6.25$	Divide each side by 4.

Exercises

Solve each proportion.

44. $\frac{3}{7} = \frac{9}{x}$

45. $\frac{-8}{10} = \frac{y}{5}$

46. $\frac{6}{15} = \frac{a}{4}$

47. $\frac{3}{-7} = \frac{-9}{t}$

48. $\frac{b+3}{7} = \frac{b-3}{6}$

49. $\frac{5}{2c-3} = \frac{3}{7c+4}$

50. Models An airplane has a wingspan of 25 ft and a length of 20 ft. You are designing a model of the airplane with a wingspan of 15 in. What will the length of your model be?

51. Projections You project a drawing 7 in. wide and $4\frac{1}{2}$ in. tall onto a wall. The projected image is 27 in. tall. How wide is the projected image?

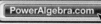
37. 78 in.

38. 71 oz

39. 2.25 min

40. 3960 yd

41. 240 loaves

42. about 6 lb

43. $\frac{5}{11}$ s or about 0.45 s

44. 21

45. −4

46. 1.6

47. 21

48. 39

49. −1

50. 12 in.

51. 42 in.

Answers

Chapter Review (continued)

52. 300%

53. 108

54. 170

55. 60 seeds

56. 30%

57. 72 students

58. increase; 11%

59. decrease; 20%

60. decrease; 11%

61. increase; 32%

62. about 47%

63. about 39%

64. Yes; 50% of 38° is 19° and 38° + 19° = 57°.

2-9 Percents

Quick Review

A percent is a ratio that compares a number to 100. If you write a percent as a fraction, you can use a proportion to solve a percent problem.

Example

What percent of 84 is 105?

$$\frac{105}{84} = \frac{p}{100} \qquad \text{Write the percent proportion.}$$

$$100(105) = 84p \qquad \text{Cross Products Property}$$

$$10{,}500 = 84p \qquad \text{Simplify.}$$

$$125 = p \qquad \text{Divide each side by 84.}$$

105 is 125% of 84.

Exercises

52. What percent of 37 is 111?

53. What is 72% of 150?

54. 60% of what number is 102?

55. **Gardening** A gardener expects that 75% of the seeds she plants will produce plants. She wants 45 plants. How many seeds should she plant?

56. **Fundraising** A charity sent out 700 fundraising letters and received 210 contributions in response. What was the percent of response?

57. **Surveys** In a survey, 60% of students prefer bagels to donuts. If 120 students were surveyed, how many students prefer bagels?

2-10 Change Expressed as a Percent

Quick Review

Percent change $p\%$ is the ratio of the amount of change to the original amount.

$$p\% = \frac{\text{amount of increase or decrease}}{\text{original amount}}$$

You can use the percent change formula to express changes as percents.

Example

A bookstore buys a book for $16 and marks it up to $28. What is the markup expressed as a percent change?

$$\text{percent change} = \frac{\text{new amount} - \text{original amount}}{\text{original amount}}$$

$$= \frac{28 - 16}{16} \qquad \text{Substitute.}$$

$$= \frac{12}{16} \qquad \text{Simplify.}$$

$$= 0.75 \text{ or } 75\% \qquad \text{Write the result as a percent.}$$

The price of the book increased by 75%.

Exercises

Tell whether each percent change is an increase or decrease. Then find the percent change. Round to the nearest percent.

58. original amount: 27
new amount: 30

59. original amount: 250
new amount: 200

60. original amount: 873
new amount: 781

61. original amount: 4.7
new amount: 6.2

62. **Demographics** In 1970, the U.S. population was about 205 million people. In 2007, it was about 301 million. What was the percent increase?

63. **Astronomy** The time from sunrise to sunset on the shortest day of the year in Jacksonville, Florida, is about 10 h 11 min. On the longest day, the time is 14 h 7 min. What is the percent increase?

64. **Weather** This morning the temperature was 38°F. This afternoon it is 57°F. Did the temperature increase by 50%? Explain.

2 Chapter Test

 **MathXL® for School**
Go to PowerAlgebra.com

Do you know HOW?

Solve each proportion.

1. $\frac{8}{k} = \frac{12}{30}$

2. $\frac{3}{5} = \frac{y+1}{9}$

Solve each equation. Check your answer.

3. $3w + 2 = w - 4$

4. $\frac{1}{4}(k - 1) = 7$

5. $6y = 12.8$

6. $\frac{5n + 1}{8} = \frac{3n - 5}{4}$

7. **Bicycling** You are riding your bicycle to prepare for a race. It takes you 12 min to go 2.5 mi. What was your speed in miles per hour?

The figures in each pair are similar. Find the missing length.

8.

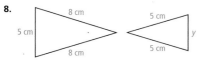

9.

10. **Shadows** In the late afternoon, a 3.5-ft child casts a 60-in. shadow. The child is next to a telephone pole that casts a 50-ft shadow, forming similar triangles. How tall is the telephone pole?

Tell whether each percent change is an increase or decrease. Then find the percent change.

11. original amount: $5000
   new amount: $6500

12. original amount: 150 lb
   new amount: 135 lb

Define a variable and write an equation to model each situation. Then solve.

13. **Farming** You have 100 ft of fencing to build a circular sheep pen.

   a. What is the diameter of the largest pen you can build? Use 3.14 for π.

   b. What is the area of the largest pen you can build?

14. **Maps** The scale on a map is 1 in. : 25 mi. You measure 6.5 in. between two towns. What is the actual distance?

15. **Birds** In a bird sanctuary, 30% of the birds are hummingbirds. If there are about 350 birds in the sanctuary at any given time, how many are hummingbirds?

Do you UNDERSTAND?

16. **Reasoning** Explain which is more accurate: measuring to the nearest millimeter or to the nearest eighth of an inch.

17. **Writing** A 30-pack of blank CDs costs $9.50. A 50-pack of blank CDs costs $13. How can you tell which is the better buy?

18. **Error Analysis** Average attendance at a school's basketball games increased from 1000 to 1500 last year. One student said that represented a 150% increase. Explain the student's error. What is the actual percent increase?

Answers

Chapter Test

1. -20
2. 4.4
3. -3
4. 29
5. $2\frac{2}{15}$
6. 11
7. 12.5 mi/h
8. 3.125 cm
9. 4.5 ft
10. 35 ft
11. increase; 30%
12. decrease; 10%

13. **a.** d = diameter; $100 = 3.14d$; about 31.8 ft
   b. d = diameter; $A = 3.14\left(\frac{d}{2}\right)^2$; about 794 ft²

14. 162.5 mi

15. 105 hummingbirds

16. Nearest millimeter; $\frac{1}{8}$ in. is about 3.175 mm. This is a larger unit of measure, so it is not as accurate.

17. Find the unit cost per CD by dividing the number of CDs by the cost. The lower unit cost is the better buy.

18. Answers may vary. Sample: The student added the percent of increase to 100%; 50%.

PowerAlgebra.com

MathXL for School
Prepare students for the Mid-Chapter Quiz and Chapter Test with online practice and review.

Item Number	Lesson
1	1-7
2	2-7
3	1-7
4	1-4
5	2-7
6	1-7
7	1-8
8	1-2
9	1-8
10	1-4
11	1-4
12	2-6
13	1-2
14	2-10
15	1-9
16	2-5
17	1-8
18	2-7
19	2-10
20	2-2
21	2-6
22	2-2
23	2-5
24	2-1
25	2-6
26	2-3

2 Cumulative Test Prep

TIPS FOR SUCCESS

Some questions on tests ask you to write a short response. Short response questions in this textbook are usually worth 2 points. To get full credit for an answer, you must give the correct answer (including appropriate units, if applicable) and justify your reasoning or show your work.

TIP 1

If you write the correct expression but make an error when calculating your answer, you might earn one point.

Mandy is selling copies of historic photos to raise money for a class trip. She can order each photo for $2.75 and each frame for $4.25. Mandy plans to sell each photo with a frame for $10.00. Write an expression to represent the total amount of money Mandy will have after selling n framed photos. Evaluate your expression for 12 framed photos. Show your work.

Solution

She makes $3n$ after selling n framed photos.

She earns $3(12) = \$36$ after selling 12 framed photos.

TIP 2

You also might earn one point if you do not write an expression but you show a method for getting to the correct answer.

Think It Through

It costs Mandy $\$2.75 + \$4.25 = \$7$ to make each framed photo. She makes $\$10 - (\$7) = \$3$ after selling one framed photo. So, she makes $3n$ after selling n framed photos. She earns $3(12) = \$36$ after selling 12 framed photos. This answer is complete and earns 2 points.

Vocabulary Builder

As you solve test items, you must understand the meanings of mathematical terms. Match each term with its mathematical meaning.

A. variable

B. similar

C. scale factor

D. perimeter

E. formula

I. the distance around the outside of a figure

II. two figures with the exact same shape, but not necessarily the same size

III. a math sentence that defines the relationship between quantities

IV. a symbol that represents a number or numbers

V. the ratio of the lengths of corresponding sides in similar figures

Multiple Choice

Read each question. Then write the letter of the correct answer on your paper.

1. Which expression is equivalent to $2b - 3a + b + a$?

A $b - 2a$

B $b - 4a$

C $3b - 4a$

D $3b - 2a$

2. Belle surveyed her classmates in music class. The ratio of students who prefer playing string instruments to those who prefer wind instruments is $2 : 5$. There are 28 students in Belle's class. How many students prefer playing string instruments?

F 5

G 8

H 20

I 25

Answers

Cumulative Test Prep

A. IV

B. II

C. V

D. I

E. III

1. D

2. G

3. Which equation is equivalent to
$2(3x - 1) - 3(5x - 3) = 4$?

- Ⓐ $-3x - 5 = 4$
- Ⓒ $-9x - 11 = 4$
- Ⓑ $-9x - 4 = 4$
- Ⓓ $-9x + 7 = 4$

4. The statement $-2 \cdot (7 \cdot 4) = (-2 \cdot 7) \cdot 4$ is an example of which property?

- Ⓕ Commutative Property of Multiplication
- Ⓖ Identity Property of Multiplication
- Ⓗ Distributive Property
- Ⓘ Associative Property of Multiplication

5. Jim uses 3 cups of peaches to yield 4 jars of peach jam. He also makes strawberry-peach jam. He uses equal amounts of strawberries and peaches. How many cups of strawberries does Jim need to yield 10 jars of strawberry-peach jam?

- Ⓐ $3\frac{3}{4}$ c
- Ⓒ $7\frac{1}{2}$ c
- Ⓑ $4\frac{1}{2}$ c
- Ⓓ 9 c

6. $3(6x + 2) - 2(5x + 3)$ is equivalent to which of the following expressions?

- Ⓕ $8x$
- Ⓗ $8x + 9$
- Ⓖ $8x + 5$
- Ⓘ $8x + 12$

7. Sabrina's car has traveled 28,000 mi. If she drives 36 mi each day, which equation can be used to find the total number of miles m Sabrina's car will have traveled after she drives it for d days?

- Ⓐ $d = 36m + 28{,}000$
- Ⓑ $m = 36d + 28{,}000$
- Ⓒ $m + 36d = 28{,}000$
- Ⓓ $d = 28{,}000m + 36$

8. Which operation should be done first to simplify the expression $12 + 6 \cdot 3 - (35 - 14 \div 7)$?

- Ⓕ $12 + 6$
- Ⓗ $35 - 14$
- Ⓖ $6 \cdot 3$
- Ⓘ $14 \div 7$

9. Erica is making feathered caps for her school play. Each cap must have 3 feathers. Which equation represents the number of feathers f Erica needs to make c caps?

- Ⓐ $c = 3f$
- Ⓒ $c = f + 3$
- Ⓑ $f = 3c$
- Ⓓ $f = c + 3$

10. Which property is shown by the equation
$8 \times (7 \times 9) = (7 \times 9) \times 8$?

- Ⓕ Commutative Property of Multiplication
- Ⓖ Associative Property of Multiplication
- Ⓗ Identity Property of Multiplication
- Ⓘ Closure Property of Multiplication

11. Use the diagram below, which shows similar triangles formed by the shadows of a person and a tree.

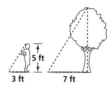

5 ft

3 ft   7 ft

What is the approximate height of the tree?

- Ⓐ 4 ft
- Ⓒ 12 ft
- Ⓑ 9 ft
- Ⓓ 105 ft

12. Which of the following fractions is equivalent to $\frac{36}{153}$?

- Ⓕ $\frac{13}{47}$
- Ⓗ $\frac{4}{17}$
- Ⓖ $\frac{1}{9}$
- Ⓘ $\frac{9}{34}$

13. Which product is equal to -36?

- Ⓐ $12(2 - 12)$
- Ⓑ $6(2 + 12)$
- Ⓒ $12(1 - 22)$
- Ⓓ $3(10 - 22)$

3. D
4. I
5. A
6. F
7. B
8. I
9. B
10. F
11. C
12. H
13. D

Answers

Cumulative Test Prep (continued)

14. F

15. D

16. I

17. A

18. 2.36

19. 182

20. 10.5

21. 36

22. 40

23. [2] $.35 + $.25n (OR equivalent expression)
$3.60 = 0.35 + 0.25n$
$3.25 = 0.25n$
$13 = n$
(OR equivalent strategy)
[1]   correct expression OR correct substitution

24. [2] $A = h \cdot \frac{1}{2}h$ (OR equivalent equation)
$A = 4$ in. $\cdot \frac{1}{2} \cdot 4$ in. $= 8$ in^2.
(OR equivalent strategy)
[1]   incorrect equation OR incorrect strategy

25. [2]   9 curtains; 4 yd $\cdot \frac{36 \text{ in.}}{1 \text{ yd}} = 144$ in. total,
144 in. $\div$ 16 in. $= 9$
[1]   correct answer without correct strategy
OR incorrect answer with appropriate strategy

26. [2] $25.00d + $.30(14)d
(OR equivalent expression)
$25.00(4) + $.30(14)(4) =
$100 + $16.80 = $116.80
(OR equivalent strategy)
[1]   correct expression OR correct substitution

---

14. Last year, Conner paid 15% of his earnings in federal taxes. He paid $3000. Jose also paid 15% of his earnings in federal taxes, but he paid $3600. How much more did Jose earn than Conner?

- (F) $4000
- (G) $6000
- (H) $20,000
- (I) $24,000

15. The table shows the price of a bus ticket based on the number of miles traveled. Which equation represents the relationship between the ticket price p and the number of miles traveled m?

Miles	Price
100	$50
150	$70
200	$90
250	$110

- (A) $p = 2m$
- (B) $p = 0.5m$
- (C) $p = 2m + 10$
- (D) $p = 0.4m + 10$

16. The formula for the volume V of a cone is $V = \frac{1}{3}\pi r^2 h$, where h is the height of the cone and r is the radius of the base. The height of a cone is 5 in. and the radius of the base is 2 in. What is the approximate volume of the cone? Use 3.14 for π.

- (F) 2 in.^{3}
- (G) 6 in.^{3}
- (H) 15 in.^{3}
- (I) 21 in.^{3}

17. During a trip, Josh recorded the amount of time it took him to travel the distances shown in the table below.

Time (hours)	2	5	7	8
Distance (miles)	60	150	210	240

Which equation represents the relationship between distance d and time t?

- (A) $d = 30t$
- (B) $t = 30d$
- (C) $d = 30 + t$
- (D) $t = d + 30$

Record your answers in a grid.

18. What is the value of x when $\frac{13}{55} = \frac{x}{10}$? Round your answer to the nearest hundredth.

19. When Paige left middle school and entered high school, her class size increased by 225%. There were 56 students in her middle school class. How many students are in her high school class?

20. The perimeter of a rectangle is given by the equation $2w + 33 = 54$. What is w, the width of the rectangle?

21. Pablo can wash 6 cars in 40 min. At this rate, how many cars can Pablo wash in 4 h?

22. The formula for the time that a certain traffic light remains yellow is $t = \frac{1}{8}s + 1$, where t represents the time in seconds and s represents the speed limit in miles per hour. If the light is yellow for 6 s, what is the speed limit in miles per hour?

Short Response

23. The cost for using a phone card is 35 cents per call plus 25 cents per minute. Write an expression for the cost of a call that is n minutes long. A certain call costs $3.60. How many minutes long was the call? Show your work.

24. Travis sells black and white photos of cities across the country. Each photo's width is half its height. Write an equation to represent the area A of a photo given its height h. Use this equation to find the area of a photo that is 4 in. tall.

25. Carroll has a piece of fabric that is 4 yd long to make curtains. Each curtain requires a piece of fabric that is 16 in. long. How many curtains can Carroll make?

26. A rental car company charges $25.00 per day plus $.30 for every mile the car is driven. Dale rents a car while his own car is being repaired, and he only drives it to and from work each day. Dale drives 7 mi each way to and from work. Write an expression to represent Dale's cost of renting a car for d days. Dale rents the car for 4 days. How much does Dale owe for the rental?

Get Ready!

See Lesson 1-3 **Ordering Rational Numbers**

Complete each statement with <, =, or >.

1. $-3 \blacksquare -5$ **2.** $7 \blacksquare \frac{14}{2}$ **3.** $-8 \blacksquare -8.4$ **4.** $-\frac{5}{2} \blacksquare 2.5$

See Lesson 1-5 **Absolute Value**

Simplify each expression.

5. $5 + |4 - 6|$ **6.** $|30 - 28| - 6$ **7.** $|-7 + 2| - 4$

See Lesson 2-1 **Solving One-Step Equations**

Solve each equation. Check your solution.

8. $x - 4 = -2$ **9.** $b + 4 = 7$ **10.** $-\frac{3}{4}y = 9$ **11.** $\frac{m}{12} = 2.7$

12. $-8 + x = 15$ **13.** $n - 7 = 22.5$ **14.** $-\frac{12}{7}z = 48$ **15.** $\frac{5y}{4} = -15$

See Lesson 2-2 **Solving Two-Step Equations**

Solve each equation. Check your solution.

16. $-5 + \frac{b}{4} = 7$ **17.** $4.2m + 4 = 25$ **18.** $-12 = 6 + \frac{3}{4}x$

19. $6 = -z - 4$ **20.** $4m + 2.3 = 9.7$ **21.** $\frac{5}{8}t - 7 = -22$

22. $-4.7 = 3y + 1.3$ **23.** $12.2 = 5.3x - 3.7$ **24.** $5 - \frac{1}{3}x = -15$

See Lessons 2-3 and 2-4 **Solving Multi-Step Equations**

Solve each equation. Check your solution.

25. $4t + 7 + 6t = -33$ **26.** $2a + 5 = 9a - 16$ **27.** $\frac{1}{3} + \frac{4y}{6} = \frac{2}{3}$

28. $6(y - 2) = 8 - 2y$ **29.** $n + 3(n - 2) = 10.4$ **30.** $\frac{1}{3}w + 3 = \frac{2}{3}w - 5$

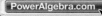

Looking Ahead Vocabulary

31. You make a *compound* word, such as houseboat, by joining two words together. Why do you think $-4 < x < 7$ is called a *compound inequality*?

32. The *intersection* of two roads is the place where the roads cross. How would you define the *intersection* of two groups of objects?

Get Ready!

Assign this diagnostic assessment to determine if students have the prerequisite skills for Chapter 3.

Lesson	Skill
1-3	Ordering Rational Numbers
1-5	Absolute Value
2-1	Solving One-Step Equations
2-2	Solving Two-Step Equations
2-3 and 2-4	Solving Multi-Step Equations

To remediate students, select from these resources (available for every lesson).
• Online Problems (PowerAlgebra.com)
• Reteaching (All-in-One Teaching Resources)
• Practice (All-in-One Teaching Resources)

Why Students Need These Skills

ORDERING RATIONAL NUMBERS
Students who understand how to order rational numbers will more readily understand the graphs of inequalities on number lines.

ABSOLUTE VALUE
Absolute values are important for motivating the concept of compound inequalities.

SOLVING ONE-STEP EQUATIONS
Properties used in solving one-step equations will be extended to solving one-step inequalities.

SOLVING TWO-STEP AND MULTI-STEP EQUATIONS
The processes used in solving two-step and multi-step equations will be extended to solving two-step and multi-step inequalities.

Looking Ahead Vocabulary

COMPOUND INEQUALITY Ask students to name other examples of compound words.

INTERSECTION Show students Venn diagrams and discuss regions of intersection.

Answers

Get Ready!

1. >
2. =
3. >
4. <
5. 7
6. −4
7. 1
8. 2
9. 3
10. −12
11. 32.4
12. 23
13. 29.5
14. −28
15. −12
16. 48
17. 5
18. −24
19. −10
20. 1.85
21. −24
22. −2
23. 3
24. 60
25. −4
26. 3
27. $\frac{1}{2}$
28. 2.5
29. 4.1
30. 24
31. Answers may vary. Sample: Two inequalities are joined together.
32. Answers may vary. Sample: the part that the two groups of objects have in common

Chapter 3 Overview

UbD Understanding by Design

Chapter 3 connects and extends the Big Ideas introduced in the last chapter to solving inequalities. In this chapter, students will develop the answers to the Essential Questions posed on the opposite page as they learn the concepts and skills bulleted below.

BIG idea Variable

ESSENTIAL QUESTION How do you represent relationships between quantities that are not equal?
- Students will learn to write and graph inequalities.

BIG idea Equivalence

ESSENTIAL QUESTION Can inequalities that appear to be different be equivalent?
- Students will use properties to generate equivalent inequalities.

BIG idea Solving Equations and Inequalities

ESSENTIAL QUESTION How can you solve inequalities?
- Equivalent inequalities are generated by using the properties of inequalities.
- Inequality symbols are reversed when multiplying or dividing both sides of an inequality by a negative number.

Indiana Academic Standard

A1.2.5 Solve problems that can be modeled using linear equations and inequalities, interpret the solutions, and determine whether the solutions are reasonable.

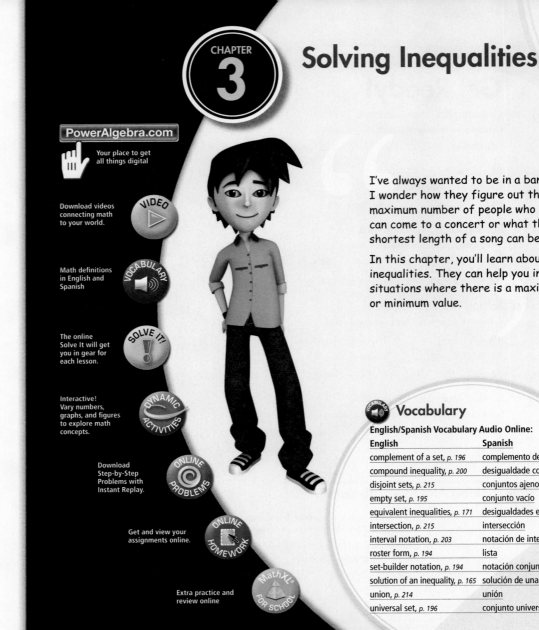

CHAPTER 3 Solving Inequalities

I've always wanted to be in a band! I wonder how they figure out the maximum number of people who can come to a concert or what the shortest length of a song can be.

In this chapter, you'll learn about inequalities. They can help you in situations where there is a maximum or minimum value.

Vocabulary

English/Spanish Vocabulary Audio Online:

English	Spanish
complement of a set, *p. 196*	complemento de un conjunto
compound inequality, *p. 200*	desigualdade compuesta
disjoint sets, *p. 215*	conjuntos ajenos
empty set, *p. 195*	conjunto vacío
equivalent inequalities, *p. 171*	desigualdades equivalentes
intersection, *p. 215*	intersección
interval notation, *p. 203*	notación de intervalo
roster form, *p. 194*	lista
set-builder notation, *p. 194*	notación conjuntista
solution of an inequality, *p. 165*	solución de una desigualdad
union, *p. 214*	unión
universal set, *p. 196*	conjunto universal

My Math Video

00:04:04

BIG ideas

1 **Variable**
Essential Question How do you represent relationships between quantities that are not equal?

2 **Equivalence**
Essential Question Can inequalities that appear to be different be equivalent?

3 **Solving Equations and Inequalities**
Essential Question How can you solve inequalities?

Chapter Preview

PowerAlgebra.com   Chapter 3   Solving Inequalities   163

My Math Video
FACILITATE Music and math have always been closely related. The Pythagoreans discovered the ratios between notes in a scale. Later, the French mathematician Joseph Fourier discovered a method for representing sound waves as series of numbers. Fourier series have been applied to synthesizers, and more recently, to digital music files.

Q What is your favorite instrument? Why? **[Answers will vary.]**

Q How would you describe the range of sounds created by that instrument? **[Answers will vary.]**

Q How is the pitch of a note measured? **[It is measured in the frequency of the sound waves it creates. The units are Hertz.]**

Q How could you mathematically describe the sounds that an instrument is capable of making? **[Write the lowest frequency and highest frequency in set notation or in an inequality.]**

EXTENSION
Have students research the frequencies that can be heard by various animals. Students should present the ranges as inequalities. Students can identify the animals with the best and worst hearing, those that hear low sounds best or high sounds best. Ask students to describe how each animal may use this range to its advantage.

 Increase students' depth of knowledge with interactive online activities.

 Show Problems from each lesson solved step by step. Instant replay allows students to go at their own pace when studying online.

 Assign homework to individual students or to an entire class.

 Prepare students for the Mid-Chapter Quiz and Chapter Test with online practice and review.

Variable

BIG idea Quantities are used to form expressions, equations, and inequalities. An expression refers to a quantity but does not make a statement about it. An equation (or an inequality) is a statement about the quantities it mentions. Using variables in place of numbers in equations (or inequalities) allows the statement of relationships among numbers that are unknown or unspecified.

ESSENTIAL UNDERSTANDINGS

3-1   An inequality is a mathematical sentence that uses an inequality symbol to compare the values of two expressions. Inequalities can be represented with symbols. Their solutions can be represented on a number line.

3-2 to 3-6 Just as properties of equality can be used to solve equations, properties of inequality can be used to solve inequalities (including multi-step and compound inequalities.)

Equivalence

BIG idea A single quantity may be represented by many different expressions. The facts about a quantity may be expressed by many different equations (or inequalities).

ESSENTIAL UNDERSTANDINGS

3-2 to 3-6 Just as equivalent equations can be used to solve equations, equivalent inequalities can be used to solve inequalities (including multi-step and compound inequalities.)

3-7   An equivalent pair of linear equations or inequalities can be used to solve absolute value equations and inequalities.

Solving Equations & Inequalities

BIG idea Solving an equation is the process of rewriting the equation to make what it says about its variable(s) as simple as possible. Properties of numbers and equality can be used to transform an equation (or inequality) into equivalent, simpler equations (or inequalities) in order to find solutions. Useful information about equations and inequalities (including solutions) can be found by analyzing graphs or tables. The numbers and types of solutions vary predictably, based on the type of equation.

ESSENTIAL UNDERSTANDINGS

3-2 to 3-6 Just as equations can be solved using the properties of equality, inequalities (including multi-step and compound inequalities) can be solved using the properties of inequality.

3-7   Absolute value equations and inequalities can be solved by first isolating the absolute value expression, if necessary, then writing an equivalent pair of linear equations or inequalities.

Graphing Inequalities

The solutions of a simple inequality can be graphed on a number line by an arrow that points left or right from an open or closed circle. If the solution includes the value ($\leq$ or $\geq$), then the circle will be closed. If the solution does not include the value ($<$ or $>$), then the circle will be open. The solutions of the inequality $x + 1 \leq 3$ are shown.

$$x + 1 - 1 \leq 3 - 1$$
$$x \leq 2$$

The solutions of a compound inequality can also be represented on a number line. Compound inequalities are simple inequalities joined by either the word *and* or the word *or*.

The solutions of a compound inequality with the word *and* are the intersection of the solutions of both the simple inequalities. The solutions of a compound inequality with the word *or* are the union of the solutions of both the simple inequalities.

The solutions of a compound inequality $4 < x < 10$ are the intersection of the solutions of the two simple inequalities $4 < x$ and $x < 10$. Its graph has an open circle at 4 and an open circle at 10 with the line between the circles shaded.

One type of inequality that may result in a compound inequality is an absolute value inequality.

$$|x + 1| < 3$$
$$x + 1 - 1 < 3 - 1 \quad \text{and} \quad x + 1 - 1 > -3 - 1$$
$$x < 2 \qquad\qquad\qquad x > -4$$

Common Errors With Graphing Equalities

Graphing compound inequalities requires that students remember that *and* means intersection and *or* means union. Explain that *and* implies that both inequalities are true, so the solutions must satisfy both inequalities. *Or* implies that either of the inequalities can be true, so all solutions are included in the set.

Equivalent Inequalities

Given an inequality like $x \leq 2$, it is clear that the solutions are any number less than or equal to 2.

However, given an inequality like $-2x \geq 6$, the solutions are not clear. You can solve the inequality by using the properties of inequality to write equivalent inequalities. Equivalent inequalities have the same solution set, but are in different forms.

The process of simplifying an inequality may require finding an equivalent inequality by multiplying or dividing each side of the inequality by a negative number. In these situations, the direction of the inequality symbol must be reversed.

$$-2x \geq 6$$
$$\frac{-2x}{-2} \leq \frac{6}{-2} \qquad \text{Divide each side by } -2.$$
$$x \leq -3 \qquad \text{Simplify.}$$

```
<---+---+---•---+---+---+---+---+---+--->
   -6  -4  -2   0   2   4
```

The inequalities $-2x \geq 6$ and $x \leq -3$ are equivalent.

Common Errors With Equivalent Inequalities

Multiplying and dividing an inequality by a negative number requires students to remember to reverse the inequality symbol. Students make two common errors with regards to this rule.
- They simply forget to change the symbol.
- They change the symbol when there is a negative number in the problem, even though the problem may not require multiplying or dividing by a negative. For example, $4x > -12$.

Set Notation

Sets can be written in roster form and set-builder notation.

Set	Whole numbers less than 6	Integers greater than -4
Roster Form	$\{5, 4, 3, 2, 1, 0\}$	$\{-3, -2, -1, \ldots\}$
Set-Builder Notation	$\{x \mid x \text{ is a whole number, } x < 6\}$	$\{x \mid x \text{ is an integer, } x > -4\}$

When dealing with sets of non-discrete real numbers use set-builder notation.

Set	Set-Builder Notation
$x < 6$	$\{x \mid x < 6\}$ "The set of all values of x such that x is less than 6."
$x > -4$	$\{x \mid x > -4\}$ "The set of all values of x such that x is greater than -4."

Notice how the intersection of the two inequalities above is the set of the solutions of the inequality $|x - 1| < 5$.

$$|x - 1| < 5$$
$$x - 1 < 5 \qquad \text{and} \qquad x - 1 > -5$$
$$x < 6 \qquad\qquad\qquad x - 1 > -4$$

The solution in set-builder notation can be written $\{x \mid x > -4\} \cap \{x \mid x < 6\}$ where $\cap$ means intersection.

A diagram can help students write the solution more simply.

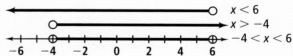

Common Errors With Set Notation

Students often forget to state the domain in set-builder notation when the domain is a subset of the real numbers.

SOLVING INEQUALITIES
Pacing and Assignment Guide

		TRADITIONAL			BLOCK
Lesson	Teaching Day(s)	Basic	Average	Advanced	Block
3-1	1	Problems 1-5 Exs. 8–39 all, 40–58 even, 65–79	Problems 1-5 Exs. 9–39 odd, 40–59, 65–79	Problems 1-5 Exs. 9–39 odd, 40–79	**Day 1** Problems 1-5 Exs. 9–39 odd, 40–59, 65–79
3-2	1	Problems 1-4 Exs. 9–44 all, 46–70 even, 81–92	Problems 1-4 Exs. 9–43 odd, 45–75, 81–92	Problems 1-4 Exs. 9–43 odd, 45–92	Problems 1-4 Exs. 9–43 odd, 45–75, 81–92
3-3	1	Problems 1-2 Exs. 7–18 all, 46–48 even, 49, 59	Problems 1-4 Exs. 7–31 odd, 33–62, 65–76	Problems 1-4 Exs. 7–31 odd, 33–76	**Day 2** Problems 1-4 Exs. 7–31 odd, 33–62, 65–76
	2	Problems 3-4 Exs. 19–32 all, 34–44 even, 49, 50–56 even, 60, 65–76			
3-4	1	Problems 1-3 Exs. 9–22 all, 44	Problems 1-3 Exs. 9–21 odd, 44, 47–48	Problems 1-5 Exs. 9–33 odd, 35–68	Problems 1-3 Exs. 9–21 odd, 44, 47–48
	2	Problems 4-5 Exs. 23–34 all, 36–42 even, 46, 51, 53–54, 58–68	Problems 4-5 Exs. 23–33 odd, 35–43, 45–46, 49–54, 58–68		**Day 3** Problems 4-5 Exs. 23–33 odd, 35–43, 45–46, 49–54, 58–68
3-5	1	Problems 1-4 Exs. 9–29 all, 30–38 even, 39, 40–48 even, 53–66	Problems 1-4 Exs. 9–27 odd, 29–49, 53–66	Problems 1-4 Exs. 9–27 odd, 29–66	Problems 1-4 Exs. 9–27 odd, 29–49, 53–66
3-6	1	Problems 1-3 Exs. 9–16 all, 43	Problems 1-3 Exs. 9–15 odd, 43–47	Problems 1-3 Exs. 9–15 odd, 43–47	**Day 4** Problems 1-5 Exs. 9–29 odd, 31–50, 53–64
	2	Problems 4-5 Exs. 17–30 all, 32–40 even, 48–50, 53–64	Problems 4-5 Exs. 17–29 odd, 31–42, 48–50, 53–64	Problems 4-5 Exs. 9–29 odd, 31–42, 48–64	
3-7	1	Problems 1-3 Exs. 9–31 all, 63, 64, 76	Problems 1-3 Exs. 9–31 odd, 63, 64, 66, 68	Problems 1-3 Exs. 9–31 odd, 63, 64, 66, 68, 77–82	**Day 5** Problems 1-5 Exs. 9–47 odd, 49–76, 83–97
		Problems 4-5 Exs. 32–48 all, 50–60 even, 61, 62, 65, 69, 72–74 even, 83–97	Problems 4-5 Exs. 33–47 odd, 49–62, 65, 67, 69–76, 83–97	Problems 4-5 Exs. 33–47 odd, 49–62, 65, 67, 69–76, 83–97	
3-8	1	Problems 1-2 Exs. 10–21	Problems 1-2 Exs. 11–21 odd, 33–43	Problems 1-2 Exs. 11–21 odd, 33–43	**Day 6** Problems 1-5 Exs. 11–31 odd, 33–43, 46–63
	2	Problems 3-5 Exs. 22–32 all, 36–43, 46–63	Problems 3-5 Exs. 23–31 odd, 46–63	Problems 3-5 Exs. 23–31 odd, 44–60	
Review	1	Chapter 3 Review	Chapter 3 Review	Chapter 3 Review	**Day 7** Chapter 3 Review
Assess	1	Chapter 3 Test	Chapter 3 Test	Chapter 3 Test	Chapter 3 Test
Total		**15 Days**	**14 Days**	**13 Days**	**7 Days**

Note: Pacing does not include Concept Bytes and other feature pages.

Resources

	For the Chapter	3-1	3-2	3-3	3-4	3-5	3-6	3-7	3-8
Planning									
Teacher Center Online Planner & Grade Book	I	I	I	I	I	I	I	I	I
Interactive Learning & Guided Instruction									
My Math Video	I								
Solve It!		I TM	I TM	I TM	I TM	I TM	I TM	I TM	I TM
Student Companion (SP)*		P M	P M	P M	P M	P M	P M	P M	P M
Vocabulary Support		I P M	I P M	I P M	I P M	I P M	I P M	I P M	I P M
Got It? Support		I P	I P	I P	I P	I P	I P	I P	I P
Dynamic Activity		I		I			I		
Online Problems		I	I	I	I	I	I	I	I
Additional Problems		M	M	M	M	M	M	M	M
English Language Learner Support (TR)		E P M	E P M	E P M	E P M	E P M	E P M	E P M	E P M
Activities, Games, and Puzzles		E M	E M	E M	E M	E M	E M	E M	E M
Teaching With TI Technology With CD-ROM									
TI-Nspire™ Support CD-ROM		✓	✓	✓	✓	✓	✓	✓	✓
Lesson Check & Practice									
Student Companion (SP)*		P M	P M	P M	P M	P M	P M	P M	P M
Lesson Check Support		I P	I P	I P	I P	I P	I P	I P	I P
Practice and Problem Solving Workbook (SP)		P	P	P	P	P	P	P	P
Think About a Plan (TR)*		E P M	E P M	E P M	E P M	E P M	E P M	E P M	E P M
Practice Form G (TR)*		E P M	E P M	E P M	E P M	E P M	E P M	E P M	E P M
Standardized Test Prep (TR)*		P M	P M	P M	P M	P M	P M	P M	P M
Practice Form K (TR)*		E P M	E P M	E P M	E P M	E P M	E P M	E P M	E P M
Extra Practice	E M								
Find the Errors!	M								
Enrichment (TR)		E P M	E P M	E P M	E P M	E P M	E P M	E P M	E P M
Answers and Solutions CD-ROM	✓	✓	✓	✓	✓	✓	✓	✓	✓
Assess & Remediate									
ExamView CD-ROM	✓	✓	✓	✓	✓	✓	✓	✓	✓
Lesson Quiz		I TM	I TM	I TM	I TM	I TM	I TM	I TM	I TM
Quizzes and Tests Form G (TR)*	E P M				E P M				E P M
Quizzes and Tests Form K (TR)*	E P M				E P M				E P M
Reteaching (TR)*		E P M	E P M	E P M	E P M	E P M	E P M	E P M	E P M
Performance Tasks (TR)*	P M								
Cumulative Review (TR)*	P M								
Progress Monitoring Assessments	I P M								

(TR) Available in All-In-One Teaching Resources   * Spanish available

1 Interactive Learning

Solve It!

PURPOSE To introduce an inequality relationship in a real-world context

PROCESS Students may draw a diagram of the street and label it with dimensions or write a number sentence using the given information.

FACILITATE

Q What is an expression that models the width of the street? [*x* = **number of lanes in the street, 10***x*]

Q What is an inequality that models the maximum height of the building? [*x* = **number of lanes,** *h* = **height of building,** *h* ≤ 10*x* + 20]

ANSWER See Solve It in Answers on next page.
CONNECT THE MATH The height determined in the Solve It is a maximum height. Students should realize that buildings along Pennsylvania Avenue can be other heights and that it is not possible to list all heights within the law. Therefore, an inequality is the only way to write a statement that includes all possible heights.

2 Guided Instruction

Problem 1

Q How can you determine which direction the inequality symbol opens? [**The symbol opens to the greater of the two quantities and points to the lesser of the two quantities.**]

3-1 Inequalities and Their Graphs

Indiana Academic Standard
A1.2.5 Solve problems that can be modeled using linear equations and inequalities, interpret the solutions, and determine whether the solutions are reasonable.

Objective To write, graph, and identify solutions of inequalities

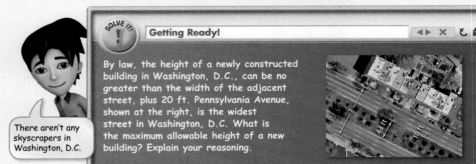

Getting Ready!

By law, the height of a newly constructed building in Washington, D.C., can be no greater than the width of the adjacent street, plus 20 ft. Pennsylvania Avenue, shown at the right, is the widest street in Washington, D.C. What is the maximum allowable height of a new building? Explain your reasoning.

There aren't any skyscrapers in Washington, D.C.

Lesson Vocabulary
• solution of an inequality

The Solve It involves comparing two quantities—the height of a building and the width of the street adjacent to it. You can use an inequality to compare such quantities.

Essential Understanding An inequality is a mathematical sentence that uses an inequality symbol to compare the values of two expressions. You can use a number line to visually represent the values that satisfy an inequality.

Problem 1 Writing Inequalities

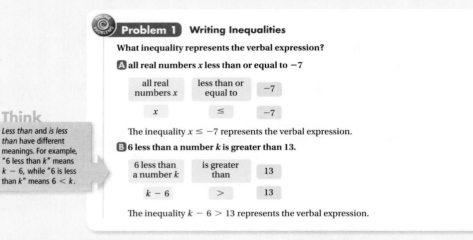

What inequality represents the verbal expression?

Ⓐ all real numbers *x* less than or equal to −7

all real numbers *x*	less than or equal to	−7
x	≤	−7

The inequality $x \le -7$ represents the verbal expression.

Ⓑ 6 less than a number *k* is greater than 13.

6 less than a number *k*	is greater than	13
k − 6	>	13

The inequality $k - 6 > 13$ represents the verbal expression.

Think

Less than and *is less than* have different meanings. For example, "6 less than *k*" means $k - 6$, while "6 is less than *k*" means $6 < k$.

3-1 Preparing to Teach

BIG idea **Variable**   **UbD**

ESSENTIAL UNDERSTANDINGS
• An inequality is a mathematical sentence that uses an inequality symbol to compare the values of two expressions.
• Inequalities can be represented with symbols.
• The solution of an inequality can be represented on a number line.

Math Background

An equation such as *x* = 7 has only one solution. It can be graphed on a number line as:

The solutions of the inequality *x* > 7 are all real numbers greater than 7. They can be graphed on a number line as:

The open dot at 7 indicates that 7 is not included in the solution.

The solutions of the inequality *x* ≥ 7 are all numbers equal to or greater than 7. They can be graphed as:

The closed dot at 7 indicates that 7 is part of the solution.

Label some irrational numbers, fractions, and whole numbers on the graph of *x* ≥ 7. Help students see that the answer set includes all of these and is an infinite set.

Support Student Learning

Use the **Algebra 1 Companion** to engage and support students during instructions. See Lesson Resources at the end of this lesson for details.

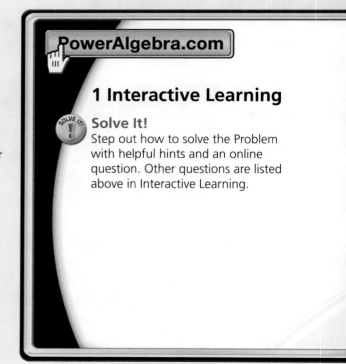

PowerAlgebra.com

1 Interactive Learning

Solve It!

Step out how to solve the Problem with helpful hints and an online question. Other questions are listed above in Interactive Learning.

Got It? **1.** What is an inequality that represents the verbal expression?
    a. all real numbers p greater than or equal to 1.5
    b. The sum of t and 7 is less than -3.

A **solution of an inequality** is any number that makes the inequality true. The solutions of the inequality $x < 5$ are all real numbers x that are less than 5. You can evaluate an expression to determine whether a value is a solution of an inequality.

 Problem 2 Identifying Solutions by Evaluating

Is the number a solution of $2x + 1 > -3$?

A -3

$$2x + 1 > -3$$
$$2(-3) + 1 \overset{?}{>} -3 \qquad \leftarrow \text{Substitute for } x. \rightarrow$$
$$-6 + 1 \overset{?}{>} -3 \qquad \leftarrow \text{Simplify.} \rightarrow$$
$$-5 \not> -3 \qquad \leftarrow \text{Compare.} \rightarrow$$

-3 does not make the original inequality true, so -3 is *not* a solution.

B -1

$$2x + 1 > -3$$
$$2(-1) + 1 \overset{?}{>} -3$$
$$-2 + 1 \overset{?}{>} -3$$
$$-1 > -3$$

-1 does make the original inequality true, so -1 is a solution.

Think

Is -1 the *only* solution to the inequality?
No. *Any* number that makes the original inequality true is a solution of the inequality. The solution -1 is one of an infinite number of solutions.

 Got It? **2. a.** Consider the numbers $-1, 0, 1,$ and 3. Which are solutions of
    $13 - 7y \le 6$?
  b. Reasoning In Problem 2, how is the solution of the related equation
    $2x + 1 = -3$ related to the solutions of the inequality?

You can use a graph to indicate all of the solutions of an inequality.

Inequality   **Graph**

$n < 1$

The open dot shows that 1 is *not* a solution. Shade to the left of 1.

$a \ge 0$

The closed dot shows that 0 is a solution. Shade to the right of 0.

$f > -3$

The open dot shows that -3 is *not* a solution. Shade to the right of -3.

$-2 \ge x$

The closed dot shows that -2 is a solution. Shade to the left of -2.

You can also write $-2 \ge x$ as $x \le -2$.

Encourage students to break the verbal expression into three parts, one for the left side of the inequality, one for the inequality symbol, and one for the right side of the inequality.

Problem 2
Students must substitute values into the algebraic inequality and then determine if the resulting numerical inequality is true or false.

Q After substituting the given value into the inequality, how do you determine which operation to perform? **[Use the order of operations.]**

Q Can a solution of the inequality $2x + 1 > -3$ be a number that is not an integer? Give an example. **[Yes; any number greater than -2 is a solution of the inequality.]**

Got It?   **VISUAL LEARNERS**
It may be helpful to students to make a three-column table such as the one below.

Given Value	Result	Solution? (Y/N)

Answers

Solve It!
143 ft; explanations may vary.

Got It?
  1. a. $p \ge 1.5$
    b. $t + 7 < -3$
  2. a. 1 and 3
    b. The solution of the equation is -2. The solution of the inequality is all real numbers greater than -2.

---

2 Guided Instruction

Each Problem is worked out and supported online.

Problem 1
Writing Inequalities

Problem 2
Identifying Solutions by Evaluating
        Animated

Problem 3
Graphing an Inequality
        Animated

Problem 4
Writing an Inequality From a Graph
        Animated

Problem 5
Writing Real-World Inequalities

Support in Algebra 1 Companion
• Vocabulary
• Key Concepts
• Got It?

Problem 3

Q Why is the first step to rewrite $2 \geq a$ as $a \leq 2$? **[An inequality with the variable on the left side is easier to graph.]**

Q Why does the solution to $a \leq 2$ look like

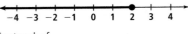

instead of

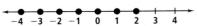

[The dots only represent the integer solutions, while the shading includes all real number solutions.]

Got It?

Q How is the inequality symbol related to the shading on the number line in 3a and 3b? **[When the inequality is written with the variable on the left, the inequality symbol points in the direction of the shading.]**

Problem 4   ERROR PREVENTION

Make sure students accurately describe the graph before writing the inequality.

Q How can you describe the graph in 4A? **[all real numbers greater than or equal to −1]**

Q How can you describe the graph in 4B? **[all real numbers less than 4]**

Got It?

To reinforce the meaning of the inequality symbols, ask students to write two inequalities—one with the variable on the left and one with the variable on the right.

Problem 3   **Graphing an Inequality**

What is the graph of $2 \geq a$?

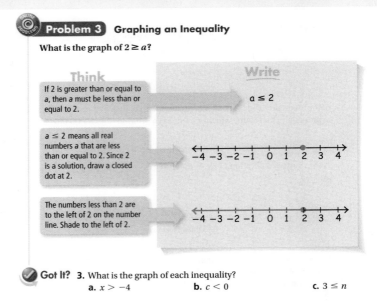

Got It? 3. What is the graph of each inequality?
    a. $x > -4$ **b.** $c < 0$ **c.** $3 \leq n$

Problem 4   **Writing an Inequality From a Graph**

What inequality represents the graph?

Plan

How do you know which inequality symbol to use?
Look at the arrow to see whether the solution is for quantities greater than or less than the endpoint. Look at the endpoint to see whether "equal to" is included in the solution.

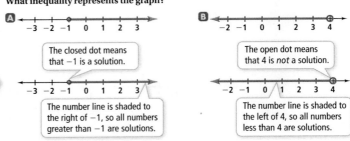

The inequality $x \geq -1$ represents the graph.   The inequality $x < 4$ represents the graph.

Got It? 4. What inequality represents each graph?

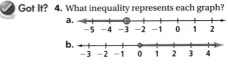

Additional Problems

1. What inequality represents the verbal expression?
  a. all real numbers x that are less than or equal to 5
  b. 4 less than a number y is greater than 10
  ANSWER a. $x \leq 5$, **b.** $y - 4 > 10$

2. Is each number a solution of $3x - 2 < -1$?
  a. 4
  b. −3
  ANSWER a. no **b.** yes

3. What is the graph of $4 \geq b$?
  ANSWER

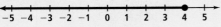

4. What inequality represents the graph?
  a.

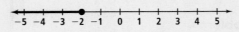

  b.

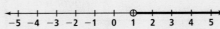

  ANSWER a. $x \leq -2$, **b.** $x > 1$

5. What inequality describes each situation? Be sure to define a variable.
  a.

You must be at least 4 feet tall to ride this roller coaster

  b.

SPEED LIMIT **35** MPH

ANSWER a. Let h be the height in feet. The sign indicates that $h \geq 4$.
b. Let s be the speed in miles per hour. The sign indicates that $s \leq 35$.

Problem 5 Writing Real-World Inequalities

What inequality describes the situation? Be sure to define a variable.

Plan

How do you know which inequality symbol to use?
The phrase "starting at $19.99" implies that the cost of a trail ride starts at $19.99 and goes up. So the cost is greater than or equal to 19.99.

A

Let c = the cost of a trail ride in dollars.
The sign indicates that $c \geq 19.99$.

B

Let s = a legal speed in miles per hour.
The sign indicates that $s \leq 8$.

 Got It? 5. **Reasoning** In part (B) of Problem 5, can the speed be *all* real numbers less than or equal to 8? Explain.

 take note

Concept Summary Representing Inequalities

Words	Symbols	Graph
x is less than 3.	$x < 3$	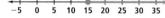
x is greater than -2.	$x > -2$	
x is less than or equal to 0.	$x \leq 0$	
x is greater than or equal to 1.	$x \geq 1$	

✓ **Lesson Check**

Do you know HOW?

1. What algebraic inequality represents all real numbers y that are greater than or equal to 12?

2. Is the number a solution of $6x - 3 \geq 10$?
   a. -1 b. 0   c. 3   d. 4

3. What is the graph of $2 > p$?

4. What inequality represents the graph?

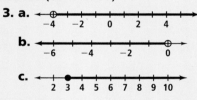

Do you UNDERSTAND?

5. **Vocabulary** How do you decide whether a number is a solution of an inequality?

6. **Compare and Contrast** What are some situations you could model with $x \geq 0$? How do they differ from situations you could model with $x > 0$?

7. **Open-Ended** What is a real-world situation that you can represent with the following graph?

Problem 5

Q Do all numbers that are solutions to the inequality $c \geq 20$ make sense in the real-world situation? Explain. **[No; only numbers with two decimal places or no decimal places are typically used to represent money.]**

Got It?

Q What inequality could be used in conjunction with $s \leq 7\ 1/2$ to indicate all possible legal speeds? Why? **[$s \geq 0$; speed cannot be negative.]**

Take Note
Reinforce that the inequality $x \leq 0$ is a combination of an inequality ($x < 0$) and an equation ($x = 0$).

3 Lesson Check

Do you know HOW?
• If students have difficulty with Exercise 2, have them review the steps presented in Problem 2.

Do you UNDERSTAND?
• If students have difficulty with Exercise 7, first have them write the inequality as an equation.

Close

Q How can you be sure you wrote a correct inequality for a real-world situation? **[Sample: Substitute a value for the variable and verify the resulting inequality is true.]**

Answers

Got It? (continued)

3. a.
   b.
   c.

4. a. $x < -3$
   b. $x \geq 0$

5. No; the speed limit can only be nonnegative real numbers.

Lesson Check

1. $y \geq 12$

2. a. no
   b. no
   c. yes
   d. yes

3.

4. $x \leq -3$

5. Substitute the number for the variable and simplify. If the number makes the inequality true, then it is a solution of the inequality.

6. Answers may vary. Sample: $x \geq 0$, whole numbers, a baseball team's score during an inning, amount in cubic centimeters of liquid in a chemistry beaker; $x > 0$, counting numbers, length of a poster, distance in blocks between your house and a park

7. Check students' work.

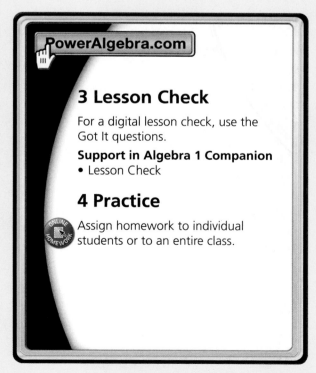

PowerAlgebra.com

3 Lesson Check

For a digital lesson check, use the Got It questions.

Support in Algebra 1 Companion
• Lesson Check

4 Practice

Assign homework to individual students or to an entire class.

4 Practice

ASSIGNMENT GUIDE

Basic: 8–39 all, 40–58 even

Average: 9–39 odd, 40–59

Advanced: 9–39 odd, 40–64

Standardized Test Prep: 65–68

Mixed Review: 69–79

Reasoning exercises have blue headings.

Applications exercises have red headings.

EXERCISE 56: Use the Think About a Plan worksheet in the **Practice and Problem Solving Workbook** (also available in the Teaching Resources in print and online) to further support students' development in becoming independent learners.

HOMEWORK QUICK CHECK

To check students' understanding of key skills and concepts, go over Exercises 13, 29, 50, 56, and 58.

Practice and Problem-Solving Exercises

 Practice   Write an inequality that represents each verbal expression.   ◆ See Problem 1.

8. v is greater than or equal to 5.   **9.** b is less than 4.

10. 3 less than g is less than or equal to 17.   **11.** The quotient of k and 9 is greater than $\frac{1}{3}$.

Determine whether each number is a solution of the given inequality.   ◆ See Problem 2.

12. $3y - 8 > 22$	**a.** 2	**b.** 0	**c.** 5
13. $8m - 6 \leq 10$	**a.** 2	**b.** 3	**c.** −1
14. $4x + 2 < -6$	**a.** 0	**b.** −2	**c.** 1
15. $\frac{6 - n}{n} \geq 11$	**a.** 0.5	**b.** 2	**c.** 4
16. $m(m - 3) < 54$	**a.** −10	**b.** 0	**c.** 9

Match each inequality with its graph.   ◆ See Problem 3.

17. $x < -1$ **18.** $x \geq -1$ **19.** $-1 < x$ **20.** $-1 \geq x$

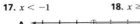

Graph each inequality.

21. $y > 2$ **22.** $t < -4$ **23.** $z \leq -5$ **24.** $v \geq -2$

25. $-3 < f$ **26.** $-\frac{9}{4} \leq c$ **27.** $8 \geq b$ **28.** $5.75 > d$

Write an inequality for each graph.   ◆ See Problem 4.

29.   **30.**

31.   **32.**

33.   **34.**

Define a variable and write an inequality to model each situation.   ◆ See Problem 5.

35. The restaurant can seat at most 172 people.

36. A person must be at least 35 years old to be elected President of the United States.

37. A light bulb can be no more than 75 watts to be safely used in this light fixture.

38. At least 475 students attended the orchestra concert Thursday night.

39. A law clerk has earned more than $20,000 since being hired.

Answers

Practice and Problem-Solving Exercises

8. $v \geq 5$

9. $b < 4$

10. $g - 3 \leq 17$

11. $\frac{k}{9} > \frac{1}{3}$

12. a. no
  b. no
  c. no

13. a. yes
  b. no
  c. yes

14. a. no
  b. no
  c. no

15. a. yes
  b. no
  c. no

16. a. no
  b. yes
  c. no

17. D   **18.** B

19. A   **20.** C

21.

22.

23.

24.

25.

26.

27.

28.

29. $x > -4$

30. $x \leq 8$

31. $x \geq 2$

32. $x < -7$

33. $x \geq 5$

34. $x < 2$

35. Let p = the number of people seated; $p \leq 172$.

36. Let a = age of person being elected; $a \geq 35$.

37. Let w = number of watts of the light bulb; $w \leq 75$.

38. Let s = number of students at concert; $s \geq 475$.

39. Let m = amount of money earned; $m > 20,000$.

B **Apply**

40. Error Analysis A student claims that the inequality $3x + 1 > 0$ is always true because multiplying a number by 3 and then adding 1 to the result always produces a number greater than 0. Explain the student's error.

41. Open-Ended Describe a situation that you can model with $x \geq 25$.

42. Ticket Sales Suppose your school plans a musical. The director's goal is ticket sales of at least $4500. Adult tickets are $7.50 and student tickets $5.00. Let a represent the number of adult tickets and s represent the number of student tickets. Which inequality represents the director's goal?

    Ⓐ $5a + 7.5s < 4500$ Ⓒ $7.5a + 5s \leq 4500$

    Ⓑ $7.5a + 5s > 4500$ Ⓓ $7.5a + 5s \geq 4500$

43. Physics According to Albert Einstein's special theory of relativity, no object can travel faster than the speed of light, which is approximately 186,000 mi/s. What is an inequality that represents this information?

Write each inequality in words.

44. $n < 5$ **45.** $b > 0$ **46.** $7 \geq x$ **47.** $z \geq 25.6$

48. $4 > q$ **49.** $21 \geq m$ **50.** $35 \geq w$ **51.** $g - 2 < 7$

52. $a \leq 3$ **53.** $6 + r > -2$ **54.** $8 \leq h$ **55.** $1.2 > k$

56. Class Party You are making muffins for a class party. You need 2 cups of flour to make a pan of 12 muffins. You have a 5-lb bag of flour, which contains 18 cups. What is an inequality that represents the possible numbers of muffins you can make?

57. Writing Explain what the phrases *no more than* and *no less than* mean when writing inequalities that model real-world situations.

Use the map at the right for Exercises 58 and 59.

58. Think About a Plan You plan to go from Portland to Tucson. Let x be the distance in miles of any flight between Portland and Tucson. What is a true statement about the mileage of any route from Portland to Tucson? Assume that no route visits the same city more than once and that each route has no more than one layover.
- How many routes exist between Portland and Tucson? What are they? Which route is the shortest?
- Can you write an inequality that represents the mileage of any route from Portland to Tucson?

59. Air Travel Your travel agent is making plans for you to go from San Diego to Seattle. A direct flight is not available. Option A consists of flights from San Diego to Boise to Seattle. Option B consists of flights from San Diego to Las Vegas to Seattle. What inequality compares the flight distances of these two options?

40. Answers may vary. Sample: You can use a counterexample to explain the student's error. For instance, when $x = -1$, $3(-1) + 1 = -3 + 1 = -2$, and $-2 \not> 0$.

41. Check students' work.

42. D

43. $x \leq 186{,}000$

44. n is less than 5.

45. b is greater than 0.

46. 7 is greater than or equal to x.

47. z is greater than or equal to 25.6.

48. 4 is greater than q.

49. 21 is greater than or equal to m.

50. 35 is greater than or equal to w.

51. 2 less than g is less than 7.

52. a is less than or equal to 3.

53. r more than 6 is greater than -2.

54. 8 is less than or equal to h.

55. 1.2 is greater than k.

56. $m \leq 108$

57. Answers may vary. Sample: *No more than* means "is less than or equal to," since the amount cannot be greater than the given number. *No less than* means "is greater than or equal to," since the amount cannot be less than the given number.

58. $x \geq 973$ mi

59. $998 > 978$, so Option A > Option B.

Answers

Practice and Problem-Solving Exercises
(continued)

60. D; answers may vary. Sample: Use reasoning or guess and check to see that values of x that are less than 3 make the inequality true.

61. Answers may vary. Sample: If $0 > -2$, then $0^2 > (-2)^2$, or $0 > 4$, which is false.

62. x and y are additive inverses.

63.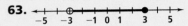

64.

65. C

66. F

67. A

68. [2]

completed	to be repaired

⊢------------ 1263 ft ------------⊣

(OR equivalent diagram) $f > 842$ (OR equivalent inequality)

[1] incorrect diagram or incorrect inequality

69. increase; 20%

70. decrease; 10%

71. decrease; 67%

72. 44

73. $-\frac{5}{24}$

74. -3

75. $-1\frac{3}{7}$

76. 11

77. -2

78. -11

79. $-\frac{1}{9}$

 Challenge

60. Reasoning Which is the correct graph of $-3 < -x$? Explain.

61. Reasoning Give a counterexample for this statement: If $x > y$, then $x^2 > y^2$.

62. Reasoning Describe the numbers x and y such that if $x > y$, then $x^2 = y^2$.

Graph on a number line.

63. all values of p such that $p > -3$ and $p \le 3$

64. all values of q such that $q < -2$ or $q > 5$

Standardized Test Prep

SAT/ACT

65. Which inequality has the same solutions as $k > 6$?

  Ⓐ $k < -6$ Ⓑ $k < 6$ Ⓒ $6 < k$ Ⓓ $-k > -6$

66. What is the value of the expression $\frac{2^3 \cdot 4 - (-3)^2}{(-3)^2 + 4 \cdot 5}$?

  Ⓕ $\frac{23}{29}$ Ⓖ $\frac{41}{29}$ Ⓗ $\frac{23}{11}$ Ⓘ $\frac{41}{11}$

67. Last season, Betsy scored 36 points. This is 8 less than twice the number of points that Amy scored. How many points did Amy score?

  Ⓐ 22   Ⓑ 36   Ⓒ 44   Ⓓ 72

Short Response

68. At an airport, a runway 1263 ft long is being repaired. The project foreman reports that less than one third of the job is complete. Draw a diagram of the runway that shows how much of it has been repaired. What is an inequality that represents the number of feet f that still need to be repaired?

Mixed Review

Tell whether each percent change is an *increase* or *decrease*. Then find the percent change. Round to the nearest percent.   ◀ See Lesson 2-10.

69. original amount: $10
new amount: $12

70. original amount: 20 in.
new amount: 18 in.

71. original amount: 36°
new amount: 12°

Find each product or quotient.   ◀ See Lesson 1-6.

72. $-4(-11)$ **73.** $\frac{5}{6} \cdot \left(-\frac{1}{4}\right)$ **74.** $-3.9 \div 1.3$ **75.** $\frac{4}{7} \div \left(-\frac{2}{5}\right)$

Get Ready!   To prepare for Lesson 3-2, do Exercises 76–79.

Solve each equation.   ◀ See Lesson 2-1.

76. $y - 5 = 6$ **77.** $p - 4 = -6$ **78.** $v + 5 = -6$ **79.** $k + \frac{2}{3} = \frac{5}{9}$

Additional Instructional Support

Algebra 1 Companion

Students can use the **Algebra 1 Companion** worktext (4 pages) as you teach the lesson. Use the Companion to support

- New Vocabulary
- Key Concepts
- Got It for each Problem
- Lesson Check

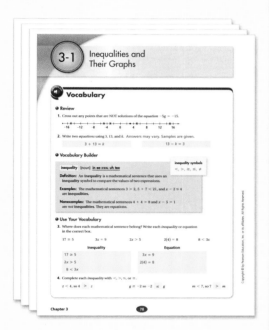

ELL Support

Focus on Language Investigate the word *inequality*. Analyze the word for the root, prefix, and suffix. "Equal" is the same as, the prefix "in" is a negative force, and the suffix "ity" is a state or condition. Invite students to give the meaning of inequality (the condition of not being the same). Write several sentences about math expressions. Have students complete the sentences and then write the sentence using symbols.

Sample sentences:

1. The numbers 5 and ___ can be written as an inequality. **[sample: 9; 5 < 9]**
2. The expression $7 - 3$ and ___ can be written as an inequality. **[sample: 0; $7 - 3 > 0$]**
3. The expression $x +$ ___ and $x -$ ___ can be written as an inequality. **[sample: 8; 2; $x + 8 > x - 2$]**

5 Assess & Remediate

Lesson Quiz

1. What inequality represents each verbal expression?
   a. all real numbers x that are greater than 2
   b. 6 more than a number k is less than or equal to 12
2. Is -2 a solution of the inequality $-2x + 5 \geq 9$?
3. **a.** Graph the inequality $c \leq 3$.
   b. How is the graph of $c < 3$ different from $c \leq 3$?
4. **Do you UNDERSTAND?** What inequality is shown in the graph? What are some inequalities that have this solution?

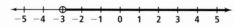

ANSWERS TO LESSON QUIZ

1. a. $x > 2$, **b.** $k + 6 \leq 12$

2. yes

3. a.

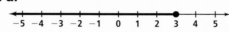

   b. The dot at 3 is open for $c < 3$ and closed for $c \leq 3$.

4. $x > -3$; Answers may vary. Samples: $2x > -6$, $-6x < 18$, $6x + 10 > x - 5$

PRESCRIPTION FOR REMEDIATION
Use the student work on the Lesson Quiz to prescribe a differentiated review assignment.

Points	Differentiated Remediation
0–1	Intervention
2–3	On-level
4	Extension

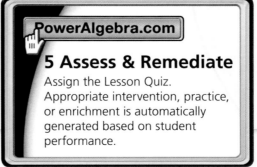

PowerAlgebra.com

5 Assess & Remediate

Assign the Lesson Quiz. Appropriate intervention, practice, or enrichment is automatically generated based on student performance.

Intervention

- **Reteaching** (2 pages) Provides reteaching and practice exercises for the key lesson concepts. Use with struggling students or absent students.
- **English Language Learner Support** Helps students develop and reinforce mathematical vocabulary and key concepts.

All-in-One Resources/Online
Reteaching

3-1 **Reteaching**
Inequalities and Their Graphs

You use the following symbols for inequalities.

> is greater than   ≥ is greater than or equal to
< is less than   ≤ is less than or equal to

Problem

What inequality represents "5 plus a number y is less than -10"?

5 plus a number y is less than -10
$5 + y$ $<$ -10

The inequality $5 + y < -10$ represents the phrase.

Exercises

Write an inequality that represents each verbal expression.

1. p is greater than or equal to 5 $p \geq 5$ 2. a is less than or equal to -4 $a \leq -4$
3. 2 times d is less than 10 $2d < 10$ 4. r divided by 5 is greater than 0 $\frac{r}{5} > 0$

Problem

Is -2 a solution of $3t + 10 \geq 5$?

$3t + 10 \geq 5$ Original inequality
$3(-2) + 10 \geq 5$ Substitute -2 for t.
$-6 + 10 \geq 5$ Simplify.
$4 \geq 5$ -2 is not a solution.

Exercises

Determine whether each number is a solution of the given inequality.

5. $5b - 7 > 13$ a. -4 b. -4 c. 8
   no   no   yes
6. $2(m + 1) < -6$ a. -6 b. -4 c. -2
   yes   no   no
7. $\frac{8 + h}{2} \leq 8$ a. 6   b. 8   c. 10
   yes   yes   no

All-in-One Resources/Online
English Language Learner Support

3-1 **ELL Support**
Inequalities and Their Graphs

For Exercises 1–5, draw a line from the inequality in Column A to its matching verbal expression in Column B. The first one is done for you.

Column A   Column B
1. $t > 42$ 3 less than a number n is greater than 9
2. $s \leq 55$ x is less than negative 5
3. $n - 3 > 9$ children under 3 are admitted free
4. $x < -5$ the speed limit is less than or equal to 55 miles per hour
5. $c < 3$ must be over 42 inches tall to ride

For Exercises 6–10, draw a line from each verbal expression in Column A to its graph in Column B.

Column A   Column B
6. p is greater than 3
7. g is greater than or equal to 4
8. b is less than or equal to 2
9. the quotient of r and 4 is greater than 2
10. v is less than -3

Differentiated Remediation *continued*

On-Level

- **Practice** (2 pages) Provides extra practice for each lesson. For simpler practice exercises, use the Form K Practice pages found in the All-in-One Teaching Resources and online.

- **Think About a Plan** Helps students develop specific problem-solving skills and strategies by providing scaffolded guiding questions.

- **Standardized Test Prep** Focuses on all major exercises, all major question types, and helps students prepare for the high-stakes assessments.

Extension

- **Enrichment** Provides students with interesting problems and activities that extend the concepts of the lesson.

- **Activities, Games, and Puzzles** Worksheets that can be used for concepts development, enrichment, and for fun!

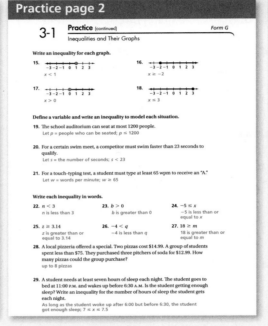

Practice and Problem Solving WKBK/ All-in-One Resources/Online
Practice page 1

Practice and Problem Solving WKBK/ All-in-One Resources/Online
Practice page 2

All-in-One Resources/Online
Enrichment

Practice and Problem Solving WKBK/ All-in-One Resources/Online
Think About a Plan

Practice and Problem Solving WKBK/ All-in-One Resources/Online
Standardized Test Prep

Online Teacher Resource Center
Activities, Games, and Puzzles

3-2 Solving Inequalities Using Addition or Subtraction

Indiana Academic Standard
A1.2.5 Solve problems that can be modeled using linear equations and inequalities, interpret the solutions, and determine whether the solutions are reasonable.

Objective To use addition or subtraction to solve inequalities

There's a minimum number of states you need to win to get elected president.

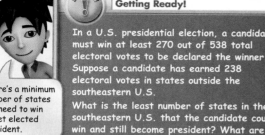

Dynamic Activity
Linear Inequalities

Lesson Vocabulary
• equivalent inequalities

You can model the situation in the Solve It with the inequality $238 + x \geq 270$, where x represents the number of electoral votes needed. You can find its solutions using one of the *properties of inequality*.

Essential Understanding Just as you used properties of equality to solve equations in Chapter 2, you can use properties of inequality to solve inequalities.

The Addition Property of Inequality is shown below. Applying this property to an inequality produces an equivalent inequality. **Equivalent inequalities** are inequalities that have the same solutions.

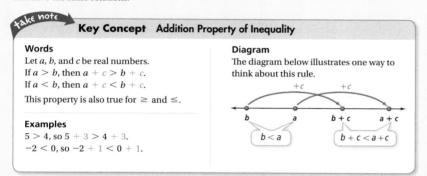

Key Concept Addition Property of Inequality

Words
Let a, b, and c be real numbers.
If $a > b$, then $a + c > b + c$.
If $a < b$, then $a + c < b + c$.
This property is also true for $\geq$ and $\leq$.

Examples
$5 > 4$, so $5 + 3 > 4 + 3$.
$-2 < 0$, so $-2 + 1 < 0 + 1$.

Diagram
The diagram below illustrates one way to think about this rule.

3-2 Preparing to Teach

BIG ideas Variable
Equivalence
Solving Equations and Inequalities

ESSENTIAL UNDERSTANDINGS
• In the same way equations are solved using properties of equality, inequalities are solved using properties of inequality.
• The Addition and Subtraction Properties of Inequality can be used to solve inequalities.

Math Background
Students are familiar with the Addition and Subtraction Properties of Equality. In this lesson, they will learn the Addition and Subtraction Properties of Inequality. These properties are closely related.

The Addition Property of Equality states that if $a = b$, then $a + c = b + c$. In

UbD the Addition Property of Inequality, the only difference is that the equality symbol is replaced with an inequality symbol: If $a < b$ then $a + c < b + c$.

If students think about the properties of inequality in terms of the corresponding Properties of Equality, these properties should be easier to remember and understand.

Support Student Learning
Use the **Algebra 1 Companion** to engage and support students during instructions. See Lesson Resources at the end of this lesson for details.

1 Interactive Learning

Solve It!
PURPOSE To use prior knowledge of equations and inequalities to solve a real-world problem involving an inequality relationship
PROCESS Students may use an organized list, trial and error, a process of elimination, or write an inequality.

FACILITATE

Q If x represents the number of electoral votes still needed, what equation models the minimum number of additional electoral votes needed to reach 270? **[$238 + x = 270$]**

Q How can you systematically determine the least number of states that yield sufficient electoral votes? **[Using a process of elimination, check to see if the state with the most electoral votes provides enough votes. Then add the state with the second most electoral votes and recheck, etc.]**

ANSWER See Solve It in Answers on next page.
CONNECT THE MATH In the Solve It, students modeled a real-world situation with an inequality. In this lesson students will solve an inequality using the Addition and Subtraction Properties of Inequality.

2 Guided Instruction

Take Note

Q How does the Addition Property of Inequality compare to the Addition Property of Equality? **[Adding a real number to both sides of an equation or an inequality maintains the relationship.]**

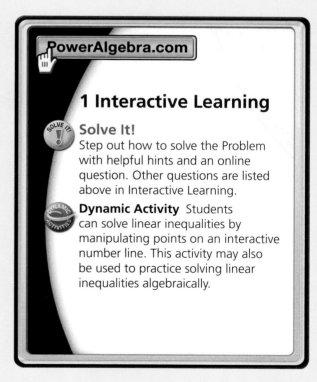

PowerAlgebra.com

1 Interactive Learning

Solve It!
Step out how to solve the Problem with helpful hints and an online question. Other questions are listed above in Interactive Learning.

Dynamic Activity Students can solve linear inequalities by manipulating points on an interactive number line. This activity may also be used to practice solving linear inequalities algebraically.

Problem 1

Students will solve a linear inequality by applying the Addition Property of Inequality to form an equivalent inequality.

> **Q** Why is 15 added to both sides? **[to isolate the variable x]**

Got It?

> **Q** What number must be added to both sides to solve the inequality? **[5]**

Problem 2

Students will solve a linear inequality and display the solutions on a number line.

> **Q** What happens to the original inequality when you substitute a number greater than 13 for *x*? **[The original inequality will be a false statement.]**

Got It?

> **Q** What inequality describes numbers that do not make the inequality true? **[m < 9]**

Problem 1 Using the Addition Property of Inequality

Think

Do you know how to solve a related problem?
Yes. You know how to solve the related equation $x - 15 = -12$ using the Addition Property of Equality.

What are the solutions of $x - 15 > -12$? Graph the solutions.

$$x - 15 > -12$$
$$x - 15 + 15 > -12 + 15 \qquad \text{Add 15 to each side.}$$
$$x > 3 \qquad \text{Simplify.}$$

The solutions of $x > 3$ are all real numbers greater than 3.

Got It? 1. What are the solutions of $n - 5 < -3$? Graph the solutions.

In Problem 1, how can you check that the final inequality $x > 3$ describes the solutions of the original inequality $x - 15 > -12$? The original inequality has infinitely many solutions, so you cannot check them all. However, you can verify that the final inequality is correct by checking its endpoint and the direction of the inequality symbol. You will do this in Problem 2.

Problem 2 Solving an Inequality and Checking Solutions

What are the solutions of $10 \geq x - 3$? Graph and check the solutions.

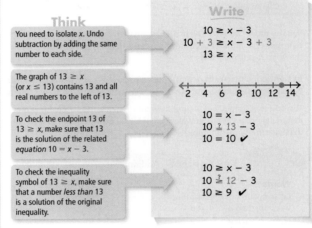

Think	Write
You need to isolate *x*. Undo subtraction by adding the same number to each side.	$10 \geq x - 3$ $10 + 3 \geq x - 3 + 3$ $13 \geq x$
The graph of $13 \geq x$ (or $x \leq 13$) contains 13 and all real numbers to the left of 13.	
To check the endpoint 13 of $13 \geq x$, make sure that 13 is the solution of the related *equation* $10 = x - 3$.	$10 = x - 3$ $10 \overset{?}{=} 13 - 3$ $10 = 10 \checkmark$
To check the inequality symbol of $13 \geq x$, make sure that a number *less than* 13 is a solution of the original inequality.	$10 \geq x - 3$ $10 \overset{?}{\geq} 12 - 3$ $10 \geq 9 \checkmark$

Got It? 2. What are the solutions of $m - 11 \geq -2$? Graph and check the solutions.

Answers

Solve It!
2; Florida and any other state, except Delaware or Washington, D.C.; explanations may vary.

Got It?

1. $n < 2$

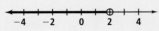

2. $m \geq 9$

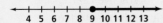

PowerAlgebra.com

2 Guided Instruction

Each Problem is worked out and supported online.

Problem 1
Using the Addition Property of Inequality
Animated

Problem 2
Solving an Inequality and Checking Solutions
Animated

Problem 3
Using the Subtraction Property of Inequality

Problem 4
Writing and Solving an Inequality
Animated

Support in Algebra 1 Companion
- Vocabulary
- Key Concepts
- Got It?

The Subtraction Property of Inequality is shown below.

Key Concept Subtraction Property of Inequality

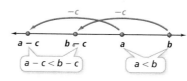

Words

Let a, b, and c be real numbers.
If $a > b$, then $a - c > b - c$.
If $a < b$, then $a - c < b - c$.
This property is also true for $\geq$ and $\leq$.

Examples

$-3 < 5$, so $-3 - 2 < 5 - 2$.
$3 > -4$, so $3 - 1 > -4 - 1$.

Diagram

The diagram below illustrates one way to think about this rule.

Problem 3 Using the Subtraction Property of Inequality

Think

How is this inequality different from others you have seen before?
The expression $t + 6$ involves addition, so you have to use subtraction to undo the addition and isolate the variable.

What are the solutions of $t + 6 > -4$? Graph the solutions.

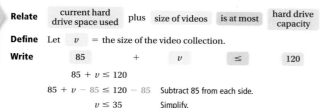

$t + 6 > -4$

$t + 6 - 6 > -4 - 6$ Subtract 6 from each side.

$t > -10$ Simplify.

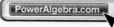

The solutions of $t > -10$ are all real numbers to the right of -10.

Got It? 3. What are the solutions of $-1 \geq y + 12$? Graph the solutions.

Problem 4 Writing and Solving an Inequality

Think

How do you know which inequality symbol to use?
Words and phrases like *at most*, *no more than*, and *maximum* may indicate that you should use $\leq$.

Computers The hard drive on your computer has a capacity of 120 gigabytes (GB). You have used 85 GB. You want to save some home videos to your hard drive. What are the possible sizes of the home video collection you can save?

Relate current hard drive space used plus size of videos is at most hard drive capacity

Define Let v = the size of the video collection.

Write 85 + v $\leq$ 120

$85 + v \leq 120$

$85 + v - 85 \leq 120 - 85$ Subtract 85 from each side.

$v \leq 35$ Simplify.

The home video collection can be any size less than or equal to 35 GB.

Take Note

Q How do you know when to use the Addition Property of Inequality and when to use the Subtraction Property of Inequality? **[The Addition Property of Inequality is used when a number is being subtracted from the variable and the Subtraction Property of Inequality is used when a number is added to the variable.]**

Problem 3
Students will solve a linear inequality by applying the Subtraction Property of Inequality to form an equivalent inequality.

Q What happens if you mistakenly add 6 to each side of the inequality? **[You still have an equivalent inequality, but you did not isolate the variable.]**

Got It?

Q What steps must be followed in order to check the solutions for the inequality? **[First check the endpoint by substituting its value into the related equation. Then check a value from the shaded part of the number line.]**

Problem 4
Students will write a linear inequality and determine which property of inequality to use to solve it. Students will use the solutions of the inequality to answer the question.

Q What are two alternate inequalities that model the real-world situation? **[v + 85 $\leq$ 120; 120 $\geq$ v + 85]**

Additional Problems

1. What are the solutions of $x + 9 < 12$? Graph the solutions.

   ANSWER $x < 3$

   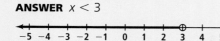

2. What are the solutions of $7 \leq x + 3$? Graph the solutions.

   ANSWER $4 \leq x$

   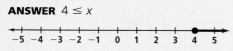

3. What are the solutions of $t + 3 > -1$? Graph the solutions.

   ANSWER $t > -4$

   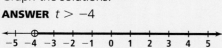

4. The hard drive on your computer has a capacity of 250 gigabytes (GB). You used 115 GB. You want to save some home videos to your hard drive. What are the possible sizes of the home video collection you can save?

   ANSWER less than or equal to 135 GB

Answers

Got It? (continued)

3. $y \leq -13$

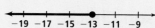

Got It?

After students write and solve an inequality for 4b, ensure they choose a solution and verify the inequality they wrote is correct.

3 Lesson Check

Do you know HOW?

• If students have difficulty with Exercise 5, have them utilize the Relate, Define, Write method presented in Problem 4. They should write the verbal representation first, and then translate to algebraic symbols.

Do you UNDERSTAND?

• If students have difficulty with Exercise 7, have them review the addition and subtraction properties of inequality and try each one for each part.

Close

> **Q** What is a general rule for properties of equations or inequalities? **[Answers may vary. Sample: What you do to one side of the sentence must be done to the other side.]**

PowerAlgebra.com

3 Lesson Check

For a digital lesson check, use the Got It questions.

Support in Algebra 1 Companion
• Lesson Check

4 Practice

Assign homework to individual students or to an entire class.

 Got It? 4. a. A club has a goal to sell at least 25 plants for a fundraiser. Club members sell 8 plants on Wednesday and 9 plants on Thursday. What are the possible numbers of plants the club can sell on Friday to meet their goal?

b. Reasoning Can you use the same inequality symbol to represent phrases like *at least, no less than,* and *greater than or equal to?* Explain.

 ### Lesson Check

Do you know HOW?

Solve each inequality. Graph and check your solutions.

1. $p - 4 < 1$

2. $8 \geq d - 2$

3. $y + 5 < -7$

4. $4 + c > 7$

5. A cyclist takes her bicycle on a chairlift to the top of a slope. The chairlift can safely carry 680 lb. The cyclist weighs 124 lb, and the bicycle weighs 32 lb. What are the possible additional weights the chairlift can safely carry?

Do you UNDERSTAND?

6. Writing How can you use the addition and subtraction properties of inequality to produce equivalent inequalities?

7. Reasoning What can you do to the first inequality in each pair in order to get the second inequality?

    a. $x + 4 \leq 10; x \leq 6$

    b. $m - 1 > 3; m > 4$

    c. $5 \geq 3 + n; 2 \geq n$

    d. $-6 < y - 2; -4 < y$

8. Compare and Contrast Suppose you solve the two inequalities $y + 4 \leq 6$ and $y - 4 \leq 6$. How are your methods of solving the inequalities similar? How are they different?

Practice and Problem-Solving Exercises

A Practice Tell what number you would add to each side of the inequality to solve the inequality. ◀ See Problems 1 and 2.

9. $f - 6 \geq -3$ **10.** $1 < d - 7$ **11.** $a - 3.3 \geq 2.6$ **12.** $5 > -18 + m$

Solve each inequality. Graph and check your solutions.

13. $y - 2 > 11$ **14.** $v - 4 < -3$ **15.** $-6 > c - 2$ **16.** $8 \leq f - 4$

17. $t - 4 \geq -7$ **18.** $s - 10 \leq 1$ **19.** $9 < p - 3$ **20.** $-3 \geq x - 1$

21. $0 < -\frac{1}{3} + f$ **22.** $z - 12 \leq -4$ **23.** $-\frac{3}{4} > r - \frac{3}{4}$ **24.** $y - 1 \geq 1.5$

25. $4.3 > -0.4 + s$ **26.** $-2.5 > n - 0.9$ **27.** $c - \frac{4}{7} < \frac{6}{7}$ **28.** $p - 1\frac{1}{2} > 1\frac{1}{2}$

Tell what number you would subtract from each side of the inequality to solve the inequality. ◀ See Problem 3.

29. $x + 3 > 0$ **30.** $9 < \frac{7}{5} + s$ **31.** $6.8 \geq m + 4.2$ **32.** $\ell + \frac{1}{3} \geq \frac{7}{3}$

Answers

Got It? (continued)

4. a. $p \geq 8$

    b. Yes. The $\geq$ symbol can be used to represent all 3 phrases.

Lesson Check

1. $p < 5$

2. $d \leq 10$

3. $y < -12$

4. $c > 3$

5. $w \leq 524$

6. Add or subtract the same number from each side of the inequality.

7. a. Subtract 4 from each side.

    b. Add 1 to each side.

    c. Subtract 3 from each side.

    d. Add 2 to each side.

8. They are similar in that 4 is being added to or subtracted from each side of the inequalities. They are different in that one inequality adds 4 and the other subtracts 4.

Practice and Problem-Solving Exercises

9. 6   **10.** 7   **11.** 3.3   **12.** 18

13–28. See back of book.

29. 3   **30.** $\frac{7}{5}$ **31.** 4.2   **32.** $\frac{1}{3}$

Solve each inequality. Graph and check your solutions.

33. $x + 5 \le 10$ **34.** $n + 6 > -2$ **35.** $2 < 9 + c$

36. $-1 \ge 5 + b$ **37.** $\frac{1}{4} + a \ge -\frac{3}{4}$ **38.** $8.6 + z < 14$

39. $\frac{1}{3} < n + 3$ **40.** $3.8 \ge b + 4$ **41.** $\frac{3}{5} + d \ge -\frac{2}{5}$

42. Exercise Your goal is to take at least 10,000 steps per day. According to your pedometer, you have walked 5274 steps. Write and solve an inequality to find the possible numbers of steps you can take to reach your goal. ⬅ **See Problem 4.**

43. Fundraising The environmental club is selling indoor herb gardens for Earth Day. Each member is encouraged to sell at least 10 gardens. You sell 3 gardens on Monday and 4 gardens on Tuesday. Write and solve an inequality to find the possible numbers of gardens you can sell to reach your goal.

44. Monthly Budget You earn $250 per month from your part-time job. You are in a kayaking club that costs $20 per month, and you save at least $100 each month. Write and solve an inequality to find the possible amounts you have left to spend each month.

 B **Apply**

Tell what you can do to the first inequality in order to get the second.

45. $36 \le -4 + y; 40 \le y$ **46.** $9 + b > 24; b > 15$ **47.** $m - \frac{1}{2} < \frac{3}{8}; m < \frac{7}{8}$

Tell whether the two inequalities in each pair are equivalent.

48. $45 \le -5 + z; 40 \le z$ **49.** $7 + c > 33; c > 26$ **50.** $n - \frac{1}{4} < \frac{5}{4}; n < 1$

You can draw a model to represent an inequality. For example, the model below represents the inequality $85 + v < 120$. Draw a model to represent each inequality below.

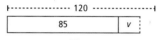

51. $17 + x < 51$ **52.** $12 + y > 18$ **53.** $-3 + m \le 13$

Solve each inequality. Justify each step.

54. $y - 4 + 2 \ge 10$ **55.** $\frac{3}{5} + d \le 2\frac{3}{5}$ **56.** $z - 1.4 < 3.9$

57. $-5 > p - \frac{1}{5}$ **58.** $a + 5.2 < -4.6$ **59.** $-3.1 > z - 1.9$

60. $\frac{5}{8} + v - \frac{7}{16} > 0$ **61.** $-4p - 2 + 5p > 10$ **62.** $5y + 5 - 4y < 8$

63. $h - \frac{1}{8} \ge -1$ **64.** $8v - 7v - 3 \ge -6$ **65.** $5 \ge m - \frac{7}{16}$

66. Government The U.S. Senate is composed of 2 senators from each of the 50 states. In order for a treaty to be ratified, at least two thirds of the senators present must approve the treaty. Suppose all senators are present and 48 of them have voted in favor of a treaty. What are the possible numbers of additional senators who must vote in favor of the treaty in order to ratify it?

ASSIGNMENT GUIDE

Basic: 9–44 all, 46–70 even

Average: 9–43 odd, 45–75

Advanced: 9–43 odd, 45–80

Standardized Test Prep: 81–84

Mixed Review: 85–92

Reasoning exercises have blue headings.

Applications exercises have red headings.

EXERCISE 66: Use the Think About a Plan worksheet in the **Practice and Problem Solving Workbook** (also available in the Teaching Resources in print and online) to further support students' development in becoming independent learners.

HOMEWORK QUICK CHECK

To check students' understanding of key skills and concepts, go over Exercises 15, 35, 66, 68, and 70.

---

33. $x \le 5$

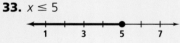

34. $n > -8$

35. $c > -7$

36. $b \le -6$

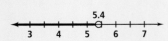

37. $a \ge -1$

38. $z < 5.4$

39. $n > -2\frac{2}{3}$

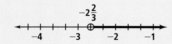

40. $b \le -0.2$

41. $d \ge -1$

42. $5274 + s \ge 10{,}000; s \ge 4726$

43. $3 + 4 + g \ge 10; g \ge 3$

44. $d \le 250 - 20 - 100; d \le 130$

45. Add 4 to each side.

46. Subtract 9 from each side.

47. Add $\frac{1}{2}$ to each side.

48. no

49. yes

50. no

51.
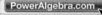

52.

53.
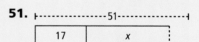

54. $y \ge 12$ **55.** $d \le 2$
56. $z < 5.3$ **57.** $-4\frac{4}{5} > p$
58. $a < -9.8$ **59.** $-1.2 > z$
60. $v > -\frac{3}{16}$ **61.** $p > 12$
62. $y < 3$ **63.** $h \ge -\frac{7}{8}$
64. $v \ge -3$
65. $5\frac{7}{16} \ge m$
66. at least 19 senators

Answers

Practice and Problem-Solving Exercises
(continued)

67. a. yes

b. No; in the first inequality, r is greater than or equal to the amount. In the second inequality, r is less than or equal to the amount.

c. In part (a), these are equations with only one solution. In part (b), because the inequality relationship is different, there is no relationship between the two inequalities.

68. any three numbers greater than or equal to 8.3 and less than or equal to 10; sample: 8.4, 8.5, 8.6

69. Answers may vary. Sample: 94, 95, or 96.

70. 3 should be added to both sides of the inequality;
$-3 + x + 3 > 1 + 3, x > 4$.

71. The graph should be shaded to the right, not the left.

72. a. Check students' work.

b. Check students' work.

73. a. No; the solution should be $a \geq 8.6 - 3.2$, or $a \geq 5.4$.

b. Answers may vary. Sample: Other numbers that are not substituted could also be solutions to the inequality.

74. a. acute

b. right

c. obtuse

---

67. a. If $56 + 58 = t$, does $t = 56 + 58$?

b. If $56 + 58 \leq r$, is $r \leq 56 + 58$? Justify your answer.

c. Explain the differences between these two examples.

68. Think About a Plan You want to qualify for a regional diving competition. At today's competition, you must score at least 53 points. Out of a possible 10 points, your scores on each of the first 5 dives are shown at the right. What scores can you earn on the armstand dive that will qualify you for the regional diving competition?

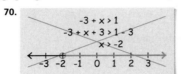

OFFICIAL SCORE CARD	
DIVE	SCORE
Front Dive	9.8
Back Dive	8.9
Reverse Dive	8.4
Inward Dive	8.2
Twisting Dive	9.4
Armstand Dive	?

- What information do you know? What information do you need?
- How might writing and solving an inequality help you?
- What does the solution of the inequality mean in terms of the original situation?

69. Qualifying Scores To enter a competition, students must score a total of at least 450 points on five qualifying tests. Each test is worth 100 points. On the first four tests, your scores were 94, 88, 79, and 95. What are three possible scores you can earn on the last test to enter the competition?

Error Analysis Describe and correct the error in solving each inequality or in graphing the solution.

70.

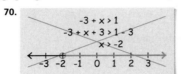

71.

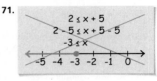

72. a. Open-Ended Use each of the inequality symbols $<$, $\leq$, $>$ and $\geq$ to write four inequalities involving addition or subtraction.

b. Solve each inequality from part (a) and graph your solutions.

73. a. Mallory says that she can solve the inequality $a + 3.2 \geq 8.6$ by replacing a with 5, 6, and 7. When $a = 5$, the inequality is false. When $a = 6$ and when $a = 7$, the inequality is true. So Mallory says that the solution is $a \geq 6$. Is her reasoning correct? Justify your answer.

b. Reasoning Explain why substituting values into the inequality does not guarantee that Mallory's solution is correct.

74. Geometry Suppose a triangle has side lengths a, b, and c, where c is the length of the longest side. You can use the following equation and inequalities to determine whether the triangle is right, acute, or obtuse.

- If $a^2 + b^2 = c^2$, then the triangle is right.
- If $a^2 + b^2 > c^2$, then the triangle is acute.
- If $a^2 + b^2 < c^2$, then the triangle is obtuse.

Classify each triangle with the following side lengths as *right*, *acute*, or *obtuse*.

a. 4 in., 5 in., 6 in.   **b.** 3 cm, 4 cm, 5 cm   **c.** 10 m, 15 m, 20 m

75. Banking To avoid a service fee, your checking account balance must be at least $500 at the end of each month. Your current balance is $536.45. You use your debit card to spend $125.19. What possible amounts can you deposit into your account by the end of the month to avoid paying the service fee?

 Challenge

Reasoning Decide whether each inequality is true for all real numbers. If the inequality is not true, give a counterexample.

76. $x + y > x - y$

77. If $x \le y$, then $x + w \le y + w$.

78. If $w < z$, then $x - w > x - z$.

79. If $x > y$, then $x > y + w$.

80. Reasoning Find real numbers a, b, c, and d for which it is true that $a < b$ and $c < d$, but it is not true that $a - c < b - d$.

Standardized Test Prep

SAT/ACT

81. What is the solution of $-21 + p > 30$?

    Ⓐ $p < 9$ Ⓑ $p > 9$ Ⓒ $p < 51$ Ⓓ $p > 51$

82. Richard won a 130-mi bike race. He finished in 11 h and 45 min. What was his average speed?

    Ⓕ 11.8 mi/h   Ⓖ 11.4 mi/h   Ⓗ 11.1 mi/h   Ⓘ 10.8 mi/h

83. The variable a is an integer. Which of the following values could NOT equal a^3?

    Ⓐ -27 Ⓑ -8 Ⓒ 16   Ⓓ 64

Short Response

84. The leading scorer in your high school's soccer division finished the season with an average of 4 goals per game for 15 games. As the division's second-leading scorer, you have an average of 4 goals per game for 14 games. You still have to play your last game. How many goals must you score in the final game to overtake the division's leading scorer? Show your work.

Mixed Review

Define a variable and write an inequality to model each situation.   ◀ **See Lesson 3-1.**

85. A hummingbird migrates more than 1850 mi.   **86.** An octopus can be up to 18 ft long.

Simplify.   ◀ **See Lesson 1-2.**

87. $7^2 + 23$ **88.** $3(4 - 5)^2 - 4$ **89.** $0.4 + 0.2(4.2 - 3.4)$

Get Ready! To prepare for Lesson 3-3, do Exercises 90–92.

Solve each equation.   ◀ **See Lesson 2-1.**

90. $10 = \frac{v}{2}$ **91.** $15 = -22y$ **92.** $\frac{3}{4}z = -18$

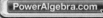
---

75. at least $88.74

76. not true; sample: $x = 5$ and $y = -2$

77. true

78. true

79. not true; sample: $x = 5$, $y = 3$, $w = 4$

80. Answers may vary. Sample: $a = 1$, $b = 2$, $c = -3$, $d = 0$

81. D

82. H

83. C

84. [2] more than 4; $4 \times 15 = 60$ and $4 \times 14 = 56$, $56 + g > 60$, so $g > 4$ (OR equivalent work)

    [1] incorrect solution with appropriate work OR correct solution with no work shown or incorrect work shown

85. Let h = distance in miles the hummingbird migrates; $h > 1850$.

86. Let o = length of octopus in feet; $o \le 18$.

87. 72

88. -1

89. 0.56

90. 20

91. $-\frac{15}{22}$

92. -24

Additional Instructional Support

Algebra 1 Companion
Students can use the **Algebra 1 Companion** worktext (4 pages) as you teach the lesson. Use the Companion to support

• New Vocabulary
• Key Concepts
• Got It for each Problem
• Lesson Check

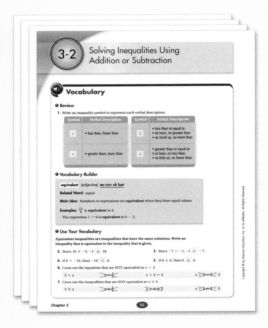

ELL Support
Use Graphic Organizers Ask students to make a table that shows a correspondence between inequalities and verbal phrases like the one below.

>	<	≥	≤
greater than	less than	greater than or equal to	less than or equal to
more than	up to	at least	at most
		not less than	not more than

5 Assess & Remediate

Lesson Quiz
1. Solve the inequality $x - 4 \le -1$. Graph the solutions.
2. Solve the inequality $6 \ge x + 4$. Graph the solutions.
3. What are the solutions of the inequality $h - 2 > 2$? Graph the solutions.
4. **Do you UNDERSTAND?** The hard drive on your computer has a capacity of 160 gigabytes (GB). You have used 122 GB. You want to save some home videos to your hard drive. What are the possible sizes of the home video collection you can save? If u represents the amount of space used, write an inequality that determines a, the amount of space available.

ANSWERS TO LESSON QUIZ
1. $x \le 3$

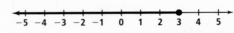

2. $2 \ge x$ or $x \le 2$

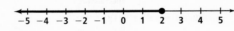

3. $h > 4$

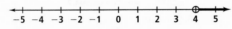

4. at most 38 GB; $a \le 160 - u$

PRESCRIPTION FOR REMEDIATION
Use the student work on the Lesson Quiz to prescribe a differentiated review assignment.

Points	Differentiated Remediation
0–2	Intervention
3	On-level
4	Extension

PowerAlgebra.com

5 Assess & Remediate
Assign the Lesson Quiz. Appropriate intervention, practice, or enrichment is automatically generated based on student performance.

Intervention

• **Reteaching** (2 pages) Provides reteaching and practice exercises for the key lesson concepts. Use with struggling students or absent students.
• **English Language Learner Support** Helps students develop and reinforce mathematical vocabulary and key concepts.

All-in-One Resources/Online
Reteaching

3-2 **Reteaching**
Solving Inequalities Using Addition or Subtraction

You can add the same number to each side of an equation. You can also add the same number to each side of an inequality.

Problem

What are the solutions of $b - 4 > -2$? Graph and check the solutions.
$b - 4 > -2$ Original inequality.
$b - 4 + 4 > -2 + 4$ Add 4 to each side.
$b > 2$ Simplify.

To graph $b > 2$, place an open circle at 2 and shade to the right.

To check the endpoint of $b > 2$, make sure that 2 is the solution of the related equation $b - 4 = -2$.
$b - 4 = -2$
$2 - 4 \stackrel{?}{=} -2$
$-2 = -2 ✓$

Then check to see if a number greater than 2 is a solution of the inequality. 5 is greater than 2.
$b - 4 > -2$
$5 - 4 \stackrel{?}{>} -2$
$1 > -2 ✓$

Exercises

Solve each inequality. Graph and check your solutions.

1. $m - 14 \ge -10$ $m \ge 4$
2. $t - 2 < 4$ $t < 6$
3. $y - 3 \le 4$ $y \le 7$
4. $d - 9 \ge -12$ $d \ge -3$
5. $w - 17 > 13$ $w > 30$
6. $a - 22 < -7$ $a < 15$

7. **Writing** Explain how you would solve $t - 15 \le 5$. add 15 to both sides

8. Anita is baking dinner rolls and pumpkin bread. She needs 4 cups of flour for the rolls. She needs at least 7 cups of flour left for the pumpkin bread. Write and solve an inequality to determine how much flour Anita needs before she starts baking. at least 11 cups

All-in-One Resources/Online
English Language Learner Support

3-2 **ELL Support**
Solving Inequalities Using Addition or Subtraction

Complete the vocabulary chart by filling in the missing information.

Word or Word Phrase	Definition	Picture or Example
Addition Property of Inequality	If $a < b$, then $a + c < b + c$. If $a > b$, then $a + c > b + c$.	$6 > 5$, so $6 + 4 > 5 + 4$
endpoint	An *endpoint* is the beginning or ending point of a segment or the beginning point of a ray.	
equivalent inequalities	*Equivalent inequalities* are inequalities that have the same solution.	$x - 3 \ge 6$ and $x - 9 \ge 0$
isolate	To *isolate* is to get the variable by itself.	$12 > x + 4$ $12 - 4 > x + 4 - 4$ $8 > x$
Subtraction Property of Inequality	If $a < b$, then $a - c < b - c$. If $a > b$, then $a - c > b - c$.	$-2 < 3$, so $-2 - 4 < 3 - 4$

Differentiated Remediation *continued*

On-Level

- **Practice** (2 pages) Provides extra practice for each lesson. For simpler practice exercises, use the Form K Practice pages found in the All-in-One Teaching Resources and online.

- **Think About a Plan** Helps students develop specific problem-solving skills and strategies by providing scaffolded guiding questions.

- **Standardized Test Prep** Focuses on all major exercises, all major question types, and helps students prepare for the high-stakes assessments.

Extension

- **Enrichment** Provides students with interesting problems and activities that extend the concepts of the lesson.

- **Activities, Games, and Puzzles** Worksheets that can be used for concepts development, enrichment, and for fun!

Practice and Problem Solving WKBK/ All-in-One Resources/Online
Practice page 1

Practice and Problem Solving WKBK/ All-in-One Resources/Online
Practice page 2

All-in-One Resources/Online
Enrichment

Practice and Problem Solving WKBK/ All-in-One Resources/Online
Think About a Plan

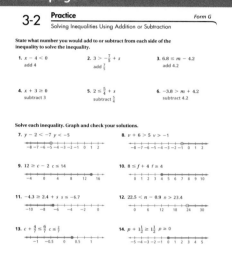

Practice and Problem Solving WKBK/ All-in-One Resources/Online
Standardized Test Prep

Online Teacher Resource Center
Activities, Games, and Puzzles

1 Interactive Learning

Solve It!

PURPOSE To use a pattern to derive the Multiplication Property of Inequality

PROCESS Students may
- use trial and error.
- use number sense.

FACILITATE

Q If the table is extended either with numbers greater than 4 or with numbers less than −3, will the pattern of inequality symbols change? Explain. **[No, the existing pattern extends infinitely in both directions.]**

ANSWER See Solve It in Answers on next page.

CONNECT THE MATH Students may use the pattern in the Solve It to understand the Multiplication Property of Inequality. This lesson will reinforce the idea that when multiplying or dividing both sides of an inequality by a negative number, the direction of the inequality sign is reversed.

2 Guided Instruction

Take Note

Q What are the rules when using the Multiplication Property of Inequality? **[When multiplying both sides of an inequality by a positive number, the direction of the inequality symbol does not change. When multiplying both sides of an inequality by a negative number, the direction of the inequality symbol reverses.]**

Solving Inequalities Using Multiplication or Division

Indiana Academic Standard
A1.2.5 Solve problems that can be modeled using linear equations and inequalities, interpret the solutions, and determine whether the solutions are reasonable.

Objective To use multiplication or division to solve inequalities

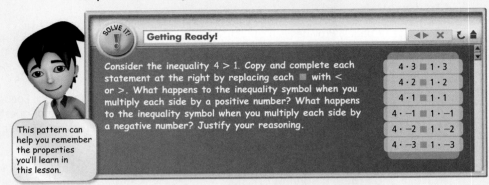

Getting Ready!

Consider the inequality $4 > 1$. Copy and complete each statement at the right by replacing each ■ with < or >. What happens to the inequality symbol when you multiply each side by a positive number? What happens to the inequality symbol when you multiply each side by a negative number? Justify your reasoning.

$4 \cdot 3 \ \blacksquare \ 1 \cdot 3$
$4 \cdot 2 \ \blacksquare \ 1 \cdot 2$
$4 \cdot 1 \ \blacksquare \ 1 \cdot 1$
$4 \cdot -1 \ \blacksquare \ 1 \cdot -1$
$4 \cdot -2 \ \blacksquare \ 1 \cdot -2$
$4 \cdot -3 \ \blacksquare \ 1 \cdot -3$

This pattern can help you remember the properties you'll learn in this lesson.

Dynamic Activity Solving Inequalities

In the Solve It, you may have noticed that multiplying both sides of an inequality by a negative number affects the inequality symbol.

Essential Understanding Just as you used multiplication and division to solve equations in Chapter 2, you can use multiplication and division to solve inequalities.

take note

Key Concept Multiplication Property of Inequality

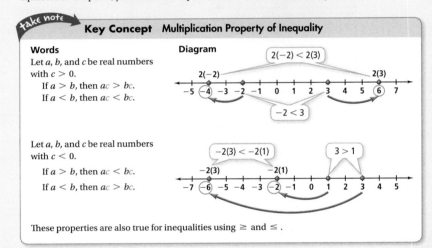

Words
Let a, b, and c be real numbers with $c > 0$.
  If $a > b$, then $ac > bc$.
  If $a < b$, then $ac < bc$.

Let a, b, and c be real numbers with $c < 0$.
  If $a > b$, then $ac < bc$.
  If $a < b$, then $ac > bc$.

These properties are also true for inequalities using $\geq$ and $\leq$.

Preparing to Teach

BIG ideas Variable
         Equivalence
         Solving Equations and Inequalities   **UbD**

ESSENTIAL UNDERSTANDINGS
- In the same way multiplication and division are used to solve equations, multiplication and division can be used to solve inequalities.
- When multiplying or dividing by a negative number, it is necessary to reverse the inequality sign.

Math Background

The Multiplication and Division Properties of Equality are related to the Multiplication and Division Properties of Inequality.

The Multiplication Property of Equality states: If $a = b$, then $ac = bc$. The Multiplication Property of Inequality states: If $a < b$ and $c > 0$, then $ac < bc$. The only difference is that the equality symbol has been replaced with an inequality symbol.

However, if both sides of an inequality are multiplied by a negative number, then students must remember to change the direction of the inequality. In symbols, if $a < b$ and $c < 0$, then $ac > bc$.

Discuss why multiplication by a negative number changes the direction of inequalities. Graph 2 and 4 on a number line and ask students to write the appropriate inequality, $2 < 4$. Multiply both by −2 to get −4 and −8, and graph these values on a number line. Ask students to write the appropriate inequality, $-4 > -8$.

Support Student Learning

Use the **Algebra 1 Companion** to engage and support students during instructions. See Lesson Resources at the end of this lesson for details.

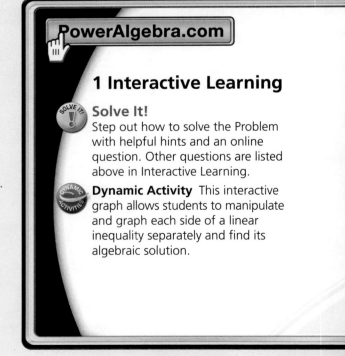

PowerAlgebra.com

1 Interactive Learning

Solve It!
Step out how to solve the Problem with helpful hints and an online question. Other questions are listed above in Interactive Learning.

Dynamic Activity This interactive graph allows students to manipulate and graph each side of a linear inequality separately and find its algebraic solution.

Here's Why It Works Multiplying or dividing each side of an inequality by a negative number changes the meaning of the inequality. You need to reverse the inequality symbol to make the inequality true. Here is an example:

$$3 > 1$$
$$-2(3) \ \blacksquare \ -2(1) \quad \text{Multiply by } -2.$$
$$-6 \ \blacksquare \ -2 \quad \text{Simplify.}$$
$$-6 < -2 \quad \text{Reverse the inequality symbol to make the inequality true.}$$

 Problem 1 Multiplying by a Positive Number

What are the solutions of $\frac{x}{3} < -2$? Graph the solutions.

Think

Why multiply by 3?
You can multiply by any multiple of 3. But multiplying by 3 isolates the variable.

$$\frac{x}{3} < -2$$
$$3\left(\frac{x}{3}\right) < 3(-2) \quad \text{Multiply each side by 3.}$$
$$x < -6 \quad \text{Simplify.}$$

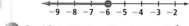
$$\begin{array}{ccccccccc} & & & & & & & & \\ \hline -9 & -8 & -7 & -6 & -5 & -4 & -3 & -2 \end{array}$$

 Got It? **1.** What are the solutions of $\frac{c}{8} > \frac{1}{4}$? Graph the solutions.

 **Problem 2** Multiplying by a Negative Number

What are the solutions of $-\frac{3}{4} w \geq 3$? Graph and check the solutions.

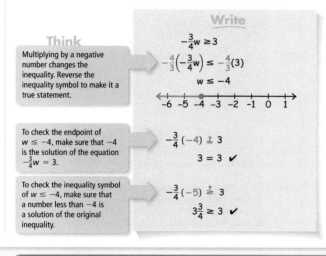

Think

Multiplying by a negative number changes the inequality. Reverse the inequality symbol to make it a true statement.

To check the endpoint of $w \leq -4$, make sure that -4 is the solution of the equation $-\frac{3}{4}w = 3$.

To check the inequality symbol of $w \leq -4$, make sure that a number less than -4 is a solution of the original inequality.

Write
$$-\frac{3}{4}w \geq 3$$
$$-\frac{4}{3}\left(-\frac{3}{4}w\right) \leq -\frac{4}{3}(3)$$
$$w \leq -4$$

$$\begin{array}{cccccccc} & & & & & & & \\ \hline -6 & -5 & -4 & -3 & -2 & -1 & 0 & 1 \end{array}$$

$$-\frac{3}{4}(-4) \stackrel{?}{=} 3$$
$$3 = 3 \ ✔$$

$$-\frac{3}{4}(-5) \stackrel{?}{\geq} 3$$
$$3\frac{3}{4} \geq 3 \ ✔$$

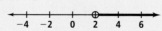

Here's Why It Works

Be sure students do not automatically reverse the direction of the inequality symbol when a negative number is included in one of the equivalent expressions. The direction of the inequality symbol reverses only when both sides of an inequality are multiplied by a negative number.

Problem 1

Q What operation does the fraction bar represent? **[The fraction bar represents division.]**

Q Does the -2 on the right side of the inequality affect the inequality symbol? Explain. **[No, both sides of the inequality are multiplied by 3, which is a positive number.]**

Got It? ERROR PREVENTION

Q What operation will isolate the variable c? **[multiplying both sides of the inequality by 8]**

Problem 2

Q What is the result of multiplying a number by its reciprocal? **[The product is always 1.]**

Q What number may be a more convenient number to use than -5 when checking the solutions? Explain. **[Answers may vary. Sample: -8; it is a multiple of -4 and will result in an integer on the left side of the inequality.]**

---

2 Guided Instruction

Each Problem is worked out and supported online.

Problem 1
Multiplying by a Positive Number

Alternative Problem 1
Multiplying by a Positive Number
Animated

Problem 2
Multiplying by a Negative Number
Animated

Alternative Problem 2
Multiplying by a Negative Number

Problem 3
Dividing by a Positive Number

Problem 4
Dividing by a Negative Number
Animated

Support in Algebra 1 Companion
• Vocabulary
• Key Concepts
• Got It?

Answers

Solve It!

$>$, $>$, $>$, $<$, $<$, $<$. The inequality symbol stays the same. The inequality symbol reverses. Explanations may vary.

Got It?

1. $c > 2$

$$\begin{array}{ccccccc} & & & & & & \\ \hline -4 & -2 & 0 & 2 & 4 & 6 \end{array}$$

Got It? VISUAL LEARNER

Point out that an alternate way to express this inequality is $-\frac{1}{3}n < -1$.

Take Note SYNTHESIZING

Use the table below to help students connect all four properties of inequalities.

Inequality Property	Symbol remains unchanged	Symbol reverses
Addition and Subtraction	Always	Never
Multiplication and Division	Multiplier/ Divisor is positive	Multiplier/ Divisor is negative

Problem 3

Q Is it possible to earn exactly $75 in your dog walking business? Explain. **[No, because 75 is not evenly divisible by 4.5.]**

Q What does a graph of the solutions look like for this real-world situation?

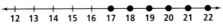

Got It?

Q What other subset of numbers that are part of the solutions do not make sense in this real-world situation? **[negative numbers]**

 Got It? 2. What are the solutions of $-\frac{n}{3} < -1$? Graph and check.

Solving inequalities using division is similar to solving inequalities using multiplication. If you divide each side of an inequality by a negative number, you need to reverse the direction of the inequality symbol.

take note
Key Concept Division Property of Inequality

Let a, b, and c be real numbers with $c > 0$.

If $a > b$, then $\frac{a}{c} > \frac{b}{c}$.

If $a < b$, then $\frac{a}{c} < \frac{b}{c}$.

Let a, b, and c be real numbers with $c < 0$.

If $a > b$, then $\frac{a}{c} < \frac{b}{c}$.

If $a < b$, then $\frac{a}{c} > \frac{b}{c}$.

Examples

$6 > 3$, so $\frac{6}{3} > \frac{3}{3}$.

$9 < 12$, so $\frac{9}{3} < \frac{12}{3}$.

$6 > 3$, so $\frac{6}{-3} < \frac{3}{-3}$.

$9 < 12$, so $\frac{9}{-3} > \frac{12}{-3}$.

These properties are also true for inequalities using $\geq$ and $\leq$.

 Problem 3 Dividing by a Positive Number

Part-Time Job You walk dogs in your neighborhood after school. You earn $4.50 per dog. How many dogs do you need to walk to earn at least $75?

Relate cost per dog times number of dogs is at least amount wanted

Define Let d = the number of dogs.

Write 4.50 · d $\geq$ 75

$$4.50d \geq 75$$

$$\frac{4.50d}{4.50} \geq \frac{75}{4.50} \quad \text{Divide each side by 4.50.}$$

$$d \geq 16\tfrac{2}{3} \quad \text{Simplify.}$$

However, since d represents the number of dogs, it must be a positive integer. So you must walk at least 17 dogs to earn at least $75.

Think
What types of solutions make sense for this situation? Only whole-number solutions make sense because you cannot walk part of a dog.

Got It? 3. a. A student club plans to buy food for a soup kitchen. A case of vegetables costs $10.68. The club can spend at most $50 for this project. What are the possible numbers of cases the club can buy?

b. Reasoning In Problem 3, why do you round to the greater whole number?

Additional Problems

1. What are the solutions of $\frac{x}{2} < -3$? Graph the solutions.

ANSWER $x < -6$

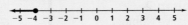

2. What are the solutions of $-\frac{2}{3}w \geq 2$? Graph the solutions.

ANSWER $w \leq -3$

3. A cheerleading squad earns $5.50 per car washed. How many cars does the squad need to wash to earn at least $77?

ANSWER at least 14 cars

4. What are the solutions of $-5a \geq 20$? Graph the solutions.

ANSWER $a \leq -4$

Answers

Got It? (continued)

2. $n > 3$

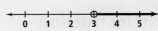

3. a. 1, 2, 3, or 4 cases

b. $\frac{75}{4.50} = 16\frac{2}{3}$, but you cannot walk $\frac{2}{3}$ of a dog. If you round down to 16, you will only make $72. So round up to 17.

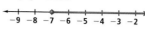

Problem 4 Dividing by a Negative Number

Think

How is this inequality different from the one in Problem 3?
The coefficient is negative. You can still use the properties of inequality to solve, but pay attention to the direction of the symbol.

What are the solutions of $-9y \le 63$? Graph the solutions.

$$-9y \le 63$$

$$\frac{-9y}{-9} \ge \frac{63}{-9} \qquad \text{Divide each side by } -9. \text{ Reverse the inequality symbol.}$$

$$y \ge -7 \qquad \text{Simplify each side.}$$

 Got It? **4.** What are the solutions of $-5x > -10$? Graph the solutions.

 Lesson Check

Do you know HOW?

Match the inequality with its graph.

1. $x + 2 > -1$ **A.**
2. $-\frac{x}{3} < -1$ **B.**
3. $x - 4 \le -1$
4. $-3x \ge 9$ **C.**

  D.

Do you UNDERSTAND?

5. Which operation would you use to solve the inequality? Explain.

  a. $1 \le -\frac{x}{2}$ **b.** $y - 4 > -5$ **c.** $-6w < -36$

6. Error Analysis Describe and correct the error in the solution.

 Practice and Problem-Solving Exercises

A **Practice** Solve each inequality. Graph and check your solution.   See Problems 1 and 2.

7. $\frac{x}{5} \ge -2$ **8.** $\frac{w}{6} < 1$ **9.** $4 > \frac{p}{8}$ **10.** $1 \le -\frac{5}{4}y$

11. $-\frac{v}{2} \ge 1.5$ **12.** $-3 < \frac{x}{3}$ **13.** $-7 \le \frac{7}{3}x$ **14.** $8 > \frac{2}{3}k$

15. $0 \le -\frac{3}{11}m$ **16.** $-\frac{3}{2}b < 6$ **17.** $-\frac{3}{4} < -\frac{3}{8}m$ **18.** $-5 \ge -\frac{5}{9}y$

Solve each inequality. Graph and check your solution.   See Problems 3 and 4.

19. $3m \ge 6$ **20.** $4t < -12$ **21.** $-30 > -5c$ **22.** $-4w \le 20$

23. $11z > -33$ **24.** $56 < -7d$ **25.** $18b \le -3$ **26.** $-7y \ge 17$

27. $-5h < 65$ **28.** $8t \le 64$ **29.** $63 \ge 7q$ **30.** $-12x > 132$

Problem 4

Q How could you use the Multiplication Property of Inequality to solve this inequality? **[Multiply both sides of the inequality by $-\frac{1}{9}$.]**

Got It?

Show students an alternate solution method. Have them add $5x$ to both sides and then add 10 to both sides. This does not require a reversal of the inequality symbol during the solution process.

3 Lesson Check

Do you know HOW?
• Have students substitute values from the graphs into the inequality to ensure they matched the graphs correctly.

Do you UNDERSTAND?
• If students have difficulty with Exercise 6, then have them solve the inequality first, and then compare their solutions to the one shown.

Close

Q When should you reverse the direction of the inequality symbol? **[When multiplying or dividing both sides of an inequality by a negative number.]**

Got It? (continued)

4. $x < 2$

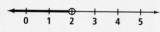

Lesson Check

1. D   **2.** B   **3.** A   **4.** C

5. a. Multiplication by -2; it is the inverse of division by -2.
  b. Addition of 4; it is the inverse of subtraction of 4.
  c. Division by -6; it is the inverse of multiplication by -6.

6. The inequality symbol was not reversed when multiplying by a negative.

$$-5\left(-\frac{n}{5}\right) < -5(2),\ n < -10$$

Practice and Problem-Solving Exercises

7–30. See back of book.

PowerAlgebra.com

3 Lesson Check

For a digital lesson check, use the Got It questions.

Support In Algebra 1 Companion
• Lesson Check

4 Practice

Assign homework to individual students or to an entire class.

4 Practice

ASSIGNMENT GUIDE

Basic: 7–32 all, 34–48 even, 49, 50–56 even, 59–60

Average: 7–31 odd, 33–62

Advanced: 7–31 odd, 33–64

Standardized Test Prep: 65–67

Mixed Review: 68–76

Reasoning exercises have blue headings.

Applications exercises have red headings.

EXERCISE 59: Use the Think About a Plan worksheet in the **Practice and Problem Solving Workbook** (also available in the Teaching Resources in print and online) to further support students' development in becoming independent learners.

HOMEWORK QUICK CHECK

To check students' understanding of key skills and concepts, go over Exercises 13, 27, 49, 59, and 60.

---

31. Text Messages Text messages cost $.15 each. You can spend no more than $10. How many text messages can you send?

32. Aquarium Fish Tetras cost $3.99 each. You can spend at most $25. How many tetras can you buy for your aquarium?

 Apply

Write four solutions to each inequality.

33. $\frac{x}{2} \le -1$ **34.** $\frac{r}{3} \ge -4$ **35.** $-1 \ge \frac{r}{3}$ **36.** $0.5 > \frac{1}{2}c$

Tell what you can do to the first inequality in order to get the second.

37. $-\frac{c}{4} > 3; c < -12$ **38.** $\frac{n}{5} \le -2; n \le -10$ **39.** $5z > -25; z > -5$ **40.** $\frac{3}{4}b \le 3; b \le 4$

Replace each ■ with the number that makes the inequalities equivalent.

41. ■$s > 14; s < -7$ **42.** ■$x \ge 25; x \le -5$ **43.** $-8u \le$ ■$; u \ge -0.5$ **44.** $-2a >$ ■$; a < -9$

Determine whether each statement is *always*, *sometimes*, or *never* true. Justify your answer.

45. If $x > 3$ and $y < 1$, then $xy > 0$.

46. If $x < 0$ and $y < 0$, then $xy > 0$.

47. If $x \ge 0$ and $y > 1$, then $xy > 0$.

48. If $x > 0$ and $y \ge 0$, then $xy > 0$.

49. Think About a Plan A friend calls you and asks you to meet at the park 2 mi away in 25 min. You set off on your skateboard after the call. At what speeds (in miles per minute) can you ride your skateboard to be at the park in at most 25 min?
* How are the distance you travel, your speed, and time related?
* How can an inequality help you solve the problem?
* How can the model below help you solve the problem?

|← 2 →|
| 25r |

Solve each inequality. Justify each step.

50. $-4.5 > 9p$ **51.** $-1 \ge \frac{t}{3}$ **52.** $\frac{3}{4}n < 4$ **53.** $0.5 \le \frac{1}{2}c$

54. $-8u < 4$ **55.** $\frac{n}{5} \le -2$ **56.** $-12 > 4a$ **57.** $1 < -\frac{5}{7}s$

58. Trip A family is taking a cross-country trip by car. They drive at an average speed of 55 mi/h, and their goal is to travel at least 400 mi/day. How many hours per day do they need to drive?

59. Lunch You have $30. You are going to buy a sandwich and a drink for yourself and two friends from the menu at the right. You will spend the remainder on snacks. What is the least number of snacks you can afford? What is the greatest number of snacks you can afford? Explain.

Drinks	Sandwiches	
Sm $1	Veggie	$4
Med $1.50	Chicken	$5
Lg $2	Roast Beef	$7
	Snacks	
Pretzels $1	Ice Cream $2	
	Brownie $3	

Answers

Practice and Problem-Solving Exercises
(continued)

31. no more than 66 text messages

32. at most 6 tetras

33–36. Answers may vary. Samples are given.

33. $-5, -4, -3, -2$

34. $-12, -11, -10, -9$

35. $-6, -5, -4, -3$

36. $-3, -2, -1, 0$

37. Multiply each side by -4 and reverse the inequality symbol.

38. Multiply each side by 5.

39. Divide each side by 5.

40. Multiply each side by $\frac{4}{3}$.

41. -2 **42.** -5 **43.** 4   **44.** 18

45. Sometimes true; sample: It is true when $x = 4$ and $y = 0.5$ but false when $x = 4$ and $y = -2$.

46. Always true; the product of two negative numbers is always greater than 0.

47. Sometimes true; sample: It is true when $x = 4$ and $y = 2$ but false when $x = 0$ and $y = 2$.

48. Sometimes true; sample: It is true when $x = 4$ and $y = 2$ but false when $x = 4$ and $y = 0$.

49. at least 0.08 mi per min

50. $\frac{-4.5}{9} > \frac{9p}{9}$ Div. Prop. of Ineq.
$-0.5 > p$ Simplify.

51. $3(-1) \ge 3\left(\frac{t}{3}\right)$ Mult. Prop. of Ineq.
$-3 \ge t$ Simplify.

52. $\frac{4}{3}\left(\frac{3}{4}n\right) < \frac{4}{3}(4)$ Mult. Prop. of Ineq.
$n < \frac{16}{3}$ Simplify.

53. $2(0.5) \le 2\left(\frac{1}{2}c\right)$ Mult. Prop. of Ineq.
$1 \le c$ Simplify.

54. $\frac{-8u}{-8} > \frac{4}{-8}$ Div. Prop. of Ineq.
$u > -\frac{1}{2}$ Simplify.

55. $5\left(\frac{n}{5}\right) \le 5(-2)$ Mult. Prop. of Ineq.
$n \le -10$ Simplify.

56. $\frac{-12}{4} > \frac{4a}{4}$ Div. Prop. of Ineq.
$-3 > a$ Simplify.

57. $-\frac{7}{5}(1) > -\frac{7}{5}\left(-\frac{5}{7}s\right)$ Mult. Prop. of Ineq.
$-\frac{7}{5} > s$ Simplify.

58. at least $7\frac{3}{11}$ h

59. If the most expensive sandwiches and drinks are ordered, the cost is $3(7) + 3(2) = 27$, leaving $3. If the most expensive snack is bought, the least number of snacks you can afford is 1. If the least expensive sandwiches and drinks are ordered, the cost is $3(4) + 3(1) = 15$, leaving $15. If the least expensive snack is bought, the greatest number of snacks you can afford is 15.

60. Open-Ended Write an inequality that can be solved by dividing by a negative number and has the solution $x < \frac{1}{3}$.

61. Patterns Consider the pattern of inequalities $\frac{x}{2} < 10, \frac{x}{3} < 10, \frac{x}{4} < 10, \ldots$. Suppose a real number a is a solution of a certain inequality in the pattern. What other inequalities in the pattern do you know have a as a solution? Explain.

62. Reasoning If $ax \le ay$ and $ay \le az$, is $x \le z$? Explain.

Ⓒ Challenge

63. Construction A contractor is building a rectangular walkway $3\frac{1}{3}$ ft wide by 35 ft long using square cement pavers. Each paver has an area of $\frac{4}{9}$ ft². What is the least number of pavers he needs to make the walkway?

64. Basketball A company sells men's basketballs with a circumference of 29.5 in. They also sell youth basketballs with a circumference of 27.75 in. The company has cube-shaped packaging boxes with edges that are either 8 in., 9 in., or 10 in. long. What is the smallest box in which each ball can be packaged?

Standardized Test Prep

65. The mayor of Renee's town chose 160 students from her school to attend a city debate. This amount is no more than $\frac{1}{4}$ of the students in Renee's school. What is the least possible number of students that attend Renee's school?

    Ⓐ 40   Ⓑ 160   Ⓒ 320   Ⓓ 640

66. An art teacher has a box of 100 markers. The teacher gives 7 markers to each student in the class and has 16 markers left over. How many students are in the class?

    Ⓕ 11   Ⓖ 12   Ⓗ 13   Ⓘ 14

Short Response

67. The width of a rectangle is 3 in. shorter than the length. The perimeter of the rectangle is 18 in. What is the length of the rectangle? Show your work.

Mixed Review

Solve each inequality.

◀ See Lesson 3-2.

68. $x + 5 \le -6$
    69. $y - 4.7 \ge 8.9$
    70. $q - 5 < 0$

71. $\frac{1}{2} > \frac{3}{4} + c$
    72. $-\frac{2}{3} < b + \frac{1}{3}$
    73. $y - 21 \le 54$

Get Ready!   **To prepare for Lesson 3-4, do Exercises 74–76.**

Solve each equation.

◀ See Lesson 2-3.

74. $-x + 8 + 4x = 14$
    75. $-6(2y + 2) = 12$
    76. $0.5t + 3.5 - 2.5t = 1.5t$

60. Check students' work.

61. $x < 20, x < 30, x < 40, \ldots$; any inequality following the one that a is a solution to. This is because each following inequality has the same solutions as the previous inequalities, with more values as solutions.

62. Yes for $g > 0$; because of the Mult. Prop. of Ineq., $x \le y$ and $y \le z$, so it follows that $x \le z$. If $g < 0$, $x < z$.

63. $\frac{4}{9}p \ge 116\frac{2}{3}$; $p \ge 262\frac{1}{2}$, so the least number of pavers needed is 263.

64. $3.14d > 29.5$ and $d > 9.4$, so the men's basketballs need a 10-in. box; $3.14d > 27.75$, $d > 8.8$ so the youth basketballs need a 9-in. box.

65. D

66. G

67. [2] $w = \ell - 3$, $18 = 2\ell + 2(\ell - 3)$, $18 = 4\ell - 6, 24 = 4\ell$, so $\ell = 6$ in. (OR equivalent work)

    [1] incorrect solution with appropriate work OR correct solution with no work shown or incorrect work shown

68. $x \le -11$

69. $y \ge 13.6$

70. $q < 5$

71. $-\frac{1}{4} > c$

72. $-1 < b$

73. $y \le 75$

74. 2

75. -2

76. 1

Additional Instructional Support

Algebra 1 Companion

Students can use the **Algebra 1 Companion** worktext (4 pages) as you teach the lesson. Use the Companion to support

- New Vocabulary
- Key Concepts
- Got It for each Problem
- Lesson Check

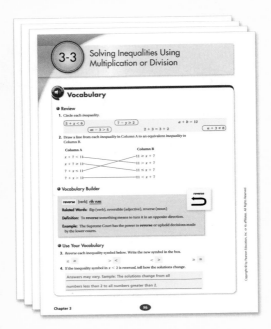

ELL Support

Assess Understanding Write the inequality $5 < 7$ on the board. Read the inequality aloud and ask if it is a true sentence. Then multiply each side of the inequality by -2. Rewrite the inequality again under the first line. Point to each side of the inequality as you state that you are multiplying both sides by -2. Then ask whether the sentence $-10 < -14$ is true. Use a number line. Ask how the sentence can be made true. If the inequality symbol were reversed, would the sentence be true? Now write $6 > 3$ on the board. Invite a student to multiply both sides by a negative number, such as -4. Scaffold to an inequality, such as $-4x > 16$, and repeat the steps above to show why the symbol reverses.

5 Assess & Remediate

Lesson Quiz

1. What are the solutions of $\frac{x}{3} > -1$? Graph the solutions.

2. What are the solutions of $-\frac{1}{4}m < 2$? Graph the solutions.

3. What must you do to the first inequality to get to the second inequality?
   a. $\frac{n}{4} < 5$; $n < 20$
   b. $-\frac{n}{4} < 5$; $n > -20$

4. Solve $-\frac{n}{7} \geq 3$.

5. **Do you UNDERSTAND?** You rake leaves in your neighborhood after school and earn \$6.50 per yard you rake. How many yards do you need to rake to earn at least \$52? What inequality models this situation?

ANSWERS TO LESSON QUIZ

1. $x > -3$

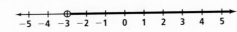

2. $m > -8$

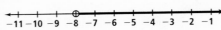

3. **a.** Multiply each side by 4.
   b. Multiply each side by -4 and reverse the inequality sign.

4. $n \leq -21$

5. at least 8 yards; $6.50y \geq 52.00$, $y =$ number of yards raked

PRESCRIPTION FOR REMEDIATION

Use the student work on the Lesson Quiz to prescribe a differentiated review assignment.

Points	Differentiated Remediation
0–2	Intervention
3–4	On-level
5	Extension

PowerAlgebra.com

5 Assess & Remediate

Assign the Lesson Quiz. Appropriate intervention, practice, or enrichment is automatically generated based on student performance.

Intervention

- **Reteaching** (2 pages) Provides reteaching and practice exercises for the key lesson concepts. Use with struggling students or absent students.

- **English Language Learner Support** Helps students develop and reinforce mathematical vocabulary and key concepts.

All-in-One Resources/Online
Reteaching

3-3 **Reteaching**
Solving Inequalities Using Multiplication or Division

You can solve inequalities using multiplication or division using these two important rules.
- You can multiply or divide each side of an inequality by a positive number.
- You can multiply or divide each side of an inequality by a negative number *only if you reverse the inequality sign.*

Problem
What are the solutions of $\frac{c}{5} \leq -2$? Graph the solutions.
$\frac{c}{5} \leq -2$ Original inequality
$5(\frac{c}{5}) \leq 5(-2)$ Multiply each side by 5. Keep the inequality symbol the same.
$c \leq -10$ Simplify.
To graph $c \leq -10$, place a closed circle at -10 and shade to the left.

Problem
What are the solutions of $-\frac{2}{3}t > 9$? Graph the solutions.
$-\frac{2}{3}t > 4$ Original inequality
$-\frac{3}{2}(-\frac{2}{3}t) < -\frac{3}{2}(4)$ Multiply each side by $-\frac{3}{2}$. Reverse the inequality symbol.
$t < -6$ Simplify.
To graph $t < -6$, place an open circle at -6 and shade to the left.

All-in-One Resources/Online
English Language Learner Support

3-3 **ELL Support**
Solving Inequalities Using Multiplication or Division

Use the list below to complete the Venn diagram.

If $a < b$ and $c > 0$, then $ac < bc$. If $a > b$ and $c > 0$, then $ac > bc$.	If $a < b$ and $c < 0$, then $\frac{a}{c} > \frac{b}{c}$. If $a > b$ and $c < 0$, then $\frac{a}{c} < \frac{b}{c}$.	Use inverse operations to solve.
If $a < b$ and $c < 0$, then $ac > bc$. If $a > b$ and $c < 0$, then $ac < bc$.	If you multiply or divide both sides of an inequality by a negative number, you need to reverse the inequality symbol to make the inequality true.	If $a < b$ and $c > 0$, then $\frac{a}{c} < \frac{b}{c}$. If $a > b$ and $c > 0$, then $\frac{a}{c} > \frac{b}{c}$.

Differentiated Remediation *continued*

On-Level

- **Practice** (2 pages) Provides extra practice for each lesson. For simpler practice exercises, use the Form K Practice pages found in the All-in-One Teaching Resources and online.

- **Think About a Plan** Helps students develop specific problem-solving skills and strategies by providing scaffolded guiding questions.

- **Standardized Test Prep** Focuses on all major exercises, all major question types, and helps students prepare for the high-stakes assessments.

Extension

- **Enrichment** Provides students with interesting problems and activities that extend the concepts of the lesson.

- **Activities, Games, and Puzzles** Worksheets that can be used for concepts development, enrichment, and for fun!

Practice and Problem Solving WKBK/All-in-One Resources/Online
Practice page 1

Practice and Problem Solving WKBK/All-in-One Resources/Online
Practice page 2

All-in-One Resources/Online
Enrichment

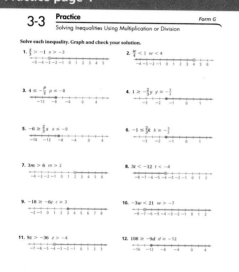

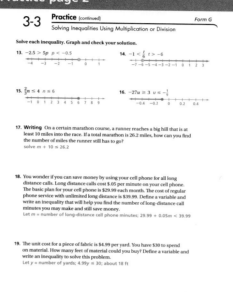

Practice and Problem Solving WKBK/All-in-One Resources/Online
Think About a Plan

Practice and Problem Solving WKBK/All-in-One Resources/Online
Standardized Test Prep

Online Teacher Resource Center
Activities, Games, and Puzzles

Guided Instruction

PURPOSE To review the Reflexive, Symmetric, and Transitive properties of equality and introduce the Transitive Property of Inequality

PROCESS Students will

- differentiate between the Reflexive, Symmetric, and Transitive properties of equality.
- use the properties through real-world situations and algebraic relationships.

DISCUSS

Advise students that they will use the Reflexive, Symmetric, and Transitive properties of equality in both algebra and geometry. These properties will be used in proofs of geometric theorems.

Illustrate the Transitive Property of Inequality by using heights of students. For example, if Wendy is shorter than Sam, and Sam is shorter than Henry, what can logically be concluded? **[Wendy is shorter than Henry.]**

EXAMPLE

Q How does the Transitive Property of Equality differ from the Transitive Property of Inequality? **[The comparison symbol is an equals sign rather than $<$, $>$, $\leq$, or $\geq$.]**

The following properties can help you understand algebraic relationships.

Reflexive, Symmetric, and Transitive Properties of Equality

For all real numbers a, b, and c:

Property	Examples
Reflexive Property $a = a$	$5x = 5x$, $\$1 = \$1$
Symmetric Property If $a = b$, then $b = a$.	If $15 = 3t$, then $3t = 15$. If 1 pair $=$ 2 socks, then 2 socks $=$ 1 pair.
Transitive Property If $a = b$ and $b = c$, then $a = c$.	If $d = 3y$ and $3y = 6$, then $d = 6$. If 36 in. $=$ 3 ft and 3 ft $=$ 1 yd, then 36 in. $=$ 1 yd.

Transitive Property of Inequality

For all real numbers a, b, and c, if $a < b$ and $b < c$, then $a < c$.

Examples If $8x < 7$ and $7 < y$, then $8x < y$.
If 1 cup $<$ 1 qt and 1 qt $<$ 1 gal, then 1 cup $<$ 1 gal.

Example

Use the property given in parentheses to complete each statement.

A If $7x < y$ and $y < z + 2$, then $7x < $ ▪. (Transitive Property of Inequality)
If $7x < y$ and $y < z + 2$, then $7x < z + 2$.

B If 2000 lb $=$ 1 ton, then 1 ton $=$ _?_ . (Symmetric Property)
If 2000 lb $=$ 1 ton, then 1 ton $=$ 2000 lb.

Exercises

Name the property that each statement illustrates.

1. If $3.8 = n$, then $n = 3.8$.
2. 6 in. $=$ 6 in.
3. If $x = 7$ and $7 = 5 + 2$, then $x = 5 + 2$.

4. If math class is earlier than art class and art class is earlier than history class, then math class is earlier than history class.

5. Complete the following sentence. If Amy is shorter than Greg and Greg is shorter than Lisa, then Amy is shorter than _?_ .

Answers

Exercises

1. Sym. Prop. of Equality
2. Refl. Prop. of Equality
3. Transitive Prop. of Equality
4. Transitive Prop. of Inequality
5. Lisa

Sometimes you need to perform two or more steps to solve an inequality. Models can help you understand how to solve multi-step inequalities.

Activity

Model and solve $2x - 3 < 1$.

Inequality	Model	Think
$2x - 3 < 1$		The tiles model the inequality.
$2x - 3 + 3 < 1 + 3$		Add 3 yellow tiles to each side.
$2x < 4$		Simplify by removing the zero pairs.
$\frac{2x}{2} < \frac{4}{2}$		Divide each side into two equal groups.
$x < 2$		Each green tile is less than two yellow tiles, so $x < 2$.

Exercises

Write an inequality for each model. Use tiles to solve each inequality.

1.

2.

Use tiles to model and solve each inequality.

3. $2n - 5 \geq 3$ 4. $-9 > 4x - 1$ 5. $3w + 4 < -5$

6. $z + 6 \leq 2z + 2$ 7. $3m + 7 \geq m - 5$ 8. $5b + 6 > 3b - 2$

Guided Instruction

PURPOSE To use algebra tiles to model and solve multi-step inequalities

PROCESS Students will
• model a multi-step inequality using algebra tiles.
• use algebra tiles to apply properties of inequalities and inverse operations.

DISCUSS
Relate the concept of balancing inequalities to a balance scale. Connect this concept to the importance of balancing inequalities. Any operation done to one side of an inequality must be done to the other side of the inequality.

Q In a multi-step equation or inequality, how do you know which step to complete first? **[Reverse the order of operations. Whichever operation was done last is the first operation to undo by using inverse operations.]**

Q In the example shown, why are three yellow tiles added to both sides? **[To form a zero pair with -3 (3 red tiles), $+3$ (3 yellow tiles) needs to be added.]**

Q How can you make sure you solved the inequality correctly? **[Based on the solution $x < 2$, choose a number less than 2 to substitute into the original inequality and verify the resulting statement is true.]**

Answers

Exercises

1. $3x + 5 > -4$; $x > -3$
2. $6 \leq 4x + 2$; $1 \leq x$
3. $n \geq 4$
4. $x < -2$
5. $w < -3$
6. $z \geq 4$
7. $m \geq -6$
8. $b > -4$

1 Interactive Learning

Solve It!

PURPOSE To use equations to model a real-world situation using a multi-step inequality

PROCESS Students may use a chart, use trial and error, or write an inequality.

FACILITATE

Q Is it possible for the Math Club to raise exactly $500 by Friday? Explain. **[No, because 500 is not evenly divisible by 7.5.]**

Q Why is the inequality $7.5t \geq 500$ not an accurate expression of the situation? **[It does not take into account the $337.50 already raised.]**

ANSWER See Solve It in Answers on next page.
CONNECT THE MATH In the Solve It, students solved a real-world problem that involves an inequality and requires more than one step to solve. In this lesson, they will learn strategies for solving multi-step inequalities.

2 Guided Instruction

Problem 1

Students should check the solutions by using the procedure introduced in Lesson 3-2.

Q Why is the Subtraction Property of Inequality used before the Division Property of Inequality to isolate the variable? **[to avoid introducing fractions in the equivalent expressions]**

3-4 Solving Multi-Step Inequalities

Indiana Academic Standard
A1.2.5 Solve problems that can be modeled using linear equations and inequalities, interpret the solutions, and determine whether the solutions are reasonable.

Objectives To solve multi-step inequalities

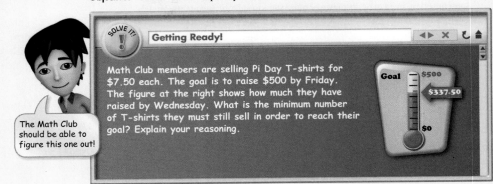

The Math Club should be able to figure this one out!

> **SOLVE IT!** **Getting Ready!**
>
> Math Club members are selling Pi Day T-shirts for $7.50 each. The goal is to raise $500 by Friday. The figure at the right shows how much they have raised by Wednesday. What is the minimum number of T-shirts they must still sell in order to reach their goal? Explain your reasoning.
>
> Goal $500
> $337.50
> $0

You can model the situation in the Solve It with the inequality $337.50 + 7.50x \geq 500$. In this lesson, you will learn how to write and solve multi-step inequalities like this one.

Essential Understanding You solve a multi-step inequality in the same way you solve a one-step inequality. You use the properties of inequality to transform the original inequality into a series of simpler, equivalent inequalities.

Problem 1 Using More Than One Step

What are the solutions of $9 + 4t > 21$? Check the solutions.

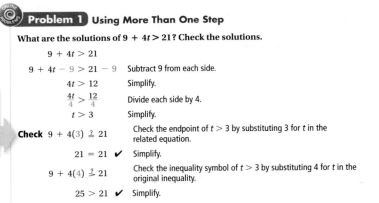

$$9 + 4t > 21$$
$$9 + 4t - 9 > 21 - 9 \quad \text{Subtract 9 from each side.}$$
$$4t > 12 \quad \text{Simplify.}$$
$$\frac{4t}{4} > \frac{12}{4} \quad \text{Divide each side by 4.}$$
$$t > 3 \quad \text{Simplify.}$$

Check $9 + 4(3) \stackrel{?}{=} 21$ Check the endpoint of $t > 3$ by substituting 3 for t in the related equation.

$$21 = 21 \ ✔ \quad \text{Simplify.}$$

$9 + 4(4) \stackrel{?}{>} 21$ Check the inequality symbol of $t > 3$ by substituting 4 for t in the original inequality.

$$25 > 21 \ ✔ \quad \text{Simplify.}$$

Plan

How can you check the solutions? Check the endpoint, 3. Then choose a value greater than 3 and check the inequality symbol.

3-4 Preparing to Teach

BIG ideas   Variable   **UbD**
Equivalence
Solving Equations and Inequalities

ESSENTIAL UNDERSTANDINGS

- In the same way multi-step equations are solved using properties of equality, multi-step inequalities are solved using properties of inequality.
- The properties of inequality are used to transform the original inequality into a series of simpler, equivalent inequalities.

Math Background

Students will use the same techniques to solve multi-step inequalities as they have used to solve multi-step equations.

For example, to solve the equation $3x + 4 = 16$, first subtract 4 from both sides to get $3x = 12$. Then divide both sides by 3 to get $x = 4$. To solve $3x + 4 < 16$, carry out the exact same steps to get $x < 4$. Explain to students that the only difference

is that the equality symbol is replaced with an inequality symbol.

The Distributive Property can also be used in inequalities in the same way it is used in equations. For example, the Distributive Property can be used to rewrite $2(x + 2) - x = 1$ as $2x + 4 - x = 1$. Combine like terms to get $x + 4 = 1$. Discuss how the exact same steps can be used to rewrite $2(x + 2) - x < 1$ as $x + 4 < 1$.

Encourage students to make connections between solving multi-step equations and multi-step inequalities. Remind them that when multiplying or dividing by a negative number, they must remember to reverse the inequality sign.

Support Student Learning

Use the **Algebra 1 Companion** to engage and support students during instructions. See Lesson Resources at the end of this lesson for details.

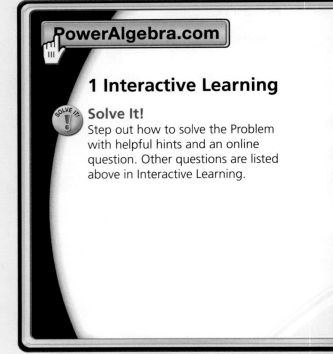

PowerAlgebra.com

1 Interactive Learning

SOLVE IT! **Solve It!**
Step out how to solve the Problem with helpful hints and an online question. Other questions are listed above in Interactive Learning.

Got It? **1.** What are the solutions of the inequality? Check your solutions.

a. $-6a - 7 \leq 17$ **b.** $-4 < 5 - 3n$ **c.** $50 > 0.8x + 30$

You can adapt familiar formulas to write inequalities. You use the real-world situation to determine which inequality symbol to use.

 Problem 2   **Writing and Solving a Multi-Step Inequality**

Geometry In a community garden, you want to fence in a vegetable garden that is adjacent to your friend's garden. You have at most 42 ft of fence. What are the possible lengths of your garden?

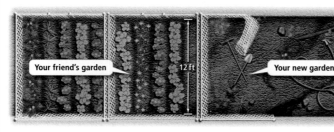

Your friend's garden   12 ft   Your new garden

Relate   Since the fence will surround the garden, you can use the perimeter formula
$P = 2\ell + 2w$.

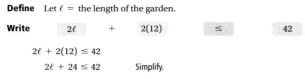

| twice the length | plus | twice the width | is at most | the amount of fence |

Define   Let ℓ = the length of the garden.

Write 2ℓ + $2(12)$ $\leq$ 42

$$2\ell + 2(12) \leq 42$$
$$2\ell + 24 \leq 42 \quad \text{Simplify.}$$
$$2\ell + 24 - 24 \leq 42 - 24 \quad \text{Subtract 24 from each side.}$$
$$2\ell \leq 18 \quad \text{Simplify.}$$
$$\frac{2\ell}{2} \leq \frac{18}{2} \quad \text{Divide each side by 2.}$$
$$\ell \leq 9 \quad \text{Simplify.}$$

The length of the garden must be 9 ft or less.

 Got It? **2.** You want to make a rectangular banner that is 18 ft long. You have no more than 48 ft of trim for the banner. What are the possible widths of the banner?

Problem 2

Q Could the inequality $\ell + 12 < 21$ also be used to model this situation? Explain. **[Yes, when both sides of the original inequality are divided by 2, the result is the inequality $\ell + 12 \leq 21$.]**

Q Is the solution set for this real-world situation limited to only whole numbers? Explain. **[No, the width of a fence can be measured in fractions or decimals.]**

Q What additional inequality should be used to state the possible widths for the garden? Explain. **[Because the width of the garden must be greater than 0, the inequality $w > 0$ should be used.]**

Got It?   **VISUAL LEARNERS**
Encourage students to sketch and label a picture of the banner before writing the inequality to model the situation.

2 Guided Instruction

 Each Problem is worked out and supported online.

Problem 1
Using More Than One Step

Problem 2
Writing and Solving a Multi-Step Inequality
Animated

Problem 3
Using the Distributive Property
Animated

Alternative Problem 3
Using the Distributive Property
Animated

Problem 4
Solving an Inequality With Variables on Both Sides

Problem 5
Inequalities With Special Solutions

Support in Algebra 1 Companion
• Vocabulary
• Key Concepts
• Got It?

Answers

Solve It!
22 T-shirts; explanations may vary.

Got It?
   1. a. $a \geq -4$
     b. $n < 3$
     c. $x < 25$
   2. any width greater than 0 ft and less than or equal to 6 ft

Problem 3

Q Which answer choice(s) would appear to be correct if the inequality symbol was not reversed? **[All answer choices would appear to be correct.]**

Q Is it possible to solve this inequality without reversing the inequality symbol? Explain. **[Yes, if you add t to both sides of the inequality $-t + 3 \geq -5$, and then add 5 to both sides of the resulting inequality, you would not divide by a negative number.]**

Got It?   ERROR PREVENTION

Students may incorrectly distribute 2 instead of -2. Ensure that they show their work and verify the Distributive Property was used correctly.

Problem 4

Q Why is $3n$ subtracted from both sides of the inequality as opposed to $6n$? **[so that the coefficient on the variable term is positive]**

Q Can the first two steps of the solution process be reversed? Explain. **[Yes, because the two steps involve addition and subtraction, they can be performed in the reverse order.]**

Got It?

Q What are the two possible first steps for gathering the variable terms on one side of the inequality in 4a? **[You could subtract $3b$ from each side or add $2b$ to each side.]**

Think

You can use reasoning and *guess-and-check* to solve the problem. If either 9 or 10 is a solution, at least one other answer choice would also be a solution. So, eliminate 9 and 10 as possible answers. Guess that either 8 or 11 is correct and check your guess.

Think

Why subtract $3n$ instead of $6n$ from each side of the inequality? You can subtract either $3n$ or $6n$ from each side. However, subtracting $3n$ gives you a variable term with a positive coefficient.

Problem 3   **Using the Distributive Property**

Multiple Choice Which is a solution of $3(t + 1) - 4t \geq -5$?

  (A) 8   (B) 9   (C) 10   (D) 11

$$3(t + 1) - 4t \geq -5$$

$3t + 3 - 4t \geq -5$	Distributive Property
$-t + 3 \geq -5$	Combine like terms.
$-t + 3 - 3 \geq -5 - 3$	Subtract 3 from each side.
$-t \geq -8$	Simplify.
$\dfrac{-t}{-1} \leq \dfrac{-8}{-1}$	Divide each side by -1. Reverse the inequality symbol.
$t \leq 8$	Simplify.

8 is a solution of the inequality $t \leq 8$. The correct answer is A.

✓ **Got It? 3.** What are the solutions of $15 \leq 5 - 2(4m + 7)$? Check your solutions.

Some inequalities have variables on both sides of the inequality symbol. You need to gather the variable terms on one side of the inequality and the constant terms on the other side.

Problem 4   **Solving an Inequality With Variables on Both Sides**

What are the solutions of $6n - 1 > 3n + 8$?

$$6n - 1 > 3n + 8$$

$6n - 1 - 3n > 3n + 8 - 3n$	To gather variables on the left, subtract $3n$ from each side.
$3n - 1 > 8$	Simplify.
$3n - 1 + 1 > 8 + 1$	To gather the constants on the right, add 1 to each side.
$3n > 9$	Simplify.
$\dfrac{3n}{3} > \dfrac{9}{3}$	Divide each side by 3.
$n > 3$	Simplify.

✓ **Got It? 4. a.** What are the solutions of $3b + 12 > 27 - 2b$? Check your solutions.
     b. Reasoning The first step in solving Problem 4 was to subtract $3n$ from each side of the inequality. What else could have been the first step in solving the inequality? Explain.

Additional Problems

1. What are the solutions of $6 + 3t > 15$?

   ANSWER $t > 3$

2. You want to fence in a rose bed that is adjacent to a deck. The length of your deck is 14 ft. You have at most 44 ft of fence. What are the possible widths of the rose bed?

   ANSWER The width of the rose bed must be 15 ft or less.

3. Which is a solution of $2(t - 1) + 3t < 2$?

   A. 0

   B. 1

   C. 2

   D. 3

   ANSWER A

4. What are the solutions of $4n + 2 < 7n - 13$?

   ANSWER $n > 5$

5. Solve each inequality.

   a. $14 - 6n \leq 2(7 - 3n)$

   b. $4p + 3 > 9p + 6 - 5p$

   ANSWER a. all real numbers,
   b. no solution

Answers

Got It? (continued)

   3. $m \leq -3$

   4. a. $b > 3$

      b. Answers may vary. Sample: adding 1 to each side. This would gather the constant terms onto one side of the inequality.

Sometimes solving an inequality gives a statement that is *always* true, such as $4 > 1$. In that case, the solutions are all real numbers. If the statement is *never* true, as is $9 \le -5$, then the inequality has no solution.

 Problem 5 Inequalities With Special Solutions

Think

Is there another way to solve this inequality?
Yes. Instead of using the Distributive Property, you can first divide each side by 2.

A What are the solutions of $10 - 8a \ge 2(5 - 4a)$?

$$10 - 8a \ge 2(5 - 4a)$$
$$10 - 8a \ge 10 - 8a \qquad \text{Distributive Property}$$
$$10 - 8a + 8a \ge 10 - 8a + 8a \qquad \text{Add } 8a \text{ to each side.}$$
$$10 \ge 10 \qquad \text{Simplify.}$$

Since the inequality $10 \ge 10$ is always true, the solutions of $10 - 8a \ge 2(5 - 4a)$ are all real numbers.

Think

Without solving, how can you tell that this inequality has no solution?
The variable terms on each side of the inequality are equal, but -5 is *not* greater than 7.

B What are the solutions of $6m - 5 > 7m + 7 - m$?

$$6m - 5 > 7m + 7 - m$$
$$6m - 5 > 6m + 7 \qquad \text{Simplify.}$$
$$6m - 5 - 6m > 6m + 7 - 6m \qquad \text{Subtract } 6m \text{ from each side.}$$
$$-5 > 7 \qquad \text{Simplify.}$$

Since the inequality $-5 > 7$ is never true, the inequality $6m - 5 > 7m + 7 - m$ has no solution.

Got It? **5.** What are the solutions of each inequality?
　　　a. $9 + 5n \le 5n - 1$　　　　　**b.** $8 + 6x \ge 7x + 2 - x$

 **Lesson Check**

Do you know HOW?

Solve each inequality, if possible. If the inequality has no solution, write *no solution*. If the solutions are all real numbers, write *all real numbers*.

1. $7 + 6a > 19$

2. $2(t + 2) - 3t \ge -1$

3. $6z - 15 < 4z + 11$

4. $18x - 5 \le 3(6x - 2)$

5. The perimeter of a rectangle is at most 24 cm. Two opposite sides are each 4 cm long. What are the possible lengths of the other two sides?

Do you UNDERSTAND?

6. Reasoning How can you tell that the inequality $3t + 1 > 3t + 2$ has no solution just by looking at the terms in the inequality?

7. Reasoning Can you solve the inequality $2(x - 3) \le 10$ *without* using the Distributive Property? Explain.

8. Error Analysis Your friend says that the solutions of the inequality $-2(3 - x) > 2x - 6$ are all real numbers. Do you agree with your friend? Explain. What if the inequality symbol were $\ge$?

Q If the inequality symbol in 5A is replaced with ">", will the solutions still be all real numbers? Explain. **[No, because the inequality 10 > 10 is never true. There would be no solution.]**

Q If the inequality symbol in 5B is replaced with "$\ge$", does the inequality still have no solution? Explain. **[Yes, because the inequality $-5 \ge 7$ is never true. There would be no solution.]**

Got It?

Q What are the solutions of an inequality where the variable terms cancel? **[If a true statement occurs, the solution is all real numbers. If a false statement occurs, there is no solution.]**

3 Lesson Check

Do you know HOW?
• If students have difficulty with Exercise 5, then encourage them to draw a diagram to model the problem.

Do you UNDERSTAND?
• If students have difficulty with Exercise 6, then have them review Problem 5.

Close

Q How can you be sure you solved an inequality correctly? **[Answers will vary. Sample answer: Substitute a value in the solution set into the inequality and verify the resulting statement is true.]**

Got It? (continued)
5. a. no solution
　　b. all real numbers

Lesson Check
1. $a > 2$

2. $t \le 5$

3. $z < 13$

4. no solution

5. greater than 0 cm and less than or equal to 8 cm

6. The variable terms cancel each other out and a false inequality results.

7. Yes; each side can be divided by 2 first.

8. No; there is no solution, since -6 is not greater than itself. If the inequality symbol were $\ge$, your friend would be correct.

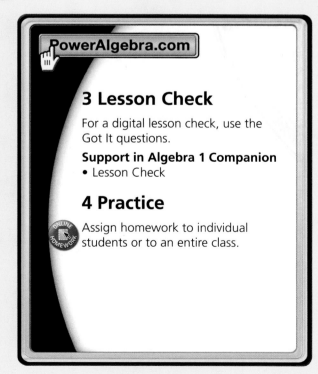

PowerAlgebra.com

3 Lesson Check

For a digital lesson check, use the Got It questions.

Support in Algebra 1 Companion
• Lesson Check

4 Practice

Assign homework to individual students or to an entire class.

4 Practice

ASSIGNMENT GUIDE

Basic: 9–34 all, 36–46 even, 51, 53–54

Average: 9–33 odd, 35–54

Advanced: 9–33 odd, 35–57

Standardized Test Prep: 58–61

Mixed Review: 62–68

Reasoning exercises have blue headings.

Applications exercises have red headings.

EXERCISE 51: Use the Think About a Plan worksheet in the **Practice and Problem Solving Workbook** (also available in the Teaching Resources in print and online) to further support students' development in becoming independent learners.

HOMEWORK QUICK CHECK

To check students' understanding of key skills and concepts, go over Exercises 11, 17, 44, 51, and 54.

Practice and Problem-Solving Exercises

 A Practice

Solve each inequality. Check your solutions. ◀ **See Problem 1.**

9. $5f + 7 \le 22$
10. $6n - 3 > -18$
11. $-5y - 2 < 8$
12. $6 - 3p \ge -9$
13. $9 \le -12 + 6r$
14. $6 \le 12 + 4j$

Write and solve an inequality. ◀ **See Problem 2.**

15. Family Trip On a trip from Buffalo, New York, to St. Augustine, Florida, a family wants to travel at least 250 mi in the first 5 h of driving. What should their average speed be in order to meet this goal?

16. Geometry An isosceles triangle has at least two congruent sides. The perimeter of a certain isosceles triangle is at most 12 in. The length of each of the two congruent sides is 5 in. What are the possible lengths of the remaining side?

Solve each inequality. ◀ **See Problems 3 and 4.**

17. $3(k - 5) + 9k \ge -3$
18. $-(7c - 18) - 2c > 0$
19. $-3(j + 3) + 9j < -15$
20. $-4 \le 4(6y - 12) - 2y$
21. $30 > -(5z + 15) + 10z$
22. $-4(d + 5) - 3d > 8$
23. $4x + 3 < 3x + 6$
24. $4v + 8 \ge 6v + 10$
25. $5f + 8 \ge 2 + 6f$
26. $6 - 3p \le 4 - p$
27. $3m - 4 \le 6m + 11$
28. $4t + 17 > 7 + 5t$

Solve each inequality, if possible. If the inequality has no solution, write *no solution*. If the solutions are all real numbers, write *all real numbers*. ◀ **See Problem 5.**

29. $-3(w - 3) \ge 9 - 3w$
30. $-5r + 6 \le -5(r + 2)$
31. $-2(6 + s) \ge -15 - 2s$
32. $9 + 2x < 7 + 2(x - 3)$
33. $2(n - 8) < 16 + 2n$
34. $6w - 4 \le 2(3w + 6)$

B Apply

Solve each inequality, if possible. If the inequality has no solution, write *no solution*. If the solutions are all real numbers, write *all real numbers*.

35. $-3(x - 3) \ge 5 - 4x$
36. $3s + 6 \le -5(s + 2)$
37. $3(2 + t) \ge 15 - 2t$
38. $\frac{4}{3}s - 3 < s + \frac{2}{3} - \frac{1}{3}s$
39. $4 - 2n \le 5 - n + 1$
40. $-2(0.5 - 4t) \ge -3(4 - 3.5t)$
41. $4(a - 2) - 6a \le -9$
42. $4(3n - 1) \ge 2(n + 3)$
43. $17 - (4k - 2) \ge 2(k + 3)$

44. Think About a Plan Your cell phone plan costs $39.99 per month plus $.15 for each text message you send or receive. You have at most $45 to spend on your cell phone bill. What is the maximum number of text messages that you can send or receive next month?

• What information do you know? What information do you need?
• What inequality can you use to find the maximum number of text messages that you can send or receive?
• What are the solutions of the inequality? Are they reasonable?

Answers

Practice and Problem-Solving Exercises

9. $f \le 3$
10. $n > -2.5$
11. $y > -2$
12. $p \le 5$
13. $r \ge 3.5$
14. $j \ge -1.5$
15. $5s \ge 250; s \ge 50$ mph
16. $10 + s \le 12; s \le 2$ but greater than 0
17. $k \ge 1$
18. $c < 2$
19. $j < -1$
20. $y \ge 2$

21. $z < 9$
22. $d < -4$
23. $x < 3$
24. $v \le -1$
25. $f \le 6$
26. $p \ge 1$
27. $m \ge -5$
28. $t < 10$
29. all real numbers
30. no solution
31. all real numbers
32. no solution
33. all real numbers
34. all real numbers
35. $x \ge -4$
36. $s \le -2$

37. $t \ge \frac{9}{5}$
38. $s < 5\frac{1}{2}$
39. $n \ge -2$
40. $t \le 4.4$
41. $a \ge 0.5$
42. $n \ge 1$
43. $k \le \frac{13}{6}$
44. 33 text messages

45. Rental Rates The student council wants to rent a ballroom for the junior prom. The ballroom's rental rate is $1500 for 3 h and $125 for each additional half hour. Suppose the student council raises $2125. What is the maximum number of hours for which they can rent the ballroom?

46. Writing Suppose a friend is having difficulty solving $3.75(q - 5) > 4(q + 3)$. Explain how to solve the inequality, showing all the necessary steps and identifying the properties you would use.

47. Biology The average normal body temperature for humans is 98.6°F. An abnormal increase in body temperature is classified as hyperthermia, or fever. Which inequality represents the body temperature in degrees Celsius of a person with hyperthermia? (*Hint*: To convert from degrees Celsius C to degrees Fahrenheit F, use the formula $F = \frac{9}{5}C + 32$.)

Ⓐ $\frac{9}{5}C + 32 \geq 98.6$ Ⓑ $\frac{9}{5}C + 32 \leq 98.6$ Ⓒ $\frac{9}{5}C + 32 < 98.6$ Ⓓ $\frac{9}{5}C + 32 > 98.6$

48. Open-Ended Write two different inequalities that you can solve by subtracting 3 from each side and then dividing each side by −5. Solve each inequality.

49. a. Solve $6v + 5 \leq 9v - 7$ by gathering the variable terms on the left side and the constant terms on the right side of the inequality.
   b. Solve $6v + 5 \leq 9v - 7$ by gathering the constant terms on the left side and the variable terms on the right side of the inequality.
   c. Compare the results of parts (a) and (b).
   d. Which method do you prefer? Explain.

50. Mental Math Determine whether each inequality is *always true* or *never true*.
   a. $5s + 7 \geq 7 + 5s$ **b.** $4t + 6 > 4t - 3$ **c.** $5(m + 2) < 5m - 4$

51. Commission A sales associate in a shoe store earns $325 per week, plus a commission equal to 4% of her sales. This week her goal is to earn at least $475. At least how many dollars' worth of shoes must she sell in order to reach her goal?

52. A student uses the table below to help solve $7y + 2 < 6(4 - y)$.

y	$7y + 2$	$<$	$6(4 - y)$
0.5	$7(0.5) + 2 = 5.5$	True	$6(4 - 0.5) = 21$
1	$7(1) + 2 = 9$	True	$6(4 - 1) = 18$
1.5	$7(1.5) + 2 = 12.5$	True	$6(4 - 1.5) = 15$
2	$7(2) + 2 = 16$	False	$6(4 - 2) = 12$

   a. Reasoning Based on the table, would you expect the solution of $7y + 2 < 6(4 - y)$ to be of the form $y < c$ or $y > c$, where c is a real number? Explain.
   b. Estimate Based on the table, estimate the value of c.
   c. Solve the inequality. Compare the actual solution to your estimated solution.

45. 5.5 h

46. Answers may vary. Sample: $3.75q - 18.75 > 4q + 12$, Distr. Prop. $-18.75 > 0.25q + 12$; subtr. $3.75q$ from each side. $-30.75 > 0.25q$; subtr. 12 from each side $-123 > q$; div. each side by 0.25.

47. D

48. Check students' work.

49. a. $v \geq 4$
   b. $4 \leq v$
   c. They are equivalent.
   d. Check students' work.

50. a. always true
   b. always true
   c. never true

51. at least $3750

52. a. $y < c$; answers may vary. Sample: The values of y that are less than 2 make the inequality true.
   b. Answers may vary. Sample: 1.75
   c. $y < \frac{22}{13}$, which is about 1.69; the solutions are close.

Answers

Practice and Problem-Solving Exercises
(continued)

53. $3y$ was subtracted from instead of added to each side; $7y \leq 2$, $y \leq \frac{2}{7}$.

54. 5 wasn't fully distributed; $5p + 15 > 4p + 2$, $p + 15 > 2$, $p > -13$.

55. $-5, -4, -3, -2, -1, 0, 1, 2, 3, 4, 5,$ and 6

56. 10 h

57. a. 73 boxes

   b. 4 trips

58. 9.6 kg

59. 3

60. 8

61. $8.13

62. $m \leq -4$

63. $y \geq -8$

64. $y > -20$

65. $t \geq -3$

66. whole numbers

67. natural numbers

68. integers

Error Analysis Describe and correct the error in each solution.

53.

$$4y + 4 \leq -3y + 6$$
$$4y \leq -3y + 2$$
$$y \leq 2$$

54.

$$5(p + 3) > 4p + 2$$
$$5p + 3 > 4p + 2$$
$$5p > 4p - 1$$
$$p > -1$$

C Challenge

55. Geometry The base of a triangle is 12 in. Its height is $(x + 6)$ in. Its area is no more than 72 in.². What are the possible integer values of x?

56. Part-Time Jobs You can earn money by tutoring for $8 per hour and by walking dogs for $7.50 per hour. You have 15 h available to work. What is the greatest number of hours you can spend walking dogs and still make at least $115?

57. Freight Handling The elevator of a building can safely carry no more than 4000 lb. A worker moves supplies in 50-lb boxes from the loading dock to the fourth floor of the building. The worker weighs 210 lb. The cart he uses weighs 95 lb.
   a. What is the greatest number of boxes he can move in one trip?
   b. The worker needs to deliver 275 boxes. How many trips must he make?

Standardized Test Prep

GRIDDED RESPONSE

SAT/ACT

58. The Science Club hopes to collect at least 200 kg of aluminum cans for recycling during a 21-week semester. The graph shows the first week's results. Let x represent the minimum average mass of cans required per week for the remainder of the semester. What is x?

59. What is the solution of $2x + 8 = 4x + 2$?

60. What is the solution of $-5n - 16 = -7n$?

61. Great Gifts pays its supplier $65 for each box of 12 bells. The owner wants to determine the minimum amount x he can charge his customers per bell in order to make at least a 50% profit per box. What is x? Round to the nearest hundredth if necessary.

Aluminum Cans Collected in Week 1

Mixed Review

Solve each inequality.

← See Lesson 3-3.

62. $-9m \geq 36$ **63.** $-24 \leq 3y$ **64.** $\frac{y}{5} > -4$ **65.** $-\frac{t}{3} \leq 1$

Get Ready! To prepare for Lesson 3-5, do Exercises 66–68.

Determine whether each set represents the set of *natural numbers*, *whole numbers*, or *integers*.

← See Lesson 1-3.

66. the nonnegative integers   **67.** the counting numbers   **68.** $\ldots, -3, -2, -1, 0, 1, 2, 3, \ldots$

Additional Instructional Support

Algebra 1 Companion

Students can use the **Algebra 1 Companion** worktext (4 pages) as you teach the lesson. Use the Companion to support

- New Vocabulary
- Key Concepts
- Got It for each Problem
- Lesson Check

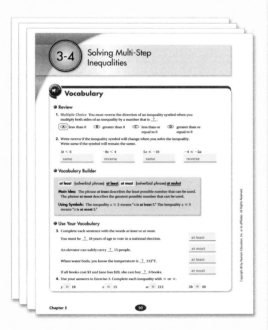

ELL Support

Assess Understanding Pair students so there is a more proficient student with a less proficient student. Write $5y + 5 \leq 8 - y$ on the board. Tell students to ask each other to describe the steps to solve the inequality. Encourage students to ask questions like: What is the first thing you would do?, What is that property?, What operation are you using?, or Is there another way to do that? It would be a good idea to have a student pair model the procedure so that the class can observe their interactions.

Ask students to make a graphic organizer like the one below to help recognize an inequality with the possible solution sets.

Solutions to Inequalities	
No solution	a numeric inequality which is false
All Real Numbers	a numeric inequality which is true
A set of real numbers	an inequality with a variable on one side and a constant on the other

5 Assess & Remediate

Lesson Quiz

1. What are the solutions of $4 + 5t < 19$?
2. **Do you UNDERSTAND?** At a community center, you want to rope off an area that is adjacent to a building. The length of the building is 10 ft. You have 42 ft of rope. What are the possible widths of the roped-off area?
3. Which is a solution of $3(x + 4) - x > 4$?
   - **A.** -6
   - **B.** -5
   - **C.** -4
   - **D.** -3
4. What are the solutions of $6t - 1 \geq 4t + 13$?
5. What are the solutions of $3(2m - 1) \leq 6m - 2$?

ANSWERS TO LESSON QUIZ

1. $t < 3$
2. The width of the roped-off area must be 16 ft or less.
3. D
4. $t \geq 7$
5. all real numbers

PRESCRIPTION FOR REMEDIATION

Use the student work on the Lesson Quiz to prescribe a differentiated review assignment.

Points	Differentiated Remediation
0–2	Intervention
3–4	On-level
5	Extension

PowerAlgebra.com

5 Assess & Remediate

Assign the Lesson Quiz. Appropriate intervention, practice, or enrichment is automatically generated based on student performance.

Intervention

- **Reteaching** (2 pages) Provides reteaching and practice exercises for the key lesson concepts. Use with struggling students or absent students.
- **English Language Learner Support** Helps students develop and reinforce mathematical vocabulary and key concepts.

All-in-One Resources/Online
Reteaching

All-in-One Resources/Online
English Language Learner Support

Differentiated Remediation *continued*

On-Level

- **Practice** (2 pages) Provides extra practice for each lesson. For simpler practice exercises, use the Form K Practice pages found in the All-in-One Teaching Resources and online.

- **Think About a Plan** Helps students develop specific problem-solving skills and strategies by providing scaffolded guiding questions.
- **Standardized Test Prep** Focuses on all major exercises, all major question types, and helps students prepare for the high-stakes assessments.

Extension

- **Enrichment** Provides students with interesting problems and activities that extend the concepts of the lesson.
- **Activities, Games, and Puzzles** Worksheets that can be used for concepts development, enrichment, and for fun!

Practice and Problem Solving WKBK/All-in-One Resources/Online
Practice page 1

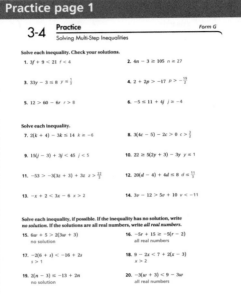

Practice and Problem Solving WKBK/All-in-One Resources/Online
Practice page 2

3-4 Practice (continued)   Form G
Solving Multi-Step Inequalities

21. A grandmother says her grandson is two years older than her granddaughter and that together, they are at least 12 years old. How old are her grandson and granddaughter?
The granddaughter is at least 5 years old and the grandson is at least 7 years old.

22. A family decides to rent a boat for the day while on vacation. The boat's rental rate is $500 for the first two hours and $50 for each additional half hour. Suppose the family can spend $700 for the boat. What inequality represents the number of hours for which they can rent the boat?
$500 + 100(x - 2) \leq 700$

23. **Writing** Suppose a friend is having difficulty solving $-1.75(q - 5) > 3(q + 2.5)$. Explain how to solve the inequality, showing all the necessary steps and identifying the properties you would use.
$-1.75q + 8.75 > 3q + 7.5$ Use the Dist. Prop.
$-4.75q > -1.25$ Add. Prop. of Inequal.
$q < \frac{5}{19}$ Mult. Prop. of Inequal.

24. **Open-Ended** Write two different inequalities that you can solve by adding 2 to each side and then dividing each side by −12. Solve each inequality.
Answers may vary. Samples:
$-12x - 2 < 10$; $x > 1$
$-12x - 2 \geq 10$; $x \leq -1$

25. **Reasoning a.** Solve $3v - 5 \leq 2v + 10$ by gathering the variable terms on the left side and the constant terms on the right side of the inequality. $v \leq 15$

b. Solve $3v - 5 \leq 2v + 10$ by gathering the constant terms on the left side and the variable terms on the right side of the inequality. $15 \geq v$

c. Compare the results of parts (a) and (b). they are equivalent

d. Which method do you prefer? Explain.
Sample: I prefer the first method because you do not need to divide by a negative number and reverse the inequality sign.

All-in-One Resources/Online
Enrichment

3-4 Enrichment
Solving Multi-Step Inequalities

Often you are given an inequality and asked to solve it. However, it is also possible to start with the solution and write an inequality that would produce that solution. Start with the solution and perform the same operation on both sides to produce a new inequality. Continue performing operations until you have reached an inequality that meets the desired conditions.

For example, start with $x < 1$.

$x < 1$	
$3x < 3$	Multiply each side by 3.
$3x + 4 < 7$	Add 4 to each side.
$5x + 4 < 2x + 7$	Add 2x to each side.
$10x + 8 < 4x + 14$	Multiply each side by 2.

The example used only operations that did not require switching the direction of the inequality symbol. But you can multiply or divide by negative numbers as long as you remember to switch the direction of the inequality symbol.

Write a multi-step inequality that has the given inequality as its solution.

1. $y > 4$
Answers may vary. Sample:
$6y + 3 > 4y + 11$

2. $n \geq -3$
Answers may vary. Sample:
$3n + 5 \geq n - 4$

3. $z \leq 8$
Answers may vary. Sample:
$8z - 25 \leq 4z + 7$

4. $p < 0$
Answers may vary. Sample:
$3(p + 2) + p < p + 6$

Write a multi-step inequality that has the given inequality as its solution. Use at least one operation that requires changing the direction of the inequality symbol.

5. $q \geq 4$
Answers may vary. Sample:
$q + 3 \geq 3q - 5$

6. $r < -5$
Answers may vary. Sample:
$2r + 3 > 3r + 8$

7. $t > 8$
Answers may vary. Sample:
$2t + 18 < 5t - 6$

8. $w \leq 0$
Answers may vary. Sample:
$3w + 5 \geq 5w + 5$

Practice and Problem Solving WKBK/All-in-One Resources/Online
Think About a Plan

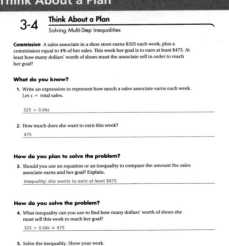

Practice and Problem Solving WKBK/All-in-One Resources/Online
Standardized Test Prep

3-4 Standardized Test Prep
Solving Multi-Step Inequalities

Multiple Choice

For Exercises 1–6, choose the correct letter.

1. What is the solution of $6w - 8 \geq 22$? D
A. $w > \frac{7}{3}$ B. $w \leq \frac{7}{3}$ C. $w > 5$ D. $w \geq 5$

2. What is the solution of $2(y + 5) + 7y \leq 19$? G
F. $y < 1$ G. $y \leq 1$ H. $y > 1$ I. $y \geq 1$

3. What is the solution of $25 > -3(4n - 3)$? C
A. $n < -\frac{4}{3}$ B. $n < \frac{4}{3}$ C. $n > -\frac{4}{3}$ D. $n > \frac{4}{3}$

4. Which graph represents the solution of $-12 > -k - (3k + 4)$? G

5. You have already saved $55. You earn $9 per hour at your job. You are saving for a bicycle that costs $199. What inequality represents the minimum number of hours you need to work to save for the bicycle? C
A. $h < 16$ B. $h \leq 16$ C. $h \geq 16$ D. $h > 16$

6. Admission to the fair costs $7.75. Each ride costs you $.50. You have $15 to spend at the fair including admission. Which inequality represents the number of rides you can ride? H
F. $r > 14$ G. $r < 14$ H. $r \leq 14$ I. $r \leq 15$

Short Response

7. The perimeter of a rectangle is at least 32 cm. The length of the rectangle is 9 cm. What are the possible widths of the rectangle? Show your work.
at least 7 cm
[2] Question answered correctly.
[1] Answer is incomplete.
[0] Answer is wrong.

Online Teacher Resource Center
Activities, Games, and Puzzles

3-4 Game: Points for Each Line
Solving Multi-Step Inequalities

This game is for two teams of three or four and a host. The host receives a sheet of inequalities with solutions. Each inequality is assigned a point value. The point values are shown in the grid below.

10	20	30	40	50	60	70	80	90	100
10	20	30	40	50	60	70	80	90	100
10	20	30	40	50	60	70	80	90	100

Members of each team take turns solving the inequalities. A student from each team gets to solve an inequality during each round. There are 15 rounds. Before receiving an inequality to solve, the student who is solving the inequality selects an available point value from the grid. Inequalities with a greater point value are more difficult. The host then asks the student to solve the inequality with that point value. The student must use only mental math to solve the inequality.

If the student gives a correct answer, then the point value of the question is earned for the team. If the student gives an incorrect answer, then the host asks the next student of the other team to solve the inequality. If the next student is correct, then that team can add that point value to their score for the current round. The point value is crossed out from the grid and the host crosses out the inequality on the sheet. Use the scorecard on the right to keep score.

Play continues until all the point values have been crossed out. The team with the most points wins!
See Teacher Instructions page.

Round	Team 1	Team 2
1		
2		
3		
4		
5		
6		
7		
8		
9		
10		
11		
12		
13		
14		
15		
Total		

Do you know HOW?

Write an inequality that represents each verbal expression or graph.

1. all real numbers y greater than or equal to 12

2. 8 more than a number m is less than 5.

3.

4. The product of -3 and t is greater than 11.

5. c less than 7 is less than or equal to -3.

6.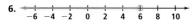

7. A cat weighs no more than 8 lb.

Solve each inequality. Graph the solutions.

8. $8d + 2 < 5d - 7$

9. $2n + 1 \geq -3$

10. $-2x + 7 \leq 45$

11. $5s - 3 + 1 < 8$

12. $5(3p - 2) > 50$

13. $\frac{y}{2} < -3$

14. $6 \geq -\frac{4}{5}n$

15. $-1.5d > 18$

16. A baseball team wants to collect at least 160 cans of food for an upcoming food drive. Team members brought 42 cans of food on Monday and 65 cans of food on Wednesday. Write and solve an inequality to describe how many cans of food the team must collect on Friday to make or exceed their goal.

17. Suppose you earn $7.25 per hour working part-time for a florist. Write and solve an inequality to find how many *full* hours you must work to earn at least $125.

Solve each inequality, if possible. If the inequality has no solution, write *no solution*. If the solutions are all real numbers, write *all real numbers*.

18. $7 - 6b \leq 19$

19. $15f + 9 > 3(5f + 3)$

20. $6z - 15 \geq 4z + 11$

21. $-3(4 - m) \geq 2(4m - 14)$

22. $8z + 5 - 2z \leq 3(2z + 1) + 2$

23. The cheerleaders are making a rectangular banner for a football game. The length of the banner is 30 ft. The cheerleaders can use no more than 96 ft of trim around the outside of the banner. What are the possible widths of the banner?

Do you UNDERSTAND?

24. **a. Error Analysis** A student claims that the graph below represents the solutions of the inequality $-3 < x$. What error did the student make?

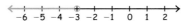

   b. What inequality is actually represented by the graph?

Decide whether the two inequalities in each pair are equivalent. Explain.

25. $36 \leq -4 + y;\ 40 \leq y$

26. $9 + b > 24;\ b > 33$

27. $m - \frac{1}{2} < \frac{3}{8};\ m < \frac{7}{8}$

28. **Reasoning** A local gym offers a trial membership for 3 months. It discounts the regular monthly fee x by $25. If the total cost of the trial membership is less than $100, you will consider signing up. What inequality can you use to determine whether you should sign up?

13. $y < -6$
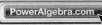

14. $n \geq -7\frac{1}{2}$

15. $d < -12$

16. $42 + 65 + c \geq 160;\ c \geq 53$

17. $7.25h \geq 125;\ h \geq 18$

18. $b \geq -2$

19. no solution

20. $z \geq 13$

21. $m \leq 3.2$

22. all real numbers

23. any width greater than 0 ft and less than or equal to 18 ft

24. **a.** The student misread the direction of the inequality symbol.

   b. $x < -3$

25. Yes; when 4 is added to both sides of the first inequality, $40 \leq y$ results.

26. No; subtracting 9 from each side of the first inequality does not result in $b > 33$.

27. Yes; when $\frac{1}{2}$ is added to both sides of the first inequality, $m < \frac{7}{8}$ results.

28. $3(x - 25) < 100$

Answers

Mid-Chapter Quiz

1. $y \geq 12$

2. $m + 8 < 5$

3. $x \geq -1$

4. $-3t > 11$

5. $7 - c \leq -3$

6. $x < 6$

7. $c \leq 8$

8. $d < -3$
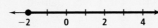

9. $n \geq -2$
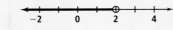

10. $x \geq -19$
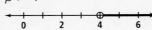

11. $s < 2$

12. $p > 4$

PowerAlgebra.com

MathXL for School
Prepare students for the Mid-Chapter Quiz and Chapter Test with online practice and review.

1 Interactive Learning

Solve It!

PURPOSE To use prior knowledge to solve a real-world problem by creating a subset of a set of elements

PROCESS Students may use trial and error, an organized list, a tree diagram, or the process of elimination.

FACILITATE

Q How can you determine how many two-letter combinations exist? **[Use the Fundamental Counting Principle. 3 × 3 = 9]**

Q How can you be certain that you have not left out any possible words from your list? Explain. **[Make an organized list of each two-letter combination.]**

ANSWER See Solve It in Answers on next page.

CONNECT THE MATH In the Solve It students found the subsets of a set. In this lesson students learn to write sets and determine the subsets and complements of a set.

2 Guided Instruction

Problem 1

Q What are natural numbers? **[Natural numbers are the counting numbers starting with 1.]**

Q If the symbol "≤" were used in the set-builder notation instead of "<," what other changes need to be made to the notation? **[The 6 needs to be changed to 5.]**

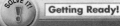 

3-5 Working With Sets

Objectives To write sets and identify subsets
To find the complement of a set

> Be careful! Your phone chooses from a lot of combinations.

Getting Ready!

Most numbers on a telephone keypad correspond to a set of letters. Suppose you're sending a text message. You press 4, 6, 6, and 3, in that order—one number for each letter. What word might your telephone think you're trying to spell? What words could you be trying to spell? Explain your reasoning.

Lesson Vocabulary
• roster form
• set-builder notation
• empty set
• universal set
• complement of a set

Recall from Lesson 1-3 that a *set* is a collection of distinct elements. A *subset* contains elements from a set. For example, the number 6 on the telephone keypad corresponds to the set {M, N, O}. The set {M, O} is one subset of this set.

Essential Understanding Sets are the basis of mathematical language. You can write sets in different ways and form smaller sets of elements from a larger set. You can also describe the elements that are *not* in a given set.

Roster form is one way to write sets. Roster form lists the elements of a set within braces, { }. For example, you write the set containing 1 and 2 as {1, 2}, and you write the set of multiples of 2 as {2, 4, 6, 8, . . .}.

Set-builder notation is another way to write sets. It describes the properties an element must have to be included in a set. For example, you can write the set {2, 4, 6, 8, . . . } in set-builder notation as {x | x is a multiple of 2}. You read this as "the set of all real numbers x, such that x is a multiple of 2."

Plan

How are roster form and set-builder notation different? Roster form *lists* the elements of a set. Set-builder notation *describes* the properties of those elements.

Problem 1 Using Roster Form and Set-Builder Notation

How do you write "*T* is the set of natural numbers that are less than 6" in roster form? In set-builder notation?

Roster form	**Set-builder notation**
Write "*T* is" as "*T* =."	List all natural numbers that are less than 6.	Use a variable.	Describe the limits on the variable.

$$T = \{1, 2, 3, 4, 5\}$$

$$T = \{x \mid x \text{ is a natural number}, x < 6\}$$

3-5 Preparing to Teach

ESSENTIAL UNDERSTANDINGS   UbD
• Sets are the basis of mathematical language.
• Sets are written in different ways, including roster form and set-builder notation.
• Smaller sets of elements can be formed from a larger set.
• The elements *not* in a given set are the complement of a set.

Math Background
It is necessary that students understand sets before they work with compound inequalities in Lesson 3–6.

Students learn two ways to write sets in this lesson. Roster notation may be easier for students to use at first, but it will become difficult or even impossible to use as sets become larger. Discuss with students why roster notation cannot be used to write sets such as the real numbers.

Beyond their use with compound inequalities, sets are important because many mathematical objects are defined in terms of sets. For example, functions map elements in one set, the domain, to elements in another set, the range.

Discuss with students how to compare the sizes of sets. It is easy to see that two finite sets are the same size if they have the same number of elements, but the size of infinite sets is more difficult to understand. For example, the set of even integers is a subset of the set of integers, and yet both sets are infinite.

Support Student Learning
Use the **Algebra I Companion** to engage and support students during instruction. See Lesson Resources at the end of this lesson for details.

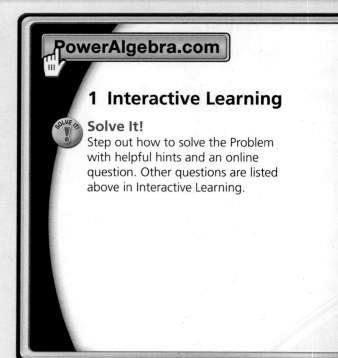

PowerAlgebra.com

1 Interactive Learning

Solve It!
Step out how to solve the Problem with helpful hints and an online question. Other questions are listed above in Interactive Learning.

Got It? **1.** *N* is the set of even natural numbers that are less than or equal to 12. How do you write *N* in roster form? In set-builder notation?

You can use set-builder notation to write the solutions of a linear inequality.

 Problem 2 **Inequalities and Set-Builder Notation**

Multiple Choice In set-builder notation, how do you write the solutions of $-5x + 7 \leq 17$?

Ⓐ $x \geq -2$ Ⓒ $\{-2, -1, 0, \ldots\}$

Ⓑ $\{x \mid x \geq -2\}$ Ⓓ $\{x \mid x \leq -2\}$

$$-5x + 7 \leq 17$$
$$-5x + 7 - 7 \leq 17 - 7 \quad \text{Subtract 7 from each side.}$$
$$-5x \leq 10 \quad \text{Simplify.}$$
$$\frac{-5x}{-5} \geq \frac{10}{-5} \quad \text{Divide each side by } -5. \text{ Reverse the inequality symbol.}$$
$$x \geq -2 \quad \text{Simplify.}$$

In set-builder notation, the solutions are given by $\{x \mid x \geq -2\}$. The answer is B.

 Got It? **2.** In set-builder notation, how do you write the solutions of $9 - 4n > 21$?

You know that a set *A* is a subset of a set *B* if each element of *A* is also an element of *B*. For example, if $B = \{-2, -1, 0, 1, 2, 3\}$ and $A = \{-1, 0, 2\}$, then *A* is a subset of *B*. You can write this relationship as $A \subseteq B$.

The **empty set,** or *null set,* is the set that contains no elements. The empty set is a subset of every set. Use $\emptyset$ or $\{\ \}$ to represent the empty set.

 Problem 3 **Finding Subsets**

What are all the subsets of the set $\{3, 4, 5\}$?

$\emptyset$	Start with the empty set.
$\{3\}, \{4\}, \{5\}$	List the subsets with one element.
$\{3, 4\}, \{3, 5\}, \{4, 5\}$	List the subsets with two elements.
$\{3, 4, 5\}$	List the original set. It is always considered a subset.

The eight subsets of $\{3, 4, 5\}$ are $\emptyset$, $\{3\}$, $\{4\}$, $\{5\}$, $\{3, 4\}$, $\{3, 5\}$, $\{4, 5\}$, and $\{3, 4, 5\}$.

 Got It? **3. a.** What are the subsets of the set $P = \{a, b\}$? Of the set $S = \{a, b, c\}$?
    b. Reasoning Let $A = \{x \mid x < -3\}$ and $B = \{x \mid x \leq 0\}$. Is *A* a subset of *B*? Explain your reasoning.

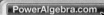
Plan

How is this problem similar to others you've solved?
It requires using properties of inequality to solve a multi-step inequality, as you did in Lesson 3-4.

Think

Why is the original set considered a subset?
It's a subset because it contains elements from the original set. In this case, it's the subset that contains all three elements.

Got It?
If further practice is needed, then provide students with a set given in set-builder notation. Ask students to write the corresponding roster form and give a verbal description of the set.

Problem 2
Note that three of the four choices provide for accurate ways to write the solution of the inequality. However, the intent of the question is to determine which choice shows set-builder notation.

> **Q** Why is the roster form in Choice C not an appropriate way to express the solutions of this inequality? **[Roster form cannot be used to express all of the non-integer numbers that are included in the solutions.]**

Got It?
Explain to students that "$x \mid$" means that all real numbers are part of the set except those which do not meet the requirements stated in the rest of the notation.

Problem 3

> **Q** Which set is a subset of all 8 sets listed in the solution? Explain. **[The empty set is a subset of itself and the other 7 sets.]**

Got It?   **VISUAL LEARNERS**

> **Q** Why are all of the subsets of *P* also subsets of *S*? **[The subsets of *P* are also subsets of *S*, because *P* is a subset of *S*.]**

Encourage students to sketch a graph of sets A and B prior to answering 3b.

---

 2 Guided Instruction

Each Problem is worked out and supported online.

Problem 1
Using Roster Form and Set-Builder Notation

Problem 2
Inequalities and Set-Builder Notation
Animated

Problem 3
Finding Subsets
Animated

Problem 4
Finding the Complement of a Set
Animated

Support in Algebra 1 Companion
• Vocabulary
• Key Concepts
• Got It?

Answers

Solve It!
Answers may vary. Sample: home, gone, hoof, good, goof, home, hone, hood; explanations may vary.

Got It?

1. $N = \{2, 4, 6, 8, 10, 12\}$; $N = \{x \mid x \text{ is an even natural number, } x \leq 12\}$

2. $\{n \mid n < -3\}$

3. a. $\{\ \}$ or $\emptyset$, $\{a\}$, $\{b\}$, $\{a, b\}$; $\{\ \}$ or $\emptyset$, $\{a\}$, $\{b\}$, $\{c\}$, $\{a, b\}$, $\{a, c\}$, $\{b, c\}$, $\{a, b, c\}$

    b. Yes; every element of set *A* is part of set *B*, since $-3 < 0$.

When working with sets, you call the largest set you are using the **universal set**, or universe. The **complement of a set** is the set of all elements in the universal set that are *not* in the set. You denote the complement of A by A'.

In the Venn diagrams below, U represents the universal set. Notice that $A \subseteq U$ and $A' \subseteq U$.

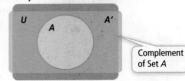

Set A is shaded.

The complement of set A is shaded.

Set A

Complement of Set A

Problem 4 Finding the Complement of a Set

Universal set U = {king, queen, bishop, knight, rook, pawn} and set A is the set of chess pieces that move side to side. What is the complement of set A?

King

Queen

Bishop

Knight

Rook

Pawn

Know
• The elements of set U
• The elements of set A

Need
• The elements of A'

Plan
Use a Venn diagram to find all the elements in set U that are *not* in set A.

The Venn diagram shows the relationship between sets A and U. The elements in set U that are *not* in set A are bishop, knight, and pawn.

So, A' = {bishop, knight, pawn}.

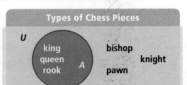

Types of Chess Pieces

U

king
queen
rook

A

bishop

knight

pawn

 Got It? **4.** Universal set U = {months of the year} and set A = {months with exactly 31 days}. What is the complement of set A? Write your answer in roster form.

Problem 4

Q How many elements are in U? **[6]**

Q How many elements are in A? **[3]**

Q How can you determine how many elements are in A'? **[You can subtract the number of elements in set A from the number of elements in set U.]**

Got It?

Q Is it possible for an element of set U to be in neither set A' nor set A? Explain. **[No, by the definition of a complement, all elements in set U that are not in set A are in set A'.]**

Additional Problems

1. How do you write "M is the set of whole numbers that are less than 5" in roster form? In set-builder notation?

ANSWER M = {0, 1, 2, 3, 4}; M = {$x \mid x$ is a whole number less than 5}

2. In set-builder notation, how do you write the solutions of $-4x + 3 < 15$?

a. $x > -3$

b. {$x \mid x > -3$}

c. all real numbers greater than -3

d. {$-2, -1, 0, 1, \ldots$}

ANSWER b

3. What are all the subsets of the set {1, 2, 3}?

ANSWER { }, {1}, {2}, {3}, {1, 2}, {2, 3}, {1, 3}, and {1, 2, 3}

4. Given that the universal set U = {car, truck, van, school bus, bicycle} and that set A is the set of vehicles that have 4 wheels, what is the complement of set A?

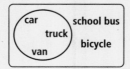

car
truck
van

school bus

bicycle

ANSWER A' = {school bus, bicycle}

Answers

Got It? (continued)

4. A' = {February, April, June, September, November}

Lesson Check

Do you know HOW?

1. How do you write "G is the set of odd natural numbers that are less than 18" in roster form? In set-builder notation?

2. In set-builder notation, how do you write the solutions of $5 + d \leq 8$?

3. What are all the subsets of $\{4, 8, 12\}$?

4. Given the universal set $U = \{$seasons of the year$\}$ and $W = \{$winter$\}$, what is W'?

Do you UNDERSTAND?

5. **Vocabulary** What is the complement of A'? Explain.

6. Is the first set in each pair a subset of the second set? Explain.
   a. $\emptyset$; $\{1, 3, 5\}$ b. $\{1, 3, 5\}$; $\{1, 3\}$ c. $\{3\}$; $\{1, 3, 5\}$

7. **Reasoning** A nonempty set is a set that contains at least one element. Given nonempty sets A and B, suppose that $A \subseteq B$. Is $B \subseteq A$ *always*, *sometimes*, or *never* true?

8. **Error Analysis** A student says sets A and B below are the same. What error did the student make?
   $A = \{x \mid x$ is a whole number less than 5$\}$
   $B = \{1, 2, 3, 4\}$

Practice and Problem-Solving Exercises

Ⓐ Practice

Write each set in roster form and in set-builder notation. ◀ See Problem 1.

9. M is the set of integers that are greater than -1 and less than 4.

10. N is the set of real numbers that are factors of 12.

11. P is the set of natural numbers that are less than 11.

12. R is the set of even natural numbers that are less than 2.

Write the solutions of each inequality in set-builder notation. ◀ See Problem 2.

13. $4y + 7 \geq 23$ 14. $5r + 8 < 63$ 15. $13 - 9m < 58$

16. $7 - 3d \geq 28$ 17. $2(3p - 11) \geq -16$ 18. $3(2k + 12) < -42$

List all the subsets of each set. ◀ See Problem 3.

19. $\{a, e, i, o\}$ 20. $\{0, 1, 2\}$ 21. $\{$dog, cat, fish$\}$

22. $\{-2, 2\}$ 23. $\{1\}$ 24. $\{+, -, \times, \div\}$

25. Suppose $U = \{1, 2, 3, 4, 5\}$ is the universal set and $A = \{2, 3\}$. What is A'? ◀ See Problem 4.

26. Suppose $U = \{1, 2, 3, 4, 5, 6, 7, 8\}$ is the universal set and $P = \{2, 4, 6, 8\}$. What is P'?

27. Suppose $U = \{\ldots, -3, -2, -1, 0, 1, 2, 3, \ldots\}$ is the universal set and $R = \{\ldots, -3, -1, 1, 3, \ldots\}$. What is R'?

28. Suppose $U = \{1, 2\}$ is the universal set and $T = \{1\}$. What is T'?

---

3 Lesson Check

Do you know HOW?
- If students have difficulty with Exercise 4, then encourage them to list all of the seasons in a year.

Do you UNDERSTAND?
- If students have difficulty with Exercise 7, then have them assign their own elements to sets A and B and explore the relationships.

Close

Q How can you be sure you listed all of the elements in the complement of set B? **[Answers will vary. Sample: List elements in the universal set. Cross out the elements that are part of set B to identify the complement.]**

Answers

Lesson Check

1. $G = \{1, 3, 5, 7, 9, 11, 13, 15, 17\}$;
   $G = \{x \mid x$ is an odd natural number, $x < 18\}$

2. $\{d \mid d \leq 3\}$

3. $\{\}$ or $\emptyset$, $\{4\}$, $\{8\}$, $\{12\}$, $\{4, 8\}$, $\{4, 12\}$, $\{8, 12\}$, $\{4, 8, 12\}$

4. $W' = \{$spring, summer, fall$\}$

5. A; Its complement is the set of all elements in the universal set that are not in A'.

6. a. Yes; the empty set is a subset of every set.
   b. No; the number 5 in the first set is not an element of the second set.
   c. Yes; the element in the first set is also an element of the second set.

7. sometimes

8. The student forgot that 0 is also a whole number.

Practice and Problem-Solving Exercises

9. $\{0, 1, 2, 3\}$; $\{m \mid m$ is an integer, $-1 < m < 4\}$

10. $\{1, 2, 3, 4, 6, 12\}$; $\{n \mid n$ is a real number that is a factor of 12$\}$

11. $\{1, 2, 3, 4, 5, 6, 7, 8, 9, 10\}$; $\{p \mid p$ is a natural number, $p < 11\}$

12. $\{\}$ or $\emptyset$; $\{r \mid r$ is an even natural number, $r < 2\}$

13. $\{y \mid y \geq 4\}$ 14. $\{r \mid r < 11\}$

15. $\{m \mid m > -5\}$ 16. $\{d \mid d \leq -7\}$

17. $\{p \mid p \geq 1\}$ 18. $\{k \mid k < -13\}$

19–22. See back of book.

23–28. See next page.

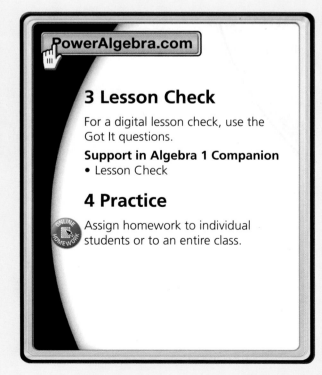

4 Practice

ASSIGNMENT GUIDE

Basic: 9–29 all, 30–38 even, 39, 40–48 even

Average: 9–27 odd, 29–49

Advanced: 9–27 odd, 29–52

Standardized Test Prep: 53–57

Mixed Review: 58–66

Reasoning exercises have blue headings.

Applications exercises have red headings.

EXERCISE 39: Use the Think About a Plan worksheet in the **Practice and Problem Solving Workbook** (also available in the Teaching Resources in print and online) to further support students' development in becoming independent learners.

HOMEWORK QUICK CHECK

To check students' understanding of key skills and concepts, go over Exercises 9, 25, 29, 39, and 48.

 Apply

29. **Think About a Plan** Universal set U and set A are defined below. What are the elements of A'?
    $U = \{$days of the week$\}$
    $A = \{$days of the week that contain the letter N$\}$
    - What are the elements of the universal set?
    - What are the elements of set A?
    - How can you find the complement of set A?

Suppose $U = \{0, 1, 2, 3, 4, 5, 6\}$, $A = \{2, 4, 6\}$, and $B = \{1, 2, 3\}$. Tell whether each statement is *true* or *false*. Explain your reasoning.

30. $A \subseteq U$ 31. $U \subseteq B$ 32. $B \subseteq A$ 33. $\emptyset \subseteq B$

Write each set in set-builder notation.

34. $B = \{11, 12, 13, 14, \ldots\}$ 35. $M = \{1, 3, 5, 7, 9, 11, 13, 17, 19\}$

36. $S = \{1, 2, 3, 4, 6, 12\}$ 37. $G = \{\ldots, -2, -1, 0, 1, 2, \ldots\}$

38. Universal set U and set B are defined below. What are the elements of B'?
    $U = \{$states of the United States$\}$
    $B = \{$states that do not start with the letter A$\}$

39. Universal set $U = \{$planets in Earth's solar system$\}$ and set $P = \{$planets farther from the sun than Earth is from the sun$\}$. What is the complement of set P? Write your answer in roster form.

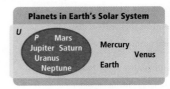

Planets in Earth's Solar System

Solve each inequality. Write your solutions in set-builder notation.

40. $-2(3x + 7) > -14$ 41. $-2(3x + 7) > -14 - 6x$

42. $-2(3x + 7) \geq -14 - 6x$ 43. $-3(4x + 8) + 1 \geq -23$

44. $-3(4x + 8) + 1 \geq -23 - 12x$ 45. $-3(4x + 8) + 1 < -23 - 12x$

46. Suppose $U = \{x \mid x$ is a multiple of 2, $x < 18\}$ is the universal set and $C = \{4, 8, 12, 16\}$. What is C'?

47. Suppose $U = \{x \mid x$ is an integer, $x \leq 12\}$ is the universal set and $T = \{x \mid x$ is a natural number, $x \leq 12\}$. What is T'?

48. **Open-Ended** Write a two-step inequality with solutions that are given by $\{n \mid n > 0\}$.

49. How many elements are in the set $\{x \mid x$ is an even prime number, $x < 100\}$?

Answers

Practice and Problem-Solving Exercises
(continued)

23. $\{\ \}$ or $\emptyset$, $\{1\}$

24. $\{\ \}$ or $\emptyset$, $\{+\}$, $\{-\}$, $\{\times\}$, $\{\div\}$, $\{+, -\}$, $\{+, \times\}$, $\{+, \div\}$, $\{-, \times\}$, $\{-, \div\}$, $\{\times, \div\}$, $\{+, -, \times\}$, $\{+, -, \div\}$, $\{+, \times, \div\}$, $\{-, \times, \div\}$, $\{+, -, \times, \div\}$

25. $\{1, 4, 5\}$

26. $\{1, 3, 5, 7\}$

27. $\{\ldots, -4, -2, 0, 2, 4, \ldots\}$

28. $\{2\}$

29. $A' = \{$Tuesday, Thursday, Friday, Saturday$\}$

30. True; every element of A is an element of U.

31. False; some elements of U are not elements of B.

32. False; some elements of B are not elements of A.

33. True; the empty set is a subset of every set.

34. $B = \{b \mid b$ is an integer, $b \geq 11\}$

35. $M = \{m \mid m$ is odd integer, $1 \leq m \leq 19\}$

36. $S = \{s \mid s$ is a factor of 12$\}$

37. $G = \{g \mid g$ is an integer$\}$

38. $\{$Alabama, Alaska, Arkansas, Arizona$\}$

39. $\{$Mercury, Venus, Earth$\}$

40. $\{x \mid x < 0\}$

41. $\{\ \}$ or $\emptyset$

42. $\{x \mid x$ is a real number$\}$

43. $\{x \mid x \leq 0\}$

44. $\{x \mid x$ is a real number$\}$

45. $\{\ \}$ or $\emptyset$

46. $C' = \{2, 6, 10, 14\}$

47. $T' = \{x \mid x$ is an integer, $x \leq 0\}$

48. Answers may vary. Sample:
    $2n - 5 > -5$

49. 1

50. Reasoning Without listing each subset of a set, how can you determine the number of subsets that the set has?

Use your answer from Exercise 50. Determine how many subsets each set has.

51. $R = \{$positive even numbers less than 20$\}$ **52.** $Q = \{0\}$

Standardized Test Prep

53. Let the universal set be $U = \{x \mid x \text{ is a natural number}\}$, and let set $E = \{2, 4, 6, 8, \ldots\}$. What is E'?

Ⓐ $\{1, 3, 5, 7, \ldots\}$ Ⓒ $\{$all positive integers$\}$
Ⓑ $\{0, 2, 4, 6, 8, \ldots\}$ Ⓓ $\{2, 4, 6, 8, \ldots\}$

54. Which set represents the solutions of $-9x + 17 \geq -64$?

Ⓕ $\{x \mid x \leq 9\}$ Ⓖ $\{x \mid x \geq 9\}$ Ⓗ $\left\{x \mid x \leq -\frac{47}{9}\right\}$ Ⓘ $\left\{x \mid x \geq -\frac{47}{9}\right\}$

55. In the diagram below, $\triangle ABC \sim \triangle EFG$. What is FG?

Ⓐ $3\frac{8}{9}$ Ⓑ $6\frac{3}{7}$ Ⓒ 11 Ⓓ $12\frac{3}{5}$

56. What is the least whole-number solution of $-10n \leq 5$?

Ⓕ -1 Ⓖ 0 Ⓗ 1 Ⓘ 2

57. Mum's Florist sells two dozen roses for $24.60. First Flowers Florist sells 6 roses for $7.50. Which florist has the lower cost per rose? Explain.

Mixed Review

Solve each inequality.   ◀ See Lesson 3-4.

58. $3b + 2 > 26$ **59.** $2(t + 2) - 3t \geq -1$ **60.** $6z - 15 < 4z + 11$

Evaluate each expression for the given value of the variable.   ◀ See Lesson 1-2.

61. $3n - 6; n = 4$ **62.** $7 - 2b; b = 5$ **63.** $\frac{2d - 3}{5}; d = 9$

Get Ready! To prepare for Lesson 3-6, do Exercises 64–66.

Graph each pair of inequalities on one number line.   ◀ See Lesson 3-1.

64. $c < 8; c \geq 10$ **65.** $t \geq -2; t \leq -5$ **66.** $m \leq 7; m > 12$

50. Determine the number of elements in the set. Raise 2 to that number.

51. 512

52. 2

53. A

54. F

55. D

56. G

57. [2] Mum's Florist: $24.60 ÷ 24 = $1.025 each. First Flowers Florist: $7.50 ÷ 6 = $1.25 each. Mum's Florist has a lower cost per rose.

[1] incorrect solution with appropriate work OR correct solution with no work shown or incorrect work shown

58. $b > 8$

59. $t \leq 5$

60. $z < 13$

61. 6

62. −3

63. 3

64.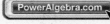

65.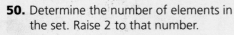

66.

Additional Instructional Support

Algebra 1 Companion

Students can use the **Algebra 1 Companion** worktext (4 pages) as you teach the lesson. Use the Companion to support

• New Vocabulary
• Key Concepts
• Got It for each Problem
• Lesson Check

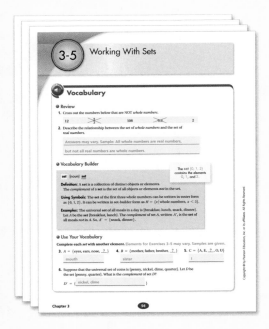

ELL Support

Focus on Communication Write the objectives for the lesson on the board and read them aloud. Question the meaning of the objectives, for example: What does it mean to 'write sets'? Have students skim the text for the meaning of key words. Guide students to rephrase the objectives using their own words. The goal is to rewrite the objectives on the board in understandable, meaningful terms. After the objectives are clearly communicated, leave the objectives where they can be seen and repeat the appropriate parts of the objectives that support the classroom tasks at hand.

5 Assess & Remediate

Lesson Quiz

1. How do you write "S is the set of natural numbers that are less than 8" in roster form?
2. In set-builder notation, how do you write the solutions of $2x - 7 \geq 11$?
3. What are all the subsets of the set {7, 8, 9}?
4. Suppose $U = \{1, 2, 3, 4, 5\}$ is the universal set and $A = \{1, 5\}$. What is A'?
5. **Do you UNDERSTAND?** Given that the universal set U = {baseball, basketball, football, tennis ball, soccer ball, volleyball} and that set A is the set of sports balls that are spherical, what is the complement of set A?

ANSWERS TO LESSON QUIZ

1. S = {1, 2, 3, 4, 5, 6, 7}
2. $\{x \mid x \geq 9\}$
3. { } or ∅, {7}, {8}, {9}, {7, 8}, {8, 9}, {7, 9}, {7, 8, 9}
4. $A' = \{2, 3, 4\}$
5. $A' = \{football\}$

PRESCRIPTION FOR REMEDIATION
Use the student work on the Lesson Quiz to prescribe a differentiated review assignment.

Points	Differentiated Remediation
0–2	Intervention
3–4	On-level
5	Extension

PowerAlgebra.com

5 Assess & Remediate

Assign the Lesson Quiz. Appropriate intervention, practice, or enrichment is automatically generated based on student performance.

Intervention

• **Reteaching** (2 pages) Provides reteaching and practice exercises for the key lesson concepts. Use with struggling students or absent students.
• **English Language Learner Support** Helps students develop and reinforce mathematical vocabulary and key concepts.

All-in-One Resources/Online
Reteaching

3-5 **Reteaching**
Working With Sets

There are two ways to write a set.
• Roster form lists the elements of a set within braces, { }.
• Set-builder notation describes the properties an element must have to be included in a set.

Problem

How do you write "R is the set of even whole numbers less than 10" in roster form and in set-builder notation?

Roster Form
List the numbers 0, 2, 4, 6, and 8 in braces.
$R = \{0, 2, 4, 6, 8\}$

Set-Builder Notation
Describe the properties.
$R = \{x \mid x \text{ is an even whole number, } x < 10\}$
This is read as "the set of all even whole numbers x such that x is less than 10."

Exercises

Write each set in roster form and in set-builder notation.

1. D is the set of integers greater than −5 and less than 5.
   $D = \{-4, -3, -2, -1, 0, 1, 2, 3, 4\}; D = \{x \mid x \text{ is an integer, } -5 < x < 5\}$
2. N is the set of odd natural numbers less than 14.
   $N = \{1, 3, 5, 7, 9, 11, 13\}; N = \{x \mid x \text{ is an odd integer, } x < 14\}$
3. P is the set of natural numbers less than or equal to 7.
   $P = \{1, 2, 3, 4, 5, 6, 7\}; P = \{x \mid x \text{ is a natural number, } x \leq 7\}$
4. T is the set of real numbers that are factors of 18.
   $T = \{1, 2, 3, 6, 9, 18\}; T = \{x \mid x \text{ is a real number, } x \text{ is a factor of 18}\}$
5. A is the set of integers between −3 and 5.
   $A = \{-2, -1, 0, 1, 2, 3, 4\}; A = \{x \mid x \text{ is an integer, } -3 < x < 5\}$

Write the solutions of each inequality in set-builder notation.

6. $4b + 8 > -12$
   $\{b \mid b \text{ is a real number; } b > -5\}$
7. $7n - 14 \geq 28$
   $\{n \mid n \text{ is an integer; } n \geq 6\}$
8. $5s - 15 \leq 18 - 2s$
   $\{s \mid s \text{ is a real number; } s \leq \frac{33}{7}\}$
9. $2(3p - 5) - 7p < -2$
   $\{p \mid p \text{ is a real number; } p > -8\}$

All-in-One Resources/Online
English Language Learner Support

3-5 **ELL Support**
Working With Sets

Concept List

$B \subseteq A$	empty set or null set	multiples of 3
roster form	set-builder notation	subset
$T = \{0, 1, 2, 3, 4\}$	the complement of set A	universal set

Choose the concept from the list above that best represents the item in each box.

1. U	2.	3. { } or ∅
universal set	$B \subseteq A$	empty set or null set
4. $T = \{x \mid x \text{ is a whole number} < 5\}$	5. $\{x \mid x > 1\}$	6. $\subseteq$
$T = \{0, 1, 2, 3, 4\}$	set builder notation	subset
7. {1}	8.	9. {3, 6, 9, ...}
roster form	the complement of set A	multiples of 3

Differentiated Remediation *continued*

On-Level

- **Practice** (2 pages) Provides extra practice for each lesson. For simpler practice exercises, use the Form K Practice pages found in the All-in-One Teaching Resources and online.

- **Think About a Plan** Helps students develop specific problem-solving skills and strategies by providing scaffolded guiding questions.

- **Standardized Test Prep** Focuses on all major exercises, all major question types, and helps students prepare for the high-stakes assessments.

Extension

- **Enrichment** Provides students with interesting problems and activities that extend the concepts of the lesson.

- **Activities, Games, and Puzzles** Worksheets that can be used for concepts development, enrichment, and for fun!

Practice and Problem Solving WKBK/ All-in-One Resources/Online
Practice page 1

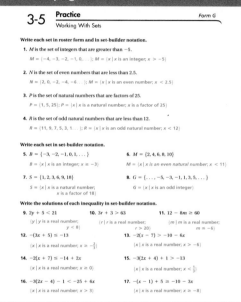

Practice and Problem Solving WKBK/ All-in-One Resources/Online
Practice page 2

(Practice (continued), Form G, 3-5 Working With Sets)

All-in-One Resources/Online
Enrichment

(Enrichment, 3-5 Working With Sets)

Practice and Problem Solving WKBK/ All-in-One Resources/Online
Think About a Plan

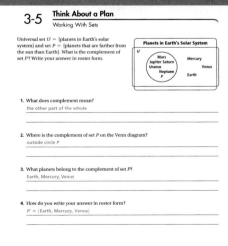

Practice and Problem Solving WKBK/ All-in-One Resources/Online
Standardized Test Prep

(Standardized Test Prep, 3-5 Working With Sets)

Online Teacher Resource Center
Activities, Games, and Puzzles

(Game: Thanks for the (Math) Memories, 3-5 Working With Sets)

1 Interactive Learning

Solve It!

PURPOSE To use inequalities to find a range of answers for a real-world situation

PROCESS Students may use the endpoints of the graph to determine a verbal description of the range of values that represents the expected earnings. Students may use a compound inequality to represent the expected earnings.

> **FACILITATE**
>
> **Q** Is it possible to describe the orange production of a tree using a single inequality? Explain. **[No, a single inequality has an endpoint and then continues infinitely in one direction.]**
>
> **Q** What is the range of the possible orange production for a tree? Let b represent the number of boxes of oranges. **[b is between 1.3 and 4; $b \geq 1.3$ and $b \leq 4$]**
>
> **Q** What is the range of the expected earnings, e? Write an inequality if possible. **[e is between 12.35 and 38; $e \geq 12.35$ and $e \leq 38$.]**

ANSWER See Solve It in Answers on next page.
CONNECT THE MATH Students will sometimes use the word *and* to connect two inequalities. Ask students to justify the use of the word *and*. To introduce the concepts later in the lesson, ask students to write two inequalities to represent earnings that should be unexpected by the grower. Ask students if the word *and* can be used to connect these two inequalities.

Objectives To solve and graph inequalities containing the word *and*
To solve and graph inequalities containing the word *or*

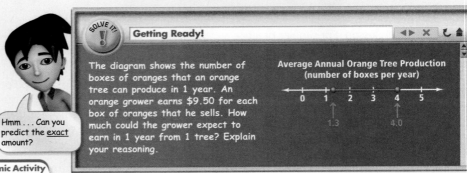

Hmm . . . Can you predict the <u>exact</u> amount?

Dynamic Activity Compound Inequalities

Lesson Vocabulary
- compound inequality
- interval notation

> **Getting Ready!**
>
> The diagram shows the number of boxes of oranges that an orange tree can produce in 1 year. An orange grower earns $9.50 for each box of oranges that he sells. How much could the grower expect to earn in 1 year from 1 tree? Explain your reasoning.
>
> **Average Annual Orange Tree Production**
> (number of boxes per year)

The Solve It involves a value that is between two numbers. You can use a compound inequality to represent this relationship. A **compound inequality** consists of two distinct inequalities joined by the word *and* or the word *or*.

Essential Understanding You find the solutions of a compound inequality either by identifying where the solution sets of the distinct inequalities overlap or by combining the solution sets to form a larger solution set.

The graph of a compound inequality with the word *and* contains the *overlap* of the graphs of the two inequalities that form the compound inequality.

The graph of a compound inequality with the word *or* contains *each* graph of the two inequalities that form the compound inequality.

You can rewrite a compound inequality involving *and* as a single inequality. For instance, in the inequality above, you can write $x \geq 3$ and $x \leq 7$ as $3 \leq x \leq 7$. You read this as "x is greater than or equal to 3 and less than or equal to 7." Another way to read it is "x is between 3 and 7, inclusive." In this example, *inclusive* means the solutions of the inequality include both 3 and 7.

3-6 Preparing to Teach

BIG ideas Variable
Equivalence
Solving Equations and Inequalities

UbD

ESSENTIAL UNDERSTANDINGS

- The solutions of a compound inequality are either the overlap or combination of the solution sets of distinct inequalities.
- The graph of a compound inequality with the word *and* contains the overlap of the graphs of the two inequalities.
- The graph of a compound inequality with the word *or* contains each graph of the two inequalities.

Math Background

To satisfy the inequality $x < 7$, a number only needs to be less than 7. To satisfy a compound inequality, a number may need to meet two conditions. These conditions are either expressed by the word *and* or the word *or*.

For example, a solution of the compound inequality $x > 3$ and $x < 7$ must be both greater than 3 and less than 7. The graph of all solutions looks like:

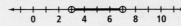

A solution of the compound inequality $x < 3$ or $x > 7$ must be either less than three, or greater than 7. The graph of the solution looks like:

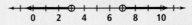

Support Student Learning

Use the **Algebra 1 Companion** to engage and support students during instructions. See Lesson Resources at the end of this lesson for details.

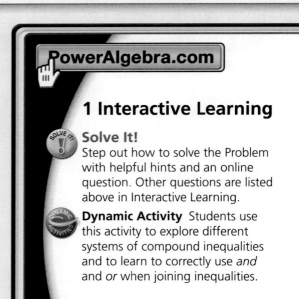

PowerAlgebra.com

1 Interactive Learning

Solve It!
Step out how to solve the Problem with helpful hints and an online question. Other questions are listed above in Interactive Learning.

Dynamic Activity Students use this activity to explore different systems of compound inequalities and to learn to correctly use *and* and *or* when joining inequalities.

Problem 1 Writing a Compound Inequality

What compound inequality represents the phrase? Graph the solutions.

A all real numbers that are greater than −2 and less than 6

$n > -2$ and $n < 6$

$-2 < n$ and $n < 6$

$-2 < n < 6$

B all real numbers that are less than 0 or greater than or equal to 5

$t < 0$ or $t \geq 5$

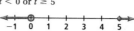

Think

Why can you write an *and* inequality without the word *and*?
The compound inequality $-2 < n$ and $n < 6$ means n is greater than −2 and n is less than 6. This means n is between −2 and 6. You write this as $-2 < n < 6$.

 Got It? **1.** For parts (a) and (b) below, write a compound inequality that represents each phrase. Graph the solutions.

    a. all real numbers that are greater than or equal to −4 and less than 6

    b. all real numbers that are less than or equal to $2\frac{1}{2}$ or greater than 6

    c. Reasoning What is the difference between "x is between −5 and 7" and "x is between −5 and 7, inclusive"?

A solution of a compound inequality involving *and* is any number that makes *both* inequalities true. One way you can solve a compound inequality is by separating it into two inequalities.

 Problem 2 Solving a Compound Inequality Involving *And*

What are the solutions of $-3 \leq m - 4 < -1$? Graph the solutions.

$$-3 \leq m - 4 < -1$$

$-3 \leq m - 4$	and	$m - 4 < -1$

Write the compound inequality as two inequalities joined by the word *and*.

$-3 + 4 \leq m - 4 + 4$	and	$m - 4 + 4 < -1 + 4$

Add 4 to each side of each inequality.

$1 \leq m$	and	$m < 3$

Simplify.

$$1 \leq m < 3$$

Write the solutions as a single inequality.

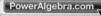

Plan

How do you know to join the two inequalities with *and*?
The compound inequality $-3 \leq m - 4 < -1$ means that the quantity $m - 4$ is between −3 and −1, including −3. So use the word *and*.

 Got It? **2.** What are the solutions of $-2 < 3y - 4 < 14$? Graph the solutions.

You can also solve an inequality like $-3 \leq m - 4 < -1$ by working on all three parts of the inequality at the same time. You work to isolate the variable between the inequality symbols. This method is used in Problem 3.

---

2 Guided Instruction

Problem 1

> **Q** Should the graph for 1A have closed circles or open circles at the endpoints? Explain. **[The graph should have open circles because the inequality symbols are not inclusive.]**
>
> **Q** Is it possible to use the word "between" when describing the value of t in 1B? Explain. **[No, t is not contained in a distinct range of numbers.]**

Got It?

Point out to students that the phrase "greater than or equal to −4" in 1a is a compound statement which contains the word *or*. Therefore, it is a combination of the numbers greater than 4 or numbers equal to 4.

Problem 2

Students rewrite the compound inequality as two distinct inequalities prior to solving the inequality.

> **Q** Does this compound inequality represent two inequalities joined by *or* or by *and*? **[and]**
>
> **Q** Will the graph of the solutions contain one shaded region or two shaded regions? **[one]**

Got It?   ERROR PREVENTION

Point out to students that if the solutions of the two distinct inequalities do not contain an "overlap," then there is likely a mistake in the solution process. However, it is possible that the solution is the empty set.

---

2 Guided Instruction

 Each Problem is worked out and supported online.

Problem 1
Writing a Compound Inequality
Animated

Problem 2
Solving a Compound Inequality Involving *And*

Problem 3
Writing and Solving a Compound Inequality
Animated

Problem 4
Solving a Compound Inequality Involving *Or*
Animated

Problem 5
Using Interval Notation

Support in Algebra 1 Companion
• Vocabulary
• Key Concepts
• Got It?

Answers

Solve It!
Between $12.35 and $38; explanations may vary.

Got It?

1. a. $-4 \leq x < 6$

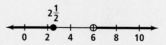

    b. $x \leq 2\frac{1}{2}$ or $x > 6$

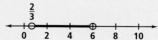

    c. x is between −5 and 7 does not include −5 or 7. *Inclusive* means that −5 and 7 are included.

2. $\frac{2}{3} < y < 6$

Problem 3

Students solve a compound inequality without rewriting it as two distinct inequalities.

> **Q** How would you find the average of the four test scores? **[You would add the scores together and then divide by 4, but because one of the test scores is unknown, use x.]**
>
> **Q** What property is used to remove the denominator of 4 from the compound inequality? **[Multiplication Property of Inequality]**

Got It?

Encourage students to answer this question by modifying the inequality $336 \leq 251 + x \leq 344$ to $336 \leq 235 + x \leq 344$.

Problem 4

Students find the solutions of a compound inequality by combining the solutions of the two distinct inequalities.

> **Q** Are all of the numbers which are solutions to the inequality $t < -3$ also solutions of both original inequalities? Explain. **[No, solutions of a compound inequality containing "or" only have to make one inequality true.]**
>
> **Q** What is a statement that describes the unshaded portion of the number line? **[Answers may vary. Sample: The numbers on the unshaded portion of the number line do not solve either inequality.]**

Got It?   ERROR PREVENTION

If students determine that the solutions for this compound inequality overlap, then they likely forgot to reverse the inequality symbol when solving the first inequality.

Think

What is another way to solve this problem?
You can *work backward* to solve this problem. You can start with the inequality $84 \leq x \leq 86$ where x represents the average of your test scores. Then rewrite the inequality in terms of the sum of your 4 test scores.

 Problem 3 **Writing and Solving a Compound Inequality**

Test Average To earn a B in your algebra course, you must achieve an unrounded test average between 84 and 86, inclusive. You scored 86, 85, and 80 on the first three tests of the grading period. What possible scores can you earn on the fourth and final test to earn a B in the course?

Know	Need	Plan
• Test average must be between 84 and 86, inclusive • First 3 test scores	Possible scores you can earn on the last test to get a B in the course	Write an expression for your test average. Then write and solve a compound inequality.

$$84 \leq \frac{86 + 85 + 80 + x}{4} \leq 86 \quad \text{Write a compound inequality.}$$

$$4(84) \leq 4\left(\frac{251 + x}{4}\right) \leq 4(86) \quad \text{Multiply each part by 4.}$$

$$336 \leq 251 + x \leq 344 \quad \text{Simplify.}$$

$$336 - 251 \leq 251 + x - 251 \leq 344 - 251 \quad \text{Subtract 251 from each part.}$$

$$85 \leq x \leq 93 \quad \text{Simplify.}$$

Your score on the fourth test must be between 85 and 93, inclusive.

 Got It? 3. Reasoning Suppose you scored 78, 78, and 79 on the first three tests. Is it possible for you to earn a B in the course? Assume that 100 is the maximum grade you can earn in the course and on the test. Explain.

A solution of a compound inequality involving *or* is any number that makes *either* inequality true. To solve a compound inequality involving *or*, you must solve separately the two inequalities that form the compound inequality.

Plan

How is this inequality different from others you've solved?
It contains the word *or*. Unlike an *and* inequality, it's formed by two inequalities with solutions that do not overlap.

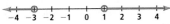 **Problem 4** **Solving a Compound Inequality Involving Or**

What are the solutions of $3t + 2 < -7$ or $-4t + 5 < 1$? Graph the solutions.

$$3t + 2 < -7 \qquad \text{or} \qquad -4t + 5 < 1$$

$$3t + 2 - 2 < -7 - 2 \qquad \text{or} \qquad -4t + 5 - 5 < 1 - 5$$

$$3t < -9 \qquad \text{or} \qquad -4t < -4$$

$$\frac{3t}{3} < \frac{-9}{3} \qquad \text{or} \qquad \frac{-4t}{-4} > \frac{-4}{-4}$$

$$t < -3 \qquad \text{or} \qquad t > 1$$

> Reverse the inequality symbol when you divide by a negative number.

The solutions are given by $t < -3$ or $t > 1$.

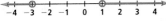

 Got It? 4. What are the solutions of $-2y + 7 < 1$ or $4y + 3 \leq -5$? Graph the solutions.

Additional Problems

1. What compound inequality represents each given phrase?

    a. all real numbers that are greater than 1 and less than 5

    b. all real numbers that are less than 10 or greater than 15

    ANSWER a. $1 < x < 5$
    b. $x < 10$ or $x > 15$

2. What are the solutions of $-2 < x + 2 \leq 5$? Graph the solutions.

    ANSWER $-4 < x \leq 3$

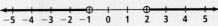

3. To win the recycling contest, you must collect between 83 and 87 pop tabs each week, inclusive. Suppose you collected 82, 86, and 84 pop tabs during the first three weeks of the competition. What are the possible numbers of pop tabs you can collect during the fourth and final week in order to win the recycling contest?

    ANSWER between 80 and 96 pop tabs inclusive

4. What are the solutions to $2n - 1 < -3$ or $-3n + 2 < -4$? Graph the solutions.

    ANSWER $n < -1$ or $n > 2$

You can use an inequality such as $x \le -3$ to describe a portion of the number line called an *interval*. You can also use *interval notation* to describe an interval on the number line. **Interval notation** includes the use of three special symbols. These symbols include

parentheses: Use (or) when a $<$ or $>$ symbol indicates that the interval's endpoints are *not* included.

brackets: Use [or] when a $\le$ or $\ge$ symbol indicates that the interval's endpoints *are* included.

infinity: Use ∞ when the interval continues forever in a *positive* direction. Use $-\infty$ when the interval continues forever in a *negative* direction.

Inequality	Graph	Interval Notation
$x \ge 2$	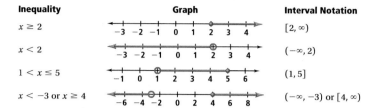	$[2, \infty)$
$x < 2$		$(-\infty, 2)$
$1 < x \le 5$		$(1, 5]$
$x < -3$ or $x \ge 4$		$(-\infty, -3)$ or $[4, \infty)$

Problem 5 Using Interval Notation

A What is the graph of $[-4, 6)$? How do you write $[-4, 6)$ as an inequality?

The bracket indicates that -4 is included. So use a closed circle at -4.

The parenthesis indicates that 6 is *not* included. So use an open circle at 6.

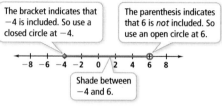

Shade between -4 and 6.

The inequality $-4 \le x < 6$ represents the interval notation $[-4, 6)$.

B What is the graph of $x \le -1$ or $x > 2$? How do you write $x \le -1$ or $x > 2$ in interval notation?

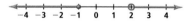

The interval notation $(-\infty, -1]$ or $(2, \infty)$ represents the inequality $x \le -1$ or $x > 2$.

Got It? 5. a. What is the graph of $(-2, 7]$? How do you write $(-2, 7]$ as an inequality?
b. What is the graph of $y > 7$? How do you write $y > 7$ in interval notation?

Plan

How do you write interval notation as an inequality?

It may help to read its meaning aloud first. $[-4, 6)$ means all real numbers greater than or equal to -4 and less than 6.

Problem 5

Q How is the symbol "[" represented on a graph? In inequality symbols? **[closed circle; $\ge$]**

Q How is the symbol ")" represented on a graph? In inequality symbols? **[open circle; $<$]**

Q How can the inequality $-4 \le x < 6$ be written as two inequalities? **[$x \ge -4$ and $x < 6$]**

Q What is a verbal translation of the inequality in 5B? **[All real numbers less than or equal to -1 or greater than 2.]**

Got It?

Q How does the graph of $(-2, 7]$ differ from the graph of $[-2, 7)$? **[In the graph of $(-2, 7]$, -2 has an open circle and 7 has a closed circle. The location of the open circle and the closed circle is reversed in the graph of $[-2, 7)$.]**

Answers

Got It? (continued)

3. Answers may vary. Sample: No, to get a B, the average of the 4 tests must be at least 84. If x is the 4th test score, $\frac{78 + 78 + 79 + x}{4} \ge 84$, $235 + x \ge 336$, and $x \ge 101$, which is impossible.

4. $y > 3$ or $y \le -2$

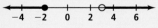

5. a. $-2 < x \le 7$

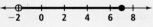

b. $(7, \infty)$

3 Lesson Check

Do you know HOW?
- If students have difficulty with Exercise 3, then have them review Problem 3.

Do you UNDERSTAND?
- If students have difficulty with Exercise 7, then have them graph $3x - 7 \leq 14$ and $4x - 8 > 20$ to determine the solutions.

Close

Q Explain how you know when to use a parentheses or a bracket when writing an inequality in interval notation. **[Answers will vary. Sample answer: Use parentheses when the interval is not inclusive. Use brackets when the interval is inclusive.]**

Lesson Check
Do you know HOW?

1. What compound inequality represents the phrase "all real numbers that are greater than or equal to 0 and less than 8"? Graph the solutions.

2. What are the solutions of $-4 \leq r - 5 < -1$? Graph the solutions.

3. Your test scores in science are 83 and 87. What possible scores can you earn on your next test to have a test average between 85 and 90, inclusive?

4. Write the interval represented on the number line below as an inequality and in interval notation.

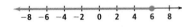

Do you UNDERSTAND?

5. **Vocabulary** Which of the following are compound inequalities?

   A. $x > 4$ or $x < -4$ B. $x \geq 6$

   C. $8 \leq 5x < 30$ D. $7x > 42$ or $-5x \leq 10$

6. **Error Analysis** A student writes the inequality $x \geq 17$ in interval notation as $[17, \infty]$. Explain why this is incorrect.

7. **Reasoning** What are the solutions of $3x - 7 \leq 14$ or $4x - 8 > 20$? Write your solutions as a compound inequality and in interval notation.

8. **Writing** Compare the graph of a compound inequality involving *and* with the graph of a compound inequality involving *or*.

Practice and Problem-Solving Exercises

A Practice **Write a compound inequality that represents each phrase. Graph the solutions.** See Problem 1.

9. all real numbers that are between -5 and 7

10. The circumference of a women's basketball must be between 28.5 in. and 29 in., inclusive.

Solve each compound inequality. Graph your solutions. See Problems 2 and 3.

11. $-4 < k + 3 < 8$ 12. $5 \leq y + 2 \leq 11$ 13. $3 < 4p - 5 \leq 15$

14. $15 \leq \frac{20 + 11 + k}{3} \leq 19$ 15. $\frac{1}{4} < \frac{2x - 7}{2} < 5$ 16. $-3 \leq \frac{6 - q}{9} \leq 3$

Solve each compound inequality. Graph your solutions. See Problem 4.

17. $6b - 1 < -7$ or $2b + 1 > 5$ 18. $5 + m > 4$ or $7m < -35$

19. $4d + 5 \geq 13$ or $7d - 2 < 12$ 20. $7 - c < 1$ or $4c \leq 12$

21. $5y + 7 \leq -3$ or $3y - 2 \geq 13$ 22. $5z - 3 > 7$ or $4z - 6 < -10$

Write each interval as an inequality. Then graph the solutions. See Problem 5.

23. $(-\infty, 2]$ 24. $[-4, 5]$ 25. $(-\infty, -1]$ or $(3, \infty)$ 26. $[6, \infty)$

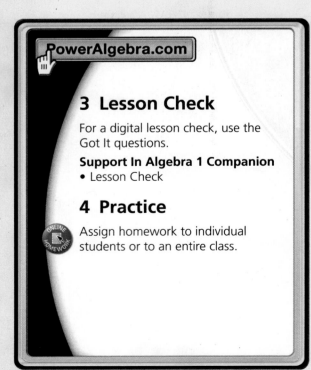

PowerAlgebra.com

3 Lesson Check

For a digital lesson check, use the Got It questions.

Support In Algebra 1 Companion
- Lesson Check

4 Practice

Assign homework to individual students or to an entire class.

Answers

Lesson Check

1. $0 \leq x < 8$

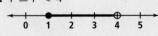

2. $1 \leq r < 4$

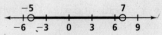

3. $85 \leq x \leq 100$

4. $x \leq 6$; $(-\infty, 6]$

5. A, C, and D

6. Answers may vary. Sample: The bracket indicates a specific number is part of the solution. The symbol ∞ means that the numbers continue without end. So a parenthesis should follow.

7. $x \leq 7$ or $x > 7$; $(-\infty, \infty)$

8. The graph of a compound inequality with the word *and* contains the overlap of the graphs that form the inequality. The graph of a compound inequality with the word *or* contains both of the graphs that form the inequality.

Practice and Problem-Solving Exercises

9. $-5 < x < 7$

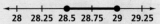

10. $28.5 \leq x \leq 29$

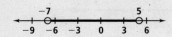

11. $-7 < k < 5$

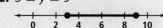

12. $3 \leq y \leq 9$

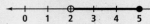

13. $2 < p \leq 5$

Write each inequality in interval notation. Then graph the interval.

27. $x > -2$ **28.** $x \le 0$ **29.** $x < -2$ or $x \ge 1$ **30.** $-3 \le x < 4$

B Apply

Solve each inequality. Write each set in interval notation.

31. $7 < x + 6 \le 12$

32. $-9 < 3m + 6 \le 18$

33. $f + 14 < 9$ or $-9f \le -45$

34. $12h - 3 \ge 15h$ or $5 > -0.2h + 10$

Write a compound inequality that each graph could represent.

35. 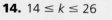   **36.** 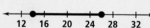   **37.**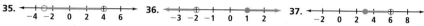

Solve each compound inequality. Justify each step.

38. $4r - 3 > 11$ or $4r - 3 \le -11$

39. $2 \le 0.75v \le 4.5$

40. $\frac{4y + 2}{5} - 5 > 3$ or $\frac{4 - 3y}{6} > 4$

41. $-\frac{4}{3} \le \frac{1}{7}w - \frac{3}{4} < 1$

42. Chemistry The acidity of the water in a swimming pool is considered normal if the average of three pH readings is between 7.2 and 7.8, inclusive. The first two readings for a swimming pool are 7.4 and 7.9. What possible values for the third reading p will make the average pH normal?

43. Think About a Plan The Triangle Inequality Theorem states that the sum of the lengths of any two sides of a triangle is greater than the length of the third side. The lengths of two sides of a triangle are given. What are the possible lengths x of the third side of the triangle?
- Is there an upper limit on the value of x? Is there a lower limit?
- How can you use your answers to the previous question to write one or more inequalities involving x?

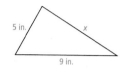

Use your answers to Exercise 43 to answer Exercises 44–47. The lengths of two sides of a triangle are given. Find the possible lengths of the third side.

44. 3.75 in., 7 in.   **45.** 15 ft, 21 ft   **46.** 14 mm, 35 mm   **47.** 6 m, 17 m

48. Physics The force exerted on a spring is proportional to the distance the spring is stretched from its relaxed position. Suppose you stretch a spring a distance of d inches by applying a force of F pounds. For your spring, $\frac{d}{F} = 0.8$. You apply forces between 25 lb and 40 lb, inclusive. What inequality describes the distances the spring is stretched?

49. Reasoning Describe the solutions of $4x - 9 < 7$ or $3x - 10 > 2$.

50. Nutrition A sedentary 15-year-old male should consume no more than 2200 Calories per day. A moderately active 15-year-old male should consume between 2400 and 2800 Calories per day. An active 15-year-old male should consume between 2800 and 3200 Calories per day. Model these ranges on a number line. Represent each range of calories using interval notation.

4 Practice

ASSIGNMENT GUIDE

Basic: 9–30 all, 32–40 even, 43, 48–50

Average: 9–29 odd, 31–50

Advanced: 9–29 odd, 31–52

Standardized Test Prep: 53–55

Mixed Review: 56–64

Reasoning exercises have blue headings.

Applications exercises have red headings.

EXERCISE 48: Use the Think About a Plan worksheet in the **Practice and Problem Solving Workbook** (also available in the Teaching Resources in print and online) to further support students' development in becoming independent learners.

HOMEWORK QUICK CHECK

To check students' understanding of key skills and concepts, go over Exercises 13, 23, 43, 48, and 49.

---

14. $14 \le k \le 26$

15. $3\frac{3}{4} < x < 8\frac{1}{2}$

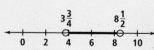

16. $-21 \le q \le 33$

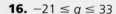

17. $b < -1$ or $b > 2$

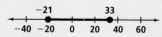

18. $m > -1$ or $m < -5$

19. $d \ge 2$ or $d < 2$

20. $c \le 3$ or $c > 6$

21. $y \le -2$ or $y \ge 5$

22. $z > 2$ or $z < -1$

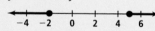

23. $x \le 2$

24. $-4 \le x \le 5$

25. $x \le -1$ or $x > 3$

26. $x \ge 6$

27. $(-2, \infty)$

28. $(-\infty, 0]$

29. $(-\infty, -2)$ or $[1, \infty)$

30. $[-3, 4)$

31. $(1, 6]$

32. $(-5, 4]$

33. $(-\infty, -5)$ or $[5, \infty)$

34. $(-\infty, -1]$ or $(25, \infty)$

35. $-3 < x < 4$

36. $x < -2$ or $x \ge 1$

37–50. See next page.

Answers

Practice and Problem-Solving Exercises
(continued)

37. $3 \le x < 6$

38. $r > 3.5$ or $r \le -2$

39. $2\frac{2}{3} \le v \le 6$

40. $y > 9\frac{1}{2}$ or $y < -6\frac{2}{3}$

41. $-4\frac{1}{12} \le w < 12\frac{1}{4}$

42. between 6.3 and 8.1, inclusive

43. $4 < x < 14$

44. any length greater than 3.25 in. and less than 10.75 in.

45. any length greater than 6 ft and less than 36 ft

46. any length greater than 21 mm and less than 49 mm

47. any length greater than 11 m and less than 23 m

48. $20 \le d \le 32$

49. any real number except 4

50. $(0, 2200]$

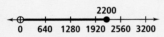

(2400, 2800)

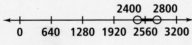

(2800, 3200)

2800

51. $F < -37.966$ or $F > 673.844$; $(-\infty, -37.966)$ or $(673.844, \infty)$

52. a. $102.5 \le R \le 184.5$

    b. 22 years old

53. B

54. F

55. [2] $35 \le 10.4 + 0.0059g \le 50$,
$24.6 \le 0.0059g \le 39.6$,
$4169.49 \le g \le 6711.86$; minimum water consumption is 4169 gal and maximum water consumption is 6712 gal (OR equivalent work).

    [1] incorrect solution with appropriate work OR correct solution with no work shown or incorrect work shown

 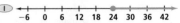
206   Chapter 3   Solving Inequalities

56. { } or ∅, {1}, {3}, {5}, {7}, {1, 3}, {1, 5}, {1, 7}, {3, 5}, {3, 7}, {5, 7}, {1, 3, 5}, {1, 3, 7}, {1, 5, 7}, {3, 5, 7}, {1, 3, 5, 7}

57. $B' = \{1, 2, 3, 5, 7, 15\}$

58. no

59. $\frac{1}{3} < b$

60. $n \le 3$

61. $7 \ge r$

62. $=$

63. $>$

64. $>$

Additional Instructional Support

Algebra 1 Companion

Students can use the **Algebra 1 Companion** worktext (4 pages) as you teach the lesson. Use the Companion to support

- New Vocabulary
- Key Concepts
- Got It for each Problem
- Lesson Check

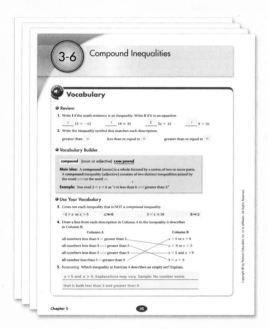

ELL Support

Focus on Language Have students write the differences between compound inequalities that are joined with *and* or with *or* using their own words. Ask, what does a compound inequality with *and* mean? Ask, what does a compound inequality with *or* mean? How are the graphs of the solutions for each different?

Pair students by academic ability or by language levels so there is a more proficient student with a less proficient student. Ask them to read their paragraphs to each other. Encourage questions, clarification (What do you mean?), and peer assistance in learning.

5 Assess & Remediate

Lesson Quiz

1. Write the phrase "all real numbers that are greater than -4 and less than or equal to 7" as a compound inequality.
2. What are the solutions of $-1 \leq x - 3 < 4$? Graph the solutions.
3. What are the solutions of $\frac{1}{5} < \frac{2x - 4}{3} < 6$?
4. **Do you UNDERSTAND?** To earn a fitness award, your average heart rate while walking must be between 80 and 89 beats per minute, inclusive. Suppose you recorded 85, 81, and 87 beats per minute on your first three recordings. What are the possible heart rates you can have on the fourth and final recording in order to earn a fitness award?
5. What are the solutions to $3n - 1 > 8$ or $4n + 3 < -1$? Graph the solutions.

ANSWERS TO LESSON QUIZ

1. $-4 < x \leq 7$
2. $2 \leq x < 7$

3. $2\frac{3}{10} < x < 11$
4. between 67 and 103 beats per minute inclusive
5. $n < -1$ or $n > 3$

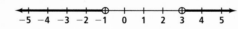

PRESCRIPTION FOR REMEDIATION

Use the student work on the Lesson Quiz to prescribe a differentiated review assignment.

Points	Differentiated Remediation
0–2	Intervention
3–4	On-level
5	Extension

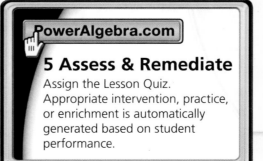

PowerAlgebra.com

5 Assess & Remediate

Assign the Lesson Quiz. Appropriate intervention, practice, or enrichment is automatically generated based on student performance.

Intervention

- **Reteaching** (2 pages) Provides reteaching and practice exercises for the key lesson concepts. Use with struggling students or absent students.
- **English Language Learner Support** Helps students develop and reinforce mathematical vocabulary and key concepts.

All-in-One Resources/Online
Reteaching

3-6 Reteaching
Compound Inequalities

A compound inequality with the word *or* means one or both inequalities must be true. The graph of the compound inequality $a < -4$ or $a \geq 3$ is shown below.

A compound inequality with the word *and* means both inequalities must be true. The graph of the compound inequality $b \leq 4$ and $b > -1$ is shown below.

To solve a compound inequality, solve the simple inequalities from which it is made.

Problem

What are the solutions of $17 \leq 2x + 7 \leq 29$? Graph the solutions.

$17 \leq 2x + 7 \leq 29$ is the same as $17 \leq 2x + 7$ and $2x + 7 \leq 29$. You can solve it as two inequalities.

$17 \leq 2x + 7$	and	$2x + 7 \leq 29$
$17 - 7 \leq 2x + 7 - 7$	and	$2x + 7 - 7 \leq 29 - 7$
$10 \leq 2x$	and	$2x \leq 22$
$\frac{10}{2} \leq \frac{2x}{2}$	and	$\frac{2x}{2} \leq \frac{22}{2}$
$5 \leq x$	and	$x \leq 11$

To graph the compound inequality, place closed circles at 5 and 11. Shade between the two circles.

All-in-One Resources/Online
English Language Learner Support

3-6 ELL Support
Compound Inequalities

Complete the vocabulary chart by filling in the missing information.

Word or Word Phrase	Definition	Picture or Example
and	A solution of a compound inequality involving *and* is any number that makes *both* inequalities true.	$x > 3$ and $x < 5$
compound inequality	A *compound inequality* consists of two distinct inequalities joined by the word *and* or the word *or*.	$2 < x < 7$
inclusive	*Inclusive* means to include the end points as part of the solution.	$2 \leq x \leq 7$
infinity	*Infinity* continues forever.	∞ or $-\infty$ $(-\infty, 3)$ means $x < 3$
interval	An *interval* is a portion of the number line, such as the numbers between 1 and 5.	
interval notation	You can also use *interval notation* to describe an interval on the number line. Interval notation includes the use of three special symbols.	(2,3) means $2 < x < 3$ [2,3) means $2 \leq x < 3$ [2,3] means $2 \leq x \leq 3$ [2, ∞) means $x \geq 2$
or	A solution of a compound inequality involving *or* is any number that makes either inequality true.	$x > 5$ or $x \leq 3$

Differentiated Remediation *continued*

On-Level

- **Practice** (2 pages) Provides extra practice for each lesson. For simpler practice exercises, use the Form K Practice pages found in the All-in-One Teaching Resources and online.

- **Think About a Plan** Helps students develop specific problem-solving skills and strategies by providing scaffolded guiding questions.

- **Standardized Test Prep** Focuses on all major exercises, all major question types, and helps students prepare for the high-stakes assessments.

Extension

- **Enrichment** Provides students with interesting problems and activities that extend the concepts of the lesson.

- **Activities, Games, and Puzzles** Worksheets that can be used for concepts development, enrichment, and for fun!

Practice and Problem Solving WKBK/ All-in-One Resources/Online
Practice page 1

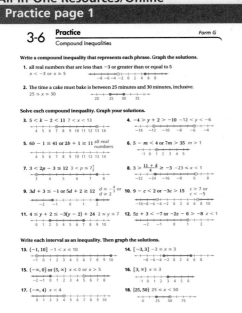

Practice and Problem Solving WKBK/ All-in-One Resources/Online
Practice page 2

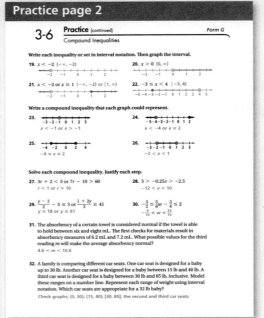

All-in-One Resources/Online
Enrichment

Practice and Problem Solving WKBK/ All-in-One Resources/Online
Think About a Plan

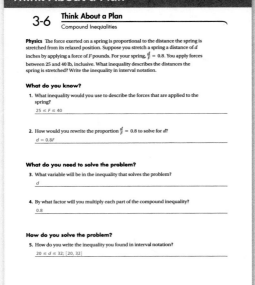

Practice and Problem Solving WKBK/ All-in-One Resources/Online
Standardized Test Prep

Online Teacher Resource Center
Activities, Games, and Puzzles

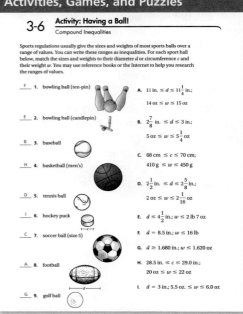

3-7 Absolute Value Equations and Inequalities

Objective To solve equations and inequalities involving absolute value

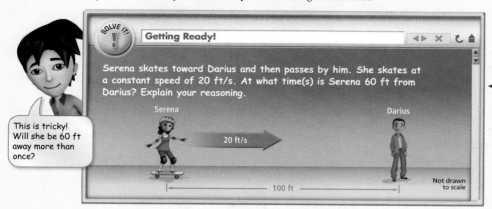

This is tricky! Will she be 60 ft away more than once?

Getting Ready!

Serena skates toward Darius and then passes by him. She skates at a constant speed of 20 ft/s. At what time(s) is Serena 60 ft from Darius? Explain your reasoning.

Serena

Darius

20 ft/s

100 ft

Not drawn to scale

In the Solve It, Serena's distance from Darius decreases and then increases. You can use absolute value to model such changes.

Essential Understanding You can solve absolute value equations and inequalities by first isolating the absolute value expression, if necessary. Then write an equivalent pair of linear equations or inequalities.

Think

How many solutions does the equation have?

There are two values on a number line that are 7 units from 0: 7 and −7. So the equation has two solutions.

Problem 1 Solving an Absolute Value Equation

What are the solutions of $|x| + 2 = 9$? Graph and check the solutions.

$$|x| + 2 = 9$$
$$|x| + 2 - 2 = 9 - 2 \qquad \text{Subtract 2 from each side.}$$
$$|x| = 7 \qquad \text{Simplify.}$$
$$x = 7 \text{ or } x = -7 \qquad \text{Definition of absolute value}$$

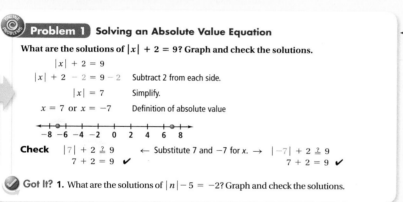

Check $|7| + 2 \stackrel{?}{=} 9 \qquad \leftarrow$ Substitute 7 and −7 for x. $\rightarrow \qquad |-7| + 2 \stackrel{?}{=} 9$
$7 + 2 = 9 \checkmark \qquad\qquad\qquad\qquad\qquad\qquad 7 + 2 = 9 \checkmark$

Got It? **1.** What are the solutions of $|n| - 5 = -2$? Graph and check the solutions.

PowerAlgebra.com | Lesson 3-7 Absolute Value Equations and Inequalities | **207**

3-7 Preparing to Teach

BIG ideas Equivalence
Solving Equations and Inequalities

UbD

ESSENTIAL UNDERSTANDINGS
- An equivalent pair of linear equations or inequalities can be used to represent absolute value equations and inequalities.
- Absolute value equations and inequalities can be solved by first isolating the absolute value expression, if necessary, then writing an equivalent pair of linear equations or inequalities.

Math Background

Absolute value is an example of a mathematical concept which cannot be defined using only one condition. The absolute value brackets in an equation or inequality are representative of two separate conditions. Students must identify the two conditions to be satisfied and write either a

pair of equations or a pair of inequalities to represent the conditions.

You can think of absolute value using an algebraic definition or a geometric definition.

Algebraic Definition:

$|x| = x$, when $x \geq 0$, and $|x| = -x$, when $x < 0$.

Geometric Definition:

$|x|$ is the distance x is from zero (either to the right or to the left) on a number line.

Using the algebraic definition of absolute value, $|2x| = 36$ means $2x = 36$ and $2x = -36$. The solutions are $x = 18$ and $x = -18$.

Using the geometric definition, think what distances doubled are 36 units from 0. The solutions are distances 18 units to the right of 0 and 18 units to the left of 0.

---

1 Interactive Learning

Solve It!

PURPOSE To use inequalities and problem solving to understand absolute value in a real-world situation
PROCESS Students may use trial and error, make a table, or write an absolute value equation.

FACILITATE

Q What expression represents the distance remaining between Serena and Darius as Serena skates towards Darius? **[100 − 20t]**

Q What is the value of the expression for $t = 8$? **[−60]**

ANSWER See Solve It in Answers on next page.
CONNECT THE MATH There are two values of time for each distance between Serena and Darius. Students will visualize this concept when presented with absolute values shown on a number line.

2 Guided Instruction

Problem 1

Q If x is 7 units away from 0 on a number line, what are the two possible values of x? **[−7, 7]**

Q How would you write the solution set for the equation in roster form? In set-builder notation? **[{−7, 7}; {x | x = 7 or x = −7}]**

Got It? **ERROR PREVENTION**

If students get solutions of $n = 3$ and $n = 7$, then they likely wrote the pair of equations $|n| - 5 = -2$ and $|n| - 5 = 2$ prior to isolating the absolute value expression.

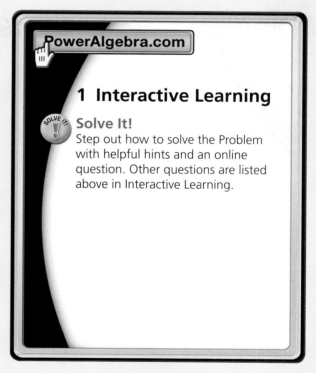

PowerAlgebra.com

1 Interactive Learning

Solve It!
Step out how to solve the Problem with helpful hints and an online question. Other questions are listed above in Interactive Learning.

Lesson 3-7 **207**

Q For what value of b does $|A| = b$ require solving only one equation? **[$b = 0$]**

Q Why is it impossible to solve $|A| = b$ when $b < 0$? **[The absolute value of an expression cannot equal a negative number.]**

Problem 2

Q What absolute value equation represents this real-world situation? **[$|100 - 2t| = 40$]**

Q How can you eliminate choices A, B, and D prior to solving the equations? **[You can eliminate choices A and B, because each contains a negative time.]**

Got It?

Q Why should you use the original absolute value equation to check answers? **[You might have made an error when writing the equivalent pair of equations.]**

Problem 3

Q Is it possible to decide that the absolute value equation $3|2z + 9| = -2$ does not have any solutions without first dividing each side of the equation by 3? Explain. **[Yes; the product of an absolute value and a positive number is positive.]**

Got It?   VISUAL LEARNERS

Show students this equation has no solution by demonstrating that it is impossible to be -2 units away from 0 on a number line.

Some equations, such as $|2x - 5| = 13$, have variable expressions within absolute value symbols. The equation $|2x - 5| = 13$ means that the distance on a number line from $2x - 5$ to 0 is 13 units. There are two points that are 13 units from 0: 13 and -13. So to find the values of x, solve the equations $2x - 5 = 13$ and $2x - 5 = -13$. You can generalize this process as follows.

 Key Concept   Solving Absolute Value Equations

To solve an equation in the form $|A| = b$, where A represents a variable expression and $b > 0$, solve $A = b$ and $A = -b$.

 Problem 2   Solving an Absolute Value Equation

Multiple Choice Starting from 100 ft away, your friend skates toward you and then passes by you. She skates at a constant speed of 20 ft/s. Her distance d from you in feet after t seconds is given by $d = |100 - 20t|$. At what times is she 40 ft from you?

   Ⓐ -2 s and 8 s   Ⓑ -3 s and 7 s   Ⓒ 3 s and 7 s   Ⓓ 2 s and 8 s

Plan

What must be true of the expression $100 - 20t$?
Its absolute value is 40, so $100 - 20t$ must equal either 40 or -40. Use this fact to write and solve two equations.

$$100 - 20t = 40 \qquad \leftarrow \text{Write two equations.} \rightarrow \qquad 100 - 20t = -40$$
$$-20t = -60 \qquad \leftarrow \text{Subtract 100 from each side.} \rightarrow \qquad -20t = -140$$
$$t = 3 \qquad \leftarrow \text{Divide each side by } -20. \rightarrow \qquad t = 7$$

The solutions are 3 s and 7 s. The correct answer is C.

✓ **Got It? 2.** What are the solutions of $|3x - 1| = 8$? Check the solutions.

Recall that absolute value represents distance from 0 on a number line. Distance is always nonnegative. So any equation that states that the absolute value of an expression is negative has no solutions.

 Problem 3   Solving an Absolute Value Equation With No Solution

What are the solutions of $3|2z + 9| + 12 = 10$?

$$3|2z + 9| + 12 = 10$$
$$3|2z + 9| = -2 \qquad \text{Subtract 12 from each side.}$$
$$|2z + 9| = -\frac{2}{3} \qquad \text{Divide each side by 3.}$$

The absolute value of an expression cannot be negative, so there is no solution.

Plan

How can you make the equation look like one you've solved before?
Use properties of equality to isolate the absolute value expression on one side of the equal sign.

✓ **Got It? 3.** What are the solutions of $|3x - 6| - 5 = -7$?

Answers

Solve It!
2 s and 8 s; explanations may vary.

Got It?
1. $n = 3$ and $n = -3$

2. $x = 3$ or $x = -\frac{7}{3}$

3. no solution

 PowerAlgebra.com

2 Guided Instruction

Each Problem is worked out and supported online.

Problem 1
Solving an Absolute Value Equation
    Animated

Problem 2
Solving an Absolute Value Equation
    Animated

Problem 3
Solving an Absolute Value Equation With No Solution

Problem 4
Solving an Absolute Value Inequality Involving $\geq$

Problem 5
Solving an Absolute Value Inequality Involving $\leq$
    Animated

Support in Algebra 1 Companion
• Vocabulary
• Key Concepts
• Got It?

You can write absolute value inequalities as compound inequalities. The graphs below show two absolute value inequalities.

$|n - 1| < 2$

$|n - 1| < 2$ represents all numbers with a distance from 1 that is less than 2 units. So $|n - 1| < 2$ means $-2 < n - 1 < 2$.

$|n - 1| > 2$

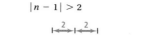

$|n - 1| > 2$ represents all numbers with a distance from 1 that is greater than 2 units. So $|n - 1| > 2$ means $n - 1 < -2$ or $n - 1 > 2$.

Key Concept   Solving Absolute Value Inequalities

To solve an inequality in the form $|A| < b$, where A is a variable expression and $b > 0$, solve the compound inequality $-b < A < b$.

To solve an inequality in the form $|A| > b$, where A is a variable expression and $b > 0$, solve the compound inequality $A < -b$ or $A > b$.

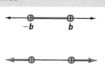

Similar rules are true for $|A| \leq b$ or $|A| \geq b$.

Problem 4   Solving an Absolute Value Inequality Involving ≥

What are the solutions of $|8n| \geq 24$? Graph the solutions.

Think

The inequality says that $8n$ is at least 24 units from 0 on a number line.

To be at least 24 units from 0, $8n$ can be less than or equal to -24 or greater than or equal to 24.

You need to isolate n. Undo multiplication by dividing each side by the same number.

Write

$|8n| \geq 24$

$8n \leq -24$ or $8n \geq 24$

$\dfrac{8n}{8} \leq \dfrac{-24}{8}$ or $\dfrac{8n}{8} \geq \dfrac{24}{8}$

$n \leq -3$ or $n \geq 3$

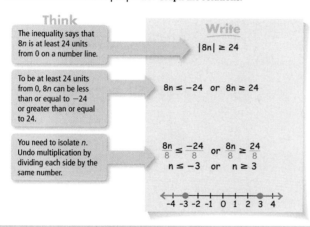

Use the graphic organizer to help students sort out the equivalent pairs of inequalities.

$\|ax + c\| < b$	$ax + c < b$ and $ax + c > -b$
$\|ax + c\| > b$	$ax + c > b$ or $ax + c < -b$
$\|ax + c\| \leq b$	$ax + c \leq b$ and $ax + c \geq -b$
$\|ax + c\| \geq b$	$ax + c \geq b$ or $ax + c \leq -b$

Problem 4

Q What two steps should you follow to check your solutions for this inequality? **[First, you should substitute each endpoint into the original inequality and verify the statement is true. Second, you should substitute a number from each shaded region into the original inequality to see if the statement is true.]**

Additional Problems

1. What are the solutions of $|x| + 3 = 7$? Graph the solutions.

   ANSWER $x = -4$ or $x = 4$

2. Your cousin was standing along a parade route when she spotted a float 750 ft from her. The parade was traveling at 158 ft/min. The distance d from your cousin in feet after t minutes is given by $d = |750 - 158t|$.
At what times is the float 200 ft from your cousin? Round to the nearest tenth.

   A. -3.5 min and -6.0 min

   B. -3.5 min and 6.0 min

   C. 2 min and 4.5 min

   D. 3.5 min and 6.0 min

   ANSWER D

3. What are the solutions of $5|3x - 1| + 6 = 3$?

   ANSWER no solution

4. What are the solutions of $|5x| \geq 20$? Graph the solutions.

   ANSWER $x \leq -4$ or $x \geq 4$

5. A professional athlete normally runs one mile in 224 seconds. The athlete wants to run within 6 seconds of his normal time. What is the range of allowable times for the athlete?

   ANSWER $218 \leq t \leq 230$

Got It?

Q What two inequalities do you solve for this absolute value inequality? **[2x + 4 > 5 or 2x + 4 < −5]**

Problem 5

Q What inequality implies that $w − 213$ is less than 5 units away from 0 in the positive direction on the number line? **[w − 213 < 5]**

Q What inequality implies that $w − 213$ is less than 5 units away from 0 in the negative direction on the number line? **[w − 213 > −5]**

Got It?

Q What inequality states that the difference between the actual and ideal weights is at most 0.05 ounces? **[|w − 32| ≤ 0.05 or |32 − w ≤ 0.05]**

3 Lesson Check

Do you know HOW?
• If students have difficulty with Exercise 2, then remind them to isolate the absolute value expression first.

Do you UNDERSTAND?
• If students have difficulty with Exercise 7, then have them review Problem 3.

Close

Q Explain why there are two inequalities written from a single absolute value inequality. **[Answers may vary. Sample: When the absolute value is less than or less than or equal to, an "and" statement applies. When the absolute value is greater than or greater than or equal to, an "or" statement applies.]**

Problem 5   Solving an Absolute Value Inequality Involving ≤

Manufacturing A company makes boxes of crackers that should weigh 213 g. A quality-control inspector randomly selects boxes to weigh. Any box that varies from the weight by more than 5 g is sent back. What is the range of allowable weights for a box of crackers?

Relate | difference between actual and ideal weights | is at most | 5 g |

Define Let w = the actual weight in grams.

Write | $|w − 213|$ | ≤ | 5 |

$$|w − 213| \leq 5$$
$$-5 \leq w − 213 \leq 5 \quad \text{Write a compound inequality.}$$
$$208 \leq w \leq 218 \quad \text{Add 213 to each expression.}$$

The weight of a box of crackers must be between 208 g and 218 g, inclusive.

Think

How else could you write this inequality?
You could break the compound inequality into two parts:
$w − 213 \geq −5$ and
$w − 213 \leq 5$.

 Got It?   **5. a.** A food manufacturer makes 32-oz boxes of pasta. Not every box weighs exactly 32 oz. The allowable difference from the ideal weight is at most 0.05 oz. Write and solve an absolute value inequality to find the range of allowable weights.
  b. Reasoning In Problem 5, could you have solved the inequality $|w − 213| \leq 5$ by first adding 213 to each side? Explain your reasoning.

Lesson Check

Do you know HOW?

Solve and graph each equation or inequality.

1. $|x| = 5$

2. $|n| − 3 = 4$

3. $|2t| = 6$

4. $|h − 3| < 5$

5. $|x + 2| \geq 1$

Do you UNDERSTAND?

6. **Reasoning** How many solutions do you expect to get when you solve an absolute value equation? Explain.

7. **Writing** Explain why the absolute value equation $|3x| + 8 = 5$ has no solution.

8. **Compare and Contrast** Explain the similarities and differences in solving the equation $|x − 1| = 2$ with solving the inequalities $|x − 1| \leq 2$ and $|x − 1| \geq 2$.

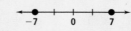

3 Lesson Check

For a digital lesson check, use the Got It questions.

Support in Algebra 1 Companion
• Lesson Check

4 Practice

Assign homework to individual students or to an entire class.

Answers

Got It? (continued)
4. $x \geq 0.5$ or $x \leq −4.5$

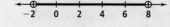

5. a. $|w − 32| \leq 0.05$; $31.95 \leq w \leq 32.05$
  b. No; 213 is part of the absolute value expression. You cannot add 213 until after you write the absolute value inequality as a compound inequality.

Lesson Check
1. $x = 5$ or $x = −5$

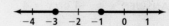

2. $n = 7$ or $n = −7$

3. $t = 3$ or $t = −3$

4. $−2 < h < 8$

5. $x \leq −3$ or $x \geq −1$

6. 2; there are two values on a number line that are the same distance from 0.

7. The absolute value cannot be equal to a negative number since distance from 0 on a number line must be nonnegative.

8. Answers may vary. Sample: The equation is set equal to 2 and −2. The first inequality is set to be ≤ 2 and ≥ −2. The second inequality is set to be ≥ 2 or ≤ −2.

Practice and Problem-Solving Exercises

 Practice

Solve each equation. Graph and check your solutions. ◄ **See Problem 1.**

9. $|b| = \frac{1}{2}$ **10.** $4 = |y|$ **11.** $|n| + 3 = 7$ **12.** $7 = |s| - 3$

13. $|x| - 10 = -2$ **14.** $5|d| = 20$ **15.** $-3|m| = -9$ **16.** $|y| + 3 = 3$

Solve each equation. If there is no solution, write *no solution*. ◄ **See Problems 2 and 3.**

17. $|r - 8| = 5$ **18.** $|c + 4| = 6$ **19.** $2 = |g + 3|$

20. $3 = |m + 2|$ **21.** $-2|7d| = 14$ **22.** $-3|2w| = -12$

23. $3|v - 3| = 9$ **24.** $2|d + 4| = 8$ **25.** $|4f + 1| - 2 = 5$

26. $|3t - 2| + 6 = 2$ **27.** $4|2y - 3| - 1 = 11$ **28.** $3|x + 2| + 4 = 13$

29. $-4|k| = 12$ **30.** $|-3n| - 2 = 4$ **31.** $-4|k + 1| = 16$

Solve and graph each inequality. ◄ **See Problems 4 and 5.**

32. $|x| \geq 3$ **33.** $|x| < 5$ **34.** $|x + 3| < 5$

35. $|y + 8| \geq 3$ **36.** $|y - 2| \leq 1$ **37.** $|p - 7| \leq 3$

38. $|2c - 5| < 9$ **39.** $|3t + 1| > 8$ **40.** $|4w + 1| > 11$

41. $|5t - 4| \geq 16$ **42.** $|4x + 7| > 19$ **43.** $|2v - 1| \leq 9$

44. $|3d - 7| > 28$ **45.** $|2f + 9| \leq 13$ **46.** $|5m - 9| \geq 24$

47. Quality Control The ideal length of one type of model airplane is 90 cm. The actual length may vary from ideal by at most 0.05 cm. What are the acceptable lengths for the model airplane?

48. Basketball The ideal circumference of a women's basketball is 28.75 in. The actual circumference may vary from the ideal by at most 0.25 in. What are the acceptable circumferences for a women's basketball?

 Apply

Solve each equation or inequality. If there is no solution, write *no solution*.

49. $|2d| + 3 = 21$ **50.** $1.2|5p| = 3.6$ **51.** $\left|d + \frac{1}{2}\right| + \frac{3}{4} = 0$

52. $|f| - \frac{2}{3} = \frac{5}{6}$ **53.** $3|5y - 7| - 6 = 24$ **54.** $|t| + 2.7 = 4.5$

55. $-2|c - 4| = -8.4$ **56.** $\frac{|y|}{-3} = 5$ **57.** $|n| - \frac{5}{4} < 5$

58. $\frac{7}{8} < |c + 7|$ **59.** $4 - 3|m + 2| > -14$ **60.** $|-3d| \geq 6.3$

61. Think About a Plan The monthly average temperature T for San Francisco, California, is usually within 7.5°F of 56.5°F, inclusive. What is the monthly average temperature in San Francisco?
- Should you model this situation with an equation or an inequality?
- How can you use the given information to write the equation or inequality?

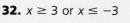
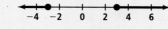
---

4 Practice

ASSIGNMENT GUIDE

Basic: 9–48 all, 50–60 even, 61–65, 69, 72–76 even

Average: 9–47 odd, 49–76

Advanced: 9–47 odd, 49–82

Standardized Test Prep: 83–87

Mixed Review: 88–97

Reasoning exercises have blue headings.

Applications exercises have red headings.

EXERCISE 69: Use the Think About a Plan worksheet in the **Practice and Problem Solving Workbook** (also available in the Teaching Resources in print and online) to further support students' development in becoming independent learners.

HOMEWORK QUICK CHECK

To check students' understanding of key skills and concepts, go over Exercises 19, 33, 61, 64, and 69.

Answers

Practice and Problem-Solving Exercises

9. $b = -\frac{1}{2}$ or $b = \frac{1}{2}$

10. $y = 4$ or $y = -4$

11. $n = 4$ or $n = -4$

12. $s = 10$ or $s = -10$

13. $x = 8$ or $x = -8$

14. $d = 4$ or $d = -4$

15. $m = 3$ or $m = -3$

16. $y = 0$

17. $r = 13$ or $r = 3$

18. $c = 2$ or $c = -10$

19. $g = -1$ or $g = -5$

20. $m = 1$ or $m = -5$

21. no solution

22. $w = 2$ or $w = -2$

23. $v = 6$ or $v = 0$

24. $d = 0$ or $d = -8$

25. $f = 1.5$ or $f = -2$

26. no solution

27. $y = 3$ or $y = 0$

28. $x = 1$ or $x = -5$

29. no solution

30. $n = 2$ or $n = -2$

31. no solution

32. $x \geq 3$ or $x \leq -3$

33. $-5 < x < 5$

34. $-8 < x < 2$

35. $y \leq -11$ or $y \geq -5$

36. $1 \leq y \leq 3$

37. $4 \leq p \leq 10$

38–61. See next page.

Answers

Practice and Problem-Solving Exercises
(continued)

38. $-2 < c < 7$

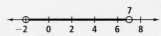

39. $t < -3$ or $t > \frac{7}{3}$

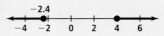

40. $w < -3$ or $w > 2.5$

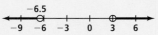

41. $t \le -2.4$ or $t \ge 4$

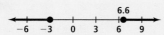

42. $x < -6.5$ or $x > 3$

43. $-4 \le v \le 5$

44. $d < -7$ or $d > 11\frac{2}{3}$

45. $-11 \le f \le 2$

46. $m \le -3$ or $m \ge 6.6$

47. any length between 89.95 cm and 90.05 cm, inclusive

48. any length between 28.5 in. and 29 in., inclusive

49. $d = 9$ or $d = -9$

50. $p = 0.6$ or $p = -0.6$

51. no solution

52. $f = 1\frac{1}{2}$ or $f = -1\frac{1}{2}$

53. $y = 3.4$ or $y = -0.6$

54. $t = 1.8$ or $t = -1.8$

55. $c = 8.2$ or $c = -0.2$

56. no solution

57. $-6\frac{1}{4} < n < 6\frac{1}{4}$

58. $c < -7\frac{7}{8}$ or $c > -6\frac{1}{8}$

59. $-8 < m < 4$

60. $d \le -2.1$ or $d \ge 2.1$

61. $49°F \le T \le 64°F$

62. $99°F \le T \le 100.8°F$

63. $t = 4\frac{4}{9}$ s and $17\frac{7}{9}$ s

---

62. Biology A horse's body temperature T is considered to be normal if it is within at least 0.9°F of 99.9°F. Find the range of normal body temperatures for a horse.

63. Biking Starting from 200 ft away, your friend rides his bike toward you and then passes by you at a speed of 18 ft/s. His distance d (in feet) from you t seconds after he started riding his bike is given by $d = |200 - 18t|$. At what time(s) is he 120 ft from you?

Error Analysis Find and correct the mistake in solving each equation or inequality.

64.
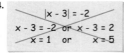

65.
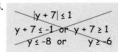

66. Open-Ended Write an absolute value equation that has 2 and 6 as solutions.

67. Reasoning Explain why you can rewrite $|x + 5| > 1$ as a compound inequality involving *or*.

68. Polling According to a poll for an upcoming school board election, 40% of voters are likely to vote for the incumbent. The poll shows a margin of error of ±3 percentage points. Write and solve an absolute value equation to find the least and the greatest percents of voters v likely to vote for the incumbent.

69. Banking The official weight of a nickel is 5 g, but the actual weight can vary from this amount by up to 0.194 g. Suppose a bank weighs a roll of 40 nickels. The wrapper weighs 1.5 g.
a. What is the range of possible weights for the roll of nickels?
b. Reasoning If all of the nickels in the roll each weigh the official amount, then the roll's weight is $40(5) + 1.5 = 201.5$ g. Is it possible for a roll to weigh 201.5 g and contain nickels that do not weigh the official amount? Explain.

70. Oil Production An oil refinery aims to produce 900,000 barrels of oil per day. The daily production varies by up to 50,000 barrels from this goal, inclusive. What are the minimum and maximum numbers of barrels of oil produced each day?

Write an absolute value inequality that represents each set of numbers.

71. all real numbers less than 4 units from 0

72. all real numbers at most 7 units from 0

73. all real numbers more than 2 units from 6

74. all real numbers at least 2 units from -1

75. Manufacturing The ideal diameter of a piston for one type of car engine is 90.000 mm. The actual diameter can vary from the ideal by at most 0.008 mm. What is the range of acceptable diameters for the piston?

76. Farm Maintenance For safety, the recommended height of a horse fence is 5 ft. Because of uneven ground surfaces, the actual height of the fence can vary from this recommendation by up to 3 in. Write and solve an absolute value equation to find the maximum and minimum heights of the fence.

---

64. There is no solution since the absolute value cannot be a negative number.

65. $-1 \le y + 7 \le 1$, $-8 \le y \le -6$

66. Check students' work. Sample: $|x - 4| = 2$

67. Answers may vary. Sample: To be more than 1 unit away from -5 on a number line means $x + 5 > 1$ or $x + 5 < -1$.

68. $|v - 0.4| \le 0.03$; $0.37 \le v \le 0.43$

69. a. between 193.74 g and 209.26 g, inclusive
b. Yes; answers may vary. Sample: Some nickels could weigh more and some could weigh less, and their average could be the official amount.

70. minimum 850,000 barrels, maximum 950,000 barrels

71. $|x| < 4$

72. $|x| \le 7$

73. $|x - 6| > 2$

74. $|x + 1| \ge 2$

75. between 89.992 mm and 90.008 mm, inclusive

76. $|x - 5| \le 0.25$; minimum 4.75 ft, maximum 5.25 ft

Solve each equation. Check your solutions.

77. $|x + 4| = 3x$ **78.** $\lceil 4t - 5 \rceil = 2t + 1$ **79.** $\frac{4}{3}|2y + 3| = 4y$

Determine whether each statement is *always*, *sometimes*, or *never* true for real numbers *a* and *b*.

80. $|ab| = |a| \cdot |b|$ **81.** $\left|\frac{a}{b}\right| = \frac{|a|}{|b|}, b \neq 0$ **82.** $|a + b| = |a| + |b|$

Standardized Test Prep

GRIDDED RESPONSE

83. The expected monthly rainfall in a certain town is shown for June, July, and August. The actual rainfall generally varies from the expected amount by up to 0.015 in. What is the maximum amount of rainfall the town can expect to receive in July?

Expected Monthly Rainfall (inches)		
June	July	August
4.12	4.25	4.41

84. What is the solution of the equation $\frac{x}{4} - 3 = 7$?

85. What is the solution of the equation $3w + 2 = 4w - 3$?

86. Jose is purchasing 4 dress shirts that cost $28 each and 2 pairs of pants that cost $38 each. The items are all on sale for 35% off. How much money will Jose save by purchasing them on sale instead of at full price?

87. 75% of what number is 90?

Mixed Review

Write a compound inequality to model each situation. ◀ See Lesson 3-6.

88. The highest elevation in North America is 20,320 ft above sea level at Mount McKinley, Alaska. The lowest elevation in North America is 282 ft below sea level at Death Valley, California.

89. Normal human body temperature *T* is within 0.3°C of 37.2°C.

Simplify each expression. ◀ See Lesson 1-7.

90. $2(x + 5)$ **91.** $-3(y - 7)$ **92.** $4(\ell + 3) - 7$ **93.** $-(m - 4) + 8$

Get Ready! To prepare for Lesson 3-8, do Exercises 94–97.

Write each set in set-builder notation. ◀ See Lesson 3-5.

94. $A = \{0, 1, 2, 3, 4, 5, 6, 7, 8, 9\}$ **95.** $B = \{1, 3, 5, 7\}$

Write each set in roster form.

96. $C = \{n \mid n$ is an even number between -15 and $-5\}$

97. $D = \{k \mid k$ is a composite number between 7 and 17$\}$

77. 2
78. $\frac{2}{3}$, 3
79. 3
80. always
81. always
82. sometimes
83. 4.265
84. 40
85. 5
86. $65.80
87. 120
88. $-282 \leq e \leq 20{,}320$
89. $36.9 \leq T \leq 37.5$
90. $2x + 10$
91. $-3y + 21$
92. $4\ell + 5$
93. $-m + 12$
94. $A = \{x \mid x$ is a whole number, $x < 10\}$
95. $B = \{x \mid x$ is an odd integer, $1 \leq x \leq 7\}$
96. $C = \{-14, -12, -10, -8, -6\}$
97. $D = \{8, 9, 10, 12, 14, 15, 16\}$

Additional Instructional Support

Algebra 1 Companion

Students can use the **Algebra 1 Companion** worktext (4 pages) as you teach the lesson. Use the Companion to support

- New Vocabulary
- Key Concepts
- Got It for each Problem
- Lesson Check

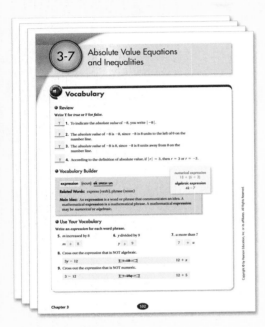

ELL Support

Focus on Language Read the Key Understanding sentence to the class. Invite students to underline or highlight the key words. Ask students for cognates (same base word) and familiar words related to any key words. Discuss which key words are related to words they already know and which are unique.

Use Role Playing Divide students into 5 or 6 small groups. Have students write an absolute value equation or inequality, and on a separate paper graph the solution. Have groups trade their graphs and then match the graph with the correct mathematical sentence. Each student should act as the instructor to check the group's work and answer questions about his or her equation and graph.

5 Assess & Remediate

Lesson Quiz

1. What are the solutions of $|x| - 2 = 3$? Graph the solutions.

2. What are the solutions of $2|x - 6| = 10$?

3. Your neighbor leaves his yard, which is 120 ft from the bus stop, and begins to walk toward you at the bus stop, but passes you. He is walking at a speed of 4 ft/s. His distance d from you after t seconds is given by $d = |120 - 4t|$. After how many seconds is your neighbor 30 ft from you?

4. What are the solutions of $\frac{1}{4}|8x + 9| = -7$?

5. **Do you UNDERSTAND?** A manufacturer makes shipments of building block sets that should ideally have 315 pieces. A quality-control inspector randomly selects a set. Any set that varies from the ideal number of pieces by more than 8 blocks is sent back. What is the range of allowable number of blocks for a building block set?

ANSWERS TO LESSON QUIZ

1. $x = -5$ or $x = 5$

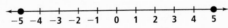

2. 1, 11
3. 22.5 s and 37.5 s
4. no solution
5. $307 \leq p \leq 323$

PRESCRIPTION FOR REMEDIATION

Use the student work on the Lesson Quiz to prescribe a differentiated review assignment.

Points	Differentiated Remediation
0–2	Intervention
3–4	On-level
5	Extension

PowerAlgebra.com

5 Assess & Remediate

Assign the Lesson Quiz. Appropriate intervention, practice, or enrichment is automatically generated based on student performance.

Intervention

- **Reteaching** (2 pages) Provides reteaching and practice exercises for the key lesson concepts. Use with struggling students or absent students.

- **English Language Learner Support** Helps students develop and reinforce mathematical vocabulary and key concepts.

All-in-One Resources/Online
Reteaching

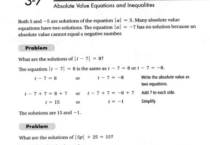

All-in-One Resources/Online
English Language Learner Support

Differentiated Remediation *continued*

On-Level

- **Practice** (2 pages) Provides extra practice for each lesson. For simpler practice exercises, use the Form K Practice pages found in the All-in-One Teaching Resources and online.

- **Think About a Plan** Helps students develop specific problem-solving skills and strategies by providing scaffolded guiding questions.

- **Standardized Test Prep** Focuses on all major exercises, all major question types, and helps students prepare for the high-stakes assessments.

Extension

- **Enrichment** Provides students with interesting problems and activities that extend the concepts of the lesson.

- **Activities, Games, and Puzzles** Worksheets that can be used for concepts development, enrichment, and for fun!

Practice and Problem Solving WKBK/All-in-One Resources/Online
Practice page 1

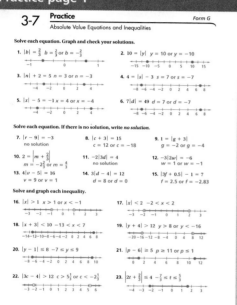

Practice and Problem Solving WKBK/All-in-One Resources/Online
Practice page 2

All-in-One Resources/Online
Enrichment

Practice and Problem Solving WKBK/All-in-One Resources/Online
Think About a Plan

Practice and Problem Solving WKBK/All-in-One Resources/Online
Standardized Test Prep

Online Teacher Resource Center
Activities, Games, and Puzzles

1 Interactive Learning

Solve It!

PURPOSE To use Venn diagrams to introduce students to the concepts of unions and intersections of sets

PROCESS Students may
- use trial and error.
- make a table.
- write an absolute value equation to solve the problem.

FACILITATE

Q What set relationship do each of the seven regions in the Venn diagram represent? **[From left to right: RC only, RC and SC only, SC only, RC and TC only, RC, SC and TC, SC and TC only, TC only]**

Q Which data from the table can be transferred to the Venn diagram? Which data cannot be transferred to the Venn diagram? **[The last four entries can be transferred. The first two entries cannot be transferred.]**

Q How many students are in RC only? **[22 − (8 + 3 + 5) = 6]**

Q How many students are in SC only? **[22 − (8 + 3 + 6) = 5]**

Q How many students are in TC only? **[50 − (6 + 8 + 5 + 5 + 3 + 6) = 17]**

ANSWER See Solve It in Answers on next page.
CONNECT THE MATH In the Solve It students use a Venn diagram to solve the problem. In this lesson students will explore the unions and intersections of sets.

3-8 Unions and Intersections of Sets

Objective To find the unions and intersections of sets

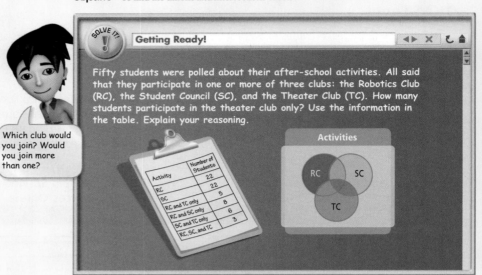

Which club would you join? Would you join more than one?

Lesson Vocabulary
- union
- intersection
- disjoint sets

Certain regions of the Venn diagram in the Solve It show *unions* and *intersections* of sets.

Essential Understanding Given two or more sets, you can describe which elements belong to *at least one* set. You can also describe which elements belong to *all* of the sets. You use symbols to represent these relationships.

The **union** of two or more sets is the set that contains all elements of the sets. The symbol for union is ∪. To find the union of two sets, list the elements that are in either set, or in both sets. An element is in the union if it belongs to *at least one* of the sets. In the Venn diagram below, $A \cup B$ is shaded.

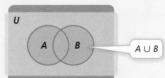

3-8 Preparing to Teach

ESSENTIAL UNDERSTANDINGS UbD
- Given two or more sets, the set of elements belonging to *at least one* set is the union of the sets.
- Given two or more sets, the set of elements belonging to *all* of the sets is the intersection of the sets.

Math Background
In Lesson 3-5, students learned how two sets of numbers relate as a foundation for learning how two inequalities interact. This lesson introduces the set operations of union and intersection and then connects these operations to *or* and *and* compound inequalities, respectively. Venn diagrams are effective tools for helping students visualize the concepts of intersection and union.

Naming the union and intersection of sets is not a difficult task for students to learn. What students find difficult is remembering what each symbol means.

You can share mnemonic devices to help students remember the differences between the operations of union and intersection.

Tools for remembering Union
- The verb form of union is unite. Unite means to *put together to make a single unit*.
- The symbol for union ∪ looks like an uppercase U, which is the first letter in union.

Tools for remembering Intersection
- The verb form of intersection is intersect. Intersect means to *share a common area*.
- The symbol for intersection ∩ looks like a lowercase n, which is the beginning sound of intersection.

Support Student Learning
Use the **Algebra 1 Companion** to engage and support students during instructions. See Lesson Resources at the end of this lesson for details.

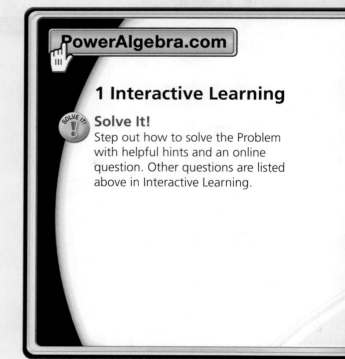

PowerAlgebra.com

1 Interactive Learning

Solve It!
Step out how to solve the Problem with helpful hints and an online question. Other questions are listed above in Interactive Learning.

In your left pocket, you have a quarter, a paper clip, and a key. In your right pocket, you have a penny, a quarter, a pencil, and a marble. What is a set that represents the different items in your pockets?

Step 1 Write sets that represent the contents of each pocket.
Left pocket: $L = \{$quarter, paper clip, key$\}$
Right pocket: $R = \{$penny, quarter, pencil, marble$\}$

Step 2 Write the union of the sets, which represents the different items that are in your pockets.
$L \cup R = \{$quarter, paper clip, key, penny, pencil, marble$\}$

Think

What if an item is in both sets?
Sets L and R each contain a quarter, so a quarter is in the union of L and R. You should list it only once, though.

Got It? 1. a. Write sets P and Q below in roster form. What is $P \cup Q$?
$P = \{x \mid x$ is a whole number less than 5$\}$
$Q = \{y \mid y$ is an even natural number less than 5$\}$
b. Reasoning What is true about the union of two distinct sets if one set is a subset of the other?

The **intersection** of two or more sets is the set of elements that are common to every set. An element is in the intersection if it belongs to *all* of the sets. The symbol for intersection is ∩. When you find the intersection of two sets, list only the elements that are in both sets. In the Venn Diagram below, $A \cap B$ is shaded.

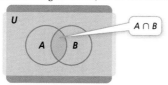

Disjoint sets have no elements in common. The intersection of disjoint sets is the empty set. The diagram below shows two disjoint sets.

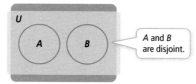

2 Guided Instruction

Problem 1

Q What is the union of the contents of the pocket? **[The objects that are either in one or both of the pockets.]**

Q Which object in the union is in both pockets? **[quarter]**

Got It? VISUAL LEARNER

Use the following graphical representations of sets P and Q to help students visualize the union of the two sets.

P: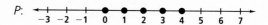

Q: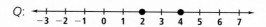

Q Which set is a subset of the other? **[Q is a subset of P.]**

2 Guided Instruction

 Each Problem is worked out and supported online.

Problem 1
Union of Sets

Problem 2
Intersection of Sets
Animated

Problem 3
Making a Venn Diagram

Problem 4
Using a Venn Diagram to Show Numbers of Elements
Animated

Problem 5
Writing Solutions of an Inequality

Support in Algebra 1 Companion
• Vocabulary
• Key Concepts
• Got It?

Answers

Solve It!
17 students; explanations may vary.

Got It?
1. a. $P = \{0, 1, 2, 3, 4\}$; $Q = \{2, 4\}$;
$P \cup Q = \{0, 1, 2, 3, 4\}$

b. Answers may vary. Sample: If $B \subseteq A$, then $A \cup B$ will contain the same elements as A.

Problem 2

Q What is an integer? **[An integer is a natural number, the opposite of a natural number, or 0.]**

Q What is the least natural number less than 19? **[1]**

Q How do you find the multiples of the number 6? **[6 multiplied by any integer is a multiple of 6.]**

Got It? VISUAL LEARNERS

If students are having difficulty understanding the meaning of "intersection," remind them of examples of intersection. Have students sketch two streets that meet and then identify the intersection of the streets. Have students sketch two streets that are parallel to emphasize the meaning of "disjoint."

Problem 3

Q What items do the yellow bag and the red bag have in common that are not also in the blue bag? **[pan]**

Q What items in the yellow bag are not found in any other backpack? **[flashlight, sunglasses]**

Q What items in the red bag are not found in any other backpack? **[rope]**

Q What items in the blue bag are not found in any other backpack? **[camera]**

 Problem 2 Intersection of Sets

Set $X = \{x \mid x$ is a natural number less than 19$\}$, set $Y = \{y \mid y$ is an odd integer$\}$, and set $Z = \{z \mid z$ is a multiple of 6$\}$.

A What is $X \cap Z$?

List the elements that are both natural numbers less than 19 and multiples of 6:
$X \cap Z = \{6, 12, 18\}$.

B What is $Y \cap Z$?

List the elements that are both odd integers and multiples of 6. There are no multiples of 6 that are also odd, so Y and Z are disjoint sets. They have no elements in common. $Y \cap Z = \emptyset$, the empty set.

Think

Why are sets Y and Z disjoint?
Every element of Z is a multiple of 6, so every element of Z is even. Y contains only *odd* numbers. So no element of Z belongs to Y.

✓ **Got It? 2.** Let $A = \{2, 4, 6, 8\}$, $B = \{0, 2, 5, 7, 8\}$, and $C = \{n \mid n$ is an odd whole number$\}$.
  a. What is $A \cap B$?   **b.** What is $A \cap C$?   **c.** What is $C \cap B$?

You can draw Venn diagrams to solve problems involving relationships between sets.

 Problem 3 Making a Venn Diagram

Camping Three friends are going camping. The items in each of their backpacks form a set. Which items do all three friends have in common?

Think

How do you know where in the diagram to place each item?
Items that the friends have in common belong in an intersection. Use the Venn diagram to determine the correct intersection.

Draw a Venn diagram to represent the union and intersection of the sets.

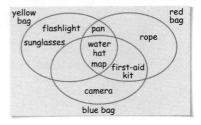

All three friends have a hat, a map, and a bottle of water in their backpacks.

216 Chapter 3 Solving Inequalities

Additional Problems

1. Suppose that in a box, there is a brush, marker, and pencil. In another box, there is a calculator, marker, ribbon, and brush. What items are in either box?

ANSWER a brush, marker, pencil, calculator, and ribbon

2. Set $X = \{x \mid x$ is a whole number less than 15$\}$, set $Y = \{y \mid y$ is an odd integer$\}$, and set $Z = \{z \mid z$ is a multiple of 4$\}$.
  a. What is $X \cap Z$?
  b. What is $Y \cap Z$?

ANSWER a. $\{4, 8, 12\}$
b. empty set

3. Three friends are learning new languages. Draw a Venn diagram to represent the union and intersection of these sets. Which language do all three friends have in common?

Matt: Spanish, German, Italian
Rob: Spanish, German
Jane: Russian, Chinese, Spanish

ANSWER Spanish

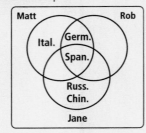

4. Of 125 students in the fifth grade, some have music on Tuesday, some have art on Tuesday, and some have both classes on Tuesday. Sixty-eight have music on Tuesday and 33 have both classes on Tuesday. How many students have art on Tuesday?

ANSWER 90

5. What are the solutions of $|2x - 1| < 5$? Write the solutions as either the union or the intersection of two sets.

ANSWER
$\{x \mid x > -2\} \cap \{x \mid x < 3\}$

Got It? **3.** Let $A = \{x \mid x$ is one of the first five letters in the English alphabet$\}$, $B = \{x \mid x$ is a vowel$\}$, and $C = \{x \mid x$ is a letter in the word VEGETABLE$\}$. Which letters are in all three sets?

You can also use Venn diagrams to show the *number* of elements in the union or intersection of sets.

 Problem 4 **Using a Venn Diagram to Show Numbers of Elements**

Polling Of 500 commuters polled, some drive to work, some take public transportation, and some do both. Two hundred commuters drive to work and 125 use both types of transportation. How many commuters take public transportation?

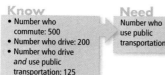

Know	Need	Plan
• Number who commute: 500 • Number who drive: 200 • Number who drive *and* use public transportation: 125	Number who use public transportation	• Draw a Venn diagram • Calculate the number of commuters who only drive • Calculate the number of commuters who only use public transportation

Step 1 Draw a Venn diagram. Let D = commuters who drive and P = commuters who take public transportation.

Step 2 The intersection of D and P represents the commuters who use both methods of transportation: $D \cap P$ has 125 commuters.

Step 3 Find the number of commuters who only drive: $200 - 125 = 75$. Enter 75 into the Venn diagram.

Step 4 The total number of commuters is 500. Subtract to find the number of commuters who use only public transportation: $500 - 200 = 300$.

The number of commuters using public transportation is $300 + 125 = 425$.

 Got It? **4.** Of 30 students in student government, 20 are honor students and 9 are officers and honor students. All of the students are officers, honor students, or both. How many are officers but not honor students?

Recall from Lesson 3-6 that the graph of a compound inequality with the word *and* contains the *overlap* of the graphs of the two inequalities that form the compound inequality. You can think of the overlap as the intersection of two sets. Similarly, you can think of the solutions of an *or* inequality as the union of two sets.

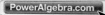
Got It?

Q Which letters are in two sets, but not three sets? **[B]**

Q Which letters are in the union of all three sets? **[V, E, G, T, A, B, L, C, D, I, O, U]**

Problem 4

Q What are the two sets that will be represented by the two circles in the Venn diagram? **[the set of commuters who drive and the set of commuters who use public transportation]**

Q Is it necessary to know the elements of the sets in order to draw the Venn diagram? Explain. **[No, the Venn diagram can also be used to represent the quantity of elements in the sets and in the subsets.]**

Q What will be the sum of each region once the Venn diagram is drawn? Explain. **[The sum will be 500 because all people polled must be represented in the diagram.]**

Got It? ERROR PREVENTION

Q How many circles do you need in the Venn diagram? Explain. **[You need two circles because there are two sets of data.]**

Q Which of the three region(s) of the Venn diagram are not stated explicitly in the problem? **[the region representing those who are officers but not honors students and the region representing those who are honors students but not officers]**

Answers

Got It? (continued)

2. a. $A \cap B = \{2, 8\}$

   b. $A \cap C = \varnothing$

   c. $C \cap B = \{5, 7\}$

3. A and E

4. 10

Problem 5

Students solve an absolute value inequality and identify the solutions as either an intersection or a union of two sets.

> **Q** Is it possible to use roster notation to denote the two solution sets? Explain. **[No, the solutions are real numbers that cannot be explicitly listed.]**

Got It?   VISUAL LEARNERS

In Question 5a, have students graph the solution sets on a number line. Point out that the overlapping region is the intersection of the two sets.

3 Lesson Check

Do you know HOW?
- If students have difficulty with Exercise 5, then have them review Problem 4. Make sure they draw their Venn diagram correctly.

Do you UNDERSTAND?
- If students have difficulty with Exercise 7, then have them review Problem 3.

Close

> **Q** Explain the main difference between a union and an intersection. **[Answers may vary. Sample: A union lists all the elements in all sets. An intersection lists the elements all of the sets have in common.]**

 Problem 5 Writing Solutions of an Inequality

What are the solutions of $|2x - 1| < 3$? Write the solutions as either the union or the intersection of two sets.

$$|2x - 1| < 3$$
$$-3 < 2x - 1 < 3 \quad \text{Write a compound inequality.}$$
$$-2 < \quad 2x \quad < 4 \quad \text{Add 1 to each expression.}$$
$$-1 < \quad x \quad < 2 \quad \text{Divide each side by 2.}$$

The solutions of the inequality are given by $-1 < x < 2$. You can write this as $x > -1$ and $x < 2$. This compound inequality is the intersection of two sets, which you can write as follows: $\{x \mid x > -1\} \cap \{x \mid x < 2\}$.

 Think

Is the solution of the inequality a union or an intersection?
The solution is a compound inequality joined by the word *and*. So the solution is an intersection.

 Got It? 5. Solve each inequality. Write the solutions as either the union or the intersection of two sets.
  a. $8 \le x + 5 < 11$ b. $|4x - 6| > 14$

 Lesson Check

Do you know HOW?

Let $X = \{2, 4, 6, 8, 10\}$, $Y = \{1, 2, 3, 4, 5, 6, 7, 8, 9, 10\}$, and $Z = \{1, 3, 5, 7, 9\}$. Find each union or intersection.

1. $X \cup Y$ 2. $X \cap Y$ 3. $X \cap Z$ 4. $Y \cup Z$

5. In a survey of 80 people who use their cell phones to take pictures and play games, 49 take pictures and 35 take pictures and play games. How many people only use their cell phones to play games?

Do you UNDERSTAND?

6. **Vocabulary** Suppose A and B are nonempty sets. Which set contains more elements: $A \cup B$ or $A \cap B$? Explain your reasoning.

7. **Compare and Contrast** How are unions and intersections of sets different?

Determine whether each statement is *true* or *false*.

8. If x is an element of set A and x is not an element of set B, then x is an element of $A \cup B$.

9. If x is not an element of set A and x is an element of set B, then x is an element of $A \cap B$.

Practice and Problem-Solving Exercises

A Practice   Find each union or intersection. Let $A = \{1, 3, 4\}$, $B = \{x \mid x \text{ is an even whole number less than 9}\}$, $C = \{2, 5, 7, 10\}$, and $D = \{x \mid x \text{ is an odd whole number less than 10}\}$.   **See Problems 1 and 2.**

10. $A \cup B$ 11. $A \cup C$ 12. $A \cup D$ 13. $B \cup C$
14. $B \cup D$ 15. $C \cup D$ 16. $A \cap B$ 17. $A \cap C$
18. $A \cap D$ 19. $B \cap C$ 20. $B \cap D$ 21. $C \cap D$

3 Lesson Check

For a digital lesson check, use the Got It questions.

Support In Algebra 1 Companion
- Lesson Check

4 Practice

Assign homework to individual students or to an entire class.

Answers

Got It? (continued)
5. a. $\{x \mid x \ge 3\} \cap \{x \mid x < 6\}$
   b. $\{x \mid x < -2\} \cup \{x \mid x > 5\}$

Lesson Check
1. $X \cup Y = \{1, 2, 3, 4, 5, 6, 7, 8, 9, 10\}$
2. $X \cap Y = \{2, 4, 6, 8, 10\}$
3. $X \cap Z = \varnothing$
4. $Y \cup Z = \{1, 2, 3, 4, 5, 6, 7, 8, 9, 10\}$
5. 31 people
6. $A \cup B$ contains more elements because it contains all the elements in both sets.
7. The union of sets is the set that contains all elements of each set. The intersection of sets is the set of elements that are common to each set.
8. true
9. false

Practice and Problem-Solving Exercises
10. $A \cup B = \{0, 1, 2, 3, 4, 6, 8\}$
11. $A \cup C = \{1, 2, 3, 4, 5, 7, 10\}$
12. $A \cup D = \{1, 3, 4, 5, 7, 9\}$
13. $B \cup C = \{0, 2, 4, 5, 6, 7, 8, 10\}$
14. $B \cup D = \{0, 1, 2, 3, 4, 5, 6, 7, 8, 9\}$
15. $C \cup D = \{1, 2, 3, 5, 7, 9, 10\}$
16. $A \cap B = \{4\}$
17. $A \cap C = \varnothing$
18. $A \cap D = \{1, 3\}$
19. $B \cap C = \{2\}$
20. $B \cap D = \varnothing$
21. $C \cap D = \{5, 7\}$

Draw a Venn diagram to represent the union and intersection of these sets.
⬅ See Problem 3.

22. The letters in the words ALGEBRA, GEOMETRY, and CALCULUS are represented by the sets $V = \{A, L, G, E, B, R\}$, $W = \{G, E, O, M, T, R, Y\}$, and $X = \{C, A, L, U, S\}$, respectively.

23. Let $E = \{x \mid x \text{ is a positive, composite number less than } 10\}$, $F = \{1, 2, 4, 5, 6, 8, 9\}$, and $G = \{x \mid x \text{ is a positive, even number less than or equal to } 10\}$.

24. Let $L = \{A, B, C, 1, 2, 3, \text{horse}, \text{cow}, \text{pig}\}$, $M = \{-1, 0, 1, B, Y, \text{pig}, \text{duck}, \Delta\}$, and $N = \{C, 3, \text{duck}, \Delta\}$.

25. **Camping** Twenty-eight girls went camping. There were two main activities: volleyball and swimming. Fourteen girls went swimming, 5 participated in both activities, and 4 girls did neither. How many girls only played volleyball?
⬅ See Problem 4.

26. **Winter Sports** A ski shop owner surveys 200 people who ski or snowboard. If 196 people ski and 154 people do both activities, how many people snowboard?

Solve each inequality. Write the solutions as either the union or intersection of two sets.
⬅ See Problem 5.

27. $|3x - 5| < 14$
28. $-6 < n + 7 \le 21$
29. $|8w - 1| \ge 7$
30. $3 \le |5d + 11|$
31. $2|x - 7| > 28$
32. $|4.5t - 1.5| \le 12$

ⓑ Apply

Find each union or intersection. Let $W = \{5, 6, 7, 8\}$, $X = \{3, 6, 9\}$, $Y = \{2, 3, 7, 8\}$, **and** $Z = \{x \mid x \text{ is an even whole number less than } 10\}$.

33. $W \cup Y \cup Z$
34. $X \cap Y \cap Z$
35. $W \cap X \cap Z$

36. **Writing** Let $M = \{x \mid x \text{ is a multiple of } 3\}$ and $N = \{x \mid x \text{ is a multiple of } 5\}$. Describe the intersection of M and N.

37. **Think About a Plan** Blood type is determined partly by which *antigens* a red blood cell has. An antigen is a protein on the surface of a red blood cell. Type A contains the A antigen. Type B contains the B antigen. Type AB contains both A and B antigens. Type O does not have any antigens. A hospital has 25 patients with the A antigen, 17 with the B antigen, 10 with the A and B antigens, and 30 without A or B antigens. How many patients are represented by the data?
• How can a Venn diagram help you solve the problem?
• What strategies can you use to complete the Venn diagram?

38. **Sports** In a survey of students about favorite sports, the results include 22 who like tennis, 25 who like football, 9 who like tennis and football, 17 who like tennis and baseball, 20 who like football and baseball, 6 who like all three sports, and 4 who like none of the sports. How many students like only tennis and football? How many students like only tennis and baseball? How many students like only baseball and football?

39. **Reasoning** Suppose A and B are sets such that $A \subseteq B$. What is true about $A \cap B$?

4 Practice

ASSIGNMENT GUIDE

Basic: 10–32, 36–43

Average: 11–31 odd, 33–43

Advanced: 11–31 odd, 33–45

Standardized Test Prep: 46–48

Mixed Review: 49–63

Reasoning exercises have blue headings.

Applications exercises have red headings.

EXERCISE 38: Use the Think About a Plan worksheet in the **Practice and Problem Solving Workbook** (also available in the Teaching Resources in print and online) to further support students' development in becoming independent learners.

HOMEWORK QUICK CHECK

To check students' understanding of key skills and concepts, go over Exercises 11, 23, 37, 38, and 39.

22.
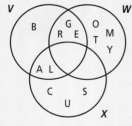

24.
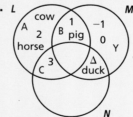

23.
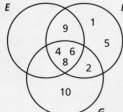

32. $\left\{t \mid t \ge -2\frac{1}{3}\right\} \cap \{t \mid t \le 3\}$
33. $W \cup Y \cup Z = \{0, 2, 3, 4, 5, 6, 7, 8\}$
34. $X \cap Y \cap Z = \varnothing$
35. $W \cap X \cap Z = \{6\}$
36. $M \cap N = \{x \mid x \text{ is a multiple of } 15\}$
37. 62 patients
38. 3; 11; 14
39. $A \cap B = A$

25. 10 girls
26. 158 people
27. $\{x \mid x > -3\} \cap \left\{x \mid x < \frac{19}{3}\right\}$
28. $\{n \mid n > -13\} \cap \{n \mid n \le 14\}$
29. $\left\{w \mid w \le -\frac{3}{4}\right\} \cup \{w \mid w \ge 1\}$
30. $\{d \mid d \le -2.8\} \cup \{d \mid d \ge -1.6\}$
31. $\{x \mid x < -7\} \cup \{x \mid x > 21\}$

Answers

Practice and Problem-Solving Exercises
(continued)

40. {(1, −3), (1, −2), (1, −1), (1, 0), (2, −3), (2, −2), (2, −1), (2, 0), (3, −3), (3, −2), (3, −1), (3, 0)}

41. {(π, 2), (π, 4), (2π, 2), (2π, 4), (3π, 2), (3π, 4), (4π, 2), (4π, 4)}

42. {(grape, jam), (grape, juice), (apple, jam), (apple, juice), (orange, jam), (orange, juice)}

43. {(reduce, plastic), (reuse, plastic), (recycle, plastic)}

44. false, since

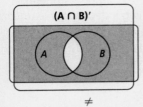

$\neq$

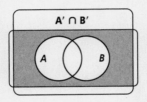

45. Sometimes; when A=B=C, the statement is true. When A, B, and C are distinct sets the statement is false.

46. B

47. F

48. [2] The $20 raise is greater since the weekly rate will be $100. The 20% raise will only give $80 + $80(0.2) = $96 a week. (OR equivalent explanation)

[1] incorrect answer with appropriate explanation OR correct answer with no explanation or incorrect explanation

---

The *cross product* of two sets A and B, denoted by $A \times B$, is the set of all ordered pairs with the first element in A and with the second element in B. In set-builder notation, you write:

$$A \times B = \{(a, b) \mid a \text{ is an element of } A, b \text{ is an element of } B\}$$

For example, suppose $A = \{1, 2\}$ and $B = \{7, 10, 12\}$. Then:

$$A \times B = \{(1, 7), (1, 10), (1, 12), (2, 7), (2, 10), (2, 12)\}$$

Given sets A and B, find $A \times B$.

40. $A = \{1, 2, 3\}$, $B = \{-3, -2, -1, 0\}$

41. $A = \{\pi, 2\pi, 3\pi, 4\pi\}$, $B = \{2, 4\}$

42. $A = \{\text{grape, apple, orange}\}$, $B = \{\text{jam, juice}\}$

43. $A = \{\text{reduce, reuse, recycle}\}$, $B = \{\text{plastic}\}$

Challenge

44. Use a Venn diagram to determine whether the statement $(A \cap B)' = A' \cap B'$ is *true* or *false*.

45. Reasoning Is the statement $(A \cup B) \cap C = A \cup (B \cap C)$ *always*, *sometimes*, or *never* true? Justify your answer.

Standardized Test Prep

SAT/ACT

46. Set $X = \{x \mid x \text{ is a factor of } 12\}$ and set $Y = \{y \mid y \text{ is a factor of } 16\}$. Which set represents $X \cap Y$?

Ⓐ $\emptyset$ Ⓑ $\{1, 2, 4\}$ Ⓒ $\{0, 1, 2, 4\}$ Ⓓ $\{1, 2, 3, 4, 6, 8, 12, 16\}$

47. Which compound inequality is equivalent to $|x + 4| < 8$?

Ⓕ $-12 < x < 4$ Ⓗ $-12 > x > 4$

Ⓖ $x < -12$ or $x > 4$ Ⓘ $x > -12$ or $x < 4$

Short Response

48. Suppose you earn $80 per week at your summer job. Your employer offers you a $20 raise or a 20% raise. Which should you take? Explain.

Mixed Review

Solve each equation or inequality.   ◆ See Lesson 3-7.

49. $|x| = 4$ **50.** $|n| + 7 = 9$ **51.** $4|f - 5| = 12$ **52.** $3|3y + 2| = 18$

53. $|4d| \leq 20$ **54.** $|x - 3| \geq 7$ **55.** $|2w + 6| > 24$ **56.** $2|3x| + 1 = 9$

Tell whether the ordered pair is a solution to the given equation.   ◆ See Lesson 1-9.

57. $x + 3 = y$; (1, 4)   **58.** $2x - 5 = y$; (−1, 8)   **59.** $\frac{1}{2}x + 7 = y$; (8, 11)

Get Ready!   **To prepare for Lesson 4-1, do Exercises 60–63.**

Graph each point on the same coordinate grid.   ◆ See Review p. 60.

60. (1, 4)   **61.** (−1, −5)   **62.** (3, −6)   **63.** (−2, 1)

---

49. $x = 4$ or $x = -4$

50. $n = 2$ or $n = -2$

51. $f = 2$ or $f = 8$

52. $y = \frac{4}{3}$ or $y = -\frac{8}{3}$

53. $-5 \leq d \leq 5$

54. $x \leq -4$ or $x \geq 10$

55. $w < -15$ or $w > 9$

56. $x = \frac{4}{3}$ or $x = -\frac{4}{3}$

57. yes

58. no

59. yes

60–63.

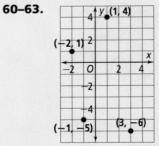

Additional Instructional Support

Algebra 1 Companion

Students can use the **Algebra 1 Companion** worktext (4 pages) as you teach the lesson. Use the Companion to support

- New Vocabulary
- Key Concepts
- Got It for each Problem
- Lesson Check

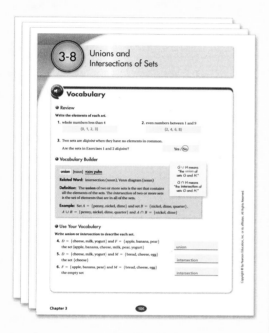

ELL Support

Focus on Language Examine the word *union*. Ask students for other words that look like or sound like union. (unified, unity, united). Then ask students for synonyms for union. Remind students that a synonym is a word that means the same thing. Examples may include joint, combined, organization, and connection. Ask for antonyms, such as disconnected and separate.

Union used as a noun means the joining of two or more things, an association of people or groups, or a coalition of an idea or action. The idea is becoming one from more than one.

5 Assess & Remediate

Lesson Quiz

1. Use the Venn diagram below. How many students play soccer and baseball, but not volleyball? How many play exactly 2 sports?

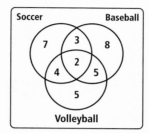

2. Do you UNDERSTAND? Of 350 students polled, some have a cat, some have a dog, and some have both. One hundred seventy-five students have a cat and 140 have both types of pets. How many students have a dog only? Explain.

3. Set $X = \{x \mid x$ is a whole number less than or equal to 10\} and set $Y = \{y \mid 5, 10, 15, 20\}$.
  a. What is $X \cap Y$?
  b. What is $X \cup Y$?

ANSWERS TO LESSON QUIZ

1. 3; 12
2. 175; since 175 have a cat or a cat and a dog, then the number that have a dog only is $350 - 175 = 175$.
3. a. $X \cap Y = \{5, 10\}$; **b.** $X \cup Y = \{0, 1, 2, 3, 4, 5, 6, 7, 8, 9, 10, 15, 20\}$

PRESCRIPTION FOR REMEDIATION

Use the student work on the Lesson Quiz to prescribe a differentiated review assignment.

Points	Differentiated Remediation
0–1	Intervention
2	On-level
3	Extension

PowerAlgebra.com

5 Assess & Remediate

Assign the Lesson Quiz. Appropriate intervention, practice, or enrichment is automatically generated based on student performance.

Intervention

- **Reteaching** (2 pages) Provides reteaching and practice exercises for the key lesson concepts. Use with struggling students or absent students.
- **English Language Learner Support** Helps students develop and reinforce mathematical vocabulary and key concepts.

All-in-One Resources/Online
Reteaching

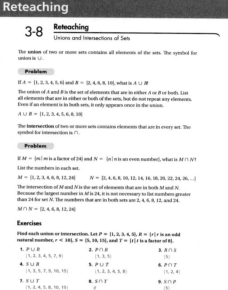

All-in-One Resources/Online
English Language Learner Support

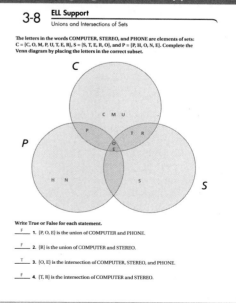

Differentiated Remediation *continued*

On-Level

- **Practice** (2 pages) Provides extra practice for each lesson. For simpler practice exercises, use the Form K Practice pages found in the All-in-One Teaching Resources and online.

- **Think About a Plan** Helps students develop specific problem-solving skills and strategies by providing scaffolded guiding questions.

- **Standardized Test Prep** Focuses on all major exercises, all major question types, and helps students prepare for the high-stakes assessments.

Extension

- **Enrichment** Provides students with interesting problems and activities that extend the concepts of the lesson.

- **Activities, Games, and Puzzles** Worksheets that can be used for concepts development, enrichment, and for fun!

Practice and Problem Solving WKBK/ All-in-One Resources/Online
Practice page 1

3-8 Practice *Form G*
Unions and Intersections of Sets

Find each union or intersection. Let $A = \{1, 3, 5, 7, 9\}$, $B = \{x \mid x$ is a positive odd integer less than 10$\}$, $C = \{1, 2, 4, 7\}$, and $D = \{x \mid x$ is a negative integer between -5 and $-1\}$.

1. $A \cup B$ 2. $A \cap C$ 3. $A \cap D$
{1, 3, 5, 7, 9}   {1, 7}   ∅

4. $B \cup C$ 5. $B \cap D$ 6. $C \cup D$
{1, 2, 3, 4, 5, 7, 9}   ∅   {−4, −3, −2, 1, 2, 4, 7}

7. $A \cap B$ 8. $A \cup C$ 9. $A \cup D$
{1, 3, 5, 7, 9}   {1, 2, 3, 4, 5, 7, 9}   {−4, −3, −2, 1, 3, 5, 7, 9}

10. $A \cap B \cap C$ 11. $D \cup C \cup B$ 12. $A \cup B \cup D$
{1, 7}   {−4, −3, −2, 1, 2, 3, 4, 5, 7, 9}   {−4, −3, −2, 1, 2, 3, 4, 5, 7, 9}

13. $A \cap B \cap D$ 14. $A \cup C \cup D$ 15. $B \cap C \cap D$
∅   {−4, −3, −2, 1, 2, 3, 4, 5, 7, 9}   ∅

Draw a Venn diagram to represent the union and intersection of these sets.

16. Let $V = \{p, m, b, a, d, e\}$, $W = \{i, t, b, p\}$, and $X = \{g, e, r, z, p\}$.

17. Let $L = \{$all negative odd integers$\}$, $M = \{$all negative integers greater than or equal to $-5\}$, and $N = \{-3, -1, 0, 3, 1\}$.

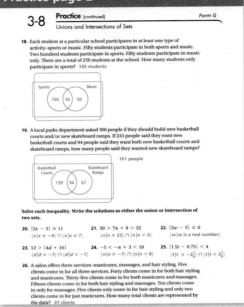

Practice and Problem Solving WKBK/ All-in-One Resources/Online
Think About a Plan

3-8 Think About a Plan
Unions and Intersections of Sets

In a survey of students about favorite sports, the results include 22 who like tennis, 25 who like football, 9 who like tennis and football, 17 who like tennis and baseball, 20 who like football and baseball, 6 who like all three sports, and 4 who like none of the sports. How many students like only tennis and football? How many students like only baseball and football?

1. How can a Venn diagram help you solve the problem?
Answers may vary. Sample: A Venn diagram can help you organize the information visually because there is a designated region for every possibility.

2. How many circles will you need in your diagram? three

3. What strategies can you use to complete the Venn diagram?
Answers may vary. Sample: You can start with the number of students who like all three and work out, using subtraction and variables where necessary.

a. Which parts of the Venn diagram can you complete? all parts except those who like only baseball

b. Where will you place the students who like all 3 sports? in the center, where all three circles overlap

c. Where will you place the students who like none of the sports? outside the circles

4. How many students like only tennis and football? 3

5. How many students like only tennis and baseball? 11

6. How many students like only baseball and football? 14

Practice and Problem Solving WKBK/ All-in-One Resources/Online
Practice page 2

3-8 Practice *(continued)* *Form G*
Unions and Intersections of Sets

18. Each student at a particular school participates in at least one type of activity–sports or music. Two hundred students participate in both sports and music. Fifty students participate in music only. There are a total of 250 students at the school. How many students only participate in sports? 150 students

Sports   Music
150   50   50

19. A local parks department asked 300 people if they should build new basketball courts and/or new skateboard ramps. If 233 people said they want new basketball courts and 94 people said they want both new basketball courts and skateboard ramps, how many people said they wanted new skateboard ramps?
161 people

Basketball Courts   Skateboard Ramps
139   94   67

Solve each inequality. Write the solutions as either the union or intersection of two sets.

20. $|2x - 3| \le 11$
$\{x \mid x \ge -4\} \cap \{x \mid x \le 7\}$

21. $50 > 7n + 8 > 22$
$\{n \mid n > 23\} \cap \{n \mid n < 6\}$

22. $|2w - 5| \ge 0$
$\{w \mid w$ is a real number$\}$

23. $12 > |4d + 16|$
$\{d \mid d > -7\} \cap \{d \mid d < -1\}$

24. $-5 < -n + 3 < 10$
$\{n \mid n > -7\} \cap \{n \mid n < 8\}$

25. $|1.5t - 0.75| < 4$
$\{t \mid t > -2\frac{1}{6}\} \cap \{t \mid t < 3\frac{1}{6}\}$

26. A salon offers three services–manicures, massages, and hair styling. Five clients come in for all three services. Forty clients come in for both hair styling and manicures. Thirty-five clients come in for both manicures and massages. Fifteen clients come in for both hair styling and massages. Ten clients come in only for massages. Five clients only come in for just two clients come in for just manicures. How many total clients are represented by the data? 97 clients

---

Practice and Problem Solving WKBK/ All-in-One Resources/Online
Standardized Test Prep

3-8 Standardized Test Prep
Unions and Intersections of Sets

Gridded Response

Solve each exercise and enter your answer on the grid provided.

1. Let $A = \{1, 3, 5\}$ and $B = \{x \mid x$ is an integer less than 2$\}$. Find $A \cap B$. 1

2. Let $C = \{1, 2, 3, 4, 5\}$ and $D = \{x \mid x$ is a positive, even integer less than 7$\}$. How many elements are in $C \cup D$? 6

3. Let $X = \{8, 10, 12\}$, $Y = \{6, 7, 8\}$, and $Z = \{-4, 4, 8\}$. Find $X \cap Y \cap Z$. 8

4. Let $M = \{1, 3, 5, 7\}$, $N = \{x \mid x$ is an even whole number less than 12$\}$, and $P = \{x \mid x$ is an odd whole number less than 4$\}$. How many elements are in $(M \cup N) \cap P$? 2

5. Let $F = \{-1, 0, 1, 2, 3\}$, $G = \{1, 3, 5, 7\}$, and $H = \{2, 4, 6, 8\}$. What is the difference of the number of elements of $G \cup H$ and the number of elements of $F \cap G$? 6

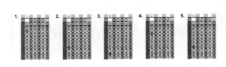

All-in-One Resources/Online
Enrichment

3-8 Enrichment
Unions and Intersections of Sets

For each statement, write *true* or *false*. If you write *true*, explain. If you write *false*, give a counterexample to show that the statement is false. Assume that sets A, B, and C have at least one element each.

1. The union of two sets always has more elements than either of the two sets.
false; $A = \{2\}$, $B = \{2, 3\}$; Union = {2, 3}

2. The intersection of two sets never has more elements than either of the two sets. true

3. If two sets have at least one element each, then the union of those two sets must have at least one element. true

4. For any two sets A and B, $A \cup B = B \cup A$. true

5. For any two sets A and B, $A \cap B = B \cap A$. true

6. For any two sets A and B, $(A \cup B) \cap A$ has more elements than A.
false; $A = \{2\}$, $B = \{2, 3\}$; Intersection = {2} = A

7. For any two sets A and B, $(A \cup B) \cup A$ has more elements than A.
false; $A = \{2, 3, 4\}$, $B = \{2, 3\}$; Intersection = {2, 3, 4} = A

8. For any three sets A, B, and C, $(A \cup B) \cup C = A \cup (B \cup C)$. true

---

Online Teacher Resource Center
Activities, Games, and Puzzles

3-8 Puzzle: Math Darts
Unions and Intersections of Sets

All of the real numbers are members of sets. You can see the target below as a Venn diagram representing subsets of real numbers.

- The region within each circle of the target, along with the space outside the target, represents different subsets of the real numbers. For Exercises 1–5, match the type of subset to sets A, B, C, D, and E in the target below. Then for Exercises 6–10, match each number to sets A, B, C, D, and E that most closely describes the number. Take your best shot!

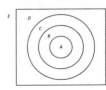

C	1. integers	A. set A
E	2. irrational numbers	B. set B
A	3. counting numbers	C. set C
D	4. rational numbers	D. set D
B	5. whole numbers	E. set E
E	6. $\sqrt{13}$	
C	7. -5	
B	8. 0	
D	9. $2\frac{5}{8}$	
A	10. 47	

3 *Pull It* **All Together**

> To solve these problems you will pull together many concepts and skills that you have studied about solving inequalities.

BIG idea Variable

You can use algebraic inequalities to represent relationships between quantities that are not equal.

Task 1

A camping supply store carries tents usually priced from \$68 to \$119. The store is having a sale. What is the range of possible prices you could pay for a tent?

ALL TENTS ON SALE
10% to 25% Off
▶ Shop Now

BIG idea Equivalence

You can represent an inequality using symbols in an infinite number of ways. Equivalent representations have the same solutions as the original inequality.

Task 2

For each figure, find the values of x such that the area A of the figure satisfies the given condition.

$A \leq 72$

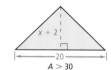

$A > 30$

BIG idea Solving Equations and Inequalities

You can use properties of inequality to transform an inequality into equivalent, simpler inequalities and then find solutions.

Task 3

You have a photograph 12 in. wide and 18 in. long. You surround the photograph with a mat x in. wide, as shown at the right. You want to make a frame for the matted photograph, but you only have an 80-in. length of wood to use for the frame. What are the dimensions of the largest frame you can make?

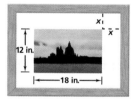

Performance Task

Pull It All Together

The concepts and skills required to solve these problems are from several lessons within this chapter and from the previous chapter. As students solve these problems, they will demonstrate their reasoning strategies and their growth as independent problem solvers.

The following questions are designed for you to:
- Help support students as they do the Tasks.
- Gauge the amount of support a student needs as they progress to becoming an independent problem solver.

Task 1
- How can you determine the minimum price of a tent?
- How can you determine the maximum price of a tent?
- How can you show the range of possible prices of tents?

Task 2
- What is an inequality that represents the area of the rectangle?
- What is the formula for the area of a triangle?

Task 3
- What problem-solving strategy can you use to solve the problem?
- How much area does the photograph take up?

Assess
Performance UbD

Pull It All Together

See p. 67 for a holistic scoring rubric to gauge a student's progress on Understanding the Problem, Planning a Solution, Getting an Answer, and Developing Autonomy.

SOLUTIONS OUTLINES

Task 1

Possible plan: Recognize that a 25% discount is the same as paying 75% of the regular price and a 10% discount is the same as paying 90% of the regular price. Find the lowest possible sale price for a tent by multiplying the least expensive tent by the greatest discount ($0.75 \times 68 = 51$). Find the greatest possible sale price for a tent by multiplying the most expensive tent by the lowest discount ($0.9 \times 119 = 107.10$). Write an inequality to represent the situation. (Answer: $51 \leq p \leq 101.70$)

Task 2

Possible plan: Find the area of each figure (Rectangle: $3x$; Triangle: $\frac{1}{2}(20)(x + 2) = 10x + 20$). Substitute the area for A in each inequality (Rectangle: $3x \leq 72$; Triangle: $10x + 20 > 30$). Solve each inequality. (Answer: Rectangle: $0 < x \leq 24$; Triangle: $x > 1$) Note: The width of the rectangle cannot be less than or equal to zero.

Task 3

Possible plan: Find the width and length of the matted photograph ($w = 12 + 2x$), ($\ell = 18 + 2x$). Find the perimeter of the matted photograph ($P = 2(18 + 2x + 12 + 2x) = 8x + 60$). Write an inequality representing that the perimeter of the matted photograph must be less than or equal to 80 ($8x + 60 \leq 80$). Solve the inequality ($x \leq 2.5$). Substitute 2.5 for x in the width and length expressions to find the dimensions of the largest frame you can make. (Answer: 17 in. by 23 in.)

Essential Questions

BIG idea **Variable**
ESSENTIAL QUESTION How do you represent relationships between quantities that are not equal?
ANSWER You can use algebraic inequalities to represent relationships between quantities that are not equal.

BIG ideas **Equivalence**
ESSENTIAL QUESTION Can inequalities that appear to be different be equivalent?
ANSWER You can represent an inequality in many ways. Equivalent representations have the same solutions as the original inequality.

BIG idea **Solving Equations and Inequalities**
ESSENTIAL QUESTION How can you solve inequalities?
ANSWER You can use properties of inequality to transform an inequality into equivalent, simpler inequalities and then find solutions.

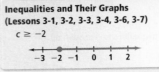

3 Chapter Review

Connecting **BIG** ideas and Answering the Essential Questions

1 Variable
You can use algebraic inequalities to represent relationships between quantities that are not equal.

Inequalities and Their Graphs
(Lessons 3-1, 3-2, 3-3, 3-4, 3-6, 3-7)
$$c \geq -2$$

$$-3 \quad -2 \quad -1 \quad 0 \quad 1 \quad 2$$

2 Equivalence
You can represent an inequality in many ways. Equivalent representations have the same solutions as the original inequality.

Solving One-Step Inequalities
(Lessons 3-2, 3-3)
The inequalities in each pair are equivalent.
$$f - 4 \geq -3 \qquad 6y < 24$$
$$f \geq 1 \qquad\quad y < 4$$

3 Solving Equations and Inequalities
You can use properties of inequality to transform an inequality into equivalent, simpler inequalities and then find solutions.

Solving Multi-Step Inequalities
(Lesson 3-4)
$$7z + 10 \leq 24$$
$$7z + 10 - 10 \leq 24 - 10$$
$$7z \leq 14$$
$$\frac{7z}{7} \leq \frac{14}{7}$$
$$z \leq 2$$

Solving Compound and Absolute Value Inequalities
(Lessons 3-6, 3-7)
$$|3m + 2| \leq 14$$
$$-14 \leq \; 3m + 2 \; \leq 14$$
$$-16 \leq \qquad 3m \quad \leq 12$$
$$-\frac{16}{3} \leq \qquad m \quad \leq 4$$

Chapter Vocabulary

- complement of a set (p. 196)
- compound inequality (p. 200)
- disjoint sets (p. 215)
- empty set (p. 195)
- equivalent inequalities (p. 171)
- intersection (p. 215)
- interval notation (p. 203)
- roster form (p. 194)
- set-builder notation (p. 194)
- solution of an inequality (p. 165)
- union (p. 214)
- universal set (p. 196)

Choose the correct term to complete each sentence.

1. The set $\{5, 10, 15, 20, \ldots\}$ represents the multiples of 5 written in ? .

2. The ? of two or more sets is the set that contains all elements of the sets.

3. The set that contains no elements is the ? .

4. The ? is a number that makes the inequality true.

5. The inequalities $6a \geq 12$ and $a \geq 2$ are ? .

Summative Questions

Use the following prompts as you review this chapter with your students. The prompts are designed to help you assess your students' understanding of the Big Ideas they have studied.

- How do you use a number line to show an inequality?
- What properties can you use to generate equivalent inequalities?
- Compare the process of solving equations with solving inequalities?
- What considerations must be taken into account when using the Multiplication and Division Properties of Inequality?

Answers

Chapter Review

1. roster form

2. union

3. empty set

4. solution of an inequality

5. equivalent inequalities

3-1 Inequalities and Their Graphs

Quick Review

A **solution of an inequality** is any number that makes the inequality true. You can indicate all the solutions of an inequality on the graph. A closed dot indicates that the endpoint is a solution. An open dot indicates that the endpoint is *not* a solution.

Example

What is the graph of $x \le -4$?

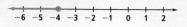

Exercises

Graph each inequality.

6. $x > 5$

7. $h \le -1$

8. $10 \ge p$

9. $r < 3.2$

Write an inequality for each graph.

10.

11.

12.

3-2 Solving Inequalities Using Addition or Subtraction

Quick Review

You can use the addition and subtraction properties of inequality to transform an inequality into a simpler, equivalent inequality.

Example

What are the solutions of $x + 4 \le 5$?

$x + 4 \le 5$

$x + 4 - 4 \le 5 - 4$ Subtract 4 from each side.

$x \le 1$ Simplify.

Exercises

Solve each inequality. Graph your solutions.

13. $w + 3 > 9$

14. $v - 6 < 4$

15. $-4 < t + 8$

16. $n - \frac{1}{2} \ge \frac{3}{4}$

17. $22.3 \le 13.7 + h$

18. $q + 0.5 > -2$

19. Allowance You have at most $15.00 to spend. You want to buy a used CD that costs $4.25. Write and solve an inequality to find the possible additional amounts you can spend.

6.
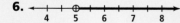

7.
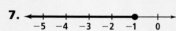

8.

9.
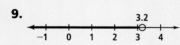

10. $x > 5$

11. $x \le -2$

12. $x > -5.5$

13. $w > 6$

14. $v < 10$

15. $-12 < t$

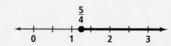

16. $n \ge \frac{5}{4}$

17. $8.6 \le h$

18. $q > -2.5$

19. $4.25 + x \le 15.00; \ x \le 10.75$

Answers

Chapter Review (continued)

20. $x < 3$

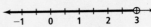

21. $t < -3$

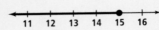

22. $y \le 6$

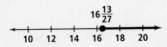

23. $h > -24$

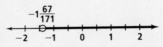

24. $g > 4$

25. $n \le 15$

26. $d \ge 16\frac{13}{27}$

27. $m > -1\frac{67}{171}$

28. $7.25h \ge 200$; at least 28 full hours

29. $k \ge -0.5$

30. $c < -2$

31. $t < -6$

32. $y \le -56$

33. $x < 2\frac{2}{3}$

34. $x \le -13$

35. $a \le 5.8$

36. $w > 0.35$

37. $200 + 0.04s \ge 450$; $s \ge 6250$

3-3 Solving Inequalities Using Multiplication or Division

Quick Review
You can use the multiplication and division properties of inequality to transform an inequality. When you multiply or divide each side of an inequality by a negative number, you have to reverse the inequality symbol.

Example
What are the solutions of $-3x > 12$?

$$-3x > 12$$

$$\frac{-3x}{-3} < \frac{12}{-3}$$ Divide each side by -3. Reverse the inequality symbol.

$$x < -4$$ Simplify.

Exercises
Solve each inequality. Graph your solutions.

20. $5x < 15$

21. $-6t > 18$

22. $\frac{y}{3} \le 2$

23. $-\frac{h}{4} < 6$

24. $25.5g > 102$

25. $-\frac{3}{5}n \ge -9$

26. $44.5 \le 2.7d$

27. $-17.1m < 23.8$

28. Part-Time Job You earn $7.25 per hour baby-sitting. Write and solve an inequality to find how many full hours you must work to earn at least $200.

3-4 Solving Multi-Step Inequalities

Quick Review
When you solve inequalities, sometimes you need to use more than one step. You need to gather the variable terms on one side of the inequality and the constant terms on the other side.

Example
What are the solutions of $3x + 5 > -1$?

$$3x + 5 > -1$$

$$3x > -6$$ Subtract 5 from each side.

$$x > -2$$ Divide each side by 3.

Exercises
Solve each inequality.

29. $4k - 1 \ge -3$

30. $6(c - 1) < -18$

31. $3t > 5t + 12$

32. $-\frac{6}{7}y - 6 \ge 42$

33. $4 + \frac{x}{2} > 2x$

34. $3x + 5 \le 2x - 8$

35. $13.5a + 7.4 \le 85.7$

36. $42w > 2(w + 7)$

37. Commission A salesperson earns $200 per week plus a commission equal to 4% of her sales. This week her goal is to earn no less than $450. Write and solve an inequality to find the amount of sales she must have to reach her goal.

3-5 Working With Sets

Quick Review

The **complement** of a set A is the set of all elements in the universal set that are *not* in A.

Example

Suppose $U = \{1, 2, 3, 4, 5, 6\}$ and $Y = \{2, 4, 6\}$. What is Y'?

The elements in U that are *not* in Y are 1, 3, and 5.
So $Y' = \{1, 3, 5\}$.

Exercises

List all the subsets of each set.

38. $\{s, t\}$

39. $\{5, 10, 15\}$

40. How do you write "A is the set of even whole numbers that are less than 18" in roster form? How do you write A using set-builder notation?

41. Suppose $U = \{1, 2, 3, 4, 5, 6, 7, 8\}$ and $B = \{2, 4, 6, 8\}$. What is B'?

3-6 Compound Inequalities

Quick Review

Two inequalities that are joined by the word *and* or the word *or* are called **compound inequalities**. A solution of a compound inequality involving *and* makes both inequalities true. A solution of an inequality involving *or* makes either inequality true.

Example

What are the solutions of $-3 \le z - 1 < 3$?

$-3 \le z - 1 < 3$

$-2 \le z < 4$ Add 1 to each part of the inequality.

Exercises

Solve each compound inequality.

42. $-2 \le d + \frac{1}{2} < 4\frac{1}{2}$

43. $0 < -8b \le 12$

44. $2t \le -4$ or $7t \ge 49$

45. $5m < -10$ or $3m > 9$

46. $-1 \le a - 3 \le 2$

47. $9.1 > 1.4p \ge -6.3$

48. Climate A town's high temperature for a given month is 88°F and the low temperature is 65°F. Write a compound inequality to represent the range of temperatures for the given month.

38. { } or Ø, {s}, {t}, {s, t}

39. { } or Ø, {5}, {10}, {15}, {5, 10}, {5, 15}, {10, 15}, {5, 10, 15}

40. $A = \{0, 2, 4, 6, 8, 10, 12, 14, 16\}$; $A = \{x \mid x$ is an even whole number less than 18$\}$

41. $B' = \{1, 3, 5, 7\}$

42. $-2\frac{1}{2} \le d < 4$

43. $-1.5 \le b < 0$

44. $t \le -2$ or $t \ge 7$

45. $m < -2$ or $m > 3$

46. $2 \le a \le 5$

47. $6.5 > p \ge -4.5$

48. $65 \le t \le 88$

Answers

Chapter Review (continued)

49. $y = 3$ or $y = -3$

50. $n = 2$ or $n = -6$

51. $r = 1$ or $r = -5$

52. no solution

53. $-3 \leq x \leq 3$

54. no solution

55. $x < 3$ or $x > 4$

56. $k < -7$ or $k > -3$

57. any length between 19.6 mm and 20.4 mm, inclusive

58. $A \cup B = A$

59.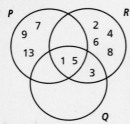

60. $N \cap P = \{x \mid x \text{ is a multiple of } 6\}$

61. 5 cats

3-7 Absolute Value Equations and Inequalities

Quick Review

Solving an equation or inequality that contains an absolute value expression is similar to solving other equations and inequalities. You will need to write two equations or inequalities using positive and negative values. Then solve the equations.

Example

What is the solution of $|x| - 7 = 3$?

$$|x| - 7 = 3$$
$$|x| = 10 \qquad \text{Add 7 to each side.}$$
$$x = 10 \text{ or } x = -10 \qquad \text{Definition of absolute value}$$

Exercises

Solve each equation or inequality. If there is no solution, write *no solution*.

49. $|y| = 3$

50. $|n + 2| = 4$

51. $4 + |r + 2| = 7$

52. $|x + 3| = -2$

53. $|5x| \leq 15$

54. $|3d + 5| < -2$

55. $|2x - 7| - 1 > 0$

56. $4|k + 5| > 8$

57. Manufacturing The ideal length of a certain nail is 20 mm. The actual length can vary from the ideal by at most 0.4 mm. Find the range of acceptable lengths of the nail.

3-8 Unions and Intersections of Sets

Quick Review

The **union** of two or more sets is the set that contains all elements of the sets. The **intersection** of two or more sets is the set of elements that are common to all the sets. **Disjoint sets** have no elements in common.

Example

Student Activities Of 100 students who play sports or take music lessons, 70 students play a sport and 50 students play a sport and take music lessons. How many students *only* take music lessons?

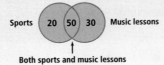

Both sports and music lessons

So, 30 students take only music lessons.

Exercises

58. Given $A = \{1, 2, 3, 4, 5, 6, 7, 8, 9\}$ and $B = \{2, 4, 6, 8\}$, what is $A \cup B$?

59. Let $P = \{1, 5, 7, 9, 13\}$, $R = \{1, 2, 3, 4, 5, 6, 8\}$, and $Q = \{1, 3, 5\}$. Draw a Venn diagram that represents the intersection and union of the sets.

60. Let $N = \{x \mid x \text{ is a multiple of 2}\}$ and $P = \{x \mid x \text{ is a multiple of 6}\}$. Describe the intersection of N and P.

61. Cats There are 15 cats. Ten are striped and 7 are striped and have green eyes. The rest of the cats have green eyes but are not striped. How many cats have green eyes but are not striped?

3 Chapter Test

Do you know HOW?

Write an inequality for each graph.

1.
$$-12\ -10\ -8\ -6\ -4\ -2\ \ 0\ \ 2\ \ 4$$

2.
$$-2\ -1\ \ 0\ \ 1\ \ 2\ \ 3\ \ 4\ \ 5\ \ 6$$

3.
$$-6\ -5\ -4\ -3\ -2\ -1\ \ 0\ \ 1\ \ 2$$

4.
$$-3\ -2\ -1\ \ 0\ \ 1\ \ 2\ \ 3\ \ 4\ \ 5$$

Solve each inequality. Graph the solutions.

5. $z + 7 \le 9$

6. $-\frac{1}{3}x < 2$

7. $5w \ge -6w + 11$

8. $-\frac{7}{2}(m - 2) < 21$

9. $|x - 5| \ge 3$

10. $9 \le 6 - b < 12$

11. $4 + 3n \ge 1$ or $-5n > 25$

12. $10k < 75$ and $4 - k \le 0$

List the subsets of each set.

13. $\{1, 3, 5, 7\}$

14. $\{red, blue, yellow\}$

15. Quality Control A manufacturer is cutting fabric into rectangles that are 18.55 in. long by 36.75 in. wide. Each rectangle's length and width must be within 0.05 in. of the desired size. Write and solve inequalities to find the acceptable range for the length ℓ and the width w.

Write a compound inequality that each graph could represent.

16.
$$-10\ -8\ -6\ -4\ -2\ \ 0\ \ 2\ \ 4\ \ 6$$

17.
$$-4\ -3\ -2\ -1\ \ 0\ \ 1\ \ 2\ \ 3\ \ 4$$

18. Multiple Choice Suppose $A = \{x \mid x > -1\}$ and $B = \{x \mid -3 \le x \le 2\}$. Which statement is true?

Ⓐ $A \cup B = \{\}$

Ⓑ $A' = \{x \mid x < -1\}$

Ⓒ $A \cap B = \{x. \mid -1 < x \le 2\}$

Ⓓ $B \subseteq \{x \mid x < 2\}$

Solve each equation. Check your solution.

19. $|4k - 2| = 11$

20. $23 = |n + 10|$

21. $|3c + 1| - 4 = 13$

22. $4|5 - t| = 20$

23. Fundraising A drama club wants to raise at least $500 in ticket sales for its annual show. The members of the club sold 50 tickets at a special $5 rate. The usual ticket price the day of the show is $7.50. At least how many tickets do they have to sell the day of the show to meet the goal?

24. Of 145 runners, 72 run only on weekends and 63 run on both weekends and during the week. How many of the runners run only during the week?

Do You UNDERSTAND?

25. Open-Ended Write an absolute value inequality that has 3 and -5 as two of its solutions.

26. Writing Compare and contrast the Multiplication Property of Equality and the Multiplication Property of Inequality.

27. Describe the region labeled C in terms of set A and set B.

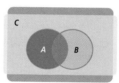

28. Suppose set A has 9 elements. What is the greatest number of elements a subset of A can have?

15. $|\ell - 18.55| \le 0.05, 18.5 \le \ell \le 18.6$; $|w - 36.75| \le 0.05, 36.7 \le w \le 36.8$

16. $x \le -6$ or $x > 2$

17. $-3 < x < 2$

18. C

19. $k = 3.25$ or $k = -2.25$

20. $n = 13$ or $n = -33$

21. $c = 5\frac{1}{3}$ or $c = -6$

22. $t = 0$ or $t = 10$

23. 34 tickets

24. 10 runners

25. Check students' work.

26. Answers may vary. Sample: The mult. props. of eq. and inequality allow each side of the equation or inequality to be multiplied by the same positive number without changing its solutions. Also, with the inequality prop., multiplying by a negative number requires the inequality sign to be reversed.

27. $(A \cup B)'$

28. 9 elements

Answers

Chapter Test

1. $x < -7$

2. $x \le 4.5$

3. $x > -5$

4. $x > 1.5$

5. $z \le 2$
$$-4\ -2\ \ 0\ \ 2\ \ 4$$

6. $x > -6$
$$-6\ -4\ -2\ \ 0\ \ 2$$

7. $w \ge 1$
$$0\ \ 1\ \ 2\ \ 3\ \ 4$$

8. $m > -4$
$$-4\ -2\ \ 0\ \ 2\ \ 4$$

9. $x \le 2$ or $x \ge 8$
$$-2\ \ 0\ \ 2\ \ 4\ \ 6\ \ 8\ \ 10$$

10. $-6 < b \le -3$
$$-6\ -4\ -2\ \ 0\ \ 2$$

11. $n < -5$ or $n \ge -1$
$$-7\ -5\ -3\ -1\ \ 1\ \ 3\ \ 5$$

12. $4 \le k < 7.5$
$$0\ \ 2\ \ 4\ \ 6\ \ 8\ \ 10$$

13. $\{\}$ or $\varnothing$, $\{1\}$, $\{3\}$, $\{5\}$, $\{7\}$, $\{1, 3\}$, $\{1, 5\}$, $\{1, 7\}$, $\{3, 5\}$, $\{3, 7\}$, $\{5, 7\}$, $\{1, 3, 5\}$, $\{1, 3, 7\}$, $\{1, 5, 7\}$, $\{3, 5, 7\}$, $\{1, 3, 5, 7\}$

14. $\{\}$ or $\varnothing$, $\{red\}$, $\{blue\}$, $\{yellow\}$, $\{red, blue\}$, $\{red, yellow\}$, $\{blue, yellow\}$, $\{red, blue, yellow\}$

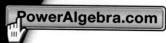

PowerAlgebra.com

MathXL for School
Prepare students for the Mid-Chapter Quiz and Chapter Test with online practice and review.

Item Number	Lesson
1	1-9
2	3-3
3	3-3
4	2-4
5	3-3
6	2-10
7	3-4
8	2-7
9	2-6
10	1-2
11	1-7
12	3-4
13	3-8
14	3-4
15	3-6
16	3-6
17	1-9
18	3-4
19	1-9
20	2-6
21	2-6
22	2-7
23	3-8
24	2-10
25	2-4
26	2-8
27	3-4
28	2-3
29	1-9
30	3-6

TIPS FOR SUCCESS

Some questions on tests ask you to write an extended response. In this textbook, an extended response question is usually worth a maximum of 4 points. Sometimes these questions have multiple parts. To get full credit, you need to answer each part and show all your work or justify your reasoning.

TIP 1

A 1-point response might show an incorrect equation without giving the number of children who must attend to cover costs.

The Theatre Club needs to raise $440 to cover the cost of its children's play. The ticket prices are $14 for an adult and $2 for a child. The club expects that three times as many children as adults will attend the play. Write and solve an equation to find how many adult and child tickets the club needs to sell to cover the cost.

Solution

x = number of adults

$3x$ = number of children

$$14(x) + 2(3x) = 440$$
$$14x + 6x = 440$$
$$20x = 440$$
$$x = 22$$
$$3x = 66$$

So, 22 adults and 66 children must attend.

TIP 2

A 3-point response might approach the problem correctly, but have an error.

Think It Through

A 4-point response defines variables, shows the work, and gives a written answer to the problem. So relate what is given to what has been asked. Identify the variables and make a model that you can use to write an equation. Then show your work as you use this equation to find the solution.

Vocabulary Builder

As you solve test items, you must understand the meanings of mathematical terms. Choose the correct term to complete each sentence.

A. Two inequalities that are joined by the word *and* or the word *or* form a (*compound, connected*) inequality.

B. (*Equivalent, Similar*) inequalities are inequalities with the same solutions.

C. Any number that makes an inequality true is a (*union, solution*) of the inequality.

D. A (*proportion, conversion factor*) is an equation that states that two ratios are equal.

E. A(n) (*open, closed*) dot on the graph of an inequality shows that the point is a solution of the inequality.

Multiple Choice

Read each question. Then write the letter of the correct answer on your paper.

1. You are making bracelets to sell at a fair. The table shows the total cost c of making b bracelets. Which equation represents the relationship between the number of bracelets you make and the total cost?

Bracelets, b	Cost, c
10	$9.00
15	$13.50
20	$18.00
25	$22.50

(A) $c = 9b$

(B) $c = 0.9b$

(C) $9c = b$

(D) $0.9c = b$

2. What are the solutions of $2u + 5.2 \leq 9.4 + u$?

(F) $u \geq 4.2$

(G) $u \leq 48.9$

(H) $u \leq 14.6$

(I) $u \leq 4.2$

Answers

Cumulative Test Prep

A. compound

B. equivalent

C. solution

D. proportion

E. closed

1. B

2. I

3. A baseball team can spend up to $1500 on bats. Bats cost $32 each. Which inequality represents the number of bats b they can buy?

(A) $32b \le 1500$

(B) $32b \ge 1500$

(C) $32b + b \le 1500$

(D) $32b + b \ge 1500$

4. What is the solution of $w - 4 = 18 + 3w$?

(F) -11 (H) 3.5

(G) -3.5 (I) 11

5. Which graph represents the solutions to the inequality $3n \le -6$?

(A)
```
  +---+---+---+---+---+--o--+---+
 -3  -2  -1   0   1   2   3
```

(B)
```
  +---+--●--+---+---+---+---+---+
 -3  -2  -1   0   1   2   3
```

(C)
```
  +---+---+---+---+---+--●--+---+
 -3  -2  -1   0   1   2   3
```

(D)
```
  +--o--+---+---+---+---+---+---+
 -3  -2  -1   0   1   2   3
```

6. In the spring, you could serve a tennis ball at a rate of 43 mi/h. The speed of your serve increased 12% after practicing all summer. About how fast is your serve after practicing?

(F) 38 mi/h   (H) 51 mi/h

(G) 48 mi/h   (I) 55 mi/h

7. The cost of a hardcover book x is at least $3 more than twice the cost of the paperback book y. Which inequality represents this situation?

(A) $2y + 3 \ge x$ (C) $2y + 3 \le x$

(B) $x + 3 \le 2y$ (D) $x + 2y \le 3$

8. What is the solution of $\frac{18}{x} = \frac{5}{7}$?

(F) 12.9   (G) 20   (H) 25.2   (I) 35

9. A fox runs at a rate of 42 mi/h and a cat runs at a rate of 44 ft/s. What is the difference in their speeds? (*Hint:* 1 mi = 5280 ft)

(A) 12 ft/s   (C) 17.6 mi/h

(B) 17.6 ft/s   (D) 30 mi/h

10. When simplifying the expression $206 - 4(17 - 3^2)$, which part of the expression do you simplify first?

(F) $206 - 4$ (H) $17 - 3$

(G) 3^2 (I) $4(17)$

11. Which expression is equivalent to $8y - (6y - 5)$?

(A) $2y - 5$

(B) $14y - 5$

(C) $2y + 5$

(D) $14y + 5$

12. Max saved $16,000 and bought a car that costs $10,500. He will pay $1200 each year for car insurance. Which inequality can you use to find the maximum number of years he can pay for insurance with his remaining savings?

(F) $10{,}500 + 1200x \le 16{,}000$

(G) $10{,}500 - 1200x \le 16{,}000$

(H) $16{,}000 + 1200x \le 10{,}500$

(I) $16{,}000 - 1200x \le 10{,}500$

13. Let $L = \{3, 4, 5\}$, $M = \{x \mid x$ is a negative integer greater than $-5\}$, and $N = \{-1, 0, 1\}$. What is $L \cap M$?

(A) $\{3, 4, 5\}$ (C) $\{-4, -3, -2, -1, 3, 4, 5\}$

(B) $\{-5, -4, -3\}$ (D) $\{\,\}$

14. What are the solutions of $-\frac{1}{9}a + 1 < 8$?

(F) $a > 7$ (H) $a > -63$

(G) $a < 7$ (I) $a < -63$

15. Which choice best describes the following statement?
If $x < 0$ and $y \ge 0$, then $xy < 0$.

(A) always true

(B) sometimes true, when $y < 0$

(C) sometimes true, when $y > 0$

(D) never true

16. What are the solutions of $4 < 6b - 2 \le 28$?

(F) $\frac{1}{3} < b \le \frac{13}{3}$

(G) $6 < b \le 30$

(H) $\frac{2}{3} < b \le \frac{14}{3}$

(I) $1 < b \le 5$

3. A

4. F

5. B

6. G

7. C

8. H

9. B

10. G

11. C

12. F

13. D

14. H

15. C

16. I

Answers

Cumulative Test Prep (continued)

17. C

18. I

19. 3600

20. 13.64

21. 9216

22. 6.429

23. 7

24. 12.5

25. 3

26. 15.75

27. [2] $25 + 0.10(m - 500) \geq 30$ (OR equivalent inequality); $27.50 (OR equivalent amount)

[1] incorrect inequality OR incorrect amount

28. [2] $c = \$30.60 + \$0.0176k$ (OR equivalent equation); $53.96 (OR equivalent amount)

[1] incorrect equation OR incorrect amount

29. [2] $n = -33d + 360$; the number of snacks n decreases by 33 each day (OR equivalent explanation).

[1] appropriate methods with one computational error

30. [4] Let b = number of boxes;
$1400 \leq (1 - 0.1)(32b) \leq 1500$
(OR equivalent inequality);
$1400 \leq 28.80b \leq 1500$, so rounded to the whole box, $49 \leq b \leq 52$, or between 49 and 52 boxes, inclusive (OR equivalent work).

[3] appropriate methods, but with one computational error

[2] correct inequality and correct number of boxes, but no work shown, OR appropriate methods, with more than one computational error

[1] correct inequality OR correct number of boxes with no work shown

---

17. You count the number of melons you use based on the number of bowls of fruit salad made, as shown in the table at the right. Which equation describes the relationship between the number of bowls of fruit salad f and the number of melons used m?

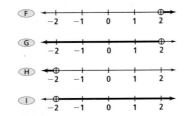

Fruit salad, f	Melons, m
2	1
4	2
6	3
8	4
10	5

Ⓐ $f = 0.5m$ Ⓒ $m = 0.5f$

Ⓑ $2f = m$ Ⓓ $2m = 0.5f$

18. Which graph represents the solutions to the inequality $3(f + 2) > 2f + 4$?

Ⓕ [number line from −2 to 2, open circle at 2, shaded right]

Ⓖ [number line from −2 to 2, open circle at 2, shaded left]

Ⓗ [number line from −2 to 2, open circle at −2, shaded left]

Ⓘ [number line from −2 to 2, open circle at −2, shaded left]

GRIDDED RESPONSE

Record your answers in a grid.

19. You can mow 400 ft² of grass if you work for 5 min, 800 ft² if you work for 10 min, 1200 ft² of grass if you work for 15 min, and so on. How many square feet can you mow in 45 min?

20. An insect flies 20 ft in 1 s. How fast does the insect fly in miles per hour? Round to the nearest hundredth if necessary.

21. Isabella is covering a square tabletop with square mosaic tiles. The tabletop is 2 ft long and 2 ft wide. Each tile is $\frac{1}{4}$ in. long and $\frac{1}{4}$ in. wide. What is the minimum number of tiles needed to cover the tabletop?

22. What is the solution of $\frac{7}{5} = \frac{9}{x}$? Round your answer to the nearest thousandth if necessary.

23. Suppose $P = \{-2, 6, 7, 9\}$ and $Q = \{0, 2, 4, 6\}$. How many elements are in the set $P \cup Q$?

24. A family visited an amusement park. A person must be 3 ft tall to ride the roller coaster. One child is 4 in. short of the height regulation. By what percent must the child's height increase so that the whole family can ride the roller coaster?

25. What is the value of d when $11(d + 1) = 4(d + 8)$?

26. You are making a scale model of a sports field. The actual field is a rectangle with a length of 315 ft and a width of 300 ft. Your scale model is 15 in. wide. What is its length in inches?

Short Response

27. You have a wireless phone plan that costs $25 per month. You must also pay $.10 per minute for each minute over 500 min. Your phone bill was more than $30 last month. Write an inequality to represent the number of minutes m you spent on the phone last month. Suppose you use 525 min next month. How much will your bill be?

28. An electric company charges a monthly fee of $30.60 plus $.0176 for each kilowatt-hour (kWh) of energy used. Write an equation to represent the cost of the family's electric bill each month. Suppose the family used 1327 kWh of energy. How much was their bill?

29. A vending machine starts with 360 snacks. After 1 day it has 327 snacks, after 2 days it has 294 snacks, after 3 days it has 261 snacks, and so on. Describe the pattern of the number of snacks n based on the number of days d.

Extended Response

30. A company has $1500 in its budget for paper this year. The regular price of paper is $32 per box, with a 10% discount for bulk orders. If the company spends at least $1400 on paper, the shipping is free. Write a compound inequality to represent the number of boxes the company can buy with the discount and receive free shipping. What are the possible numbers of boxes the company can buy with the discount and free shipping?

Get Ready!

Get Ready!

Lesson 1-2 ◆ Evaluating Expressions

Evaluate each expression for the given value(s) of the variable(s).

1. $3x - 2y; x = -1, y = 2$　　　　**2.** $-w^2 + 3w; w = -3$

3. $\frac{3 + k}{k}; k = 3$　　　　**4.** $h - (h^2 - 1) \div 2; h = -1$

Lesson 1-9 ◆ Using Tables, Equations, and Graphs

Use a table, an equation, and a graph to represent each relationship.

5. Bob is 9 years older than his dog.

6. Sue swims 1.5 laps per minute.

7. Each carton of eggs costs \$3.

Review, page 60 ◆ Graphing in the Coordinate Plane

Graph the ordered pairs in the same coordinate plane.

8. $(3, -3)$　　　　**9.** $(0, -5)$　　　　**10.** $(-2, 2)$　　　　**11.** $(-2, 0)$

Lesson 2-2 ◆ Solving Two-Step Equations

Solve each equation. Check your answer.

12. $5x + 3 = -12$　　**13.** $\frac{n}{6} - 1 = 10$　　**14.** $7 = \frac{x + 8}{2}$　　**15.** $\frac{x - 1}{4} = \frac{3}{4}$

Lesson 3-7 ◆ Solving Absolute Value Equations

Solve each equation. If there is no solution, write *no solution*.

16. $|r + 2| = 2$　　　　　　**17.** $-3|d - 5| = -6$

18. $-3.2 = |8p|$　　　　　　**19.** $5|2x - 7| = 20$

 ## Looking Ahead Vocabulary

20. The amount of money you earn from a summer job is *dependent* upon the number of hours you work. What do you think it means when a variable is *dependent* upon another variable?

21. A *relation* is a person to whom you are related. If $(1, 2)$, $(3, 4)$, and $(5, 6)$ form a mathematical *relation*, to which number is 3 related?

22. When a furnace runs *continuously*, there are no breaks or interruptions in its operation. What do you think a *continuous* graph looks like?

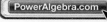 PowerAlgebra.com 　　 Chapter 4　An Introduction to Functions　　　231

Get Ready!

Assign this diagnostic assessment to determine if students have the prerequisite skills for Chapter 4.

Lesson	Skill
1-2	Evaluating Expressions
1-9	Using Tables, Equations, and Graphs
Review, page 60	Graphing in the Coordinate Plane
2-2	Solving Two-Step Equations
3-7	Solving Absolute Value Equations

To remediate students, select from these resources (available for every lesson).
- Online Problems (PowerAlgebra.com)
- Reteaching (All-in-One Teaching Resources)
- Practice (All-in-One Teaching Resources)

Why Students Need These Skills
EVALUATING EXPRESSIONS
Students will evaluate functions for a given input value.

USING TABLES, EQUATIONS, AND GRAPHS
Functions will be graphed by using tables and equations.

GRAPHING IN THE COORDINATE PLANE
Students will graph discrete and continuous functions in coordinate planes.

SOLVING TWO-STEP EQUATIONS
Students will write and solve function rules.

SOLVING ABSOLUTE VALUE EQUATIONS
Students will determine whether a relation is a function using the vertical line test.

Looking Ahead Vocabulary
DEPENDENT Ask students to name other examples of items that are dependent on one another.

RELATION Ask students to write a relation of age and height.

CONTINUOUS Have students draw a continuous graph. Have students draw a graph that is not continuous.

Answers

Get Ready!
1. -7
2. -18
3. 2
4. -1
5–11. See back of book.
12. -3　　　**13.** 66　　　**14.** 6
15. 4　　　**16.** $0, -4$　　　**17.** $3, 7$
18. no solution　　　**19.** $\frac{11}{2}, \frac{3}{2}$
20. Its value is based on the first value.
21. 4
22. There are no breaks in the graph.

Chapter 4 Overview

UbD Understanding by Design

Chapter 4 introduces the topic of functions. In this chapter, students will develop the answers to the Essential Questions posed on the opposite page as they learn the concepts and skills bulleted below.

BIG idea **Functions**

ESSENTIAL QUESTION How can you represent and describe functions?

- Students will represent functions using tables, equations, and graphs.
- Students will use function notation.
- Students will represent arithmetic sequences using function rules.

BIG idea **Modeling**

ESSENTIAL QUESTION Can functions describe real-world situations?

- Graphs will be used to relate two quantities.
- Students will model real-world situations that are continuous and real-world situations that are discrete.

Indiana Academic Standards

A1.1.1 Determine whether a relation represented by a table, graph, words or equation is a function or not a function and translate among tables, graphs, words and equations.

A1.1.2 Identify the domain and range of relations represented by tables, graphs, words, and equations.

A1.2.1 Translate among various representations of linear functions including tables, graphs, words and equations.

A1.2.5 Solve problems that can be modeled using linear equations and inequalities, interpret the solutions, and determine whether the solutions are reasonable.

A1.5.5 Sketch and interpret linear and non-linear graphs representing given situations and identify independent and dependent variables.

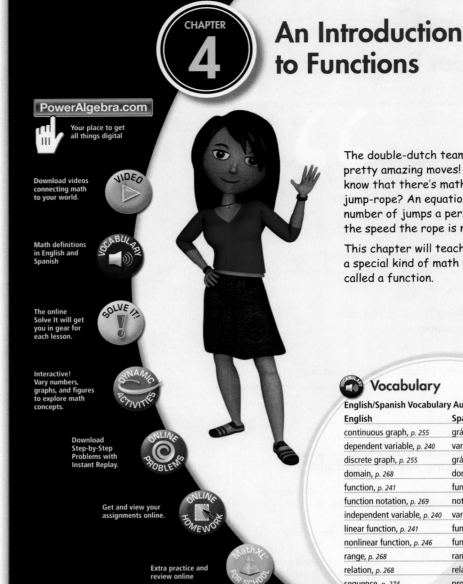

CHAPTER 4

An Introduction to Functions

PowerAlgebra.com

Your place to get all things digital

Download videos connecting math to your world.

Math definitions in English and Spanish

The online Solve It will get you in gear for each lesson.

Interactive! Vary numbers, graphs, and figures to explore math concepts.

Download Step-by-Step Problems with Instant Replay.

Get and view your assignments online.

Extra practice and review online

The double-dutch team has some pretty amazing moves! Did you know that there's math involved in jump-rope? An equation relates the number of jumps a person makes to the speed the rope is moving.

This chapter will teach you about a special kind of math relationship called a function.

Vocabulary

English/Spanish Vocabulary Audio Online:

English	Spanish
continuous graph, *p. 255*	gráfica continua
dependent variable, *p. 240*	variable dependiente
discrete graph, *p. 255*	gráfica discreta
domain, *p. 268*	dominio
function, *p. 241*	función
function notation, *p. 269*	notación de una función
independent variable, *p. 240*	variable independiente
linear function, *p. 241*	función lineal
nonlinear function, *p. 246*	función no lineal
range, *p. 268*	rango
relation, *p. 268*	relación
sequence, *p. 274*	progresión

PowerAlgebra.com

Chapter 4 Overview

Use these online assets to engage your students. There is support for the Solve It and step-by step solutions for Problems.

 Show the student-produced video demonstrating relevant and engaging applications of the new concepts in the chapter.

 Find online definitions for new terms in English and Spanish.

 Start each lesson with an attention-getting Problem. View the Problem online with helpful hints.

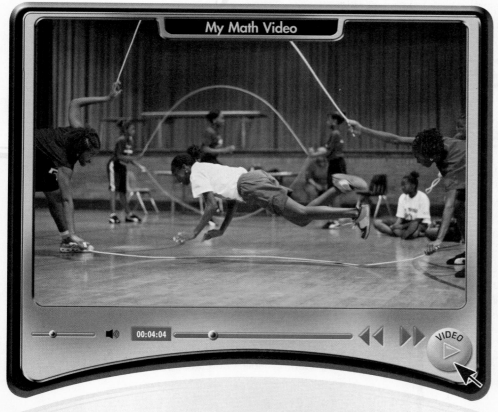

My Math Video

My Math Video

FACILITATE Use this photo to discuss the concept of recognizing patterns. In order to understand relations and functions, students should be prepared to look for patterns in numbers and graphs.

Q How do you jump rope? **[You jump just before the rope hits the ground so that you are in the air when it is touches the ground.]**

Q How can the girls in the photo know when to jump, or bend down? **[Answers may vary. Sample: The girls must recognize the pattern in the timing of the rope and the timing of the jumper.]**

Q What are other examples of situations that occur outdoors where you might recognize a pattern? Explain. **[Answers may vary. Sample: crossing the street: judge the speed of the cars]**

EXTENSION

Provide students with tiles or blocks to create patterns of shapes like the ones shown below. Have students create the shapes in the first row and make a table of the number of blocks contained in each shape. Then, challenge students to predict the number of blocks that will be contained in the 5th version of the pattern. Students should repeat with the other rows of shapes. [9, 25, 36]

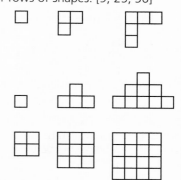

BIG ideas

1 **Functions**
Essential Question How can you represent and describe functions?

2 **Modeling**
Essential Question Can functions describe real-world situations?

Chapter Preview

PowerAlgebra.com | Chapter 4 An Introduction to Functions | 233

 Increase students' depth of knowledge with interactive online activities.

 Show Problems from each lesson solved step by step. Instant replay allows students to go at their own pace when studying online.

 Assign homework to individual students or to an entire class.

 Prepare students for the Mid-Chapter Quiz and Chapter Test with online practice and review.

Math Background

Functions

BIG idea A function is a relationship between variables in which each value of the input variable is associated with a unique value of the output variable. Functions can be represented in a variety of ways, such as graphs, tables, equations, or words. Each representation is particularly useful in certain situations.

ESSENTIAL UNDERSTANDINGS

4-2 The value of one variable may be uniquely determined by the value of another variable. Such relationships may be represented using words, tables, equations, sets of ordered pairs, and graphs.

4-3 to 4-6 Functions (linear and nonlinear) are a special type of relation where each value in the domain is paired with exactly one value in the range. Some functions can be graphed or represented by equations.

4-7 Some sequences have function rules that can be used to find any term of the sequence.

Modeling

BIG idea Many real-world mathematical problems can be represented algebraically. These representations can lead to algebraic solutions. A function that models a real-world situation can then be used to make estimates or predictions about future occurrences.

ESSENTIAL UNDERSTANDINGS

4-1 Graphs can be used to visually represent the relationship between two variable quantities as they change.

4-4 The set of all solutions of an equation forms its graph. A graph may include solutions that do not appear in a table. A real-world graph should show only points that make sense in the given situation.

4-5 Many real-world functional relationships can be represented by equations. Equations can be used to find the solution of given real-world problems.

Linear Functions

Linear functions are functions that can be defined by linear equations. **Linear equations** are first-degree equations. **First-degree equations** are equations in which variables are raised to an exponent of 1, but no higher.

Equations in the form $y = mx + b$ are in slope-intercept form.

Using function notation $f(x)$, the slope-intercept form can be written as a linear function: $f(x) = mx + b$.

When $m = 2$ and $b = 3$, for example, the function is $f(x) = 2x + 3$.

Ordered pairs that are included in the set defined by the function can be generated by assigning values to independent variable x and finding the corresponding dependent values y.

$f(x) = 2x + 3$	$(x, f(x))$
$f(0) = 2(0) + 3 = 0 + 3 = 3$	$(0, 3)$
$f(1) = 2(1) + 3 = 2 + 3 = 5$	$(1, 5)$
$f(2) = 2(2) + 3 = 4 + 3 = 7$	$(2, 7)$
$f(3) = 2(3) + 3 = 6 + 3 = 9$	$(3, 9)$

The pattern represents a linear function.

Common Errors With Linear Functions

Given an equation in the form $x = k$, students might identify it as a linear function.

Although this is a linear equation, it is not a linear function. An equation in this form is represented on a graph by a vertical line.

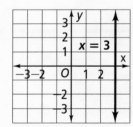

The graph of a linear function must pass the vertical line test: there must not be any vertical line that can include any two points of the graph. A vertical line, like the graph at the right, does not pass the vertical line test at all, since there is a vertical line that can include all its points.

Another test is that for every x-value there is one and only one y. In the case of a vertical line, for every x-value there are an infinite number of y-values.

Functions

You can use tables to determine if patterns describe linear functions or not.

If the differences between consecutive independent values are all equal and the differences between consecutive function values are all equal, then the pattern describes a linear function.

For example:

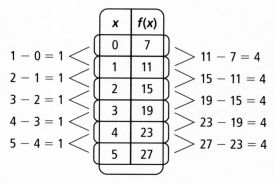

x	$f(x)$
0	7
1	11
2	15
3	19
4	23
5	27

$1 - 0 = 1$ $11 - 7 = 4$
$2 - 1 = 1$ $15 - 11 = 4$
$3 - 2 = 1$ $19 - 15 = 4$
$4 - 3 = 1$ $23 - 19 = 4$
$5 - 4 = 1$ $27 - 23 = 4$

If the differences between consecutive independent values are all equal and the differences between consecutive function values are not all equal, then the pattern does not describe a linear function.

x	$f(x)$
0	1
1	2
2	6
3	10
4	17
5	25

$1 - 0 = 1$ $2 - 1 = 1$
$2 - 1 = 1$ $6 - 2 = 4$
$3 - 2 = 1$ $10 - 6 = 4$
$4 - 3 = 1$ $17 - 10 = 7$
$5 - 4 = 1$ $25 - 17 = 8$

Common Errors With Nonlinear Functions

When using a table with consecutive *x*-values to determine if a function is linear or not, *all* of the differences must be the same. If most of the differences are the same but one or two are not, students who do not check enough values might conclude that the pattern describes a linear function when it does not.

Sequences

An **arithmetic sequence** is a sequence in which the differences between successive values are all the same.

Sequence: 1, −1, −3, −5, −7, . . .

$-1 - 1 = -2$
$-3 - (-1) = -2$
$-5 - (-3) = -2$
$-7 - (-5) = -2$

The differences between successive values are all −2, so the sequence is an arithmetic sequence. The difference −2 is called the **common difference** of the arithmetic sequence.

To write a rule for an arithmetic sequence you can begin by making a table.

Term number, n	1	2	3	4	5
Value of term, A_n	1	−1	−3	−5	−7

The rule for an arithmetic sequence is $A_n = A_1 + (n - 1)d$, where d is the common difference.

You can use this rule to find any term in the sequence. The value of the 10th term in the sequence above is 17.

$$A_{10} = 1 + (9)(-2) = 1 - 18 = -17$$

Common Errors With Sequences

When finding the differences between consecutive values of a sequence, students might subtract succeeding terms instead of preceding terms. For example, in the above sequence this error would yield:

$1 - (-1) = 2$
$-1 - (-3) = 2$
$-3 - (-5) = 2$
$-5 - (-7) = 2$

This indicates that the common difference is 2, when in fact it is −2.

AN INTRODUCTION TO FUNCTIONS
Pacing and Assignment Guide

		TRADITIONAL			BLOCK
Lesson	Teaching Day(s)	Basic	Average	Advanced	Block
4-1	1	Problems 1-3 Exs. 5–15, 17–18, 21–29	Problems 1-3 Exs. 5–13 odd, 14–18, 21–29	Problems 1-3 Exs. 5–13 odd, 14–29	**Day 1** Problems 1-3 Exs. 5–13 odd, 14–18, 21–29
4-2	1	Problems 1-2 Exs. 6–14, 17–18, 21–27	Problems 1-2 Exs. 7–13 odd, 14–18, 21–27	Problems 1-2 Exs. 7–13 odd, 14–27	Problems 1-2 Exs. 7–13 odd, 14–18, 21–27
4-3	1	Problems 1-3 Exs. 6–17, 19–20, 23–29	Problems 1-3 Exs. 7–15 odd, 17–20, 23–29	Problems 1-3 Exs. 7–15 odd, 17–29	**Day 2** Problems 1-3 Exs. 7–15 odd, 17–20, 23–29
4-4	1	Problems 1-4 Exs. 9–32, 33, 36–39, 42–58	Problems 1-4 Exs. 9–31 odd, 33–39, 42–58	Problems 1-4 Exs. 9–31 odd, 33–58	Problems 1-4 Exs. 9–31 odd, 33–39, 42–58
4-5	1	Problems 1-3 Exs. 8–21, 23, 26–27, 29–30, 33–56	Problems 1-3 Exs. 9–21 odd, 22–30, 33–56	Problems 1-3 Exs. 9–21 odd, 22–56	**Day 3** Problems 1-3 Exs. 9–21 odd, 22–30, 33–56
4-6	1	Problems 1-3 Exs. 8–17 all, 26	Problems 1-3 Exs. 9–17 odd, 27, 31–34	Problems 1-3 Exs. 9–17 odd, 27, 31–34, 36	Problems 1-3 Exs. 9–17 odd, 27, 31–34
	2	Problems 4-5 Exs. 18–23 all, 24, 28, 29, 41–50	Problems 4-5 Exs. 19–23 odd, 24–26, 28–30, 35, 41–50	Problems 4-5 Exs. 19–23 odd, 24–26, 28–30, 35, 37–50	**Day 4** Problems 4-5 Exs. 19–23 odd, 24–26, 28–30, 35, 41–50
4-7	1	Problems 1-3 Exs. 9–39 all, 40–52 even, 58–69	Problems 1-3 Exs. 9–39 odd, 40–54, 48–69	Problems 1-3 Exs. 9–39 odd, 40–69	Problems 1-3 Exs. 9–39 odd, 40–54, 48–69
Review	1	Chapter 4 Review	Chapter 4 Review	Chapter 4 Review	**Day 5** Chapter 4 Review
Assess	1	Chapter 4 Test	Chapter 4 Test	Chapter 4 Test	Chapter 4 Test
Total		10 Days	10 Days	10 Days	5 Days

Note: Pacing does not include Concept Bytes and other feature pages.

Resources

	For the Chapter	4-1	4-2	4-3	4-4	4-5	4-6	4-7
Planning								
Teacher Center Online Planner & Grade Book	I	I	I	I	I	I	I	I
Interactive Learning & Guided Instruction								
My Math Video	I							
Solve It!		I TM	I TM	I TM	I TM	I TM	I TM	I TM
Student Companion (SP)*		P M	P M	P M	P M	P M	P M	
Vocabulary Support		I P M	I P M	I P M	I P M	I P M	I P M	I P M
Got It? Support		I P	I P	I P	I P	I P	I P	I P
Dynamic Activity							I	
Online Problems		I	I	I	I	I	I	I
Additional Problems		M	M	M	M	M	M	M
English Language Learner Support (TR)		E P M	E P M	E P M	E P M	E P M	E P M	E P M
Activities, Games, and Puzzles		E M	E M	E M	E M	E M	E M	E M
Teaching With TI Technology With CD-ROM								
TI-Nspire™ Support CD-ROM		✓	✓	✓	✓	✓	✓	✓
Lesson Check & Practice								
Student Companion (SP)*		P M	P M	P M	P M	P M	P M	P M
Lesson Check Support		I P	I P	I P	I P	I P	I P	I P
Practice and Problem Solving Workbook (SP)		P	P	P	P	P	P	P
Think About a Plan (TR)*		E P M	E P M	E P M	E P M	E P M	E P M	E P M
Practice Form G (TR)*		E P M	E P M	E P M	E P M	E P M	E P M	E P M
Standardized Test Prep (TR)*		P M	P M	P M	P M	P M	P M	P M
Practice Form K (TR)*		E P M	E P M	E P M	E P M	E P M	E P M	E P M
Extra Practice	E M							
Find the Errors!	M							
Enrichment (TR)		E P M	E P M	E P M	E P M	E P M	E P M	E P M
Answers and Solutions CD-ROM	✓	✓	✓	✓	✓	✓	✓	✓
Assess & Remediate								
ExamView CD-ROM	✓	✓	✓	✓	✓	✓	✓	✓
Lesson Quiz		I TM	I TM	I TM	I TM	I TM	I TM	I TM
Quizzes and Tests Form G (TR)*	E P M			E P M				E P M
Quizzes and Tests Form K (TR)*	E P M			E P M				E P M
Reteaching (TR)*		E P M	E P M	E P M	E P M	E P M	E P M	E P M
Performance Tasks (TR)*	P M							
Cumulative Review (TR)*	P M							
Progress Monitoring Assessments	I P M							

(TR) Available in All-In-One Teaching Resources   * Spanish available

1 Interactive Learning

Solve It!
PURPOSE To interpret a graph that reflects the changing relationship between two variable quantities

PROCESS Students may visualize the filling of each container or may interpret the relationship in each graph to visualize the amount of water contained.

FACILITATE
Q If each of the first two containers holds the same amount of water, which container would have the greater water height? Explain. **[The second container would have the greater water height since the diameter of the first container is greater.]**

Q Does a constant increase in volume result in the same increase in height in the third container? Explain. **[No, at the top, constant increase in volume results in slower increase in height.]**

ANSWER See Solve It in Answers on next page.
CONNECT THE MATH In the Solve It, students use a graph to compare relationships among containers. In this lesson, students will interpret characteristics of graphs to describe a real-world situation.

2 Guided Instruction

Problem 1

Q Does the person blowing up the balloon pause the same amount of time for each breath? Explain. **[Yes, the horizontal-line portions of the graph appear to be the same length.]**

4-1 Using Graphs to Relate Two Quantities

Indiana Academic Standard
A1.5.5 Sketch and interpret linear and non-linear graphs representing given situations and identify independent and dependent variables.

Objective To represent mathematical relationships using graphs

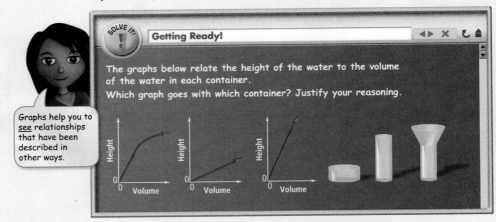

Graphs help you to <u>see</u> relationships that have been described in other ways.

Getting Ready!

The graphs below relate the height of the water to the volume of the water in each container.
Which graph goes with which container? Justify your reasoning.

As you may have noticed in the Solve It, the change in the height of the water as the volume increases is related to the shape of the container.

Essential Understanding You can use graphs to visually represent the relationship between two variable quantities as they both change.

Think
How can you analyze the relationship in a graph?
Read the titles. The axis titles tell you what variables are related. The graph itself represents the relationship as the variables change.

Problem 1 Analyzing a Graph

The graph shows the volume of air in a balloon as you blow it up, until it pops. What are the variables? Describe how the variables are related at various points on the graph.

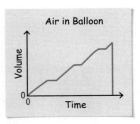

Air in Balloon

The variables are volume and time. The volume increases each time you blow, and it stays constant each time you pause to breathe. When the balloon pops in the middle of the fourth blow, the volume decreases to 0.

234 **Chapter 4** An Introduction to Functions

4-1 Preparing to Teach

BIGidea **Modeling** **UbD**

ESSENTIAL UNDERSTANDINGS
- Graphs can be used to visually represent the relationship between two variable quantities as they each change.
- Tables and graphs can both show relationships between variables.

Math Background
Functions can be represented in various ways, including verbal descriptions, equations, tables, and graphs. A graph in the coordinate plane is the most immediately understandable way of showing how one variable changes in respect to another variable. A table is often useful to provide points for a sketched outline of a graph.

In this lesson, students use mathematics to represent real-world situations from daily life. By graphing functions, students explore the idea of change, including changes in speed,

altitude, distance, volume, time, and other variable quantities. In addition to change, students investigate relationships between quantities by using graphs.

Support Student Learning
Use the **Algebra 1 Companion** to engage and support students during instructions. See Lesson Resources at the end of this lesson for details.

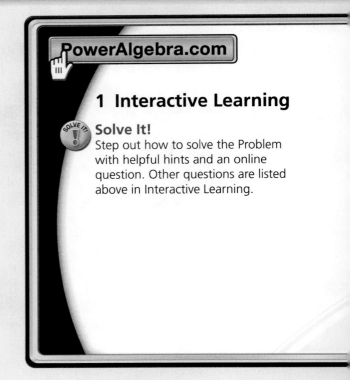

PowerAlgebra.com

1 Interactive Learning

Solve It!
Step out how to solve the Problem with helpful hints and an online question. Other questions are listed above in Interactive Learning.

Got It? **1.** What are the variables in each graph? Describe how the variables are related at various points on the graph.

a.

Board Length

b.
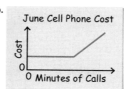
June Cell Phone Cost

Got It?

Q In 1a, what does the vertical line segment represent in terms of the length of the board? in terms of the time that passes? **[The board is cut to a shorter length. Each cut is more or less instantaneous.]**

Q How many times is the board cut? How many pieces of board are there at the end of the time shown? **[three cuts; four pieces of board]**

Q In 1b, what does the horizontal line portion of the graph represent? **[This cell phone plan provides a set number of minutes for a fixed cost.]**

Tables and graphs can both show relationships between variables. Data from a table are often displayed using a graph to visually represent the relationship.

Problem 2 **Matching a Table and a Graph**

Multiple Choice A band allowed fans to download its new video from its Web site. The table shows the total number of downloads after 1, 2, 3, and 4 days. Which graph could represent the data shown in the table?

Video Downloads

Day	Total Downloads
1	346
2	1011
3	3455
4	10,426

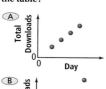
Ⓐ

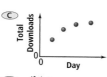
Ⓒ

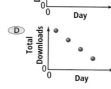
Ⓑ Ⓓ

Know	Need	Plan
The relationship represented by a table	A graph that could represent the relationship	Compare the pattern of changes in the table to each graph.

In the table, the total number of downloads increases each day, and each increase is noticeably greater than the previous increase. So the graph should rise from left to right, and each rise should be steeper than the previous rise. The correct answer is B.

Problem 2

Q Should the horizontal distance between the points shown in the correct graph be constant? Explain. **[Yes, the increase in the day column is always one.]**

Q Should the vertical distance between the points shown in the correct graph be constant? Explain. **[No, the increase in the Total Downloads column is not constant.]**

Q Would a graph of only the new downloads each day be similar to or different from the graph of the total downloads each day? Explain. **[It would be similar to the graph of the total downloads because the increase in the number of new downloads each day is greater than the previous increase.]**

2 Guided Instruction

 Each Problem is worked out and supported online.

Problem 1
Analyzing a Graph
Animated

Problem 2
Matching a Table and a Graph
Animated

Problem 3
Sketching a Graph
Animated

Support in Algebra 1 Companion
• Vocabulary
• Key Concepts
• Got It?

Answers

Solve It!
The first graph describes the third container. The second graph describes the first container. The third graph describes the second container.

Got It?
1. a. Time, length; the length of the board remains constant for a time before another piece is cut off.

  b. Time, cost; the cost remains constant for a certain number of minutes.

Got It?

Q Should the horizontal distance between the points shown in the correct graph be constant? Explain. **[Yes, the increase in the use column is always 1 use.]**

Q Should the vertical distance between the points shown in the correct graph be constant? Explain. **[Yes, the decrease in the ounces column is constant.]**

Q How can you determine by visual inspection that choice A is not correct? **[Choice A is not correct because it indicates that the amount of spray is zero after 3 uses.]**

Q According to the data, approximately how many uses does the can of bug repellent contain? Explain. **[Each spray uses 0.2 ounces and there are 5 ounces in the can, so there are approximately 25 uses.]**

Problem 3

Q Should the "rising" section of the graph be a straight line? Explain. **[No, the increases in height slow down as the engine begins to burn out.]**

Q Should the "falling slowly" section of the graph be a straight line? Explain. **[Yes, the decrease in height remains constant for each constant increase in seconds.]**

Got It?   VISUAL LEARNERS

Q Visualize a photographer standing in front of the swing and snapping a picture every quarter-second, and then arranging all the pictures in a row. What would it be like to trace the path of the swing across the row of pictures? **[The swing would seem to travel in a wavelike pattern up and down across the pictures.]**

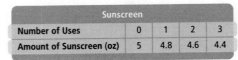

Got It? 2. The table shows the amount of sunscreen left in a can based on the number of times the sunscreen has been used. Which graph could represent the data shown in the table?

Sunscreen				
Number of Uses	0	1	2	3
Amount of Sunscreen (oz)	5	4.8	4.6	4.4

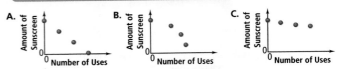

In Problem 1, the number of downloads, which is on the vertical axis of each graph, depends on the day, which is on the horizontal axis. When one quantity depends on another, show the independent quantity on the horizontal axis and the dependent quantity on the vertical axis.

Problem 3 Sketching a Graph

Rocketry A model rocket rises quickly and then slows to a stop as its fuel burns out. It begins to fall quickly until the parachute opens, after which it falls slowly back to Earth. What sketch of a graph could represent the height of the rocket during its flight? Label each section.

Think
How can you get started?
Identify the two variables that are being related, such as *height* and *time*. Then look for key words that describe the relationship, such as *rises quickly* or *falls slowly*.

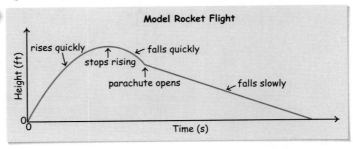

Got It? 3. a. Suppose you start to swing yourself on a playground swing. You move back and forth and swing higher in the air. Then you slowly swing to a stop. What sketch of a graph could represent how your height from the ground might change over time? Label each section.

b. Reasoning If you jumped from the swing instead of slowly swinging to a stop, how would the graph in part (a) be different? Explain.

Additional Problems

1. The graph below shows the amount of gasoline in Jamie's car after she fills up her tank. What are the variables? Describe how they are related at various points on the graph.

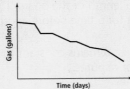

ANSWER The variables are the amount of gas (in gallons) and time (in days). The amount of gas decreases each time Jamie drives somewhere and stays constant when she is not driving.

2. The table shows the total number of customers at a car wash after 1, 2, 3, and 4 days of its grand opening. Which graph could represent the data shown in the table?

Car Wash Grand Opening

Day	Total Customers
1	61
2	125
3	177
4	242

A.

B.

C.

D.

ANSWER A

3. When Malcolm jogs on the treadmill, he gradually increases his speed until he reaches a certain level. Then he jogs at this level for several minutes. Then he slows to a stop and stretches. After this he increases to a speed that is slightly lower than before and jogs at this speed for a short while before slowing to a stop again. What is a possible sketch of a graph that shows Malcolm's jogging speed during his workout? Label each section.

ANSWER

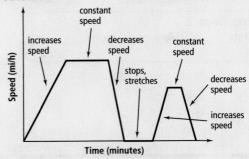

Lesson Check

Do you know HOW?

1. What are the variables in the graph at the right? Use the graph to describe how the variables are related.

2. Describe the relationship between time and temperature in the table below.

Time (number of hours after noon)	1	3	5	7
Temperature (°F)	61	62	58	51

Do you UNDERSTAND?

3. Match one of the labeled segments in the graph below with each of the following verbal descriptions: *rising slowly*, *constant*, and *falling quickly*.

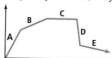

4. **Reasoning** Describe a real-world relationship that could be represented by the graph sketched above.

Practice and Problem-Solving Exercises

 Practice

What are the variables in each graph? Describe how the variables are related at various points on the graph. ◀ See Problem 1.

5.

6.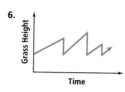

7.

Match each graph with its related table. Explain your answers. ◀ See Problem 2.

8.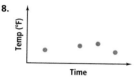

9.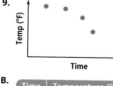

10.

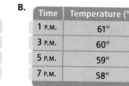

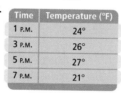

A.
Time	Temperature (°F)
1 P.M.	91°
3 P.M.	89°
5 P.M.	81°
7 P.M.	64°

B.
Time	Temperature (°F)
1 P.M.	61°
3 P.M.	60°
5 P.M.	59°
7 P.M.	58°

C.
Time	Temperature (°F)
1 P.M.	24°
3 P.M.	26°
5 P.M.	27°
7 P.M.	21°

---

3 Lesson Check

Do you know HOW?

- If students have difficulty with Exercise 1, then suggest that they think of "fuel used" as being "fuel used to travel 20 miles." Do that so students will be able to attach possible numeric values to the points on the graph.

Do you UNDERSTAND?

- If students have difficulty with Exercise 4, then ask them to verbalize how each of the five sections of the graph is representative of their real-world relationship.

Close

Q What does a nonvertical, nonhorizontal straight line on a graph imply about the two variables? **[A straight line implies that the change in both variables remains constant.]**

Answers

Got It? (continued)

2. C

3. a. Answers may vary. Sample:

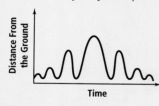

b. The end of the graph would decrease sharply.

Lesson Check

1. Car weight, fuel used; the heavier the car, the more the fuel used.

2. The temperature rises slightly in the first 2 h and then falls over the next 4 h.

3. rising slowly: B; constant: C; falling quickly: D

4. Answers may vary. Sample: the depth of water in a stream bed over time

Practice and Problem-Solving Exercises

5. Number of pounds, total cost; as the number of pounds increases, the total cost goes up, at first quickly and then more slowly.

6. Time, grass height; the grass grows and you cut it, then it grows again and you cut it. This is repeated three times.

7. Area painted, paint in can; the more you paint, the less paint left in the can. You are using the paint at a constant rate.

8. C   **9.** A   **10.** B

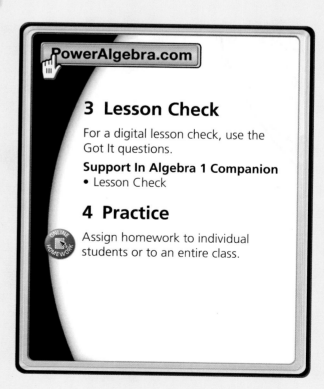

3 Lesson Check

For a digital lesson check, use the Got It questions.

Support In Algebra 1 Companion
- Lesson Check

4 Practice

Assign homework to individual students or to an entire class.

4 Practice

ASSIGNMENT GUIDE

Basic: 5–15, 17–18

Average: 5–13 odd, 14–18

Advanced: 5–13 odd, 14–20

Standardized Test Prep: 21–23

Mixed Review: 24–29

Reasoning exercises have blue headings.

Applications exercises have red headings.

EXERCISE 17: Use the Think About a Plan worksheet in the **Practice and Problem Solving Workbook** (also available in the Teaching Resources in print and online) to further support students' development in becoming independent learners.

HOMEWORK QUICK CHECK

To check students' understanding of key skills and concepts, go over Exercises 7, 11, 14, 17, and 18.

Sketch a graph to represent each situation. Label each section.

 See Problem 3.

11. hours of daylight each day over the course of one year

12. your distance from the ground as you ride a Ferris wheel

13. your pulse rate as you watch a scary movie

B Apply

14. Think About a Plan The *shishi-odoshi*, a popular Japanese garden ornament, was originally designed to frighten away deer. Using water, it makes a sharp rap each time a bamboo tube rises. Sketch a graph that could represent the volume of water in the bamboo tube as it operates.

Tube begins filling.   Full tube begins falling.   Tube falls and empties water.   Tube rises and hits rock, making noise.

- What quantities vary in this situation?
- How are these quantities related?

15. Error Analysis T-shirts cost $12.99 each for the first 5 shirts purchased. Each additional T-shirt costs $4.99 each. Describe and correct the error in the graph at the right that represents the relationship between total cost and number of shirts purchased.

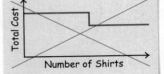

16. Open-Ended Describe a real-world relationship between the area of a rectangle and its width, as the width varies and the length stays the same. Sketch a graph to show this relationship.

17. Skiing Sketch a graph of each situation. Are the graphs the same? Explain.
 a. your speed as you travel on a ski lift from the bottom of a ski slope to the top
 b. your speed as you ski from the top of a ski slope to the bottom

18. Reasoning The diagram at the left below shows a portion of a bike trail.
 a. Explain whether the graph below is a reasonable representation of how the speed might change for the rider of the blue bike.

Blue Bike's Speed

 b. Sketch two graphs that could represent a bike's speed over time. Sketch one graph for the blue bike, and the other for the red bike.

Answers

Practice and Problem-Solving Exercises
(continued)

11. Answers may vary. Sample:

12. Answers may vary. Sample:

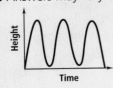

13. Answers may vary. Sample:

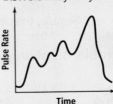

14. Answers may vary. Sample:

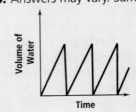

15. The graph shown represents the relationship between the number of shirts and the cost per shirt, not the total cost.

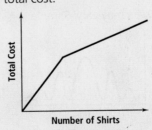

16. Check students' work.

Challenge

19. Track The sketch at the right shows the distance three runners travel during a race. Describe what occurs at times A, B, C, and D. In what order do the runners finish? Explain.

Three-Person Race

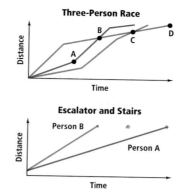

20. Reasoning The graph at the right shows the vertical distance traveled as Person A walks up a set of stairs and Person B walks up an escalator next to the stairs. Copy the graph. Then draw a line that could represent the vertical distance traveled as Person C rides the escalator standing still. Explain your reasoning.

Escalator and Stairs

Standardized Test Prep

 SAT/ACT

21. The graph at the right shows your distance from home as you walk to the bus stop, wait for the bus, and then ride the bus to school. Which point represents a time that you are waiting for the bus?

Distance From Home

Ⓐ A   Ⓒ C
Ⓑ B   Ⓓ D

22. What is the solution of $-2x < 4$?

Ⓕ $x < 2$ Ⓖ $x > 2$ Ⓗ $x < -2$ Ⓘ $x > -2$

 Short Response

23. You earn $8.50 per hour. Then you receive a raise to $9.35 per hour. Find the percent increase. Then find your pay per hour if you receive the same percent increase two more times. Show your work.

Mixed Review

Let $A = \{-3, 1, 4\}$, $B = \{x \mid x$ is an odd number greater than -2 and less than 10$\}$, and $C = \{1, 4, 7, 12\}$. Find each union or intersection.

◆ See Lesson 3-8.

24. $A \cup B$ **25.** $A \cap B$ **26.** $B \cup C$ **27.** $A \cap C$

Get Ready! To prepare for Lesson 4-2, do Exercises 28 and 29.

Use a table, an equation, and a graph to represent each relationship. ◆ See Lesson 1-9.

28. Donald is 4 years older than Connie.   **29.** You make 3 cards per hour.

17. No, they are not the same. Your speed on the ski lift is constant. Your speed going downhill is not.

a.

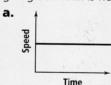

b.

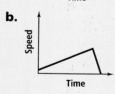

18. a. No, the graph is not reasonable. Your speed should decrease as you ride uphill.

b.

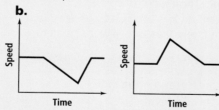

19. The three runners start at the same time. At time A, one runner has a fast start, and the other two are a little slower. At B, the second-place runner catches up to the first-place runner and passes the first-place runner in order to win at time C. At C, the runner that was in third place catches up to the original first-place runner to finish second. At D, only the original first-place runner remains in the race.

20.

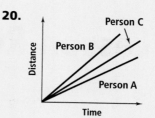

21. B   **22.** I

23. [2] $\frac{9.35 - 8.50}{8.50} = 0.10$, or a 10% increase. Another 10% increase would bring your hourly wage to $1.1(9.35) = 10.285$, or $10.29. One further 10% increase would bring your rate to $1.1(10.29) = 11.3135$, or $11.32.

[1] correct methods used with one minor computational error

24. $\{-3, -1, 1, 3, 4, 5, 7, 9\}$

25. $\{1\}$

26. $\{-1, 1, 3, 4, 5, 7, 9, 12\}$

27. $\{1, 4\}$

28.

Connie's Age	Donald's Age
0	4
1	5
2	6
3	7

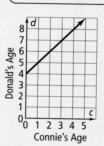

$d = c + 4$

29.

Time (hours)	Number of Cards
0	0
1	3
2	6
3	9

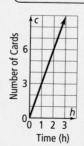

$c = 3h$

4-1 Lesson Resources

Differentiated Remediation

Additional Instructional Support

Algebra 1 Companion

Students can use the **Algebra 1 Companion** worktext (4 pages) as you teach the lesson. Use the Companion to support

- New Vocabulary
- Key Concepts
- Got It for each Problem
- Lesson Check

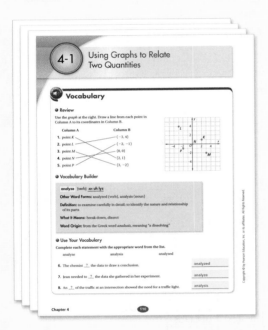

ELL Support

Connect to Prior Knowledge Ask students what they have learned about graphs. Remind them of previous lessons if necessary. Ask students when they have used graphs. Encourage students to provide ideas of places they might see a graph, such as a textbook, a newspaper, the Internet, or a magazine. Have students contribute as you write a list on the board of the characteristics of graphs. What do they notice when they see a graph? What will they expect or usually see?

5 Assess & Remediate

Lesson Quiz

1. The graph below shows the height of a hot air balloon during a trip. What are the variables? Describe how they are related at various points on the graph.

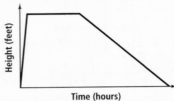

2. Do you UNDERSTAND? The table shows the total number of people in attendance at a drama club after 1, 2, 3, and 4 weeks. Sketch a graph that could represent the data.

Drama Club

Week	1	2	3	4
Total in Attendance	4	9	15	33

ANSWERS TO LESSON QUIZ

1. The variables are height and time. The balloon rises quickly to a certain height, levels off for a while, and then gradually returns to earth.

2.

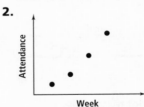

PRESCRIPTION FOR REMEDIATION

Use the student work on the Lesson Quiz to prescribe a differentiated review assignment.

Points	Differentiated Remediation
0	Intervention
1	On-level
2	Extension

PowerAlgebra.com

5 Assess & Remediate

Assign the Lesson Quiz. Appropriate intervention, practice, or enrichment is automatically generated based on student performance.

Intervention

- **Reteaching** (2 pages) Provides reteaching and practice exercises for the key lesson concepts. Use with struggling students or absent students.
- **English Language Learner Support** Helps students develop and reinforce mathematical vocabulary and key concepts.

All-in-One Resources/Online
Reteaching

All-in-One Resources/Online
English Language Learner Support

Differentiated Remediation continued

On-Level

- **Practice** (2 pages) Provides extra practice for each lesson. For simpler practice exercises, use the Form K Practice pages found in the All-in-One Teaching Resources and online.

- **Think About a Plan** Helps students develop specific problem-solving skills and strategies by providing scaffolded guiding questions.

- **Standardized Test Prep** Focuses on all major exercises, all major question types, and helps students prepare for the high-stakes assessments.

Extension

- **Enrichment** Provides students with interesting problems and activities that extend the concepts of the lesson.

- **Activities, Games, and Puzzles** Worksheets that can be used for concepts development, enrichment, and for fun!

Practice and Problem Solving WKBK/ All-in-One Resources/Online
Practice page 1

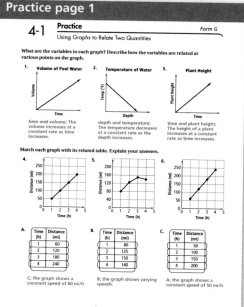

Practice and Problem Solving WKBK/ All-in-One Resources/Online
Practice page 2

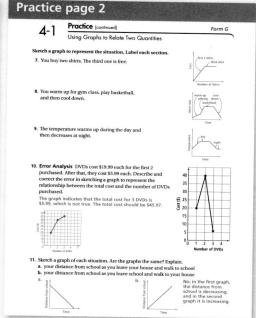

All-in-One Resources/Online
Enrichment

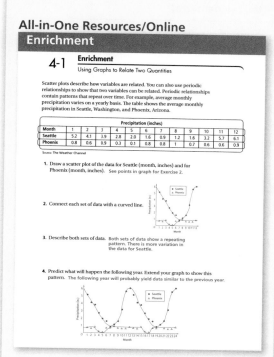

Practice and Problem Solving WKBK/ All-in-One Resources/Online
Think About a Plan

Practice and Problem Solving WKBK/ All-in-One Resources/Online
Standardized Test Prep

Online Teacher Resource Center
Activities, Games, and Puzzles

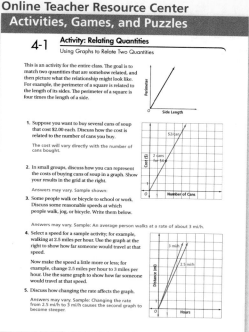

1 Interactive Learning

Solve It!

PURPOSE To identify pairs of variables in which a change in one variable leads to a change in the other variable

PROCESS Students may identify all variables in the picture, and then look for relationships between pairs of the identified variables.

FACILITATE

Q Is the number of children playing at a playground a constant or a variable quantity? Explain. **[A variable quantity because the number of children at the playground will change.]**

Q What other variables might affect the number of children at the playground? **[the time of day or the temperature]**

ANSWER See Solve It in Answers on next page.

CONNECT THE MATH Students see a situation where the value of one variable may be uniquely matched with the value of another variable, such as in the relationship between the time of day and the number of children on the playground. In this lesson, students will learn about relationships where one variable is dependent on another variable.

2 Guided Instruction

Problem 1

Q How do you determine the perimeter of a rectangular figure? **[You add the lengths of all four sides.]**

4-2 Patterns and Linear Functions

Indiana Academic Standards
A1.2.1 Translate among various representations of linear functions including tables, graphs, words and equations.
A1.5.5 Sketch and interpret linear and non-linear graphs representing given situations and identify independent and dependent variables.

Objective To identify and represent patterns that describe linear functions

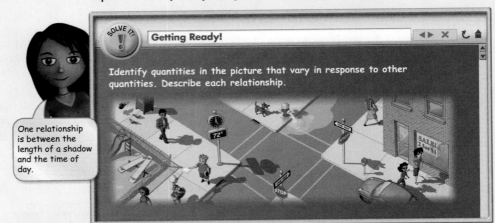

Getting Ready!

Identify quantities in the picture that vary in response to other quantities. Describe each relationship.

One relationship is between the length of a shadow and the time of day.

Lesson Vocabulary
- dependent variable
- independent variable
- input
- output
- function
- linear function

In the Solve It, you identified variables whose value *depends* on the value of another variable. In a relationship between variables, the **dependent variable** changes in response to another variable, the **independent variable.** Values of the independent variable are called **inputs.** Values of the dependent variable are called **outputs.**

Essential Understanding The value of one variable may be uniquely determined by the value of another variable. Such relationships may be represented using tables, words, equations, sets of ordered pairs, and graphs.

Problem 1 Representing a Geometric Relationship

In the diagram below, what is the relationship between the number of rectangles and the perimeter of the figure they form? Represent this relationship using a table, words, an equation, and a graph.

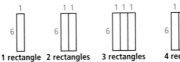

1 rectangle   2 rectangles   3 rectangles   4 rectangles

BIG idea Functions UbD

ESSENTIAL UNDERSTANDINGS
- The value of one variable may be uniquely determined by the value of another variable.
- Such relationships may be represented using words, tables, equations, sets of ordered pairs, and graphs.

Math Background

This lesson extends the representation of functions from graphs into verbal descriptions, tables, and equations. Besides dealing with functions in all these forms, students need to learn that all these forms are essentially the same thing: they all represent some kind of rule that maps a value of an input variable to a value of an output variable. The same rule that generates an equation is the rule that generates a table and a graph. Students also need to understand how independent and dependent variables are handled in equations,

graphs, and tables. They should understand that calling the independent variable x and the dependent variable y is a customary representation but not the only one. They should understand the idea of an ordered pair in which every y-value is the output value of a function applied to an x-value.

Support Student Learning

Use the **Algebra 1 Companion** to engage and support students during instructions. See Lesson Resources at the end of this lesson for details.

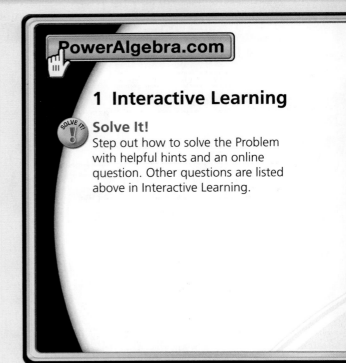

PowerAlgebra.com

1 Interactive Learning

Solve It!
Step out how to solve the Problem with helpful hints and an online question. Other questions are listed above in Interactive Learning.

Think

Which variable is the dependent variable?
The perimeter *depends* on the number of rectangles, so perimeter is the dependent variable.

Step 1 Make a table. Use *x* as the independent variable and *y* as the dependent variable.
Let *x* = the number of rectangles.
Let *y* = the perimeter of the figure.

Write each pair of input and output values *x* and *y* as an ordered pair (*x, y*).

Number of Rectangles, x	Perimeter, y	Ordered Pair (x, y)
1	2(1) + 2(6) = 14	(1, 14)
2	2(2) + 2(6) = 16	(2, 16)
3	2(3) + 2(6) = 18	(3, 18)
4	2(4) + 2(6) = 20	(4, 20)

Step 2 Look for a pattern in the table. Describe the pattern in words so you can write an equation to represent the relationship.

Words Multiply the number of rectangles in each figure by 2 to get the total length of the top and bottom sides of the combined figure. Then add 2(6), or 12, for the total length of the left and right sides of the combined figure to get the entire perimeter.

Equation $y = 2x + 12$

Step 3 Use the table to make a graph.

With a graph, you can see a pattern formed by the relationship between the number of rectangles and the perimeter of the combined figure.

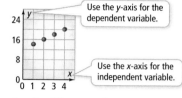

Use the y-axis for the dependent variable.

Use the x-axis for the independent variable.

✓ **Got It?** 1. In the diagram below, what is the relationship between the number of triangles and the perimeter of the figure they form? Represent this relationship using a table, words, an equation, and a graph.

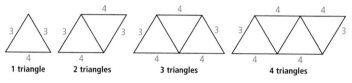

| 1 triangle | 2 triangles | 3 triangles | 4 triangles |

You can describe the relationship in Problem 1 by saying that the perimeter is a function of the number of rectangles. A **function** is a relationship that pairs each input value with exactly one output value.

You have seen that one way to represent a function is with a graph. A **linear function** is a function whose graph is a nonvertical line or part of a nonvertical line.

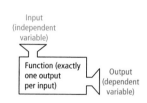

Input (independent variable)

Function (exactly one output per input)

Output (dependent variable)

Problem 1 (continued)

Q What pattern exists in the *x*-values of the table? **[The *x*-values constantly increase by 1.]**

Q What pattern exists in the *y*-values of the table? **[The *y*-values constantly increase by 2.]**

Q What pattern can you use to determine a *y*-value in the table if you are given an *x*-value? **[Multiply the *x*-value by 2 and then add 12.]**

Q How would the graph change if the dependent variable represented the area of the figure? Explain. **[The graph would be a steeper straight line, because the *y*-values would increase at a faster rate.]**

Got It?   VISUAL LEARNERS

After students have completed the graph for this relationship, ask them to explain why the points on the graph should not be connected with a straight line.

---

2 Guided Instruction

Each Problem is worked out and supported online.

Support in Algebra 1 Companion
• Vocabulary
• Key Concepts
• Got It?

Problem 1
Representing a Geometric Relationship
Animated

Problem 2
Representing a Linear Function
Animated

Answers

Solve It!
Answers may vary. Samples: The temperature on the thermometer will vary with the amount of sunshine falling on it. The distance traveled by the joggers will increase with time. The amount of water discharged from the fire hydrant will increase with time until the leak is repaired.

Got It?
1.

Number of Triangles	1	2	3	4
Perimeter	10	14	18	22

Multiply the number of triangles by 4 and add 6; $y = 4x + 6$.

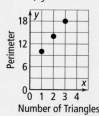

Number of Triangles

Problem 2

Q What is the size of the memory chip on the camera? Explain. **[It is a 512 MB chip. That is how much memory is available when no photos have been taken.]**

Q How much memory does each picture require when it is be stored? Explain. **[Because the amount of available memory decreases to 509 MB when 1 photo is stored, you can determine that one photo requires 3 MB of memory.]**

Q What equation represents the maximum number of photos that can be stored on your camera? Explain. **[512 − 3x = 0; This equation represents the number of photos that would result in no more available memory.]**

Got It?

VISUAL LEARNERS

Make certain that students understand that the x-value of 1 being paired with both 4 and 8 as a y-value prevents the set of ordered pairs from being a function in 2b. Then have students make a graph of the ordered pairs. Ask students to note the physical relationship of the points (1, 4) and (1, 8).

Problem 2 Representing a Linear Function

Photography The table shows the relationship between the number of photos x you take and the amount of memory y in megabytes (MB) left on your camera's memory chip. Is the relationship a linear function? Describe the relationship using words, an equation, and a graph.

Camera Memory

Number of Photos, x	Memory (MB), y
0	512
1	509
2	506
3	503

Think

How can you tell whether a relationship in a table is a function?
If each input is paired with *exactly* one output, then the relationship is a function.

Know
The amount of memory left given the number of pictures taken, as shown in the table

Need
Other representations that describe the relationship

Plan
Look for a pattern that you can describe in words to write an equation. Make a graph to show the pattern.

The amount y of memory left is uniquely determined by the number x of photos you take. You can see this in the table above, where each input value of x corresponds to exactly one output value of y. So y is a function of x. To describe the relationship, look at how y changes for each change in x in the table below.

Camera Memory

Memory is 512 MB before any photos are taken.

The independent variable x increases by 1 each time.

Number of Photos, x	Memory (MB), y
0	512
1	509
2	506
3	503

The dependent variable y decreases by 3 each time x increases by 1.

Words The amount of memory left on the chip is 512 minus the quantity 3 times the number of photos taken.

Equation $y = 512 - 3x$

Graph You can use the table to make a graph. The points lie on a line, so the relationship between the number of photos taken and the amount of memory remaining is a linear function.

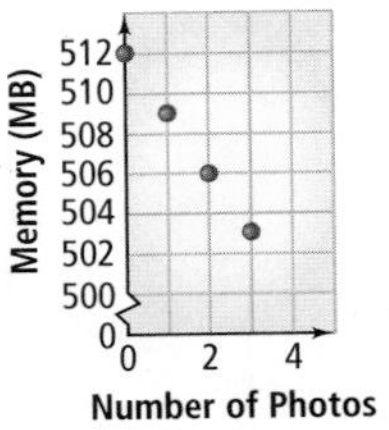

[Graph: Memory (MB) vs Number of Photos, showing points descending from 512]

✓ **Got It?** **2. a.** Is the relationship in the table below a linear function? Describe the relationship using words, an equation, and a graph.

Input, x	0	1	2	3
Output, y	8	10	12	14

b. Reasoning Does the set of ordered pairs (0, 2), (1, 4), (3, 5), and (1, 8) represent a linear function? Explain.

242 Chapter 4 An Introduction to Functions

Additional Problems

1. In the diagram below, what is the relationship between the figure number and the number of squares in the figure? How can it be represented?

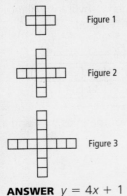

Figure 1

Figure 2

Figure 3

ANSWER $y = 4x + 1$

2. The table shows the amount of water y in a tank after x minutes of being drained. Is the relationship a function? Describe the relationship using words and an equation.

Car Wash Grand Opening

Time, x (minutes)	Water, y (gallons)
0	440
1	428
2	416
3	404

ANSWER The relationship is a function. The amount of water in gallons left in the tank is 440 minus 12 times the number of minutes, or $y = 440 - 12x$.

Answers

Got It? (continued)

2. a. Yes; the value of y is 8 more than twice the value of x; $y = 2x + 8$.

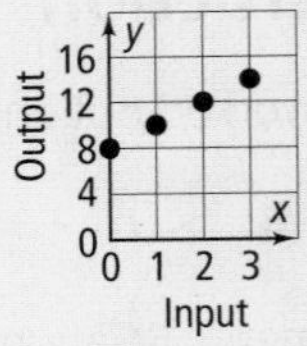

b. No; the input value 1 has more than one output value.

Lesson Check

Do you know HOW?

1. Graph each set of ordered pairs. Use words to describe the pattern shown in the graph.
   a. (0, 0), (1, 1), (2, 2), (3, 3), (4, 4)
   b. (0, 8), (1, 6), (2, 4), (3, 2), (4, 0)
   c. (3, 0), (3, 1), (3, 2), (3, 3), (3, 4)

2. Use the diagram below. Copy and complete the table showing the relationship between the number of squares and the perimeter of the figure they form.

Number of Squares	Perimeter
1	4
2	6
3	■
4	■
10	■
■	62
n	■

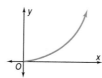

1 square   2 squares   3 squares

Do you UNDERSTAND?

3. **Vocabulary** The amount of toothpaste in a tube decreases each time you brush your teeth. Identify the independent and dependent variables in this relationship.

4. **Reasoning** Tell whether each set of ordered pairs in Exercise 1 represents a function. Justify your answers.

5. **Reasoning** Does the graph below represent a linear function? Explain.

Practice and Problem-Solving Exercises

A Practice

For each diagram, find the relationship between the number of shapes and the perimeter of the figure they form. Represent this relationship using a table, words, an equation, and a graph.

◀ See Problem 1.

6.

1 pentagon   2 pentagons   3 pentagons

7.

1 hexagon   2 hexagons   3 hexagons

For each table, determine whether the relationship is a linear function. Then represent the relationship using words, an equation, and a graph.

◀ See Problem 2.

8.
x	y
0	5
1	8
2	11
3	14

9.
x	y
0	−3
1	2
2	7
3	12

10.
x	y
0	43
1	32
2	21
3	10

---

3 Lesson Check

Do you know HOW?

- If students have difficulty with Exercise 2, then encourage them to look for a pattern, describe the pattern in words, and then write an equation to represent the pattern to complete the missing numbers in the table.

Do you UNDERSTAND?

- In Exercise 3, if students have trouble naming dependent and independent variables, suggest that "independent" means "free to choose." Are you free to choose when you brush your teeth? Is the toothpaste free to choose how much of it gets used?

Close

Q What are the ways to represent the relationship between an independent and dependent variable? **[You can represent the relationship using words, a table, a graph, and an equation.]**

Lesson Check

1. a.

   y increases by 1 for each increase of 1 for x.

   b.

   For each increase of 1 in x, y decreases by 2.

   c.

   x is 3 for any value of y.

2.
Number of Squares	1	2	3	4	10	30	n
Perimeter	4	6	8	10	22	62	2n + 2

3. independent: number of times you brush your teeth; dependent: amount of toothpaste

4. a and b are functions because for each input there is a unique output, but c is not a function because there is more than one output value for the input value 3.

5. No; the graph is not a line.

6-10. See back of book.

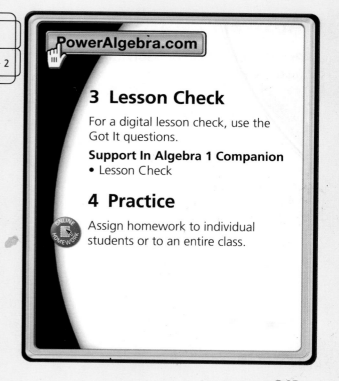

PowerAlgebra.com

3 Lesson Check

For a digital lesson check, use the Got It questions.

Support In Algebra 1 Companion
- Lesson Check

4 Practice

Assign homework to individual students or to an entire class.

ASSIGNMENT GUIDE

Basic: 6–14, 17–18

Average: 7–13 odd, 14–18

Advanced: 7–13 odd, 14–20

Standardized Test Prep: 21–24

Mixed Review: 25–27

Reasoning exercises have blue headings.

Applications exercises have red headings.

EXERCISE 18: Use the Think About a Plan worksheet in the **Practice and Problem Solving Workbook** (also available in the Teaching Resources in print and online) to further support students' development in becoming independent learners.

HOMEWORK QUICK CHECK

To check students' understanding of key skills and concepts, go over Exercises 7, 9, 14, 17, and 18.

For each table, determine whether the relationship is a linear function. Then represent the relationship using words, an equation, and a graph.

11. Mountain Climbing

Number of Hours Climbing, x	Elevation (ft), y
0	1127
1	1219
2	1311
3	1403

12. Grocery Bill

Number of Soup Cans, x	Total Bill, y
0	$52.07
1	$53.36
2	$54.65
3	$55.94

13. Gas in Tank

Miles Traveled, x	Gallons of Gas, y
0	11.2
17	10.2
34	9.2
51	8.2

B Apply

14. Error Analysis A bakery makes bread in batches. Several loaves per batch are rejected for sale due to defects. Your friend says that the total number of defective loaves is the independent variable. Explain and correct the error.

15. Gardening You can make 5 gal of liquid fertilizer by mixing 8 tsp of powdered fertilizer with water. Represent the relationship between the teaspoons of powder used and the gallons of fertilizer made using a table, an equation, and a graph. Is the amount of fertilizer made a function of the amount of powder used? Explain.

16. Reasoning Graph the set of ordered pairs $(-2, -3)$, $(0, -1)$, $(1, 0)$, $(3, 2)$, and $(4, 4)$. Determine whether the relationship is a linear function. Explain how you know.

17. Think About a Plan Gears are common parts in many types of machinery. In the diagram below, Gear A turns in response to the cranking of Gear B. Describe the relationship between the number of turns of Gear B and the number of turns of Gear A. Use words, an equation, and a graph.

- What are the independent and dependent variables?
- How much must you turn Gear B to get Gear A to go around once?

18. Electric Car An automaker produces a car that can travel 40 mi on its charged battery before it begins to use gas. Then the car travels 50 mi for each gallon of gas used. Represent the relationship between the amount of gas used and the distance traveled using a table, an equation, and a graph. Is total distance traveled a function of the amount of gas used? What are the independent and dependent variables? Explain.

Answers

Practice and Problem-Solving Exercises (continued)

11. Yes; for each additional hour of climbing, you gain 92 ft of elevation; $y = 92x + 1127$.

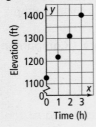

12. Yes; each additional can of soup costs $1.29. $y = 1.29x + 52.07$.

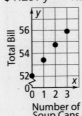

13. Yes; for every 17 mi traveled, the amount of gas in your tank goes down by 1 gallon; $y = -\frac{1}{17}x + 11.2$.

14. The number of defective loaves depends on the total number of loaves made. Therefore, the number of defective loaves is the dependent variable.

15. $y = \frac{8}{5}x$, where x is the number of gallons of water and y is the number of teaspoons of fertilizer. To calculate the powder needed to make a certain volume, use the equation $x = \frac{5}{8}y$.

x	y
0	0
5	8
10	16
15	24
20	32

yes, because there is a unique y for each x

19. Athletics The graph at the right shows the distance a runner has traveled as a function of the amount of time (in minutes) she has been running. Draw a graph that shows the time she has been running as a function of the distance she has traveled.

20. Movies When a movie on film is projected, a certain number of frames pass through the projector per minute. You say that the length of the movie in minutes is a function of the number of frames. Someone else says that the number of frames is a function of the length of the movie. Can you both be right? Explain.

Running Distance

Standardized Test Prep

21. A 3-ft fire hydrant is next to a road sign. The shadow of the fire hydrant is 4.5 ft long. The shadow of the road sign is 12 ft long. The shadows form similar triangles. What is the height in feet of the sign?

Ⓐ 1.6875 Ⓑ 8 Ⓒ 12 Ⓓ 16.5

22. What is the solution of $5d + 6 - 3d = 12$?

Ⓕ 2.25 Ⓖ 3 Ⓗ 9 Ⓘ 18

23. What are the solutions of $|4x - 11| = 13$?

Ⓐ 6 and -6 Ⓑ 24 and 6 Ⓒ -0.5 and 6 Ⓓ no solution

24. The table below shows the relationship between the number of sprays x a bottle of throat spray delivers and the amount of spray y (in milligrams) left in the bottle. Describe the relationship using words, an equation, and a graph.

Throat Spray					
Number of Sprays, x	0	1	2	3	4
Spray Left (mg), y	62,250	62,200	62,150	62,100	62,050

Mixed Review

25. A spring day begins cool and warms up as noon approaches. The temperature levels off just after noon. It drops more and more rapidly as sunset approaches. Draw a sketch of a graph that shows the possible temperature during the course of the day. Label each section.   ◀ See Lesson 4-1.

Get Ready! To prepare for Lesson 4-3, do Exercises 26 and 27.

Use a table, an equation, and a graph to represent each relationship.   ◀ See Lesson 1-9.

26. The number of mustard packets used is two times the number of hot dogs sold.

27. You are three places ahead of your friend while waiting in a long line.

PowerAlgebra.com   Lesson 4-2 Patterns and Linear Functions   245

19.

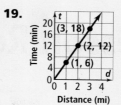

20. Yes, you can use either quantity as the independent variable. No matter which quantity you choose as the independent variable, there will be only one output for each input.

21. B   **22.** G   **23.** C

24. [2] For each spray, the amount left decreases by 50 mg; $y = -50x + 62,250$.

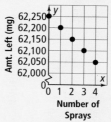

[1] correct methods used with one minor computational or graphing error

25.

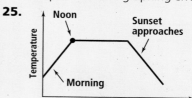

26.

Number of Hot Dogs	Number of Packets
0	0
1	2
2	4
3	6

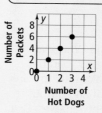

$y = 2x$

27.

Your Place	Friend's Place
0	3
1	4
2	5
3	6

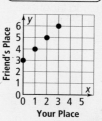

$y = x + 3$

16.

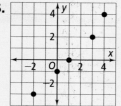

No; all points are not on a straight line.

17. Gear A will make one-half turn for 1 complete turn of Gear B; $y = \frac{1}{2}x$.

18.

Gas Used, x	Distance, y
0	40
1	90
2	140
3	190

$y = 50x + 40$

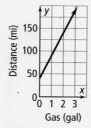

Either distance or gas could be the independent variable, depending on what information is supplied and what is to be calculated.

Additional Instructional Support

Algebra 1 Companion

Students can use the **Algebra 1 Companion** worktext (4 pages) as you teach the lesson. Use the Companion to support

- New Vocabulary
- Key Concepts
- Got It for each Problem
- Lesson Check

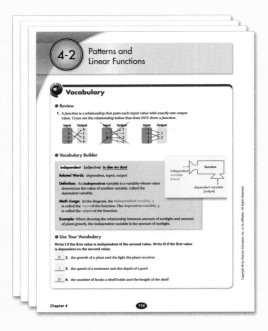

ELL Support

Connect to Prior Knowledge Whenever you discuss a functional relationship in this lesson or in following ones, take time to think aloud as you identify the input and output, or independent and dependent variables. Use voice inflection and gestures as you illustrate "what goes in and what comes out." Compare real-life examples, such as earnings for hours worked, or distance traveled for time traveled.

Assess Understanding Arrange students into small groups. Tell students to provide five examples of functions in real life. Have instructional conversations with students to identify the variables. Use function language, for example: So, the number of apples is a *function* of the money spent.

5 Assess & Remediate

Lesson Quiz

1. What is the relationship between the number of vertices in each polygon and the number of isosceles triangles?

Use the table below for Questions 2–4.

x	0	1	2	3
y	8	1	−6	−13

2. Do you UNDERSTAND? Is the relationship a linear function? How do you know?

3. What is an equation that describes the relationship?

ANSWERS TO LESSON QUIZ

1. The number of vertices equals the number of isosceles triangles.

2. Yes; the change in *x* is constant and the change in *y* in constant.

3. $y = 8 - 7x$

PRESCRIPTION FOR REMEDIATION

Use the student work on the Lesson Quiz to prescribe a differentiated review assignment.

Points	Differentiated Remediation
0–1	Intervention
2	On-level
3	Extension

PowerAlgebra.com

5 Assess & Remediate

Assign the Lesson Quiz. Appropriate intervention, practice, or enrichment is automatically generated based on student performance.

Intervention

- **Reteaching** (2 pages) Provides reteaching and practice exercises for the key lesson concepts. Use with struggling students or absent students.

- **English Language Learner Support** Helps students develop and reinforce mathematical vocabulary and key concepts.

All-in-One Resources/Online
Reteaching

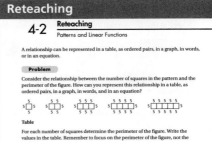

All-in-One Resources/Online
English Language Learner Support

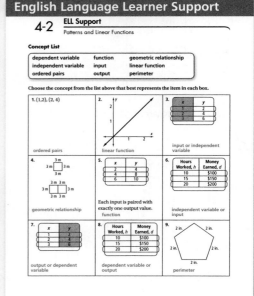

Differentiated Remediation *continued*

On-Level

- **Practice** (2 pages) Provides extra practice for each lesson. For simpler practice exercises, use the Form K Practice pages found in the All-in-One Teaching Resources and online.

- **Think About a Plan** Helps students develop specific problem-solving skills and strategies by providing scaffolded guiding questions.

- **Standardized Test Prep** Focuses on all major exercises, all major question types, and helps students prepare for the high-stakes assessments.

Extension

- **Enrichment** Provides students with interesting problems and activities that extend the concepts of the lesson.

- **Activities, Games, and Puzzles** Worksheets that can be used for concepts development, enrichment, and for fun!

Practice and Problem Solving WKBK/ All-in-One Resources/Online
Practice page 1

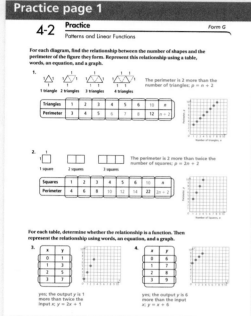

Practice and Problem Solving WKBK/ All-in-One Resources/Online
Practice page 2

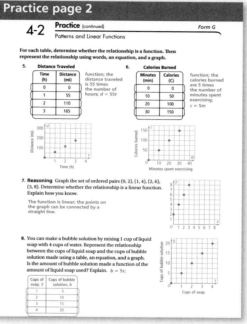

All-in-One Resources/Online
Enrichment

4-2 Enrichment — Patterns and Linear Functions

Representing Number Patterns With Linear Equations

Many number patterns can be represented by a linear equation. For example, the positive even integers 2, 4, 6, 8, . . . , can be represented by the equation $y = 2x$, where x represents the position in the sequence. The fourth even integer ($x = 4$) is $y = 2(4)$ or 8. If you can determine an equation to describe the number pattern, you can use the equation to determine the value of any number in the pattern. For example, the 300th positive even integer is $y = 2(300)$ or 600. Using the equation makes determining the values faster and easier than writing out the entire list.

Exercises

1. Write a linear equation to describe the number pattern 3, 6, 9, . . . $y = 3x$

2. Write a linear equation to describe the number pattern 0, 5, 10, 15, . . . $y = 5x$

3. Write a linear equation to describe the number pattern 4, 7, 10, . . . $y = 3x + 4$

4. Write a linear equation to describe the number pattern that starts with 8 and continues with numbers that are one more than a positive multiple of 7. $y = 7x + 8$

5. Write a linear equation to describe the number pattern that starts with 3 and continues with positive odd integers. $y = 2x + 3$

6. Write a linear equation to describe the number pattern that starts with –2 and continues with negative even integers. $y = -2x - 2$

7. Write a linear equation to describe the number pattern that starts with –8 and continues with negative multiples of 8. $y = -8x - 8$

8. **Open-Ended** Write a number pattern of your own. Can you write a linear equation to describe the pattern? If so, write the linear equation. If you cannot determine a linear equation for the pattern, write a new pattern for which you can write a linear equation.
Answers will vary. Sample answer: 1, 4, 7, 10; yes; $y = 3x + 1$

Practice and Problem Solving WKBK/ All-in-One Resources/Online
Think About a Plan

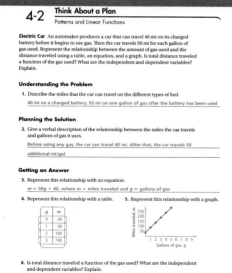

Practice and Problem Solving WKBK/ All-in-One Resources/Online
Standardized Test Prep

4-2 Standardized Test Prep — Patterns and Linear Functions

Multiple Choice

For Exercises 1–4, choose the correct letter.

1. Which equation represents the relationship shown in the table at the right? C
   A. $y = -x - 3$
   B. $y = x - 3$
   C. $y = 2x - 3$
   D. $y = -2x + 3$

x	y
0	-3
1	-1
2	1
3	3

2. In a relationship between variables, what is the variable called that changes in response to another variable? I
   F. function
   G. input function
   H. independent variable
   I. dependent variable

3. A lawn care company charges a $10 trip fee plus $0.15 per square foot of x square feet of lawn for fertilization. Which equation represents the relationship? B
   A. $x = 0.10y + 15$ B. $y = 0.15x + 10$ C. $y = 10x + 0.15$ D. $x = 10y + 0.15$

4. Which equation represents the relationship shown in the graph? G
   F. $y = -2x$
   G. $y = 2x$
   H. $y = -\frac{1}{2}x$
   I. $y = \frac{1}{2}x$

Short Response

5. The table below shows the relationship between the number of teachers and the number of students going on a field trip. How can the relationship be described using words, an equation, and a graph?

		Field Trip			
Teachers	2	3	4	5	6
Students	34	51	68	85	102

The number of students is 17 times the number of teachers; $s = 17t$;
[2] All parts answered correctly.
[1] One or two parts answered correctly.
[0] No parts answered correctly.

Online Teacher Resource Center
Activities, Games, and Puzzles

4-2 Activity: Common Themes — Patterns and Linear Functions

Your teacher will select a student to read aloud each function below. Then your teacher will write the function on the board.

A. $y = 2x + 1$ B. $y = -0.5x - 3$ C. $y = \frac{1}{2}x + 7$

D. $y = -3x - 5$ E. $y = -\frac{1}{2}x + 1$ F. $y = 1.5x + 8$

- In small groups, choose one of the functions above.
- In the table below, write the letter of the function your group chose. Complete the table of values by calculating each value of y for the given values of x.

Function Letter					
x	0	1	2	3	4
y					

Look for a pattern in the values of x in the table. Describe the pattern below.
Each value of x increases by 1 from one value of x to the next.

Look for a pattern in the values of y in your table. Describe the pattern below.
Answers may vary. Sample: In Function A, the y-value increases by 2 each time.

Write a function like the one at the right by choosing a value $y = mx + b$
of m from −2, −1, 1, or 2 and a value of b from −3, −2, −1, 1, 2, 3.
Complete the table of values below using the numbers you chose for m and b.

x	0	1	2	3	4
y					

Describe the pattern you see in the y-values.
Answers may vary. Sample: $y = -2x + 3$; the y-value decreases by 2 each time.

1 Interactive Learning

Solve It!

PURPOSE To introduce a nonlinear function, to highlight the differences between linear and nonlinear functions

PROCESS Students may complete the table of values by using a pattern or drawing figures. They may discover a pattern by graphing the data.

FACILITATE

Q Does the column for the "number of steps" reflect a constant increase or decrease in values? Explain. **[Yes, a constant increase; the number of steps increases by 1 each time.]**

Q Does the column for the "number of blocks" reflect a constant increase or decrease in values? Explain. **[No, the increases are not constant; the increases themselves keep increasing by 1.]**

ANSWER See Solve It in Answers on next page.
CONNECT THE MATH In linear relationships a constant change in the input value always produces a corresponding constant (not necessarily equal) change in the output value. In the Solve It, the change in the number of blocks is not constant, so the relationship is not linear.

2 Guided Instruction

Take Note

Q What is a function? **[a relationship pairing each input value with exactly one output value]**

Q How can you read the output value for a given input from a graph? **[Look for the point with the given x-coordinate and find the y-coordinate for that point.]**

4-3 Patterns and Nonlinear Functions

Indiana Academic Standard
A1.5.5 Sketch and interpret linear and non-linear graphs representing given situations and identify independent and dependent variables.

Objective To identify and represent patterns that describe nonlinear functions

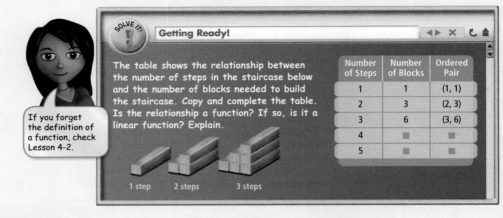

If you forget the definition of a function, check Lesson 4-2.

Lesson Vocabulary
• nonlinear function

The relationship in the Solve It is an example of a nonlinear function. A **nonlinear function** is a function whose graph is not a line or part of a line.

Essential Understanding Just like linear functions, nonlinear functions can be represented using words, tables, equations, sets of ordered pairs, and graphs.

take note

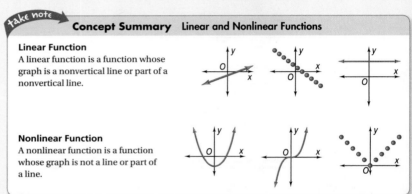

Concept Summary Linear and Nonlinear Functions

Linear Function
A linear function is a function whose graph is a nonvertical line or part of a nonvertical line.

Nonlinear Function
A nonlinear function is a function whose graph is not a line or part of a line.

4-3 Preparing to Teach

BIG idea Functions UbD

ESSENTIAL UNDERSTANDINGS

• Just like linear functions, nonlinear functions can be represented using words, tables, equations, sets of ordered pairs, and graphs.
• A nonlinear function is a function whose graph is not a line or part of a line.

Math Background

In the real world, some situations are modeled using linear functions, while many other situations must be modeled using nonlinear functions. Introducing students to both nonlinear and linear functions provides a framework for making sense of real-world data. Linear functions will be studied in depth first.

Later in the text and in advanced math courses, students will begin their study of nonlinear functions such as: absolute value, quadratic, exponential, radical, and rational functions.

Students need to understand that any function that does not form a straight line is a nonlinear function and that functions fit one of two categories: linear or nonlinear.

Support Student Learning
Use the **Algebra 1 Companion** to engage and support students during instructions. See Lesson Resources at the end of this lesson for details.

PowerAlgebra.com

1 Interactive Learning

Solve It!
Step out how to solve the Problem with helpful hints and an online question. Other questions are listed above in Interactive Learning.

(C) **Problem 1** Classifying Functions as Linear or Nonlinear

Pizza The area A, in square inches, of a pizza is a function of its radius r, in inches. The cost C, in dollars, of the sauce for a pizza is a function of the weight w, in ounces, of sauce used. Graph these functions shown by the tables below. Is each function *linear* or *nonlinear*?

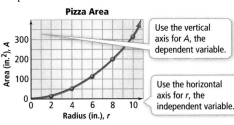

Pizza Area

Radius (in.), r	Area (in.²), A
2	12.57
4	50.27
6	113.10
8	201.06
10	314.16

Sauce Cost

Weight (oz), w	Cost, C
2	$.80
4	$1.60
6	$2.40
8	$3.20
10	$4.00

Know
The relationships shown in the tables are functions.

Need
To classify the functions as *linear* or *nonlinear*

Plan
Use the tables to make graphs.

Think
How can a graph tell you if a function is linear or nonlinear?
The graph of a linear function is a nonvertical line or part of a line, but the graph of a nonlinear function is not.

Graph A as a function of r.

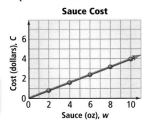

Use the vertical axis for A, the dependent variable.

Use the horizontal axis for r, the independent variable.

Graph C as a function of w.

The graph is a curve, not a line, so the function is nonlinear.

The graph is a line, so the function is linear.

 Got It? **1. a.** The table below shows the fraction A of the original area of a piece of paper that remains after the paper has been cut in half n times. Graph the function represented by the table. Is the function *linear* or *nonlinear*?

Cutting Paper				
Number of Cuts, n	1	2	3	4
Fraction of Original Area Remaining, A	$\frac{1}{2}$	$\frac{1}{4}$	$\frac{1}{8}$	$\frac{1}{16}$

b. Reasoning Will the area A in part (a) ever reach zero? Explain.

Problem 1

Q Is the change in the values of both radius and area for the pizza problem constant? Explain. **[No, the change in the radius is constant, but the change in the area is not.]**

Q Using the tables, for which relation is it easier to tell the value of the dependent variable when the value of the independent variable is 11? Explain. **[The relation between cheese and sauce is easy because the change is constant. For every increase of 2 oz in weight, the cost increases by $0.80. So, for a 1-oz additional weight, the cost increases by $0.40.]**

Q How can you tell by inspecting the graphs which function is linear? **[Linear functions form straight lines and nonlinear ones do not.]**

Got It?
Students may need help setting up an appropriate scale for graphing this table of values. Make sure students examine the range of numbers in the table before marking a scale on the y-axis.

2 Guided Instruction

(C) Each Problem is worked out and supported online.

Problem 1
Classifying Functions as Linear or Nonlinear
Animated

Problem 2
Representing Patterns and Nonlinear Functions
Animated

Problem 3
Writing a Rule to Describe a Nonlinear Function
Animated

Support in Algebra 1 Companion
• Vocabulary
• Key Concepts
• Got It?

Answers

Solve It!
10, (4, 10); 15, (5, 15); yes; no

Got It?
1. a.

nonlinear

b. No; you can always multiply a number by $\frac{1}{2}$. The denominator of the fraction will get larger and larger, so the value of the fraction will approach 0 but never reach it.

Problem 2

Q Is the functional relationship shown in the table a linear function? Explain. **[No; the change in the independent variable is constant but the change in the dependent variable is not.]**

Q If the total number of cubes in a similar block is 1728, how many blocks are on one edge of the cube? **[12 because 12 × 12 × 12 = 1728]**

Got It?

ERROR PREVENTION

If students have difficulty writing the correct equation for this function, suggest that they rewrite the y-values as powers of 3, such as: 3^1, 3^2, 3^3, etc.

 Problem 2 Representing Patterns and Nonlinear Functions

The table shows the total number of blocks in each figure below as a function of the number of blocks on one edge.

1   2   3

Number of Blocks on Edge, x	Total Number of Blocks, y	Ordered Pair (x, y)
1	1	(1, 1)
2	8	(2, 8)
3	27	(3, 27)
4	▪	▪
5	▪	▪

What is a pattern you can use to complete the table? Represent the relationship using words, an equation, and a graph.

Draw the next two figures to complete the table.

Think

How can you use a pattern to complete the table?
You can draw figures with 4 and 5 blocks on an edge. Then analyze the figures to determine the total number of blocks they contain.

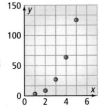
4   5

A cube with 4 blocks on an edge contains 4 · 4 · 4 = 64 blocks. A cube with 5 blocks on an edge contains 5 · 5 · 5 = 125 blocks.

Number of Blocks on Edge, x	Total Number of Blocks, y	Ordered Pair (x, y)
1	1	(1, 1)
2	8	(2, 8)
3	27	(3, 27)
4	64	(4, 64)
5	125	(5, 125)

Words The total number of blocks y is the cube of the number of blocks on one edge x.

Equation $y = x^3$

You can use the table to make a graph. The points do not lie on a line. So the relationship between the number of blocks on one edge and the total number of blocks is a nonlinear function.

 Got It? **2.** The table shows the number of new branches in each figure of the pattern below. What is a pattern you can use to complete the table? Represent the relationship using words, an equation, and a graph.

1   2   3

Number of Figure, x	1	2	3	4	5
Number of New Branches, y	3	9	27	▪	▪

Additional Problems

1. The number of centimeters is a function of the number of inches as shown in the table. Is the function *linear* or *nonlinear*?

Converting Inches to Centimeters

Inches	Centimeters
1	2.54
2	5.08
3	7.62
4	10.16

ANSWER linear

2. The table shows the number of calls made in a phone tree during each level. Identify the pattern to complete the table. How can you represent the relationship using words, an equation, and a graph?

Phone Tree

Level, x	Number of Calls, y	Ordered Pair (x, y)
1	2	(1, 2)
2	4	(2, 4)
3	8	(3, 8)
4		
5		

ANSWER The number of calls made at a level is equal to 2 raised to the level number. As an equation: $y = 2^x$. The missing ordered pairs are (4, 16) and (5, 32).

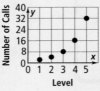

3. The ordered pairs (1, 1), (2, 8), (3, 27), (4, 64), and (5, 125) represent a function. What is a rule that represents this function?

ANSWER $y = x^3$

A function can be thought of as a rule that you apply to the input in order to get the output. You can describe a nonlinear function with words or with an equation, just as you did with linear functions.

 Problem 3 Writing a Rule to Describe a Nonlinear Function

The ordered pairs (1, 2), (2, 4), (3, 8), (4, 16), and (5, 32) represent a function. What is a rule that represents this function?

Make a table to organize the *x*- and *y*-values. For each row, identify rules that produce the given *y*-value when you substitute the *x*-value. Look for a pattern in the *y*-values.

Think

How can you use reasoning to write a rule?
You can *solve a simpler problem* by writing a rule based on the first one or two rows of the table. Then see if the rule works for the other rows.

x	y
1	2
2	4
3	8
4	16
5	32

What rule produces 2, given an *x*-value of 1? The rules $y = 2x$, $y = x + 1$, and $y = 2^x$ work for (1, 2).

$y = x + 1$ does not work for (2, 4). $y = 2x$ works for (2, 4), but not for (3, 8). $y = 2^x$ works for all three pairs.

$8 = 2 \cdot 2 \cdot 2$ and $16 = 2 \cdot 2 \cdot 2 \cdot 2$. The pattern of the *y*-values matches $2^1, 2^2, 2^3, 2^4, 2^5$, or $y = 2^x$.

The function can be represented by the rule $y = 2^x$.

 Got It? 3. What is a rule for the function represented by the ordered pairs (1, 1), (2, 4), (3, 9), (4, 16), and (5, 25)?

Lesson Check

Do you know HOW?

1. Graph the function represented by the table below. Is the function *linear* or *nonlinear*?

x	0	1	2	3	4
y	12	13	14	15	16

2. The ordered pairs (0, −2), (1, 1), (2, 4), (3, 7), and (4, 10) represent a function. What is a rule that represents this function?

3. Which rule could represent the function shown by the table below?

x	0	1	2	3	4
y	0	−1	−4	−9	−16

A. $y = x^2$ B. $y = -x^3$ C. $y = -x^2$

Do you UNDERSTAND?

4. **Vocabulary** Does the graph represent a *linear function* or a *nonlinear function*? Explain.

a.   b.

5. **Error Analysis** A classmate says that the function shown by the table at the right can be represented by the rule $y = x + 1$. Describe and correct your classmate's error.

x	y
0	1
1	2
2	5
3	10
4	17

Problem 3

Q What pattern exists in the *y*-values in the table of values? **[Each successive *y*-value is the previous *y*-value multiplied by 2.]**

Q What mathematical operation corresponds to repeated multiplication by the same number? **[raising a number to a power]**

Q Using the rule, what is the output for an input of 10? Explain. **[$2^{10} = 1024$]**

Got It?   ERROR PREVENTION

Students should be sure to check the equation they wrote by substituting each ordered pair from the table into the equation. Each ordered pair should satisfy the equation.

3 Lesson Check

Do you know HOW?

• If students have difficulty with Exercise 1, then have them review Problem 1 to determine the appearance of a linear function and the appearance of a nonlinear function.

Do you UNDERSTAND?

• If students cannot identify the error made by the classmate in Exercise 5, then have them find the change in *x*-values and the change in *y*-values to determine the equation that represents the relationship shown in the table.

Close

Q How can you describe the rule for a function? **[You can describe the rule in words or with an equation.]**

Answers

Got It? (continued)

2. The number of branches is 3 raised to the *x*th power; $y = 3^x$; 81, 243.

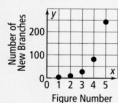

Figure Number

3. $y = x^2$

Lesson Check

1.

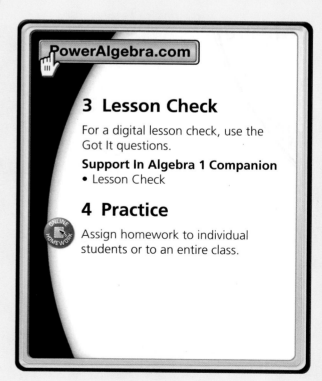

linear

2. $y = 3x - 2$ 3. C

4. a. linear function
   b. nonlinear function

5. Only the first two pairs fit this rule. The rule that fits all the pairs is $y = x^2 + 1$.

PowerAlgebra.com

3 Lesson Check

For a digital lesson check, use the Got It questions.

Support In Algebra 1 Companion
• Lesson Check

4 Practice

Assign homework to individual students or to an entire class.

4 Practice

ASSIGNMENT GUIDE

Basic: 6–17, 19–20

Average: 7–15 odd, 17–20

Advanced: 7–15 odd, 17–22

Standardized Test Prep: 23–25

Mixed Review: 26–29

Reasoning exercises have blue headings.

Applications exercises have red headings.

EXERCISE 20: Use the Think About a Plan worksheet in the **Practice and Problem Solving Workbook** (also available in the Teaching Resources in print and online) to further support students' development in becoming independent learners.

HOMEWORK QUICK CHECK

To check students' understanding of key skills and concepts, go over Exercises 9, 13, 17, 19, and 20.

Practice and Problem-Solving Exercises

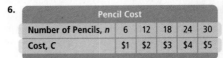

A Practice The cost C, in dollars, for pencils is a function of the number n of pencils purchased. The length L of a pencil, in inches, is a function of the time t, in seconds, it has been sharpened. Graph the function shown by each table below. Tell whether the function is *linear* or *nonlinear*.

◀ See Problem 1.

6.

Pencil Cost					
Number of Pencils, n	6	12	18	24	30
Cost, C	$1	$2	$3	$4	$5

7.

Pencil Sharpening						
Time (s), t	0	3	6	9	12	15
Length (in.), L	7.5	7.5	7.5	7.5	7.4	7.3

Graph the function shown by each table. Tell whether the function is *linear* or *nonlinear*.

8.

x	y
0	5
1	5
2	5
3	5

9.

x	y
0	−4
1	−3
2	0
3	5

10.

x	y
0	0
1	1
2	−5
3	8

11.

x	y
0	0
1	3
2	6
3	9

12. For the diagram below, the table gives the total number of small triangles y in figure number x. What pattern can you use to complete the table? Represent the relationship using words, an equation, and a graph.

◀ See Problem 2.

Figure 1   Figure 2   Figure 3

Figure Number, x	Total Small Triangles, y	Ordered Pair (x, y)
1	3	(1, 3)
2	12	(2, 12)
3	27	(3, 27)
4	■	■
5	■	■

Each set of ordered pairs represents a function. Write a rule that represents the function.

◀ See Problem 3.

13. $(0, 0), (1, 4), (2, 16), (3, 36), (4, 64)$

14. $\left(1, \frac{2}{3}\right), \left(2, \frac{4}{9}\right), \left(3, \frac{8}{27}\right), \left(4, \frac{16}{81}\right), \left(5, \frac{32}{243}\right)$

15. $(1, 2), (2, 16), (3, 54), (4, 128), (5, 250)$

16. $(0, 0), (1, 0.5), (2, 2), (3, 4.5), (4, 8)$

B Apply **17. Writing** The rule $V = \frac{4}{3}\pi r^3$ gives the volume V of a sphere as a function of its radius r. Identify the independent and dependent variables in this relationship. Explain your reasoning.

18. Open-Ended Write a rule for a nonlinear function such that y is negative when $x = 1$, positive when $x = 2$, negative when $x = 3$, positive when $x = 4$, and so on.

Answers

Practice and Problem-Solving Exercises

6.
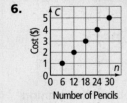
linear

7.
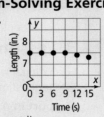
nonlinear

8.
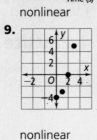
linear

9.
nonlinear

10.
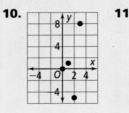
nonlinear

11.
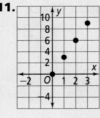
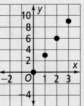
linear

12. 48, (4, 48), 75, (5, 75); square the value of x and then multiply it by 3; $y = 3x^2$.

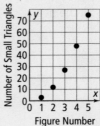

13. $y = 4x^2$

14. $y = \left(\frac{2}{3}\right)^x$

15. $y = 2x^3$

16. $y = 0.5x^2$

17. Independent: r, dependent: V; volume depends on the length of the radius.

18. Answers will vary. Sample: $y = (-1)^x$

19. Think About a Plan Concrete forming tubes are used as molds for cylindrical concrete supports. The volume V of a tube is the product of its length ℓ and the area A of its circular base. You can make $\frac{2}{3}$ ft^3 of cement per bag. Write a rule to find the number of bags of cement needed to fill a tube 4 ft long as a function of its radius r. How many bags are needed to fill a tube with a 4-in. radius? A 5-in. radius ? A 6-in. radius?

* What is a rule for the volume V of any tube?
* What operation do you use to find the number of bags needed for a given volume?

20. Fountain A designer wants to make a circular fountain inside a square of grass as shown at the right. What is a rule for the area A of the grass as a function of r?

 Challenge

21. Reasoning What is a rule for the function represented by $\left(0, \frac{2}{19}\right), \left(1, 1\frac{2}{19}\right), \left(2, 4\frac{2}{19}\right), \left(3, 9\frac{2}{19}\right), \left(4, 16\frac{2}{19}\right),$ and $\left(5, 25\frac{2}{19}\right)$? Explain your reasoning.

22. Reasoning A certain function fits the following description: As the value of x increases by 1 each time, the value of y continually decreases by a smaller amount each time, and never reaches a value as low as 1. Is this function *linear* or *nonlinear*? Explain your reasoning.

Standardized Test Prep

SAT/ACT

23. The ordered pairs $(-2, 1), (-1, -2), (0, -3), (1, -2),$ and $(2, 1)$ represent a function. Which rule could represent the function?

   Ⓐ $y = -3x - 5$ Ⓑ $y = x^2 - 3$ Ⓒ $y = x + 3$ Ⓓ $y = x^2 + 5$

24. You are making a model of the library. The floor plans for the library and the plans for your model are shown. What is the value of x?

   Ⓕ 1.4 in.   Ⓗ 23.2 in.

   Ⓖ 2.8 in.   Ⓘ 437.5 in.

Short Response

25. A 15-oz can of tomatoes costs \$.89, and a 29-oz can costs \$1.69. Which can has the lower cost per ounce? Justify your answer.

Mixed Review

26. Determine whether the relationship in the table is a function. Then describe the relationship using words, an equation, and a graph.

◀ See Lesson 4-2.

Get Ready! To prepare for Lesson 4-4, do Exercises 27–29.

Evaluate each expression for $x = -3$, $x = 0$, and $x = 2.5$.   ◀ See Lesson 1-2.

27. $7x - 3$ **28.** $1 + 4x$ **29.** $-2x^2$

---

19. Let y = number of bags, and $y = 6\pi r^2$; 3 bags; 4 bags; 5 bags

20. $A = 4r^2 - \pi r^2$

21. $y = x^2 + \frac{2}{19}$; the value of y is $\frac{2}{19}$ more than the square of x.

22. Nonlinear; if the function were linear, then there would be a value of x for which the value of y was less than 1.

23. B   **24.** G

25. [2]   \$.89/15 oz $\approx$ \$.0593/oz, \$1.69/29 oz $\approx$ \$.0583; the 29-oz can has the lower cost per ounce.

    [1]   one computational error

26. The value of y is 3 more than twice x; $y = 2x + 3$.

27. $-24, -3, 14.5$

28. $-11, 1, 11$

29. $-18, 0, -12.5$

Lesson Resources

Additional Instructional Support

Algebra 1 Companion

Students can use the **Algebra 1 Companion** worktext (4 pages) as you teach the lesson. Use the Companion to support

• New Vocabulary

• Key Concepts

• Got It for each Problem

• Lesson Check

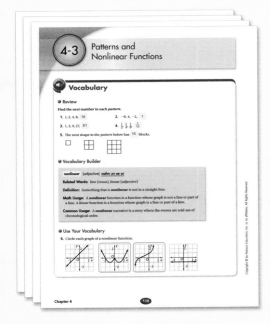

ELL Support

Use Graphic Organizers Divide students in pairs. Model a Venn diagram on the board. Ask: What does it mean to compare? to contrast? Show students how to compare and contrast a triangle and a rectangle. Model the process on the board as you think aloud: What characteristics are the same? What characteristics are different? Have students compare and contrast linear and nonlinear functions using their diagram. Discuss their work. Confirm the goals of the lesson were met.

5 Assess & Remediate

Lesson Quiz

1. **Do you UNDERSTAND?** The surface area of a cube is a function of the side length of the cube as shown in the table. Is the function *linear* or *nonlinear*?

Surface Area of a Cube

Side Length (in.), x	Surface Area (in.²), x
1	6
2	24
3	54
4	96

2. The ordered pairs (1, 2), (2, 5), (3, 10), (4, 17), and (5, 26) represent a function. What is a rule that could represent this function?

3. Tell whether the function shown by the table below is *linear* or *nonlinear*.

x	y
0	−3
1	2
2	7
3	12
4	17

ANSWERS TO LESSON QUIZ

1. nonlinear

2. $y = x^2 + 1$

3. linear

PRESCRIPTION FOR REMEDIATION

Use the student work on the Lesson Quiz to prescribe a differentiated review assignment.

Points	Differentiated Remediation
0–1	Intervention
2	On-level
3	Extension

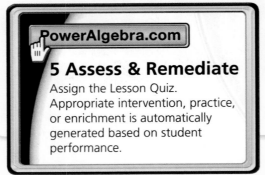

PowerAlgebra.com

5 Assess & Remediate

Assign the Lesson Quiz. Appropriate intervention, practice, or enrichment is automatically generated based on student performance.

Intervention

• **Reteaching** (2 pages) Provides reteaching and practice exercises for the key lesson concepts. Use with struggling students or absent students.

• **English Language Learner Support** Helps students develop and reinforce mathematical vocabulary and key concepts.

All-in-One Resources/Online
Reteaching

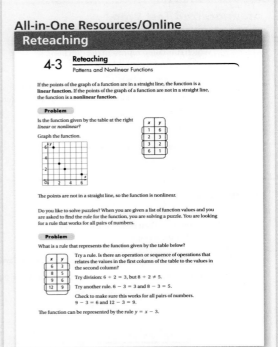

All-in-One Resources/Online
English Language Learner Support

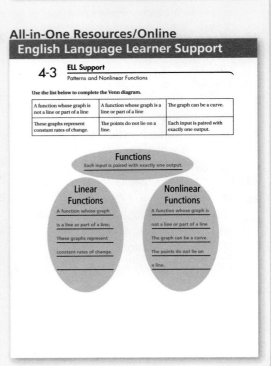

Differentiated Remediation *continued*

On-Level

- **Practice** (2 pages) Provides extra practice for each lesson. For simpler practice exercises, use the Form K Practice pages found in the All-in-One Teaching Resources and online.

- **Think About a Plan** Helps students develop specific problem-solving skills and strategies by providing scaffolded guiding questions.

- **Standardized Test Prep** Focuses on all major exercises, all major question types, and helps students prepare for the high-stakes assessments.

Extension

- **Enrichment** Provides students with interesting problems and activities that extend the concepts of the lesson.

- **Activities, Games, and Puzzles** Worksheets that can be used for concepts development, enrichment, and for fun!

Practice and Problem Solving WKBK/ All-in-One Resources/Online
Practice page 1

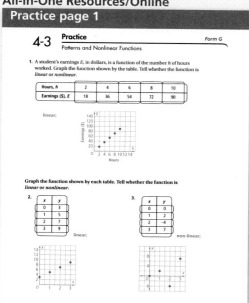

Practice and Problem Solving WKBK/ All-in-One Resources/Online
Practice page 2

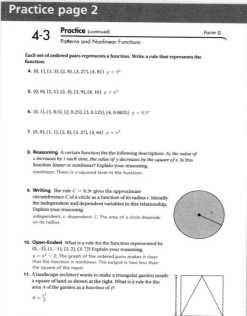

All-in-One Resources/Online
Enrichment

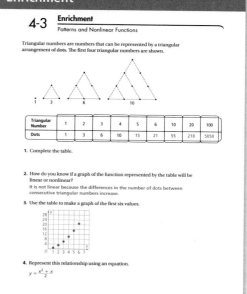

Practice and Problem Solving WKBK/ All-in-One Resources/Online
Think About a Plan

Practice and Problem Solving WKBK/ All-in-One Resources/Online
Standardized Test Prep

Online Teacher Resource Center
Activities, Games, and Puzzles

Answers

Mid-Chapter Quiz

1. Time of day, number of pieces of French toast on a serving tray; the tray starts off with a number of pieces and it remains constant at first. Then a large number of pieces are taken followed by a period where a piece is taken every once in a while. The tray is then refilled with the amount that it started with. Some pieces are taken occasionally and then it remains constant until the end.

2.
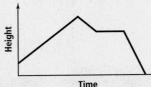

Height of Disk

The increasing slope represents the rising of the flying disk into the air. At its highest point, it hits the tree, then falls to the roof, which is represented by the downward-sloped line. The horizontal line represents the time it is sitting on the roof. The last downward-sloping line represents the fall back to the ground.

3.
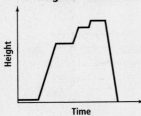

Height of Elevator

The horizontal lines represent when the elevator is stopped and people are getting on or off. The positive-sloped lines are when the elevator is rising, and the negative-sloped lines are when the elevator is descending.

4. Number of cans, total amount of soda in ounces; each can contains 12 oz of soda; $y = 12x$.

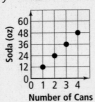

MathXL for School

Prepare students for the Mid-Chapter Quiz and Chapter Test with online practice and review.

Do you know HOW?

1. **Buffet** The graph shows the number of slices of French toast in a serving dish at a breakfast buffet as time passes. What are the variables? Describe how the variables are related at various points on the graph.

French Toast

(Graph: Number of Slices of French Toast vs. Time)

Sketch a graph of the height of each object over time. Label each section.

2. **Recreation** You throw a flying disc into the air. It hits a tree branch on its way up and comes to rest on a roof. It stays on the roof for a minute before the wind blows it back to the ground.

3. **Elevator** An elevator fills with people on the ground floor. Most get off at the seventh floor, and the remainder get off at the ninth floor. Then two people get on at the tenth floor and are carried back to the ground floor without any more stops.

For each table, identify the independent and dependent variables. Then describe the relationship using words, an equation, and a graph.

4. **Ounces of Soda**

Number of Cans	Soda (oz)
1	12
2	24
3	36
4	48

5. **Dog Biscuits Left**

Number of Tricks	Number of Biscuits
1	20
2	17
3	14
4	11

Tell whether the function shown by each table is *linear* or *nonlinear*.

6.

x	1	2	3	4
y	6	8	10	12

7.

x	0	2	4	6
y	5	5	5	5

8.

x	0	1	2	3
y	−3	−4	−5	6

Do you UNDERSTAND?

9. **Vocabulary** Does each graph represent a *linear function* or a *nonlinear function*? Explain.

a.

b.

c.

d.

10. **Writing** The size of a bees' nest increases as time passes. Your friend says that time is the dependent variable because size depends on time. Is your friend correct? Explain.

11. **Open-Ended** With some functions, the value of the dependent variable decreases as the value of the independent variable increases. What is a real-world example of this?

---

5. Number of tricks; number of dog biscuits left; starting with 23 biscuits in the box, the dog gets 3 biscuits for each trick; $y = -3x + 23$.

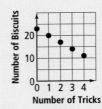

6. linear

7. linear

8. nonlinear

9. a. Nonlinear; the graph is not a line.

   b. Linear; the graph is a line.

   c. Nonlinear; the graph is not a line.

   d. Linear; the points on the graph lie on a line.

10. No; time is the independent variable and size is the dependent variable because the size increases as time passes.

11. Answers will vary. Sample: The number of miles you have traveled going to a destination and the number of miles left to travel before you get there.

4-4 Graphing a Function Rule

Indiana Academic Standard
A1.2.1 Translate among various representations of linear functions including tables, graphs, words and equations.

Objective To graph equations that represent functions

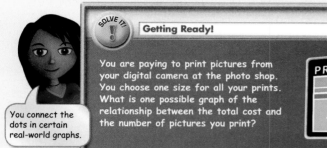

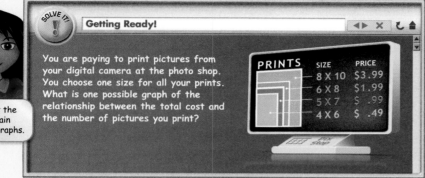

Getting Ready!

You are paying to print pictures from your digital camera at the photo shop. You choose one size for all your prints. What is one possible graph of the relationship between the total cost and the number of pictures you print?

PRINTS	SIZE	PRICE
	8 X 10	$3.99
	6 X 8	$1.99
	5 X 7	$ .99
	4 X 6	$ .49

> You connect the dots in certain real-world graphs.

You can use a table of values to help you make a graph in the Solve It.

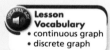

Lesson Vocabulary
• continuous graph
• discrete graph

Essential Understanding The set of all solutions of an equation forms the equation's graph. A graph may include solutions that do not appear in a table. A real-world graph should only show points that make sense in the given situation.

Think

What input values make sense here?
It is possible to use any input *x* in the equation and get an output *y*. Choose integer values of *x* to produce integer values of *y*, which are easier to graph.

Problem 1 Graphing a Function Rule

What is the graph of the function rule $y = -2x + 1$**?**

Step 1 Make a table of values.

x	y = -2x + 1	(x, y)
-1	y = -2(-1) + 1 = 3	(-1, 3)
0	y = -2(0) + 1 = 1	(0, 1)
1	y = -2(1) + 1 = -1	(1, -1)
2	y = -2(2) + 1 = -3	(2, -3)

Step 2 Graph the ordered pairs.

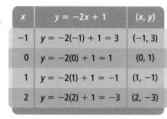

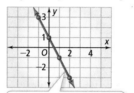
Connect the points with a line to represent *all* solutions.

Got It? 1. What is the graph of the function rule $y = \frac{1}{2}x - 1$?

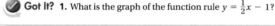

PowerAlgebra.com   Lesson 4-4   Graphing a Function Rule   253

---

1 Interactive Learning

Solve It!

PURPOSE To graph a discrete linear function using a table of values

PROCESS Students may create a table of values using a rule to write ordered pairs or by expressing the function rule as an equation.

FACILITATE

Q How do you determine the total cost for a given number of prints? **[You multiply the number of prints by the price per print.]**

Q What is the least value for the independent variable? Explain. **[0, because you cannot print a negative number of pictures.]**

ANSWER See Solve It in Answers on next page.
CONNECT THE MATH In the Solve It, the points are not connected because you cannot print and be charged for "parts" of a picture. In this lesson, students learn about continuous and discrete data points on a graph.

2 Guided Instruction

Problem 1

Q Do more ordered pairs satisfy the function rule besides those given in the table? Explain. **[Yes; every value of *x* has a corresponding *y*.]**

Q When you graph a line, how does that show all possible ordered-pair solutions? **[The line between the points shows non-integral solutions, and the arrows indicate the line continues infinitely.]**

Got It?   VISUAL LEARNERS

Emphasize that although the tables of values constructed by the students may differ, all graphs are identical once the line is graphed.

4-4 Preparing to Teach

BIG ideas Functions
              Modeling

UbD

ESSENTIAL UNDERSTANDINGS
• The set of all solutions of an equation forms its graph.
• A graph may include solutions that do not appear in a table.
• A real-world graph should show only points that make sense in the given situation.

Math Background

Quantities in the world of mathematics are either discrete or continuous. Students had experience with discrete versus continuous sets when they studied the sets of real numbers. While the set of whole numbers is discrete, the set of real numbers is continuous. In this lesson, students extend the concepts of discrete and continuous to

apply to functions in which an input value is defined to be either discrete or continuous.

Discrete data is represented on a coordinate grid by graphing points but not connecting them with line segments.

Continuous data is represented on a coordinate grid by graphing points and then connecting the points with line segments. In many situations, it is also appropriate to place arrows on one or both ends of the segment to show that the possible solutions continue indefinitely.

Support Student Learning

Use the **Algebra 1 Companion** to engage and support students during instructions. See Lesson Resources at the end of this lesson for details.

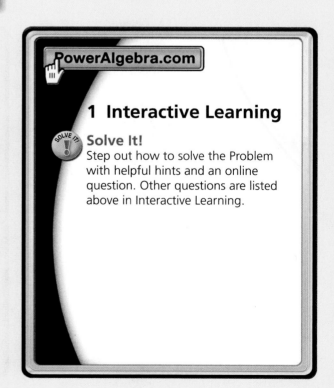

PowerAlgebra.com

1 Interactive Learning

Solve It!

Step out how to solve the Problem with helpful hints and an online question. Other questions are listed above in Interactive Learning.

Problem 2

Q What are the independent and dependent variables? **[The number of cubic feet of concrete is the independent variable and the total weight in pounds is the dependent variable.]**

Q What does the 30,000 represent in the given function? **[the weight of the truck when it is empty]**

Q How much does each cubic foot of concrete weigh? **[146 lb]**

Q What is the range of values for the dependent variable? **[from 30,000 lb to about 60,000 lb]**

Q Does it make sense to put arrows on the line in the graph? **[No, the c values are limited to between 0 and 200 ft³.]**

Got It?

Q What values should you use for the independent variable in a table of values? **[Answers may vary. Sample: every 50 gallons from 0 to 250]**

Q Why does it make sense to connect the points with part of a straight line? **[Because the number of gallons of water can be any real number between 0 and 250.]**

When you graph a real-world function rule, choose appropriate intervals for the units on the axes. Every interval on an axis should represent the same change in value. If all the data are nonnegative, show only the first quadrant.

Problem 2 Graphing a Real-World Function Rule

Trucking The function rule $W = 146c + 30,000$ represents the total weight W, in pounds, of a concrete mixer truck that carries c cubic feet of concrete. If the capacity of the truck is about 200 ft³, what is a reasonable graph of the function rule?

Plan
How do you choose values for a real-world independent variable?
Look for information about what the values can be. The independent variable c in this problem is limited by the capacity of the truck, 200 ft³.

Step 1
Make a table to find ordered pairs (c, W).

The truck can hold 0 to 200 ft³ of concrete. So only c-values from 0 to 200 are reasonable.

c	W = 146c + 30,000	(c, W)
0	$W = 146(0) + 30,000 = 30,000$	(0, 30,000)
50	$W = 146(50) + 30,000 = 37,300$	(50, 37,300)
100	$W = 146(100) + 30,000 = 44,600$	(100, 44,600)
150	$W = 146(150) + 30,000 = 51,900$	(150, 51,900)
200	$W = 146(200) + 30,000 = 59,200$	(200, 59,200)

Step 2
Graph the ordered pairs from the table.

W reaches almost 60,000 lb. So W-values from 0 to 60,000 in grid increments of 10,000 make sense.

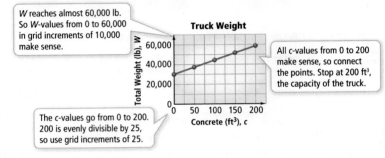

All c-values from 0 to 200 make sense, so connect the points. Stop at 200 ft³, the capacity of the truck.

The c-values go from 0 to 200. 200 is evenly divisible by 25, so use grid increments of 25.

Got It? **2. a.** The function rule $W = 8g + 700$ represents the total weight W, in pounds, of a spa that contains g gallons of water. What is a reasonable graph of the function rule, given that the capacity of the spa is 250 gal?
b. Reasoning What is the weight of the spa when empty? Explain.

In Problem 2, the truck could contain any amount of concrete from 0 to 200 ft³, such as 27.3 ft³ or $105\frac{2}{3}$ ft³. You can connect the data points from the table because any point between the data points has meaning.

Some graphs may be composed of isolated points. For example, in the Solve It you graphed only points that represent printing whole numbers of photos.

Answers

Solve It!
Answers may vary. Sample:

Got It?
1.

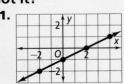

2. See page 256.

PowerAlgebra.com

2 Guided Instruction

Each Problem is worked out and supported online.

Problem 1
Graphing a Function Rule
Animated

Problem 2
Graphing a Real-World Function Rule

Problem 3
Identifying Continuous and Discrete Graphs
Animated

Problem 4
Graphing Nonlinear Function Rules
Animated

Support in Algebra 1 Companion
• Vocabulary
• Key Concepts
• Got It?

Key Concept   Continuous and Discrete Graphs

Continuous Graph
A **continuous graph** is a graph that is unbroken.

Discrete Graph
A **discrete graph** is composed of distinct, isolated points.

Take Note
Make note that a continuous function can be represented by a line, as is shown in the example graph. A continuous function can also be represented by a line segment, as in Problem 2, or a ray, as in Problem 3.

A discrete function is used to represent data that has holes—that is functions where only the values of certain data points make sense.

Problem 3

Q What type of numbers can you use as the domain for the function that describes the relationship between the milk used and the amount of cheese made? Explain. **[Positive real numbers; the number of gallons of milk used cannot be negative, but it can be a fraction or a decimal.]**

Q What type of numbers can you use as the domain for the function that describes the relationship between the money made and the number of wheels of cheese sold? Explain. **[Whole numbers; the number of wheels of cheese sold cannot be negative, nor can it be a fraction or a decimal.]**

Q Because the domain for the function is not continuous, how can you describe the range values? **[The values of the range must be positive multiples of 9.]**

Problem 3   Identifying Continuous and Discrete Graphs

Farmer's Market A local cheese maker is making cheddar cheese to sell at a farmer's market. The amount of milk used to make the cheese and the price at which he sells the cheese are shown. Write a function for each situation. Graph each function. Is the graph *continuous* or *discrete*?

1 gal of milk makes 16 oz of cheddar cheese.

Each wheel of cheddar cheese costs $9.

Think
How can you decide if a graph is continuous or discrete?
Decide what values are reasonable for the independent variable. For example, if 3 and 4 make sense, do 3.3 and 3.7 make sense as well?

The weight *w* of cheese, in ounces, depends on the number of gallons *m* of milk used. So $w = 16m$. Make a table of values.

m	0	1	2	3	4
w	0	16	32	48	64

Graph each ordered pair (m, w).

Weight of Cheese

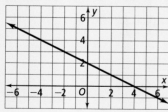

Any amount of milk makes sense, so connect the points. The graph is continuous.

The amount *a* of money made from selling cheese depends on the number *n* of wheels sold. So $a = 9n$. Make a table of values.

n	0	1	2	3	4
a	0	9	18	27	36

Graph each ordered pair (n, a)

Money Earned

He can only sell whole wheels of cheese. The graph is discrete.

PowerAlgebra.com   Lesson 4-4   Graphing a Function Rule   **255**

Additional Problems

1. What is the graph of the function rule $y = -\frac{1}{2}x + 2$?

ANSWER

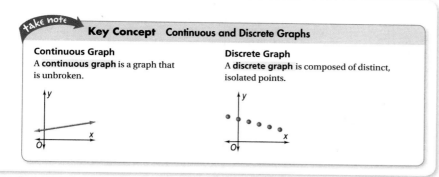

2. The function $C = 12.5h + 30$ represents the total cost of renting a truck for *h* hours. What is a reasonable graph of the function given that the daily limit is 12 hours?

ANSWER

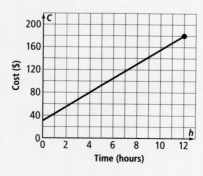
Time (hours)

3. Megan buys eggs at the supermarket for $1.75 per carton. The cost is a function of the number of cartons bought. What is the graph of the function? Is the function *continuous* or *discrete*?

ANSWER discrete

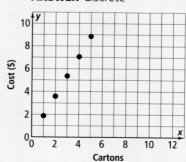
Cartons

4. What is a graph of $y = x^2 - 1$?

ANSWER

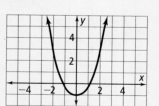

Got It?   ERROR PREVENTION

Help students distinguish between discrete and continuous functions by telling them that a discrete function is one in which the values for the independent variable can be counted, and a continuous function is one in which the values for the independent variable can be measured.

Problem 4

> **Q** How do you find the absolute value of a number? **[You determine how far the number is from zero on a number line.]**
>
> **Q** Why are all values of the dependent variable for 4B positive? **[They are all positive because the square of a number is always a positive value.]**
>
> **Q** If you are unsure of the shape to use when connecting ordered pairs on the graph, what should you do? **[Pick more x-values and determine the corresponding y-values; graph more ordered pairs.]**

Got It?   ERROR PREVENTION

If students' graphs resemble parabolas, make sure they understand that when a negative value is cubed, the product is a negative number.

 Got It? **3.** Graph each function rule. Is the graph *continuous or discrete*? Justify your answer.
  a. The amount of water w in a wading pool, in gallons, depends on the amount of time t, in minutes, the wading pool has been filling, as related by the function rule $w = 3t$.
  b. The cost C for baseball tickets, in dollars, depends on the number n of tickets bought, as related by the function rule $C = 16n$.

The function rules graphed in Problems 1–3 represent linear functions. You can also graph a nonlinear function rule. When a function rule does not represent a real-world situation, graph it as a continuous function.

 Problem 4 Graphing Nonlinear Function Rules

What is the graph of each function rule?

A $y = |x| - 4$

Step 1	Step 2
Make a table of values.	Graph the ordered pairs. Connect the points.

 Think
What input values make sense for these nonlinear functions? Include 0 as well as negative and positive values so that you can see how the graphs change.

x	y = |x| − 4	(x, y)
−4	y = |−4| − 4 = 0	(−4, 0)
−2	y = |−2| − 4 = −2	(−2, −2)
0	y = |0| − 4 = −4	(0, −4)
2	y = |2| − 4 = −2	(2, −2)
4	y = |4| − 4 = 0	(4, 0)

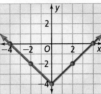

B $y = x^2 + 1$

Step 1	Step 2
Make a table of values.	Graph the ordered pairs. Connect the points.

x	y = x² + 1	(x, y)
−2	y = (−2)² + 1 = 5	(−2, 5)
−1	y = (−1)² + 1 = 2	(−1, 2)
0	y = 0² + 1 = 1	(0, 1)
1	y = 1² + 1 = 2	(1, 2)
2	y = 2² + 1 = 5	(2, 5)

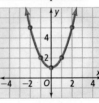

 Got It? **4.** What is the graph of the function rule $y = x^3 + 1$?

Answers

Got It? (continued)

2. a.

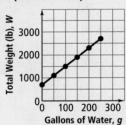

b. 700 lb; when $g = 0$, the spa is empty, and $W = 700$.

3. a.

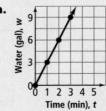

Continuous; you can have any amount of water.

b.

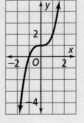

Discrete; you can only have a whole number of tickets.

4.

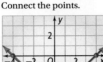

Lesson Check

Do you know HOW?

Graph each function rule.

1. $y = 2x + 4$

2. $y = \frac{1}{2}x - 7$

3. $y = 9 - x$

4. $y = -x^2 + 2$

5. The function rule $h = 18 + 1.5n$ represents the height h, in inches, of a stack of traffic cones.
 a. Make a table for the function rule.
 b. Suppose the stack of cones can be no taller than 30 in. What is a reasonable graph of the function rule?

Do you UNDERSTAND?

Vocabulary Tell whether each relationship should be represented by a *continuous* or a *discrete* graph.

6. The number of bagels b remaining in a dozen depends on the number s that have been sold.

7. The amount of gas g remaining in the tank of a gas grill depends on the amount of time t the grill has been used.

8. Error Analysis Your friend graphs $y = x + 3$ at the right. Describe and correct your friend's error.

Practice and Problem-Solving Exercises

 Practice

Graph each function rule.　　　　　　　　　　　　　◀ **See Problem 1.**

9. $y = x - 3$　　　　**10.** $y = 2x + 5$　　　　**11.** $y = 3x - 2$

12. $y = 5 + 2x$　　　**13.** $y = 3 - x$　　　　**14.** $y = -5x + 12$

15. $y = 10x$　　　　　**16.** $y = 4x - 5$　　　　**17.** $y = 9 - 2x$

18. $y = 2x - 1$　　　　**19.** $y = \frac{3}{4}x + 2$　　　**20.** $y = -\frac{1}{2}x + \frac{1}{2}$

Graph each function rule. Explain your choice of intervals on the axes　◀ **See Problems 2 and 3.**
of the graph. Tell whether the graph is *continuous* or *discrete*.

21. Beverages The height h, in inches, of the juice in a 20-oz bottle depends on the amount of juice j, in ounces, that you drink. This situation is represented by the function rule $h = 6 - 0.3j$.

22. Trucking The total weight w, in pounds, of a tractor-trailer capable of carrying 8 cars depends on the number of cars c on the trailer. This situation is represented by the function rule $w = 37{,}000 + 4200c$.

23. Food Delivery The cost C, in dollars, for delivered pizza depends on the number p of pizzas ordered. This situation is represented by the function rule $C = 5 + 9p$.

---

3 Lesson Check

Do you know HOW?

- If students have difficulty with Exercise 4, then tell them to rewrite the function as $y = -1 \cdot (x)^2 + 2$, and remind students that squaring takes precedence over multiplying according to the order of operations.

Do you UNDERSTAND?

- If students have difficulty with Exercise 8, then remind them that a function rule such as $y = x + 3$ is defined for all real number values of x, unless otherwise stated.

Close

Q How can you determine whether or not to connect the points on a graph with a line or portion of a line? **[You connect the points if the numbers between any two data values in the table have meaning in terms of the real-world situation.]**

Lesson Check

1.

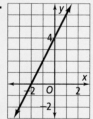

2.

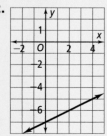

3.

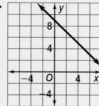

4.

5–8. See back of book.

Practice and Problem-Solving Exercises

9–23. See back of book.

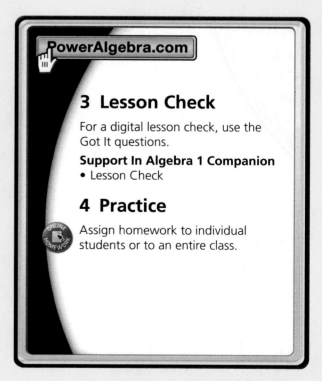

PowerAlgebra.com

3 Lesson Check

For a digital lesson check, use the Got It questions.

Support In Algebra 1 Companion
- Lesson Check

4 Practice

Assign homework to individual students or to an entire class.

4 Practice

ASSIGNMENT GUIDE

Basic: 9–32, 33, 36–39

Average: 9–31 odd, 33–39

Advanced: 9–31 odd, 33–41

Standardized Test Prep: 42–45

Mixed Review: 46–58

Reasoning exercises have blue headings.

Applications exercises have red headings.

EXERCISE 39: Use the Think About a Plan worksheet in the **Practice and Problem Solving Workbook** (also available in the Teaching Resources in print and online) to further support students' development in becoming independent learners.

HOMEWORK QUICK CHECK

To check students' understanding of key skills and concepts, go over Exercises 9, 21, 33, 38, and 39.

See Problem 4.

Graph each function rule.

24. $y = |x| - 7$ **25.** $y = |x| + 2$ **26.** $y = 2|x|$

27. $y = x^3 - 1$ **28.** $y = 3x^3$ **29.** $y = -2x^2$

30. $y = |-2x| - 1$ **31.** $y = -x^3$ **32.** $y = |x - 3| - 1$

 Apply

33. Error Analysis The graph at the right shows the distance d you run, in miles, as a function of time t, in minutes, during a 5-mi run. Your friend says that the graph is not continuous because it stops at $d = 5$, so the graph is discrete. Do you agree? Explain.

5-Mile Run

34. Writing Is the point $\left(2, 2\frac{1}{2}\right)$ on the graph of $y = x + 2$? How do you know?

35. Geometry The area A of an isosceles right triangle depends on the length ℓ of each leg of the triangle. This is represented by the rule $A = \frac{1}{2}\ell^2$. Graph the function rule. Is the graph *continuous* or *discrete*? How do you know?

36. Which function rule is graphed below?

   Ⓐ $y = -\frac{1}{2}x + 1$

   Ⓑ $y = \frac{1}{2}x - 1$

   Ⓒ $y = \left|\frac{1}{2}x\right| - 1$

   Ⓓ $y = \frac{1}{2}x + 1$

37. Sporting Goods The amount a basketball coach spends at a sporting goods store depends on the number of basketballs the coach buys. The situation is represented by the function rule $a = 15b$.
   a. Make a table of values and graph the function rule. Is the graph *continuous* or *discrete*? Explain.
   b. Suppose the coach spent $120 before tax. How many basketballs did she buy?

38. Think About a Plan The height h, in inches, of the vinegar in the jars of pickle chips shown at the right depends on the number of chips p you eat. About how many chips must you eat to lower the level of the vinegar in the jar on the left to the level of the jar on the right? Use a graph to find the answer.
   • What should the maximum value of p be on the horizontal axis?
   • What are reasonable values of p in this situation?

$h = 4.75 - 0.22p$

4 in.

39. Falling Objects The height h, in feet, of an acorn that falls from a branch 100 ft above the ground depends on the time t, in seconds, since it has fallen. This is represented by the rule $h = 100 - 16t^2$. About how much time does it take for the acorn to hit the ground? Use a graph and give an answer between two consecutive whole-number values of t.

Answers

Practice and Problem-Solving Exercises
(continued)

24.

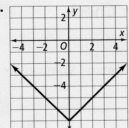

25.

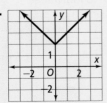

26.

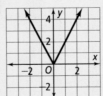

27.

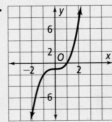

28.

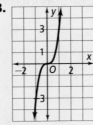

29.

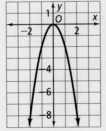

30.

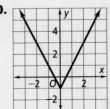

31.

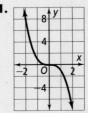

40. Reasoning Graph the function rules below in the same coordinate plane.

$$y = |x| + 1 \qquad y = |x| + 4 \qquad y = |x| - 3$$

In the function rule $y = |x| + k$, how does changing the value of k affect the graph?

41. Reasoning Make a table of values and a graph for the function rules $y = 2x$ and $y = 2x^2$. How does the value of y change when you double the value of x for each function rule?

Standardized Test Prep

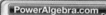GRIDDED RESPONSE

42. A plumber's bill b is based on $125 for materials and $50 per hour for t hours of labor. This situation can be represented by the function rule $b = 50t + 125$. Suppose the plumber works for $3\frac{1}{4}$ h. How much is the bill?

43. No more than $\frac{1}{10}$ of the people attending an auto race will be given a free hat. If maximum attendance is 3510 people, what is the greatest number of free hats that can be given away?

44. What is the solution of $\frac{12}{b} = \frac{36}{51}$?

45. What is the solution of $2(x - 5) = 2 - x$?

Mixed Review

Tell whether the function shown in each table is *linear* or *nonlinear*. ◀ See Lesson 4-3.

46.

x	0	1	2	3	4
y	0	−1	−1	−3	−2

47.

x	0	1	2	3	4
y	−7	−6	−5	−4	−3

Solve each equation. If there is no solution, write *no solution*. ◀ See Lesson 3-7.

48. $|x - 5| = 7$ **49.** $|x + 3| = 4$ **50.** $6 = |a - 7|$

51. $20 = |n + 11|$ **52.** $-3|4q| = 10$ **53.** $-2|5y| = -40$

54. $8|z - 1| = 24$ **55.** $|b + 2| + 5 = 1$ **56.** $3|t + 1| + 1 = 7$

Get Ready! To prepare for Lesson 4-5, do Exercises 57 and 58.

Define a variable and write an equation for each situation. Then solve the problem. ◀ See Lesson 2-2.

57. Shopping You have $14. Ice-cream cones cost $4, and the store offers $2 off the price of the first ice-cream cone. How many ice-cream cones can you buy?

58. Gardening You order 5 yd of mulch and pay a delivery fee of $35. The total cost including the delivery fee is $200. What is the cost of each yard of mulch?

32.

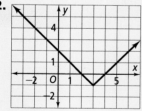

Continuous; lengths and areas can be any number.

36. B

37. a.

b	0	1	2	3
a	0	15	30	45

33. No; the graph is continuous over the appropriate values of d and t.

34. No; when you substitute the values $x = 2$ and $y = 2\frac{1}{2}$ in $y = \frac{1}{3}x = 2$, you do not get a true statement.

35.

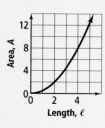

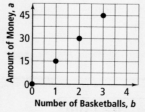

Discrete; you can only have whole numbers of basketballs.

b. 8

38. about 3 or 4 pickle chips

39. between 2 and 3 s

40.

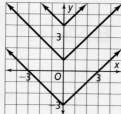

The value of k tells how many units the graph of $y = |x|$ has been shifted up or down on the y-axis.

41.

x	−2	−1	0	1	2
y	−4	−2	0	1	2

x	−2	−1	0	1	2
y	8	2	0	2	8

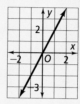

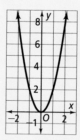

For $y = 2x$, the value of y doubles when the value of x doubles. For $y = 2x^2$, the value of y quadruples when the value of x doubles.

42. $287.50   **43.** 351

44. 17   **45.** 4

46. nonlinear   **47.** linear

48. −2, 12   **49.** −7, 1

50. 1, 13   **51.** −31, 9

52. no solution   **53.** −4, 4

54. −2, 4   **55.** no solution

56. −3, 1

57. Let x = number of cones purchased at $4. Then $14 = 4x - 2$; 4.

58. Let x = cost of each yard of mulch. Then $200 = 35 + 5x$; $33.

Additional Instructional Support

Algebra 1 Companion

Students can use the **Algebra 1 Companion** worktext (4 pages) as you teach the lesson. Use the Companion to support

- New Vocabulary
- Key Concepts
- Got It for each Problem
- Lesson Check

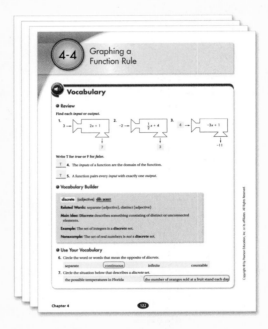

ELL Support

Focus on Language Draw a graph of a continuous function and a discrete function. Ask the following questions. What is the base word of *continuous*? [continue] Why do you call the function continuous? [no break in the line] Point to the space between points. Is there data here? If so, what is it? Turn to the graph of the discrete function. Point to the space between points. Is there data here?

Make a list such as minutes and distance, cars and number of occupants, or cost and weight of fruit purchased. Ask which situations are continuous and discrete. Ask students to contribute ideas.

5 Assess & Remediate

Lesson Quiz

1. What is the graph of the function rule $y = \frac{1}{3}x - 1$?
2. **Do you UNDERSTAND?** Kenny buys mixed nuts at a corner market for $4.50 per pound. The cost is a function of the number of pounds of nuts bought. What is the graph of the function? Is the function *continuous* or *discrete*?

ANSWERS TO LESSON QUIZ

1.

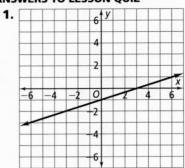

2. continuous

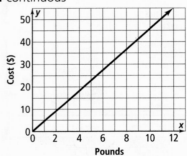

PRESCRIPTION FOR REMEDIATION

Use the student work on the Lesson Quiz to prescribe a differentiated review assignment.

Points	Differentiated Remediation
0	Intervention
1	On-level
2	Extension

PowerAlgebra.com

5 Assess & Remediate

Assign the Lesson Quiz. Appropriate intervention, practice, or enrichment is automatically generated based on student performance.

Intervention

- **Reteaching** (2 pages) Provides reteaching and practice exercises for the key lesson concepts. Use with struggling students or absent students.
- **English Language Learner Support** Helps students develop and reinforce mathematical vocabulary and key concepts.

All-in-One Resources/Online
Reteaching

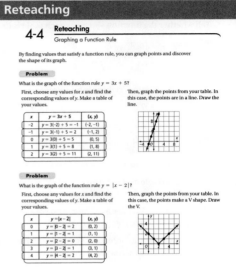

All-in-One Resources/Online
English Language Learner Support

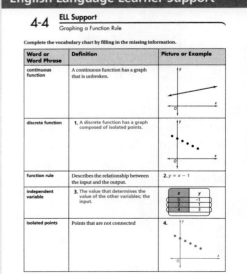

Differentiated Remediation continued

On-Level

- **Practice** (2 pages) Provides extra practice for each lesson. For simpler practice exercises, use the Form K Practice pages found in the All-in-One Teaching Resources and online.

- **Think About a Plan** Helps students develop specific problem-solving skills and strategies by providing scaffolded guiding questions.

- **Standardized Test Prep** Focuses on all major exercises, all major question types, and helps students prepare for the high-stakes assessments.

Extension

- **Enrichment** Provides students with interesting problems and activities that extend the concepts of the lesson.

- **Activities, Games, and Puzzles** Worksheets that can be used for concepts development, enrichment, and for fun!

Practice and Problem Solving WKBK/ All-in-One Resources/Online
Practice page 1

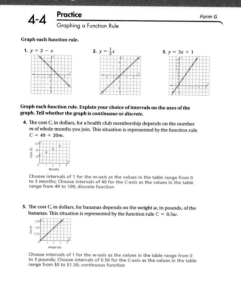

Practice and Problem Solving WKBK/ All-in-One Resources/Online
Practice page 2

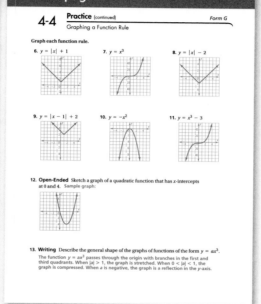

All-in-One Resources/Online
Enrichment

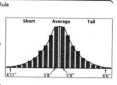

Practice and Problem Solving WKBK/ All-in-One Resources/Online
Think About a Plan

Practice and Problem Solving WKBK/ All-in-One Resources/Online
Standardized Test Prep

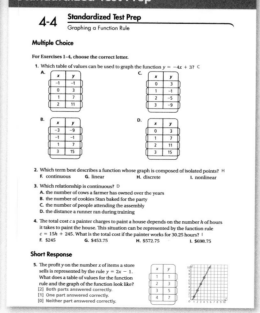

Online Teacher Resource Center
Activities, Games, and Puzzles

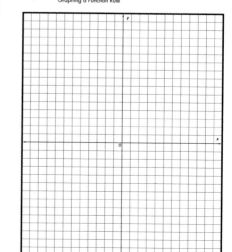

Guided Instruction

PURPOSE To use a graphing calculator to graph functions and solve linear equations

PROCESS Students will graph functions that represent two sides of a linear equation and determine the point of intersection for the equations.

DISCUSS Show students an equation. Discuss the parts of the equation. Have students describe what it means to be a solution of an equation.

Example 1

In this Example students use a graphing calculator to input an equation and enter predetermined window settings in order to view the important parts of the graph. If students get an error message after entering the Xmin or Ymin values, remind them that negative values must be entered using the unary minus key $\boxed{(-)}$ rather than the subtraction operator $\boxed{-}$.

Concept Byte
Use With Lesson 4-4
TECHNOLOGY

Graphing Functions and Solving Equations

Indiana Academic Standard
A1.2.1 Translate among various representations of linear functions including tables, graphs, words and equations.

You have learned to graph function rules by making a table of values. You can also use a graphing calculator to graph function rules.

Example 1

Graph $y = \frac{1}{2}x - 4$ using a graphing calculator.

Step 1 Press the $\boxed{y=}$ key. To the right of $Y_1 =$, enter $\frac{1}{2}x - 4$ by pressing $\boxed{(}$ 1 $\boxed{÷}$ 2 $\boxed{)}$ $\boxed{x,t,\theta,n}$ $\boxed{-}$ 4.

Step 2 The screen on the graphing calculator is a "window" that lets you look at only part of the graph. Press the $\boxed{window}$ key to set the borders of the graph. A good window for this function rule is the standard viewing window, $-10 \le x \le 10$ and $-10 \le y \le 10$.

You can have the axes show 1 unit between tick marks by setting **Xscl** and **Yscl** to 1, as shown.

Step 3 Press the $\boxed{graph}$ key. The graph of the function rule is shown.

Answers

Exercises

1.
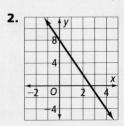

2.

3.
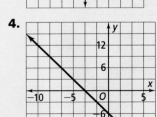

4.

5.
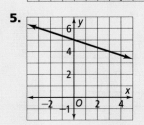

In Chapter 2 you learned how to solve equations in one variable. You can also solve equations by using a graphing calculator to graph each side of the equation as a function rule. The x-coordinate of the point where the graphs intersect is the solution of the equation.

Example 2

Solve $7 = -\frac{3}{4}k + 3$ using a graphing calculator.

Step 1 Press [Y=]. Clear any equations. Then enter each side of the given equation. For $Y_1 =$, enter 7. For $Y_2 =$, enter $-\frac{3}{4}x + 3$ by pressing ((-) 3 ÷ 4) [x,t,θ,n] + 3. Notice that you must replace the variable k with x.

Step 2 Graph the function rules. Use a standard graphing window by pressing [zoom] 6. This gives a window defined by $-10 \le x \le 10$ and $-10 \le y \le 10$.

Step 3 Use the **CALC** feature. Select **INTERSECT** and press [enter] 3 times to find the point where the graphs intersect.

The calculator's value for the x-coordinate of the point of intersection is -5.333333. The actual x-coordinate is $-5\frac{1}{3}$.

The solution of the equation $7 = -\frac{3}{4}k + 3$ is $-5\frac{1}{3}$.

Example 2
In this Example students locate the point of intersection of two equations using a graphing calculator.

Q Why is it important to use the CALC feature when identifying the solution rather than simply examining the graph? **[The solution may not be located at an integer value, and examining the graph for the solution is not very precise.]**

Q Once the point of intersection is found, how can you check to make sure the point is actually a solution to the equation? **[Substitute the coordinates of the point for x and y and verify that a true statement results.]**

Exercises

Graph each function rule using a graphing calculator.

1. $y = 6x + 3$

2. $y = -3x + 8$

3. $y = 0.2x - 7$

4. $y = -1.8x - 6$

5. $y = -\frac{1}{3}x + 5$

6. $y = \frac{8}{3}x - 5$

7. Open-Ended Graph $y = -0.4x + 8$. Using the [window] screen, experiment with values for **Xmin**, **Xmax**, **Ymin**, and **Ymax** until you can see the graph crossing both axes. What values did you use for **Xmin**, **Xmax**, **Ymin**, and **Ymax**?

8. Reasoning How can you graph the equation $2x + 3y = 6$ on a graphing calculator?

Use a graphing calculator to solve each equation.

9. $8a - 12 = 6$

10. $-4 = -3t + 2$

11. $-5 = -0.5x - 2$

12. $4 + \frac{3}{2}n = -7$

13. $\frac{5}{4}d - \frac{1}{2} = 6$

14. $-3y - 1 = 3.5$

6.

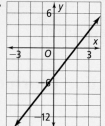

7. Answers may vary. Sample:
$-10 \le x \le 22$ and $-10 \le y \le 10$

8. First solve the equation for y:
$y = -\frac{2}{3}x + 2$.

9. 2.25   **10.** 2   **11.** 6

12. $-7\frac{1}{3}$ **13.** 5.2   **14.** -1.5

1 Interactive Learning

Solve It!
PURPOSE To analyze a real-world situation and write a linear function to represent it
PROCESS Students may interpret the function rule by creating a table of values or by analyzing the verbal phrases. Student will use the results to write the function rule as an equation.

FACILITATE
Q When your friend has swum x meters, how far have you swum? Explain. **[$x - 15$ m; I will always be 15 m behind my friend.]**

Q Is this function continuous or discrete? Explain. **[It is continuous, because the number of meters swum can be any positive real number.]**

ANSWER See Solve It in Answers on next page.
CONNECT THE MATH An equation can be written that represents the distance your friend has swum depending on the distance you have swum. In the lesson, students learn that a function rule defines the relationship between the independent and dependent variables.

2 Guided Instruction

Problem 1

Q What are the independent and dependent variables? **[The number of chirps in a minute is the independent variable and the temperature is the dependent variable.]**

Q What mathematical operations can you use to find $\frac{1}{4}$ of a number? **[Multiply by one-fourth or divide by 4.]**

4-5 Writing a Function Rule

Indiana Academic Standard
A1.2.1 Translate among various representations of linear functions including tables, graphs, words and equations.

Objective To write equations that represent functions

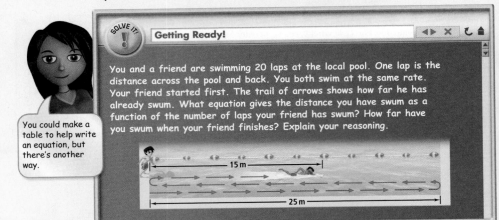

You could make a table to help write an equation, but there's another way.

Getting Ready!

You and a friend are swimming 20 laps at the local pool. One lap is the distance across the pool and back. You both swim at the same rate. Your friend started first. The trail of arrows shows how far he has already swum. What equation gives the distance you have swum as a function of the number of laps your friend has swum? How far have you swum when your friend finishes? Explain your reasoning.

In the Solve It, you can see how the value of one variable depends on another. Once you see a pattern in a relationship, you can write a rule.

Essential Understanding Many real-world functional relationships can be represented by equations. You can use an equation to find the solution of a given real-world problem.

Think
How can a model help you visualize a real-world situation? Use a model like the one below to represent the relationship that is described.

Problem 1 Writing a Function Rule

Insects You can estimate the temperature by counting the number of chirps of the snowy tree cricket. The outdoor temperature is about 40°F more than one fourth the number of chirps the cricket makes in one minute. What is a function rule that represents this situation?

Relate temperature is 40°F more than $\frac{1}{4}$ of the number of chirps in 1 min

Define Let T = the temperature. Let n = the number of chirps in 1 min.

Write $T \quad = \quad 40 \quad + \quad \frac{1}{4} \quad \cdot \quad n$

A function rule that represents this situation is $T = 40 + \frac{1}{4}n$.

BIG ideas Functions
Modeling

ESSENTIAL UNDERSTANDINGS
- Many real-world functional relationships can be represented by equations.
- Equations can be used to find the solution of given real-world problems.

Math Background
When students write a rule for a table of values, they must make sure that the apparent pattern does indeed hold true for each pair of points listed in the table. While two points are enough to determine a line, at least a third point should be used as a check to find and correct errors in calculation.

Using algebra to solve real-world problems involves two major steps. The first step is to model the real-world situation with an algebraic function or equation. The second step is to either evaluate

the function or solve the equation. This lesson provides students with an in-depth look at writing an algebraic function to model a real-world situation.

Support Student Learning
Use the **Algebra 1 Companion** to engage and support students during instructions. See Lesson Resources at the end of this lesson for details.

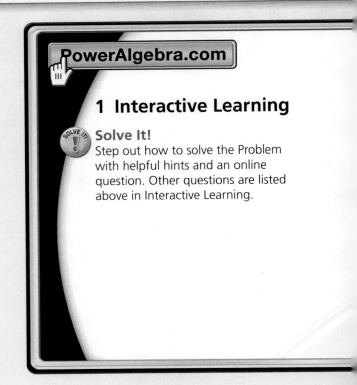

PowerAlgebra.com

1 Interactive Learning

Solve It!
Step out how to solve the Problem with helpful hints and an online question. Other questions are listed above in Interactive Learning.

Got It? 1. A landfill has 50,000 tons of waste in it. Each month it accumulates an average of 420 more tons of waste. What is a function rule that represents the total amount of waste after *m* months?

Problem 2 Writing and Evaluating a Function Rule

Concert Revenue A concert seating plan is shown below. Reserved seating is sold out. Total revenue from ticket sales will depend on the number of general-seating tickets sold. Write a function rule to represent this situation. What is the maximum possible total revenue?

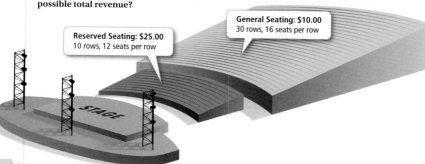

General Seating: $10.00
30 rows, 16 seats per row

Reserved Seating: $25.00
10 rows, 12 seats per row

STAGE

Plan

How can a model help you write an equation?
A model like the one below can help you write an expression for the general-seating revenue.

|←— Gen. seating —→|
| 10 |---------------|
| *n* tickets |

Add the reserved-seating revenue to get the total revenue.

Relate   total revenue   is $\boxed{\text{general seating revenue}}$ plus $\boxed{\text{reserved seating revenue}}$

$\boxed{\text{price per ticket}} \cdot \boxed{\text{number of tickets sold}}$

Define   Let   *R*   = the total revenue.

Let   *n*   = the number of general-seating tickets sold.

Write R =   10   ·   *n*   + $(25 \cdot 10 \cdot 12)$

$R = 10n + 3000$

The function rule $R = 10n + 3000$ represents this situation. There are $30 \cdot 16 = 480$ general-seating tickets. Substitute 480 for *n* to find the maximum possible revenue.

$R = 10(480) + 3000 = 7800$

The maximum possible revenue from ticket sales is $7800.

 Got It? 2. a. A kennel charges $15 per day to board dogs. Upon arrival, each dog must have a flea bath that costs $12. Write a function rule for the total cost for *n* days of boarding plus a bath. How much does a 10-day stay cost?
   b. Reasoning Does a 5-day stay cost half as much as a 10-day stay? Explain.

PowerAlgebra.com   Lesson 4-5   Writing a Function Rule   263

Got It?

Q How would you determine the total tons of waste in the dump after *x* months? **[Multiply *x* by 420 and then add 50,000.]**

Problem 2

Q What are the independent and dependent variables? **[The number of general seating tickets sold is the independent variable and the total revenue is the dependent variable.]**

Q How much money has already been generated though the sale of reserved seating? **[$3000]**

Q What algebraic expression represents the revenue generated by selling *n* general seating tickets? **[10*n*]**

Q What algebraic expression represents the total revenue for the concert if *n* general seating tickets are sold? **[10*n* + 3000]**

Q How many general seating tickets are available? Explain. **[30 · 16 = 480 tickets]**

Got It?

Q Do you have to calculate the cost of a 5-day stay to answer the question in 2b? Explain. **[No, without the $12 charge for the flea bath the cost of a 5-day stay would be half the cost of a 10-day stay. The flea bath is paid no matter how many days the stay is.]**

---

2 Guided Instruction

 Each Problem is worked out and supported online.

Problem 1
Writing a Function Rule
Animated

Problem 2
Writing and Evaluating a Function Rule
Animated

Problem 3
Writing a Nonlinear Function Rule
Animated

Support in Algebra 1 Companion
• Vocabulary
• Key Concepts
• Got It?

Answers

Solve It!
$d = 50\ell - 65$; 935 m

Got It?
1. $W = 50{,}000 + 420m$
2. a. $C = 12 + 15n$; $162
   b. No; making the stay shorter only halves the daily charge, not the bath charge.

Problem 3

Q If the variable *w* represents the width, what expression represents 5 more than the width? Explain. **[w + 5]**

Q How do you determine the area of a rectangle? **[Multiply the length by the width.]**

Q What property can you use to simplify the expression $(w + 5)w$? **[Distributive Property]**

Q Is this function continuous or discrete? Explain. **[It is continuous, because the measurement for the width of a rectangle can be any positive number.]**

Got It?

Q If the variable *b* represents the length of the base, what expression represents 4 less than twice the length of the base? **[2b − 4]**

3 Lesson Check

Do you know HOW?
• If students have difficulty with Exercise 4, then remind them how to calculate the volume of a cube.

Do you UNDERSTAND?
• If students have difficulty with Exercise 7, then remind them that in a discrete function, the independent variable can be counted, while in a continuous function, the independent variable can only be measured.

Close

Q Is it necessary to create a table of values for a real-world situation in order to write an equation that represents the function? Explain. **[No, you can use the verbal description as a model for the equation or write the equation from a graph.]**

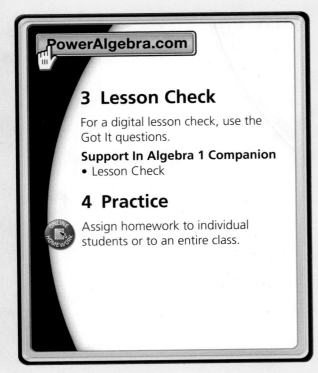

PowerAlgebra.com

3 Lesson Check

For a digital lesson check, use the Got It questions.

Support In Algebra 1 Companion
• Lesson Check

4 Practice

Assign homework to individual students or to an entire class.

Problem 3 Writing a Nonlinear Function Rule   GRIDDED RESPONSE

Geometry Write a function rule for the area of a rectangle whose length is 5 ft more than its width. What is the area of the rectangle when its width is 9 ft?

Think

How can *drawing a diagram* help you to write a rule?
A diagram visually represents information in the problem. It can give you a clearer understanding of how variables are related.

Step 1 Represent the general relationship first. The area *A* of a rectangle is the product of its length ℓ and its width *w*.

$A = \ell \cdot w$

Step 2 Revise the model to show that the length is 5 ft more than the width.

The length is 5 ft more than the width. You can substitute $w + 5$ for ℓ.

Step 3 Use the diagram in Step 2 to write the function rule. The function rule $A = (w + 5)w$, or $A = w^2 + 5w$, represents the rectangle's area. Substitute 9 for *w* to find the area when the width is 9 ft.

$A = 9^2 + 5(9)$

$= 81 + 45$

$= 126$

When the width of the rectangle is 9 ft, its area is 126 ft^2.

Got It? 3. a. Write a function rule for the area of a triangle whose height is 4 in. more than twice the length of its base. What is the area of the triangle when the length of its base is 16 in.?

b. Reasoning Graph the function rule from Problem 3. How do you know the rule is nonlinear?

Lesson Check

Do you know HOW?

Write a function rule to represent each situation.

1. the total cost *C* for *p* pounds of copper if each pound costs $3.57

2. the height *f*, in feet, of an object when you know the object's height *h* in inches

3. the amount *y* of your friend's allowance if the amount she receives is $2 more than the amount *x* you receive

4. the volume *V* of a cube-shaped box whose edge lengths are 1 in. greater than the diameter *d* of the ball that the box will hold

Do you UNDERSTAND?

5. Vocabulary Suppose you write an equation that gives *a* as a function of *b*. Which is the dependent variable and which is the independent variable?

6. Error Analysis A worker has dug 3 holes for fence posts. It will take 15 min to dig each additional hole. Your friend writes the rule $t = 15n + 3$ for the time *t*, in minutes, required to dig *n* additional holes. Describe and correct your friend's error.

7. Reasoning Is the graph of a function rule that relates a square's area to its side length *continuous* or *discrete*? Explain.

Additional Problems

1. Carolyn has 420 CDs in her collection. Each month, she adds 12 more CDs to her collection. What equation is a function rule that represents this situation?

ANSWER $y = 420 + 12x$

2. An archery club charges an annual membership fee of $65 plus $2 per visit. Write a function rule for the total cost of belonging to the club if you make *v* visits in a year. How much would it cost if you use the club 15 times in a year?

ANSWER $C = 65 + 2v$; $95

3. Write a function rule for the area of a rectangle whose length is 3 in. more than the width. What is the area of the rectangle when its width is 7 in.?

ANSWER $A = w^2 + 3w$; 70 in.^{2}

Practice and Problem-Solving Exercises

A Practice Write a function rule that represents each sentence. ← **See Problem 1.**

8. y is 5 less than the product of 4 and x.

9. C is 8 more than half of n.

10. 7 less than three fifths of b is a.

11. 2.5 more than the quotient of h and 3 is w.

Write a function rule that represents each situation.

12. Wages A worker's earnings e are a function of the number of hours n worked at a rate of $8.75 per hour.

13. Pizza The price p of a pizza is $6.95 plus $.95 for each topping t on the pizza.

14. Weight Loads The load L, in pounds, of a wheelbarrow is the sum of its own 42-lb weight and the weight of the bricks that it carries, as shown at the right.

The wheelbarrow holds n 4-lb bricks.

15. Baking The almond extract a remaining in an 8-oz bottle decreases by $\frac{1}{6}$ oz for each batch b of waffle cookies made.

16. Aviation A helicopter hovers 40 ft above the ground. Then the helicopter climbs at a rate of 21 ft/s. Write a rule that represents the helicopter's height h above the ground as a function of time t. What is the helicopter's height after 45 s? ← **See Problem 2.**

17. Diving A team of divers assembles at an elevation of -10 ft relative to the surface of the water. Then the team dives at a rate of -50 ft/min. Write a rule that represents the team's depth d as a function of time t. What is the team's depth after 3 min?

18. Publishing A new book is being planned. It will have 24 pages of introduction. Then it will have c 12-page chapters and 48 more pages at the end. Write a rule that represents the total number of pages p in the book as a function of the number of chapters. Suppose the book has 25 chapters. How many pages will it have?

19. Write a function rule for the area of a triangle with a base 3 cm greater than 5 times its height. What is the area of the triangle when its height is 6 cm? ← **See Problem 3.**

20. Write a function rule for the volume of the cylinder shown at the right with a height 3 in. more than 4 times the radius of the cylinder's base. What is the volume of the cylinder when it has a radius of 2 in.?

21. Write a function rule for the area of a rectangle with a length 2 ft less than three times its width. What is the area of the rectangle when its width is 2 ft?

B Apply **22. Open-Ended** Write a function rule that models a real-world situation. Evaluate your function for an input value and explain what the output represents.

h
r
$V = \pi r^2 h$

---

4 Practice

ASSIGNMENT GUIDE

Basic: 8–21, 23, 26–27, 29–30

Average: 9–21 odd, 22–30

Advanced: 9–21 odd, 22–32

Standardized Test Prep: 33–36

Mixed Review: 37–56

Reasoning exercises have blue headings.

Applications exercises have red headings.

EXERCISE 29: Use the Think About a Plan worksheet in the **Practice and Problem Solving Workbook** (also available in the Teaching Resources in print and online) to further support students' development in becoming independent learners.

HOMEWORK QUICK CHECK

To check students' understanding of key skills and concepts, go over Exercises 9, 17, 23, 26, and 29.

Answers

Got It? (continued)

3. a. $A = b^2 + 2b$; 288 in.^{2}

b.

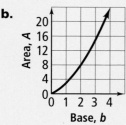

The graph is not a line.

Lesson Check

1. $C = 3.57p$ **2.** $f = \frac{h}{12}$

3. $y = x + 2$ **4.** $V = (d + 1)^3$

5. dependent, a; independent, b

6. You can't add holes and minutes. The correct rule is $t = 15n$.

7. Continuous; side length and area can be any positive real numbers.

Practice and Problem-Solving Exercises

8. $y = 4x - 5$ **9.** $C = 8 + \frac{1}{2}n$

10. $a = \frac{3}{5}b - 7$ **11.** $\frac{h}{3} + 2.5 = w$

12. $e = 8.75n$

13. $p = 6.95 + 0.95t$

14. $L = 42 + 4n$ **15.** $a = 8 - \frac{1}{6}b$

16. $h = 40 + 21t$; 985 ft

17. $d = -10 - 50t$; -160 ft

18. $p = 72 + 12c$; 372 pages

19. $A = \frac{3}{2}h + \frac{5}{2}h^2$; 99 cm^2

20. $V = \pi r^2(3 + 4r)$; 138.16 in.^{3}, or 44π in.^{3}

21. $A = 3w^2 - 2w$; 8 ft^2

22. Check students' work.

Answers

Practice and Problem-Solving Exercises
(continued)

23. Answers may vary. Sample: The rule covers all values, whereas the table only represents some of the values.

24. $A = 1.6w^2$

25. $d = -3.5 - 1.8s$; -435.5 m

26. $h = \frac{10}{-64}j + 10$; 2.66 in.

27. a.

Cost of Meal	$15	$21	$24	$30
Money Left	$37.75	$30.85	$27.40	$20.50

b. $m = 55 - 1.15c$

c.

28. a. $b = 42.95d + 45.60$

b. $432.15

29. a. $d = 1.8w$

b. No; the room is not wide enough.

c. $6\frac{2}{3}$ ft

30. $r = \frac{1}{2}d^2 + 1$

---

23. Writing What advantage(s) can you see of having a rule instead of a table of values to represent a function?

24. History of Math The golden ratio has been studied and used by mathematicians and artists for more than 2000 years. A golden rectangle, constructed using the golden ratio, has a length about 1.6 times its width. Write a rule for the area of a golden rectangle as a function of its width.

25. Whales From an elevation of 3.5 m below the surface of the water, a northern bottlenose whale dives at a rate of 1.8 m/s. Write a rule that gives the whale's depth d as a function of time in minutes. What is the whale's depth after 4 min?

26. Think About a Plan The height h, in inches, of the juice in the pitcher shown at the right is a function of the amount of juice j, in ounces, that has been poured out of the pitcher. Write a function rule that represents this situation. What is the height of the juice after 47 oz have been poured out?
- What is the height of the juice when half of it has been poured out?
- What fraction of the juice would you pour out to make the height decrease by 1 in.?

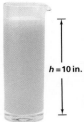

$h = 10$ in.

volume = 64 oz

27. Tips You go to dinner and decide to leave a 15% tip for the server. You had $55 when you entered the restaurant.
- **a.** Make a table showing how much money you would have left after buying a meal that costs $15, $21, $24, or $30.
- **b.** Write a function rule for the amount of money m you would have left if the meal costs c dollars before the tip.
- **c.** Graph the function rule.

28. Car Rental A car rental agency charges $29 per day to rent a car and $13.95 per day for a global positioning system (GPS). Customers are charged for their full tank of gas at $3.80 per gallon.
- **a.** A car has a 12-gal tank and a GPS. Write a rule for the total bill b as a function of the number of days d the car is rented.
- **b.** What is the bill for a 9-day rental?

29. Projectors You consult your new projector's instruction manual before mounting it on the wall. The manual says to multiply the desired image width by 1.8 to find the correct distance of the projector lens from the wall.
- **a.** Write a rule to describe the distance of the lens from the wall as a function of desired image width.
- **b.** The diagram shows the room in which the projector will be installed. Will you be able to project an image 7 ft wide? Explain.
- **c.** What is the maximum image width you can project in the room?

12 ft — ? ft

30. Reasoning Write a rule that is an example of a nonlinear function that fits the following description.

When d is 4, r is 9, and r is a function of d.

Make a table and a graph of each set of ordered pairs (x, y). Then write a function rule to represent the relationship between x and y.

31. $(-4, 7), (-3, 6), (-2, 5), (-1, 4), (0, 3), (1, 2), (2, 1), (3, 0), (4, -1)$

32. $(-4, 15), (-3, 8), (-2, 3), (-1, 0), (0, -1), (1, 0), (2, 3), (3, 8), (4, 15)$

Standardized Test Prep

SAT/ACT

33. You buy x pounds of cherries for $2.99/lb. What is a function rule for the amount of change C you receive from a $50 bill?

Ⓐ $C = 2.99x - 50$ Ⓒ $C = 50x - 2.99$
Ⓑ $C = 50 - 2.99x$ Ⓓ $C = 2.99 - 50x$

34. What is the solution of $-5 < h + 2 < 11$?

Ⓕ $-3 < h < 11$ Ⓖ $-7 < h < 9$ Ⓗ $-7 > h > 9$ Ⓘ $h < -7$ or $h > 9$

35. Which equation do you get when you solve $-ax + by^2 = c$ for b?

Ⓐ $b = \frac{c - ax}{y^2}$ Ⓑ $b = y^2(c + ax)$ Ⓒ $b = \frac{c + ax}{y^2}$ Ⓓ $b = \frac{c}{y^2} + ax$

Extended Response

36. The recommended dosage D, in milligrams, of a certain medicine depends on a person's body mass m, in kilograms. The function rule $D = 0.1m^2 + 5m$ represents this relationship.
  a. What is the recommended dosage for a person whose mass is 60 kg? Show your work.
  b. One pound is equivalent to approximately 0.45 kg. Explain how to find the recommended dosage for a 200-lb person. What is this dosage?

Mixed Review

Graph each function rule.   ◀ **See Lesson 4-4.**

37. $y = 9 - x$ **38.** $y = 4 + 3x$ **39.** $y = x + 1.5$

40. $y = 4x - 1$ **41.** $y = 6x$ **42.** $y = 12 - 3x$

Convert the given amount to the given unit.   ◀ **See Lesson 2-6.**

43. 8.25 lb; ounces   **44.** 450 cm; meters   **45.** 17 yd; feet

46. 90 s; minutes   **47.** 216 h; days   **48.** 9.5 km; meters

Get Ready! To prepare for Lesson 4-6, do Exercises 49–56.

Find each product. Simplify if necessary.   ◀ **See Lesson 1-6.**

49. $-4(9)$ **50.** $-3(-7)$ **51.** $-7.2(-15.5)$ **52.** $-6(1.5)$

53. $-4\left(-\frac{7}{2}\right)$ **54.** $-\frac{4}{9}\left(-\frac{9}{4}\right)$ **55.** $\frac{25}{9}\left(\frac{3}{5}\right)$ **56.** $\frac{7}{10}\left(\frac{15}{8}\right)$

31.

x	-4	-3	-2	-1	0	1	2	3	4
y	7	6	5	4	3	2	1	0	-1

$y = -x + 3$

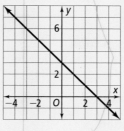

32.

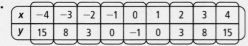

x	-4	-3	-2	-1	0	1	2	3	4
y	15	8	3	0	-1	0	3	8	15

$y = x^2 - 3$

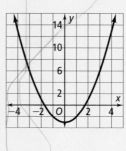

33. B   **34.** G   **35.** C

36. [4] **a.** $D = 0.1m^2 + 5m$
$$D = 0.1(60)^2 + 5(60)$$
$$= 0.1(3600) + 300$$
$$= 360 + 300$$
$$= 660$$
The dosage is 660 mg.

b. First find out the equivalent weight of a 200-lb person in kilograms.
$\frac{1}{0.45} = \frac{200}{x}$ so $x = 0.45(200) = 90$ kg
Now substitute $m = 90$ into the dosage formula. $D = 0.1(90)^2 + 5(90) = 0.1(8100) + 450 = 810 + 450 = 1260$
The correct dosage for a 200-lb person is 1260 mg.

[3] correct methods used with a minor computational error in either part (a) or (b)

[2] correct use of dosage formula, but with an error in the conversion

[1] correct answers with no work shown

37.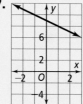

38.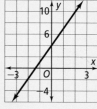

39.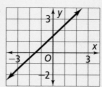

40.

41.

42.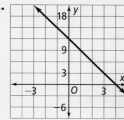

43. 132 oz   **44.** 4.5 m

45. 51 ft   **46.** 1.5 min

47. 9 days   **48.** 9500 m

49. -36 **50.** 21

51. 111.6   **52.** -9

53. 14   **54.** 1

55. $\frac{5}{3}$ **56.** $\frac{21}{16}$

Additional Instructional Support

Algebra 1 Companion

Students can use the **Algebra 1 Companion** worktext (4 pages) as you teach the lesson. Use the Companion to support

- New Vocabulary
- Key Concepts
- Got It for each Problem
- Lesson Check

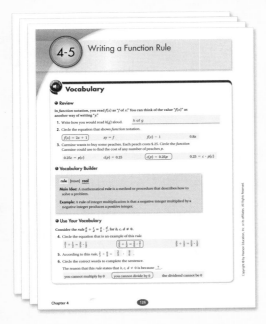

ELL Support

Use Graphic Organizers Project a word problem on the overhead projector. Read aloud as you point to the words. Model how to highlight information used to write the function rule. Display another problem and have students decide what the problem is asking for and what information is given. Help students make a chart to list independent and dependent variables and the units that describe them. Students should cultivate the habit of finding these facts before they write the function rule.

Focus on Communication Write a function rule, such as $s = 90 \div 5x$. Then state a verbal problem the function rule could represent. Encourage students to contribute their own ideas. As you say the words, gesture and point to the variables and operations the words represent.

5 Assess & Remediate

Lesson Quiz

1. The school cafeteria has 285 cartons of juice in stock. Each day, a total of 60 cartons are sold. What equation is a function rule that represents this situation?

2. **Do you UNDERSTAND?** A plumber charges a service fee of $40 plus $25 per hour for labor. Write a function rule for the total cost of hiring the plumber for a job that takes x hours. How much would it cost to hire the plumber for a job that takes 4 hours?

3. Write a function rule for the area of a triangle whose base is 4 ft more than the height. What is the area of the triangle when its height is 6 ft?

ANSWERS TO LESSON QUIZ

1. $y = 285 - 60x$
2. $y = 40 + 25x$; $140
3. $A = 0.5h^2 + 2h$; 30 ft²

PRESCRIPTION FOR REMEDIATION
Use the student work on the Lesson Quiz to prescribe a differentiated review assignment.

Points	Differentiated Remediation
0–1	Intervention
2	On-level
3	Extension

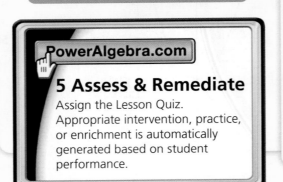

PowerAlgebra.com

5 Assess & Remediate

Assign the Lesson Quiz. Appropriate intervention, practice, or enrichment is automatically generated based on student performance.

Intervention

- **Reteaching** (2 pages) Provides reteaching and practice exercises for the key lesson concepts. Use with struggling students or absent students.

- **English Language Learner Support** Helps students develop and reinforce mathematical vocabulary and key concepts.

All-in-One Resources/Online

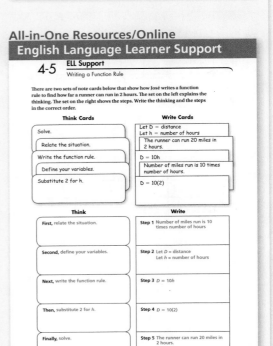

Differentiated Remediation *continued*

On-Level

- **Practice** (2 pages) Provides extra practice for each lesson. For simpler practice exercises, use the Form K Practice pages found in the All-in-One Teaching Resources and online.

- **Think About a Plan** Helps students develop specific problem-solving skills and strategies by providing scaffolded guiding questions.

- **Standardized Test Prep** Focuses on all major exercises, all major question types, and helps students prepare for the high-stakes assessments.

Extension

- **Enrichment** Provides students with interesting problems and activities that extend the concepts of the lesson.

- **Activities, Games, and Puzzles** Worksheets that can be used for concepts development, enrichment, and for fun!

Practice and Problem Solving WKBK/All-in-One Resources/Online
Practice page 1

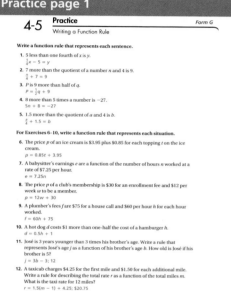

4-5 Practice — Form G
Writing a Function Rule

Write a function rule that represents each sentence.

1. 5 less than one fourth of x is y.
$\frac{1}{4}x - 5 = y$

2. 7 more than the quotient of a number n and 4 is 9.
$\frac{n}{4} + 7 = 9$

3. P is 9 more than half of q.
$P = \frac{1}{2}q + 9$

4. 8 more than 5 times a number is -27.
$5n + 8 = -27$

5. 1.5 more than the quotient of a and 4 is b.
$\frac{a}{4} + 1.5 = b$

For Exercises 6–10, write a function rule that represents each situation.

6. The price p of an ice cream is $3.95 plus $0.85 for each topping t on the ice cream.
$p = 0.85t + 3.95$

7. A babysitter's earnings e are a function of the number of hours n worked at a rate of $7.25 per hour.
$e = 7.25n$

8. The price p of a club's membership is $30 for an enrollment fee and $12 per week w to be a member.
$p = 12w + 30$

9. A plumber's fees f are $75 for a house call and $60 per hour h for each hour worked.
$f = 60h + 75$

10. A hot dog costs $1 more than one-half the cost of a hamburger h.
$d = 0.5h + 1$

11. José is 3 years younger than 3 times his brother's age. Write a rule that represents José's age j as a function of his brother's age b. How old is José if his brother is 5?
$j = 3b - 3; 12$

12. A taxicab charges $4.25 for the first mile and $1.50 for each additional mile. Write a rule for describing the total rate r as a function of the total miles m. What is the taxi rate for 12 miles?
$r = 1.5(m - 1) + 4.25; \$20.75$

Practice and Problem Solving WKBK/All-in-One Resources/Online
Practice page 2

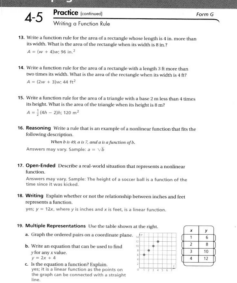

4-5 Practice (continued) — Form G
Writing a Function Rule

13. Write a function rule for the area of a rectangle whose length is 4 in. more than its width. What is the area of the rectangle when its width is 8 in.?
$A = (w + 4)w; 96$ in.^{2}

14. Write a function rule for the area of a rectangle with a length 3 ft more than two times its width. What is the area of the rectangle when its width is 4 ft?
$A = (2w + 3)w; 44$ ft^2

15. Write a function rule for the area of a triangle with a base 2 m less than 4 times its height. What is the area of the triangle when its height is 8 m?
$A = \frac{1}{2}(4h - 2)h; 120$ m^2

16. **Reasoning** Write a rule that is an example of a nonlinear function that fits the following description.
When b is 49, a is 7, and a is a function of b.
Answers may vary. Sample: $a = \sqrt{b}$

17. **Open-Ended** Describe a real-world situation that represents a nonlinear function.
Answers may vary. Sample: The height of a soccer ball is a function of the time since it was kicked.

18. **Writing** Explain whether or not the relationship between inches and feet represents a function.
yes; $y = 12x$, where y is inches and x is feet, is a linear function.

19. **Multiple Representations** Use the table shown at the right.
a. Graph the ordered pairs on a coordinate plane.
b. Write an equation that can be used to find y for any x value.
$y = 2x + 4$
c. Is the equation a function? Explain.
yes; it is a linear function as the points on the graph can be connected with a straight line.

x	y
1	6
2	8
3	10
4	12

Practice and Problem Solving WKBK/All-in-One Resources/Online
Think About a Plan

4-5 Think About a Plan
Writing a Function Rule

Projectors You consult your new projector's instruction manual before mounting it to the ceiling. The manual says *multiply the desired image width by 1.8 to find the correct distance of the projector lens from the wall.*
a. Write a rule to describe the distance of the lens from the wall as a function of desired image width.
b. The diagram shows the room in which the projector will be installed. Will you be able to project an image 7 ft wide? Explain.
c. What is the maximum image width you can project in the room?

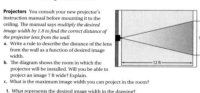

1. What represents the desired image width in the drawing?
The "?"

2. What variables will you use in writing the rule and what do they represent?
Let d = the distance between the wall and the lens and let w = the desired image width.

3. Write a rule to describe the distance of the lens from the wall as a function of desired image width.
$d = 1.8w$

4. How can you determine if the room is large enough to project an image that is 7 ft wide?
Substitute 7 for w in the equation and simplify.

5. Is the room large enough to project an image that is 7 ft wide? Explain.
no; $d = 1.8(7) = 12.6$

6. How can you determine the maximum image width that can be projected in this room?
Substitute 12 for d in the equation and solve for w.

7. What is the maximum image width you can project in the room? Show your work.
$6\frac{2}{3}$ ft; $12 = 1.8w$ so $w = 6\frac{2}{3}$

Practice and Problem Solving WKBK/All-in-One Resources/Online
Standardized Test Prep

4-5 Standardized Test Prep
Writing a Function Rule

Multiple Choice

For Exercises 1–5, choose the correct letter.

1. Jill earns $45 per hour. Using p for her pay and h for the hours she works, what function rule represents the situation? B
A. $h = 45p$ B. $p = 45h$ C. $h = p + 45$ D. $p = h + 45$

2. What is a function rule for the perimeter P of a building with a rectangular base if the width w is two times the length l? H
F. $p = 2l$ G. $p = 2w$ H. $p = 6l$ I. $p = 6w$

3. Which function rule can be used to represent the area of a triangle with a base b 8 in. longer than twice the height h in terms of the height h? C
A. $A = \frac{1}{2}bh$ C. $A = h^2 + 4h$
B. $A = \frac{1}{2}h(h + 8)$ D. $A = \frac{1}{2}(2h)(h + 8)$

4. Which equation represents the sentence "d is 17 less than the quotient of n and 4"? F
F. $d = \frac{n}{4} - 17$ H. $d = 4n - 17$
G. $d = \frac{n}{4} + 17$ I. $d - 17 = \frac{n}{4}$

5. The function rule for the profit a company expects to earn is $P = 1500m + 2700$, where P represents profit and m represents the number of months the company has been in business. How much profit should the company earn after 12 months in business? D
A. $15,700   B. $17,700   C. $18,000   D. $20,700

Extended Response

6. A plane was flying at an altitude of 30,000 feet when it began the descent toward the airport. The airplane descends at a rate of 850 feet per minute.
a. What is the function rule that describes this situation? $A = 30,000 - 850m$
b. What is the altitude of the plane after it has descended for 8 minutes? Show your work. 23,200 ft
c. How long will it take for the airplane to land on the ground if it continues to descend at the same rate? Show your work. about 35 min
[2] All parts answered correctly.
[1] One or two parts answered correctly.
[0] No parts answered correctly.

All-in-One Resources/Online
Enrichment

4-5 Enrichment
Writing a Function Rule

The inverse of a function is the set of ordered pairs found by swapping the first and second elements of each pair in the original function. If f is a given function, then f^{-1} represents the inverse of f. To find an inverse, simply swap the x and y coordinates. This new inverse will be a relation, but may not be a function. You can test that inverses are functions by using the vertical line test.

Problem

If $f(x) = x + 2$, find $f^{-1}(x)$.

$y = x + 2$	Original equation
$x = y + 2$	Swap x and y.
$y + 2 = x$	Reflexive Property of Equality
$y + 2 - 2 = x - 2$	Subtract 2 from each side.
$y = x - 2$	Simplify.

So, $f^{-1} = x - 2$.

For any ordered pair that makes $f(x) = x + 2$ true, the reverse ordered pair will make $f^{-1} = x - 2$ true.

$f(x) = x + 2$	
-5	-3
-3	-1
1	3
3	5

$f^{-1}(x) = x - 2$	
-3	-5
-1	-3
3	1
5	3

Exercises

1. Graph $f(x) = x + 2$ and $f^{-1} = x - 2$ to verify they are inverse functions.

Find the inverse of each function. Then graph the function and its inverse.

2. $f(x) = x - 3$
$f^{-1}(x) = x + 3$

3. $f(x) = 2x$
$f^{-1}(x) = \frac{x}{2}$

Online Teacher Resource Center
Activities, Games, and Puzzles

4-5 Puzzle: Chasing Down the Clues
Writing a Function Rule

The 12 clues given below lead you up a winding path from the value of b to the value of x. Notice that the value of b is given in the path at the right.

- For each clue below, write and solve a linear equation in two variables. Place each answer in the appropriate box.
- Using the value of b, start with clue 12 and work your way up the path.
- Use the chain of clues to find the value of x. (Hint: You have correctly answered all the clues if the value of x equals the greatest perfect square less than 100.)

1. I am a number x that is three times a less 15.

2. I am a number a that is twice the sum of 4 and d.

3. I am a number d that is twice h plus 12.

4. I am a number h that is twice n.

5. I am n. I am twice r less 10.

6. I am a number r three times less than c.

7. I am c and -2 times q.

8. I am q. Find me by multiplying m by 2 and then subtracting 70.

9. I am m, twice s plus 5.

10. I am s and 2 more than twice p.

11. I am p and twice z less 40.

12. I am z. To find me, multiply b by 3, then subtract 7.

$x = 81$
$a = 32$
$d = 12$
$b = 0$
$n = 0$
$r = 5$
$c = 8$
$q = -4$
$m = 33$
$s = 14$
$p = 6$
$z = 23$
$b = 10$

1 Interactive Learning

Solve It!

PURPOSE To familiarize students with the concept that one input can sometimes be paired with more than one possible output

PROCESS Students may work backward, use trial and error, or use the process of elimination.

FACILITATE

Q If your friend's first roll was a "3," what space would he end on? Explain. **[He would first land on the space marked with a "+4" and then move 4 ahead to end on the space marked "8."]**

Q How would the answer to the Solve It change if there were no "move" directions marked on the board? **[There would only be one possible answer for where he started.]**

ANSWER See Solve It in Answers on next page.
CONNECT THE MATH In the Solve It, the independent variable is the current space and the dependent variable is the previous space. Students should realize that the Solve It differs from previously studied functions because more than one output corresponds to one input.

2 Guided Instruction

Problem 1

Q Does any domain value in 1A have more than one arrow originating from it? Explain. **[No, each input has only one arrow.]**

Q Can a mapping diagram in which a range value has more than one arrow pointing to it represent a function? Explain. **[Yes, two different domain values can be mapped to the same range value.]**

4-6 Formalizing Relations and Functions

Indiana Academic Standard
A1.1.1 Determine whether a relation represented by a table, graph, words or equation is a function or not a function and translate among tables, graphs, words and equations.
A1.1.2 Identify the domain and range of relations represented by tables, graphs, words, and equations.

Objectives To determine whether a relation is a function
To find domain and range and use function notation

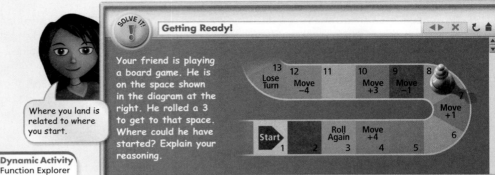

Where you land is related to where you start.

Dynamic Activity
Function Explorer

Lesson Vocabulary
• relation
• domain
• range
• vertical line test
• function notation

A **relation** is a pairing of numbers in one set, called the **domain,** with numbers in another set, called the **range.** A relation is often represented as a set of ordered pairs (x, y). In this case, the domain is the set of x-values and the range is the set of y-values.

Essential Understanding A function is a special type of relation in which each value in the domain is paired with exactly one value in the range.

Think
When is a relation *not* a function?
A function maps each domain value to exactly one range value. So a relation that maps a domain value to more than one range value cannot be a function.

Problem 1 Identifying Functions Using Mapping Diagrams

Identify the domain and range of each relation. Represent the relation with a mapping diagram. Is the relation a function?

A $\{(-2, 0.5), (0, 2.5), (4, 6.5), (5, 2.5)\}$
The domain is $\{-2, 0, 4, 5\}$.
The range is $\{0.5, 2.5, 6.5\}$.

Domain	Range
-2	0.5
0	2.5
4	6.5
5	

Each domain value is mapped to only one range value. The relation is a function.

B $\{(6, 5), (4, 3), (6, 4), (5, 8)\}$
The domain is $\{4, 5, 6\}$.
The range is $\{3, 4, 5, 8\}$.

Domain	Range
4	3
5	4
6	5
	8

The domain value 6 is mapped to two range values. The relation is not a function.

4-6 Preparing to Teach

BIG idea Functions **UbD**

ESSENTIAL UNDERSTANDINGS
• A function is a special type of relation where each value in the domain is paired with one value in the range.
• The vertical line test shows whether a relation is a function.

Math Background
The notion of functions being a subset of relations is an important concept that will be expounded upon in future mathematics courses. An important subset of functions is one-to-one functions. A one-to-one function is a function in which no two different elements in the domain are paired with the same element in the range. An understanding of one-to-one functions is necessary for the study of inverse functions.

Four common ways to represent a discrete relation are with ordered pairs, with a table, with a map,

or with a graph. When relations are continuous, they are typically represented with an equation or with a graph. Give students a discrete relation in one of the four forms and have them represent it in three other ways.

Support Student Learning
Use the **Algebra 1 Companion** to engage and support students during instructions. See Lesson Resources at the end of this lesson for details.

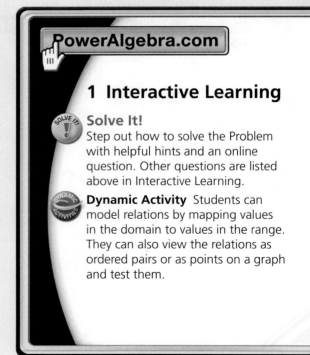

PowerAlgebra.com

1 Interactive Learning

Solve It!
Step out how to solve the Problem with helpful hints and an online question. Other questions are listed above in Interactive Learning.

Dynamic Activity Students can model relations by mapping values in the domain to values in the range. They can also view the relations as ordered pairs or as points on a graph and test them.

Got It? **1.** Identify the domain and range of each relation. Represent the relation with a mapping diagram. Is the relation a function?
   a. {(4.2, 1.5), (5, 2.2), (7, 4.8), (4.2, 0)}   **b.** {(−1, 1), (−2, 2), (4, −4), (7, −7)}

Another way to decide if a relation is a function is to analyze the graph of the relation using the **vertical line test.** If any vertical line passes through more than one point of the graph, then for some domain value there is more than one range value. So the relation is not a function.

 Problem 2 **Identifying Functions Using the Vertical Line Test**

Is the relation a function? Use the vertical line test.

Ⓐ {(−4, 2), (−3, 1), (0, −2), (−4, −1), (1, 2)}   Ⓑ $y = -x^2 + 3$

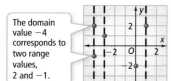
The domain value −4 corresponds to two range values, 2 and −1.

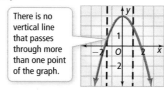
There is no vertical line that passes through more than one point of the graph.

The relation is not a function.   The relation is a function.

 Got It? **2.** Is the relation a function? Use the vertical line test.
   a. {(4, 2), (1, 2), (0, 1), (−2, 2), (3, 3)}   **b.** {(0, 2), (1 −1), (−1, 4), (0, −3), (2, 1)}

You have seen functions represented as equations involving *x* and *y*, such as $y = -3x + 1$. Below is the same equation written using **function notation.**

$$f(x) = -3x + 1$$

Notice that $f(x)$ replaces *y*. It is read "*f* of *x*." The letter *f* is the name of the function, not a variable. Function notation is used to emphasize that the function value $f(x)$ depends on the independent variable *x*. Other letters besides *f* can also be used, such as *g* and *h*.

 Problem 3 **Evaluating a Function**

Reading The function $w(x) = 250x$ represents the number of words $w(x)$ you can read in *x* minutes. How many words can you read in 8 min?

$w(x) = 250x$

$w(8) = 250(8)$ Substitute 8 for *x*.

$w(8) = 2000$ Simplify.

You can read 2000 words in 8 min.

---

2 Guided Instruction

 Each Problem is worked out and supported online.

Problem 1
Identifying Functions Using Mapping Diagrams
Animated

Problem 2
Identifying Functions Using the Vertical Line Test
Animated

Problem 3
Evaluating a Function

Problem 4
Finding the Range of a Function

Problem 5
Identifying a Reasonable Domain and Range
Animated

Support in Algebra 1 Companion
• Vocabulary
• Key Concepts
• Got It?

Got It?
Point out to students that in 1a, there are more elements in the range than are in the domain. When this is the case, a domain element must be mapped to more than one range element, and the relation is not a function.

Problem 2

Q Does a relation need to pass a horizontal line test also in order to be a function? Explain. **[No, a function can have more than one input paired with a particular output.]**

Q What method can you use to generate the graph of $y = -x^2 + 3$? **[Make a table of values.]**

Q What is the range for the function $y = -x^2 + 3$? **[all numbers less than or equal to 3]**

Got It?

Q What ordered pair could be added to the set for 1a that would prevent the relation from being a function? **[Answers may vary. Sample: (0, 5)]**

Problem 3

Q According to the function, what is your rate for reading, in words per minute? **[250 words/min]**

Q If you read 1250 words, how many minutes did you read? Explain. **[5 min; $\frac{1250}{250} = 5$]**

Answers

Solve It!
Answer may vary. Samples: 4, 5, 9

Got It?
1. a. domain: {4.2, 5, 7}; range: {0, 1.5, 2.2, 4.8}.

not a function

b. domain: {−2, −1, 4, 7}; range: {1, 2, −4, −7}.

function

2. a. function
   b. not a function

Got It?

ERROR PREVENTION

Make sure students understand that $w(8)$ is function notation and does not mean "w times 8." Tell them that it is read w of 8.

Problem 4

Q Are the numbers listed in the domain possible values for the independent variable or for the dependent variable? Explain. **[Independent variable; they are possible input values.]**

Q Does the number of elements in the domain always equal the number of elements in the range for a function? Explain. **[No, it is possible to have the same range value for two different domain values, in which case the range would have fewer values.]**

Got It?

Discuss with students the English usage of the terms *domain* and *range*. The phrases "a King's domain" and "a voice's range" can help reinforce mathematical understanding of these words.

Problem 5

Q If the function were changed to $A(q) = 150q$, would the reasonable domain change? Would the range change? Explain. **[The domain would stay the same, because you would still have the same amount of paint available. The range would change, because the area needing paint would be modified.]**

Q Does it make sense to connect the ordered pairs in the graph? **[The ordered pairs should be connected. It is possible to use fractions of cans of paint.]**

Think

What is another way to think of the domain and range?
The domain is the set of input values for the function. The range is the set of output values.

Got It? 3. Use the function in Problem 3. How many words can you read in 6 min?

Problem 4 Finding the Range of a Function

Multiple Choice The domain of $f(x) = -1.5x + 4$ is $\{1, 2, 3, 4\}$. What is the range?

Ⓐ $\{-2, -0.5, 1, 2.5\}$ Ⓒ $\{-2.5, -1, -0.5, 2\}$
Ⓑ $\{-2.5, -1, 0.5, 2\}$ Ⓓ $\{-2.5, -0.5, 1, 2\}$

Step 1 Make a table. List the domain values as the x-values.

x	$-1.5x + 4$	$f(x)$
1	$-1.5(1) + 4$	2.5
2	$-1.5(2) + 4$	1
3	$-1.5(3) + 4$	-0.5
4	$-1.5(4) + 4$	-2

Step 2 Evaluate $f(x)$ for each domain value. The values of $f(x)$ form the range.

The range is $\{-2, -0.5, 1, 2.5\}$. The correct answer is A.

Got It? 4. The domain of $g(x) = 4x - 12$ is $\{1, 3, 5, 7\}$. What is the range?

Problem 5 Identifying a Reasonable Domain and Range

Painting You have 3 qt of paint to paint the trim in your house. A quart of paint covers 100 ft². The function $A(q) = 100q$ represents the area $A(q)$, in square feet, that q quarts of paint cover. What domain and range are reasonable for the function? What is the graph of the function?

Know
• One quart of paint covers 100 ft².
• You have 3 qt of paint.

Need
Reasonable domain and range values in order to graph the function

Plan
Find the least and greatest amounts of paint you can use and areas of trim you can cover. Use these values to make a graph.

The least amount of paint you can use is none. So the least domain value is 0. You have only 3 qt of paint, so the most paint you can use is 3 qt. The greatest domain value is 3. The domain is $0 \le q \le 3$.

To find the range, evaluate the function using the least and greatest domain values.

$$A(0) = 100(0) = 0 \qquad A(3) = 100(3) = 300$$

The range is $0 \le A(q) \le 300$.

To graph the function, make a table of values. Choose values of q that are in the domain. The graph is a line segment that extends from $(0, 0)$ to $(3, 300)$.

q	$A(q)$
0	0
1	100
2	200
3	300

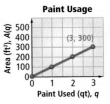

Paint Usage

Additional Problems

1. Identify the domain and range of each relation. Represent the relation with a mapping diagram. Is the relation a function?

a. $\{(-3, 1), (0, 2), (1, 1), (2, 4)\}$
b. $\{(4, 6), (5, 1), (7, 2), (5, 2)\}$

ANSWER a. The domain is $\{-3, 0, 1, 2\}$.
The range is $\{1, 2, 4\}$. The relation is a function.

Domain   Range

b. The domain is $\{4, 5, 7\}$. The range is $\{1, 2, 6\}$. The relation is not a function.

Domain   Range

2. Is the relation a function? Use the vertical line test.

a. $\{(-4, -4), (-2, 3), (3, 0), (5, 1), (6, 1)\}$

b. $y = 2x^2 + 1$

ANSWER a. yes **b.** yes

3. The function $T(x) = 65x$ represents the number of words $T(x)$ that Rachel can type in x minutes. How many words can she type in 7 minutes?

ANSWER 455 words

4. What is the range of $f(x) = 3x - 2$ with domain $\{1, 2, 3, 4\}$?

A. $\{3, 6, 9, 12\}$
B. $\{-1, 2, 5, 8\}$
C. $\{2, 4, 6, 8\}$
D. $\{1, 4, 7, 10\}$

ANSWER D

5. Lorena has 4 rolls of ribbon to make party favors. Each roll can be used to make 30 favors. The function $F(r) = 30r$ represents the number of favors $F(r)$ that can be made with r rolls. What are a reasonable domain and range of the function? What is a graph of the function?

ANSWER The domain is $0 \le r \le 4$. The range is $0 \le F(r) \le 120$.

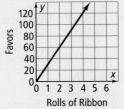

Rolls of Ribbon

Got It? **5. a.** If you have 7 qt of paint, what domain and range are reasonable for Problem 5?

b. Reasoning Why does it *not* make sense to have domain values less than 0 or greater than 3 in Problem 5?

Lesson Check

Do you know HOW?

1. Identify the domain and range of the relation $\{(-2, 3), (-1, 4), (0, 5), (1, 6)\}$. Represent the relation with a mapping diagram. Is the relation a function?

2. Is the relation in the graph shown at the right a function? Use the vertical line test.

3. What is $f(2)$ for the function $f(x) = 4x + 1$?

4. The domain of $f(x) = \frac{1}{2}x$ is $\{-4, -2, 0, 2, 4\}$. What is the range?

Do you UNDERSTAND?

5. **Vocabulary** Write $y = 2x + 7$ using function notation.

6. **Compare and Contrast** You can use a mapping diagram or the vertical line test to tell if a relation is a function. Which method do you prefer? Explain.

7. **Error Analysis** A student drew the dashed line on the graph shown and concluded that the graph represented a function. Is the student correct? Explain.

Practice and Problem-Solving Exercises

A Practice

Identify the domain and range of each relation. Use a mapping diagram to determine whether the relation is a function. ◀ See Problem 1.

8. $\{(3, 7), (3, 8), (3, -2), (3, 4), (3, 1)\}$

9. $\{(6, -7), (5, -8), (1, 4), (7, 5)\}$

10. $\{(0.04, 0.2), (0.2, 1), (1, 5), (5, 25)\}$

11. $\{(4, 2), (1, 1), (0, 0), (1, -1), (4, -2)\}$

Use the vertical line test to determine whether the relation is a function. ◀ See Problem 2.

12. 13. 14. 15.

16. **Physics** Light travels about 186,000 mi/s. The function $d(t) = 186,000t$ gives the distance $d(t)$, in miles, that light travels in t seconds. How far does light travel in 30 s? ◀ See Problem 3.

17. **Shopping** You are buying orange juice for $4.50 per container and have a gift card worth $7. The function $f(x) = 4.50x - 7$ represents your total cost $f(x)$ if you buy x containers of orange juice and use the gift card. How much do you pay to buy 4 containers of orange juice?

PowerAlgebra.com | Lesson 4-6 Formalizing Relations and Functions | 271

Got It?
Remind students that a stated domain such as $0 \le q \le 7$, states the values for which the function is defined. Tell students that in the future, they may be asked to state the values for which a function is undefined.

3 Lesson Check

Do you know HOW?

• If students have difficulty with Exercise 2, then remind them how to perform the vertical line test with a pencil. A full description of this process is on page 269.

Do you UNDERSTAND?

• If students have difficulty with Exercise 5, then make sure they understand that when using function notation x represents the independent variable and $f(x)$ represents the dependent variable.

Close

Q How are functions and relations related? **[Every function is a relation, but not every relation is a function. For a relation to be a function, each domain value in the relation must be paired with exactly one range value.]**

Answers

Got It? (continued)

3. 1500 words

4. $\{-8, 0, 8, 16\}$

5. a. domain: $0 \le q \le 7$, range: $0 \le A(q) \le 700$

   b. The least amount of paint you can use is 0 quarts. The greatest amount you can use is 3 quarts.

Lesson Check

1. domain: $\{-2, -1, 0, 1\}$, range: $\{3, 4, 5, 6\}$.

function

2. yes   3. 9

4. $\{-2, -1, 0, 1, 2\}$ 5. $f(x) = 2x + 7$

6. Answers may vary. Sample: Both methods can be used to determine whether there is more than one

output for any given input. A mapping diagram does not represent a function if any domain value is mapped to more than one range value. A graph does not represent a function if it fails the vertical line test.

7. No; there exists a vertical line that intersects the graph in more than one point, so the graph does not represent a function.

Practice and Problem-Solving Exercises

8. domain $\{3\}$, range $\{-2, 1, 4, 7, 8\}$; no

9. domain $\{1, 5, 6, 7\}$, range $\{-8, -7, 4, 5\}$; yes

10. domain $\{0.04, 0.2, 1, 5\}$, range $\{0.2, 1, 5, 25\}$; yes

11. domain $\{0, 1, 4\}$, range $\{-2, -1, 0, 1, 2\}$; no

12. not a function   13. not a function

14. function   15. function

16–17. See next page.

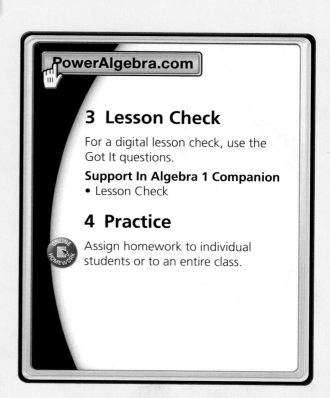

PowerAlgebra.com

3 Lesson Check

For a digital lesson check, use the Got It questions.

Support In Algebra 1 Companion
• Lesson Check

4 Practice

Assign homework to individual students or to an entire class.

Lesson 4-6 **271**

4 Practice

ASSIGNMENT GUIDE

Basic: 8–23 all, 24–28 even, 29

Average: 9–23 odd, 24–35

Advanced: 9–23 odd, 24–40

Standardized Test Prep: 41–44

Mixed Review: 45–50

Reasoning exercises have blue headings.

Applications exercises have red headings.

EXERCISE 29: Use the Think About a Plan worksheet in the **Practice and Problem Solving Workbook** (also available in the Teaching Resources in print and online) to further support students' development in becoming independent learners.

HOMEWORK QUICK CHECK

To check students' understanding of key skills and concepts, go over Exercises 11, 19, 26, 28, and 29.

Find the range of each function for the given domain. ◆ See Problem 4.

18. $f(x) = 2x - 7; \{-2, -1, 0, 1, 2\}$

19. $g(x) = -4x + 1; \{-5, -1, 0, 2, 10\}$

20. $h(x) = x^2; \{-1.2, 0, 0.2, 1.2, 4\}$

21. $f(x) = 8x - 3; \left\{-\frac{1}{2}, \frac{1}{4}, \frac{3}{4}, \frac{1}{8}\right\}$

Find a reasonable domain and range for each function. Then graph the function. ◆ See Problem 5.

22. Fuel A car can travel 32 mi for each gallon of gasoline. The function $d(x) = 32x$ represents the distance $d(x)$, in miles, that the car can travel with x gallons of gasoline. The car's fuel tank holds 17 gal.

23. Nutrition There are 98 International Units (IUs) of vitamin D in 1 cup of milk. The function $V(c) = 98c$ represents the amount $V(c)$ of vitamin D, in IUs, you get from c cups of milk. You have a 16-cup jug of milk.

 Apply

Determine whether the relation represented by each table is a function. If the relation is a function, state the domain and range.

24.

x	0	3	3	5
y	2	1	-1	3

25.

x	-4	-1	0	3
y	-4	-4	-4	-4

26. Open-Ended Make a table that represents a relation that is not a function. Explain why the relation is not a function.

27. Reasoning If $f(x) = 6x - 4$ and $f(a) = 26$, what is the value of a? Explain.

28. Think About a Plan In a factory, a certain machine needs 10 min to warm up. It takes 15 min for the machine to run a cycle. The machine can operate for as long as 6 h per day including warm-up time. Draw a graph showing the total time the machine operates during 1 day as a function of the number of cycles it runs.
- What domain and range are reasonable?
- Is the function a linear function?

29. Carwash A theater group is having a carwash fundraiser. The group can only spend $34 on soap, which is enough to wash 40 cars. Each car is charged $5.
- **a.** If c is the total number of cars washed and p is the profit, which is the independent variable and which is the dependent variable?
- **b.** Is the relationship between c and p a function? Explain.
- **c.** Write an equation that shows this relationship.
- **d.** Find a reasonable domain and range for the situation.

30. Open-Ended What value of x makes the relation $\{(1, 5), (x, 8), (-7, 9)\}$ a function?

Determine whether each relation is a function. Assume that each different variable has a different value.

31. $\{(a, b), (b, a), (c, c), (e, d)\}$

32. $\{(b, b), (c, d), (d, c), (c, a)\}$

33. $\{(c, e), (c, d), (c, b)\}$

34. $\{(a, b), (b, c), (c, d), (d, e)\}$

Answers

Practice and Problem-Solving Exercises (continued)

16. about 5,580,000 mi

17. $11

18. $\{-11, -9, -7, -5, -3\}$

19. $\{-39, -7, 1, 5, 21\}$

20. $\{0, 0.04, 1.44, 16\}$

21. $\{-7, -2, -1, 3\}$

22. $0 \le x \le 17, 0 \le d(x) \le 544$

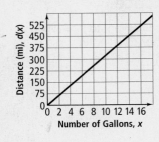
Number of Gallons, x

23. $0 \le c \le 16, 0 \le D(c) \le 1568$

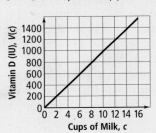
Cups of Milk, c

24. not a function

25. function; domain: $\{-4, -1, 0, 3\}$, range: $\{-4\}$

26. Check students' work.

27. 5; if $f(a) = 26$, then $6a - 4 = 26$ and $a = 5$.

28.

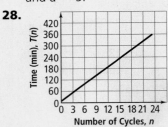
Number of Cycles, n

29. a. c is the independent variable and p is the dependent variable.

b. Yes; for each value of c, there is a unique value of p.

c. $p = 5c - 34$

d. $0 \le c \le 40, 0 \le p \le 166$

30. Answers may vary. Sample given: any value except 1 and −7

31. function

32. not a function

33. not a function

34. function

35. Reasoning Can the graph of a function be a horizontal line? A vertical line? Explain.

 Challenge

36. To form the inverse of a relation written as a set of ordered pairs, you switch the coordinates of each ordered pair. For example, the inverse of the relation $\{(1, 8), (3, 5), (7, 9)\}$ is $\{(8, 1), (5, 3), (9, 7)\}$. Give an example of a relation that is a function, but whose inverse is *not* a function.

Use the functions $f(x) = 2x$ and $g(x) = x^2 + 1$ to find the value of each expression.

37. $f(3) + g(4)$ **38.** $g(3) + f(4)$ **39.** $f(5) - 2 \cdot g(1)$ **40.** $f(g(3))$

Standardized Test Prep

GRIDDED RESPONSE

SAT/ACT

41. What is the value of the function $f(x) = 7x$ when $x = 0.75$?

42. Andrew needs x dollars for a snack. Scott needs 2 more dollars than Andrew, but Nick only needs half as many dollars as Andrew. Altogether they need $17 to pay for their snacks. How many dollars does Nick need?

43. What is the greatest number of $.43 stamps you can buy for $5?

44. What is the greatest possible width of the rectangle, to the nearest inch?

$\ell = 35$ in.

$A < 184$ in.^{2}

Mixed Review

Write a function rule to represent each situation.   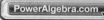 See Lesson 4-5.

45. You baby-sit for $5 per hour and get a $7 tip. Your earnings E are a function of the number of hours h you work.

46. You buy several pairs of socks for $4.50 per pair, plus a shirt for $10. The total amount a you spend is a function of the number of pairs of socks s you buy.

47. The graph shows a family's distance from home as they drive to the mountains for a vacation.
   a. What are the variables in the graph?
   b. Copy the graph. Describe how the variables are related at various points on the graph.

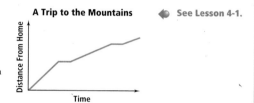

See Lesson 4-1.

Get Ready! **To prepare for Lesson 4-7, do Exercises 48–50.**

Evaluate each expression for $x = 1, 2, 3,$ and 4.   See Lesson 1-2.

48. $9 + 3(x - 1)$ **49.** $8 + 7(x - 1)$ **50.** $0.4 - 3(x - 1)$

---

35. A horizontal line is a function because each value of x has a unique value of y; a vertical line is not a function because the x-value has more than one y-value associated with it.

36. Answers may vary. Sample: $\{(1, 3), (2, 3), (3, 3)\}$ is a function, but its inverse is not.

37. 23   **38.** 18

39. 6   **40.** 20

41. 5.25   **42.** 3

43. 11 stamps   **44.** 5 in.

45. $E = 5h + 7$ **46.** $a = 4.5s + 10$

47. a. time and distance

b.

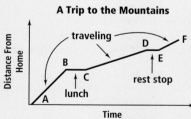

48. 9, 12, 15, 18   **49.** 8, 15, 22, 29

50. 0.4, −2.6, −5.6, −8.6

Additional Instructional Support

Algebra 1 Companion

Students can use the **Algebra 1 Companion** worktext (4 pages) as you teach the lesson. Use the Companion to support

- New Vocabulary
- Key Concepts
- Got It for each Problem
- Lesson Check

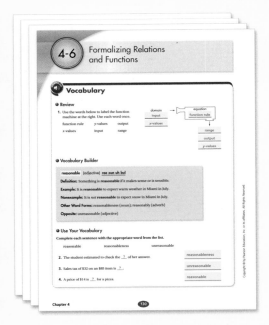

ELL Support

Focus on Language Examine the word *relation*. What other words look like or sound like *relation*? [*relate, relative, relationship*]. Ask students for synonyms of *relation*. Remind students that a synonym has the same meaning. Examples may include *link, alliance, family, correlation,* and *connection.* Ask students for antonyms of *relation*, such as *independence* or *disconnection.*

Relation means an association or significant connection among things. The word comes from Latin *relatus* (brought back), because a *related* item is one that refers *back* to another in some way.

5 Assess & Remediate

Lesson Quiz

1. Identify the domain and range of the relation {(−1, 1), (0, 2), (3, −2), (5, 2)}. Represent the relation with a mapping diagram. Is the relation a function?

2. Is the relation below a function? Use the vertical line test.
{(−6, 3), (−1, 0), (2, 4), (−1, −7), (5, 2)}

3. Do you UNDERSTAND? The function $Y(x) = \frac{1}{3}x$ represents the number of yards $Y(x)$ in x feet. How many yards are there in 1 mile? (Hint: 1mi = 5280 ft.)

4. What is the range of $f(x) = -2x + 5$ with domain {1, 2, 3, 4}?

ANSWERS TO LESSON QUIZ

1. The domain is {−1, 0, 3, 5}. The range is {−2, 1, 2}. The relation is a function.

2. no

3. 1760

4. {3, 1, −1, −3}

PRESCRIPTION FOR REMEDIATION
Use the student work on the Lesson Quiz to prescribe a differentiated review assignment.

Points	Differentiated Remediation
0–2	Intervention
3	On-level
4	Extension

PowerAlgebra.com

5 Assess & Remediate

Assign the Lesson Quiz. Appropriate intervention, practice, or enrichment is automatically generated based on student performance.

Intervention

- **Reteaching** (2 pages) Provides reteaching and practice exercises for the key lesson concepts. Use with struggling students or absent students.

- **English Language Learner Support** Helps students develop and reinforce mathematical vocabulary and key concepts.

All-in-One Resources/Online
Reteaching

All-in-One Resources/Online
English Language Learner Support

Differentiated Remediation *continued*

On-Level

- **Practice** (2 pages) Provides extra practice for each lesson. For simpler practice exercises, use the Form K Practice pages found in the All-in-One Teaching Resources and online.

- **Think About a Plan** Helps students develop specific problem-solving skills and strategies by providing scaffolded guiding questions.

- **Standardized Test Prep** Focuses on all major exercises, all major question types, and helps students prepare for the high-stakes assessments.

Extension

- **Enrichment** Provides students with interesting problems and activities that extend the concepts of the lesson.

- **Activities, Games, and Puzzles** Worksheets that can be used for concepts development, enrichment, and for fun!

Practice and Problem Solving WKBK/ All-in-One Resources/Online
Practice page 1

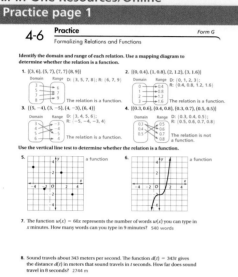

Practice and Problem Solving WKBK/ All-in-One Resources/Online
Practice page 2

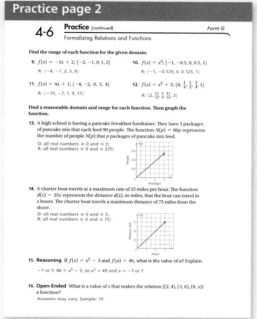

All-in-One Resources/Online
Enrichment

Practice and Problem Solving WKBK/ All-in-One Resources/Online
Think About a Plan

Practice and Problem Solving WKBK/ All-in-One Resources/Online
Standardized Test Prep

Online Teacher Resource Center
Activities, Games, and Puzzles

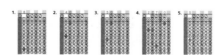

1 Interactive Learning

Solve It!

PURPOSE To determine the pattern in a sequence that can be expressed both recursively and explicitly using a function

PROCESS Students may make a table of values and determine a function rule or may analyze the sequence of the number of pieces of wood to determine a recursive pattern.

FACILITATE

Q How many pieces of wood are used in each of the three fences shown? **[4; 7; 10]**

Q What is your conjecture for how many pieces of wood are necessary for four sections of fence? Explain. **[Answers may vary. Sample: 13, since each new section requires 3 more pieces of wood.]**

Q How can you test your conjecture? **[Sketch a fence with four sections and count.]**

ANSWER See Solve It in Answers on next page.
CONNECT THE MATH In the Solve It the number of pieces of wood used for building the fence represents a sequence. In this lesson students learn to identify a pattern as a sequence.

2 Guided Instruction

Problem 1

Q If the sequence in 1A were extended backward for numbers less than 5, what would be the next three numbers? **[2, −1, −4]**

Q Even though 2.5 + 2.5 = 5, why is the pattern in 1B "add 2.5 to the previous term" not correct? **[The rule cannot be applied to every term in order to produce the next term.]**

Objectives To identify and extend patterns in sequences
To represent arithmetic sequences using function notation

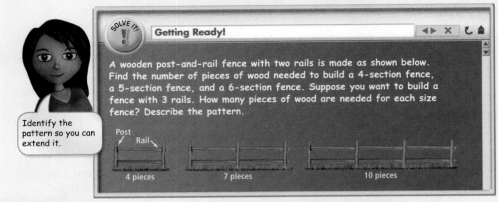

Getting Ready!

A wooden post-and-rail fence with two rails is made as shown below. Find the number of pieces of wood needed to build a 4-section fence, a 5-section fence, and a 6-section fence. Suppose you want to build a fence with 3 rails. How many pieces of wood are needed for each size fence? Describe the pattern.

Identify the pattern so you can extend it.

Post
Rail
4 pieces   7 pieces   10 pieces

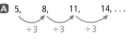
Lesson Vocabulary
• sequence
• term of a sequence
• arithmetic sequence
• common difference

In the Solve It, the numbers of pieces of wood used for 1 section of fence, 2 sections of fence, and so on, form a pattern, or a sequence. A **sequence** is an ordered list of numbers that often form a pattern. Each number in the list is called a **term of a sequence.**

Essential Understanding When you can identify a pattern in a sequence, you can use it to extend the sequence. You can also model some sequences with a function rule that you can use to find any term of the sequence.

Problem 1 Extending Sequences

Describe a pattern in each sequence. What are the next two terms of each sequence?

Ⓐ 5,   8,   11,   14, . . .
      +3   +3   +3

Ⓑ 2.5,   5,   10,   20, . . .
        ×2   ×2   ×2

Plan
How can you identify a pattern?
Look at how each term of the sequence is related to the previous term. Your goal is to identify a single rule that you can apply to every term to produce the next term.

A pattern is "add 3 to the previous term." So the next two terms are 14 + 3 = 17 and 17 + 3 = 20.

A pattern is "multiply the previous term by 2." So the next two terms are 2(20) = 40 and 2(40) = 80.

BIG ideas Functions   **UbD**
        Modeling

ESSENTIAL UNDERSTANDINGS
• Some sequences have function rules that can be used to find any term of the sequence.
• When the pattern in a sequence is identified, the sequence can be extended.

Math Background

The study of sequences in this lesson lays a foundation for the study of graphing linear equations in the next chapter. Finding patterns in sequences and using them to extend the sequence prepares students for identifying the slope as a pattern in the line, and using the slope to extend the line. Further, modeling arithmetic sequences using a function rule prepares students for writing the equation of a line.

An inductive argument reasons from observations of particular instances (for example, this crow is

black, that crow is black) to a generality (all crows are black). Not all conclusions reached in this way are correct, but this kind of reasoning is very often used in daily life and is often effective.

Students can use inductive reasoning to identify patterns, or sequences, in sets of numbers. An arithmetic sequence is formed by adding a specific number to each term after the first. Another type of sequence, the geometric sequence, will be introduced in a later chapter.

Support Student Learning

Use the **Algebra 1 Companion** to engage and support students during instructions. See Lesson Resources at the end of this lesson for details.

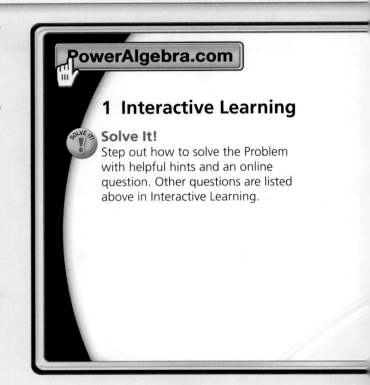

PowerAlgebra.com

1 Interactive Learning

Solve It!
Step out how to solve the Problem with helpful hints and an online question. Other questions are listed above in Interactive Learning.

Got It? **1.** Describe a pattern in each sequence. What are the next two terms of each sequence?

a. 5, 11, 17, 23, . . .   **b.** 400, 200, 100, 50, . . .
c. 2, −4, 8, −16, . . .   **d.** −15, −11, −7, −3, . . .

In an **arithmetic sequence,** the difference between consecutive terms is constant. This difference is called the **common difference.**

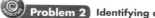 **Problem 2** Identifying an Arithmetic Sequence

Plan

How can you identify an arithmetic sequence?
The difference between every pair of consecutive terms must be the same.

Tell whether the sequence is arithmetic. If it is, what is the common difference?

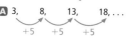 **A** 3,   8,   13,   18, . . .
          +5   +5   +5

The sequence has a common difference of 5, so it is arithmetic.

B 6,   9,   13,   17, . . .
        +3   +4   +4

The sequence does not have a common difference, so it is not arithmetic.

 Got It? **2.** Tell whether the sequence is arithmetic. If it is, what is the common difference?

a. 8, 15, 22, 30, . . .   **b.** 7, 9, 11, 13, . . .
c. 10, 4, −2, −8, . . .   **d.** 2, −2, 2, −2, . . .

A sequence is a function that relates the term number to the value of the term. Consider the sequence 7, 11, 15, 19, . . . Think of each term as the output of a function. Think of the term number as the input.

term number	1	2	3	4	← input
term	7	11	15	19	← output

You can use the common difference of the terms of an arithmetic sequence to write a function rule for the sequence. For the sequence 7, 11, 15, 19, . . . , the common difference is 4.

Let n = the term number in the sequence.
Let $A(n)$ = the value of the nth term of the sequence.

value of term 1 = $A(1) = 7$
value of term 2 = $A(2) = 7 + 4$ The common difference is 4.
value of term 3 = $A(3) = 7 + 4 + 4$ The number of 4's added is *1 less than* the term number.
value of term 4 = $A(4) = 7 + 4 + 4 + 4$
value of term n = $A(n) = 7 + 4 + 4 + \ldots + 4 = 7 + (n - 1)4$

The function rule for the sequence above is $A(n) = 7 + (n - 1)4$. You can find the tenth term by finding $A(10)$. So the tenth term is $A(10) = 7 + (10 - 1)4 = 7 + 36 = 43$.

2 Guided Instruction

 Each Problem is worked out and supported online.

Problem 1
Extending Sequences
Animated

Problem 2
Identifying an Arithmetic Sequence
Animated

Problem 3
Writing a Rule for an Arithmetic Sequence
Animated

Support in Algebra 1 Companion
• Vocabulary
• Key Concepts
• Got It?

Answers

Solve It!
13, 16, 19; 17, 21, 25; start with the number of pieces of wood it takes to build one section and add the number of pieces of wood needed to build an additional section times the number of sections.

Got It?
1. a. Add 6 to the previous term; 29, 35.
   b. Multiply each previous term by $\frac{1}{2}$; 25, 12.5.
   c. Multiply each previous term by −2; 32, −64.
   d. Add 4 to the previous term; 1, 5.
2. a. not an arithmetic sequence
   b. arithmetic sequence; 2
   c. arithmetic sequence; −6
   d. not an arithmetic sequence

Take Note

Point out the usefulness rules for arithmetic sequences by noting that without a rule, determining the 100th term in a sequence would require you to determine the 99th term, which would then require you to determine the 98th term, and so on.

Problem 3

> **Q** How can you determine the common difference for the sequence? **[You subtract from each term its previous term.]**
>
> **Q** What equation can you use to determine which bid will be $390? **[390 = 200 + (n − 1)10]**
>
> **Q** Which bid will be $390? **[the 20th bid]**

Got It?

> **Q** What is the starting value for the arithmetic sequence? **[$100]**
>
> **Q** What is the common difference? **[−$1.75]**

You can find any term of an arithmetic sequence if you know the first term and the common difference.

Key Concept Rule For an Arithmetic Sequence

The nth term of an arithmetic sequence with first term $A(1)$ and common difference d is given by

$$A(n) = A(1) + (n - 1)d$$

nth term   first term   term number   common difference

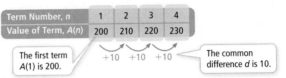 **Problem 3** Writing a Rule for an Arithmetic Sequence

Online Auction An online auction works as shown below. Write a rule to represent the bids as an arithmetic sequence. What is the twelfth bid?

First Bid: The seller sets a minimum price, which must be met by the first bid.

Following Bids: Bids increase in regular increments.

Make a table of the bids. Identify the first term and common difference.

Term Number, n	1	2	3	4
Value of Term, $A(n)$	200	210	220	230

The first term $A(1)$ is 200.   +10 +10 +10   The common difference d is 10.

Substitute $A(1) = 200$ and $d = 10$ into the formula $A(n) = A(1) + (n - 1)d$. The rule $A(n) = 200 + (n - 1)10$ represents the sequence of the auction bids. To find the twelfth bid, evaluate $A(n)$ for $n = 12$.

$$A(12) = 200 + (12 - 1)10 = 310$$

The twelfth bid is $310.

 Got It? **3. a.** A subway pass has a starting value of $100. After one ride, the value of the pass is $98.25. After two rides, its value is $96.50. After three rides, its value is $94.75. Write a rule to represent the remaining value on the card as an arithmetic sequence. What is the value of the pass after 15 rides?

b. Reasoning How many rides can be taken with the $100 pass?

Plan

What information do you need to write a rule for an arithmetic sequence?
You need the first term of the sequence and the common difference.

Additional Problems

1. Describe the pattern in each sequence. What are the next two terms of each sequence?

a. 4, 6, 8, 10, …

b. 1, 3, 9, 27, …

ANSWER a. The pattern is "add 2 to the previous term"; 12, 14.

b. The pattern is "multiply the previous term by 3"; 81, 243.

2. Tell whether the sequence is arithmetic. If it is, what is the common difference?

a. 7, 11, 16, 22, …

b. 3, 9, 15, 21, …

ANSWER a. not arithmetic;

b. arithmetic, 6

3. Justine's grandfather puts $100 in a savings account for her on her first birthday. He puts $125, $150, and $175 into the account on her next 3 birthdays. If this pattern continues, how much will Justine's grandfather put in the savings account on her 12th birthday?

ANSWER $375

Answers

Got It? (continued)

3. a. $A(n) = 100 - (n - 1)1.75$; $73.75

b. 57

Lesson Check

Do you know HOW?

Describe a pattern in each sequence. Then find the next two terms of the sequence.

1. 3, 11, 19, 27, . . .

2. 3, −6, 12, −24, . . .

Tell whether the sequence is arithmetic. If it is, identify the common difference.

3. 1, −7, −14, −21, . . .

4. 11, 20, 29, 38, . . .

5. Write a rule for an arithmetic sequence with a first term of 9 and a common difference of −2. What is the seventh term of the sequence?

Do you UNDERSTAND?

6. Vocabulary Consider the following arithmetic sequence: 25, 19, 13, 7, . . . Is the common difference 6 or −6? Explain.

7. Error Analysis Describe and correct the error below in finding the tenth term of the arithmetic sequence 4, 12, 20, 28, . . .

> first term = 4
> common difference = 8
> tenth term = 4 + 10(8) = 84

8. Reasoning Can you use the rule below to find the nth term of an arithmetic sequence with a first term $A(1)$ and a common difference d? Explain.

$$A(n) = A(1) + nd - d$$

Practice and Problem-Solving Exercises

A Practice

Describe a pattern in each sequence. Then find the next two terms of the sequence. **See Problem 1.**

9. 6, 13, 20, 27, . . . **10.** 8, 4, 2, 1, . . . **11.** 2, 6, 10, 14, . . .

12. 10, 4, −2, −8, . . . **13.** 13, 11, 9, 7, . . . **14.** 2, 20, 200, 2000, . . .

15. 1.1, 2.2, 3.3, 4.4, . . . **16.** 99, 88, 77, 66, . . . **17.** 4.5, 9, 18, 36, . . .

Tell whether the sequence is arithmetic. If it is, identify the common difference. **See Problem 2.**

18. −7, −3, 1, 5, . . . **19.** −9, −17, −26, −33, . . . **20.** 19, 8, −3, −14, . . .

21. 2, 11, 21, 32, . . . **22.** $\frac{1}{2}, \frac{1}{3}, \frac{1}{6}, 0, . . .$ **23.** 0.2, 1.5, 2.8, 4.1, . . .

24. 10, 8, 6, 4, . . . **25.** 10, 24, 36, 52, . . . **26.** 3, 6, 12, 24, . . .

27. 15, 14.5, 14, 13.5, 13, . . . **28.** 4, 4.4, 4.44, 4.444, . . . **29.** −3, −7, −10, −14, . . .

30. Garage After one customer buys 4 new tires, a garage recycling bin has 20 tires in it. After another customer buys 4 new tires, the bin has 24 tires in it. Write a rule to represent the number of tires in the bin as an arithmetic sequence. How many tires are in the bin after 9 customers buy all new tires? **See Problem 3.**

31. Cafeteria You have a cafeteria card worth $50. After you buy lunch on Monday, its value is $46.75. After you buy lunch on Tuesday, its value is $43.50. Write a rule to represent the amount of money left on the card as an arithmetic sequence. What is the value of the card after you buy 12 lunches?

---

3 Lesson Check

Do you know HOW?

- If students have difficulty with Exercise 5, then have them review Problem 3 to see how to set up a table and then find the common difference.

Do you UNDERSTAND?

- If students have difficulty with Exercise 8, then have them examine the rule given for determining the nth term of an arithmetic sequence given in the Take Note on page 276.

Close

Q Describe two ways that you can determine the 50th term in an arithmetic sequence given the first term and the common difference. **[Answers may vary. Sample: You can write a rule for the nth term and use the rule, or you can use the first term and the common difference to determine each term in the sequence up to the 50th term.]**

Lesson Check

1. Add 8 to the previous term; 35, 43.

2. Multiply the previous term by −2; 48, −96.

3. not an arithmetic sequence

4. arithmetic sequence; 9

5. $A(n) = 9 - 2(n - 1)$; −3

6. −6; the pattern is "add −6 to the previous term."

7. Evaluate $A(n) = 4 + (n - 1)8$ for $n = 10$; $A(10) = 4 + (10 - 1)8 = 76$.

8. Yes; $A(n) = A(1) + (n - 1)d = A(1) + nd - d$ by the Distributive Property.

Practice and Problem-Solving Exercises

9. Add 7 to the previous term; 34, 41.

10. Multiply the previous term by 0.5; 0.5, 0.25.

11. Add 4 to the previous term; 18, 22.

12. Add −6 to the previous term; −14, −20.

13. Add −2 to the previous term; 5, 3.

14. Multiply the previous term by 10; 20,000, 200,000.

15. Add 1.1 to the previous term; 5.5, 6.6.

16. Add −11 to the previous term; 55, 44.

17. Multiply the previous term by 2; 72, 144.

18. yes; 4

19. not an arithmetic sequence

20. yes; −11

21. not an arithmetic sequence

22. yes; $-\frac{1}{6}$

23. yes; 1.3

24. yes; −2

25. not an arithmetic sequence

26. not an arithmetic sequence

27. yes; −0.5

28. not an arithmetic sequence

29. not an arithmetic sequence

30. $A(n) = 16 + 4(n - 1)$; 52 tires

31. $A(n) = 50 - 3.25(n - 1)$; $11

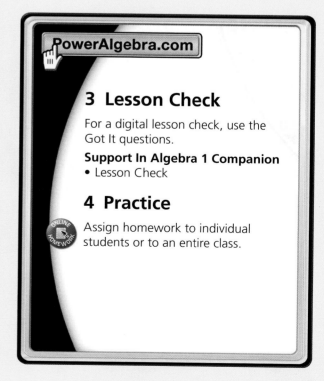

PowerAlgebra.com

3 Lesson Check

For a digital lesson check, use the Got It questions.

Support In Algebra 1 Companion
- Lesson Check

4 Practice

Assign homework to individual students or to an entire class.

4 Practice

ASSIGNMENT GUIDE

Basic: 9–39 all, 40–52 even

Average: 9–39 odd, 40–54

Advanced: 9–39 odd, 40–57

Standardized Test Prep: 58–60

Mixed Review: 61–69

Reasoning exercises have blue headings.

Applications exercises have red headings.

EXERCISE 52: Use the Think About a Plan worksheet in the **Practice and Problem Solving Workbook** (also available in the Teaching Resources in print and online) to further support students' development in becoming independent learners.

HOMEWORK QUICK CHECK

To check students' understanding of key skills and concepts, go over Exercises 11, 19, 46, 50, and 52.

Find the second, fourth, and eleventh terms of the sequence described by each rule.

32. $A(n) = 5 + (n - 1)(-3)$

33. $A(n) = -3 + (n - 1)(5)$

34. $A(n) = -11 + (n - 1)(2)$

35. $A(n) = 9 + (n - 1)(8)$

36. $A(n) = 0.5 + (n - 1)(3.5)$

37. $A(n) = -7 + (n - 1)(5)$

38. $A(n) = 1 + (n - 1)(-6)$

39. $A(n) = -2.1 + (n - 1)(-1.1)$

 Apply   Tell whether each sequence is arithmetic. Justify your answer. If the sequence is arithmetic, write a function rule to represent it.

40. 0.3, 0.9, 1.5, 2.1, . . .

41. −3, −7, −11, −15, . . .

42. 1, 8, 27, 64, . . .

43. −5, 5, −5, 5, . . .

44. 46, 31, 16, 2, . . .

45. 0.2, −0.6, −1.4, −2.2, . . .

46. Reasoning An arithmetic sequence has a common difference of zero. The thirty-eighth term of the sequence is 2.1. What is the eighty-fifth term of the sequence? Explain.

47. Open-Ended Write a function rule for a sequence that has 25 as the sixth term.

Write the first six terms in each sequence. Explain what the sixth term means in the context of the situation.

48. A cane of bamboo is 30 in. tall the first week and grows 6 in. per week thereafter.

49. You borrow $350 from a friend the first week and pay the friend back $25 each week thereafter.

50. Think About a Plan Suppose the first Friday of a new year is the fourth day of that year. Will the year have 53 Fridays regardless of whether or not it is a leap year?
- What is a rule that represents the sequence of the days in the year that are Fridays?
- How many full weeks are in a 365-day year?

51. Look For a Pattern The first five rows of Pascal's Triangle are shown at the right.
  a. Predict the numbers in the seventh row.
  b. Find the sum of the numbers in each of the first five rows. Predict the sum of the numbers in the seventh row.

52. Transportation Buses run every 9 min starting at 6:00 A.M. You get to the bus stop at 7:16 A.M. How long will you wait for a bus?

53. Multiple Representations Use the table at the right that shows an arithmetic sequence.
  a. Copy and complete the table.
  b. Graph the ordered pairs (x, y) on a coordinate plane.
  c. What do you notice about the points on your graph?

Answers

Practice and Problem-Solving Exercises (continued)

32. 2, −4, −25

33. 2, 12, 47

34. −9, −5, 9

35. 17, 33, 89

36. 4, 11, 35.5

37. −2, 8, 43

38. −5, −17, −59

39. −3.2, −5.4, −13.1

40. Yes; the common difference is 0.6; $A(n) = 0.3 + (n - 1)0.6$.

41. Yes; the common difference is −4; $A(n) = -3 + (n - 1)(-4)$.

42. No; there is no common difference.

43. No; there is no common difference.

44. No; there is no common difference.

45. Yes; the common difference is −0.8; $A(n) = 0.2 + (n - 1)(-0.8)$.

46. 2.1; if you keep adding zero, you do not change the value.

47. Answers may vary. Sample: $A(n) = 15 + 2(n - 1)$

48. 30, 36, 42, 48, 54, 60; at six weeks, the bamboo is 60 in. tall.

49. 350, 325, 300, 275, 250, 225; you owe $225 at the end of six weeks.

50. no

51. a. 1, 6, 15, 20, 15, 6, 1
  b. 1, 2, 4, 8, 16; 64

52. 5 min

53. a. 11, 14

  b.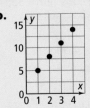

  c. The points all lie on a line.

54. Number Theory The Fibonacci sequence is 1, 1, 2, 3, 5, 8, 13, . . . After the first two numbers, each number is the sum of the two previous numbers.
   a. What is the next term of the sequence? The eleventh term of the sequence?
   b. Open-Ended Choose two other numbers to start a Fibonacci-like sequence. Write the first seven terms of your sequence.

 Challenge   Find the common difference of each arithmetic sequence. Then find the next term.

55. $4, x + 4, 2x + 4, 3x + 4, \ldots$

56. $a + b + c, 4a + 3b + c, 7a + 5b + c, \ldots$

57. a. Geometry Draw the next figure in the pattern.

   b. Reasoning What is the color of the twentieth figure? Explain.
   c. How many sides does the twenty-third figure have? Explain.

Standardized Test Prep

SAT/ACT

58. What is the seventh term of the arithmetic sequence represented by the rule $A(n) = -9 + (n - 1)(0.5)$?

   Ⓐ -7 Ⓑ -6.5 Ⓒ -6 Ⓓ -5.5

59. What is the solution of $-24 + s > 38$?

   Ⓕ $s < 14$ Ⓖ $s > 14$ Ⓗ $s < 62$ Ⓘ $s > 62$

Short Response

60. Marta's starting annual salary is $26,500. At the beginning of each new year, she receives a $2880 raise. Write a function rule to find Marta's salary $f(n)$ after n years. What will Marta's salary be after 6 yr?

Mixed Review

Find the range of each function for the domain $\{-3, -1.2, 0, 1, 10\}$.   ◀ See Lesson 4-6.

61. $f(x) = -4x$ **62.** $g(x) = 1 - 4x$ **63.** $h(x) = 3x^2$

64. $g(x) = 11 - 1.5x^2$ **65.** $h(x) = 9x + 8$ **66.** $f(x) = \frac{3}{4}x - 5$

Get Ready!   To prepare for Lesson 5-1, do Exercises 67–69.   ◀ See Lesson 2-6.

67. A pool fills at a rate of 8 gal/min. What is this rate in gallons per hour?

68. A ball is thrown at a speed of 90 mi/h. What is this speed in feet per second?

69. You buy bottled water in 12-packs that cost $3 each. If you drink 3 bottles per day, what is your cost per week?

   Lesson 4-7   Sequences and Functions   279

---

54. a. 21; 89
   b. Answers will vary. Sample: 3, 3, 6, 9, 15, 24, 39
55. x; $4x + 4$
56. $3a + 2b$; $10a + 7b + c$
57. a. Figure should be a blue pentagon.
   b. Blue; the colors rotate red, blue, and purple. Every third figure is purple, so the 21st figure is purple. The figure just before that is blue.
   c. 10 sides; figure 23 is in the 8th group of three figures; the number of sides in each group of three figures is $3 + (n - 1)$; substitute 8 for n.

58. C   **59.** I
60. [2] $f(n) = 26,500 + 2880n$; $43,780
   [1] function correct, but salary not found
   [1] correct methods used with one minor calculation error
61. $\{12, 4.8, 0, -4, -40\}$
62. $\{13, 5.8, 1, -3, -39\}$
63. $\{27, 4.32, 0, 3, 300\}$
64. $\{-2.5, 8.84, 11, 9.5, -139\}$
65. $\{-19, -2.8, 8, 17, 98\}$
66. $\{-7.25, -5.9, -5, -4.25, 2.5\}$
67. 480 gal/h
68. 132 ft/s
69. $6

Additional Instructional Support

Algebra 1 Companion

Students can use the **Algebra 1 Companion** worktext (4 pages) as you teach the lesson. Use the Companion to support

- New Vocabulary
- Key Concepts
- Got It for each Problem
- Lesson Check

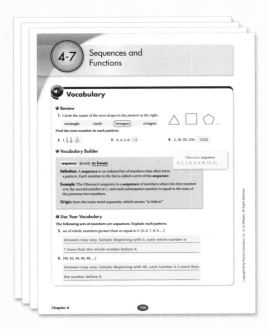

ELL Support

Focus on Language Write an arithmetic sequence such as 3, 7, 11, 15 . . . Draw arrows underneath to show that each term is the previous term + 4. Circle one term and ask what it's called. [a term] Circle one of the arrows with the rule + 4 and ask what it's called. [rule or pattern] Circle the whole sequence and ask what it's called. [sequence]

Focus on Language Pair students so that a more proficient student is with a less proficient student. Have students review the vocabulary for the chapter. Ask them to write a definition of each term in their own words. Tell them to discuss their ideas and then question each other on the meaning of each term.

5 Assess & Remediate

Lesson Quiz

1. Describe the pattern in each sequence. What are the next two terms of each sequence?

   a. 14, 11, 8, 5, ...

   b. 20, 25, 30, 35, ...

2. Tell whether the sequence is arithmetic. If it is, what is the common difference?

   a. −6, 2, 10, 18, ...

   b. 1, 2, 4, 8, ...

3. **Do you UNDERSTAND?** Jason is studying a new plant food for a science experiment. The plant is 14 cm tall when the experiment begins and grows at a rate of 1.5 cm per week. What will the height of the plant be after 5 weeks?

ANSWERS TO LESSON QUIZ

1. a. The pattern is "subtract 3 from the previous number"; 2, −1.

   b. The pattern is "add 5 to the previous number"; 40, 45.

2. a. arithmetic, 8 **b.** not arithmetic

3. 21.5 cm

PRESCRIPTION FOR REMEDIATION
Use the student work on the Lesson Quiz to prescribe a differentiated review assignment.

Points	Differentiated Remediation
0–1	Intervention
2	On-level
3	Extension

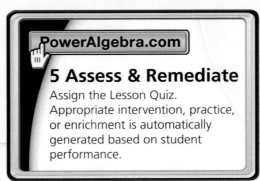

PowerAlgebra.com

5 Assess & Remediate

Assign the Lesson Quiz. Appropriate intervention, practice, or enrichment is automatically generated based on student performance.

Intervention

- **Reteaching** (2 pages) Provides reteaching and practice exercises for the key lesson concepts. Use with struggling students or absent students.

- **English Language Learner Support** Helps students develop and reinforce mathematical vocabulary and key concepts.

All-in-One Resources/Online
Reteaching

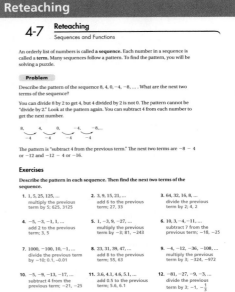

All-in-One Resources/Online
English Language Learner Support

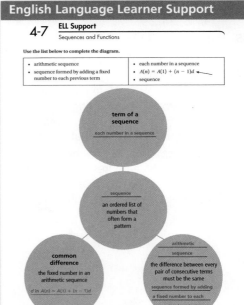

Differentiated Remediation continued

On-Level

- **Practice** (2 pages) Provides extra practice for each lesson. For simpler practice exercises, use the Form K Practice pages found in the All-in-One Teaching Resources and online.

- **Think About a Plan** Helps students develop specific problem-solving skills and strategies by providing scaffolded guiding questions.

- **Standardized Test Prep** Focuses on all major exercises, all major question types, and helps students prepare for the high-stakes assessments.

Extension

- **Enrichment** Provides students with interesting problems and activities that extend the concepts of the lesson.

- **Activities, Games, and Puzzles** Worksheets that can be used for concepts development, enrichment, and for fun!

Practice and Problem Solving WKBK/ All-in-One Resources/Online
Practice page 1

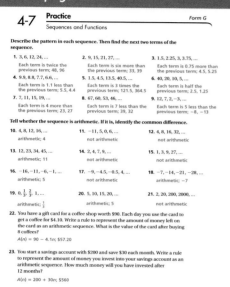

Practice and Problem Solving WKBK/ All-in-One Resources/Online
Practice page 2

All-in-One Resources/Online
Enrichment

Practice and Problem Solving WKBK/ All-in-One Resources/Online
Think About a Plan

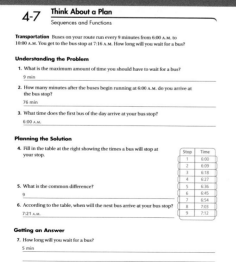

Practice and Problem Solving WKBK/ All-in-One Resources/Online
Standardized Test Prep

Online Teacher Resource Center
Activities, Games, and Puzzles

Performance Task UbD

Pull It All Together

The concepts and skills required to solve these problems are from several lessons within this chapter and from the previous chapter. As students solve these problems, they will demonstrate their reasoning strategies and their growth as independent problem solvers.

The following questions are designed to:
- Help support students as they do the Tasks.
- Gauge the amount of support students need as they become independent problem solvers.

Task 1
- What information in the situation indicates that the relationship will be linear?
- What is a reasonable domain based on the information given?
- What is a reasonable range based on the information given?

Task 2
- Why is the situation discrete?
- Does the graph being linear or nonlinear help you decide if the graphed relation is a function?

Task 3
- What are the common differences in lengths of the necklace?
- What are the common differences in amounts of string?
- Are the common differences constant?
- How can you model the data?

---

4 Pull It All Together

> To solve these problems, you will pull together many concepts and skills that you have studied about functions.

BIG idea Functions
A function is a relationship that pairs one input value with exactly one output value. You can use words, tables, equations, sets of ordered pairs, and graphs to represent functions.

Task 1
Solve. Show your work and explain your steps.

You are riding your bike at a constant speed of 30 ft/s. A friend uses a stopwatch to time you as you ride along a city block that is 264 ft long.
  a. Make a graph to represent the situation, where the independent variable is time and the dependent variable is distance traveled.
  b. Make a second graph to represent the situation, where the independent variable is time and the dependent variable is speed.
  c. Do both graphs represent functions? If so, are they linear or nonlinear? Explain.
  d. Find a reasonable domain and range for each graph.
  e. Write a function rule for each graph.

Task 2
Solve. Show your work and explain your steps.

A shop manager is ordering shopping bags. The price per bag is determined by how many bags the manager buys. The price per bag is determined by how many bags the manager buys. The graph at the right shows the price per bag based on the number of bags that are bought.
  a. Does the graph represent a function? If so, is it *linear* or *nonlinear*? Explain.
  b. Find a reasonable domain and range for the graph.
  c. How much would it cost to buy 1500 bags?

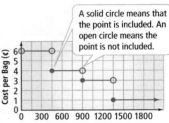

A solid circle means that the point is included. An open circle means the point is not included.

BIG idea Modeling
You can use functions to model real-world situations that pair one input value with a unique output value.

Task 3
Solve. Show your work and explain your steps.

You are making a knotted necklace. The table at the right shows the amount of string you need for different necklace lengths.
  a. Identify the independent and dependent variables.
  b. Write and graph a function rule that represents the situation.
  c. Is the graph *continuous* or *discrete*? Explain your reasoning.
  d. How much string do you need to make a 15-in. necklace?

Length of Necklace (in.)	Amount of String (in.)
10	200
11	202
12	204
13	206

Assess Performance UbD

Pull It All Together
See p. 67 for a holistic scoring rubric to gauge a student's progress on Understanding the Problem, Planning a Solution, Getting an Answer, and Assessing Autonomy.

SOLUTION OUTLINES

1. a.

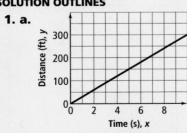

b.

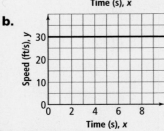

c. First step: Perform vertical line test or review definition of function. (Answer: Both are functions; linear.)

d. First step: Find maximum and minimum values for both graphs for *x* and *y*. (Answer: domain: {nonnegative real numbers}, range: {nonnegative real numbers}; domain: {nonnegative real numbers}, range: $y = 30$)

e. First step: Use the tables in parts (a) and (b) or the graphs in parts (c) and (d) to write a rule. (Answer: $D(t) = 30t$, $S(t) = 30$)

2. a. First step: Use the vertical line test. (Answer: yes; nonlinear, the graph is not a line.)

b. First step: Find domain and range values that make sense. (Answer: domain {nonnegative integers}, range {0.01, 0.03, 0.04, 0.06})

c. First step: Use the graph to find the total amount it would cost to order 1500 bags. (Answer: $15)

3. a. First step: Determine which variable depends on the other one. (Answer: length of necklace, amount of string)

b. First step: use the table to find a pattern and write a rule. (Answer: $y = 2x + 180$)

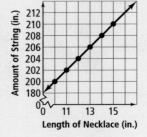

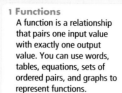

Chapter Review

Connecting **BIG** ideas and Answering the Essential Questions

1 Functions
A function is a relationship that pairs one input value with exactly one output value. You can use words, tables, equations, sets of ordered pairs, and graphs to represent functions.

Patterns and Functions (Lessons 4-2 and 4-3)

Linear

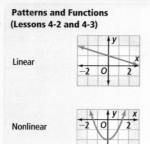

Nonlinear

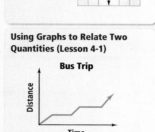

Function Notation and Sequences (Lessons 4-6 and 4-7)

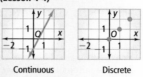

n	A(n) = 3 + (n − 1) (2)	A(n)
1	3 + (1 − 1) (2)	3
2	3 + (2 − 1) (2)	5
3	3 + (3 − 1) (2)	7

2 Modeling
You can use functions to model real-world situations that pair one input value with a unique output value.

Using Graphs to Relate Two Quantities (Lesson 4-1)

Bus Trip

Distance

Time

Graphing a Function Rule (Lesson 4-4)

Continuous   Discrete

Writing a Function Rule (Lesson 4-5)
$$C = \frac{1}{4}n + 6 \qquad A = s^2$$

Chapter Vocabulary

- arithmetic sequence, p. 275
- common difference, p. 275
- continuous graph, p. 255
- dependent variable, p. 240
- discrete graph, p. 255
- domain, p. 268
- function, p. 241
- function notation, p. 269
- input, p. 240
- independent variable, p. 240
- linear function, p. 241
- nonlinear function, p. 246
- output, p. 240
- range, p. 268
- relation, p. 268
- sequence, p. 274
- term of a sequence, p. 274
- vertical line test, p. 269

Choose the correct term to complete each sentence.

1. If the value of a changes in response to the value of b, then b is the __?__ .

2. The graph of a(n) __?__ function is a nonvertical line or part of a nonvertical line.

3. A(n) __?__ graph consists of distinct, isolated points.

4. The __?__ of a function consists of the set of all output values.

| PowerAlgebra.com | **Chapter 4** Chapter Review | 281 |

Essential Questions

BIG idea **Functions**
ESSENTIAL QUESTION How can you represent and describe functions?
ANSWER A function is a relationship that pairs one input value with exactly one output value. You can use words, tables, equations, sets of ordered pairs, and graphs to represent functions.

BIG idea **Modeling**
ESSENTIAL QUESTION Can functions describe real-world situations?
ANSWER You can use functions to model real-world situations that pair one input value with a unique output value.

Answers

SOLUTION OUTLINES (continued)

c. First step: Determine if the graph is unbroken or if it consists of discrete points. (Answer: Continuous; you can have any length of necklace.)

d. First step: Use the rule you wrote or the graph you made in part (b). (Answer: 210 in.)

Chapter Review

1. independent variable

2. linear   **3.** discrete   **4.** range

Summative Questions UbD

Use the following prompts as you review this chapter with your students. The prompts are designed to help you assess your students' understanding of the BIG Ideas they have studied.

- How can you represent discrete relations?
- How can you represent continuous relations?
- What is the difference between a linear and a nonlinear function?
- When is a relation also a function?

Answers

Chapter Review (continued)

5. Answers may vary. Sample:

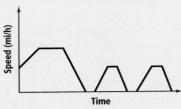

6. Answers may vary. Sample:

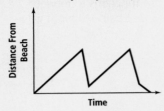

7. Chairs painted, paint left; each time p increases by 1, L decreases by 30; $L = 128 - 30p$.

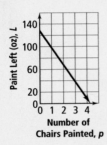

8. Snacks purchased, total cost; for each additional snack, total cost goes up by 3; $C = 18 + 3s$.

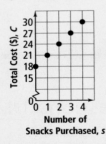

9. Independent n, dependent E; the elevation is 311 more than 15 times the number of flights climbed; $E = 15n + 311$.

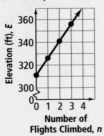

4-1 Using Graphs to Relate Two Quantities

Quick Review
You can use graphs to represent the relationship between two variables.

Example
A dog owner plays fetch with her dog. Sketch a graph to represent the distance between them and the time.

Playing Fetch

Exercises

5. Travel A car's speed increases as it merges onto a highway. The car travels at 65 mi/h on the highway until it slows to exit. The car then stops at three traffic lights before reaching its destination. Draw a sketch of a graph that shows the car's speed over time. Label each section.

6. Surfing A professional surfer paddles out past breaking waves, rides a wave, paddles back out past the breaking waves, rides another wave, and paddles back to the beach. Draw a sketch of a graph that shows the surfer's possible distance from the beach over time.

4-2 Patterns and Linear Functions

Quick Review
A **function** is a relationship that pairs each **input** value with exactly one **output** value. A **linear function** is a function whose graph is a line or part of a line.

Example
The number y of eggs left in a dozen depends on the number x of 2-egg omelets you make, as shown in the table. Represent this relationship using words, an equation, and a graph.

Number of Omelets Made, x	0	1	2	3
Number of Eggs Left, y	12	10	8	6

Look for a pattern in the table. Each time x increases by 1, y decreases by 2. The number y of eggs left is 12 minus the quantity 2 times the number x of omelets made: $y = 12 - 2x$.

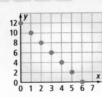

Exercises
For each table, identify the independent and dependent variables. Represent the relationship using words, an equation, and a graph.

7. Paint in Can

Number of Chairs Painted, p	Paint Left (oz), L
0	128
1	98
2	68
3	38

8. Game Cost

Number of Snacks Purchased, s	Total Cost, C
0	$18
1	$21
2	$24
3	$27

9. Elevation

Number of Flights of Stairs Climbed, n	0	1	2	3
Elevation (ft above sea level), E	311	326	341	356

4-3 Patterns and Nonlinear Functions

Quick Review

A **nonlinear function** is a function whose graph is *not* a line or part of a line.

Example

The area A of a square field is a function of the side length s of the field. Is the function *linear* or *nonlinear*?

Side Length (ft), s	10	15	20	25
Area (ft²), A	100	225	400	625

Graph the ordered pairs and connect the points. The graph is not a line, so the function is nonlinear.

Exercises

Graph the function shown by each table. Tell whether the function is *linear* or *nonlinear*.

10.

x	y
1	0
2	1
3	8
4	20

11.

x	y
1	0
2	4.5
3	9
4	13.5

12.

x	y
1	2
2	6
3	12
4	72

13.

x	y
1	−2
2	−9
3	−16
4	−23

4-4 Graphing a Function Rule

Quick Review

A **continuous graph** is a graph that is unbroken. A **discrete graph** is composed of distinct, isolated points. In a real-world graph, show only points that make sense.

Example

The total height h of a stack of cans is a function of the number n of layers of 4.5-in. cans used. This situation is represented by $h = 4.5n$. Graph the function.

n	h
0	0
1	4.5
2	9
3	13.5
4	18

The graph is discrete because only whole numbers of layers make sense.

Exercises

Graph the function rule. Explain why the graph is *continuous* or *discrete*.

14. Walnuts Your cost c to buy w pounds of walnuts at $6/lb is represented by $c = 6w$.

15. Moving A truck originally held 24 chairs. You remove 2 chairs at a time. The number of chairs n remaining after you make t trips is represented by $n = 24 - 2t$.

16. Flood A burst pipe fills a basement with 37 in. of water. A pump empties the water at a rate of 1.5 in./h. The water level ℓ, in inches, after t hours is represented by $\ell = 37 - 1.5t$.

17. Graph $y = -|x| + 2$.

14.

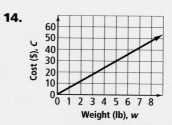

continuous because w can take on any nonnegative value

15.

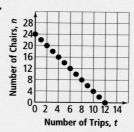

discrete because the number of trips must be a whole number

16.

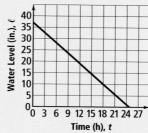

continuous because t can take on any nonnegative value between 0 and $24\frac{2}{3}$

17.

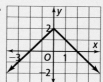

10.

nonlinear

12.

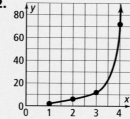

nonlinear

11.

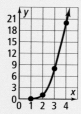

linear

13.

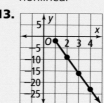

linear

Answers

Chapter Review (continued)

18. $V = 243 - 0.2s$ **19.** $C = 200 + 45h$

20. not a function   **21.** function

22. -4; 6 **23.** 53; 33

24. $\{7.2, 1.12, -4.2, -34.6\}$

25. Multiply each previous term by 5; 625, 3125.

26. Add -3 to the previous term; $-14, -17$.

27. Add 2.5 to the previous term; 14, 16.5.

28. Multiply the previous term by -2; 32, -64.

29. arithmetic; 1.2   **30.** arithmetic; 10

31. not an arithmetic sequence

32. not an arithmetic sequence

4-5 Writing a Function Rule

Quick Review
To write a function rule describing a real-world situation, it is often helpful to start with a verbal model of the situation.

Example
At a bicycle motocross (BMX) track, you pay $40 for a racing license plus $15 per race. What is a function rule that represents your total cost?

total cost = license fee + fee per race · number of races

$\quad C \quad = \quad 40 \quad + \quad 15 \quad \cdot \quad r$

A function rule is $C = 40 + 15 \cdot r$.

Exercises
Write a function rule to represent each situation.

18. Landscaping The volume V remaining in a 243-ft³ pile of gravel decreases by 0.2 ft³ with each shovelful s of gravel spread in a walkway.

19. Design Your total cost C for hiring a garden designer is $200 for an initial consultation plus $45 for each hour h the designer spends drawing plans.

4-6 Formalizing Relations and Functions

Quick Review
A **relation** pairs numbers in the **domain** with numbers in the **range**. A relation may or may not be a function.

Example
Is the relation $\{(0, 1), (3, 3), (4, 4), (0, 0)\}$ a function?

The x-values of the ordered pairs form the domain, and the y-values form the range. The domain value 0 is paired with two range values, 1 and 0. So the relation is not a function.

Exercises
Tell whether each relation is a function.

20. $\{(-1, 7), (9, 4), (3, -2), (5, 3), (9, 1)\}$

21. $\{(2, 5), (3, 5), (4, -4), (5, -4), (6, 8)\}$

Evaluate each function for $x = 2$ and $x = 7$.

22. $f(x) = 2x - 8$ **23.** $h(x) = -4x + 61$

24. The domain of $t(x) = -3.8x - 4.2$ is $\{-3, -1.4, 0, 8\}$. What is the range?

4-7 Sequences and Functions

Quick Review
A **sequence** is an ordered list of numbers, called terms, that often forms a pattern. In an **arithmetic sequence**, there is a **common difference** between consecutive terms.

Example
Tell whether the sequence is arithmetic.

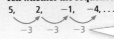

5,   2, -1, -4, . . .

$\quad -3 \quad -3 \quad -3$

The sequence has a common difference of -3, so it is arithmetic.

Exercises
Describe a pattern in each sequence. Then find the next two terms of the difference.

25. 1, 5, 25, 125, . . .   **26.** $-2, -5, -8, -11, . . .$

27. 4, 6.5, 9, 11.5, . . .   **28.** 2, -4, 8, -16, . . .

Tell whether the sequence is arithmetic. If it is, identify the common difference.

29. 2.9, 4.1, 5.3, 6.5, . . .   **30.** $-15, -5, 5, 15, . . .$

31. $-7, -13, -20, -26, . . .$ **32.** 3, 6, 12, 24, . . .

4 · Chapter Test

MathXL® for School
Go to PowerAlgebra.com

Do you know HOW?

1. **Recreation** You ride your bike to the park, sit to read for a while, and then ride your bike home. It takes you less time to ride from the park to your house than it took to ride from your house to the park. Draw a sketch of a graph that shows your possible distance traveled over time. Label each section.

2. Identify the independent and dependent variables in the table below. Then describe the relationship using words, an equation, and a graph.

Speed of Sound in Air				
Temperature (°C)	10	15	20	25
Velocity (m/s)	337	340	343	346

Graph the function shown by each table. Tell whether the function is *linear* or *nonlinear*.

3.
x	y
−3	−5
−1	−1
1	3
3	7

4.
x	y
0	1
1	2
2	5
3	10

Make a table of values for each function rule. Then graph the function.

5. $y = 1.5x - 3$

6. $y = -x^2 + 4$

Identify the domain and range of each relation. Use a mapping diagram to determine whether the relation is a function.

7. $\{(-2, 5), (8, 6), (3, 12), (5, 6)\}$

8. $\{(9, 6), (3, 8), (4, 9.5), (9, 2)\}$

9. **Baking** A bottle holds 48 tsp of vanilla. The amount A of vanilla remaining in the bottle decreases by 2 tsp per batch b of cookies. Write a function rule to represent this situation. How much vanilla remains after 12 batches of cookies?

10. **Party Favors** You are buying party favors that cost $2.47 each. You can spend no more than $30 on the party favors. What domain and range are reasonable for this situation?

Find the range of each function for the domain $\{-4, -2, 0, 1.5, 4\}$.

11. $f(x) = -2x - 3$

12. $f(x) = 5x^2 + 4$

Find the second, fourth, and eleventh terms of the sequence described by each rule.

13. $A(n) = 2 + (n - 1)(-2.5)$

14. $A(n) = -9 + (n - 1)(3)$

Tell whether each sequence is arithmetic. Justify your answer. If the sequence is arithmetic, write a function rule to represent it.

15. 128, 64, 32, 16, . . .

16. 3, 3.25, 3.5, 3.75, . . .

Do you UNDERSTAND?

Vocabulary Tell whether each relationship should be represented by a *continuous* or *discrete* graph.

17. the price of turkey that sells for $.89 per pound

18. the profit you make selling flowers at $1.50 each when each flower costs you $.80

19. **Reasoning** Can a function have an infinite number of values in its domain and only a finite number of values in its range? If so, describe a real-world situation that can be modeled by such a function.

20. **Writing** What is the difference between a relation and a function? Is every relation a function? Is every function a relation? Explain.

PowerAlgebra.com | Chapter 4 Chapter Test | 285

5.
x	−2	−1	0	1	2
y	−6	−4.5	−3	−1.5	0

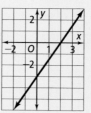

6.
x	−2	−1	0	1	2
y	0	3	4	3	0

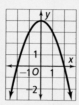

7. domain: $\{-2, 3, 5, 8\}$, range: $\{5, 6, 12\}$; function

8. domain: $\{3, 4, 9\}$, range: $\{2, 6, 8, 9.5\}$; not a function

9. $A = 48 - 2b$; 24 tsp

10. domain $\{0, 1, 2, \dots, 12\}$, range $\{0, 2.47, 4.94, 7.41, \dots, 29.64\}$

11. $\{5, 1, -3, -6, -11\}$

12. $\{84, 24, 4, 15.25, 84\}$

13. −0.5, −5.5, −23

14. −6, 0, 21

15. No, because the sequence does not have a common difference.

16. Yes, because the sequence has a common difference. $A(n) = 3 + (n - 1)(0.25)$

17. continuous

18. discrete

19. Yes; a car travels at the average rate of 55 mi/h for 4 h.

20. A relation is a set of ordered pairs. A function is a relation that assigns exactly one output value to each input value. Not every relation is a function, but every function is a relation.

Answers

Chapter Test

1.

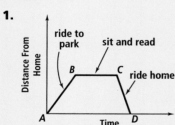

ride to park
sit and read
ride home

Distance From Home
A   B   C   D
Time

2. Temperature, velocity of sound; for every increase of 5°C, the velocity of sound increases by 3 m/s; $y = \frac{3}{5}x + 331$.

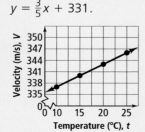

Velocity (m/s), V
350
347
344
341
338
335
0 10 15 20 25
Temperature (°C), t

3.

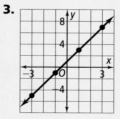

linear

4.

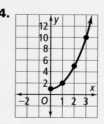

nonlinear

PowerAlgebra.com

MathXL for School
Prepare students for the Mid-Chapter Quiz and Chapter Test with online practice and review.

Chapter Test 285

Item Number	Lesson
1	1-2
2	4-2
3	1-7
4	4-6
5	2-7
6	2-2
7	2-3
8	4-1
9	1-6
10	2-7
11	4-4
12	3-6
13	2-8
14	2-2
15	4-2
16	4-3
17	2-5
18	2-2
19	4-7
20	2-8
21	2-6
22	1-2
23	2-6
24	3-8
25	1-9

4 Cumulative Test Prep

TIPS FOR SUCCESS

Some questions on standardized tests ask you to choose a graph that best represents a real-world situation. Read the question at the right. Then follow the tips to answer it.

Aiko ran at a constant speed for most of a race. Toward the end of the race, she increased her speed until she reached the finish line. Which graph best represents Aiko's distance traveled over time?

TIP 1
Aiko's speed is constant for most of the race, so the graph should be a straight line most of the time.

TIP 2
Aiko's speed increases toward the end of the race, so the graph should rise more quickly at the end.

Think It Through
Choice A shows a *constant* speed during the *entire* race.

Choice B shows an *increasing* speed near the race's *end*.

Choice C shows a *complete stop* in the *middle* of the race.

Choice D shows a *decreasing* speed near the race's *end*.

The correct answer is B.

Vocabulary Builder

As you solve test items, you must understand the meanings of mathematical terms. Match each term with its mathematical meaning.

A. dependent variable

B. equation

C. numerical expression

D. function

E. domain

I. a math sentence stating two quantities have the same value

II. a relation where each input value corresponds to exactly one output value

III. a math phrase that contains operations and numbers but no variables

IV. a variable whose value changes in response to another variable

V. the possible values for the input of a function or relation

Multiple Choice

Read each question. Then write the letter of the correct answer on your paper.

1. Which values of x and y will make the expression $5(x - y)^2$ equal to 20?

   Ⓐ $x = 0, y = 3$ Ⓒ $x = 3, y = 5$

   Ⓑ $x = 1, y = 1$ Ⓓ $x = 5, y = 1$

2. Angie uses the equation $E = 0.03s + 25{,}000$ to find her yearly earnings E based on her total sales s. What is the independent variable?

   Ⓕ E Ⓗ s

   Ⓖ 0.03 Ⓘ $25{,}000$

3. Which expression is equivalent to $6b - 3a + b + 2a$?

   Ⓐ $5b - a$ Ⓒ $7b - a$

   Ⓑ $5b - 5a$ Ⓓ $7b - 5a$

Answers

Cumulative Test Prep

A. IV

B. I

C. III

D. II

E. V

1. C

2. H

3. C

4. A point is missing from the graph of the relation at the the right. The relation is *not* a function. Which point is missing?

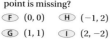

- (F) $(0, 0)$
- (H) $(-1, 2)$
- (G) $(1, 1)$
- (I) $(2, -2)$

5. Lindsey is using a map to find the distance between her house and Juanita's house. On the map, the distance is 2.5 in. If the map scale is $\frac{1}{8}$ in. : 1.5 mi, how far from Juanita does Lindsey live?

- (A) 0.5 mi
- (C) 4.8 mi
- (B) 3.75 mi
- (D) 30 mi

6. Pedro ran 2 more than $\frac{3}{4}$ the number of miles that Cierra ran. Which equation represents the relationship between the number of miles p that Pedro ran and the number of miles c that Cierra ran?

- (F) $c = \frac{3}{4}p + 2$
- (H) $c = \frac{3}{4}p - 2$
- (G) $p = \frac{3}{4}c + 2$
- (I) $p = \frac{3}{4}c - 2$

7. The relationship between degrees Fahrenheit F and degrees Celsius C is given by $C = \frac{5}{9}(F - 32)$. Manuel's pen pal from Europe said that the temperature last week was 25°C. What was the temperature in degrees Fahrenheit?

- (A) $-18°F$
- (C) $77°F$
- (B) $-4°F$
- (D) $102°F$

8. Which graph could represent the circumference of a balloon as the air is being let out?

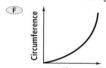

9. Mr. Washington is buying a gallon of milk for $3.99 and some boxes of cereal for $4.39 each. If Mr. Washington has $20, how many boxes of cereal can he buy?

- (A) 3
- (C) 5
- (B) 4
- (D) 6

10. During a clinical study, a medical company found that 3 out of 70 people experienced a side effect when using a certain medicine. The company predicts 63,000 people will use the medicine next year. How many people are expected to experience a side effect?

- (F) 300
- (H) 2700
- (G) 900
- (I) 21,000

11. Which equation can be used to generate the table of values at the right?

- (A) $y = x + 9$
- (B) $y = 2x + 4$
- (C) $y = x + 3$
- (D) $y = 3x - 2$

x	y
-3	-11
0	-2
3	7
6	16

12. Which number line displays the solution of the compound inequality $-5 < -2x + 7 < 15$?

(F)

(G)

(H)

(I)

13. In the diagram below, $\triangle ABC$ and $\triangle DEF$ are similar.

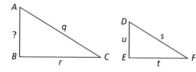

Which expression represents AB?

- (A) $\frac{qu}{s}$
- (C) $\frac{qr}{u}$
- (B) $\frac{ru}{s}$
- (D) $\frac{rs}{t}$

4. G
5. D
6. G
7. C
8. H
9. A
10. H
11. D
12. G
13. A

Answers

Cumulative Test Prep (continued)

14. I

15. B

16. G

17. 108

18. 56

19. 17

20. 29

21. 1.25

22. 86.60

23. [2] 8 h

[1] 1 computation error

24. [2] $3x < 4x + 6$ $2x + 1 < 15$

     $-x < 6$ $2x < 14$

      $x > -6$ $x < 7$

   $-6 < x < 7$

[1] correct methods used with one minor computational error

25. [4] **a.** independent: n number of loads of laundry; dependent: g gallons of water used

b. $g = 41n$

c. 13

[3] correct methods used with one minor computational error

[2] error in function but then correct term number and sequence value, or correct function representations but error in finding term number and value

[1] correct answers with no work shown

---

14. The sum of two consecutive odd integers is 24. Which equation can be used to find the first integer n?

 $n + 1 = 24$ 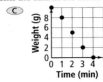 $2n + 1 = 24$

Ⓖ $n + 2 = 24$ Ⓘ $2n + 2 = 24$

15. The table below shows the relationship between how long an ice cube is in the sun and its weight.

Time (min)	0	1	2	3	4
Weight (g)	9	8	5	2	0

Which graph best represents the data in the table?

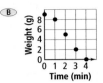

16. Which of the following situations can be represented by a linear function?

Ⓕ the height of a person, given the person's age

Ⓖ the weight of a bag of pennies, given the number of pennies

Ⓗ the length of a day, given the day of the year

Ⓘ the test grade, given the hours the student studied

GRIDDED RESPONSE

Record your answers in a grid.

17. Sasha is framing a 5 in.-by-7 in. picture with a frame that is 3 in. wide, as shown at the right. What is the frame's area in square inches?

18. The sum of two consecutive integers is -15. What is the product of the two integers?

---

19. Max writes a number pattern in which each number in the pattern is 1 less than twice the previous number. If the first number is 2, what is the fifth number?

20. The rectangles shown below are similar.

20 ft

The area of rectangle A is 180 ft². The area of rectangle B is 45 ft². What is rectangle B's perimeter in feet?

21. One lap of a swimming pool is 50 m from one end of the pool to the other. Tamara swims 25 laps in a swim meet. How many kilometers does she swim?

22. An Internet company charges $8.95 per month for the first 3 months that it hosts your Web site. Then the company charges $11.95 per month for Web hosting. How much money, in dollars, will the company charge for 8 months of Web hosting?

Short Response

23. You are taking a plane trip that begins in Seattle and ends in Boston, with a layover in Dallas. The flight from Seattle to Dallas is 2 h 55 min. The layover in Dallas is 1 h 25 min. The flight from Dallas to Boston is 3 h 40 min. How long in hours is the entire trip?

24. What values of x make both inequalities true?

$3x < 4x + 6$

$2x + 1 < 15$

Extended Response

25. A particular washing machine uses an average of 41 gallons of water for every load of laundry.

a. Identify the independent and dependent variables in this situation.

b. Write a function rule to represent the situation.

c. Suppose you used 533 gallons of water for laundry in one month. How many loads of laundry did you wash?

CHAPTER
5

Get Ready!

Lesson 1-9 ◀ **Solutions of a Two-Variable Equation**

Tell whether the given ordered pair is a solution of the equation.

1. $4y + 2x = 3; (1.5, 0)$ **2.** $y = 7x - 5; (0, 5)$ **3.** $y = -2x + 5; (2, 1)$

Lesson 2-5 ◀ **Transforming Equations**

Solve each equation for y.

4. $2y - x = 4$ **5.** $3x = y + 2$ **6.** $-2y - 2x = 4$

Lesson 2-6 ◀ **Comparing Unit Rates**

7. Transportation A car traveled 360 km in 6 h. A train traveled 400 km in 8 h. A boat traveled 375 km in 5 h. Which had the fastest average speed?

8. Plants A birch tree grew 2.5 in. in 5 months. A bean plant grew 8 in. in 10 months. A rose bush grew 5 in. in 8 months. Which grew the fastest?

Lesson 4-4 ◀ **Graphing a Function Rule**

Make a table of values for each function rule. Then graph each function.

9. $f(x) = x + 3$ **10.** $f(x) = -2x$ **11.** $f(x) = x - 4$

Lesson 4-7 ◀ **Arithmetic Sequences**

Write a rule for each arithmetic sequence.

12. $2, 5, 8, 11, \ldots$ **13.** $13, 10, 7, 4, \ldots$ **14.** $-3, -0.5, 2, 4.5, \ldots$

 Looking Ahead Vocabulary

15. A steep hill has a greater *slope* than a flat plain. What does the *slope* of a line on a graph describe?

16. Two streets are *parallel* when they go the same way and do no cross. What does it mean in math to call two lines *parallel*?

17. John was bringing a message to the principal's office when the principal *intercepted* him and took the message. When a graph passes through the y-axis, it has a *y-intercept*. What do you think a y-intercept of a graph represents?

PowerAlgebra.com | Chapter 5 Linear Functions | 289

Answers

Get Ready!

1. yes

2. no

3. yes

4. $y = \frac{1}{2}x + 2$

5. $y = 3x - 2$

6. $y = -x - 2$

7. boat

8. bean plant

9.

x	f(x)
−2	1
0	3
2	5

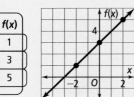

10.

x	f(x)
−1	2
0	0
1	−2

11.

x	f(x)
0	−4
2	−2
4	0

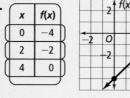

12. $A(n) = 2 + (n - 1)3$

13. $A(n) = 13 + (n - 1)(-3)$

14. $A(n) = -3 + (n - 1)2.5$

15. the steepness of the line

16. Two lines are parallel if they lie in the same plane and do not intersect.

17. A y-intercept is the y-coordinate of the point where the line crosses the y-axis.

Get Ready!

Assign this diagnostic assessment to determine if students have the prerequisite skills for Chapter 5.

Lesson	Skill
1-9	Solutions of a Two-Variable Equation
2-5	Transforming Equations
2-6	Comparing Unit Rates
4-4	Graphing a Function Rule
4-7	Arithmetic Sequences

To remediate students, select from these resources (available for every lesson).
• Online Problems (PowerAlgebra.com)
• Reteaching (All-in-One Teaching Resources)
• Practice (All-in-One Teaching Resources)

Why Students Need These Skills

SOLUTIONS OF A TWO-VARIABLE EQUATION
Students will examine if an ordered pair is a solution to an equation using substitution.

TRANSFORMING EQUATIONS
Students will solve literal equations for a variable when converting an equation from point-slope form to slope-intercept form.

COMPARING UNIT RATES
Students will find rates of change from tables in order to find slope.

GRAPHING A FUNCTION RULE
Students will write an equation representing a line and graph the line.

ARITHMETIC SEQUENCES
Students will analyze patterns to write function rules.

Looking Ahead Vocabulary

SLOPE Ask students to name other examples of real-world items that have an increasing slope and a decreasing slope.

PARALLEL Ask students to list three examples of parallel lines in the classroom.

Y-INTERCEPT Have students define another real-world definition of interception. How does their definition relate to math?

Get Ready! 289

Chapter 5 Overview

UbD Understanding by Design

Chapter 5 connects and extends the Big Ideas introduced in the last chapter to graphing equations. In this chapter, students will develop the answers to the Essential Questions posed on the opposite page as they learn the concepts and skills bulleted below.

BIG idea Proportionality

ESSENTIAL QUESTION What does the slope of a line indicate about the line?
• Students will find slope using a formula.
• Students will find slope using a graph.
• Students will analyze various slopes and describe their meaning.

BIG idea Functions

ESSENTIAL QUESTION What information does the equation of a line give you?
• The equation of a line gives its slope.
• The equation of a line gives its *y*-intercept.

BIG idea Modeling

ESSENTIAL QUESTION How can you make predictions based on a scatter plot?
• Students will find the line of best fit.
• Students will analyze trend lines in scatter plots.

Indiana Academic Standards

A1.2.1 Translate among various representations of linear functions including tables, graphs, words and equations.

A1.2.2 Graph linear equations and show that they have constant rates of change.

A1.2.3 Determine the slope, *x*-intercept, and *y*-intercept of a line given its graph, its equation, or two points on the line and determine the equation of a line given sufficient information.

A1.2.4 Write, interpret, and translate among equivalent forms of equations for linear functions (slope-intercept, point-slope, and standard), recognizing that equivalent forms reveal more or less information about a given situation.

A1.2.5 Solve problems that can be modeled using linear equations and inequalities, interpret the solutions, and determine whether the solutions are reasonable.

A1.7.1 Organize and display data using appropriate methods to detect patterns and departures from patterns. Summarize the data using measures of center (mean, median) and spread (range, percentiles, variance, standard deviation). Compare data sets using graphs and summary statistics.

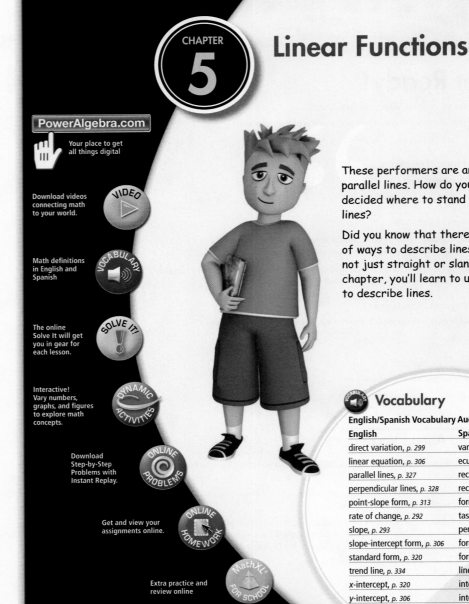

These performers are arranged in parallel lines. How do you think they decided where to stand to make the lines?

Did you know that there are lots of ways to describe lines? They're not just straight or slanted. In this chapter, you'll learn to use algebra to describe lines.

Vocabulary

English/Spanish Vocabulary Audio Online:

English	Spanish
direct variation, *p. 299*	variación directa
linear equation, *p. 306*	ecuación lineal
parallel lines, *p. 327*	rectas paralelas
perpendicular lines, *p. 328*	rectas perpendiculares
point-slope form, *p. 313*	forma punto-pendiente
rate of change, *p. 292*	tasa de cambio
slope, *p. 293*	pendiente
slope-intercept form, *p. 306*	forma pendiente-intercepto
standard form, *p. 320*	forma normal
trend line, *p. 334*	línea de tendencia
x-intercept, *p. 320*	intercepto en *x*
y-intercept, *p. 306*	intercepto en *y*

PowerAlgebra.com

Chapter 5 Overview

Use these online assets to engage your students. These include support for the Solve It and step-by-step solutions for Problems.

 Show the student-produced video demonstrating relevant and engaging applications of the new concepts in the chapter.

 Find online definitions for new terms in English and Spanish.

 Start each lesson with an attention-getting Problem. View the Problem online with helpful hints.

My Math Video

My Math Video

FACILITATE Use this photo to introduce the concept of parallel lines. Students may recall the concepts of parallel and perpendicular lines from earlier courses. This discussion prepares students to describe lines algebraically.

Q Suppose you drew lines to imitate the four lines of women. Would the lines intersect? **[No; the women form parallel lines.]**

Q A woman in one line is about 3 feet from the woman in the line next to her. Can you conclude how far apart the other pairs of women are? **[If the dancers are symmetric, they will all be 3 feet apart.]**

Q The slant of a line is described using slope in mathematics. You compare how far you move horizontally and vertically as you trace a certain part of the line. How would you describe the slope of the lines the women form? **[Their lines go right and up.]**

EXTENSION

Have students collect data that is linear. Some examples include the price of different numbers of song downloads or text messages, the perimeter of a square based on its side length, money earned for hours worked, etc. Have students graph their data on a coordinate plane and sketch the line that it creates. Challenge students to use the line to describe the relationship between the two variables in their data and make predictions about points beyond what is shown on their graphs.

BIG ideas

1 **Proportionality**
Essential Question: What does the slope of a line indicate about the line?

2 **Functions**
Essential Question: What information does the equation of a line give you?

3 **Modeling**
Essential Question: How can you make predictions based on a scatter plot?

Chapter Preview

PowerAlgebra.com | **Chapter 5** Linear Functions | **291**

 Increase students' depth of knowledge with interactive online activities.

 Show Problems from each lesson solved step by step. Instant replay allows students to go at their own pace when studying online.

 Assign homework to individual students or to an entire class.

 Prepare students for the Mid-Chapter Quiz and Chapter Test with online practice and review.

UbD

Proportionality

BIG idea Two quantities are *proportional* if they have the same ratio in each instance where they are measured together.

ESSENTIAL UNDERSTANDINGS

5–1 Ratios can be used to show a relationship between changing quantities, such as vertical and horizontal change.

5–2 If the ratio of two variables is constant, then the variables have a special relationship, called a direct variation.

Function

BIG idea A function is a relationship between variables in which each value of the input variable is associated with a unique value of the output variable. Functions can be represented in a variety of ways, such as graphs, tables, equations, or words. Each representation is particularly useful in certain situations. Some important families of functions are developed through transformations of the simplest form of the function.

ESSENTIAL UNDERSTANDINGS

5–3 to 5–5 A line on a graph can be represented by a linear equation. Forms of linear equations include the Slope–Intercept, Point–Slope, and Standard forms.

5–6 The relationship between two lines can be determined by comparing their slopes and y-intercepts.

5–8 Absolute value equations can be graphed quickly by shifting the graph of $y = |x|$.

Modeling

BIG idea Many real-world mathematical problems can be represented algebraically. These representations can lead to algebraic solutions. A function that models a real-world situation can then be used to make estimates or predictions about future occurrences.

ESSENTIAL UNDERSTANDINGS

5–7 Two sets of numerical data can be graphed as ordered pairs. If the two sets of data are related, a line on the graph can be used to estimate or predict values.

Slope

The slope of a line represents the constant rate of change of a linear function.

$$\text{slope} = \frac{\text{vertival change}}{\text{horizontal change}} = \frac{\text{rise}}{\text{run}}$$

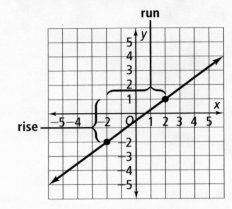

The slope of the line above can be determined from the two points shown, $(-2, -2)$ and $(2, 1)$.

The vertical change between $(-2, -2)$ and $(2, 1)$ is the difference in the y-values, $1 - (-2) = 3$. The horizontal change is the difference in the x-values, $2 - (-2) = 4$. So, slope $= \frac{3}{4}$. It does not matter which point is identified as (x_1, y_1) and which one is defined as (x_2, y_2).

For example, set $(x_1, y_1) = (-2, -2)$ and $(x_2, y_2) = (2, 1)$.

$$\text{slope} = \frac{\text{rise}}{\text{run}} = \frac{y_2 - y_1}{x_2 - x_1} = \frac{1 - (-2)}{2 - (-2)} = \frac{1 + 2}{2 + 2} = \frac{3}{4}$$

Common Errors With Slope

Although it does not matter which point is identified as (x_1, y_1) and which one is defined as (x_2, y_2), it is important that the same order is used for the numerator as for the denominator.

If students mix up the elements in the ordered pairs, the terms in the numerator and denominator are subtracted in reverse order from each other, and the slope is incorrect.

Forms of Linear Equations

The slope-intercept form is useful for graphing linear equations. Standard form and point-slope form should be manipulated into slope-intercept form to more easily graph the equation.

$y = mx + b$ slope-intercept form

$y - y_1 = m(x - x_1)$ point-slope form

$Ax + By = C$ standard form

Here are three possible situations:

GIVEN: SLOPE-INTERCEPT FORM

Given: $y = \frac{1}{2}x + 4$, the slope $= \frac{1}{2}$ and the y-intercept $= 4$.

Graph the y-intercept and use the slope to find the next point. Draw a line through the points.

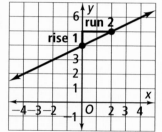

GIVEN: POINT-SLOPE FORM

Given $y - 1 = -\frac{3}{5}(x - (-2))$, solve the equation for y.

$$y - 1 = -\frac{3}{5}(x - (-2))$$

$$y - 1 = -\frac{3}{5}x - \frac{6}{5}$$

$$y = -\frac{3}{5}x - \frac{1}{5}$$

GIVEN: TWO POINTS

Given $-2x + 3y = 1$, solve the equation for y.

$$-2x + 3y = 1$$

$$y = \frac{2}{3}x + \frac{1}{3}$$

Common Errors With Forms of Linear Equations

The operation signs in the point-slope formula are subtraction, so negative x_1 and y_1 values will change the signs to addition.

In the point-slope equation $y + 3 = \frac{1}{2}(x + 7)$ the slope is $\frac{1}{2}$ and a point is $(-7, -3)$, not $(7, 3)$.

Scatter Plots

The line of best fit for a scatter plot can be drawn with varying degrees of precision. If you plot the data points using pencil and paper, you may simply draw a line of best fit by eye.

The stronger the correlation, the easier it is to draw the line of best fit by eye.

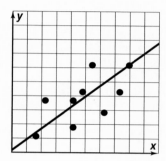

The weaker the correlation, the harder it is to draw the line of best fit by eye. It is not clear which of the lines best fit the scatter plot below.

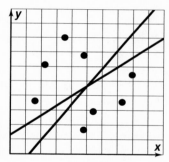

Common Errors With Scatter Plots

Negative correlation does not mean lack of correlation but rather correlation in a negative direction: it refers to a scatter plot whose line of best fit has a negative slope.

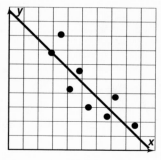

A scatter plot that shows *no* correlation has points that cover the graph in various places and do not cluster.

LINEAR FUNCTIONS
Pacing and Assignment Guide

		TRADITIONAL			BLOCK
Lesson	**Teaching Day(s)**	**Basic**	**Average**	**Advanced**	**Block**
5-1	1	Problems 1-4 Exs. 8–25 all, 26–38 even, 39, 41, 42–48 even, 59–74	Problems 1-4 Exs. 9–25 odd, 26–49, 59–74	Problems 1-4 Exs. 9–25 odd, 26–74	**Day 1** Problems 1-4 Exs. 9–25 odd, 26–49, 59–74
5-2	1	Problems 1-4 Exs. 9–29 all, 30–34 even, 35–42, 48–59	Problems 1-4 Exs. 9–29 odd, 30–43, 48–59	Problems 1-4 Exs. 9–29 odd, 30–59	Problems 1-4 Exs. 9–29 odd, 30–43, 48–59
5-3	1	Problems 1-3 Exs. 7–27 all, 52–58 even	Problems 1-3 Exs. 7–27 odd, 51–58	Problems 1-3 Exs. 7–27 odd, 51–78	**Day 2** Problems 1-6 Exs. 7–49 odd, 51–71, 76–90
	2	Problems 4-6 Exs. 28–50 all, 59–61 all, 62–68 even, 71, 76–90	Problems 4-6 Exs. 29–49 odd, 59–71, 76–90	Problems 4-6 Exs. 29–49 odd, 59–90	
5-4	1	Problems 1-2 Exs. 8–15, 24–27	Problems 1-2 Exs. 9–15 odd, 24–27	Problems 1-4 Exs. 9–23 odd, 24–43	**Day 3** Problems 1-4 Exs. 9–23 odd, 24–31, 34–43
	2	Problems 3-4 Exs. 16–23, 28–29, 31, 34–43	Problems 3-4 Exs. 17–23 odd, 28–31, 34–43		
5-5	1	Problems 1-3 Exs. 8–30 all, 39	Problems 1-3 Exs. 9–29 odd, 39, 45–50	Problems 1-3 Exs. 9–29 odd, 39, 45–50	**Day 4** Problems 1-5 Exs. 9–37 odd, 39–60, 66–79
	2	Problems 4-5 Exs. 31–38 all, 40–44, 52–60 even, 66–79	Problems 4-5 Exs. 31–37 odd, 51–60, 66–79	Problems 4-5 Exs. 31–37 odd, 51–79	
5-6	1	Problems 1-4 Exs. 7–26, 27–30, 32–33, 35, 38–47	Problems 1-4 Exs. 7–25 odd, 27–35, 38–47	Problems 1-4 Exs. 7–25 odd, 27–47	**Day 5** Problems 1-4 Exs. 7–25 odd, 27–35, 38–47
5-7	1	Problems 1-4 Exs. 7–15, 16–20, 23–33	Problems 1-4 Exs. 7–15 odd, 16–21, 23–33	Problems 1-4 Exs. 7–15 odd, 16–33	Problems 1-4 Exs. 7–15 odd, 16–21, 23–33
5-8	1	Problems 1-3 Exs. 6–20 all	Problems 1-3 Exs. 7–19 odd,	Problems 1-5 Exs. 7–31 odd, 33–59	**Day 6** Problems 1-5 Exs. 7–31 odd, 33–47, 50–59
	2	Problems 4-5 Exs. 21–32 all, 34–42 even, 43–44, 50–59	Problems 4-5 Exs. 7–19 odd, 33–47, 50–59		
Review	1	Chapter 5 Review	Chapter 5 Review	Chapter 5 Review	**Day 7** Chapter 5 Review
Assess	1	Chapter 5 Test	Chapter 5 Test	Chapter 5 Test	Chapter 5 Test
Total		**14 Days**	**14 Days**	**12 Days**	**7 Days**

Note: Pacing does not include Concept Bytes and other feature pages.

Resources

	For the Chapter	5-1	5-2	5-3	5-4	5-5	5-6	5-7	5-8
Planning									
Teacher Center Online Planner & Grade Book	I	I	I	I	I	I	I	I	I
Interactive Learning & Guided Instruction									
My Math Video	I								
Solve It!		I TM	I TM	I TM	I TM	I TM	I TM	I TM	I TM
Student Companion (SP)*		P M	P M	P M	P M	P M	P M	P M	P M
Vocabulary Support		I P M	I P M	I P M	I P M	I P M	I P M	I P M	I P M
Got It? Support		I P	I P	I P	I P	I P	I P	I P	I P
Dynamic Activity		I	I	I				I	I
Online Problems		I	I	I	I	I	I	I	I
Additional Problems		M	M	M	M	M	M	M	M
English Language Learner Support (TR)		E P M	E P M	E P M	E P M	E P M	E P M	E P M	E P M
Activities, Games, and Puzzles		E M	E M	E M	E M	E M	E M	E M	E M
Teaching With TI Technology With CD-ROM		✓ P	✓ P		✓ P		✓ P	✓ P	
TI-Nspire™ Support CD-ROM	✓	✓	✓	✓	✓	✓	✓	✓	✓
Lesson Check & Practice									
Student Companion (SP)*		P M	P M	P M	P M	P M	P M	P M	P M
Lesson Check Support		I P	I P	I P	I P	I P	I P	I P	I P
Practice and Problem Solving Workbook (SP)		P	P	P	P	P	P	P	P
Think About a Plan (TR)*		E P M	E P M	E P M	E P M	E P M	E P M	E P M	E P M
Practice Form G (TR)*		E P M	E P M	E P M	E P M	E P M	E P M	E P M	E P M
Standardized Test Prep (TR)*		P M	P M	P M	P M	P M	P M	P M	P M
Practice Form K (TR)*		E P M	E P M	E P M	E P M	E P M	E P M	E P M	E P M
Extra Practice	E M								
Find the Errors!	M								
Enrichment (TR)		E P M	E P M	E P M	E P M	E P M	E P M	E P M	E P M
Answers and Solutions CD-ROM	✓	✓	✓	✓	✓	✓	✓	✓	✓
Assess & Remediate									
ExamView CD-ROM	✓	✓	✓	✓	✓	✓	✓	✓	✓
Lesson Quiz		I TM	I TM	I TM	I TM	I TM	I TM	I TM	I TM
Quizzes and Tests Form G (TR)*	E P M					E P M			E P M
Quizzes and Tests Form K (TR)*	E P M					E P M			E P M
Reteaching (TR)*		E P M	E P M	E P M	E P M	E P M	E P M	E P M	E P M
Performance Tasks (TR)*	P M								
Cumulative Review (TR)*	P M								
Progress Monitoring Assessments	I P M								

(TR) Available in All-In-One Teaching Resources   * Spanish available

1 Interactive Learning

Solve It!

PURPOSE To provide a real-world situation in which the steepness of lines must be quantified in order to facilitate comparisons

PROCESS Students may use visual judgment or knowledge of ratios to find steepness.

FACILITATE

Q If the horizontal distance between two pairs of poles were the same, how would you use the vertical distance to determine between which pair of poles the cable is steeper? **[When the vertical distance is greater, the cable is steeper.]**

Q When the horizontal distance is not the same, how would you determine between which pair of poles the cable is the steepest? **[Between each pair of poles, divide the vertical distance by the horizontal distance.]**

ANSWER See Solve It in Answers on next page.
CONNECT THE MATH Steepness of a line can be quantified by dividing the vertical distance covered by the horizontal distance covered. In this lesson, students learn this steepness is the slope of a line.

2 Guided Instruction

Problem 1

Q How can you use the rate of change to create the next row in the table? **[Increase the time by 1 min and increase the distance by 260 ft.]**

Q Does this table represent a function? Explain. **[Yes, every input is matched with only one output.]**

Got It?

Q What is the rate of change from the first row of the table to the last row? **[260 ft/1 min]**

Indiana Academic Standards
A1.2.2 Graph linear equations and show that they have constant rates of change.
A1.2.3 Determine the slope, x-intercept, and y-intercept of a line given its graph, its equation, or two points on the line and determine the equation of a line given sufficient information.

Objectives To find rates of change from tables
To find slope

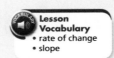

Getting Ready!

The table shows the horizontal and vertical distances from the base of the mountain at several poles along the path of a ski lift. The poles are connected by cable. Between which two poles is the cable's path the steepest? How do you know?

Pole	Horizontal Distance	Vertical Distance
A	20	30
B	40	35
C	60	60
D	100	70

Before you hit the slopes, better check the steepness of the trail!

Lesson Vocabulary
• rate of change
• slope

Essential Understanding You can use ratios to show a relationship between changing quantities, such as vertical and horizontal change.

Rate of change shows the relationship between two changing quantities. When one quantity depends on the other, the following is true.

$$\text{rate of change} = \frac{\text{change in the dependent variable}}{\text{change in the independent variable}}$$

Problem 1 Finding Rate of Change Using a Table

Think
Does this problem look like one you've seen before?
Yes. In Lesson 2-6, you wrote rates and unit rates. The rate of change in Problem 1 is an example of a unit rate.

Marching Band The table shows the distance a band marches over time. Is the rate of change in distance with respect to time constant? What does the rate of change represent?

$$\text{rate of change} = \frac{\text{change in distance}}{\text{change in time}}$$

Calculate the rate of change from one row of the table to the next.

$$\frac{520 - 260}{2 - 1} = \frac{260}{1} \qquad \frac{780 - 520}{3 - 2} = \frac{260}{1} \qquad \frac{1040 - 780}{4 - 3} = \frac{260}{1}$$

The rate of change is constant and equals $\frac{260 \text{ ft}}{1 \text{ min}}$. It represents the distance the band marches per minute.

Distance Marched

Time (min)	Distance (ft)
1	260
2	520
3	780
4	1040

Got It? 1. In Problem 1, do you get the same rate of change if you use nonconsecutive rows of the table? Explain.

BIG idea Proportionality UbD

ESSENTIAL UNDERSTANDINGS
• Ratios can show the relationship between two changing quantities, such as vertical and horizontal change.
• The slope of a line is the ratio of vertical change over horizontal change.
• The slope of a line can be positive, negative, zero, or undefined.

Math Background

Prior to an algebra course, a line is described as a straight curve that extends infinitely in either direction. In algebra, a line is described by a linear equation and is represented graphically on a coordinate plane and contains infinitely many points. A coordinate plane has two dimensions. The relationship between two points on a line can be described by a ratio of the vertical change from point to point to the horizontal change from point to point. This ratio defines a relationship between

these two changing quantities and is called slope.

Slope is the ratio of rise over run. When first studying slope, students may be confused by the order of this ratio. Students are accustomed to putting the x first when writing the coordinates of an ordered pair. This can lead them to place the difference in the x-coordinates in the numerator, when it should be in the denominator. Emphasize that slope is $\frac{\text{rise}}{\text{run}}$; rise is the vertical change and run is the horizontal change.

Support Student Learning

Use the **Algebra 1 Companion** to engage and support students during instructions. See Lesson Resources at the end of this lesson for details.

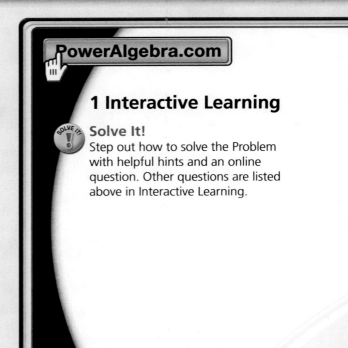

PowerAlgebra.com

1 Interactive Learning

Solve It!

Step out how to solve the Problem with helpful hints and an online question. Other questions are listed above in Interactive Learning.

The graphs of the ordered pairs (time, distance) in Problem 1 lie on a line, as shown at the right. The relationship between time and distance is linear. When data are linear, the rate of change is constant.

Notice also that the rate of change found in Problem 1 is just the ratio of the vertical change (or *rise*) to the horizontal change (or *run*) between two points on the line. The rate of change is called the *slope* of the line.

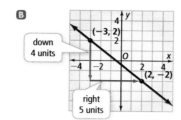
Distance Marched

$$\textbf{slope} = \frac{\text{vertical change}}{\text{horizontal change}} = \frac{\text{rise}}{\text{run}}$$

 Problem 2 Finding Slope Using a Graph

What is the slope of each line?

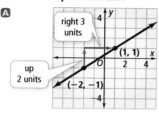
A

$$\text{slope} = \frac{\text{rise}}{\text{run}}$$
$$= \frac{2}{3}$$
The slope of the line is $\frac{2}{3}$.

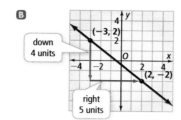
B

$$\text{slope} = \frac{\text{rise}}{\text{run}}$$
$$= \frac{-4}{5} = -\frac{4}{5}$$
The slope of the line is $-\frac{4}{5}$.

✓ **Got It? 2.** What is the slope of each line in parts (a) and (b)?

a.
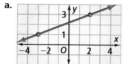

b.
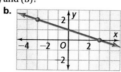

c. Reasoning In part (A) of Problem 2, pick two new points on the line to find the slope. Do you get the same slope?

Notice that the line in part (A) of Problem 2 has a positive slope and slants upward from left to right. The line in part (B) of Problem 2 has a negative slope and slopes downward from left to right.

Problem 2

Q In 2A, how can you use the slope to name another point on the line that is to the right of (1, 1)? **[From the point (1, 1), count up two units and right 3 units to name the point (4, 3).]**

Q In 2B, how can you indicate that the line falls from the left point to the right point? **[Make the rise a negative number.]**

Q In 2B, what is the slope if you start counting from the point (−3, 2) and count to the point (2, −2)? What is the slope if you start at the point (2, −2) and count to the point (−3, 2)? Are the slopes equal? $[\frac{-4}{5}; \frac{4}{-5};$ **yes]**

Got It?   **ERROR PREVENTION**
For consistency, tell students that when visually inspecting the slope of a line, it should be interpreted from left to right, just as a book is read from left to right.

2 Guided Instruction

 Each Problem is worked out and supported online.

Problem 1
Finding Rate of Change Using a Table
Animated

Problem 2
Finding Slope Using a Graph
Animated

Problem 3
Finding Slope Using Points
Animated

Problem 4
Finding Slopes of Horizontal and Vertical Lines

Support in Algebra 1 Companion
• Vocabulary
• Key Concepts
• Got It?

Answers

Solve It!
Between poles B and C; explanations may vary.

Got It?
1. Yes; the rate of change is constant.
2. a. $\frac{2}{5}$
   b. $-\frac{1}{3}$
   c. yes

Take Note

Usually students can informally state how to find the slope if given two ordered pairs on a Cartesian plane. But when students are given two points without a coordinate grid, they will not be able to count the rise and run, so they need to learn the slope formula.

Problem 3

Q Which point is to the left of the other point on the coordinate plane? **[(−1, 0) is to the left of (3, −2).]**

Q Does the line rise or fall from the left point to the right point? **[The line falls.]**

Q What does the relationship of the two given points tell you about the slope of the line? **[The line falls from left to right, so the slope is negative.]**

Got It?   ERROR PREVENTION

If students get an answer of $\frac{4}{3}$, then they probably subtracted the smaller y-value from the larger y-value and the smaller x-value from the larger x-value. Emphasize that they must choose one ordered pair as the x- and y-values to be subtracted from and the other ordered pair as the x- and y-values to subtract.

Problem 4

Q What are two other points that lie on the line shown in part A? What do all points that lie on the line have in common? **[(3, 2) and (6, 2); all points have a y-coordinate of 2.]**

Q In 4B, what do you know about the difference of the x-coordinates of any two points on the line? **[Any two x-coordinates have a difference of 0.]**

You can use any two points on a line to find its slope. Use subscripts to distinguish between the two points. In the diagram, (x_1, y_1) are the coordinates of point A, and (x_2, y_2) are the coordinates of point B. To find the slope of $\overleftrightarrow{AB}$, you can use the *slope formula*.

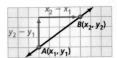

Key Concept The Slope Formula

$$\text{slope} = \frac{\text{rise}}{\text{run}} = \frac{y_2 - y_1}{x_2 - x_1}, \text{ where } x_2 - x_1 \neq 0$$

The x-coordinate you use first in the denominator must belong to the same ordered pair as the y-coordinate you use first in the numerator.

Problem 3 Finding Slope Using Points   GRIDDED RESPONSE

What is the slope of the line through $(-1, 0)$ and $(3, -2)$?

Plan

Does it matter which point is (x_1, y_1) and which is (x_2, y_2)?
No. You can pick either point for (x_1, y_1) in the slope formula. The other point is then (x_2, y_2).

Think

You need the slope, so start with the slope formula.

Substitute $(-1, 0)$ for (x_1, y_1) and $(3, -2)$ for (x_2, y_2).

Simplify to find the answer to place on the grid.

Write

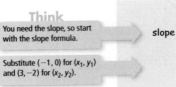

$$\text{slope} = \frac{y_2 - y_1}{x_2 - x_1}$$

$$= \frac{-2 - 0}{3 - (-1)}$$

$$= \frac{-2}{4} = -\frac{1}{2}$$

Got It? 3. What is the slope of the line through $(1, 3)$ and $(4, -1)$?

Problem 4 Finding Slopes of Horizontal and Vertical Lines

What is the slope of each line?

Think

Can you generalize these results?
Yes. All points on a horizontal line have the same y-value, so the slope is always zero. Finding the slope of a vertical line always leads to division by zero. The slope is always undefined.

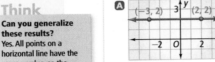

A Let $(x_1, y_1) = (-3, 2)$ and $(x_2, y_2) = (2, 2)$.

$$\text{slope} = \frac{y_2 - y_1}{x_2 - x_1} = \frac{2 - 2}{2 - (-3)} = \frac{0}{5} = 0$$

The slope of the horizontal line is 0.

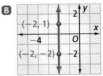

B Let $(x_1, y_1) = (-2, -2)$ and $(x_2, y_2) = (-2, 1)$.

$$\text{slope} = \frac{y_2 - y_1}{x_2 - x_1} = \frac{1 - (-2)}{-2 - (-2)} = \frac{3}{0}$$

Division by zero is undefined. The slope of the vertical line is undefined.

Additional Problems

1. The table shows the elevation of a hang glider over time. Is the rate of change in elevation with respect to time constant? What does the rate of change represent?

Hang Glider Elevation

Time (minutes)	Elevation (feet)
1	360
2	325
3	290
4	255

ANSWER The rate of change is constant and equals −35 ft/min. The hang glider is descending at a rate of 35 ft/min.

2. What is the slope of each line?

a.

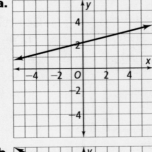

b.

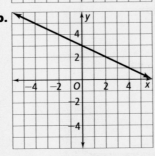

ANSWER a. $\frac{1}{4}$ **b.** $-\frac{1}{2}$

3. What is the slope of the line through $F(-3, 2)$ and $G(1, 5)$?

ANSWER $\frac{3}{4}$

4. What is the slope of each line?

a.

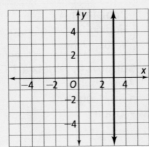

b.

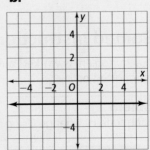

ANSWER a. undefined **b.** 0

Got It? **4.** What is the slope of the line through the given points?
      a. (4, −3), (4, 2)   **b.** (−1, −3), (5, −3)

The following summarizes what you have learned about slope.

take note

Concept Summary   Slopes of Lines

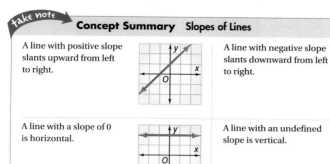

A line with positive slope slants upward from left to right.

A line with negative slope slants downward from left to right.

A line with a slope of 0 is horizontal.

A line with an undefined slope is vertical.

 Lesson Check

Do you know HOW?

1. Is the rate of change in cost constant with respect to the number of pencils bought? Explain.

Cost of Pencils				
Number of Pencils	1	4	7	12
Cost ($)	0.25	1	1.75	3

2. What is the slope of the line?

3. What is the slope of the line through (−1, 2) and (2, −3)?

Do you UNDERSTAND?

4. Vocabulary What characteristic of a graph represents the rate of change? Explain.

5. Open-Ended Give an example of a real-world situation that you can model with a horizontal line. What is the rate of change for the situation? Explain.

6. Compare and Contrast How does finding a line's slope by counting units of vertical and horizontal change on a graph compare with finding it using the slope formula?

7. Error Analysis A student calculated the slope of the line at the right to be 2. Explain the mistake. What is the correct slope?

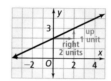

Got It?
Many students struggle to understand why division by zero is undefined. Remind students that division is the inverse of multiplication. Write the following problems side by side on the board and emphasize that they are equivalent: 6 ÷ 3 = ? and ? × 3 = 6. Ask, "What number times 3 equals 6?" [2] Then write the following two problems underneath, 6 ÷ 0 = ? and ? × 0 = 6?" [There is no such number.] Explain that there is no number times 0 that equals 6, so division by zero is undefined.

Take Note
To help students comprehend that a horizontal line has a slope of zero and a vertical line has undefined slope, have students think about skiing. Skiing on a horizontal line is possible. (It is called cross country skiing.) Skiing on a vertical line is not possible.

3 Lesson Check

Do you know HOW?
- If students have difficulty with Exercise 1, then have them look at two columns in the table and compare the difference in cost to the difference in the number of pencils.

Do you UNDERSTAND?
- If students have difficulty with Exercise 6, then ask them to plot two ordered pairs and label the point on the left as (x_1, y_1) and the one on the right as (x_2, y_2). Then have them find the slope by counting units and by using the slope formula.

Close

Q What methods can you use to find the slope of a line defined by two given points? **[Substitute points into the slope formula, or plot the points on a coordinate plane and count the rise and run between points.]**

Answers

Got It? (continued)
3. $-\frac{4}{3}$
4. a. undefined
    b. 0

Lesson Check
1. Yes; the rate of change between any two points is the same.

2. $-\frac{1}{5}$

3. $-\frac{5}{3}$

4. Slope; slope is the ratio of vertical change to horizontal change.

5. Check students' work; 0; the slope of a horizontal line is 0.

6. Answers may vary. Sample: Both methods give the same result. You need the graph to count the units of change. You need the coordinates of the points to use the slope formula.

7. The student calculated the ratio of horizontal change to vertical change, but slope is the ratio of vertical change to horizontal change; $\frac{1}{2}$.

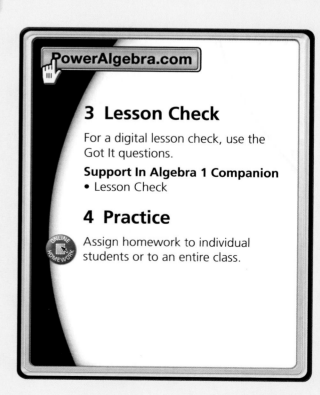

PowerAlgebra.com

3 Lesson Check

For a digital lesson check, use the Got It questions.

Support In Algebra 1 Companion
- Lesson Check

4 Practice

Assign homework to individual students or to an entire class.

4 Practice

ASSIGNMENT GUIDE

Basic: 8–25 all, 26–38 even, 39, 41, 42–48 even

Average: 9–25 odd, 26–49

Advanced: 9–25 odd, 26–58

Standardized Test Prep: 59–61

Mixed Review: 62–74

Reasoning exercises have blue headings.

Applications exercises have red headings.

EXERCISE 41: Use the Think About a Plan worksheet in the **Practice and Problem Solving Workbook** (also available in the Teaching Resources in print and online) to further support students' development in becoming independent learners.

HOMEWORK QUICK CHECK

To check students' understanding of key skills and concepts, go over Exercises 11, 21, 39, 41, and 48.

Practice and Problem-Solving Exercises

A Practice

Determine whether each rate of change is constant. If it is, find the rate of change and explain what it represents.

See Problem 1.

8. Turtle Walking

Time (min)	Distance (m)
1	6
2	12
3	15
4	21

9. Hot Dogs and Buns

Hot Dogs	Buns
1	1
2	2
3	3
4	4

10. Airplane Descent

Time (min)	Elevation (ft)
0	30,000
2	29,000
5	27,500
12	24,000

Find the slope of each line.

See Problem 2.

11.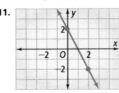

12.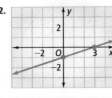

13.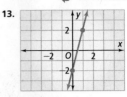

14.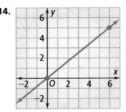

15.

16.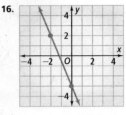

Find the slope of the line that passes through each pair of points.

See Problem 3.

17. $(0, 0), (3, 3)$

18. $(1, 3), (5, 5)$

19. $(4, 4), (5, 3)$

20. $(0, -1), (2, 3)$

21. $(-6, 1), (4, 8)$

22. $(2, -3), (5, -4)$

Find the slope of each line.

See Problem 4.

23.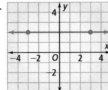

24.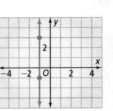

25.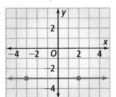

Answers

Practice and Problem-Solving Exercises

8. no

9. Yes; 1; there is one bun per hot dog.

10. Yes; −500; the plane is descending at a rate of 500 ft/min.

11. −2

12. $\frac{1}{3}$

13. 4

14. $\frac{5}{6}$

15. $\frac{3}{4}$

16. $-\frac{5}{2}$

17. 1

18. $\frac{1}{2}$

19. −1

20. 2

21. $\frac{7}{10}$

22. $-\frac{1}{3}$

23. 0

24. undefined

25. 0

Apply

Without graphing, tell whether the slope of a line that models each linear relationship is *positive*, *negative*, *zero*, or *undefined*. Then find the slope.

26. The length of a bus route is 4 mi long on the sixth day and 4 mi long on the seventeenth day.

27. A babysitter earns $9 for 1 h and $36 for 4 h.

28. A student earns a 98 on a test for answering one question incorrectly and earns a 90 for answering five questions incorrectly.

29. The total cost, including shipping, for ordering five uniforms is $66. The total cost, including shipping, for ordering nine uniforms is $114.

State the independent variable and the dependent variable in each linear relationship. Then find the rate of change for each situation.

30. Snow is 0.02 m deep after 1 h and 0.06 m deep after 3 h.

31. The cost of tickets is $36 for three people and $84 for seven people.

32. A car is 200 km from its destination after 1 h and 80 km from its destination after 3 h.

Find the slope of the line that passes through each pair of points.

33. $(-2, 1), (7, 1)$

34. $(4.25, 0), (3.5, 3)$

35. $\left(-\frac{1}{2}, \frac{4}{7}\right), \left(8, \frac{4}{7}\right)$

36. $(-5, 0.124), (-5, -0.584)$

37. $(-42.25, 5.2), (3.25, 3)$

38. $\left(-2, \frac{2}{11}\right), \left(-2, \frac{7}{13}\right)$

39. Think About a Plan The graph shows the average growth rates for three different animals. Which animal's growth shows the fastest rate of change? The slowest rate of change?
- How can you use the graph to find the rates of change?
- Are your answers reasonable?

40. Open-Ended Find two points that lie on a line with slope -9.

41. Profit John's business made $4500 in January and $8600 in March. What is the rate of change in his profit for this time period?

Rate of Growth

Each pair of points lies on a line with the given slope. Find x or y.

42. $(2, 4), (x, 8);$ slope $= -2$

43. $(4, 3), (5, y);$ slope $= 3$

44. $(2, 4), (x, 8);$ slope $= -\frac{1}{2}$

45. $(3, y), (1, 9);$ slope $= -\frac{5}{2}$

46. $(-4, y), (2, 4y);$ slope $= 6$

47. $(3, 5), (x, 2);$ undefined slope

48. Reasoning Is it true that a line with slope 1 always passes through the origin? Explain your reasoning.

26. zero

27. positive; 9

28. negative; -2

29. positive; 12

30. independent: time; dependent: depth of snow; 0.02 m/h

31. independent: number of people; dependent: cost; $12/person

32. independent: time; dependent: distance from destination; -60 km/h

33. 0

34. -4

35. 0

36. undefined

37. -0.048352

38. undefined

39. horse; mouse

40. Check students' work.

41. $2050 per month

42. 0

43. 6

44. -6

45. 4

46. 12

47. 3

48. No; the line could intercept the y-axis at any point and still have a slope of 1.

Answers

Practice and Problem-Solving Exercises
(continued)

49. a. 5

b.

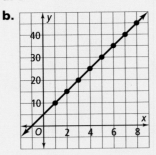

c. The slope is equal to the common difference.

50. Yes; the slopes from A to B, from B to C, and from A to C all equal $-\frac{1}{3}$.

51. Yes; the slopes from G to H, from H to I, and from G to I all equal $\frac{1}{2}$.

52. No; the slopes between all pairs of points are not the same.

53. No; the slopes between all pairs of points are not the same.

54. Yes; the slopes from G to H, from H to I, and from G to I all equal $\frac{3}{2}$.

55. No; the slopes between all pairs of points are not the same.

56. 0

57. $\frac{-n}{2m}$

58. $\frac{2d-b}{c-2a}$ or $\frac{b-2d}{2a-c}$

59. C

60. I

61. [4] **a.** $30 > 2(x + 2 + 6) > 20$ (OR equivalent inequality)

b.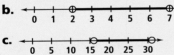

c.
```
  +--+--+--+--○--+--○--→
  0  5  10 15 20 25 30
```

[3] appropriate methods, but with one computational error

[2] correct inequality but incorrect graphs OR graphs with correct upper bounds but missing or incorrect lower bounds

[1] correct inequality and graphs, without work shown

62. 5, 9, 21

63. 1, 13, 49

64. 15, 21, 39

65. {2, 4}

66. {3}

---

49. Arithmetic Sequences Use the arithmetic sequence 10, 15, 20, 25, . . .
  a. Find the common difference of the sequence.
  b. Let $x =$ the term number, and let $y =$ the corresponding term of the sequence. Graph the ordered pairs (x, y) for the first eight terms of the sequence. Draw a line through the points.
  c. **Reasoning** How is the slope of a line from part (b) related to the common difference of the sequence?

Challenge Do the points in each set lie on the same line? Explain your answer.

50. $A(1, 3)$, $B(4, 2)$, $C(-2, 4)$ **51.** $G(3, 5)$, $H(-1, 3)$, $I(7, 7)$ **52.** $D(-2, 3)$, $E(0, -1)$, $F(2, 1)$

53. $P(4, 2)$, $Q(-3, 2)$, $R(2, 5)$ **54.** $G(1, -2)$, $H(-1, -5)$, $I(5, 4)$ **55.** $S(-3, 4)$, $T(0, 2)$, $X(-3, 0)$

Find the slope of the line that passes through each pair of points.

56. $(a, -b)$, $(-a, -b)$ **57.** $(-m, n)$, $(3m, -n)$ **58.** $(2a, b)$, $(c, 2d)$

Standardized Test Prep

SAT/ACT

59. A line has slope $\frac{4}{3}$. Through which two points could this line pass?
  Ⓐ $(24, 19)$, $(8, 10)$ Ⓑ $(10, 8)$, $(16, 0)$ Ⓒ $(28, 10)$, $(22, 2)$ Ⓓ $(4, 20)$, $(0, 17)$

60. Let the domain of the function $f(x) = \frac{1}{5}x - 12$ be $\{-5, 0, 10\}$. What is the range?
  Ⓕ $\{-5, 0, 10\}$ Ⓖ $\{0, 12, 13\}$ Ⓗ $\{-13, -12, -11\}$ Ⓘ $\{-13, -12, -10\}$

Extended Response

61. The perimeter of the rectangle at the right is less than 30 in. and greater than 20 in.
  a. What is an inequality that represents the situation?
  b. What is a graph that shows all the possible values of x?
  c. What is a graph that shows all the possible perimeters of the triangle?

Mixed Review

Find the second, fourth, and tenth terms of each sequence.   ◀ See Lesson 4-7.

62. $A(n) = 3 + (n - 1)(2)$ **63.** $A(n) = -5 + (n - 1)(6)$ **64.** $A(n) = 12 + (n - 1)(3)$

Find each union or intersection. Let $A = \{1, 2, 3, 4\}$, $B = \{2, 4, 6, 8, 10\}$, and $C = \{3, 5, 7, 8\}$.   ◀ See Lesson 3-8.

65. $A \cap B$ **66.** $A \cap C$ **67.** $B \cap C$ **68.** $B \cup C$ **69.** $A \cup C$

Get Ready! To prepare for Lesson 5-2, do Exercises 70–74.

Solve each proportion.   ◀ See Lesson 2-7.

70. $\frac{5}{8} = \frac{x}{12}$ **71.** $\frac{-4}{9} = \frac{n}{-45}$ **72.** $\frac{y}{3} = \frac{25}{15}$ **73.** $\frac{7}{n} = \frac{-35}{50}$ **74.** $\frac{14}{18} = \frac{63}{n}$

---

67. {8}

68. {2, 3, 4, 5, 6, 7, 8, 10}

69. {1, 2, 3, 4, 5, 7, 8}

70. 7.5

71. 20

72. 5

73. −10

74. 81

Additional Instructional Support

Algebra 1 Companion

Students can use the **Algebra 1 Companion** worktext (4 pages) as you teach the lesson. Use the Companion to support

- New Vocabulary
- Key Concepts
- Got It for each Problem
- Lesson Check

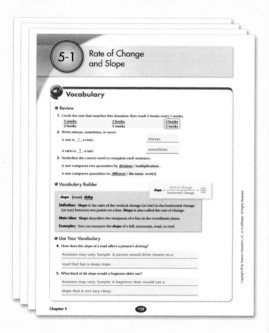

ELL Support

Connect to Prior Knowledge Write a problem from Lesson 2-6 on the board where a rate is expressed as a fraction or the unit rate is calculated. Ask students where they have seen this type of problem. Encourage volunteers to help solve the problem. Then model how to find rate of change as you think aloud.

Focus on Language Write the word *slope* on the board. Use your arm to demonstrate a slope as you move your finger down your arm. Students can investigate the classroom and find other examples of slope.

5 Assess & Remediate

Lesson Quiz

1. **Do you UNDERSTAND?** The table shows the distance a cyclist rides her bicycle over time. Is the rate of change in distance with respect to time constant? What does the rate of change represent?

Bike Riding Distance

Time (minutes)	Distance Traveled (feet)
1	1120
2	2240
3	3360
4	4480

2. What is the slope of the line shown below?

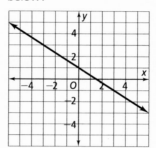

ANSWERS TO LESSON QUIZ

1. The rate of change is constant and represents a speed of 1120 ft/min. The cyclist rides her bike at a rate of 1120 ft/min.

2. $-\frac{2}{3}$

PRESCRIPTION FOR REMEDIATION

Use the student work on the Lesson Quiz to prescribe a differentiated review assignment.

Points	Differentiated Remediation
0	Intervention
1	On-level
2	Extension

PowerAlgebra.com

5 Assess & Remediate

Assign the Lesson Quiz. Appropriate intervention, practice, or enrichment is automatically generated based on student performance.

Intervention

- **Reteaching** (2 pages) Provides reteaching and practice exercises for the key lesson concepts. Use with struggling students or absent students.

- **English Language Learner Support** Helps students develop and reinforce mathematical vocabulary and key concepts.

All-in-One Resources/Online
Reteaching

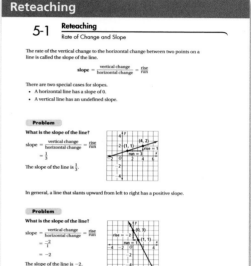

All-in-One Resources/Online
English Language Learner Support

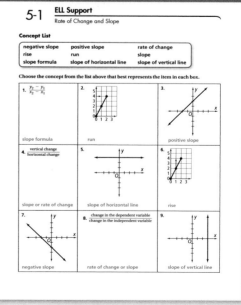

Differentiated Remediation *continued*

On-Level

- **Practice** (2 pages) Provides extra practice for each lesson. For simpler practice exercises, use the Form K Practice pages found in the All-in-One Teaching Resources and online.

- **Think About a Plan** Helps students develop specific problem-solving skills and strategies by providing scaffolded guiding questions.

- **Standardized Test Prep** Focuses on all major exercises, all major question types, and helps students prepare for the high-stakes assessments.

Extension

- **Enrichment** Provides students with interesting problems and activities that extend the concepts of the lesson.

- **Activities, Games, and Puzzles** Worksheets that can be used for concepts development, enrichment, and for fun!

Practice and Problem Solving WKBK/ All-in-One Resources/Online
Practice page 1

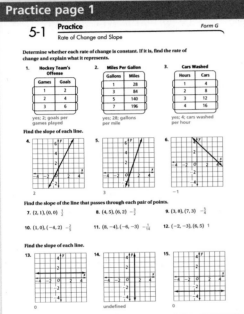

Practice and Problem Solving WKBK/ All-in-One Resources/Online
Practice page 2

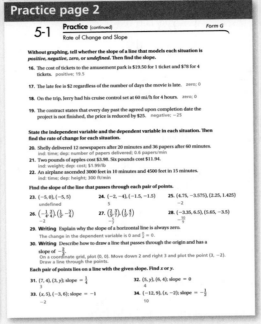

All-in-One Resources/Online
Enrichment

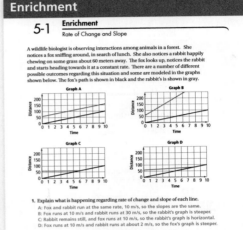

Practice and Problem Solving WKBK/ All-in-One Resources/Online
Think About a Plan

Practice and Problem Solving WKBK/ All-in-One Resources/Online
Standardized Test Prep

Online Teacher Resource Center
Activities, Games, and Puzzles

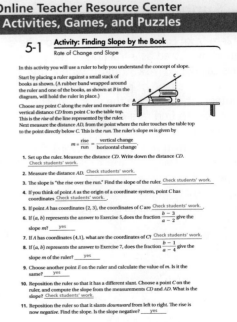

5-2 Direct Variation

Indiana Academic Standards
A1.2.1 Translate among various representations of linear functions including tables, graphs, words and equations.
A1.2.3 Determine the slope, *x*-intercept, and *y*-intercept of a line given its graph, its equation, or two points on the line and determine the equation of a line given sufficient information.

Objective To write and graph an equation of a direct variation

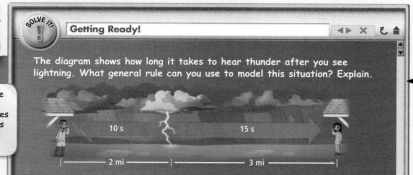

SOLVE IT! **Getting Ready!**

The diagram shows how long it takes to hear thunder after you see lightning. What general rule can you use to model this situation? Explain.

10 s   15 s

2 mi   3 mi

As your distance from lightning increases, so does the time it takes you to hear the thunder.

Dynamic Activity
Direct Variation

Lesson Vocabulary
• direct variation
• constant of variation for a direct variation

The time it takes to hear thunder *varies directly with* the distance from lightning.

Essential Understanding If the ratio of two variables is constant, then the variables have a special relationship, known as a *direct variation*.

A **direct variation** is a relationship that can be represented by a function in the form $y = kx$, where $k \neq 0$. The **constant of variation for a direct variation** k is the coefficient of x. By dividing each side of $y = kx$ by x, you can see that the ratio of the variables is constant: $\frac{y}{x} = k$.

To determine whether an equation represents a direct variation, solve it for y. If you can write the equation in the form $y = kx$, where $k \neq 0$, it represents a direct variation.

Think
Do these equations look like ones you've seen before?
Yes. They contain two variables, so they're literal equations. To determine whether they're direct variation equations, solve for y.

 Problem 1 Identifying a Direct Variation

Does the equation represent a direct variation? If so, find the constant of variation.

A $7y = 2x$

$y = \frac{2}{7}x$ ← Solve each equation for y. →

The equation has the form $y = kx$, so the equation is a direct variation. Its constant of variation is $\frac{2}{7}$.

B $3y + 4x = 8$

$3y = 8 - 4x$

$y = \frac{8}{3} - \frac{4}{3}x$

You cannot write the equation in the form $y = kx$. It is not a direct variation.

 Got It? 1. Does $4x + 5y = 0$ represent a direct variation? If so, find the constant of variation.

---

1 Interactive Learning

Solve It!
PURPOSE To use a real-world situation to familiarize students with direct variation
PROCESS Students may make a table of values of the given data and use a pattern to extend the table. Students may examine the table to write a rule verbally or algebraically.

FACILITATE

Q Using the times and distances given, how much time can you expect to pass from the time you see lightning and then hear the thunder if you are 1 mi from where the lightning strikes? **[5 s]**

Q If you hear thunder 20 s after you see lightning, how far are you from the lightning? **[4 mi]**

ANSWER See Solve It in Answers on next page.
CONNECT THE MATH The Solve It provided a real-world context for direct variation. In this lesson, students will learn the formal properties of direct variation and see additional applications.

2 Guided Instruction

Problem 1

Q What is the inverse operation of multiplying by 7? **[dividing by 7]**

Q In 1B, what part of the equation prevents you from writing it in the form $y = kx$? **[the constant term]**

Got It?   **ERROR PREVENTION**

If students state a constant of variation of $\frac{-5}{4}$, then they likely solved the equation for x rather than for y.

5-2 Preparing to Teach

BIG idea Proportionality   **UbD**

ESSENTIAL UNDERSTANDINGS
• If the ratio of two variables is constant, then the variables have a special relationship, called a direct variation.
• The graph of a direct variation equation $y = kx$ is a line that passes through (0, 0) and has a slope of k.

Math Background

A variation equation is a statement of how a change in one quantity relates to a change in another quantity. A general way to describe a direct variation relationship is that as the *x*-values increase, their corresponding *y*-values must increase also, or as the *x*-values decrease, their corresponding *y*-values must decrease also.

Students will study many types of variations. Direct variation equations are a subset of

linear equations, so they are studied within the chapter on Linear Functions. In a direct variation equation, $\frac{y}{x}$ is constant and the graph always passes through the point (0, 0). This is a condition that is true about direct variation equations, but may or may not be true about any linear equation.

Inverse variation equations are a subset of rational equations and will be studied in the chapter on Rational Functions.

Support Student Learning
Use the **Algebra I Companion** to engage and support students during instruction. See Lesson Resources at the end of this lesson for details.

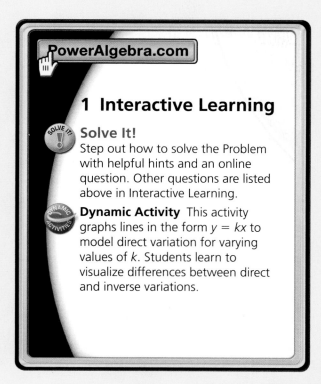

PowerAlgebra.com

1 Interactive Learning

Solve It!
Step out how to solve the Problem with helpful hints and an online question. Other questions are listed above in Interactive Learning.

Dynamic Activity This activity graphs lines in the form $y = kx$ to model direct variation for varying values of k. Students learn to visualize differences between direct and inverse variations.

Problem 2

Q What is the general form of a direct variation equation? **[y = kx]**

Q What does the variable k represent? **[the constant of variation, or the ratio of y to x]**

Q What is the value of x when y = 21? **[3]**

Got It?

Show students that they can also determine the value of y by writing a proportion and solving the equation $\frac{y}{-15} = \frac{10}{-2}$.

Problem 3

Q If an astronaut weighs 185 lb on Earth, about how much would she weigh on Mars? Explain your calculation. **[about 70 lb: 185 × 0.38 or 185 × $\frac{5}{13}$]**

Q Is the statement "weight on Earth varies directly with weight on Mars" true also? Explain. **[Yes, because the ratio of the two variables would still be constant.]**

To write an equation for a direct variation, first find the constant of variation k using an ordered pair, other than (0, 0), that you know is a solution of the equation.

Problem 2 Writing a Direct Variation Equation

Suppose y varies directly with x, and y = 35 when x = 5. What direct variation equation relates x and y? What is the value of y when x = 9?

$y = kx$ Start with the function form of a direct variation.

$35 = k(5)$ Substitute 5 for x and 35 for y.

$7 = k$ Divide each side by 5 to solve for k.

$y = 7x$ Write an equation. Substitute 7 for k in y = kx.

The equation $y = 7x$ relates x and y. When x = 9, y = 7(9), or 63.

Think
Make sure you don't stop at 7 = k. To write the direct variation equation, you have to substitute 7 for k in y = kx.

✓ **Got It? 2.** Suppose y varies directly with x, and y = 10 when x = −2. What direct variation equation relates x and y? What is the value of y when x = −15?

Problem 3 Graphing a Direct Variation

Space Exploration Weight on Mars y varies directly with weight on Earth x. The weights of the science instruments onboard the Phoenix Mars Lander on Earth and Mars are shown.

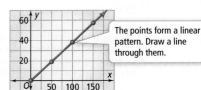
Weight on Mars
50 lb

A What is an equation that relates weight, in pounds, on Earth x and weight on Mars y?

$y = kx$ Start with the function form of a direct variation.

$50 = k(130)$ Substitute 130 for x and 50 for y.

$0.38 \approx k$ Divide each side by 130 to solve for k.

$y = 0.38x$ Write an equation. Substitute 0.38 for k in y = kx.

The equation $y = 0.38x$ gives the weight y on Mars, in pounds, of an object that weighs x pounds on Earth.

Weight on Earth
130 lb

Think
Have you graphed equations like y = 0.38x before? Yes. In Chapter 4, you graphed linear functions by making a table of values and plotting points.

B What is the graph of the equation in part (A)?

Make a table of values. Then draw the graph.

x	y
0	0.38(0) = 0
50	0.38(50) = 19
100	0.38(100) = 38
150	0.38(150) = 57

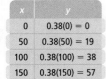

The points form a linear pattern. Draw a line through them.

Answers

Solve It!

$y = \frac{x}{5}$; explanations may vary.

Got It?

1. yes; $-\frac{4}{5}$

2. $y = -5x$; 75

3. a. $y = 0.166x$

b. 0.38; the slope is the coefficient of the x-term.

4. yes; $y = -0.75x$

PowerAlgebra.com

2 Guided Instruction

Each Problem is worked out and supported online.

Problem 1
Identifying a Direct Variation
Animated

Problem 2
Writing a Direct Variation Equation

Problem 3
Graphing a Direct Variation
Animated

Problem 4
Writing a Direct Variation From a Table
Animated

Support in Algebra 1 Companion
• Vocabulary
• Key Concepts
• Got It?

PowerAlgebra.com

Got It? 3. a. Weight on the moon y varies directly with weight on Earth x. A person who weighs 100 lb on Earth weighs 16.6 lb on the moon. What is an equation that relates weight on Earth x and weight on the moon y? What is the graph of this equation?

    b. Reasoning What is the slope of the graph of $y = 0.38x$ in Problem 3? How is the slope related to the equation?

 Concept Summary   **Graphs of Direct Variations**

The graph of a direct variation equation $y = kx$ is a line with the following properties.
- The line passes through $(0, 0)$.
- The slope of the line is k.

$k > 0$ $k < 0$

You can rewrite a direct variation equation $y = kx$ as $\frac{y}{x} = k$. When a set of data pairs (x, y) vary directly, $\frac{y}{x}$ is the constant of variation. It is the same for each data pair.

Problem 4   **Writing a Direct Variation From a Table**

For the data in the table, does y vary directly with x? If it does, write an equation for the direct variation.

A

x	y
4	6
8	12
10	15

B

x	y
−2	3.2
1	2.4
4	1.6

Find $\frac{y}{x}$ for each ordered pair.

$\frac{6}{4} = 1.5$ $\frac{12}{8} = 1.5$ $\frac{15}{10} = 1.5$

The ratio $\frac{y}{x} = 1.5$ for each data pair. So y varies directly with x. The direct variation equation is $y = 1.5x$.

Find $\frac{y}{x}$ for each ordered pair.

$\frac{3.2}{-2} = -1.6$ $\frac{2.4}{1} = 2.4$ $\frac{1.6}{4} = 0.4$

The ratio $\frac{y}{x}$ is not the same for all data pairs. So y does not vary directly with x.

Got It? 4. For the data in the table at the right, does y vary directly with x? If it does, write an equation for the direct variation.

x	y
−3	2.25
1	−0.75
4	−3

Plan

How can you check your answer?
Graph the ordered pairs in the coordinate plane. If you can connect them with a line that passes through (0, 0), then y varies directly with x.

Lesson 5-2   Direct Variation   **301**

Got It?

Ask students to compare the graphs in Question 3a and Problem 3. Ask students to tell which graph is steeper and provide a mathematical explanation for the difference in steepness.

Take Note

For some students, the notations $k > 0$ and $k < 0$ are not meaningful. Have students write the verbal translations of "k is positive" and "k is negative" beside each notation, respectively.

Problem 4

Q If a student were to mistakenly calculate the ratio $\frac{x}{y}$ for each ordered pair in part A, would they answer the question wrong? Explain. **[They would still be able to determine whether or not it was a direct variation, but they would not have the correct value for k.]**

Q Is it necessary to calculate the ratio of 1.6 and 4 in part B? Explain. **[No, The first two ratios were not constant. There is no need to calculate the third ratio.]**

Got It?

Q What operation can you perform to find the value of k so that you can write the equation of the direct variation? **[You can divide any y-value from the table by its corresponding x-value.]**

Q How do you know that the table represents a direct variation? **[The ratio of each y to x equals -0.75.]**

Additional Problems

1. Is the equation a direct variation? If it is, find the constant of variation.
  a. $4y = 5x$
  b. $2x + 3y = 6$
  ANSWER a. yes, 1.25 **b.** no

2. Suppose y varies directly with x and $y = 40$ when $x = 8$. What direct variation equation relates x and y? What is the value of y when $x = 12$?
  ANSWER $y = 5x$; 60

3. Suppose $15 (US) is worth about $150 Mexican pesos.
  a. What is an equation that relates US dollars x to Mexican pesos y?
  b. What is the graph of the equation in part (a)?
  ANSWER a. $y = 10x$
  b.

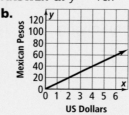

4. For the data in the table, does y vary directly with x? If it does, write an equation for the direct variation.
  a.

x	y
2	5
6	15
10	25

  b.

x	y
1	7
3	10
5	13

ANSWER a. yes, $y = 2.5x$
b. no

3 Lesson Check

Do you know HOW?
- If students have difficulty with Exercise 3, then have them set up a proportion using the number of corn muffins to number of cups of flour as the ratios.

Do you UNDERSTAND?
- If students have difficulty with Exercise 6, then have them review Problem 1B. Ask them whether the graph of $y = k + x$ will pass through (0, 0) if $k \neq 0$.

Close

> **Q** What are the characteristics of the graph of a direct variation equation? **[The graph of a direct variation equation $y = kx$, is a line with slope k that passes through the point (0, 0).]**

 Lesson Check

Do you know HOW?

1. Does the equation $6y = 18x$ represent a direct variation? If it does, what is its constant of variation?

2. Suppose y varies directly with x, and $y = 30$ when $x = 3$. What direct variation equation relates x and y?

3. A recipe for 12 corn muffins calls for 1 cup of flour. The number of muffins you can make varies directly with the amount of flour you use. You have $2\frac{1}{2}$ cups of flour. How many muffins can you make?

4. Does y vary directly with x? If it does, what is an equation for the direct variation?

x	y
-2	1
2	-1
4	-2

Do you UNDERSTAND?

Vocabulary Determine whether each statement is *always*, *sometimes*, or *never* true.

5. The ordered pair (0, 0) is a solution of the direct variation equation $y = kx$.

6. You can write a direct variation in the form $y = k + x$, where $k \neq 0$.

7. The constant of variation for a direct variation represented by $y = kx$ is $\frac{y}{x}$.

8. Reasoning Suppose q varies directly with p. Does this imply that p varies directly with q? Explain.

 Practice and Problem-Solving Exercises

 Practice Determine whether each equation represents a direct variation. If it does, find the constant of variation.   **See Problem 1.**

9. $2y = 5x + 1$ **10.** $8x + 9y = 10$ **11.** $-12x = 6y$

12. $y + 8 = -x$ **13.** $-4 + 7x + 4 = 3y$ **14.** $0.7x - 1.4y = 0$

Suppose y varies directly with x. Write a direct variation equation that relates x and y. Then find the value of y when $x = 12$.   **See Problem 2.**

15. $y = -10$ when $x = 2$.   **16.** $y = 7\frac{1}{2}$ when $x = 3$.   **17.** $y = 5$ when $x = 2$.

18. $y = 125$ when $x = -5$.   **19.** $y = 10.4$ when $x = 4$.   **20.** $y = 9\frac{1}{3}$ when $x = -\frac{1}{2}$.

Graph each direct variation equation.   **See Problem 3.**

21. $y = 2x$ **22.** $y = \frac{1}{3}x$ **23.** $y = -x$ **24.** $y = -\frac{1}{2}x$

25. Travel Time The distance d you bike varies directly with the amount of time t you bike. Suppose you bike 13.2 mi in 1.25 h. What is an equation that relates d and t? What is the graph of the equation?

26. Geometry The perimeter p of a regular hexagon varies directly with the length ℓ of one side of the hexagon. What is an equation that relates p and ℓ? What is the graph of the equation?

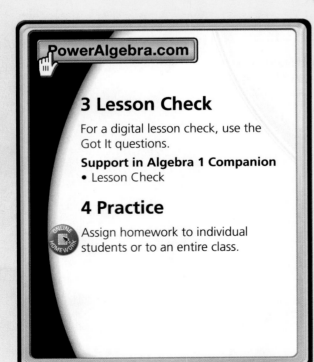

3 Lesson Check

For a digital lesson check, use the Got It questions.

Support in Algebra 1 Companion
- Lesson Check

4 Practice

Assign homework to individual students or to an entire class.

Answers

Lesson Check
1. yes; 3   **2.** $y = 10x$
3. 30 muffins   **4.** yes; $y = -\frac{1}{2}x$
5. always   **6.** never
7. sometimes
8. Yes; if $q = kp$, then $p = \frac{1}{k}q$, which is a direct variation with constant of variation $\frac{1}{k}$.

Practice and Problem-Solving Exercises
9. no   **10.** no
11. yes; -2 **12.** no
13. yes; $\frac{7}{3}$ **14.** yes; $\frac{1}{2}$
15. $y = -5x$; -60 **16.** $y = \frac{5}{2}x$; 30
17. $y = \frac{5}{2}x$; 30   **18.** $y = -25x$; -300
19. $y = 2.6x$; 31.2
20. $y = -\frac{56}{3}x$; -224

21.   **22.**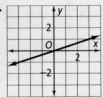

23.   **24.**

25. $d = 10.56t$

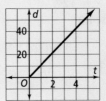

For the data in each table, tell whether y varies directly with x. If it does, write an equation for the direct variation. ◀ See Problem 4.

27.

x	y
−6	9
1	−1.5
8	−12

28.

x	y
3	5.4
7	12.6
12	21.6

29.

x	y
−2	1
3	6
8	11

B Apply

Suppose y varies directly with x. Write a direct variation equation that relates x and y. Then graph the equation.

30. $y = \frac{1}{2}$ when $x = 3$. **31.** $y = -5$ when $x = \frac{1}{4}$. **32.** $y = \frac{6}{5}$ when $x = -\frac{5}{6}$. **33.** $y = 7.2$ when $x = 1.2$.

34. Think About a Plan The amount of blood in a person's body varies directly with body weight. A person who weighs 160 lb has about 4.6 qt of blood. About how many quarts of blood are in the body of a 175-lb person?
- How can you find the constant of variation?
- Can you write an equation that relates quarts of blood to weight?
- How can you use the equation to determine the solution?

35. Electricity Ohm's Law $V = I \times R$ relates the voltage, current, and resistance of a circuit. V is the voltage measured in volts. I is the current measured in amperes. R is the resistance measured in ohms.
a. Find the voltage of a circuit with a current of 24 amperes and a resistance of 2 ohms.
b. Find the resistance of a circuit with a current of 24 amperes and a voltage of 18 volts.

Reasoning Tell whether the two quantities vary directly. Explain your reasoning.

36. the number of ounces of cereal and the number of Calories the cereal contains

37. the time it takes to travel a certain distance and the rate at which you travel

38. the perimeter of a square and the side length of the square

39. the amount of money you have left and the number of items you purchase

40. a. Graph the following direct variation equations in the same coordinate plane:
$y = x$, $y = 2x$, $y = 3x$, and $y = 4x$.
b. Look for a Pattern Describe how the graphs change as the constant of variation increases.
c. Predict how the graph of $y = \frac{1}{2}x$ would appear.

41. Error Analysis Use the table at the right. A student says that y varies directly with x because as x increases by 1, y also increases by 1. Explain the student's error.

42. Writing Suppose y varies directly with x. Explain how the value of y changes in each situation.
a. The value of x is doubled. **b.** The value of x is halved.

x	y
0	3
1	4
2	5

4 Practice

ASSIGNMENT GUIDE

Basic: 9–29 all, 30–34 even, 35–42
Average: 9–29 odd, 30–43
Advanced: 9–29 odd, 30–47
Standardized Test Prep: 48–51
Mixed Review: 52–59

Reasoning exercises have blue headings.

Applications exercises have red headings.

EXERCISE 35: Use the Think About a Plan worksheet in the **Practice and Problem Solving Workbook** (also available in the Teaching Resources in print and online) to further support students' development in becoming independent learners.

HOMEWORK QUICK CHECK
To check students' understanding of key skills and concepts, go over Exercises 13, 21, 34, 35, and 36.

26. $p = 6\ell$

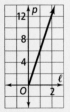

31. $y = -20x$

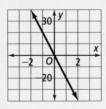

27. yes; $y = -1.5x$

28. yes; $y = 1.8x$

29. no

30. $y = \frac{1}{6}x$

32. $y = -\frac{36}{25}x$

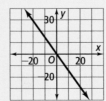

33–42. See next page.

Answers

Practice and Problem-Solving Exercises
(continued)

33. $y = 6x$

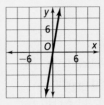

34. about 5 qt

35. a. 48 volts
   b. 0.75 ohm

36. Yes; as the number of ounces increases, the number of Calories increases. When the number of ounces is 0, the number of Calories is 0.

37. No; as the rate increases, the time decreases.

38. Yes; as the side length increases, the perimeter increases. When the side length is 0, the perimeter is 0.

39. No; as the number of items you purchase increases, the amount of money you have left decreases.

40. a.

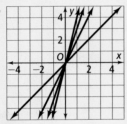

   b. The graphs get steeper.
   c. less steep than $y = x$

41. y does not vary directly with x because $y \neq 0$ when $x = 0$.

42. a. The value of y is doubled.
   b. The value of y is halved.

43. a. $\frac{2}{5}$
   b. $y = \frac{2}{5}x$; 52 lb

44. 12

45. -6

46. 8

47. a. $c = 3.85g$; yes; the constant of variation is 3.85.
   b. $c \approx 0.12m$
   c. about $28.80

48. 0.17

---

43. Physics The force you need to apply to a lever varies directly with the weight you want to lift. Suppose you can lift a 50-lb weight by applying 20 lb of force to a certain lever.
   a. What is the ratio of force to weight for the lever?
   b. Write an equation relating force and weight. What is the force you need to lift a friend who weighs 130 lb?

Challenge The ordered pairs in each exercise are for the same direct variation. Find each missing value.

44. $(3, 4)$ and $(9, y)$ **45.** $(1, y)$ and $\left(\frac{3}{2}, -9\right)$ **46.** $(-5, 3)$ and $(x, -4.8)$

47. Gas Mileage A car gets 32 mi per gallon. The number of gallons g of gas used varies directly with the number of miles m traveled.
   a. Suppose the price of gas is $3.85 per gallon. Write a function giving the cost c for g gallons of gas. Is this a direct variation? Explain your reasoning.
   b. Write a direct variation equation relating the cost of gas to the miles traveled.
   c. How much will it cost to buy gas for a 240-mi trip?

Standardized Test Prep

GRIDDED RESPONSE

SAT/ACT

48. The price p you pay varies directly with the number of pencils you buy. Suppose you buy 3 pencils for $.51. How much is each pencil, in dollars?

49. A scooter can travel 72 mi per gallon of gasoline and holds 2.3 gal. The function $d(x) = 72x$ represents the distance $d(x)$, in miles, that the scooter can travel with x gallons of gasoline. How many miles can the scooter go with a full tank of gas?

50. The table at the right shows the number of hours a clerk works per week and the amount of money she earns before taxes. If she worked 34 h per week, how much money would she earn, in dollars?

51. What is the greatest value in the range of $y = x^2 - 3$ for the domain $\{-3, 0, 1\}$?

Weekly Wages

Time (h)	Wages ($)
12	99.00
17	140.25
21	173.25
32	264.00

Mixed Review

Find the slope of the line that passes through each pair of points.   ◀ See Lesson 5-1.

52. $(2, 4), (0, 2)$ **53.** $(5, 8), (-5, 8)$ **54.** $(0, 0), (3, 18)$ **55.** $(1, -2), (-2, 3)$

Get Ready! To prepare for Lesson 5-3, do Exercises 56–59.

Evaluate each expression.   ◀ See Lesson 1-2.

56. $6a + 3$ for $a = 2$ **57.** $-2x - 5$ for $x = 3$ **58.** $\frac{1}{4}x + 2$ for $x = 16$ **59.** $8 - 5n$ for $n = 3$

49. 165.6

50. 280.50

51. 6

52. 1

53. 0

54. 6

55. $-\frac{5}{3}$

56. 15

57. -11

58. 6

59. -7

Additional Instructional Support

Algebra 1 Companion

Students can use the **Algebra 1 Companion** worktext (4 pages) as you teach the lesson. Use the Companion to support

- New Vocabulary
- Key Concepts
- Got It for each Problem
- Lesson Check

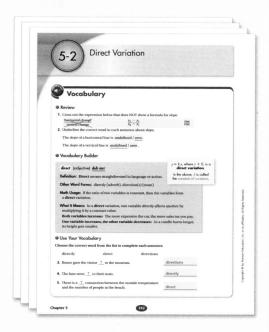

ELL Support

Assess Understanding Place students in small groups of mixed ability. Rewrite the following sentence that is under the Solve It, "your distance *varies directly* with the time it takes you to hear thunder." Discuss the meaning of this situation. Then write "_____ *varies directly* with the _____" on the board. Have students share ideas to complete the sentence with different situations of direct variation. Have students discuss their work.

5 Assess & Remediate

Lesson Quiz

1. Suppose y varies directly with x and $y = 72$ when $x = 6$. What direct variation equation relates x and y? What is the value of y when $x = 10$?

2. **Do you UNDERSTAND?** Suppose the cost of renting a scooter varies directly with the number of hours. It costs $37.50 to rent a scooter for 5 hours.
   a. What is an equation that relates the number of hours x to the rental cost y?
   b. What is the graph of the equation in part (a)?

3. For the data in the table, does y vary directly with x? If it does, write an equation for the direct variation.

x	y
3	6
5	10
7	14

ANSWERS TO LESSON QUIZ

1. $y = 12x$; 120
2. a. $y = 7.5x$ b.

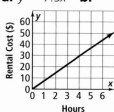

3. yes; $y = 2x$

PRESCRIPTION FOR REMEDIATION
Use the student work on the Lesson Quiz to prescribe a differentiated review assignment.

Points	Differentiated Remediation
0–1	Intervention
2	On-level
3	Extension

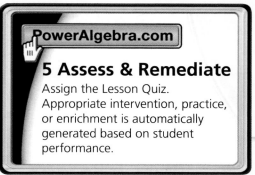

PowerAlgebra.com

5 Assess & Remediate
Assign the Lesson Quiz. Appropriate intervention, practice, or enrichment is automatically generated based on student performance.

Intervention

- **Reteaching** (2 pages) Provides reteaching and practice exercises for the key lesson concepts. Use with struggling students or absent students.
- **English Language Learner Support** Helps students develop and reinforce mathematical vocabulary and key concepts.

All-in-One Resources/Online
Reteaching

All-in-One Resources/Online
English Language Learner Support

Differentiated Remediation *continued*

On-Level

- **Practice** (2 pages) Provides extra practice for each lesson. For simpler practice exercises, use the Form K Practice pages found in the All-in-One Teaching Resources and online.

- **Think About a Plan** Helps students develop specific problem-solving skills and strategies by providing scaffolded guiding questions.

- **Standardized Test Prep** Focuses on all major exercises, all major question types, and helps students prepare for the high-stakes assessments.

Extension

- **Enrichment** Provides students with interesting problems and activities that extend the concepts of the lesson.

- **Activities, Games, and Puzzles** Worksheets that can be used for concepts development, enrichment, and for fun!

Practice and Problem Solving WKBK/ All-in-One Resources/Online
Practice page 1

Practice and Problem Solving WKBK/ All-in-One Resources/Online
Practice page 2

All-in-One Resources/Online
Enrichment

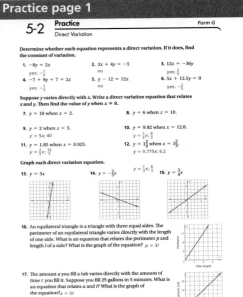

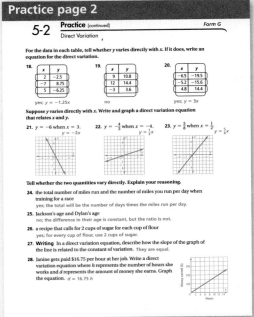

Practice and Problem Solving WKBK/ All-in-One Resources/Online
Think About a Plan

Practice and Problem Solving WKBK/ All-in-One Resources/Online
Standardized Test Prep

Online Teacher Resource Center
Activities, Games, and Puzzles

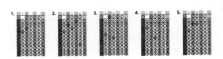

Concept Byte

Use With Lesson 5-3

TECHNOLOGY

Investigating $y = mx + b$

You can use a graphing calculator to explore the graph of an equation in the form $y = mx + b$. For this activity, choose a standard screen by pressing (zoom) 6.

1. Graph these equations on the same screen. Then complete each statement.

$y = x + 3$ $y = 2x + 3$ $y = \frac{1}{2}x + 3$

  a. The graph of __?__ is steepest.
  b. The graph of __?__ is the least steep.

2. Match each equation with the best choice for its graph.

A. $y = \frac{1}{4}x - 2$ **B.** $y = 4x - 2$ **C.** $y = x - 2$

I. 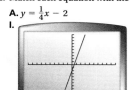   **II.** 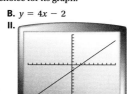   **III.**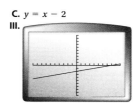

3. Graph these equations on the same screen.

    $y = 2x + 3$ $y = -2x + 3$

How does the sign of m affect the graph of the equation?

4. Reasoning How does changing the value of m affect the graph of an equation in the form $y = mx + b$?

5. Graph these equations on the same screen.

    $y = 2x + 3$ $y = 2x - 3$ $y = 2x + 2$

Where does the graph of each equation cross the y-axis? (*Hint:* Use the **ZOOM** feature to better see the points of intersection.)

6. Match each equation with the best choice for its graph.

A. $y = \frac{1}{3}x - 3$ **B.** $y = \frac{1}{3}x + 1$ **C.** $y = \frac{1}{3}x$

I. 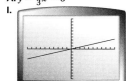   **II.** 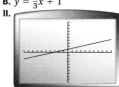   **III.**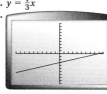

7. Reasoning How does changing the value of b affect the graph of an equation in the form $y = mx + b$?

PowerAlgebra.com   Concept Byte   Investigating $y = mx + b$ **305**

Guided Instruction

PURPOSE To use a graphing calculator to investigate the slope-intercept form of a linear equation

PROCESS Students will
• analyze lines on the same graph.
• analyze components of the equation $y = mx + b$ and how they affect the graph.
• match linear equations and graphs.

DISCUSS Ask students if they have been sled riding and the types of hills they have been on. Ask them whether a steeper hill would have a greater slope or a lesser slope. Draw some sledding hills on the board and have students rank them by the steepness of their slope.

In this Activity students focus on the components of linear equations in slope-intercept form.

Q If one equation has a slope of 2 and a second equation has a slope of 4, is the graph of the second equation twice as steep? **[yes]**

Q If the slope of an equation stays the same, but the y-intercept changes, how will this affect the graph? **[The line will move up in the coordinate plane on the value of the y-intercept.]**

Answers

Concept Byte

1 a. $y = 2x + 3$
  b. $y = \frac{1}{2}x + 3$

2. A. III, B. I, C. II

3. If m is positive, the line slants up from left to right. If m is negative, the line slants down from left to right.

4. Changing m affects the slope of the line.

5. 3, −3, 2

6. A. III, B. II, C. I

7. Changing b affects where the line crosses the y-axis.

Concept Byte   **305**

1 Interactive Learning

Solve It!

PURPOSE To acquaint students with the slope and *y*-intercept of the graph of a line

PROCESS Students may

• locate the *y*-intercept by visual inspection and use the graph labels to interpret its meaning.

• calculate the slope by formula or by counting and interpret the slope as a rate of change.

FACILITATE

Q What point is the intersection of the graph with the *y*-axis? **[(0, 20)]**

Q What are two points on the line shown in the graph? **[Answers may vary. Sample: (20, 40) and (10, 30)]**

Q What is the slope of the line? **[1]**

Q Does this graph represent a direct variation? Explain. **[No, it does not pass through the point (0, 0).]**

ANSWER See Solve It in Answers on next page.
CONNECT THE MATH The Solve It models bamboo growth with a line in slope-intercept form. In this lesson students will learn the general slope-intercept form and see several applications.

2 Guided Instruction

Take Note

Q Can the equation of a vertical line be written in slope-intercept form? Explain. **[No, the slope is undefined and cannot be substituted into the formula.]**

5-3 Slope-Intercept Form

Indiana Academic Standards
A1.2.2 Graph linear equations and show that they have constant rates of change.
A1.2.3 Determine the slope, *x*-intercept, and *y*-intercept of a line given its graph, its equation, or two points on the line and determine the equation of a line given sufficient information.

Objectives To write linear equations using slope-intercept form
To graph linear equations in slope-intercept form

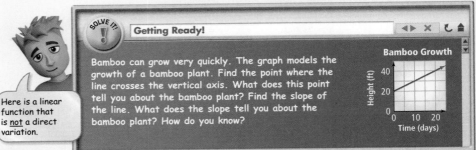

SOLVE IT!
Getting Ready!

Bamboo can grow very quickly. The graph models the growth of a bamboo plant. Find the point where the line crosses the vertical axis. What does this point tell you about the bamboo plant? Find the slope of the line. What does the slope tell you about the bamboo plant? How do you know?

Bamboo Growth

Here is a linear function that is <u>not</u> a direct variation.

Dynamic Activity
Slope-Intercept Form of a Line

Lesson Vocabulary
• parent function
• linear parent function
• linear equation
• *y*-intercept
• slope-intercept form

The function in the Solve It is a linear function, but it is not a direct variation. Direct variations are only part of the family of linear functions.

A **family of functions** is a group of functions with common characteristics. A **parent function** is the simplest function with these characteristics. The **linear parent function** is $y = x$ or $f(x) = x$. The graphs of three linear functions are shown at the right.

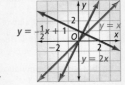

A **linear equation** is an equation that models a linear function. In a linear equation, the variables cannot be raised to a power other than 1. So $y = 2x$ is a linear equation, but $y = x^2$ and $y = 2^x$ are not. The graph of a linear equation contains all the ordered pairs that are solutions of the equation.

Graphs of linear functions may cross the *y*-axis at any point. A **y-intercept** of a graph is the *y*-coordinate of a point where the graph crosses the *y*-axis.

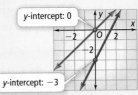

y-intercept: 0

Essential Understanding You can use the slope and *y*-intercept of a line to write and graph an equation of the line.

y-intercept: −3

take note

Key Concept Slope-Intercept Form of a Linear Equation

The **slope-intercept form** of a linear equation of a nonvertical line is $y = mx + b$.

slope   *y*-intercept

BIG idea **Function** **UbD**

ESSENTIAL UNDERSTANDINGS

• The slope and *y*-intercept of a line can be used to write and graph an equation of the line.
• One form for writing the equation of a line is the slope-intercept form.

Math Background

This lesson begins by showing students that all linear functions are related and that the slope-intercept form, $y = mx + b$, is an appropriate form to use when graphing a function. If students understand that *b* provides the ordered pair (0, *b*) and learn to generate another point from that point using the slope, they can quickly learn to graph linear functions.

When students begin to study families of functions, they should see how the parent function $f(x) = x$ is transformed to generate the slope-intercept form $f(x) = mx + b$ and how *m* and *b* affect the location of the line in the coordinate plane. The

y-intercept *b* translates the location of the graph along the *y*-axis while *m* alters the steepness of the line compared to the line $y = x$.

Support Student Learning

Use the **Algebra 1 Companion** to engage and support students during instructions. See Lesson Resources at the end of this lesson for details.

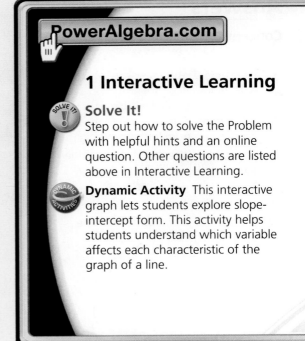

PowerAlgebra.com

1 Interactive Learning

Solve It!
Step out how to solve the Problem with helpful hints and an online question. Other questions are listed above in Interactive Learning.

Dynamic Activity This interactive graph lets students explore slope-intercept form. This activity helps students understand which variable affects each characteristic of the graph of a line.

Problem 1   Identifying Slope and *y*-Intercept

Think

Why isn't the y-intercept 2?
In slope-intercept form, the y-intercept *b* is added to the term *mx*. Instead of subtracting 2, you add the opposite, −2.

What are the slope and *y*-intercept of the graph of $y = 5x - 2$?

$$y = mx + b \quad \text{Use slope-intercept form.}$$

slope   *y*-intercept

$$y = 5x + (-2) \quad \text{Think of } y = 5x - 2 \text{ as } y = 5x + (-2).$$

The slope is 5; the *y*–intercept is −2.

Got It?   **1. a.** What are the slope and *y*-intercept of the graph of $y = -\frac{1}{2}x + \frac{2}{3}$?

     b. Reasoning How do the graph of the line and the equation in part (a) change if the *y*-intercept is moved down 3 units?

Problem 2   Writing an Equation in Slope-Intercept Form

Plan

When can you use slope-intercept form?
You can write an equation of a nonvertical line in slope-intercept form if you know its slope and *y*-intercept.

What is an equation of the line with slope $-\frac{4}{5}$ and *y*-intercept 7?

$$y = mx + b \quad \text{Use slope-intercept form.}$$

$$y = -\frac{4}{5}x + 7 \quad \text{Substitute } -\frac{4}{5} \text{ for } m \text{ and 7 for } b.$$

An equation for the line is $y = -\frac{4}{5}x + 7$.

Got It?   **2.** What is an equation of the line with slope $\frac{3}{2}$ and *y*-intercept −1?

Problem 3   Writing an Equation From a Graph

Plan

How can you use a graph to write an equation of a line?
You can use points on the graph to find the slope and the *y*-intercept of the line. Then use slope-intercept form.

Multiple Choice Which equation represents the line shown?

   Ⓐ $y = -2x + 1$ Ⓒ $y = \frac{1}{2}x - 2$

   Ⓑ $y = 2x + 1$ Ⓓ $y = 2x - 2$

Find the slope. Two points on the line are (0, −2) and (2, 2).

$$\text{slope} = \frac{2 - (-2)}{2 - 0} = \frac{4}{2} = 2$$

The *y*-intercept is −2. Write an equation in slope-intercept form.

$$y = mx + b$$

$$y = 2x + (-2) \quad \text{Substitute 2 for } m \text{ and } -2 \text{ for } b.$$

An equation for the line is $y = 2x - 2$. The correct answer is D.

Got It?   **3. a.** What is an equation of the line shown at the right?

     b. Reasoning Does the equation of the line depend on the points you use to find the slope? Explain.

---

2 Guided Instruction

 Each Problem is worked out and supported online.

Problem 1
Identifying Slope and *y* Intercept

Problem 2
Writing an Equation in Slope-Intercept Form

Problem 3
Writing an Equation From a Graph
Animated

Problem 4
Writing an Equation From Two Points
Animated

Problem 5
Graphing a Linear Equation

Problem 6
Modeling a Function
Animated

Support in Algebra 1 Companion
• Vocabulary
• Key Concepts
• Got It?

Problem 1

Q What is the ratio of rise to run for a slope of 5? **[a rise of 5 and a run of 1]**

Q What ordered pair on the graph corresponds to a *y*-intercept of −2? **[(0, −2)]**

Got It?

Q Does the graph in 1a cross the *y*-axis above or below the *x*-axis? Explain. **[It crosses above the *x*-axis since $\frac{2}{3}$ is greater than 0.]**

Problem 2

Q A student states that the given line has a slope of $-\frac{4}{5}$ and passes through the point (7, 0). Is the student correct? Explain. **[No: the slope is correct, but the *y*-intercept is (0, 7), not (7, 0).]**

Got It?   SYNTHESIZING

Using the slope-intercept form, students will write the equation $y = \frac{3}{2}x + (-1)$. Be sure students understand how to write the equation by combining the operation sign and the negative sign.

Problem 3

Q Why can you eliminate choice A by visual inspection alone? **[The line shown does not have a negative slope.]**

Q Why can you eliminate choice B by visual inspection alone? **[The *y*-intercept is not 1.]**

Got It?

Tell students that they can check the equation they choose by selecting ordered pairs (at least two) that are on the line shown in the graph. When the *x*- and *y*-values of the ordered pairs are substituted into the equation, if the math sentence is true, then the chosen equation is correct.

Answers

Solve It!

(0, 20); the initial height of the bamboo plant is 20 ft; 1; the bamboo plant grows 1 ft per day. Explanations may vary.

Got It?

   1. a. $-\frac{1}{2}, \frac{2}{3}$

     b. The graph moves down 3 units; the equation of the line changes to $y = -\frac{1}{2}x + \frac{2}{3} - 3 = -\frac{1}{2}x - \frac{7}{3}$.

   2. $y = \frac{3}{2}x - 1$

   3. a. $y = -x + 2$

     b. No; the slope is constant, so it is the same between any two points on the line.

Problem 4

Q What must you know to write the equation of a line in slope-intercept form? **[You must know the slope and the y-intercept.]**

Q How can you determine the slope of the line? **[You can substitute the points into the slope formula.]**

Q Why can you substitute either of the points into the equation in order to determine the y-intercept? **[Both of the points fall on the line, so both ordered pairs are solutions to the equation.]**

Got It?
VISUAL LEARNERS

Encourage students to check their work by graphing the line defined by the two ordered pairs. Students can check the reasonableness of the slope and y-intercept by visual inspection.

Problem 5

Q Using the slope, what is the next integral point on the line to the right of (1, 1)? **[(2, 3)]**

Q Can you use the slope to make a point to the left of the y-intercept? Explain. **[Yes, you can use the slope to plot a point that is 2 units down and 1 unit to the left.]**

Got It?
VISUAL LEARNERS

Tell students to pick a point on the line and substitute it into the given equation. If the point satisfies the equation, then the graph is correct.

Think

Can you use either point to find the y-intercept?
Yes. You can substitute the slope and the coordinates of any point on the line into the form $y = mx + b$ and solve for b.

Plan

What information can you use?
The slope tells you the ratio of vertical change to horizontal change. Plot the y-intercept. Then use the slope to plot another point on the line.

 Problem 4 **Writing an Equation From Two Points**

What equation in slope-intercept form represents the line that passes through the points (2, 1) and (5, −8)?

Know	Need	Plan
The line passes through (2, 1) and (5, −8).	An equation of the line	Use the two points to find the slope. Then use the slope and one point to solve for the y-intercept.

Step 1 Use the two points to find the slope.
$$\text{slope} = \frac{-8 - 1}{5 - 2} = \frac{-9}{3} = -3$$

Step 2 Use the slope and the coordinates of one of the points to find b.

$y = mx + b$ Use slope-intercept form.

$1 = -3(2) + b$ Substitute −3 for m, 2 for x, and 1 for y.

$7 = b$ Solve for b.

Step 3 Substitute the slope and y-intercept into the slope-intercept form.

$y = mx + b$ Use slope-intercept form.

$y = -3x + 7$ Substitute −3 for m and 7 for b.

An equation of the line is $y = -3x + 7$.

Got It? **4.** What equation in slope-intercept form represents the line that passes through the points (3, −2) and (1, −3)?

You can use the slope and y-intercept from an equation to graph a line.

 Problem 5 **Graphing a Linear Equation**

What is the graph of $y = 2x - 1$?

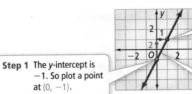

Step 1 The y-intercept is −1. So plot a point at (0, −1).

Step 2 The slope is 2, or $\frac{2}{1}$. Move up 2 units and right 1 unit. Plot another point.

Step 3 Draw a line through the two points.

Got It? **5.** What is the graph of each linear equation?
   a. $y = -3x + 4$ **b.** $y = 4x - 8$

Additional Problems

1. What are the slope and y-intercept of the graph of $y = 3x - 6$?

ANSWER slope: 3, y-intercept: −6

2. What is an equation of the line with slope 5 and y-intercept 8?

ANSWER $y = 5x + 8$

3. Which equation represents the line shown?

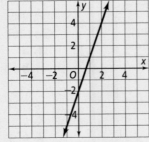

A. $y = 3x - 2$
B. $y = 3x + 2$
C. $y = -3x - 2$
D. $y = \frac{1}{3}x + 2$

ANSWER A

4. What is an equation in slope-intercept form of the line that passes through the points (1, −6) and (−3, 10)?

ANSWER $y = -4x - 2$

5. What is the graph of $y = \frac{1}{2}x - 1$?

ANSWER

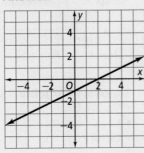

6. A carpenter charges a $45 fee plus $30 per hour for labor. Write an equation to model the total cost of a job. What graph models the total cost?

ANSWER $y = 30x + 45$

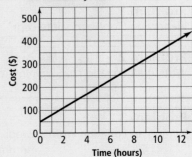

Slope-intercept form is useful for modeling real-life situations where you are given a starting value (the y-intercept) and a rate of change (the slope).

At 0 meters, the pressure is 1 atm.

 Problem 6 Modeling a Function

Physics Water pressure can be measured in atmospheres (atm). Use the information in the diagram to write an equation that models the pressure y at a depth of x meters. What graph models the pressure?

Step 1 Identify the slope and the y-intercept.

The slope is the rate of change, 0.1 atm/m.

The y-intercept is the starting value, 1 atm.

Step 2 Substitute the slope and y-intercept into the slope-intercept form.

$y = mx + b$ Use slope-intercept form.

$y = 0.1x + 1$ Substitute 0.1 for m and 1 for b.

Step 3 Graph the equation.

The y-intercept is 1. Plot the point (0, 1).

The slope is 0.1, which equals $\frac{1}{10}$. Plot a second point 1 unit above and 10 units to the right of the y-intercept. Then draw a line through the two points.

Think
How do you identify the y-intercept?
The y-intercept is the y-value when $x = 0$. So the y-intercept is the pressure at a depth of 0 m. This is the starting value, 1 atm.

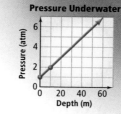
The pressure increases by 0.1 atm/m.

Pressure Underwater

Got It? **6.** A plumber charges a $65 fee for a repair plus $35 per hour. Write an equation to model the total cost y of a repair that takes x hours. What graph models the total cost?

Lesson Check

Do you know HOW?

1. What is an equation of the line with slope 6 and y-intercept -4?

2. What equation in slope-intercept form represents the line that passes through the points $(-3, 4)$ and $(2, -1)$?

3. What is the graph of $y = 5x + 2$?

Do you UNDERSTAND?

4. Vocabulary Is $y = 5$ a linear equation? Explain.

5. Reasoning Is it *always*, *sometimes*, or *never* true that an equation in slope-intercept form represents a direct variation? Support your answer with examples.

6. Writing Describe two different methods you can use to graph the equation $y = 2x + 4$. Which method do you prefer? Explain.

Problem 6

Q How do you know that the slope is positive? **[The diagram indicates that the pressure increases by 0.1 atm/m, so you know the slope is positive.]**

Q Why is the graph restricted to the 1st quadrant of the coordinate plane? **[Because water pressure is not measured using negative numbers.]**

Got It?

Q What is the slope for the equation? **[35]**

Q What is the y-intercept? **[65]**

3 Lesson Check

Do you know HOW?

- If students have difficulty with Exercise 2, then have them review the slope formula.

Do you UNDERSTAND?

- If students have difficulty with Exercise 6, then have them explain how the two different methods can be used as quick checks for each other.

Close

Q How can you use the slope and y-intercept of a line to create a graph? **[Make a point at the y-intercept, and then use the slope to create a second point. Connect the points.]**

Got It? (continued)

4. $y = \frac{1}{2}x - \frac{7}{2}$

5. a.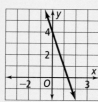

   b.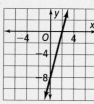

6. $y = 35x + 65$

Plumbing Repair Cost

Lesson Check

1. $y = 6x - 4$

2. $y = -x + 1$

3.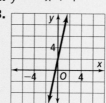

4–6. See next page.

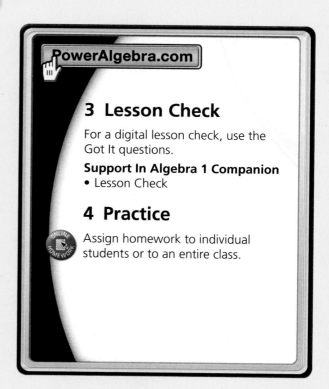

4 Practice

ASSIGNMENT GUIDE

Basic: 7–50 all, 52–58 even, 59–61 all, 62–68 even, 71

Average: 7–49 odd, 51–71

Advanced: 7–49 odd, 51–75

Standardized Test Prep: 76–80

Mixed Review: 81–90

Reasoning exercises have blue headings.

Applications exercises have red headings.

EXERCISE 71: Use the Think About a Plan worksheet in the **Practice and Problem Solving Workbook** (also available in the Teaching Resources in print and online) to further support students' development in becoming independent learners.

HOMEWORK QUICK CHECK

To check students' understanding of key skills and concepts, go over Exercises 17, 27, 59, 68, and 71.

 Practice and Problem-Solving Exercises

A Practice   Find the slope and y-intercept of the graph of each equation.   ◀ See Problem 1.

7. $y = 3x + 1$ **8.** $y = -x + 4$ **9.** $y = 2x - 5$

10. $y = -3x + 2$ **11.** $y = 5x - 3$ **12.** $y = -6x$

13. $y = 4$ **14.** $y = -0.2x + 3$ **15.** $y = \frac{1}{4}x - \frac{1}{3}$

Write an equation in slope-intercept form of the line with the given slope m and y-intercept b.   ◀ See Problem 2.

16. $m = 1, b = -1$ **17.** $m = 3, b = 2$ **18.** $m = \frac{1}{2}, b = -\frac{1}{2}$

19. $m = 0.7, b = -2$ **20.** $m = -0.5, b = 1.5$ **21.** $m = -2, b = \frac{8}{5}$

Write an equation in slope-intercept form of each line.   ◀ See Problem 3.

22.   **23.**   **24.**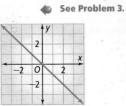

25.   **26.**   **27.**

Write an equation in slope-intercept form of the line that passes through the given points.   ◀ See Problem 4.

28. $(0, 3)$ and $(2, 5)$ **29.** $(-2, 4)$ and $(3, -1)$ **30.** $(-3, 3)$ and $(1, 2)$

31. $(-2, -1)$ and $(4, 2)$ **32.** $(-7, -3)$ and $(-12, 5)$ **33.** $(-6, 5)$ and $(1, 0)$

34. $(3, 0.5)$ and $(10, -0.2)$ **35.** $(-2, 6.9)$ and $(-4, 4.6)$ **36.** $(1.5, -2.4)$ and $(-0.5, 1.2)$

Graph each equation.   ◀ See Problem 5.

37. $y = x + 5$ **38.** $y = 3x + 4$ **39.** $y = -2x + 1$

40. $y = -4x - 1$ **41.** $y = 2x - 4$ **42.** $y = 6x - 3$

43. $y = -3x + 3$ **44.** $y = 7x$ **45.** $y = 5x + 1$

46. $y = -3x - 1$ **47.** $y = -x + 10$ **48.** $y = 15x + 5$

Answers

Lesson Check (continued)

4. Yes; it is a horizontal line with a y-intercept of 5.

5. Sometimes; answers may vary. Sample: $y = 3x$ represents direct variation, but $y = 3x + 1$ does not.

6. Answers may vary. Sample: You can plot points or you can use the slope-intercept form to plot the y-intercept and then use the slope to find a second point; check students' work.

Practice and Problem-Solving Exercises

7. 3, 1   **8.** −1, 4

9. 2, −5   **10.** −3, 2

11. 5, −3   **12.** −6, 0

13. 0, 4   **14.** −0.2, 3

15. $\frac{1}{4}, -\frac{1}{3}$ **16.** $y = x - 1$

17. $y = 3x + 2$ **18.** $y = \frac{1}{2}x - \frac{1}{2}$

19. $y = 0.7x - 2$ **20.** $y = -0.5x + 1.5$

21. $y = -2x + \frac{8}{5}$ **22.** $y = -\frac{1}{2}x + 3$

23. $y = 2x - 3$ **24.** $y = -x$

25. $y = -2x + 4$ **26.** $y = 1.5x - 2$

27. $y = \frac{5}{2}x - \frac{1}{2}$ **28.** $y = x + 3$

29. $y = -x + 2$ **30.** $y = -\frac{1}{4}x + \frac{9}{4}$

31. $y = \frac{1}{2}x$

32. $y = -1.6x - 14.2$

33. $y = -\frac{5}{7}x + \frac{5}{7}$ **34.** $y = -0.1x + 0.8$

35. $y = 1.15x + 9.2$

36. $y = -1.8x + 0.3$

37.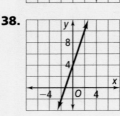

38.

39.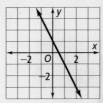

40.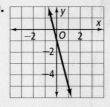

41.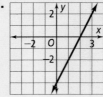

49. Retail Sales Suppose you have a $5-off coupon at a fabric store. You buy fabric that costs $7.50 per yard. Write an equation that models the total amount of money y you pay if you buy x yards of fabric. What is the graph of the equation? ◀ See Problem 6.

50. Temperature The temperature at sunrise is 65°F. Each hour during the day, the temperature rises 5°F. Write an equation that models the temperature y, in degrees Fahrenheit, after x hours during the day. What is the graph of the equation?

B Apply Find the slope and y-intercept of the graph of each equation.

51. $y - 2 = -3x$ **52.** $y + \frac{1}{2}x = 0$ **53.** $y - 9x = \frac{1}{2}$ **54.** $2y - 6 = 3x$

55. $-2y = 6(5 - 3x)$ **56.** $y - d = cx$ **57.** $y = (2 - a)x + a$ **58.** $2y + 4n = -6x$

59. Think About a Plan Polar bears are listed as a threatened species. In 2005, there were about 25,000 polar bears in the world. If the number of polar bears declines by 1000 each year, in what year will polar bears become extinct?
• What equation models the number of polar bears?
• How can graphing the equation help you solve the problem?

60. Error Analysis A student drew the graph at the right for the equation $y = -2x + 1$. What error did the student make? Draw the correct graph.

61. Computers A computer repair service charges $50 for diagnosis and $35 per hour for repairs. Let x be the number of hours it takes to repair a computer. Let y be the total cost of the repair.
  a. Write an equation in slope-intercept form that relates x and y.
  b. Graph the equation.
  c. **Reasoning** Explain why you should draw the line only in Quadrant I.

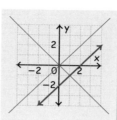

Use the slope and y-intercept to graph each equation.

62. $y = 7 - 3x$ **63.** $2y + 4x = 0$ **64.** $3y + 6 = -2x$

65. $y + 2 = 5x - 4$ **66.** $4x + 3y = 2x - 1$ **67.** $-2(3x + 4) + y = 0$

68. Reasoning How would the graph of $y = -3x + 2$ change if -3 were replaced by 4? How would it change if 2 were replaced by 0? Explain.

69. Open-Ended Write a linear equation. Identify the slope and y-intercept. Then graph your equation.

70. Writing Describe two ways you can determine whether an equation is linear.

71. Hobbies Suppose you are doing a 5000-piece puzzle. You have already placed 175 pieces. Every minute you place 10 more pieces.
  a. Write an equation in slope-intercept form to model the number of pieces placed. Graph the equation.
  b. After 50 more minutes, how many pieces will you have placed?

C Challenge Find the value of a such that the graph of the equation has the given slope m.

72. $y = 2ax + 4, m = -1$ **73.** $y = -\frac{1}{2}ax - 5, m = \frac{5}{2}$ **74.** $y = \frac{3}{4}ax + 3, m = \frac{9}{16}$

48.

49. $y = 7.5x - 5$

Price of Fabric
Price ($) / Fabric (yd)

50. $y = 5x + 65$

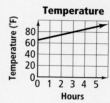
Temperature
Temperature (°F) / Hours

51. $-3, 2$ **52.** $-\frac{1}{2}, 0$ **53.** $9, \frac{1}{2}$

54. $\frac{3}{2}, 3$ **55.** $9, -15$ **56.** c, d

57. $2 - a, a$ **58.** $-3, -2n$ **59.** 2030

60. The student used the slope as the y-intercept and the y-intercept as the slope.

61–74. See next page.

42.

45.
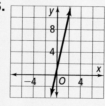

43.
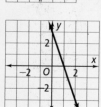

46.
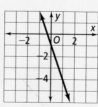

44.
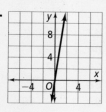

47.
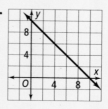

Answers

Practice and Problem-Solving Exercises
(continued)

61. a. $y = 35x + 50$

b.

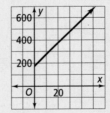

c. The amount of time the repair takes and the cost must be positive.

62.

63.

64.

65.

66.

67.

68. The slope would change to 4, so the graph would rise from left to right; the line would shift down by 2 units because the y-intercept would change from 2 to 0.

69. Check students' work.

70. Answers may vary. Samples: graph the line, determine whether the equation can be rewritten in the form $y = mx + b$.

---

75. Sailing A sailboat begins a voyage with 145 lb of food. The crew plans to eat a total of 15 lb of food per day.
    a. Write an equation in slope-intercept form relating the remaining food supply y to the number of days x.
    b. Graph your equation.
    c. The crew plans to have 25 lb of food remaining when they end their voyage. How many days does the crew expect their voyage to last?

Standardized Test Prep

SAT/ACT

76. Which equation represents the line that has slope 5 and passes through the point $(0, -2)$?
  Ⓐ $y = x - 2$ Ⓑ $y = 5x - 2$ Ⓒ $y = -2x - 5$ Ⓓ $y = 5x$

77. What is the slope of the line that passes through the points $(-5, 3)$ and $(1, 7)$?
  Ⓕ $-\frac{5}{3}$ Ⓖ $-\frac{2}{3}$ Ⓗ $\frac{2}{3}$ Ⓘ $\frac{3}{2}$

78. Which number line shows the solution of $|2x + 5| \leq 3$?
  Ⓐ   Ⓒ

  Ⓑ   Ⓓ

79. Which equation represents the graph at the right?
  Ⓕ $y = -\frac{3}{2}x + 4$ Ⓗ $y = -\frac{2}{3}x + 4$
  Ⓖ $y = -4x + \frac{3}{2}$ Ⓘ $y = 4x - \frac{2}{3}$

Short Response

80. If a, b, and c are real numbers, $a \neq 0$, and $b > c$, is the statement $ab > ac$ always, sometimes, or never true? Explain.

Mixed Review

Suppose y varies directly with x. Write a direct variation equation that relates x and y. Then find the value of y when $x = 10$.   **◀ See Lesson 5-2.**

81. $y = 5$ when $x = 1$.   **82.** $y = 8$ when $x = 4$.   **83.** $y = 9$ when $x = 3$.

Solve each equation. Justify each step.   **◀ See Lesson 2-2.**

84. $21 = -2t + 3$ **85.** $\frac{q}{3} - 3 = 6$ **86.** $8x + 5 = 61$

Get Ready!   **To prepare for Lesson 5-4, do Exercises 87–90.**

Simplify each expression.   **◀ See Lesson 1-7.**

87. $-3(x - 5)$ **88.** $5(x + 2)$ **89.** $-\frac{4}{9}(x - 6)$ **90.** $1.5(x + 12)$

---

71. a. $y = 10x + 175$

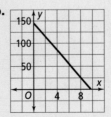

b. 675 pieces

72. $-\frac{1}{2}$

73. -5

74. $\frac{3}{4}$

75. a. $y = -15x + 145$

b.

c. 8 days

76. B   **77.** H   **78.** D   **79.** H

80. [2] Sometimes true; if $a > 0$ then $ab > ac$; otherwise $ab < ac$.
  [1] correct answer with no explanation given

81. $y = 5x$; 50   **82.** $y = 2x$; 20

83. $y = 3x$; 30   **84.** $t = -9$

85. $q = 27$ **86.** $x = 7$

87. $-3x + 15$ **88.** $5x + 10$

89. $-\frac{4}{9}x + \frac{8}{3}$ **90.** $1.5x + 18$

Additional Instructional Support

Algebra 1 Companion

Students can use the **Algebra 1 Companion** worktext (4 pages) as you teach the lesson. Use the Companion to support

- New Vocabulary
- Key Concepts
- Got It for each Problem
- Lesson Check

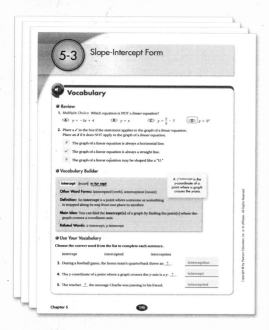

ELL Support

Use Graphic Organizers Write the words *slope-intercept form* at the top of a page. Draw an organizer with two lines extending from those words, with one line leading to the words *using a graph* and another leading to the words *using points*. Discuss the two methods of writing the equation. Then draw the graph of a line on the board. Invite volunteers to write the equation using the graph. Replace the scale and let volunteers write the equation using points from the line. After more practice, ask students to write the steps for each method on their papers.

5 Assess & Remediate

Lesson Quiz

1. What are the slope and y-intercept of the graph of $y = -\frac{1}{3}x + 1$?

2. What is an equation of a line with slope $-\frac{2}{3}$ and y-intercept of -4?

3. What equation represents the line shown?

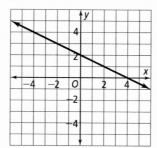

4. **Do you UNDERSTAND?** What is an equation in slope-intercept form of the line that passes through the points $(-2, -2)$ and $(1, 7)$?

ANSWERS TO LESSON QUIZ

1. slope: $-\frac{1}{3}$; y-intercept: 1
2. $y = -\frac{2}{3}x - 4$
3. $y = -\frac{1}{2}x + 2$
4. $y = 3x + 4$

PRESCRIPTION FOR REMEDIATION
Use the student work on the Lesson Quiz to prescribe a differentiated review assignment.

Points	Differentiated Remediation
0–1	Intervention
2–3	On-level
4	Extension

PowerAlgebra.com

5 Assess & Remediate

Assign the Lesson Quiz. Appropriate intervention, practice, or enrichment is automatically generated based on student performance.

Intervention

- **Reteaching** (2 pages) Provides reteaching and practice exercises for the key lesson concepts. Use with struggling students or absent students.

- **English Language Learner Support** Helps students develop and reinforce mathematical vocabulary and key concepts.

All-in-One Resources/Online
Reteaching

5-3 **Reteaching**
Slope-Intercept Form

The **slope-intercept form** of a linear equation is $y = mx + b$. In this equation, m is the slope and b is the y-intercept.

Problem

What are the slope and y-intercept of the graph of $y = -2x - 3$?

The equation is solved for y, but it is easier to determine the y-intercept if the right side is written as a sum instead of a difference.

$$y = -2x - 3$$
$$y = -2x + (-3) \quad \text{Write the subtraction as addition.}$$

The slope is -2 and the y-intercept is -3.

Problem

What is an equation for the line with slope $\frac{2}{3}$ and y-intercept 9?

When the slope and y-intercept are given, substitute the values into the slope-intercept form of a linear equation.

$$y = mx + b$$
$$y = \frac{2}{3}x + 9 \quad \text{Substitute } \frac{2}{3} \text{ for } m \text{ and 9 for } b.$$

Problem

What is an equation in slope-intercept form for the line that passes through the points $(1, -3)$ and $(3, 1)$?

Substitute the two given points into the slope formula to find the slope of the line.

$$m = \frac{1 - (-3)}{3 - 1} = \frac{4}{2} = 2$$

Then substitute the slope and the coordinates of one of the points into the slope-intercept form to find b.

$$y = mx + b \quad \text{Use slope-intercept form.}$$
$$-3 = 2(1) + b \quad \text{Substitute 2 for } m, 1 \text{ for } x, \text{ and } -3 \text{ for } y.$$
$$-5 = b \quad \text{Solve for } b.$$

Substitute the slope and y-intercept into the slope-intercept form.

$$y = mx + b \quad \text{Use slope-intercept form.}$$
$$y = 2x + (-5) \quad \text{Substitute 2 for } m \text{ and } -5 \text{ for } b.$$

All-in-One Resources/Online
English Language Learner Support

5-3 **ELL Support**
Slope-Intercept Form

Complete the vocabulary chart by filling in the missing information.

Word or Word Phrase	Definition	Picture or Example
linear equation	An equation that models a linear function	$y = 2x$
linear parent function	$y = x$ or $f(x) = x$	1.
parent function	2. A family of functions is a group of functions with common characteristics. A parent function is the simplest function with these characteristics.	$y = x$ of $y = x, y = 2x,$ and $y = 3x$
slope-intercept form	An equation of the form $y = mx + b$, where m is the slope and b is the y-intercept	3. $y = mx + b$ $y = 3x + 4$
y-intercept	4. y-coordinate of a point where the graph crosses the y-axis	$y = 2x + 1$

Differentiated Remediation *continued*

On-Level

- **Practice** (2 pages) Provides extra practice for each lesson. For simpler practice exercises, use the Form K Practice pages found in the All-in-One Teaching Resources and online.

- **Think About a Plan** Helps students develop specific problem-solving skills and strategies by providing scaffolded guiding questions.

- **Standardized Test Prep** Focuses on all major exercises, all major question types, and helps students prepare for the high-stakes assessments.

Extension

- **Enrichment** Provides students with interesting problems and activities that extend the concepts of the lesson.

- **Activities, Games, and Puzzles** Worksheets that can be used for concepts development, enrichment, and for fun!

Practice and Problem Solving WKBK/ All-in-One Resources/Online
Practice page 1

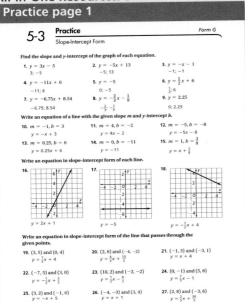

Practice and Problem Solving WKBK/ All-in-One Resources/Online
Practice page 2

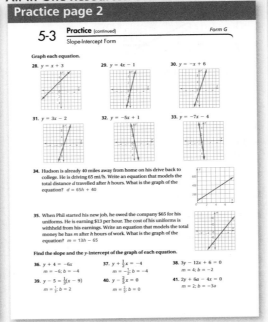

All-in-One Resources/Online
Enrichment

5-3 Enrichment — Slope-Intercept Form

Practice and Problem Solving WKBK/ All-in-One Resources/Online
Think About a Plan

5-3 Think About a Plan — Slope-Intercept Form

Hobbies Suppose you are doing a 5000-piece puzzle. You have already placed 175 pieces. Every minute you place 10 more pieces.
a. Write an equation in slope-intercept form to model the number of pieces placed. Graph the equation.
b. After 50 more minutes, how many pieces will you have placed?

Understanding the Problem

1. Is this relationship linear? How do you know?
   yes; the rate of change (10 pieces/min) is constant

Planning the Solution

2. How many pieces have you already placed? What does this represent in the slope-intercept form?
   175; the y-intercept

3. What two quantities are used to find the rate of change or slope? What is the slope of this relationship?
   number of pieces placed and change in time; 10

Getting an Answer

4. Use your answers in Steps 2 and 3 to write an equation in slope-intercept form to model the number of pieces placed.
   $y = 175 + 10x$

5. Graph the equation on a coordinate grid.

6. How many pieces will you have placed after 50 more minutes?
   675 pieces

Practice and Problem Solving WKBK/ All-in-One Resources/Online
Standardized Test Prep

5-3 Standardized Test Prep — Slope-Intercept Form

Multiple Choice

For Exercises 1–5, choose the correct letter.

1. What is an equation of the line shown in the graph at the right? C
   A. $y = -\frac{3}{2}x + 4$ C. $y = -\frac{2}{3}x + 4$
   B. $y = \frac{2}{3}x + 4$ D. $y = -\frac{3}{2}x + 6$

2. What is an equation of the line that has slope -4 and passes through the point $(-2, -5)$? G
   F. $y = -4x - 8$ H. $y = -4x - 5$
   G. $y = -4x - 13$ I. $y = -4x + 3$

3. What is an equation of the line that passes through the points $(-4, 3)$ and $(-1, 6)$? D
   A. $y = -x - 7$ B. $y = -x - 1$ C. $y = 7x + 1$ D. $y = x + 7$

4. The data shown in the table is linear. Which equation models the data? F
   F. $y = \frac{1}{2}x + 12$ H. $y = 2x + 9$
   G. $y = \frac{1}{2}x + 6$ I. $y = 2x - 3$

x	y
2	13
6	15
10	17

5. Karissa earns $200 per week plus $25 per item she sells. Which equation models the relationship between her pay p per week and the number of items n she sells? B
   A. $p = 200n + 25$ C. $n = 25p + 200$
   B. $p = 25n + 200$ D. $n = 200p + 25$

Short Response

6. What is an equation of the line that passes through $(-8, 2)$ and has slope $-\frac{3}{4}$? What is the graph of the equation?

   $y = -\frac{3}{4}x - 4$

   [2] Both parts answered correctly.
   [1] One part answered correctly.
   [0] Neither part answered correctly.

Online Teacher Resource Center
Activities, Games, and Puzzles

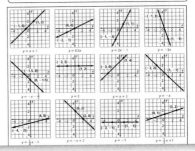

5-3 Game: It's Your Turn — Slope-Intercept Form

5-4 Point-Slope Form

Indiana Academic Standard
A1.2.4 Write, interpret, and translate among equivalent forms of equations for linear functions (slope-intercept, point-slope, and standard), recognizing that equivalent forms reveal more or less information about a given situation.

Objective To write and graph linear equations using point-slope form

Can you always use slope-intercept form? Try it here, and then learn an easier way in the lesson.

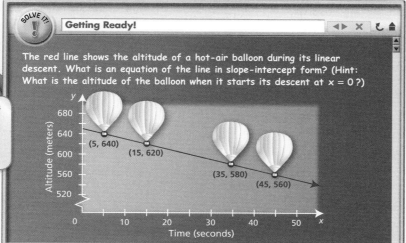

Getting Ready!

The red line shows the altitude of a hot-air balloon during its linear descent. What is an equation of the line in slope-intercept form? (Hint: What is the altitude of the balloon when it starts its descent at $x = 0$?)

(5, 640)
(15, 620)
(35, 580)
(45, 560)

Dynamic Activity
Point-Slope Form of a Line

Lesson Vocabulary
• point-slope form

You have learned how to write an equation of a line by using its y-intercept. In this lesson, you will learn how to write an equation *without* using the y-intercept.

Essential Understanding You can use the slope of a line and any point on the line to write and graph an equation of the line. Any two equations for the same line are equivalent.

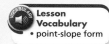

Key Concept   Point-Slope Form of a Linear Equation

Definition
The **point-slope form** of an equation of a nonvertical line with slope m and through point (x_1, y_1) is $y - y_1 = m(x - x_1)$.

Symbols
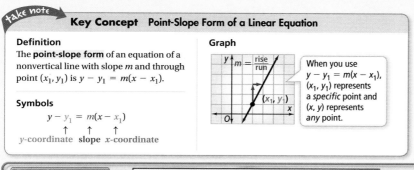

$$y - y_1 = m(x - x_1)$$

y-coordinate   **slope** x-coordinate

Graph

$m = \dfrac{\text{rise}}{\text{run}}$

(x_1, y_1)

When you use $y - y_1 = m(x - x_1)$, (x_1, y_1) represents a *specific* point and (x, y) represents *any* point.

---

1 Interactive Learning

Solve It!

PURPOSE To write the equation in slope-intercept form of a line that does not have a clearly labeled y-intercept

PROCESS Students may
• locate the y-intercept by visual inspection or by substituting a point into the slope-intercept form.
• calculate the slope formula or by counting using the slope formula.

FACILITATE

Q How can you calculate the slope of the line? **[Pick two points and substitute them into the slope formula.]**

Q Why is visual inspection not the best way to determine the y-intercept? **[Because it will only be an estimate rather than the exact value.]**

Q How can you determine the exact value of the y-intercept? **[Substitute the slope and a point on the line into the slope-intercept form, $y = mx + b$, and solve for b.]**

ANSWER See Solve It in Answers on next page.
CONNECT THE MATH Students arrived at the same equation for the line even though they used different pairs of points. In this lesson, students will explore point-slope form of a linear equation.

2 Guided Instruction

Take Note

Help students understand that the point-slope form of a linear equation provides an easier way to write the equation of a line when the y-intercept is not provided, but that the method learned in Lesson 5-3 is still valid.

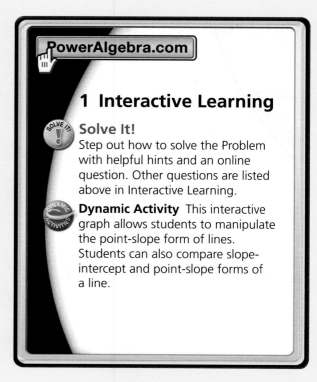

PowerAlgebra.com

1 Interactive Learning

Solve It!
Step out how to solve the Problem with helpful hints and an online question. Other questions are listed above in Interactive Learning.

Dynamic Activity This interactive graph allows students to manipulate the point-slope form of lines. Students can also compare slope-intercept and point-slope forms of a line.

5-4 Preparing to Teach

BIG idea Function   **UbD**

ESSENTIAL UNDERSTANDINGS
• The slope and y-intercept of a line can be used to write and graph an equation of the line.
• One form for writing the equation of a line is the point-slope form.
• Any two equations for the same line are equivalent.

Math Background

While all of the forms of the equation of a line are equivalent, the information provided for writing an equation will dictate the most convenient form to use.

Point out to students that using the point-slope form of a linear equation is a generalization of the more specific slope-intercept form, in which the point is specifically designed to be the y-intercept.

Students can use the point-slope form to write equations that model sets of data in which the y-intercept is not given as a point.

In calculus, students are often asked to determine the equation of a secant line for a given function evaluated at two real numbers. In this case, point-slope form is the most convenient, since the function is used to produce two ordered pairs on the curve through which the secant line passes.

Support Student Learning

Use the **Algebra I Companion** to engage and support students during instruction. See Lesson Resources at the end of this lesson for details.

Problem 1

> **Q** In the formula, both the operation signs are subtraction signs. Why is the operation sign on the right side of the equation an addition sign in the answer? **[When you substitute −3 into the formula, you have $x − (−3)$. Subtracting a negative number is the same as adding its opposite, or in this case adding 3.]**
>
> **Q** What is the slope-intercept form of the line? **[$y = −5x − 9$]**

Got It?

> **Q** In your answer, does either operation sign change to addition? Explain why or why not. **[Yes, the operation sign on the left side of the equation changes to addition because $y − (−4)$ becomes $y + 4$.]**

Problem 2

> **Q** How is using the point-slope form to graph an equation similar to using the slope-intercept form? How is it different? **[For both, you start by plotting one point and then use the slope to plot a second point. With slope-intercept form, your first point is the y-intercept. With point-slope form, your first point is the point given in the equation.]**

Got It?   ERROR PREVENTION

If students begin by graphing the point $(7, −4)$, have them first rewrite the given equation as $y − (−7) = −\frac{4}{5}(x − (4))$. Also remind them that the x-value appears first in an ordered pair, but the y-value appears first in an equation in point-slope form.

Here's Why It Works Given a point (x_1, y_1) on a line and the line's slope m, you can use the definition of slope to derive point-slope form.

$$\frac{y_2 − y_1}{x_2 − x_1} = m \qquad \text{Use the definition of slope.}$$

$$\frac{y − y_1}{x − x_1} = m \qquad \text{Let } (x, y) \text{ be any point on the line. Substitute } (x, y) \text{ for } (x_2, y_2).$$

$$\frac{y − y_1}{x − x_1} \cdot (x − x_1) = m(x − x_1) \qquad \text{Multiply each side by } (x − x_1).$$

$$y − y_1 = m(x − x_1) \qquad \text{Simplify the left side of the equation.}$$

Problem 1 Writing an Equation in Point-Slope Form

A line passes through $(−3, 6)$ and has slope $−5$. What is an equation of the line?

$$y − y_1 = m(x − x_1) \qquad \text{Use point-slope form.}$$

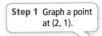 $\boxed{y_1 = 6}$ $\boxed{m = −5}$ $\boxed{x_1 = −3}$

$$y − 6 = −5[x − (−3)] \qquad \text{Substitute } (−3, 6) \text{ for } (x_1, y_1) \text{ and } −5 \text{ for } m.$$

$$y − 6 = −5(x + 3) \qquad \text{Simplify inside grouping symbols.}$$

Got It? 1. A line passes through $(8, −4)$ and has slope $\frac{2}{3}$. What is an equation in point-slope form of the line?

Problem 2 Graphing Using Point-Slope Form

What is the graph of the equation $y − 1 = \frac{2}{3}(x − 2)$?

The equation is in point-slope form, $y − y_1 = m(x − x_1)$. A point (x_1, y_1) on the line is $(2, 1)$, and the slope m is $\frac{2}{3}$.

Step 1 Graph a point at $(2, 1)$.

Step 2 Use the slope, $\frac{2}{3}$. Go up 2 units and right 3 units. Draw a point.

Step 3 Draw a line through the two points.

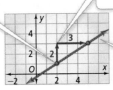

Got It? 2. What is the graph of the equation $y + 7 = −\frac{4}{5}(x − 4)$?

Think
Since you know a point and the slope, use point-slope form.

Plan
How does the equation help you make a graph?
Use the point from the equation. Use the slope from the equation to find another point. Graph using the two points.

Answers

Solve It!

$y = −2x + 650$

Got It?

1. $y + 4 = \frac{2}{3}(x − 8)$

2.

3. a. $y + 3 = \frac{7}{3}(x + 2)$

b. They are both equal to $y = \frac{7}{3}x + \frac{5}{3}$; you can use any point on a line to write an equation of the line in point-slope form.

PowerAlgebra.com

2 Guided Instruction

Each Problem is worked out and supported online.

Problem 1
Writing an Equation in Point-Slope Form

Problem 2
Graphing Using Point-Slope Form
Animated

Problem 3
Using Two Points to Write an Equation
Animated

Problem 4
Using a Table to Write an Equation
Animated

Support in Algebra 1 Companion
• Vocabulary
• Key Concepts
• Got It?

You can write the equation of a line given any two points on the line. First use the two given points to find the slope. Then use the slope and one of the points to write the equation.

Plan

How does the graph help you write an equation?
You can use two points on the line to find the slope. Then use point-slope form.

Problem 3 Using Two Points to Write an Equation

What is an equation of the line at the right?

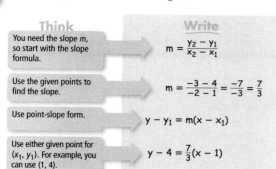

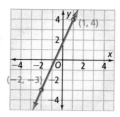

Think	Write
You need the slope m, so start with the slope formula.	$m = \dfrac{y_2 - y_1}{x_2 - x_1}$
Use the given points to find the slope.	$m = \dfrac{-3 - 4}{-2 - 1} = \dfrac{-7}{-3} = \dfrac{7}{3}$
Use point-slope form.	$y - y_1 = m(x - x_1)$
Use either given point for (x_1, y_1). For example, you can use $(1, 4)$.	$y - 4 = \dfrac{7}{3}(x - 1)$

Got It? **3. a.** In the last step of Problem 3, use the point $(-2, -3)$ instead of $(1, 4)$ to write an equation of the line.

b. Reasoning Rewrite the equations in Problem 3 and part (a) in slope-intercept form. Compare the two rewritten equations. What can you conclude?

Problem 4 Using a Table to Write an Equation

Recreation The table shows the altitude of a hot-air balloon during its linear descent. What equation in slope-intercept form gives the balloon's altitude at any time? What do the slope and y-intercept represent?

Hot-Air Balloon Descent

Time, x (s)	Altitude, y (m)
10	640
30	590
70	490
90	440

Plan

How does the table help you write an equation?
The table gives four points. You can use any two of the points to find the slope. Then use point-slope form.

$m = \dfrac{590 - 640}{30 - 10} = -2.5$ Use two points, such as $(10, 640)$ and $(30, 590)$, to find the slope.

$y - y_1 = m(x - x_1)$ Use point-slope form.

$y - 640 = -2.5(x - 10)$ Use the data point $(10, 640)$ and the slope -2.5.

$y = -2.5x + 665$ Rewrite in slope-intercept form.

The slope -2.5 represents the rate of descent of the balloon in meters per second. The y-intercept 665 represents the initial altitude of the balloon in meters.

Problem 3

Q By visual inspection, should the slope be positive or negative? Explain. **[positive; the line rises from left to right.]**

Q How can rewriting the equation in slope-intercept form be used as a check for the equation you wrote in point-slope form? **[If it is rewritten in slope-intercept form, you can compare it to the y-intercept shown in the graph.]**

Got It?   SYNTHESIZING

Have students use the method learned in Lesson 5-3 for writing an equation given two points. Ask students which method they prefer, and why.

Problem 4

Q What is the unit of measurement for the slope? **[meters per second]**

Q What is the unit of measurement for the y-intercept? **[meters]**

Additional Problems

1. A line passes through $(1, -4)$ and has slope 3. What is an equation of the line in point-slope form?

ANSWER $y + 4 = 3(x - 1)$

2. What is the graph of the equation $y + 3 = -2(x - 2)$?

ANSWER

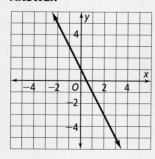

3. What is an equation in point-slope form of the line shown below?

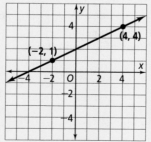

ANSWER $y - 1 = \frac{1}{2}(x + 2)$ or $y - 4 = \frac{1}{2}(x - 4)$

4. The table shows the amount of time Julio works and his total wages. What equation in slope-intercept form gives Julio's wages at any time? What do the slope and y-intercept represent?

Julio's Earnings

Hours Worked	Wages
5	$130
10	$210
15	$290
20	$370

ANSWER $y = 16x + 50$; The slope is his hourly pay rate. The y-intercept is a fixed amount of income per pay period.

Got It?

Discuss with students why the slope is expressed as a decimal when the equation represents a real-world situation.

3 Lesson Check

Do you know HOW?

• If students have difficulty with Exercise 4, then have them review Problem 3. Students should note that the ordered pairs are stated explicitly in the problem rather than graphically in a diagram.

Do you UNDERSTAND?

• If students have difficulty with Exercise 6, then tell them it is not necessary to put the equation into slope-intercept form prior to checking to see if $(-2, 1)$ satisfies the equation.

Close

Q Given the equation of a line in point-slope form, how can you determine the slope, the y-intercept, and another point that lies on the line? **[Given an equation in point-slope form $y - y_1 = m(x - x_1)$, you can determine the slope m and a point (x_1, y_1) by inspection of the equation. Rewrite the equation in slope-intercept form, $y = mx + b$, to find b, the y-intercept.]**

 Got It? **4. a.** The table shows the number of gallons of water y in a tank after x hours. The relationship is linear. What is an equation in point-slope form that models the data? What does the slope represent?

b. Reasoning Write the equation from part (a) in slope-intercept form. What does the y-intercept represent?

Volume of Water in Tank

Time, x (h)	Water, y (gal)
2	3320
3	4570
5	7070
8	10,820

 Lesson Check

Do you know HOW?

1. What is the slope and one point on the graph of $y - 12 = \frac{4}{9}(x + 7)$?

2. What is an equation of the line that passes through the point $(3, -8)$ and has slope -2?

3. What is the graph of the equation $y - 4 = 3(x + 2)$?

4. What is an equation of the line that passes through the points $(-1, -2)$ and $(2, 4)$?

Do you UNDERSTAND?

5. **Vocabulary** What features of the graph of the equation $y - y_1 = m(x - x_1)$ can you identify?

6. **Reasoning** Is $y - 4 = 3(x + 1)$ an equation of a line through $(-2, 1)$? Explain.

7. **Reasoning** Can any equation in point-slope form also be written in slope-intercept form? Give an example to explain.

 **Practice and Problem-Solving Exercises**

A Practice Write an equation in point-slope form of the line that passes through the given point and with the given slope m.

See Problem 1.

8. $(3, -4)$; $m = 6$

9. $(4, 2)$; $m = -\frac{5}{3}$

10. $(-2, -7)$; $m = \frac{4}{5}$

11. $(4, 0)$; $m = -1$

Graph each equation.

See Problem 2.

12. $y + 3 = 2(x - 1)$

13. $y - 1 = -3(x + 2)$

14. $y + 5 = -(x + 2)$

15. $y - 2 = \frac{4}{9}(x - 3)$

Write an equation in point-slope form for each line.

See Problem 3.

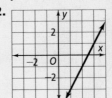

16.

17.

18.

---

3 Lesson Check

For a digital lesson check, use the Got It questions.

Support in Algebra 1 Companion
• Lesson Check

4 Practice

Assign homework to individual students or to an entire class.

Answers

Got It? (continued)

4. a. Answers may vary. Sample:
$y - 3320 = 1250(x - 2)$; the rate at which water is being added to the tank, in gallons per hour

b. $y = 1250x + 820$; the initial number of gallons of water in the tank

Lesson Check

1. $\frac{4}{9}$; $(-7, 12)$

2. $y + 8 = -2(x - 3)$

3.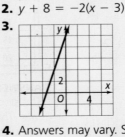

4. Answers may vary. Sample:
$y + 2 = 2(x + 1)$

5. the slope m of the line and a point (x_1, y_1) on the line

6. yes; $1 - 4 = 3(-2 + 1)$

7. Yes; answers may vary. Sample:
$y - a = m(x - b)$, $y = mx - mb + a$,
$y = mx + (a - mb)$

Practice and Problem-Solving Exercises

8. $y + 4 = 6(x - 3)$

9. $y - 2 = -\frac{5}{3}(x - 4)$

10. $y + 7 = \frac{4}{5}(x + 2)$

11. $y = -1(x - 4)$

12.

Write an equation in point-slope form of the line that passes through the given points. Then write the equation in slope-intercept form. ◀ See Problem 4.

19. $(1, 4), (-1, 1)$ **20.** $(2, 4), (-3, -6)$ **21.** $(-6, 6), (3, 3)$

Model the data in each table with a linear equation in slope-intercept form. Then tell what the slope and y-intercept represent.

22.

Time Painting, x (days)	Volume of Paint, y (gal)
2	56
3	44
5	20
6	8

23.

Time Worked, x (h)	Wages Earned, y ($)
1	8.50
3	25.50
6	51.00
9	76.50

B Apply

Graph the line that passes through the given point and has the given slope m.

24. $(-3, -2); m = 2$ **25.** $(6, -1); m = -\frac{5}{3}$ **26.** $(-3, 1); m = \frac{1}{3}$

27. Error Analysis A student graphed the equation $y - 2 = \frac{2}{3}(x - 0)$ as shown at the right. Describe and correct the student's error.

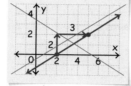

28. Think About a Plan The relationship of degrees Fahrenheit (°F) and degrees Celsius (°C) is linear. When the temperature is 50°F, it is 10°C. When the temperature is 77°F, it is 25°C. Write an equation giving the Celsius temperature C in terms of the Fahrenheit temperature F. What is the Celsius temperature when it is 59°F?
- How can point-slope form help you write the equation?
- What are two points you can use to find the slope?

29. a. Open-Ended Write an equation of a line that passes through $(-2, 5)$.
   b. Reasoning How many different equations could you write for part (a)? Explain.

30. a. Geometry Figure $ABCD$ is a rectangle. Write equations in point-slope form of the lines containing the sides of $ABCD$.
   b. Reasoning Make a conjecture about the slopes of parallel lines.
   c. Use your conjecture to write an equation of the line that passes through $(0, -4)$ and is parallel to $y - 9 = -7(x + 3)$.

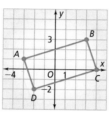

31. Boiling Point The relationship between altitude and the boiling point of water is linear. At an altitude of 8000 ft, water boils at 197.6°F. At an altitude of 4500 ft, water boils at 203.9°F. Write an equation giving the boiling point b of water, in degrees Fahrenheit, in terms of the altitude a, in feet. What is the boiling point of water at 2500 ft?

C Challenge

32. Reasoning You can use point-slope form to derive slope-intercept form. Suppose a line has slope m and y-intercept b. Show that an equation of the line is $y = mx + b$ by first writing an equation in point-slope form and then solving for y.

Answers

Practice and Problem-Solving Exercises (continued)

13.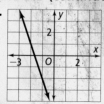

14.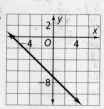

15.

16–18. Answers may vary. Samples are given.

16. $y - 3 = \frac{4}{3}(x - 1)$

17. $y - 1 = -\frac{3}{4}(x - 1)$

18. $y - 2 = \frac{3}{4}(x - 1)$

19–21. Point-slope forms may vary. Samples are given.

19. $y - 4 = \frac{3}{2}(x - 1); y = \frac{3}{2}x + \frac{5}{2}$

20. $y - 4 = 2(x - 2); y = 2x$

21. $y - 6 = -\frac{1}{3}(x + 6); y = -\frac{1}{3}x + 4$

22. $y = -12x + 80$; the slope -12 represents the change in the amount of paint in gallons per day; the y-intercept 80 represents the initial number of gallons of paint.

23. $y = 8.5x$; the slope 8.5 represents the hourly wage in dollars; the y-intercept 0 represents the amount earned for working 0 h.

24.

25.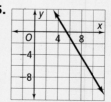

26–32. See next page.

4 Practice

ASSIGNMENT GUIDE

Basic: 8–29, 31

Average: 9–23 odd, 24–31

Advanced: 9–23 odd, 24–33

Standardized Test Prep: 34–37

Mixed Review: 38–43

Reasoning exercises have blue headings.

Applications exercises have red headings.

EXERCISE 31: Use the Think About a Plan worksheet in the **Practice and Problem Solving Workbook** (also available in the Teaching Resources in print and online) to further support students' development in becoming independent learners.

HOMEWORK QUICK CHECK

To check students' understanding of key skills and concepts, go over Exercises 9, 19, 27, 28, and 31.

Answers

Practice and Problem-Solving Exercises
(continued)

26.

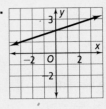

27. The student graphed the point (2, 0) instead of (0, 2).

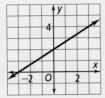

28. Answers may vary. Sample:
$C - 10 = \frac{5}{9}(F - 50)$; 15°C

29. a. Answers may vary. Sample: $y - 5 = x + 2$
b. Infinitely many; you can use any value for the slope.

30. a. Answers may vary. Samples:
$\overleftrightarrow{AB}: y - 1 = \frac{1}{3}(x + 3)$,
$\overleftrightarrow{BC}: y - 3 = -3(x - 3)$,
$\overleftrightarrow{CD}: y = \frac{1}{3}(x - 4)$,
$\overleftrightarrow{AD}: y - 1 = -3(x + 3)$
b. The slopes of parallel lines are equal.
c. $y + 4 = -7x$

31. $b = -0.0018a + 212$; 207.5°F

32. Using the point-slope form, the equation would be $y - b = m(x - 0)$, which simplifies to $y = mx + b$.

33. a. The slope between every pair of points is a constant, 2; $y = 2x$.
b. 20 in.
c. No; the rate of change is not constant.

34. A

35. H

36. D

37. [2] **a.**

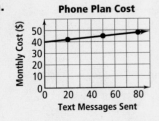

b. $c = 0.1n + 39.99$ OR equivalent equation

[1] appropriate methods, but with minor error in either the graph or the equation

---

33. Forestry A forester plants a tree and measures its circumference yearly over the next four years. The table shows the forester's measurements.

Tree Growth				
Time (yr)	1	2	3	4
Circumference (in.)	2	4	6	8

a. Show that the data are linear, and write an equation that models the data.
b. Predict the circumference of the tree after 10 yr.
c. The circumference of the tree after 10 yr was actually 43 in. After four more years, the circumference was 49 in. Based on this new information, does the relationship between time and circumference continue to be linear? Explain.

Standardized Test Prep

SAT/ACT

34. A company's revenue has been increasing by $20,000 each year. In 2011, the revenue was $730,000. Which is an equation that gives the company's revenue y (in thousands of dollars) x years after 2000?
Ⓐ $y - 730 = 20(x - 11)$ Ⓒ $y = 20x + 730$
Ⓑ $x - 11 = 20(y - 730)$ Ⓓ $x = 20y + 11$

35. Which equation is equivalent to $y + 12 = -3(x - 2)$?
Ⓕ $y = -15(x - 2)$ Ⓖ $y = -3x - 14$ Ⓗ $y = -3x - 6$ Ⓘ $y = 9x + 6$

36. Which number is NOT a solution of $6 \geq |x - 2|$?
Ⓐ -3 Ⓑ 0 Ⓒ 8 Ⓓ 10

Short Response

37. The table shows the number of text messages sent from a cellular phone and the monthly cost of the phone plan.
a. Graph the data.
b. What is an equation that represents the relationship between the number of messages sent n and the monthly cost c?

Phone Plan Cost			
Text Messages Sent	20	50	80
Monthly Cost ($)	41.99	44.99	47.99

Mixed Review

Find the slope and y-intercept of the graph of each equation.   ◀ See Lesson 5-3.

38. $y = x + 4$ **39.** $y = 6x$ **40.** $y = -x - 13$

Get Ready!   To prepare for Lesson 5-5, do Exercises 41–43.

Solve each equation for y.   ◀ See Lesson 2-5.

41. $7xy = z$ **42.** $ay - 3 = 7b$ **43.** $6(x - y) = c$

38. 1, 4
39. 6, 0
40. -1, -13
41. $y = \frac{z}{7x}$
42. $y = \frac{7b + 3}{a}$
43. $y = \frac{6x - c}{6}$

Additional Instructional Support

Algebra 1 Companion

Students can use the **Algebra 1 Companion** worktext (4 pages) as you teach the lesson. Use the Companion to support

- New Vocabulary
- Key Concepts
- Got It for each Problem
- Lesson Check

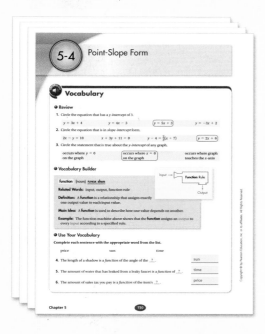

ELL Support

Focus on Language Have a word wall with vocabulary words and their definitions from each lesson. Have a separate area that shows the roots of the words. Ask students for words that share the same word base (cognates). Use the Internet or a dictionary if needed. These roots can be placed on the word wall in a separate section on different-colored paper to differentiate them.

Use Multiple Representations Have other books and texts available of varied instructional levels which define and use slope and the point-slope form.

5 Assess & Remediate

Lesson Quiz

1. **Do you UNDERSTAND?** A line passes through $(-2, 5)$ and has slope $\frac{1}{3}$. What is an equation of the line in point-slope form?

2. What is the graph of the equation $y + 3 = 2(x + 3)$?

3. What is an equation in point-slope form of the line shown below?

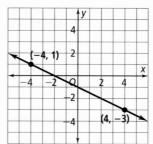

ANSWERS TO LESSON QUIZ

1. $y - 5 = \frac{1}{3}(x + 2)$

2.

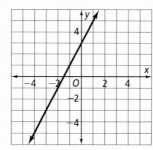

3. $y - 1 = -\frac{1}{2}(x + 4)$ or $y + 3 = -\frac{1}{2}(x - 4)$

PRESCRIPTION FOR REMEDIATION

Use the student work on the Lesson Quiz to prescribe a differentiated review assignment.

Points	Differentiated Remediation
0–1	Intervention
2	On-level
3	Extension

PowerAlgebra.com

5 Assess & Remediate

Assign the Lesson Quiz. Appropriate intervention, practice, or enrichment is automatically generated based on student performance.

Intervention

- **Reteaching** (2 pages) Provides reteaching and practice exercises for the key lesson concepts. Use with struggling students or absent students.

- **English Language Learner Support** Helps students develop and reinforce mathematical vocabulary and key concepts.

All-in-One Resources/Online
Reteaching

5-4 Reteaching
Point-Slope Form

The **point-slope form** of a nonvertical linear equation is $y - y_1 = m(x - x_1)$. In this equation, m is the slope and (x_1, y_1) is a point on the graph of the equation.

Problem

A line passes through $(5, -2)$ and has a slope -3. What is an equation for this line in point-slope form?

$y - y_1 = m(x - x_1)$ Use point-slope form.
$y - (-2) = -3(x - 5)$ Substitute $(5, -2)$ for (x_1, y_1) and -3 for m.
$y + 2 = -3(x - 5)$ Simplify.

Problem

A line passes through $(1, 4)$ and $(2, 9)$. What is an equation for this line in point-slope form? What is an equation for this line in slope-intercept form? First use the two given points to find the slope.

$m = \frac{9-4}{2-1} = \frac{5}{1} = 5$

Use the slope and one point to write an equation in point-slope form.

$y - y_1 = m(x - x_1)$ Use point-slope form.
$y - 4 = 5(x - 1)$ Substitute $(1, 4)$ for (x_1, y_1) and 5 for m.
$y - 4 = 5x - 5$ Distributive Property
$y = 5x - 1$ Add 4 to each side.

An equation in point-slope form is $y - 4 = 5(x - 1)$. An equation in slope-intercept form is $y = 5x - 1$.

Exercises

Write an equation for the line through the given point and with the given slope m.

1. $(-1, 3)$; $m = -\frac{1}{4}$ 2. $(7, -5)$; $m = 4$ 3. $(-2, -5)$; $m = \frac{2}{3}$
$y - 3 = -\frac{1}{4}(x + 1)$ $y + 5 = 4(x - 7)$ $y + 5 = \frac{2}{3}(x + 2)$

Write an equation in point-slope form of the line through the given points. Then write the equation in slope-intercept form.

4. $(1, 4)$ and $(2, 7)$ 5. $(2, 0)$ and $(3, -2)$ 6. $(4, -5)$ and $(-2, -2)$
$y - 4 = 3(x - 1)$ or $y = -2(x - 2)$ or $y + 5 = -\frac{1}{2}(x - 4)$ or
$y - 7 = 3(x - 2)$; $y + 2 = -2(x - 3)$; $y + 2 = -\frac{1}{2}(x + 2)$;
$y = 3x + 1$ $y = -2x + 4$ $y = -\frac{1}{2}x - 3$

All-in-One Resources/Online
English Language Learner Support

5-4 ELL Support
Point-Slope Form

Problem

A line passes through $(-1, 3)$ and has slope -2. What is an equation of the line? Justify your steps.

$y - y_1 = m(x - x_1)$ Use the point-slope form.
$y - 3 = -2[x - (-1)]$ Substitute $(-1, 3)$ for (x_1, y_1) and -2 for m.
$y - 3 = -2(x + 1)$ Simplify inside grouping symbols.

Exercises

A line passes through $(-3, 4)$ and has slope $\frac{1}{2}$. What is an equation of the line? Justify your steps.

$y - y_1 = m(x - x_1)$ Use the point-slope form.
$y - 4 = \frac{1}{2}[x - (-3)]$ Substitute $(-1, 4)$ for (x_1, y_1) and $\frac{1}{2}$ for m.
$y - 4 = \frac{1}{2}(x + 3)$ Simplify inside grouping symbols.

A line passes through $(2, -5)$ and has slope $\frac{1}{4}$. What is an equation of the line? Justify your steps.

$y - y_1 = m(x - x_1)$ Use the point slope form.
$y - (-5) = \frac{1}{4}(x - 2)$ Substitute $(2, -5)$ for (x_1, y_1) and $\frac{1}{4}$ for m.
$y + 5 = \frac{1}{4}(x - 2)$ Simplify inside grouping symbols.

Differentiated Remediation *continued*

Available in editable format online.

On-Level

- **Practice** (2 pages) Provides extra practice for each lesson. For simpler practice exercises, use the Form K Practice pages found in the All-in-One Teaching Resources and online.

- **Think About a Plan** Helps students develop specific problem-solving skills and strategies by providing scaffolded guiding questions.

- **Standardized Test Prep** Focuses on all major exercises, all major question types, and helps students prepare for the high-stakes assessments.

Extension

- **Enrichment** Provides students with interesting problems and activities that extend the concepts of the lesson.

- **Activities, Games, and Puzzles** Worksheets that can be used for concepts development, enrichment, and for fun!

Practice and Problem Solving WKBK/ All-in-One Resources/Online
Practice page 1

Practice and Problem Solving WKBK/ All-in-One Resources/Online
Practice page 2

All-in-One Resources/Online
Enrichment

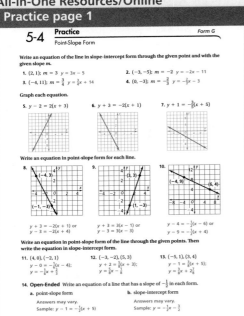

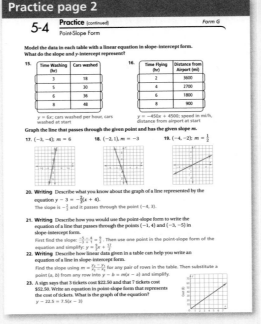

Practice and Problem Solving WKBK/ All-in-One Resources/Online
Think About a Plan

Practice and Problem Solving WKBK/ All-in-One Resources/Online
Standardized Test Prep

Online Teacher Resource Center
Activities, Games, and Puzzles

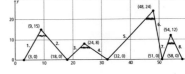

Do you know HOW?

Each rate of change is constant. Find the rate of change and explain what it means.

1. Studying for a Test

Study Time (h)	Grade
5	85
6	87
7	89
8	91

2. Distance a Car Travels

Time (s)	Distance (m)
3	75
6	150
9	225
12	300

Find the slope of the line that passes through each pair of points.

3. $(7, 3), (5, 1)$ **4.** $(-2, 1), (3, 6)$

5. $(6, -4), (6, 6)$ **6.** $(2, 5), (-8, 5)$

Tell whether each equation is a direct variation. If it is, find the constant of variation.

7. $y = 3x$

8. $5x + 3 = 8y + 3$

9. $-3x - 35y = 14$

Find the slope and y-intercept of the graph of each equation.

10. $y = \frac{1}{5}x + 3$

11. $3x + 4y = 12$

12. $6y = -8x - 18$

13. Credit Cards In 2000, people charged $1,243 billion on the four most-used types of credit cards. In 2005, people charged $1,838 billion on these same four types of credit cards. What was the rate of change?

14. Bicycling The distance a wheel moves forward varies directly with the number of rotations. Suppose the wheel moves 56 ft in 8 rotations. What distance does the wheel move in 20 rotations?

Write an equation in slope-intercept form of each line.

15.   **16.**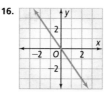

Graph each equation.

17. $y = 4x - 3$

18. $y + 3 = \frac{1}{2}(x + 2)$

Write an equation in point-slope form for the line through the given point and with the given slope m.

19. $(2, -2); m = -\frac{1}{2}$

20. $(4, 0); m = 4$

Write an equation of the line that passes through each pair of points.

21. $(4, -2)$ and $(8, -6)$

22. $(-1, -5)$ and $(2, 10)$

Do you UNDERSTAND?

23. Writing Describe two methods you can use to write an equation of a line given its graph.

24. Vocabulary How can you find the y-intercept of the graph of a linear equation?

25. Reasoning Can you graph a line if its slope is undefined? Explain.

26. Business A salesperson earns $18 per hour plus a $75 bonus for meeting her sales quota. Write and graph an equation that represents her total earnings, including her bonus. What does the independent variable represent? What does the dependent variable represent?

23. Use two points on the line to find the slope and then use the slope and one of the points to write the equation in point-slope form. Use two points on the line to find the slope and identify the y-intercept and then write the equation in slope-intercept form.

24. Answers may vary. Sample: Graph the line and find the y-coordinate of the point where the line intercepts the y-axis.

25. Yes; the graph of a line with undefined slope is a vertical line.

26. $y = 18x + 75$

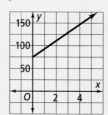

the number of hours worked; earnings

Answers

Mid-Chapter Quiz

1. 2; the grade increases by an additional 2 points for each additional hour spent studying.

2. 25; the car travels at a rate of 25 m/s.

3. 1

4. 1

5. undefined

6. 0

7. yes; 3

8. yes; $\frac{5}{8}$

9. no

10. $\frac{1}{5}$, 3

11. $-\frac{3}{4}$, 3

12. $-\frac{4}{3}$, -3

13. $119 billion per year

14. 140 ft

15. $y = \frac{1}{2}x - 1$

16. $y = -\frac{3}{2}x$

17.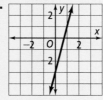

18.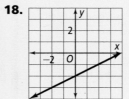

19. $y + 2 = -\frac{1}{2}(x - 2)$

20. $y = 4(x - 4)$

21–22. Answers may vary. Samples are given.

21. $y = -x + 2$

22. $y = 5x$

1 Interactive Learning

Solve It!

PURPOSE To work with an equation of a line in standard form

PROCESS Students may use the *x*- and *y*-intercepts or estimate ordered pairs to determine the number of grams of protein in the mix.

FACILITATE

Q What does each ordered pair represent? **[the number of ounces of peanuts and the number of ounces of cashews]**

Q Given an ordered pair (*c*, *p*) that falls on the line segment, what expression represents the grams of protein in the mix? **[4*c* + 7*p*]**

ANSWER See Solve It in Answers on next page.

CONNECT THE MATH The line in the Solve It can be represented with the equation $4c + 7p = 28$, which is written in standard form. By rewriting this equation in slope-intercept form, students can verify that this is the correct equation for the line.

2 Guided Instruction

Take Note

Q Why can *A* and *B* not both be zero? **[The resulting equation would be 0 = *C*.]**

Problem 1

Q What ordered pair corresponds to an *x*-intercept of 8? **[(8, 0)]**

Q What ordered pair corresponds to a *y*-intercept of 6? **[(0, 6)]**

Q Can a line have more than one *x*- or one *y*-intercept? Explain. **[No, a line cannot intersect an axis more than once.]**

Indiana Academic Standard
A1.2.4 Write, interpret, and translate among equivalent forms of equations for linear functions (slope-intercept, point-slope, and standard), recognizing that equivalent forms reveal more or less information about a given situation.

Objectives To graph linear equations using intercepts
To write linear equations in standard form

Getting Ready!

An athlete wants to make a snack mix of peanuts and cashews that will contain a certain amount of protein. Cashews have 4 g of protein per ounce, and peanuts have 7 g of protein per ounce. How many grams of protein will the athlete's mix contain? What do the points (7, 0) and (0, 4) represent? Explain.

Have you ever made a snack mix? How did you decide how much of each ingredient to use?

Snack Mix

Ounces of peanuts (vertical axis): 0 1 2 3 4
Ounces of cashews (horizontal axis): 0 1 2 3 4 5 6 7

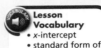

Lesson Vocabulary
• *x*-intercept
• standard form of a linear equation

In this lesson, you will learn to use intercepts to graph a line. Recall that a *y*-intercept is the *y*-coordinate of a point where a graph crosses the *y*-axis. The **x-intercept** is the *x*-coordinate of a point where a graph crosses the *x*-axis.

Essential Understanding One form of a linear equation, called *standard form*, allows you to find intercepts quickly. You can use the intercepts to draw the graph.

Key Concept Standard Form of a Linear Equation

The **standard form of a linear equation** is $Ax + By = C$, where *A*, *B*, and *C* are real numbers, and *A* and *B* are not both zero.

Problem 1 Finding *x*- and *y*-Intercepts

What are the *x*- and *y*-intercepts of the graph of $3x + 4y = 24$?

Think
Why do you substitute 0 for *y* to find the *x*-intercept?
The *x*-intercept is the *x*-coordinate of a point on the *x*-axis. Any point on the *x*-axis has a *y*-coordinate of 0.

Step 1 To find the *x*-intercept, substitute 0 for *y*. Solve for *x*.

$$3x + 4y = 24$$
$$3x + 4(0) = 24$$
$$3x = 24$$
$$x = 8$$

The *x*-intercept is 8.

Step 2 To find the *y*-intercept, substitute 0 for *x*. Solve for *y*.

$$3x + 4y = 24$$
$$3(0) + 4y = 24$$
$$4y = 24$$
$$y = 6$$

The *y*-intercept is 6.

BIG idea Function   **UbD**

ESSENTIAL UNDERSTANDING
• The standard form of a linear equation is $Ax + By = C$, where *A*, *B*, and *C* are real numbers, and *A* and *B* are not both zero.
• The standard form of a linear equation makes it possible to find intercepts and draw graphs quickly.

Math Background

A linear equation in standard form is useful for making quick graphs. An efficient way of graphing an equation in this form is to create a table of values for the equation by substituting 0 for *x* and finding the corresponding *y*-value, then substituting 0 for *y* and finding the corresponding *x*-value. If more points are needed, it may be convenient to evaluate the equation using 1 for *x* and then for *y*. Finding three points on a line is one way to be sure that the line you graph is correct. A line can

be drawn through any two points, so if an error is made when finding one of those points, the line you graph may be incorrect. By finding a third point on the line, you would likely discover that error because the three points would not be collinear.

The most common forms of a linear equation taught in high school mathematics courses are slope-intercept form, standard form, and point-slope form. However, there are many more forms that exist, including intercept form and two-point form. The form most closely related to standard form is intercept form: $\frac{x}{c} + \frac{y}{b} = 1$, where *c* is the *x*-intercept and *b* is the *y*-intercept.

Support Student Learning

Use the **Algebra 1 Companion** to engage and support students during instructions. See Lesson Resources at the end of this lesson for details.

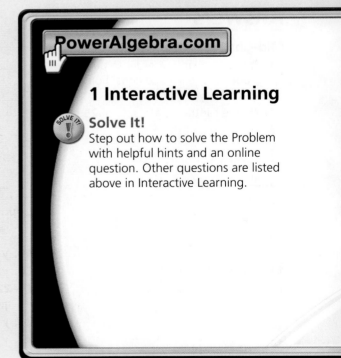

PowerAlgebra.com

1 Interactive Learning

Solve It!

Step out how to solve the Problem with helpful hints and an online question. Other questions are listed above in Interactive Learning.

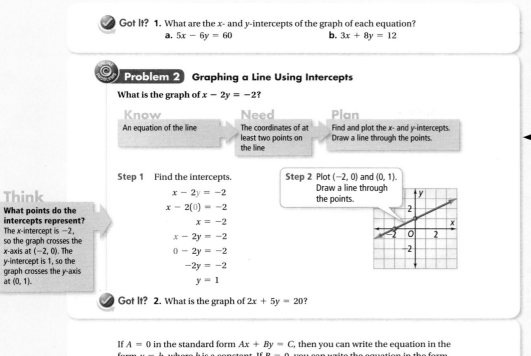

Got It? **1.** What are the x- and y-intercepts of the graph of each equation?
    a. $5x - 6y = 60$ **b.** $3x + 8y = 12$

Problem 2 Graphing a Line Using Intercepts

What is the graph of $x - 2y = -2$?

Know	Need	Plan
An equation of the line	The coordinates of at least two points on the line	Find and plot the x- and y-intercepts. Draw a line through the points.

Think

What points do the intercepts represent?
The x-intercept is -2, so the graph crosses the x-axis at $(-2, 0)$. The y-intercept is 1, so the graph crosses the y-axis at $(0, 1)$.

Step 1 Find the intercepts.
$$x - 2y = -2$$
$$x - 2(0) = -2$$
$$x = -2$$

$$x - 2y = -2$$
$$0 - 2y = -2$$
$$-2y = -2$$
$$y = 1$$

Step 2 Plot $(-2, 0)$ and $(0, 1)$. Draw a line through the points.

Got It? **2.** What is the graph of $2x + 5y = 20$?

If $A = 0$ in the standard form $Ax + By = C$, then you can write the equation in the form $y = b$, where b is a constant. If $B = 0$, you can write the equation in the form $x = a$, where a is a constant. The graph of $y = b$ is a horizontal line, and the graph of $x = a$ is a vertical line.

Problem 3 Graphing Horizontal and Vertical Lines

Think

Why write $x = 3$ in standard form?
When you write $x = 3$ in standard form, you can see that, for any value of y, $x = 3$. This form of the equation makes graphing the line easier.

What is the graph of each equation?

A $x = 3$
$1x + 0y = 3$ ← Write in standard form. →

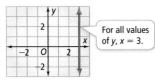

For all values of y, $x = 3$.

B $y = 3$
$0x + 1y = 3$

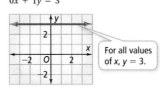

For all values of x, $y = 3$.

Got It? **3.** What is the graph of each equation?
    a. $x = 4$ **b.** $x = -1$ **c.** $y = 0$ **d.** $y = 1$

Got It?
Encourage students to check their work by substituting the intercepts as ordered pairs into the given equation. Each of the ordered pairs should satisfy the given equation.

Problem 2

Q When would this method not be a convenient method for graphing? **[if one or both of the intercepts is not an integer]**

Got It?   SYNTHESIZING
Ask students how they can determine the slope of a line written in standard form. Some students may suggest rewriting the equation in slope-intercept form, other students may suggest that you can determine the two intercepts and substitute the corresponding ordered pairs into the slope formula. Some students may also realize that they can determine the slope immediately by finding the ratio $-\frac{A}{B}$.

Problem 3

Q What do all points that are on the line $x = 3$ have in common? **[They all have an x-coordinate of 3.]**
Q What do all points that are on the line $y = 3$ have in common? **[They all have a y-coordinate of 3.]**

Got It?

Q How can you use the phrase "HOY VUX" to help you remember how to graph horizontal and vertical lines? **[Answers may vary. Sample: HOY reminds you that horizontal lines have a slope of 0 and equations that start with "$y = .$" VUX reminds you that vertical lines have undefined slope and equations that start with "$x = .$"]**

---

2 Guided Instruction

Each Problem is worked out and supported online.

Problem 1
Finding x- and y-Intercepts

Problem 2
Graphing a Line Using Intercepts
                  Animated

Problem 3
Graphing Horizontal and Vertical Lines

Problem 4
Transforming to Standard Form
                  Animated

Problem 5
Using Standard Form as a Model
                  Animated

Support in Algebra 1 Companion
• Vocabulary
• Key Concepts
• Got It?

Answers

Solve It!
28 g; (7, 0) represents a mix with 7 ounces of cashews and no peanuts; (0, 4) represents a mix with no cashews and 4 ounces of peanuts. Explanations may vary.

Got It?
1. a. $12; -10$
   b. $4; \frac{3}{2}$
2.

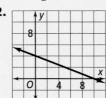

3. See back of book.

Problem 4

Q In what form is the given equation written? **[slope-intercept form]**

Q Are there other numbers that you could multiply each side by that would clear the fraction? Explain. **[Yes, you could clear the fraction by multiplying everything by any multiple of 7.]**

Got It?

Q What is the value of C for all direct variation equations written in standard form? **[0]**

Problem 5

Q If you purchase only movies, what is the maximum number of movies you can purchase? Explain. **[5, since 5 · 12 = 60]**

Q If you purchase only songs, what is the maximum number of songs you can purchase? Explain. **[60, since 1 · 60 = 60]**

Q For the cost of one movie, how many songs can you purchase? What does this number represent in the equation? **[For the cost of one movie, you can purchase 12 songs. The ratio of these numbers, $\frac{1}{12}$, is the slope of the line.]**

Given an equation in slope-intercept form or point-slope form, you can rewrite the equation in standard form using only integers.

Problem 4 Transforming to Standard Form

Plan

How can you get started? You need to clear the fraction. So, multiply each side of the equation by the denominator of the fraction.

What is $y = -\frac{3}{7}x + 5$ written in standard form using integers?

$$y = -\frac{3}{7}x + 5$$
$$7y = 7\left(-\frac{3}{7}x + 5\right) \quad \text{Multiply each side by 7.}$$
$$7y = -3x + 35 \quad \text{Distributive Property}$$
$$3x + 7y = 35 \quad \text{Add } 3x \text{ to each side.}$$

✓ **Got It? 4.** Write $y - 2 = -\frac{1}{3}(x + 6)$ in standard form using integers.

Problem 5 Using Standard Form as a Model

Online Shopping A media download store sells songs for $1 each and movies for $12 each. You have $60 to spend. Write and graph an equation that describes the items you can purchase. What are three combinations of numbers of songs and movies you can purchase?

| **Relate** | cost of a song | times | number of songs | plus | cost of a movie | times | number of movies | equals | $60 |

Define Let x = the number of songs purchased.

Let y = the number of movies purchased.

| **Write** | 1 | · | x | + | 12 | · | y | = | 60 |

Think

Is there another way to find solutions? You can *guess and check* by substituting values for one variable and solving for the other. Then check if your solution makes sense in the context of the problem. Graphing is the quickest way to see *all* the solutions.

An equation for this situation is $x + 12y = 60$. Find the intercepts.

$$x + 12y = 60 \qquad\qquad x + 12y = 60$$
$$x + 12(0) = 60 \qquad\qquad 0 + 12y = 60$$
$$x = 60 \qquad\qquad\qquad y = 5$$

Use the intercepts to draw the graph. Only points in the first quadrant make sense.

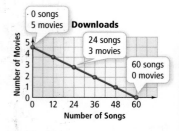

The intercepts give you two combinations of songs and movies. Use the graph to identify a third combination. Each of the red points is a possible solution.

Check for Reasonableness You cannot buy a fraction of a song or movie. The graph is a line, but only points with integer coordinates are solutions.

322 **Chapter 5** Linear Functions

Additional Problems

1. What are the x- and y-intercepts of $2x + 6y = 18$?

ANSWER 9, 3

2. What is the graph of $4x - 3y = 12$?

ANSWER

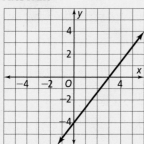

3. What is the graph of each equation?

a. $x = -1$

b. $y = 4$

ANSWER

a.

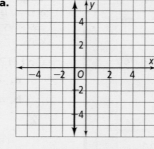

b.

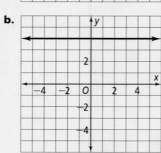

4. What is $y = -\frac{3}{5}x + 4$ in standard form using integers?

ANSWER $3x + 5y = 20$

5. A festival sells ride tickets for 50¢ each and game tickets for 20¢ each. You have $5 to spend on tickets at the festival. Write and graph an equation that describes the items you can purchase. What are three combinations of game and ride tickets you can purchase?

ANSWER Answers may vary. Sample: $2x + 5y = 50$; (5, 8), (10, 6), (15, 4)

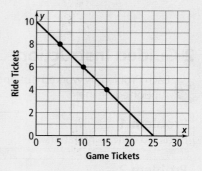

Got It? **5. a.** In Problem 5, suppose the store charged $15 for each movie. What equation describes the numbers of songs and movies you can purchase for $60?

b. **Reasoning** What domain and range are reasonable for the equation in part (a)? Explain.

Got It?

Q What is the domain of an equation? [the allowable values for *x*]

Q What is the range of an equation? [the set of all possible values for *y*, given the allowable values for *x*]

take note

Concept Summary Linear Equations

You can describe any line using one or more of these forms of a linear equation. Any two equations for the same line are equivalent.

Graph

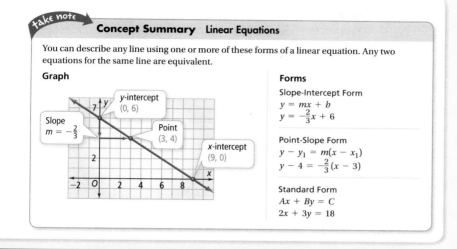

Forms

Slope-Intercept Form
$y = mx + b$
$y = -\frac{2}{3}x + 6$

Point-Slope Form
$y - y_1 = m(x - x_1)$
$y - 4 = -\frac{2}{3}(x - 3)$

Standard Form
$Ax + By = C$
$2x + 3y = 18$

Take Note
Point out to students that using different points results in different variations of the point-slope form of a linear equation and that multiplying through by different numbers results in different variations of the standard form of a linear equation. However, there is only one slope-intercept form of a linear equation.

 Lesson Check

Do you know HOW?

1. What are the *x*- and *y*-intercepts of the graph of $3x - 4y = 9$?

2. What is the graph of $5x + 4y = 20$?

3. Is the graph of $y = -0.5$ a *horizontal line*, a *vertical line*, or *neither*?

4. What is $y = \frac{1}{2}x + 3$ written in standard form using integers?

5. A store sells gift cards in preset amounts. You can purchase gift cards for $10 or $25. You have spent $285 on gift cards. Write an equation in standard form to represent this situation. What are three combinations of gift cards you could have purchased?

Do you UNDERSTAND?

6. **Vocabulary** Tell whether each linear equation is in *slope-intercept form, point-slope form,* or *standard form.*
a. $y + 5 = -(x - 2)$
b. $y = -2x + 5$
c. $y - 10 = -2(x - 1)$
d. $2x + 4y = 12$

7. **Reasoning** Which form would you use to write an equation of the line at the right: *slope-intercept form, point-slope form,* or *standard form*? Explain.

3 Lesson Check

Do you know HOW?
• If students have difficulty with Exercise 2, then encourage them to graph the line using intercepts rather than rewriting the equation in slope-intercept form.

Do you UNDERSTAND?
• If students have difficulty with Exercise 6, then refer them to the summary provided in the Take Note on this page.

Close

Q How can you determine the *x*-intercept and *y*-intercept of a linear equation written in any form? [To determine the *x*-intercept, let *y* = 0 in the equation and solve for *x*. To determine the *y*-intercept, let *x* = 0 in the equation and solve for *y*.]

Answers

Got It? (continued)

4. $x + 3y = 0$

5. a. $x + 15y = 60$

b. domain: nonnegative integers less than or equal to 60; range: {0, 1, 2, 3, 4}

Lesson Check

1. $3, -\frac{9}{4}$

2.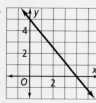

3. horizontal line

4. $x - 2y = -6$

5. $10x + 25y = 285$; answers may vary. Sample: 1 $10 card and 11 $25 cards, 6 $10 cards and 9 $25 cards, 11 $10 cards and 7 $25 cards

6. a. point-slope form
b. slope-intercept form
c. point-slope form
d. standard form

7. Answers may vary. Sample: slope-intercept form; it is easy to find the *y*-intercept and calculate the slope from the graph.

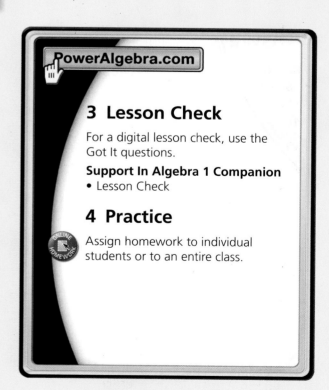

PowerAlgebra.com

3 Lesson Check

For a digital lesson check, use the Got It questions.

Support In Algebra 1 Companion
• Lesson Check

4 Practice

Assign homework to individual students or to an entire class.

4 Practice

ASSIGNMENT GUIDE

Basic: 8–44 all, 52–60 even

Average: 9–37 odd, 39–60

Advanced: 9–37 odd, 39–65

Standardized Test Prep: 66–70

Mixed Review: 71–79

Reasoning exercises have blue headings.

Applications exercises have red headings.

EXERCISE 60: Use the Think About a Plan worksheet in the **Practice and Problem Solving Workbook** (also available in the Teaching Resources in print and online) to further support students' development in becoming independent learners.

HOMEWORK QUICK CHECK

To check students' understanding of key skills and concepts, go over Exercises 9, 33, 40, 41, and 60.

Practice and Problem-Solving Exercises

(A) Practice — Find the *x*- and *y*-intercepts of the graph of each equation. ◄ See Problem 1.

8. $x + y = 9$

9. $x - 2y = 2$

10. $-3x + 3y = 7$

11. $3x - 5y = -20$

12. $7x - y = 21$

13. $-5x + 3y = -7.5$

Draw a line with the given intercepts. ◄ See Problem 2.

14. *x*-intercept: 3
    y-intercept: 5

15. *x*-intercept: −1
    y-intercept: −4

16. *x*-intercept: 4
    y-intercept: −3

Graph each equation using *x*- and *y*-intercepts.

17. $x + y = 4$

18. $x + y = -3$

19. $x - y = -8$

20. $-2x + y = 8$

21. $-4x + y = -12$

22. $6x - 2y = 18$

For each equation, tell whether its graph is a *horizontal* or a *vertical* line. ◄ See Problem 3.

23. $y = -4$

24. $x = 3$

25. $y = \frac{7}{4}$

26. $x = -1.8$

Graph each equation.

27. $y = 6$

28. $x = -3$

29. $y = -2$

30. $x = 7$

Write each equation in standard form using integers. ◄ See Problem 4.

31. $y = 2x + 5$

32. $y + 3 = 4(x - 1)$

33. $y - 4 = -2(x - 3)$

34. $y = \frac{1}{4}x - 2$

35. $y = -\frac{2}{3}x - 1$

36. $y + 2 = \frac{2}{3}(x + 4)$

37. **Video Games** In a video game, you earn 5 points for each jewel you find. You earn 2 points for each star you find. Write and graph an equation that represents the numbers of jewels and stars you must find to earn 250 points. What are three combinations of jewels and stars you can find that will earn you 250 points? ◄ See Problem 5.

38. **Clothing** A store sells T-shirts for $12 each and sweatshirts for $15 each. You plan to spend $120 on T-shirts and sweatshirts. Write and graph an equation that represents this situation. What are three combinations of T-shirts and sweatshirts you can buy for $120?

(B) Apply

39. **Writing** The three forms of linear equations you have studied are slope-intercept form, point-slope form, and standard form. Explain when each form is most useful.

40. **Think About a Plan** You are preparing a fruit salad. You want the total carbohydrates from pineapple and watermelon to equal 24 g. Pineapple has 3 g of carbohydrates per ounce and watermelon has 2 g of carbohydrates per ounce. What is a graph that shows all possible combinations of ounces of pineapple and ounces of watermelon?
    • Can you write an equation to model the situation?
    • What domain and range are reasonable for the graph?

Answers

Practice and Problem-Solving Exercises

8. 9, 9

9. 2, −1

10. $-\frac{7}{3}, \frac{7}{3}$

11. $-\frac{20}{3}, 4$

12. 3, −21

13. 1.5, −2.5

14.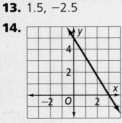

15.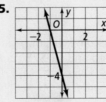

16.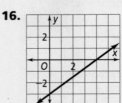

17.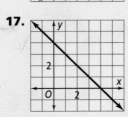

18.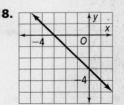

19.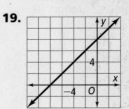

20–40. See back of book.

41. Compare and Contrast Graph $3x + y = 6$, $3x - y = 6$, and $-3x + y = 6$. How are the graphs similar? How are they different?

42. Reasoning What are the slope and y-intercept of the graph of $Ax + By = C$?

43. Error Analysis A student says the equation $y = 4x + 1$ can be written in standard form as $4x - y = 1$. Describe and correct the student's error.

44. Reasoning The coefficients of x and y in the standard form of a linear equation cannot both be zero. Explain why.

Graphing Calculator Use a graphing calculator to graph each equation. Make a sketch of the graph. Include the x- and y-intercepts.

45. $2x - 8y = -16$ **46.** $-3x - 4y = 0$ **47.** $x + 3.5y = 7$

48. $-x + 2y = -8$ **49.** $3x + 3y = -15$ **50.** $4x - 6y = 9$

For each graph, find the x- and y-intercepts. Then write an equation in standard form using integers.

51.   **52.**   **53.**

Find the x- and y-intercepts of the line that passes through the given points.

54. $(-6, 4), (3, -5)$ **55.** $(-5, -5), (4, -2)$ **56.** $(-7, 6), (-4, 11)$

57. $(-2, 8), (4, 2)$ **58.** $(3, -8), (-4, 13)$ **59.** $(5, 0.4), (-1, -2)$

60. Sports The scoreboard for a football game is shown at the right. All of the points the home team scored came from field goals worth 3 points and touchdowns with successful extra-point attempts worth 7 points. Write and graph a linear equation that represents this situation. List every possible combination of field goals and touchdowns the team could have scored.

61. Geometry Graph $x + 4y = 8$, $4x - y = -1$, $x + 4y = -12$, and $4x - y = 20$ in the same coordinate plane. What figure do the four lines appear to form?

Write an equation of each line in standard form.

62. The line contains the point $(-4, -7)$ and has the same slope as the graph of $y + 3 = 5(x + 4)$.

63. The line has the same slope as $4x - y = 5$ and the same y-intercept as the graph of $3y - 13x = 6$.

41.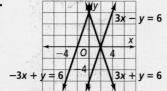

Two lines have the same slope but different y-intercepts. Two lines have the same y-intercept but different slopes.

42. $-\dfrac{A}{B}, \dfrac{C}{B}$

43. Answers may vary. Sample: The student did not subtract 1 from each side of the equation. The correct equation is $4x - y = -1$.

44. If both values are 0, then the equation becomes $0 = C$, which does not represent a line.

45.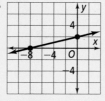

46.

47.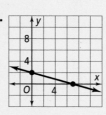

48.

49.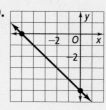

50.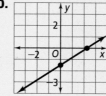

51. 4, 3; $3x + 4y = 12$

52. 2, -4; $2x - y = 4$

53. $-3, -3$; $x + y = -3$

54. $-2, -2$ **55.** 10, $-\dfrac{10}{3}$ **56.** $-\dfrac{53}{5}, \dfrac{53}{3}$

57. 6, 6   **58.** $\dfrac{1}{3}$, 1   **59.** 4, $-\dfrac{8}{5}$

60. $3f + 7t = 63$

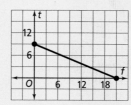

21 field goals and 0 touchdowns, 14 field goals and 3 touchdowns, 7 field goals and 6 touchdowns, 0 field goals and 9 touchdowns

61.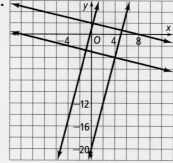

square

62. $5x - y = -13$ **63.** $4x - y = -2$

Answers

Practice and Problem-Solving Exercises
(continued)

64. a.

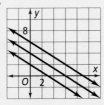

b. They are parallel.

c. Its intercepts increase and the line moves farther from the origin.

65. a. $200s + 150a = 1200$

b.

Answers may vary. Sample: student $1.50 and adult $6, student $2.25 and adult $5, student $3 and adult $4

66. C

67. H

68. B

69. H

70. [2] $C = 27t + 3$, where t is the number of tickets ordered and C is the total cost in dollars OR equivalent equation

A reasonable domain is $10 \le t \le 15$, and a reasonable range is $273 \le C \le 408$.

[1] minor error in equation, domain, or range

71–73. Point-slope forms may vary. Samples are given.

71. $y + 1 = -\frac{5}{8}(x - 5)$; $y = -\frac{5}{8}x + \frac{17}{8}$

72. $y + 2 = \frac{4}{3}x$; $y = \frac{4}{3}x - 2$

73. $y + 1 = x + 2$; $y = x + 1$

74. $-2 < t \le 3$

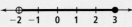

75. $1.7 \le y < 12.5$

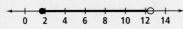

76. $x \le -1$ or $x > 3$

77. 2

78. 3

79. 0

---

64. a. Graph $2x + 3y = 6$, $2x + 3y = 12$, and $2x + 3y = 18$ in the same coordinate plane.
   b. How are the lines from part (a) related?
   c. As C increases, what happens to the graph of $2x + 3y = C$?

65. a. Fundraising Suppose your school is having a talent show to raise money for new band supplies. You think that 200 students and 150 adults will attend. It will cost $200 to put on the talent show. What is an equation that describes the ticket prices you can set for students and adults to raise $1000?
   b. Open-Ended Graph your equation. What are three possible prices you could set for student and adult tickets?

Standardized Test Prep

SAT/ACT

66. What is $y = -\frac{3}{4}x + 2$ written in standard form using integers?
   Ⓐ $\frac{3}{4}x + y = 2$ Ⓑ $3x + 4y = 2$ Ⓒ $3x + 4y = 8$ Ⓓ $-3x - 4y = 8$

67. Which of the following is an equation of a horizontal line?
   Ⓕ $3x + 6y = 0$ Ⓖ $2x + 7 = 0$ Ⓗ $-3y = 29$ Ⓘ $x - 2y = 4$

68. Which equation models a line with the same y-intercept but half the slope of the line $y = 6 - 8x$?
   Ⓐ $y = -4x + 3$ Ⓑ $y = 6 - 4x$ Ⓒ $y = 3 - 8x$ Ⓓ $y = -16x + 6$

69. What is the solution of $\frac{7}{2}x - 19 = -13 + 2x$?
   Ⓕ -9 Ⓖ -4 Ⓗ 4   Ⓘ 9

Short Response

70. The drama club plans to attend a professional production. Between 10 and 15 students will go. Each ticket costs $25 plus a $2 surcharge. There is a one-time handling fee of $3 for the entire order. What is a linear function that models this situation? What domain and range are reasonable for the function?

Mixed Review

Write an equation in point-slope form of the line that passes through the given points. Then write the equation in slope-intercept form.
See Lesson 5-4.

71. $(5, -1), (-3, 4)$ **72.** $(0, -2), (3, 2)$ **73.** $(-2, -1), (1, 2)$

Solve each compound inequality. Graph your solution.
See Lesson 3-6.

74. $-6 < 3t \le 9$ **75.** $-9.5 < 3 - y \le 1.3$ **76.** $3x + 1 > 10$ or $5x + 3 \le -2$

Get Ready!   **To prepare for Lesson 5-6, do Exercises 77–79.**

Find the slope of the line that passes through each pair of points.
See Lesson 5-1.

77. $(0, -4), (2, 0)$ **78.** $(5, 5), (3, -1)$ **79.** $(-4, 2), (5, 2)$

Lesson Resources

Additional Instructional Support

Algebra 1 Companion

Students can use the **Algebra 1 Companion** worktext (4 pages) as you teach the lesson. Use the Companion to support

- New Vocabulary
- Key Concepts
- Got It for each Problem
- Lesson Check

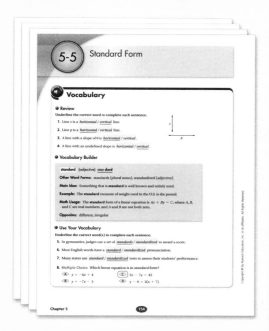

ELL Support

Focus on Communication Have students write the differences between slope-intercept form, point-slope form, and standard form in their own words. Have them identify each variable. Ask them to write why one form would be used over another. Then write two points on the board. Students will write an equation of a line using the three forms.

Use Role Playing Pair students and have them read their work to each other. Encourage questioning, clarifying, and editing as needed.

5 Assess & Remediate

Lesson Quiz

1. What are the x- and y-intercepts of $-3x + 5y = 15$?

2. What is the graph of $5x - 2y = 20$?

3. What is the graph of $x = 1$?

4. Do you UNDERSTAND? What is $y = -\frac{2}{9}x + 3$ in standard form using integers?

ANSWERS TO LESSON QUIZ

1. $-5, 3$

2.

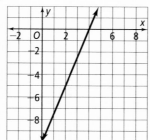

3.

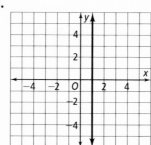

4. $2x + 9y = 27$

PRESCRIPTION FOR REMEDIATION

Use the student work on the Lesson Quiz to prescribe a differentiated review assignment.

Points	Differentiated Remediation
0–2	Intervention
3	On-level
4	Extension

5 Assess & Remediate

Assign the Lesson Quiz. Appropriate intervention, practice, or enrichment is automatically generated based on student performance.

Intervention

- **Reteaching** (2 pages) Provides reteaching and practice exercises for the key lesson concepts. Use with struggling students or absent students.

- **English Language Learner Support** Helps students develop and reinforce mathematical vocabulary and key concepts.

All-in-One Resources/Online
Reteaching

All-in-One Resources/Online
English Language Learner Support

Differentiated Remediation *continued*

On-Level

- **Practice** (2 pages) Provides extra practice for each lesson. For simpler practice exercises, use the Form K Practice pages found in the All-in-One Teaching Resources and online.

- **Think About a Plan** Helps students develop specific problem-solving skills and strategies by providing scaffolded guiding questions.

- **Standardized Test Prep** Focuses on all major exercises, all major question types, and helps students prepare for the high-stakes assessments.

Extension

- **Enrichment** Provides students with interesting problems and activities that extend the concepts of the lesson.

- **Activities, Games, and Puzzles** Worksheets that can be used for concepts development, enrichment, and for fun!

Practice and Problem Solving WKBK/ All-in-One Resources/Online
Practice page 1

Practice and Problem Solving WKBK/ All-in-One Resources/Online
Practice page 2

All-in-One Resources/Online
Enrichment

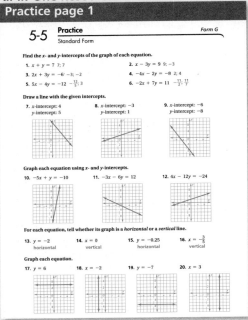

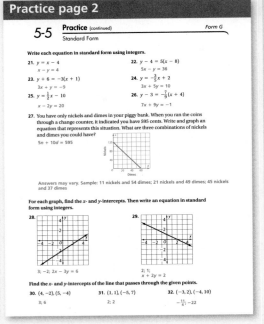

Practice and Problem Solving WKBK/ All-in-One Resources/Online
Think About a Plan

Practice and Problem Solving WKBK/ All-in-One Resources/Online
Standardized Test Prep

Online Teacher Resource Center
Activities, Games, and Puzzles

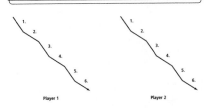

5-6 Parallel and Perpendicular Lines

Indiana Academic Standards
A1.2.2 Graph linear equations and show that they have constant rates of change.
A1.2.3 Determine the slope, x-intercept, and y-intercept of a line given its graph, its equation, or two points on the line and determine the equation of a line given sufficient information.

Objectives To determine whether lines are parallel, perpendicular, or neither
To write equations of parallel lines and perpendicular lines

> Lines that never intersect have a special relationship.

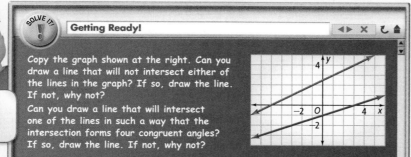

Getting Ready!

Copy the graph shown at the right. Can you draw a line that will not intersect either of the lines in the graph? If so, draw the line. If not, why not?

Can you draw a line that will intersect one of the lines in such a way that the intersection forms four congruent angles? If so, draw the line. If not, why not?

Lesson Vocabulary
• parallel lines
• perpendicular lines
• opposite reciprocals

Two distinct lines in a coordinate plane either intersect or are *parallel*. **Parallel lines** are lines in the same plane that never intersect.

Essential Understanding You can determine the relationship between two lines by comparing their slopes and y-intercepts.

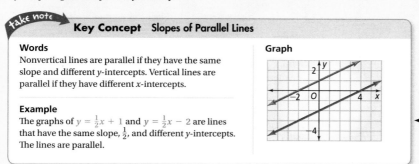

Key Concept   Slopes of Parallel Lines

Words
Nonvertical lines are parallel if they have the same slope and different y-intercepts. Vertical lines are parallel if they have different x-intercepts.

Example
The graphs of $y = \frac{1}{2}x + 1$ and $y = \frac{1}{2}x - 2$ are lines that have the same slope, $\frac{1}{2}$, and different y-intercepts. The lines are parallel.

Graph

You can use the fact that the slopes of parallel lines are the same to write the equation of a line parallel to a given line.

1 Interactive Learning

Solve It!
PURPOSE To explore the relationships between parallel and perpendicular lines in the coordinate plane
PROCESS Students may use visual judgment or prior knowledge of perpendicular and parallel lines.

FACILITATE
Q Do the two lines in the graph shown at the right intersect? Explain. **[Not in the part of the graph shown, but they will intersect somewhere in the third quadrant.]**
Q Can you draw a line such that it will not intersect one of the lines in the graph? Explain. **[Yes, if a line remains a constant distance apart from one of the two lines, then it will never intersect that line.]**

ANSWER See Solve It in Answers on next page.
CONNECT THE MATH In the Solve It, students compared intersecting lines and parallel lines. In this lesson, students study the slopes of parallel and perpendicular lines.

2 Guided Instruction

Take Note

Q How are two lines related to each other if they have the same slope and the same y-intercept? **[They are the same line.]**
Q Why are the slopes of vertical parallel lines defined differently than the slopes of nonvertical parallel lines? **[Because vertical lines have undefined slope and do not have y-intercepts.]**

5-6 Preparing to Teach

BIG idea Function   **UbD**
ESSENTIAL UNDERSTANDING
• The relationship between two lines can be determined by comparing their slopes and y-intercepts.

Math Background
To classify lines as intersecting or parallel, compare their slopes. Parallel lines have equal slopes. Intersecting lines have different slopes. If intersecting lines have slopes that are opposite reciprocals, then the lines are perpendicular.

Two lines in the same plane that have the same slope must either be parallel or coincide. In the latter case, an example of two such equivalent equations is $x + y = 1$

and $4x + 4y = 4$. There are an infinite number of ways to write equivalent equations. In the above example, the first equation is equivalent to any equation of the form $nx + ny = n$, where n is any real number.

Support Student Learning
Use the **Algebra I Companion** to engage and support students during instruction. See Lesson Resources at the end of this lesson for details.

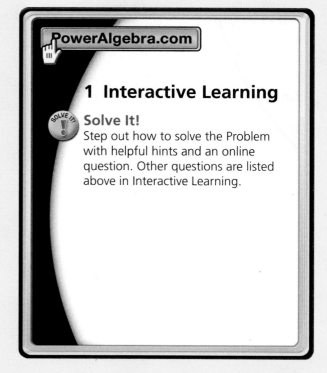

1 Interactive Learning

Solve It!
Step out how to solve the Problem with helpful hints and an online question. Other questions are listed above in Interactive Learning.

Problem 1

Q What values will you substitute into the point-slope formula and for which variables?
[**Substitute 12 for x_1, 5 for y_1, and $\frac{2}{3}$ for m.**]

Q How can you check to make certain that the graph of $y = \frac{2}{3}x - 3$ passes through the point (12, 5)? [**You can substitute the point into the equation to make sure that it satisfies the equation.**]

Q Is it possible that the line $y = \frac{2}{3}x - 1$ also passes through point (12, 5)? [**No: because the lines are parallel, they cannot have any points in common.**]

Got It?

Q What slope is shared by the two lines? Explain. [**The lines are parallel lines. Each has a slope of 2.**]

Take Note

VISUAL LEARNERS

Ask students to study examples of perpendicular lines drawn in a coordinate plane with grid lines. When students take note of the slope of each line, they can count that the rise of the first line is the same as the run of the second line and the run of the first line is the opposite of the rise of the second line.

 Problem 1 Writing an Equation of a Parallel Line

A line passes through (12, 5) and is parallel to the graph of $y = \frac{2}{3}x - 1$. What equation represents the line in slope-intercept form?

Step 1 Identify the slope of the given line. The slope of the graph of $y = \frac{2}{3}x - 1$ is $\frac{2}{3}$. The parallel line has the same slope.

Step 2 Write an equation in slope-intercept form of the line through (12, 5) with slope $\frac{2}{3}$.

 Think
Why start with point-slope form?
You know a point on the line. You can use what you know about parallel lines to find the slope. So, point-slope form is convenient to use.

$$y - y_1 = m(x - x_1) \quad \text{Start with point-slope form.}$$
$$y - 5 = \frac{2}{3}(x - 12) \quad \text{Substitute (12, 5) for } (x_1, y_1) \text{ and } \frac{2}{3} \text{ for } m.$$
$$y - 5 = \frac{2}{3}x - \frac{2}{3}(12) \quad \text{Distributive Property}$$
$$y - 5 = \frac{2}{3}x - 8 \quad \text{Simplify.}$$
$$y = \frac{2}{3}x - 3 \quad \text{Add 5 to each side.}$$

The graph of $y = \frac{2}{3}x - 3$ passes through (12, 5) and is parallel to the graph of $y = \frac{2}{3}x - 1$.

Got It? **1.** A line passes through (−3, −1) and is parallel to the graph of $y = 2x + 3$. What equation represents the line in slope-intercept form?

You can also use slope to determine whether two lines are *perpendicular*. **Perpendicular lines** are lines that intersect to form right angles.

take note

Key Concept Slopes of Perpendicular Lines

Words

Two nonvertical lines are perpendicular if the product of their slopes is −1. A vertical line and a horizontal line are also perpendicular.

Graph

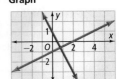

Example
The graph of $y = \frac{1}{2}x - 1$ has a slope of $\frac{1}{2}$.
The graph of $y = -2x + 1$ has a slope of −2.
Since $\frac{1}{2}(-2) = -1$, the lines are perpendicular.

Two numbers whose product is −1 are **opposite reciprocals**. So, the slopes of perpendicular lines are opposite reciprocals. To find the opposite reciprocal of $-\frac{3}{4}$, for example, first find the reciprocal, $-\frac{4}{3}$. Then write its opposite, $\frac{4}{3}$. Since $-\frac{3}{4} \cdot \frac{4}{3} = -1$, $\frac{4}{3}$ is the opposite reciprocal of $-\frac{3}{4}$.

Answers

Solve It!

No; the given lines are not parallel, so any line will intersect at least one of them; yes; answers may vary.

Got It?
1. $y = 2x + 5$

 PowerAlgebra.com

2 Guided Instruction

Each Problem is worked out and supported online.

Problem 1
Writing an Equation of a Parallel Line

Alternative Problem 1
Writing an Equation of a Parallel Line
Animated

Problem 2
Classifying Lines
Animated

Problem 3
Writing an Equation of a Perpendicular Line
Animated

Problem 4
Solving a Real-World Problem

Support in Algebra 1 Companion
• Vocabulary
• Key Concepts
• Got It?

Problem 2 Classifying Lines

Think

Why write each equation in slope-intercept form?
You can easily identify the slope of an equation in slope-intercept form. Just look at the coefficient of x.

Are the graphs of $4y = -5x + 12$ and $y = \frac{4}{5}x - 8$ *parallel, perpendicular,* or *neither*? Explain.

Step 1 Find the slope of each line by writing its equation in slope-intercept form, if necessary. Only the first equation needs to be rewritten.

$$4y = -5x + 12 \quad \text{Write the first equation.}$$

$$\frac{4y}{4} = \frac{-5x + 12}{4} \quad \text{Divide each side by 4.}$$

$$y = -\frac{5}{4}x + 3 \quad \text{Simplify.}$$

The slope of the graph of $y = -\frac{5}{4}x + 3$ is $-\frac{5}{4}$.

The slope of the graph of $y = \frac{4}{5}x - 8$ is $\frac{4}{5}$.

Step 2 The slopes are not the same, so the lines cannot be parallel. Multiply the slopes to see if they are opposite reciprocals.

$$-\frac{5}{4} \cdot \frac{4}{5} = -1$$

The slopes are opposite reciprocals, so the lines are perpendicular.

✓ **Got It? 2.** Are the graphs of the equations *parallel, perpendicular,* or *neither*? Explain.
a. $y = \frac{3}{4}x + 7$ and $4x - 3y = 9$ **b.** $6y = -x + 6$ and $y = -\frac{1}{6}x + 6$

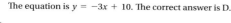 **Problem 3** Writing an Equation of a Perpendicular Line

Multiple Choice Which equation represents the line that passes through $(2, 4)$ and is perpendicular to the graph of $y = \frac{1}{3}x - 1$?

Ⓐ $y = \frac{1}{3}x + 10$ Ⓑ $y = 3x + 10$ Ⓒ $y = -3x - 2$ Ⓓ $y = -3x + 10$

Think

How do you know you have found the opposite reciprocal?
Multiply the two numbers together as a check. If the product is -1, the numbers are opposite reciprocals: $\frac{1}{3}(-3) = -1$.

Step 1 Identify the slope of the graph of the given equation. The slope is $\frac{1}{3}$.

Step 2 Find the opposite reciprocal of the slope from Step 1. The opposite reciprocal of $\frac{1}{3}$ is -3. So, the perpendicular line has a slope of -3.

Step 3 Use point-slope form to write an equation of the perpendicular line.

$$y - y_1 = m(x - x_1) \quad \text{Write point-slope form.}$$

$$y - 4 = -3(x - 2) \quad \text{Substitute } (2, 4) \text{ for } (x_1, y_1) \text{ and } -3 \text{ for } m.$$

$$y - 4 = -3x + 6 \quad \text{Distributive Property}$$

$$y = -3x + 10 \quad \text{Add 4 to each side.}$$

The equation is $y = -3x + 10$. The correct answer is D.

✓ **Got It? 3.** A line passes through $(1, 8)$ and is perpendicular to the graph of $y = 2x + 1$. What equation represents the line in slope-intercept form?

Problem 2

Q What forms of a linear equation make it easy to identify the slope of a line? **[point-slope form and slope-intercept form]**

Q How do you find the product of two fractions? **[Answers may vary. Sample: You multiply the numerators, multiply the denominators, and simplify the resulting fraction.]**

Got It?   ERROR PREVENTION

If students are incorrectly determining the relationships between these pairs of lines, they are probably not correctly identifying the slope of each line. Some students might forget that the slope is the coefficient of the x-term only when the equation is written in slope-intercept form.

Problem 3

Q What is the relationship between the given equation and the equation given in choice A? **[The equations represent lines parallel to one another.]**

Q Is it possible for perpendicular lines to share the same y-intercept? Explain. **[Yes, if the lines intersect at the y-intercept.]**

Q At what point do the graphs of the equations in choice A, choice B, and choice D intersect? Explain. **[Each graph has y-intercept of 10, so they intersect at the point (0, 10).]**

Got It?

Q How do you express 2 as a fraction? What is its opposite reciprocal? $[\frac{2}{1}; -\frac{1}{2}]$

Additional Problems

1. What is an equation in slope-intercept form of the line that passes through $(2, 15)$ and is parallel to the graph of $y = 4x - 1$?

ANSWER $y = 4x + 7$

2. Are the graphs of $2y = -3x + 6$ and $y = \frac{2}{3}x + 2$ *parallel, perpendicular,* or *neither*?

ANSWER perpendicular

3. The graph of which equation passes through $(10, 15)$ and is perpendicular to the graph of $y = -\frac{5}{6}x - 2$?

A. $y = -\frac{5}{6}x + 4$

B. $y = -\frac{5}{6}x - 6$

C. $y = \frac{6}{5}x + 3$

D. $y = \frac{6}{5}x - 5$

ANSWER C

4. Carla is using a coordinate grid to make a map of her hometown. She plots Main Street as shown. If 3rd Street is perpendicular to Main Street at $(5, 7)$, what is an equation for 3rd Street?

[A coordinate grid labeled with x and y axes, showing a line labeled "Main Street" sloping downward from about (0, 8).]

ANSWER $y = 5x - 18$

Answers

Got It? (continued)

2. a. Neither; the slopes are not equal or opposite reciprocals.

b. Parallel; the slopes are equal.

3. $y = -\frac{1}{2}x + \frac{17}{2}$

Problem 4

Q Is it necessary to write the equation that represents the existing beam? Explain. **[No, only the slope of the line is needed.]**

Q What are the equations of the lines that represent the four sides of the ceiling? What is the relationship of these lines? **[$x = 0$, $x = 12$, $y = 0$ and $y = 10$; opposite lines are parallel and adjacent lines are perpendicular.]**

Got It?

Q What does the point (0, 10) represent for the new equation? **[the y-intercept]**

3 Lesson Check

Do you know HOW?
- If students have difficulty with Exercise 3, then remind them that the product of the opposite reciprocals is -1.

Do you UNDERSTAND?
- If students have difficulty with Exercise 5, then remind them that parallel lines have the same slope.

Close

Q If two lines are neither parallel nor perpendicular, what two statements can you make about the slopes of the lines? **[The slopes are not the same and not opposite reciprocals.]**

---

3 Lesson Check

For a digital lesson check, use the Got It questions.

Support in Algebra 1 Companion
- Lesson Check

4 Practice

Assign homework to individual students or to an entire class.

 Problem 4 Solving a Real-World Problem

Architecture An architect uses software to design the ceiling of a room. The architect needs to enter an equation that represents a new beam. The new beam will be perpendicular to the existing beam, which is represented by the red line. The new beam will pass through the corner represented by the blue point. What is an equation that represents the new beam?

Plan

Have you seen a problem like this before?
Yes. You wrote the equation of a perpendicular line in Problem 3. Follow the same steps here after you calculate the slope of the line from the graph.

Step 1 Use the slope formula to find the slope of the red line that represents the existing beam.

$$m = \frac{4 - 6}{6 - 3} \quad \text{Points (3, 6) and (6, 4) are on the red line.}$$

$$= -\frac{2}{3} \quad \text{Simplify.}$$

The slope of the line that represents the existing beam is $-\frac{2}{3}$.

Step 2 Find the opposite reciprocal of the slope from Step 1. The opposite reciprocal of $-\frac{2}{3}$ is $\frac{3}{2}$.

Step 3 Use point-slope form to write an equation. The slope of the line that represents the new beam is $\frac{3}{2}$. It will pass through (12, 10). An equation that represents the new beam is $y - 10 = \frac{3}{2}(x - 12)$ or, in slope-intercept form, $y = \frac{3}{2}x - 8$.

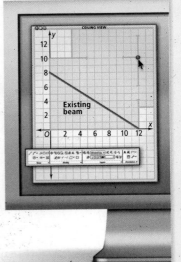

CEILING VIEW

Existing beam

Got It? **4.** What equation could the architect enter to represent a second beam whose graph will pass through the corner at (0, 10) and be parallel to the existing beam? Give your answer in slope-intercept form.

 Lesson Check

Do you know HOW?

1. Which equations below have graphs that are parallel to one another? Which have graphs that are perpendicular to one another?

$$y = -\frac{1}{6}x \qquad y = 6x \qquad y = 6x - 2$$

2. What is an equation of the line that passes through (3, −1) and is parallel to $y = -4x + 1$? Give your answer in slope-intercept form.

3. What is an equation of the line that passes through (2, −3) and is perpendicular to $y = x - 5$? Give your answer in slope-intercept form.

Do you UNDERSTAND?

4. Vocabulary Tell whether the two numbers in each pair are opposite reciprocals.

a. $-2, \frac{1}{2}$ **b.** $\frac{1}{4}, 4$ **c.** $5, -5$

5. Open-Ended Write equations of two parallel lines.

6. Compare and Contrast How is determining if two lines are parallel similar to determining if they are perpendicular? How are the processes different?

Answers

Got It? (continued)

4. $y = -\frac{2}{3}x + 10$

Lesson Check

1. $y = 6x$ and $y = 6x - 2$; $y = -\frac{1}{6}x$ and $y = 6x$, $y = -\frac{1}{6}x$ and $y = 6x - 2$

2. $y = -4x + 11$

3. $y = -x - 1$

4. a. yes
    b. no
    c. no

5. Check students' work.

6. In both cases, you compare the slopes of the lines. If the slopes are equal, then the lines are parallel. If the slopes are opposite reciprocals, the lines are perpendicular.

Practice and Problem-Solving Exercises

A Practice

Write an equation in slope-intercept form of the line that passes through the given point and is parallel to the graph of the given equation.

◀ See Problem 1.

7. $(1, 3); y = 3x + 2$ **8.** $(2, -2); y = -x - 2$ **9.** $(1, -3); y + 2 = 4(x - 1)$

10. $(2, -1); y = -\frac{3}{2}x + 6$ **11.** $(0, 0); y = \frac{2}{3}x + 1$ **12.** $(4, 2); x = -3$

Determine whether the graphs of the given equations are *parallel*, *perpendicular*, or *neither*. Explain.

◀ See Problem 2.

13. $y = x + 11$
$\quad\;\; y = -x + 2$

14. $y = \frac{3}{4}x - 1$
$\quad\;\; y = \frac{3}{4}x + 29$

15. $y = -2x + 3$
$\quad\;\; 2x + y = 7$

16. $y - 4 = 3(x + 2)$
$\quad\;\; 2x + 6y = 10$

17. $y = -7$
$\quad\;\; x = 2$

18. $y = 4x - 2$
$\quad\;\; -x + 4y = 0$

Write an equation in slope-intercept form of the line that passes through the given point and is perpendicular to the graph of the given equation.

◀ See Problem 3.

19. $(0, 0); y = -3x + 2$ **20.** $(-2, 3); y = \frac{1}{2}x - 1$ **21.** $(1, -2); y = 5x + 4$

22. $(-3, 2); x - 2y = 7$ **23.** $(5, 0); y + 1 = 2(x - 3)$ **24.** $(1, -6); x - 2y = 4$

25. Urban Planning A path for a new city park will connect the park entrance to Main Street. The path should be perpendicular to Main Street. What is an equation that represents the path?

◀ See Problem 4.

26. Bike Path A bike path is being planned for the park in Exercise 25. The bike path will be parallel to Main Street and will pass through the park entrance. What is an equation of the line that represents the bike path?

B Apply

27. Identify each pair of parallel lines. Then identify each pair of perpendicular lines.

line *a*: $y = 3x + 3$ line *b*: $x = -1$ line *c*: $y - 5 = \frac{1}{2}(x - 2)$
line *d*: $y = 3$ line *e*: $y + 4 = -2(x + 6)$ line *f*: $9x - 3y = 5$

Determine whether each statement is *always*, *sometimes*, or *never* true. Explain.

28. A horizontal line is parallel to the *x*-axis.

29. Two lines with positive slopes are parallel.

30. Two lines with the same slope and different *y*-intercepts are perpendicular.

31. Open-Ended What is an equation of a line that is parallel to the *x*-axis? What is an equation of a line that is parallel to the *y*-axis?

32. Error Analysis A student says that the graph of $y = \frac{1}{3}x + 1$ is parallel to the graph of $y = -3x + 4$. Describe and correct the student's error.

4 Practice

ASSIGNMENT GUIDE

Basic: 7–26, 27–30, 32–33, 35

Average: 7–25 odd, 27–35

Advanced: 7–25 odd, 27–37

Standardized Test Prep: 38–40

Mixed Review: 41–47

Reasoning exercises have blue headings.

Applications exercises have red headings.

EXERCISE 35: Use the Think About a Plan worksheet in the **Practice and Problem Solving Workbook** (also available in the Teaching Resources in print and online) to further support students' development in becoming independent learners.

HOMEWORK QUICK CHECK

To check students' understanding of key skills and concepts, go over Exercises 15, 21, 32, 33, and 35.

Answers

Practice and Problem-Solving Exercises

7. $y = 3x$ **8.** $y = -x$

9. $y = 4x - 7$ **10.** $y = -\frac{3}{2}x + 2$

11. $y = \frac{2}{3}x$ **12.** $x = 4$

13. Perpendicular; the slopes are opposite reciprocals.

14. Parallel; the slopes are equal.

15. Parallel; the slopes are equal.

16. Perpendicular; the slopes are opposite reciprocals.

17. Perpendicular; one line is vertical and the other line is horizontal.

18. Neither; the slopes are not equal or opposite reciprocals.

19. $y = \frac{1}{3}x$

20. $y = -2x - 1$

21. $y = -\frac{1}{5}x - \frac{9}{5}$

22. $y = -2x - 4$

23. $y = -\frac{1}{2}x + \frac{5}{2}$

24. $y = -2x - 4$

25. $y = -\frac{1}{2}x + 4$

26. $y = 2x + 4$

27. *a* and *f*; *b* and *d*, *c* and *e*

28. Sometimes; a horizontal line has the same slope as the *x*-axis. If the horizontal line is not $y = 0$, then it is parallel to the *x*-axis.

29. Sometimes; if the slopes are equal and the *y*-intercepts are not equal, then the lines are parallel.

30. Never; two lines with the same slope are parallel.

31. Answers may vary. Samples: $y = 1; x = 1$

32. The slopes are not equal, so the lines cannot be parallel. The slopes are opposite reciprocals, so the lines are perpendicular.

Answers

Practice and Problem-Solving Exercises (continued)

33. $x = 3$

34. $-\frac{3}{2}$, 24

35. $y = -100x + 600$, $y = -100x + 1000$; parallel; the slopes are the same.

36. $\overline{AB}$ is parallel to $\overline{CD}$ because they both have slope $-\frac{5}{2}$.
$\overline{BC}$ is parallel to $\overline{AD}$ because they both have slope $\frac{2}{5}$.
$\overline{AB}$ is perpendicular to $\overline{BC}$ because their slopes are opposite reciprocals.
$\overline{AD}$ is perpendicular to $\overline{CD}$ because their slopes are opposite reciprocals.

37. No; the slope of $\overline{PQ}$ is 2, the slope of $\overline{QR}$ is -1, and the slope of $\overline{PR}$ is $\frac{1}{2}$. No two slopes are opposite reciprocals, so no angle of the triangle is a right angle.

38. D

39. G

40. [2] Sal's: $\$15.50/24 = \$0.6458$ per bottle
Shopper's World: $\$8.15/12 = \$0.679$ per bottle
Since $0.6458 < 0.679$, Sal's has the better price per bottle.
[1] appropriate methods, but with one computational error

41.
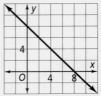

42.
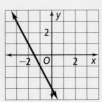

43.
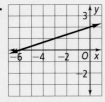

44. $y = 3x - 2$

45. $y = -\frac{2}{5}x + \frac{29}{5}$

46. $y = 0.25x + 1.875$

47. $y = -\frac{40}{7}x + \frac{660}{7}$

---

33. Think About a Plan A designer is creating a new logo, as shown at the right. The designer wants to add a line to the logo that will be perpendicular to the blue line and pass through the red point. What equation represents the new line?
- What is the slope of the blue line?
- What is the slope of the new line?

34. Reasoning For what value of k are the graphs of $12y = -3x + 8$ and $6y = kx - 5$ parallel? For what value of k are they perpendicular?

35. Agriculture Two farmers use combines to harvest corn from their fields. One farmer has 600 acres of corn, and the other has 1000 acres of corn. Each farmer's combine can harvest 100 acres per day. Write two equations for the number of acres y of corn *not* harvested after x days. Are the graphs of the equations *parallel, perpendicular,* or *neither*? How do you know?

Challenge

36. Geometry In a rectangle, opposite sides are parallel and adjacent sides are perpendicular. Figure $ABCD$ has vertices $A(-3, 3)$, $B(-1, -2)$, $C(4, 0)$, and $D(2, 5)$. Show that $ABCD$ is a rectangle.

37. Geometry A right triangle has two sides that are perpendicular to each other. Triangle PQR has vertices $P(4, 3)$, $Q(2, -1)$, and $R(0, 1)$. Determine whether PQR is a right triangle. Explain your reasoning.

Standardized Test Prep

SAT/ACT

38. Which equation represents the graph of a line parallel to the line at the right?
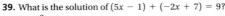
Ⓐ $y = \frac{1}{2}x + 5$ Ⓒ $y = -2x + 4$
Ⓑ $y = 2x - 6$ Ⓓ $y = -\frac{1}{2}x - 2$

39. What is the solution of $(5x - 1) + (-2x + 7) = 9$?
Ⓕ $\frac{3}{7}$ Ⓖ 1   Ⓗ 3   Ⓘ 5

Short Response

40. Sal's Supermarket sells cases of twenty-four 12-oz bottles of water for $\$15.50$. Shopper's World sells 12-packs of 12-oz bottles of water for $\$8.15$. Which store has the better price per bottle? Explain.

Mixed Review

Graph each equation using x- and y-intercepts.   ◀ See Lesson 5-5.

41. $x + y = 8$ **42.** $2x + y = -3$ **43.** $x - 3y = -6$

Get Ready! To prepare for Lesson 5-7, do Exercises 44–47.

Write an equation in slope-intercept form of the line that passes through the given points.   ◀ See Lesson 5-3.

44. $(1, 1), (3, 7)$ **45.** $(2, 5), (12, 1)$ **46.** $(0.5, 2), (4.5, 3)$ **47.** $(13, 20), (6, 60)$

Additional Instructional Support

Algebra 1 Companion

Students can use the **Algebra 1 Companion** worktext (4 pages) as you teach the lesson. Use the Companion to support

- New Vocabulary
- Key Concepts
- Got It for each Problem
- Lesson Check

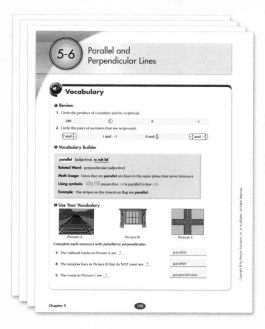

ELL Support

Use Manipulatives Have students place graph paper in a plastic page protector. Use dry eraser markers so the graph can be reused. Draw parallel lines and model finding the slope of one line by counting rise over run. Think aloud as you work using gestures to correlate the words with the object. Then use two points to find the slope of the other line. Ask students what they notice about the slopes. Discuss the definition of parallel lines. Write equations for each line. Repeat with perpendicular lines.

Assess Understanding Assist as students find slopes and write equations of parallel and perpendicular lines. Vary opportunities by providing a graphed line, two points, a point and the slope or a linear equation for students to work with.

5 Assess & Remediate

Lesson Quiz

1. What is an equation in slope-intercept form of the line that passes through (6, 10) and is parallel to the graph of $y = \frac{1}{3}x - 1$?

2. Are the graphs of $-5y = 2x + 3$ and $y = \frac{2}{5}x + 4$ parallel, perpendicular, or neither?

3. **Do you UNDERSTAND?** What is an equation in slope-intercept form of the line that passes through $(6, -7)$ and is perpendicular to the line shown below?

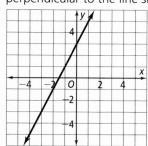

ANSWERS TO LESSON QUIZ

1. $y = \frac{1}{3}x + 8$
2. neither
3. $y = -\frac{1}{2}x - 4$

PRESCRIPTION FOR REMEDIATION

Use the student work on the Lesson Quiz to prescribe a differentiated review assignment.

Points	Differentiated Remediation
0–1	Intervention
2	On-level
3	Extension

PowerAlgebra.com

5 Assess & Remediate

Assign the Lesson Quiz. Appropriate intervention, practice, or enrichment is automatically generated based on student performance.

Intervention

- **Reteaching** (2 pages) Provides reteaching and practice exercises for the key lesson concepts. Use with struggling students or absent students.

- **English Language Learner Support** Helps students develop and reinforce mathematical vocabulary and key concepts.

All-in-One Resources/Online
Reteaching

5-6 Reteaching
Parallel and Perpendicular Lines

Nonvertical lines are parallel if they have the same slope and different y-intercepts. The graphs of $y = 2x - 6$ and $y = 2x + 3$ are parallel because they have the same slope, 2, but different y-intercepts, −6 and 3.

Problem

What is an equation in slope-intercept form of the line that passes through (8, 7) and is parallel to the graph of $y = \frac{3}{4}x + 2$?

The slope of $y = \frac{3}{4}x + 2$ is $\frac{3}{4}$. Because the desired equation is for a line parallel to a line with slope $\frac{3}{4}$, the slope of the parallel line must also be $\frac{3}{4}$. Use the slope and the given point in the point-slope form of a linear equation and then solve for y to write the equation in slope-intercept form.

$y - y_1 = m(x - x_1)$ Start with the point-slope form.
$y - 7 = \frac{3}{4}(x - 8)$ Substitute (8, 7) for (x_1, y_1) and $\frac{3}{4}$ for m.
$y - 7 = \frac{3}{4}x - 6$ Distributive Property
$y = \frac{3}{4}x + 1$ Add 7 to each side.

The graph of $y = \frac{3}{4}x + 1$ passes through (8, 7) and is parallel to the graph of $y = \frac{3}{4}x + 2$.

Exercises

1. **Writing** Are the graphs of $y = \frac{2}{3}x + 3$ and $y = \frac{3}{2}x - 4$ parallel? Explain how you know.
No, because the slopes $\frac{2}{3}$ and $\frac{3}{2}$ are not equal.

Write an equation in slope-intercept form of the line that passes through the given point and is parallel to the graph of the given equation.

2. (3, 1); $y = 2x + 4$
$y = 2x - 5$

3. (1, 3); $y = 7x + 5$
$y = 7x - 4$

4. (1, 6); $y = 9x - 5$
$y = 9x - 3$

5. (0, 0); $y = -\frac{1}{2}x - 4$
$y = -\frac{1}{2}x$

6. (−5, 7); $y = -\frac{2}{5}x - 3$
$y = -\frac{2}{5}x + 5$

7. (6, 6); $y = \frac{1}{4}x - 1$
$y = \frac{1}{4}x + 4$

All-in-One Resources/Online
English Language Learner Support

5-6 ELL Support
Parallel and Perpendicular Lines

Use the list below to complete the Venn diagram.

A vertical line and a horizontal line	Equation can be written in slope-intercept form	Lines in the same plane that never intersect
Lines that intersect to form right angles	Nonvertical lines that have the same slope and different y-intercepts	Slopes are opposite reciprocals.
Two nonvertical lines that have a product of −1 for their slopes	You can determine the relationship between two lines by comparing their slopes and y-intercepts.	Vertical lines that have different x-intercepts

Parallel Lines — **Perpendicular Lines**

Lines in the same plane that never intersect;
Nonvertical lines that have the same slope and different y-intercepts;
Vertical lines that have different x-intercepts

You can determine the relationship between two lines by comparing their slopes and y-intercepts. Equation can be written in slope-intercept form

Lines that intersect to form right angles;
Two nonvertical lines that have a product of −1 for their slopes;
A vertical line and a horizontal line;
Slopes are opposite reciprocals.

Differentiated Remediation *continued*

On-Level

- **Practice** (2 pages) Provides extra practice for each lesson. For simpler practice exercises, use the Form K Practice pages found in the All-in-One Teaching Resources and online.

- **Think About a Plan** Helps students develop specific problem-solving skills and strategies by providing scaffolded guiding questions.

- **Standardized Test Prep** Focuses on all major exercises, all major question types, and helps students prepare for the high-stakes assessments.

Extension

- **Enrichment** Provides students with interesting problems and activities that extend the concepts of the lesson.

- **Activities, Games, and Puzzles** Worksheets that can be used for concepts development, enrichment, and for fun!

Practice and Problem Solving WKBK/ All-in-One Resources/Online
Practice page 1

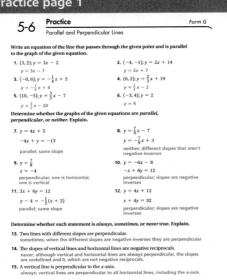

Practice and Problem Solving WKBK/ All-in-One Resources/Online
Practice page 2

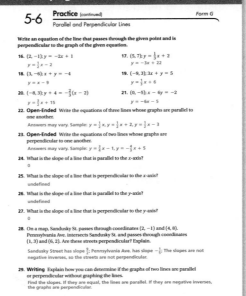

All-in-One Resources/Online
Enrichment

Practice and Problem Solving WKBK/ All-in-One Resources/Online
Think About a Plan

Practice and Problem Solving WKBK/ All-in-One Resources/Online
Standardized Test Prep

Online Teacher Resource Center
Activities, Games, and Puzzles

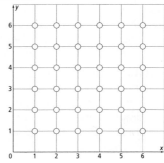

5-7 Scatter Plots and Trend Lines

Objectives To write an equation of a trend line and of a line of best fit
To use a trend line and a line of best fit to make predictions

Dynamic Activity
Exploring
Correlation

Lesson Vocabulary
• scatter plot
• positive correlation
• negative correlation
• no correlation
• trend line
• interpolation
• extrapolation
• line of best fit
• correlation coefficient
• causation

SOLVE IT!

Getting Ready!

The number of digital albums downloaded has an effect on CD sales.

The table shows the number of digital albums downloaded per year and the number of CDs sold by manufacturers per year. What relationship exists between the two sets of data? Predict the number of CDs sold and the number of albums downloaded in 2010. Explain your reasoning.

Music Sales

Year	Albums Downloaded (millions)	CDs Sold (millions)
2004	4.6	767
2005	13.6	705.4
2006	27.6	619.7
2007	42.5	511.1

Source: Recording Industry Association of America

In the Solve It, the number of albums downloaded per year and the number of CDs sold per year are related.

Essential Understanding You can determine whether two sets of numerical data are related by graphing them as ordered pairs. If the two sets of data are related, you may be able to use a line to estimate or predict values.

A **scatter plot** is a graph that relates two different sets of data by displaying them as ordered pairs. Most scatter plots are in the first quadrant of the coordinate plane because the data are usually positive numbers.

You can use scatter plots to find trends in data. The scatter plots below show the three types of relationships that two sets of data may have.

When y tends to increase as x increases, the two sets of data have a **positive correlation**.

When y tends to decrease as x increases, the two sets of data have a **negative correlation**.

When x and y are not related, the two sets of data have **no correlation**.

PowerAlgebra.com | Lesson 5-7 Scatter Plots and Trend Lines | 333

5-7 Preparing to Teach

BIG idea Modeling UbD

ESSENTIAL UNDERSTANDINGS
• Graphing ordered pairs is a way to determine whether two sets of numerical data are related.
• If two sets of data are related, it may be possible to use a line to estimate or predict values.

Math Background
Real-world data, when graphed, rarely falls exactly along a line. Data are classified as linear if the points approximate a line on a graph. When this is the case, there are techniques to approximate an equation for a line of "best fit." Graphing calculators make this task easier by correlating equations of "best fit' with actual entered data.

Statistics is the branch of mathematics concerned with the collection, analysis, interpretation, and presentation of numerical data. Linear regression, which produces a line of best fit, is an important statistical technique that is widely used in all sciences to describe relationships between variables. It ranks as one of the most important tools used in these disciplines.

Support Student Learning
Use the **Algebra I Companion** to engage and support students during instruction. See Lesson Resources at the end of this lesson for details.

1 Interactive Learning

Solve It!
PURPOSE To analyze data whose scatter plot is best represented with a linear equation
PROCESS Students may determine an "average" rise and run for the data in the table and use it to make predictions, or students may graph the data and determine the coordinates of the next ordered pair by visual inspection.

FACILITATE
Q If you plotted the data, letting the number of downloaded albums be the independent variable and the number of CDs sold be the dependent variable, what general shape would the points make? **[In general, the data points would fall on a line going down to the right.]**

Q Is there a constant rate of change in the data? Explain. **[No, the slope calculated between different pairs of points is different.]**

Q How could you determine one slope that best describes the rate of change of the data? **[Answers may vary. Sample: You could find an average slope using the slopes, such as the first and the last ordered pair.]**

ANSWER See Solve It in Answers on next page.
CONNECT THE MATH In the Solve It, data points were examined to determine a relationship among the data points. In the lesson, students make scatter plots and examine trend lines for those data sets.

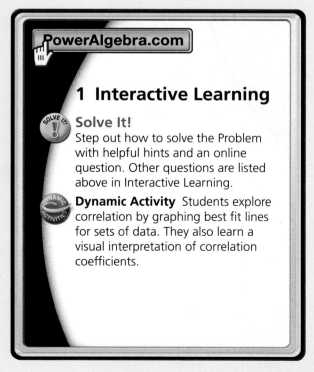

PowerAlgebra.com

1 Interactive Learning

Solve It!
Step out how to solve the Problem with helpful hints and an online question. Other questions are listed above in Interactive Learning.

Dynamic Activity Students explore correlation by graphing best fit lines for sets of data. They also learn a visual interpretation of correlation coefficients.

2 Guided Instruction

Problem 1

> **Q** Does the temperature always show a decrease as the altitude increases? Explain. **[No, but generally it shows a decrease.]**
>
> **Q** How can your knowledge of negative slope help you remember the meaning of the term *negative correlation*? **[Points that are negatively correlated resemble a line that has negative slope.]**
>
> **Q** If the temperature was plotted on the horizontal axis and the altitude was plotted on the vertical axis, would the data still be negatively correlated? **[No, the data would have a positive correlation.]**

Got It?

Ask students to identify two dependent variables that, when paired with the independent variable "population of a city," would result in a positive correlation and a negative correlation, respectively.

Problem 1 Making a Scatter Plot and Describing Its Correlation

Temperature The table shows the altitude of an airplane and the temperature outside the plane.

Plane Altitude and Outside Temperature										
Altitude (m)	0	500	1000	1500	2000	2500	3000	3500	4000	4500	5000
Temperature (°F)	59.0	59.2	61.3	55.5	41.6	29.8	29.9	18.1	26.2	12.4	0.6

Think

The highest altitude is 5000 m. So a reasonable scale on the altitude axis is 0 to 5500 with every 1000 m labeled. You can use similar reasoning to label the temperature axis.

A Make a scatter plot of the data.

Treat the data as ordered pairs. For the altitude of 1500 m and the temperature of 55.5°F, plot (1500, 55.5).

B What type of relationship does the scatter plot show?

The temperature outside the plane tends to decrease as the altitude of the plane increases. So the data have a negative correlation.

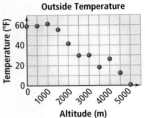

Plane Altitude and Outside Temperature

✓ **Got It?** **1. a.** Make a scatter plot of the data in the table below. What type of relationship does the scatter plot show?

Gasoline Purchases								
Dollars Spent	10	11	9	10	13	5	8	4
Gallons Bought	2.5	2.8	2.3	2.6	3.3	1.3	2.2	1.1

b. Reasoning Consider the population of a city and the number of letters in the name of the city. Would you expect a *positive correlation*, a *negative correlation*, or *no correlation* between the two sets of data? Explain your reasoning.

When two sets of data have a positive or negative correlation, you can use a trend line to show the correlation more clearly. A **trend line** is a line on a scatter plot, drawn near the points, that shows a correlation.

You can use a trend line to estimate a value between two known data values or to predict a value outside the range of known data values. **Interpolation** is estimating a value between two known values. **Extrapolation** is predicting a value outside the range of known values.

Answers

Solve It!

As the number of albums downloaded increases, the number of CDs sold decreases; about 80 million albums downloaded, about 250 million CDs sold; explanations may vary.

Got It?

1. a.

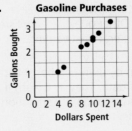

Gasoline Purchases

positive correlation

b. No correlation; the length of a city's name and the population are not related.

PowerAlgebra.com

2 Guided Instruction

Each Problem is worked out and supported online.

Problem 1
Making a Scatter Plot and Describing Its Correlation
Animated

Problem 2
Writing an Equation of a Trend Line
Animated

Problem 3
Finding the Line of Best Fit

Problem 4
Identifying Whether Relationships are Causal
Animated

Support in Algebra 1 Companion
• Vocabulary
• Key Concepts
• Got It?

Problem 2 Writing an Equation of a Trend Line

Biology Make a scatter plot of the data at the right. What is the approximate weight of a 7-month-old panda?

Weight of a Panda

Age (months)	Weight (lb)
1	2.5
2	7.6
3	12.5
4	17.1
6	24.3
8	37.9
10	49.2
12	54.9

Step 1 Make a scatter plot and draw a trend line. Estimate the coordinates of two points on the line.

Plan

How do you draw an accurate trend line?
An accurate trend line should fit the data closely. There should be about the same number of points above the line as below it.

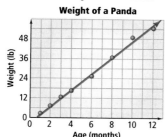

Weight of a Panda

Two points on the trend line are (4, 17.1) and (8, 37.9).

Step 2 Write an equation of the trend line.

$m = \frac{y_2 - y_1}{x_2 - x_1} = \frac{37.9 - 17.1}{8 - 4} = \frac{20.8}{4} = 5.2$ Find the slope of the trend line.

$y - y_1 = m(x - x_1)$ Use point-slope form.

$y - 17.1 = 5.2(x - 4)$ Substitute 5.2 for m and (4, 17.1) for (x_1, y_1).

$y - 17.1 = 5.2x - 20.8$ Distributive Property

$y = 5.2x - 3.7$ Add 17.1 to each side.

Step 3 Estimate the weight of a 7-month-old panda.

$y = 5.2(7) - 3.7$ Substitute 7 for x.

$y = 32.7$ Simplify.

Think

How can you check the reasonableness of your answer?
Since $x = 7$ is visible on the graph, find its corresponding y-value. When $x = 7$, $y \approx 32.7$. So the estimate is reasonable.

The weight of a 7-month-old panda is about 32.7 lb.

Got It? 2. a. Make a scatter plot of the data below. Draw a trend line and write its equation. What is the approximate body length of a 7-month-old panda?

Body Length of a Panda

Age (month)	1	2	3	4	5	6	8	9
Body Length (in.)	8.0	11.75	15.5	16.7	20.1	22.2	26.5	29.0

b. Reasoning Do you think you can use your model to extrapolate the body length of a 3-year-old panda? Explain.

Problem 2

Q Your friend thinks that the best trend line is one that intersects the most data points. Is he correct? Explain. **[No, the line might not be the best fit if it does not take into account the number of data points that fall below and above the line.]**

Q Do you need to intersect at least two data points so that you have two points to use when writing the equation of the line? Explain. **[No, you can use any two points on the line that you draw. The points do not need to be data points.]**

Q What does the y-intercept of the trend line represent? **[The number of Calories needed by a newborn.]**

Got It?   ERROR PREVENTION

Tell students to use the meanings of the words *exterior* and *interior* to help remember the difference between extrapolating data and interpolating data using a trend line.

Additional Problems

1. The table shows the amount of time spent studying for a final exam by 8 students and the grades that they earned.

Study Time vs. Grade

Study Time (hours)	Grade Earned
7	88
3	79
5	92
1	71
0	62
6	94
4	82
2	65

a. Make a scatter plot of the data.

b. What type of relationship does the scatter plot show?

ANSWER

a.

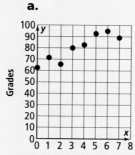

b. positive relationship

Additional Problems 2–4.
See next page.

Answers

Got It? (continued)

2. a. Answers may vary. Sample:

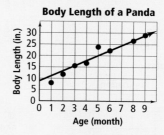

Body Length of a Panda

$y = 2.23x + 8.8$; about 24.4 in.

b. No; an adult panda does not grow at the same rate as a young panda.

Problem 3

Q By visual inspection of the table, will the slope of the line of best fit be positive or negative? Explain. **[Positive; both the dependent variable and the independent variable are increasing.]**

Q Will the correlation coefficient be a positive or a negative number? Explain. **[It will be positive because the data appears to be positively correlated.]**

Q What does the slope of the line of best fit represent? **[the approximate increase in cost per year]**

Q If the trend continues, in what academic year will the tuition and fees at a public 4-year college be approximately $10,780? **[2018-2019]**

The trend line that shows the relationship between two sets of data most accurately is called the **line of best fit.** A graphing calculator computes the equation of the line of best fit using a method called linear regression.

The graphing calculator also gives you the **correlation coefficient** r, a number from -1 to 1, that tells you how closely the equation models the data.

$$r = -1 \quad\quad r = 0 \quad\quad r = 1$$
strong negative correlation   no correlation   strong positive correlation

The nearer r is to 1 or -1, the more closely the data cluster around the line of best fit. If r is near 1, the data lie close to a line of best fit with positive slope. If r is near -1, the data lie close to a line of best fit with negative slope.

Problem 3 Finding the Line of Best Fit

College Tuition Use a graphing calculator to find the equation of the line of best fit for the data at the right. What is the correlation coefficient to three decimal places? Predict the cost of attending in the 2012–2013 academic year.

Step 1 Press **stat**. From the **EDIT** menu, choose **Edit**. Enter the years into L_1. Let $x = 2000$ represent academic year 2000–2001, $x = 2001$ represent 2001–2002, and so on. Enter the costs into L_2.

Step 2 Press **stat**. Choose **LinReg(ax + b)** from the **CALC** menu. Press **enter** to find the equation of the line of best fit and the correlation coefficient. The calculator uses the form $y = ax + b$ for the equation.

Average Tuition and Fees at Public 4-Year Colleges

Academic Year	Cost ($)
2000–2001	3508
2001–2002	3766
2002–2003	4098
2003–2004	4645
2004–2005	5126
2005–2006	5492
2006–2007	5836

Source: The College Board

LinReg
y = ax + b
a = 409.4285714 — slope
b = -815446.7143 — y-intercept
r^2 = .9919891076
r = .9959864997 — correlation coefficient

Think

What does the value of the correlation coefficient mean?
The correlation coefficient of 0.996 is close to 1. So there is a strong positive correlation between the academic year and the cost of attending college.

Round to the nearest hundredth. The equation of the line of best fit is $y = 409.43x - 815,446.71$. The correlation coefficient is about 0.996.

Step 3 Predict the cost of attending in the 2012–2013 academic year.

$y = 409.43x - 815,446.71$ Use the equation of the line of best fit.
$y = 409.43(2012) - 815,446.71$ Substitute 2012 for x.
$y \approx 8326$ Simplify. Round to the nearest whole number.

The cost of attending a four-year public college in the 2012–2013 academic year is predicted to be about $8326.

Additional Problems
(continued)

2. Make a scatter plot of the data below. Draw a trend line and write its equation. Use the equation to estimate the deer population in the 12th year of the study.

Deer Population Study

Year	Population
1	1260
2	1375
3	1310
4	1490
5	1625
6	1680
7	1740
8	1715

ANSWER $y = 75x + 1200$; 2100 deer

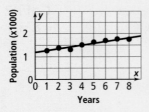

Years

3. Use a graphing calculator to find the equation of the line of best fit for the data below. What is the correlation coefficient to three decimal places? Predict the average heart rate (in beats per minute) after 12 minutes of jogging.

Heart Rate Study

Jogging Time (minutes)	Heart Rate (bpm)
1	81
2	84
3	86
4	91
5	97
6	102
7	108
8	112

ANSWER 0.992; about 130 bpm

4. In the following situations, is there likely to be a correlation? If so, does the correlation reflect a causal relationship? Explain.

a. the height of a student and the grade earned on a quiz

b. the price of bananas at a grocery store and the number of pounds of bananas bought

ANSWER a. no correlation; the height of a student has little to do with how well the student does on a quiz. **b.** correlation, causal as the price of bananas goes down, the pounds of bananas bought will increase. It is likely that a decrease in the price of bananas causes an increase in the sales of bananas; therefore, this is a causal relationship.

Got It? **3. a.** Predict the cost of attending in the 2016–2017 academic year.
b. **Reasoning** What does the slope of the line of best fit in Problem 3 tell you about the rate of change in the cost?

Causation is when a change in one quantity causes a change in a second quantity. A correlation between quantities does not always imply causation.

 Problem 4 **Identifying Whether Relationships Are Causal**

In the following situations, is there likely to be a correlation? If so, does the correlation reflect a causal relationship? Explain.

A the number of loaves of bread baked and the amount of flour used

There is a positive correlation and also a causal relationship. As the number of loaves of bread baked increases, the amount of flour used increases.

B the number of mailboxes and the number of firefighters in a city

There is likely to be a positive correlation because both the number of mailboxes and the number of firefighters tend to increase as the population of a city increases. However, installing more mailboxes will not *cause* the number of firefighters to increase, so there is no causal relationship.

Think

Causal relationships always have a correlation. However, two data sets that have a correlation may not have a causal relationship.

 Got It? **4.** In the following situations, is there likely to be a correlation? If so, does the correlation reflect a causal relationship? Explain.
a. the cost of a family's vacation and the size of their house
b. the time spent exercising and the number of Calories burned

Lesson Check

Do you know HOW?

Use the table.

Average Maximum Daily Temperature in January for Northern Latitudes							
Latitude (° N)	35	33	30	25	43	40	39
Temperature (°F)	46	52	67	76	32	37	44

SOURCE: U.S. Department of Commerce

1. Make a scatter plot of the data. What type of relationship does the scatter plot show?

2. Draw a trend line and write its equation.

3. Predict the average maximum daily temperature in January at a latitude of 50° N.

Do you UNDERSTAND?

4. **Vocabulary** Given a set of data pairs, how would you decide whether to use interpolation or extrapolation to find a certain value?

5. **Compare and Contrast** How are a trend line and the line of best fit for a set of data pairs similar? How are they different?

6. **Error Analysis** Refer to the table below. A student says that the data have a negative correlation because as x decreases, y also decreases. What is the student's error?

x	10	7	5	4	1	0
y	1	0	−2	−4	−7	−9

Got It?
Share with students how to use the calculator to plot the data as a scatter plot and graph the line of best fit onto the scatter plot.

Problem 4

Q What is a variable that would have neither a correlation nor a causal relationship with the number of pages in a book? **[Answers may vary. Sample: the number of copies of the book sold]**

Q What is a variable that will have both a correlation and a causal relationship with the number of mailboxes in a city? **[Answers may vary. Sample: the number of stops made by postal trucks in the city]**

Got It?   **VISUAL LEARNERS**
Use a Venn diagram to define the relationship between causation and correlation.

3 Lesson Check

Do you know HOW?
• If students have difficulty with Exercise 3, then have them review Problem 2.

Do you UNDERSTAND?
• If students have difficulty with Exercise 6, then suggest that they read the data in this table from right to left.

Close

Q How can predictions be made from correlated data? **[An equation of a line of best fit or a trend line can be used to make predictions.]**

Answers

Got It? (continued)

3. a. about $9964

b. The slope tells you that the cost increases at a rate of about $409.43 per year.

4. a. There may be a positive correlation, but it is not causal because a more expensive vacation does not cause a family to own a bigger house.

b. There is a positive correlation and a causal relationship. The more time you spend exercising, the more Calories you burn.

Lesson Check

1. **Average Maximum Daily Temperature in January for Northern Latitudes**

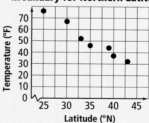

negative correlation

2–3. Answers may vary. Samples are given.

2. $y = -2x + 120$

3. about 20°F

4–6. See next page.

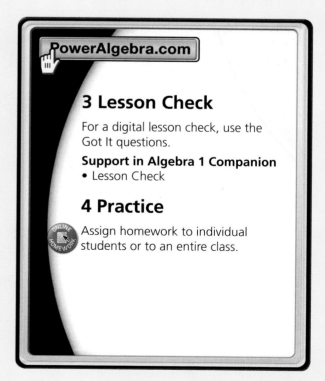

4 Practice

ASSIGNMENT GUIDE

Basic: 7–15, 16–20

Average: 7–15 odd, 16–21

Advanced: 7–15 odd, 16–22

Standardized Test Prep: 23–26

Mixed Review: 27–33

Reasoning exercises have blue headings.

Applications exercises have red headings.

EXERCISE 20: Use the Think About a Plan worksheet in the **Practice and Problem Solving Workbook** (also available in the Teaching Resources in print and online) to further support students' development in becoming independent learners.

HOMEWORK QUICK CHECK

To check students' understanding of key skills and concepts, go over Exercises 7, 13, 16, 19, and 20.

Practice and Problem-Solving Exercises

Ⓐ Practice

For each table, make a scatter plot of the data. Describe the type of correlation the scatter plot shows.

◀ See Problem 1.

7.

Jeans Sales				
Average Price ($)	21	28	36	40
Number Sold	130	112	82	65

8.

Gasoline Purchases					
Dollars Spent	10	11	9	8	13
Gallons Bought	2.6	3	2.4	2.2	3.5

Theme Parks Use the table below for Exercises 9 and 10.

◀ See Problem 2.

Attendance and Revenue at U.S. Theme Parks									
Year	1990	1992	1994	1996	1998	2000	2002	2004	2006
Attendance (millions)	253	267	267	290	300	317	324	328	335
Revenue (billions of dollars)	5.7	6.5	7.0	7.9	8.7	9.6	9.9	10.8	11.5

Source: International Association of Amusement Parks and Attractions

9. Make a scatter plot of the data pairs (year, attendance). Draw a trend line and write its equation. Estimate the attendance at U.S. theme parks in 2005.

10. Make a scatter plot of the data pairs (year, revenue). Draw a trend line and write its equation. Predict the revenue at U.S. theme parks in 2012.

11. Entertainment Use a graphing calculator to find the equation of the line of best fit for the data in the table. Find the value of the correlation coefficient r to three decimal places. Then predict the number of movie tickets sold in the U.S. in 2014.

◀ See Problem 3.

Movie Tickets Sold in U.S. by Year										
Year	1998	1999	2000	2001	2002	2003	2004	2005	2006	2007
Tickets Sold (millions)	1289	1311	1340	1339	1406	1421	1470	1415	1472	1470

Source: Motion Picture Association of America

In each situation, tell whether a correlation is likely. If it is, tell whether the correlation reflects a causal relationship. Explain your reasoning.

◀ See Problem 4.

12. the amount of time you study for a test and the score you receive

13. a person's height and the number of letters in the person's name

14. the shoe size and the salary of a teacher

15. the price of hamburger at a grocery store and the amount of hamburger sold

Ⓑ Apply

16. Open-Ended Describe three real-world situations: one with a positive correlation, one with a negative correlation, and one with no correlation.

Answers

Lesson Check (continued)

4. You use interpolation to estimate a value between two known values. You use extrapolation to predict a value outside the range of the known values.

5. Both the trend line and the line of best fit show a correlation between two sets of data. The line of best fit is the most accurate trend line.

6. If y decreases as x decreases, then there is a positive correlation because a trend line will have a positive slope.

Practice and Problem-Solving Exercises

7.

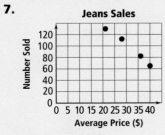

Jeans Sales

negative correlation

8.

Gasoline Purchases

positive correlation

9–10. Answers may vary. Samples are given.

9.

Attendance at U.S. Theme Parks

$y = 5x - 9690$; about 335 million

10.

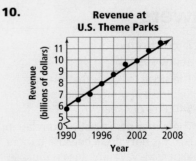

Revenue at U.S. Theme Parks

$y = 0.33x - 650.75$; about $13.2 billion

17. Writing Give two data sets that are correlated but do *not* have a causal relationship.

18. Business During one month at a local deli, the amount of ham sold decreased as the amount of turkey sold increased. Is this an example of *positive correlation*, *negative correlation*, or *no correlation*?

19. Think About a Plan Students measured the diameters and circumferences of the tops of a variety of cylinders. Below are the data that they collected. Estimate the diameter of a cylinder with circumference 22 cm.

Cylinder Tops									
Diameter (cm)	3	3	5	6	8	8	9.5	10	10	12
Circumference (cm)	9.3	9.5	16	18.8	25	25.6	29.5	31.5	30.9	39.5

- How can you use a scatter plot to find an equation of a trend line?
- How can you use the equation of the trend line to make an estimate?

20. U.S. Population Use the data below.

Estimated Population of the United States (thousands)							
Year	2000	2001	2002	2003	2004	2005	2006
Male	138,482	140,079	141,592	142,937	144,467	145,973	147,512
Female	143,734	145,147	146,533	147,858	149,170	150,533	151,886

Source: U.S. Census Bureau

a. Make a scatter plot of the data pairs (male population, female population).
b. Draw a trend line and write its equation.
c. Use your equation to predict the U.S. female population if the U.S. male population increases to 150,000,000.
d. Reasoning Consider a scatter plot of the data pairs (year, male population). Would it be reasonable to use this scatter plot to predict the U.S. male population in 2035? Explain your reasoning.

21. a. Graphing Calculator Use a graphing calculator to find the equation of the line of best fit for the data below. Let $x = 8$ represent 1998, $x = 9$ represent 1999, and so on.

U.S. Computer and Video Game Unit Sales										
Year	1998	1999	2000	2001	2002	2003	2004	2005	2006	2007
Unit Sales (in millions)	152.4	184.5	196.3	210.3	225.8	240.9	249.5	229.5	241.6	267.9

Source: The NPD Group/Retail Tracking Service

b. What is the slope of the line of best fit? What does the slope mean in terms of the number of computer and video game units sold?
c. What is the *y*-intercept of the line of best fit? What does the *y*-intercept mean in terms of the number of computer and video game units sold?

11. $y = 21.4x - 41557$; 0.942; 1542.6 million tickets

12. There is likely a correlation and a causal relationship, because the more you study, the better prepared you are for the test.

13. no correlation likely

14. no correlation likely

15. There is likely a correlation and a possible causal relationship, because the higher the price of hamburger, the less people are likely to buy.

16. Check students' work.

17. Check students' work.

18. negative correlation

19. about 7 cm

20. a.

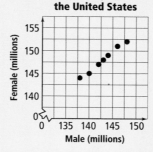

Estimated Population of the United States

Female (millions) vs Male (millions)

b–c. Answers may vary. Samples are given.

b. $y = 0.906x + 18173$

c. about 154,179,000

d. No; 2035 is too far in the future to predict. Growth rates may change by then.

21. a. $y = 10.5x + 88.2$

b. 10.5; the sales increase by about 10.5 million units each year.

c. 88.2; the estimated number of units sold in the year 1990

Answers

Practice and Problem-Solving Exercises (continued)

22. a.

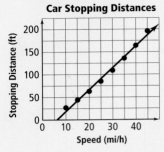

Car Stopping Distances

$y = 4.82x - 29.65$

b. about 404 ft

c. The relationship is not actually linear, so you cannot use the trend line to extrapolate the stopping distance for a speed of 90 mi/h.

d. The slope would increase and the y-intercept would decrease.

23. A

24. G

25. D

26. [2]

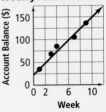

Weekly Account Balance

Using the points (1, 35) and (9, 136), the equation of the trend line is $y = 12.625x + 22.375$. So in week 6, the student has about $98.13 in the account. OR equivalent process

[1] appropriate methods, but with one calculation error

27. $y = 5x - 13$

28. $y = -x + 5$

29. $y = -\frac{2}{3}x + \frac{10}{3}$

30. 5

31. 0

32. 18

33. 12

 Challenge

22. a. Make a scatter plot of the data below. Then find the equation of the line of best fit. Draw the line of best fit on your scatter plot.

Car Stopping Distances								
Speed (mi/h)	10	15	20	25	30	35	40	45
Stopping Distance (ft)	27	44	63	85	109	136	164	196

b. Use your equation to predict the stopping distance at 90 mi/h.

c. Reasoning The actual stopping distance at 90 mi/h is close to 584 ft. Why do you think this distance is not close to your prediction?

d. Suppose you plot (90, 584) on your scatter plot. What effect would it have on the slope and y-intercept of the line of best fit you found in part (a)?

Standardized Test Prep

SAT/ACT

23. Suppose you survey each school in your state. What relationship would you expect between the number of students and the number of teachers in each school?

Ⓐ positive correlation   Ⓒ no correlation

Ⓑ negative correlation   Ⓓ none of the above

24. A horizontal line passes through (5, −2). Which other point is also on the line?

Ⓕ (5, 2)   Ⓖ (−5, −2)   Ⓗ (−5, 2)   Ⓘ (5, 0)

25. When 18 gal of water are pumped into an empty tank, the tank is filled to three fourths of its capacity. How many gallons of water does the tank hold?

Ⓐ 12   Ⓑ 13.5   Ⓒ 18.5   Ⓓ 24

Short Response

26. The table shows the balance of a student's bank account at various times. Estimate how much money is in the student's bank account in Week 6. Justify your answer.

Weekly Account Balance					
Week	1	3	4	7	9
Account Balance	$35	$68	$85	$105	$136

Mixed Review

Write an equation of the line in slope-intercept form that passes through the given point and is parallel to the graph of the given equation.   ◆ **See Lesson 5-6.**

27. $y = 5x + 1; (2, -3)$ **28.** $y = -x - 9; (0, 5)$ **29.** $2x + 3y = 9; (-1, 4)$

Get Ready! To prepare for Lesson 5-8, do Exercises 30–33.

Find each absolute value.   ◆ **See Lesson 1-5.**

30. $|2 - 7|$ **31.** $|7 - 7|$ **32.** $|56 - 38|$ **33.** $|-24 + 12|$

Additional Instructional Support

Algebra 1 Companion

Students can use the **Algebra 1 Companion** worktext (4 pages) as you teach the lesson. Use the Companion to support

- New Vocabulary
- Key Concepts
- Got It for each Problem
- Lesson Check

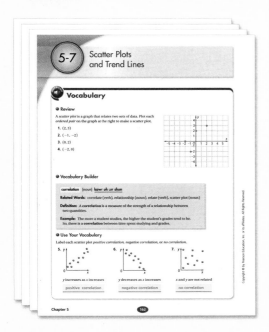

ELL Support

Focus on Language Write the lesson objectives on the board and read them aloud. Ask: What does it mean to *make predictions*? Have students skim the text for the meaning of a trend line and a line of best fit. Guide students to rephrase the objectives in their own words. Ask students to predict if it will rain that day. Offer other examples and ask students for some. Ask students how they made their predictions. What does it mean to predict? Confirm at the end of the lesson that the objectives were met.

5 Assess & Remediate

Lesson Quiz

1. **Do you UNDERSTAND?** The table shows the amount of time spent practicing the piano by 8 music students versus the number of mistakes that they made in their recital.

   Make a scatter plot of the data.

2. What type of relationship does the scatter plot show?

Practice Time vs. Mistakes Made

Practice Time (hours)	Mistakes Made
4	6
7	4
3	7
2	3
10	2
12	1
9	2
6	8

ANSWERS TO LESSON QUIZ

1.

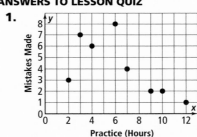

2. negative correlation

PRESCRIPTION FOR REMEDIATION

Use the student work on the Lesson Quiz to prescribe a differentiated review assignment.

Points	Differentiated Remediation
0	Intervention
1	On-level
2	Extension

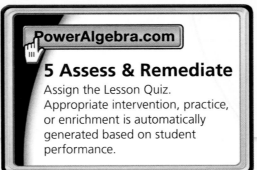

PowerAlgebra.com

5 Assess & Remediate

Assign the Lesson Quiz. Appropriate intervention, practice, or enrichment is automatically generated based on student performance.

Intervention

- **Reteaching** (2 pages) Provides reteaching and practice exercises for the key lesson concepts. Use with struggling students or absent students.
- **English Language Learner Support** Helps students develop and reinforce mathematical vocabulary and key concepts.

All-in-One Resources/Online
Reteaching

All-in-One Resources/Online
English Language Learner Support

Differentiated Remediation *continued*

On-Level

- **Practice** (2 pages) Provides extra practice for each lesson. For simpler practice exercises, use the Form K Practice pages found in the All-in-One Teaching Resources and online.

- **Think About a Plan** Helps students develop specific problem-solving skills and strategies by providing scaffolded guiding questions.

- **Standardized Test Prep** Focuses on all major exercises, all major question types, and helps students prepare for the high-stakes assessments.

Extension

- **Enrichment** Provides students with interesting problems and activities that extend the concepts of the lesson.

- **Activities, Games, and Puzzles** Worksheets that can be used for concepts development, enrichment, and for fun!

Practice and Problem Solving WKBK/ All-in-One Resources/Online
Practice page 1

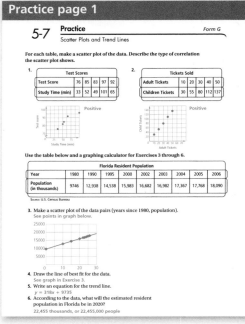

Practice and Problem Solving WKBK/ All-in-One Resources/Online
Practice page 2

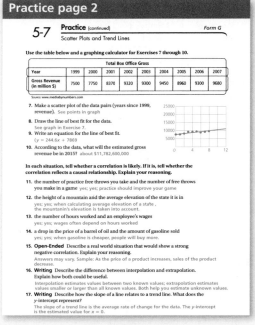

All-in-One Resources/Online
Enrichment

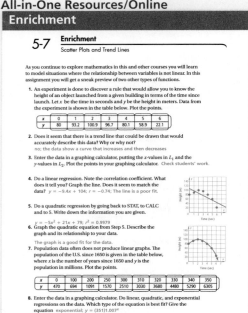

Practice and Problem Solving WKBK/ All-in-One Resources/Online
Think About a Plan

Practice and Problem Solving WKBK/ All-in-One Resources/Online
Standardized Test Prep

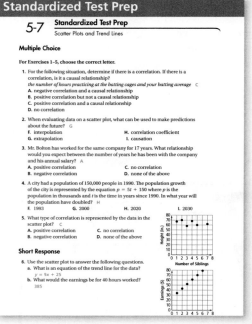

Online Teacher Resource Center
Activities, Games, and Puzzles

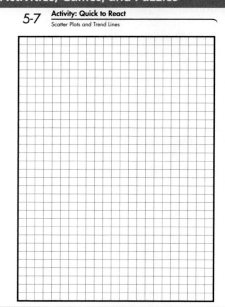

Concept Byte
Use With Lesson 5-7
Collecting Linear Data

In this activity, you will release a ball from different heights and record the maximum height after its first bounce. Complete this activity over a hard surface. Measure all heights from the bottom of the ball.

Activity

Place one end of a meter stick on the floor and tape it to the wall. Tape a second meter stick to the wall starting at the top of the first meter stick.

1. **Data Collection** Drop the ball from 50 cm. Carefully record its maximum height after the first bounce. Repeat.

2. Copy and complete the table at the right. You may make additional measurements using different starting heights.

3. Graph the data from both trials on the same coordinate plane.

4. **Reasoning** Why is it reasonable to use (0, 0) as a data point?

5. Draw a trend line that includes (0, 0).

6. **a. Predict** Use your line to predict the maximum height of the first bounce after the ball is dropped from 175 cm.
   b. From what height would you have to drop the ball for it to reach 2 m after the first bounce?

7. **a.** Use a graphing calculator to find the equation of the line of best fit for the data in the table.
   b. Predict Use your equation to predict the maximum height of the first bounce after the ball is dropped from 175 cm.
   c. How do your predictions from part (a) of Step 6 and part (b) of Step 7 compare?

Bounce Height Data

Initial Height (cm)	Maximum Height After First Bounce	
	Trial 1	Trial 2
50	▪	▪
100	▪	▪
150	▪	▪
200	▪	▪

Exercises

8. **Multiple Choice** The graph at the right shows the bounce data for a ball. Let x = the initial height in centimeters. Let y = the maximum height in centimeters. Which equation best models the data?

   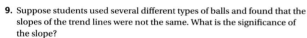 Ⓐ $y = 0.3x$ Ⓒ $y = 0.5x$
   Ⓑ $y = 0.4x$ Ⓓ $y = 0.6x$

9. Suppose students used several different types of balls and found that the slopes of the trend lines were not the same. What is the significance of the slope?

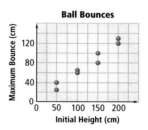

Ball Bounces

PowerAlgebra.com   Concept Byte   Collecting Linear Data   341

Guided Instruction

PURPOSE To write an equation and make predictions based on data collected from an experiment

PROCESS Students will
- conduct an experiment and collect and graph the data.
- make predictions based on the data collected.
- use a data set to form a prediction equation.

DISCUSS Emphasize to students the importance of accuracy when measuring the maximum heights of the balls and the impact on the experiment if not measured correctly.

Activity
In this activity students focus on collecting data from an experiment to help make predictions.

Q What variables impact the height of the ball? **[Answers will vary. Samples: type of ball used, firmness of floor]**

Q Why are the data points not all on the same line? **[Answers will vary. Samples: error in measurement, force of ball dropped, force of gravity is not linear]**

Answers

Activity

1–3. Check students' work.

4. A ball dropped from 0 cm will bounce 0 cm.

5–7. Check students' work.

Exercises

8. D

9. The greater the slope, the more bounce the ball has.

1 Interactive Learning

Solve It!
PURPOSE To visualize horizontal and vertical translations as a means of transforming one graph into another
PROCESS Students may use visual judgment, a physical model, or analyze equations of the lines.

FACILITATE
Q How does the equation of Line 1 compare to the equation of Line 2? **[The equations have the same slope, but different y-intercepts.]**
Q What is the vertical distance between the y-intercept of Line 1 and the y-intercept of Line 2? the horizontal distance? **[2 units, 6 units]**

ANSWER See Solve It in Answers on next page.
CONNECT THE MATH Students detect the vertical slide that maps Line 1 to Line 2, and then the horizontal slide. In the lesson, students learn to identify vertical and horizontal shifts by looking at the equations. Graphing will not be necessary to identify the translation.

2 Guided Instruction

Problem 1

Q What is one way you can visually compare the ordered pairs of the graphs of $y = |x|$ and $y = |x| - 2$? **[Answers may vary. Sample: Make a table of values.]**
Q How is the table of values for $y = |x| - 2$ related to the table of values for $y = |x|$? **[For matching x-values, the y-values for $y = |x| - 2$ are 2 less than the y-values for $y = |x|$.]**

Objectives To graph an absolute value function
To translate the graph of an absolute value function

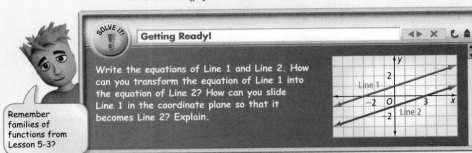

Remember families of functions from Lesson 5-3?

SOLVE IT Getting Ready!

Write the equations of Line 1 and Line 2. How can you transform the equation of Line 1 into the equation of Line 2? How can you slide Line 1 in the coordinate plane so that it becomes Line 2? Explain.

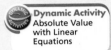

Dynamic Activity
Absolute Value with Linear Equations

Lesson Vocabulary
• absolute value function
• translation

In the Solve It you described how one line could be shifted to result in a second line. You can use a similar method to graph *absolute value functions*. An **absolute value function** has a V-shaped graph that opens up or down. The parent function for the family of absolute value functions is $y = |x|$.

A **translation** is a shift of a graph horizontally, vertically, or both. The result is a graph of the same size and shape, but in a different position.

Essential Understanding You can quickly graph absolute value equations by shifting the graph of $y = |x|$.

Problem 1 Describing Translations

Below are the graphs of $y = |x|$ and $y = |x| - 2$. How are the graphs related?

Plan
How can you compare the graphs? Look for the characteristics that you've studied with other graphs, such as shape, size, or individual points.

The graphs have the same shape. Notice each point on $y = |x| - 2$ is 2 units lower than the corresponding point on $y = |x|$. The graph of $y = |x| - 2$ is the graph of $y = |x|$ translated down 2 units.

BIG idea Function **UbD**
ESSENTIAL UNDERSTANDING
• Absolute value equations can be graphed quickly by shifting the graph of $y = |x|$.

Math Background
A family of functions is a group of functions with common characteristics. The parent function of each family is the function of simplest form. For absolute value functions, the parent function is $y = |x|$. In this lesson, translations of this parent function are studied.

Translation is one of three commonly used transformations. A translation is also called a slide. The following general forms reflect the different translations presented in this lesson.

$y = |x| + k$ is shifted up k units.
$y = |x| - k$ is shifted down k units.
$y = |x - h|$ is shifted right h units.
$y = |x + h|$ is shifted left h units.

Translations that include both horizontal and vertical shifts are not covered in this lesson but combine the general forms given above.

$y = |x - h| + k$ is shifted up k units and right h units.

Variations of this form follow according to the variations given above.

Support Student Learning
Use the **Algebra 1 Companion** to engage and support students during instructions. See Lesson Resources at the end of this lesson.

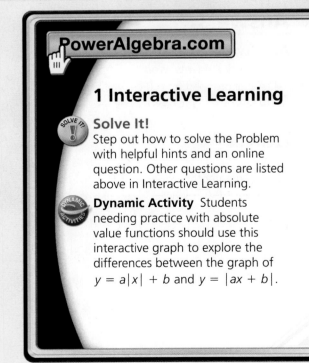

PowerAlgebra.com

1 Interactive Learning

Solve It!
Step out how to solve the Problem with helpful hints and an online question. Other questions are listed above in Interactive Learning.

Dynamic Activity Students needing practice with absolute value functions should use this interactive graph to explore the differences between the graph of $y = a|x| + b$ and $y = |ax + b|$.

Got It? **1. a.** How is the graph at the right related to the graph of $y = |x|$?

b. Reasoning What are the domain and range of each function in Problem 1?

The graph of $y = |x| + k$ is a translation of $y = |x|$. Let k be a positive number. Then $y = |x| + k$ translates the graph of $y = |x|$ up k units, while $y = |x| - k$ translates the graph of $y = |x|$ down k units.

 Problem 2 **Graphing a Vertical Translation**

What is the graph of $y = |x| + 2$?

Know	Need	Plan
• The equation of an absolute value function • The graph of $y = |x|$	The graph of the function	Identify the direction and amount of the translation. Translate the y-intercept point and one point on each side of it. Draw the graph.

Think

Why start with the graph of $y = |x|$?
Since $y = |x|$ is the parent function of $y = |x| + 2$, you can start with the graph of $y = |x|$ and shift it up.

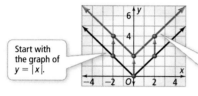

Start with the graph of $y = |x|$.

Draw the graph of $y = |x| + 2$ by translating the graph of $y = |x|$ up 2 units.

 Got It? **2.** What is the graph of $y = |x| - 7$?

If you know the direction of a translation and the number of units the function is to be translated, you can write an equation to describe the translation.

Plan

How can you get started?
For an upward translation, start with the equation $y = |x| + k$.
For a downward translation, start with the equation $y = |x| - k$.

Problem 3 **Writing Equations of Vertical Translations**

What is an equation for each translation of $y = |x|$?

A 11 units up

An equation is $y = |x| + 11$.

B 14 units down

An equation is $y = |x| - 14$.

 Got It? **3.** What is an equation for each translation of $y = |x|$?

a. 8 units up

b. 5 units down

Got It?

Tell students to examine each of the axes in the coordinate plane to determine the domain and the range. For the domain, students should note that all coordinates on the x-axis correspond to a point on the graph. For the range, students should note that some coordinates on the y-axis correspond to a point on the graph.

Problem 2

Q What are the two methods you can use to produce the graph of $y = |x| + 2$? Which method do you prefer? **[Answers may vary. Sample: Make a table of values or use a translation. Translation. It is faster.]**

Q Without graphing, how can you determine the y-intercept of an absolute value equation by visual inspection? **[The y-intercept is the number added to the absolute value term.]**

Got It?

Q What does the constant term in the equation tell you about the graph of $y = |x| - 7$ compared to the graph of $y = |x|$? **[The graph is translated down 7 units from the graph of $y = |x|$.]**

Problem 3

Q How can you describe the graph of $y = |x| + 11$ related to its parent graph? **[The graph of $y = |x| + 11$ is 11 units above its parent graph.]**

Q Is the graph of $y = |x| - 14$ the same as the graph of $y = |x| + (-14)$? Explain. **[Yes, subtraction can be rewritten as addition.]**

Got It?

Q What are the y-intercepts of each graph? **[The y-intercepts are 8 and −5 respectively.]**

---

2 Guided Instruction

Each Problem is worked out and supported online.

Problem 1
Describing Translations

Problem 2
Graphing a Vertical Translation
Animated

Problem 3
Writing Equations of Vertical Translations

Problem 4
Graphing a Horizontal Translation
Animated

Problem 5
Writing Equations of Horizontal Translations
Animated

Support in Algebra 1 Companion
• Vocabulary
• Key Concepts
• Got It?

Answers

Solve It!

$y = \frac{1}{3}x + 1$; $y = \frac{1}{3}x - 1$; subtract 2 from the y-intercept; slide the line down 2 units. Explanations may vary.

Got It?

1. a. The graph is the graph of $y = |x|$ translated 4 units up.

b. The domain of both graphs is all real numbers. The range of $y = |x|$ is $y \geq 0$. The range of $y = |x| - 2$ is $y \geq -2$.

2.

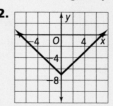

3. a. $y = |x| + 8$

b. $y = |x| - 5$

Problem 4

> **Q** Is the graph of $y = |x + 5|$ a horizontal or vertical translation? Explain. **[horizontal; the "+5" is inside the absolute value function.]**

Got It?   VISUAL LEARNERS

Have students identify how the equation in Problem 4 differs from the equation in the Got It.

Problem 5

> **Q** In 5B, what is the equation written in the general form for a horizontal translation? **[$y = |x - (-4)|$]**

Got It?   ERROR PREVENTION

Students may assume that because positive x-values are on the right side of the graph, an equation of the form $y = |x + h|$ should represent a translation to the right. But the sign of the constant term represents a translation in the opposite of the intuitively expected direction.

3 Lesson Check

Do you know HOW?

- If students have difficulty with Exercises 1–3, then remind them to use the equations to check points on the graphs.

Do you UNDERSTAND?

- If students have difficulty with Exercise 5, then have them review the graph at the top of p. 344.

Close

> **Q** What is the difference between a horizontal translation and a vertical translation? **[A vertical translation moves the graph up or down. A horizontal translation moves the graph to the left or to the right.]**

The graphs below show what happens when you graph $y = |x + 2|$ and $y = |x - 2|$.

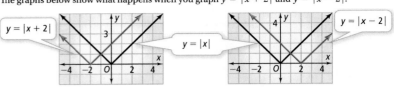

For a positive number h, $y = |x + h|$ translates the graph of $y = |x|$ left h units, and $y = |x - h|$ translates the graph of $y = |x|$ right h units.

Problem 4 Graphing a Horizontal Translation

What is the graph of $y = |x + 5|$?

Think
How can you check that the graph is correct?
You can use the equation to check that points on the graph are solutions.

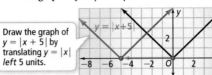

Draw the graph of $y = |x + 5|$ by translating $y = |x|$ left 5 units.

✓ **Got It?** **4.** What is the graph of $y = |x - 5|$?

Problem 5 Writing Equations of Horizontal Translations

What is an equation for each translation of $y = |x|$?

Plan
How can you get started?
To translate right, start with the equation $y = |x - h|$. To translate left, start with the equation $y = |x + h|$.

A 9 units right
An equation is $y = |x - 9|$.

B 4 units left
An equation is $y = |x + 4|$.

✓ **Got It?** **5.** What is an equation for each translation of $y = |x|$?
  a. 8 units right   **b.** 6 units left

✓ Lesson Check

Do you know HOW?

1. How is the graph of $y = |x| - 8$ different from the graph of $y = |x|$? How is it the same?

2. What is the equation for the translation of $y = |x|$ 9 units up?

3. What is the graph of $y = |x + 7|$?

Do you UNDERSTAND?

4. **Compare and Contrast** How are the graphs of $y = |x| - 4$ and $y = |x - 4|$ the same? How are they different?

5. **Error Analysis** A student is graphing the equation $y = |x - 10|$ and translates the graph of $y = |x|$ 10 units left. Describe the student's error.

Additional Problems

1. Below are the graphs of $y = |x|$ and $y = |x| + 2$. How are the graphs related?

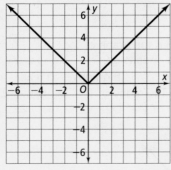

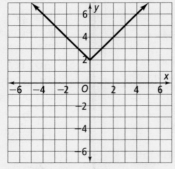

ANSWER The graph of $y = |x| + 2$ is the graph of $y = |x|$ shifted 2 units up.

2. What is the graph of $y = |x| - 3$?

ANSWER

3. What is an equation for each translation of $y = |x|$?
  a. 7 units up
  b. 5 units down

  ANSWER a. $y = |x| + 7$
  b. $y = |x| - 5$

4. What is the graph of $y = |x - 3|$?

ANSWER

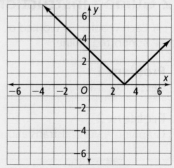

5. What is an equation for each translation of $y = |x|$?
  a. 4 units right
  b. 6 units left

  ANSWER a. $y = |x - 4|$
  b. $y = |x + 6|$

Practice and Problem-Solving Exercises

 Practice

Describe how each graph is related to the graph of $y = |x|$.
See Problem 1.

6.

7.

8.

Graph each function by translating $y = |x|$.
See Problem 2.

9. $y = |x| - 3$ **10.** $y = |x| + 7$ **11.** $y = |x| + 3$

12. $y = |x| - 6$ **13.** $y = |x| + 6$ **14.** $y = |x| - 2.5$

Write an equation for each translation of $y = |x|$.
See Problem 3.

15. 9 units up   **16.** 7 units down   **17.** 0.25 unit up

18. 3.25 units down   **19.** 5.9 units up   **20.** 1 unit down

Graph each function by translating $y = |x|$.
See Problem 4.

21. $y = |x - 3|$ **22.** $y = |x + 3|$ **23.** $y = |x - 1|$

24. $y = |x + 6|$ **25.** $y = |x - 7|$ **26.** $y = |x + 2.5|$

Write an equation for each translation of $y = |x|$.
See Problem 5.

27. left 9 units   **28.** right 9 units   **29.** right 0.5 unit

30. left $\frac{3}{2}$ units   **31.** left $\frac{5}{2}$ units   **32.** right 8.2 units

 Apply

At the right is the graph of $y = -|x|$. Graph each function by translating $y = -|x|$.

33. $y = -|x| + 3$ **34.** $y = -|x| - 3$

35. $y = -|x + 3|$ **36.** $y = -|x - 3|$

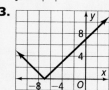

Write an equation for each translation of $y = -|x|$.

37. 2 units up   **38.** 2.25 units left

39. 15 units down   **40.** 4 units right

41. Writing Explain how the relationship between $y = |x|$ and $y = |x| + k$ is similar to the relationship between $y = mx$ and $y = mx + b$.

42. Reasoning Make a table of values for $y = |x|$ and $y = |x| + 5$. How do the y-values for corresponding x-values compare?

Answers

Got It? (continued)

4.
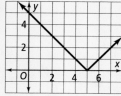

5. a. $y = |x - 8|$
   b. $y = |x + 6|$

Lesson Check

1. $y = |x| - 8$ is $y = |x|$ translated 8 units down; the graphs have the same shape.

2. $y = |x| + 9$

3.
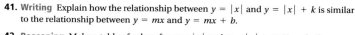
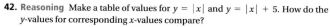

4. The graphs have the same shape; $y = |x| - 4$ is $y = |x|$ translated 4 units down and $y = |x - 4|$ is $y = |x|$ translated 4 units right.

5. The student should translate the graph 10 units to the right.

Practice and Problem-Solving Exercises

6–42. See back of book.

4 Practice

ASSIGNMENT GUIDE

Basic: 6–32 all, 34–42 even, 43–44

Average: 7–31 odd, 33–47

Advanced: 7–31 odd, 33–49

Standardized Test Prep: 50–53

Mixed Review: 54–59

Reasoning exercises have blue headings.

Applications exercises have red headings.

EXERCISE 44: Use the Think About a Plan worksheet in the **Practice and Problem Solving Workbook** (also available in the Teaching Resources in print and online) to further support students' development in becoming independent learners.

HOMEWORK QUICK CHECK

To check students' understanding of key skills and concepts, go over Exercises 11, 29, 42, 43, and 44.

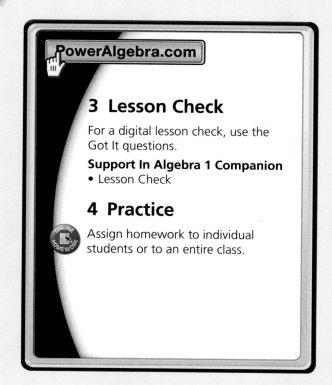

PowerAlgebra.com

3 Lesson Check

For a digital lesson check, use the Got It questions.

Support In Algebra 1 Companion
• Lesson Check

4 Practice

Assign homework to individual students or to an entire class.

Answers

Practice and Problem-Solving Exercises (continued)

43. $(-1, 3)$

44. $(-2, 5)$ and $(5, 2)$

45.

It is a translation of $y = |x|$ up 2 units and right 1 unit.

46.

It is a translation of $y = |x|$ down 1 unit and left 2 units.

47. a.

b. $(2, 3)$

c. The x-coordinate is the horizontal translation and the y-coordinate is the vertical translation; (h, k).

48. a.

x	y
-2	4
-1	2
0	0
1	2
2	4

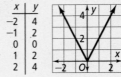

b.

c.

d.

---

43. Think About a Plan What point(s) do the graphs of $y = |x - 2|$ and $y = |x + 4|$ have in common?
- How are these graphs related?
- Could a graph or a table help you solve this problem?

44. What point(s) do the graphs of $y = -|x| + 7$ and $y = |x - 3|$ have in common?

Graph each translation of $y = |x|$. Describe how the graph is related to the graph of $y = |x|$.

45. $y = |x - 1| + 2$

46. $y = |x + 2| - 1$

47. a. Graph $y = |x - 2| + 3$.
b. The *vertex* of an absolute value function is the point at which its graph changes direction. What is the vertex of the graph of $y = |x - 2| + 3$?
c. Reasoning What relationship do you see between the vertex and the equation? What is the vertex of the graph of $y = |x - h| + k$?

Ⓒ Challenge

48. a. Graph $y = |2x|$ by making a table of values.
b. Translate $y = |2x|$ to graph $y = |2x| + 3$.
c. Translate $y = |2x|$ to graph $y = |2(x - 1)|$.
d. Translate $y = |2x|$ to graph $y = |2(x - 1)| + 3$.

49. Graph $y = -|x + 4| - 7$.

Standardized Test Prep

GRIDDED RESPONSE

SAT/ACT

50. For $f(x) = 5x - 7$, what value of x gives $f(x) = -3$?

51. What is the slope of the line at the right?

52. What is the value of $f(x) = x^2 - 4x + 6$ when $x = -3$?

53. What is the x-intercept of the line $y = -4x + 2$?

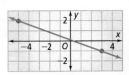

Mixed Review

The data below follow a linear model. Write an equation of a trend line or use a graphing calculator to find an equation of the line of best fit.

See Lesson 5-7.

54.

Year	1	2	3	4
Price	$5.30	$5.57	$5.82	$6.05

55.

Ounces	8	12	16	20
Calories	100	151	202	250

Get Ready! To prepare for Lesson 6-1, do Exercises 56–59.

Graph each equation.

See Lesson 5-3.

56. $y = 2x - 1$

57. $y = -3x + 5$

58. $y = \frac{1}{3}x + 2$

59. $y = -\frac{5}{2}x - 7$

49.

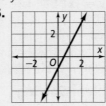

50. $\frac{4}{5}$ **51.** $-\frac{3}{8}$ **52.** 27 **53.** $\frac{1}{2}$

54–55. Answers may vary. Samples are given.

54. $y = 0.25x + 5.05$

55. $y = 12.5x$

56.

57.

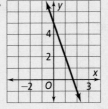

58.

59.

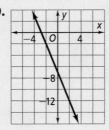

Additional Instructional Support

Algebra 1 Companion

Students can use the **Algebra 1 Companion** worktext (4 pages) as you teach the lesson. Use the Companion to support

- New Vocabulary
- Key Concepts
- Got It for each Problem
- Lesson Check

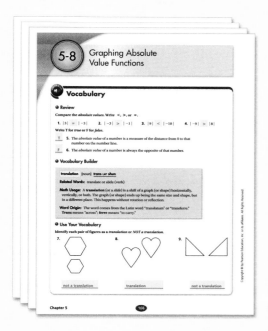

ELL Support

Use Role Playing Demonstrate vertical and horizontal motion by sliding an object across a table or moving it up and down in the air. Motion with your hands to demonstrate both directions. Relate horizontal to the horizon.

Use Graphic Organizers Have students work in pairs of mixed abilities to make a Venn diagram, labeling one circle $y = |x| + 2$ and the other $y = |x + 2|$. Tell them to write all the similarities between the equations in the overlapping area and differences in the rest of each circle. Discuss their results, verifying each statement thoroughly, creating an accurate diagram on the board that students can copy and use for later review.

5 Assess & Remediate

Lesson Quiz

1. Do you UNDERSTAND? Below are the graphs of $y = |x|$ and $y = |x| - 1$. How are the graphs related?

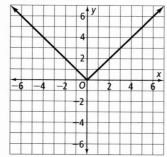

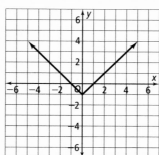

2. What is an equation for the translation of $y = |x|$ down 8 units?

3. What is an equation for the translation of $y = |x|$ left 7 units?

ANSWERS TO LESSON QUIZ

1. The graph of $y = |x| - 1$ is the graph of $y = |x|$ shifted down 1 unit.

2. $y = |x| - 8$

3. $y = |x + 7|$

PRESCRIPTION FOR REMEDIATION

Use the student work on the Lesson Quiz to prescribe a differentiated review assignment.

Points	Differentiated Remediation
0–1	Intervention
2	On-level
3	Extension

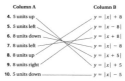

5 Assess & Remediate

Assign the Lesson Quiz. Appropriate intervention, practice, or enrichment is automatically generated based on student performance.

Intervention

- **Reteaching** (2 pages) Provides reteaching and practice exercises for the key lesson concepts. Use with struggling students or absent students.

- **English Language Learner Support** Helps students develop and reinforce mathematical vocabulary and key concepts.

All-in-One Resources/Online
Reteaching

5-8 **Reteaching**
Graphing Absolute Value Functions

The graph of $y = |x|$ is shown at the right.

The graph of $y = |x| + k$ has the same shape as the graph of $y = |x|$ but is a translation of $y = |x|$ up or down by k units. If k is positive the translation is up. If k is negative, the translation is down.

Problem

What is the graph of $y = |x| - 4$?

$y = |x| - 4$ can be rewritten as $y = |x| + (-4)$. The equation is now in the form $y = |x| + k$. In this case, $k = -4$, so translate the graph of $y = |x|$ four units down.

Exercises

Graph each function by translating $y = |x|$.

1. $y = |x| + 1$ 2. $y = |x| - 2$ 3. $y = |x| + 4$

4. **Writing** Compare and contrast the graphs of $y = |x|$ and $y = |x| - 10$.
If you translate the first graph down 10 units, you will make the second graph. They have the same shape.

All-in-One Resources/Online
English Language Learner Support

5-8 **ELL Support**
Graphing Absolute Value Functions

Use the chart below to review vocabulary. These vocabulary words will help you complete this page.

Related Words	Explanation	Example
Translation trans LAY shun	Every point in a figure is moved the same distance in the same direction	The line was a *translation* of the original line.
Conversion kun VUR zhun	To change in form	The figure was multiplied by a *conversion* factor of 3.
Paraphrase PA ruh frayz	To reword	He *paraphrased* the teacher's directions to the new student.
Version VUR zhun	An interpretation of a matter from a particular point of view	The homework had several *versions* of similar types of problems.

Use the vocabulary from above to fill in the blanks. The first one is done for you.

To *paraphrase* means to reword what was said.
Alex's notes from class ___paraphrased___ what the teacher said.

1. Each ___version___ had the same questions, but in different order.

2. To convert from decimals to percents, you multiply by the ___conversion___ factor of one hundred.

3. Jenna moved her game piece by a ___translation___ of 2 units back.

For Exercises 4–10, match each translation for $y = |x|$ in Column A with its corresponding equation in Column B.

Column A	Column B
4. 5 units up	$y = |x| + 8$
5. 5 units left	$y = |x - 8|$
6. 8 units down	$y = |x + 8|$
7. 8 units left	$y = |x| - 8$
8. 8 units up	$y = |x + 5|$
9. 8 units right	$y = |x| + 5$
10. 5 units down	$y = |x| - 5$

Differentiated Remediation continued

On-Level

- **Practice** (2 pages) Provides extra practice for each lesson. For simpler practice exercises, use the Form K Practice pages found in the All-in-One Teaching Resources and online.

- **Think About a Plan** Helps students develop specific problem-solving skills and strategies by providing scaffolded guiding questions.

- **Standardized Test Prep** Focuses on all major exercises, all major question types, and helps students prepare for the high-stakes assessments.

Extension

- **Enrichment** Provides students with interesting problems and activities that extend the concepts of the lesson.

- **Activities, Games, and Puzzles** Worksheets that can be used for concepts development, enrichment, and for fun!

Practice and Problem Solving WKBK/ All-in-One Resources/Online
Practice page 1

Practice and Problem Solving WKBK/ All-in-One Resources/Online
Practice page 2

All-in-One Resources/Online
Enrichment

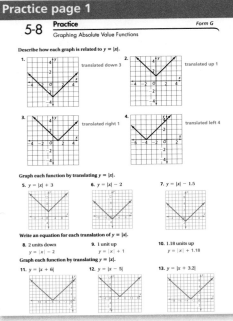

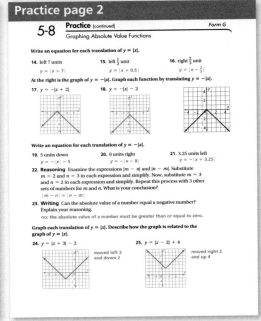

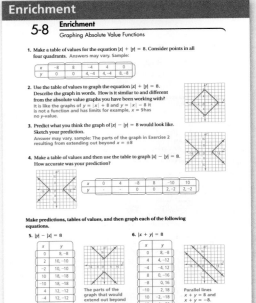

Practice and Problem Solving WKBK/ All-in-One Resources/Online
Think About a Plan

Practice and Problem Solving WKBK/ All-in-One Resources/Online
Standardized Test Prep

Online Teacher Resource Center
Activities, Games, and Puzzles

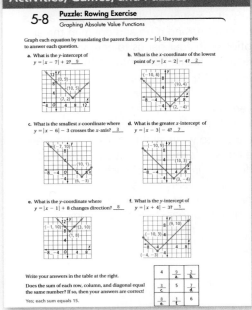

Concept Byte

Use With Lesson 5-8

EXTENSION

Characteristics of Absolute Value Graphs

In previous lessons you explored characteristics of linear graphs. Here you will explore characteristics of absolute value graphs of the form $y = a|x - h| + k$.

For a linear graph you can identify the x- and y-intercepts, the domain and range, and the slope. For an absolute value graph, you can also identify the direction the graph opens and the *vertex*. The vertex of an absolute value graph is the point at which the graph changes direction. The graph of $y = a|x - h| + k$ has vertex (h, k).

The graph of an absolute value function will always have one y-intercept, but it can have zero, one, or two x-intercepts. An absolute value graph has a different slope for each *branch*. The branches are the two rays on either side of the vertex.

Example

Graph $y = |x + 1| - 2$. **What are the slope of each branch, the x- and y-intercepts, the vertex, and the domain and range?**

Step 1 Plot the vertex $(-1, -2)$.

Step 2 Use the equation to find a point on either side of the vertex.

Step 3 Draw the two branches of the graph.

The domain is all real numbers. The range is all real numbers greater than or equal to -2.

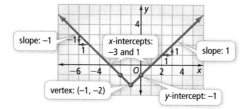

Exercises

1. a. Graph $y = -|x - 3| - 4$, $y = |x - 3| - 4$, $y = -2|x + 3| - 4$, and $y = 2|x + 3| - 4$.
  b. Which graphs open up and which graphs open down?
  c. Reasoning How does the sign of a affect the direction the graph opens?
  d. What are the slopes of the left and right branches of each graph?
  e. Reasoning How does the slope of the left branch relate to the slope of the right branch? How does a relate to the slope of the branches?

2. a. Graph $y = -2|x - 1| + 4$.
  b. What is the vertex of the graph?
  c. What are the domain and range of the function?
  d. What are the x- and y-intercepts?
  e. Reasoning How can you use the vertex and the sign of a to determine the range of the absolute value function?

Guided Instruction

PURPOSE To investigate absolute value graphs and their characteristics

PROCESS Students will
- analyze absolute value graphs.
- graph absolute value equations and translations of the parent absolute value equation.

DISCUSS Have students give the absolute value of various integers and identify them on a basic number line. Stress the point that the left side of the number line reflects the right side of the number line. Have students make a conjecture on how this connects with an absolute value graph.

Example

In this Example students focus on exploring the components of an absolute value graph.

Q What happens to the graph of an absolute value function at its vertex? **[It reverses direction.]**

Q How does a linear graph differ from an absolute value graph? **[It has a vertex, and it has two slopes (one for each branch).]**

Answers

Exercises

1. a. See back of book for graphs.
  b. $y = |x - 3| - 4$ and $y = 2|x + 3| - 4$ open up; $y = -|x - 3| - 4$ and $y = -2|x + 3| - 4$ open down.
  c. If $a > 0$, the graph opens up; if $a < 0$, the graph opens down.
  d. 1, −1; −1, 1; 2, −2; −2, 2
  e. They are opposites; $-a$ and a are the slopes of the two branches.

2. a.

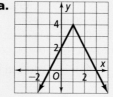

  b. $(1, 4)$
  c. domain: all real numbers; range: $y \le 4$
  d. x-intercepts: −1, 3; y-intercept: 2
  e. The y-coordinate of the vertex is k. If a is positive, the graph opens up, so the range is $y \ge k$. If a is negative, the graph opens down, so the range is $y \le k$.

Performance Task UbD

Pull It All Together

The concepts and skills required to solve these problems are from several lessons within this chapter and from the previous chapter. As students solve these problems, they will demonstrate their reasoning strategies and their growth as independent problem solvers.

The following questions are designed to:
• Help support students as they do the Tasks.
• Gauge the amount of support students need as they become independent problem solvers.

Task 1
• How can you find rate of change given a table?
• How can you find rate of change given an equation?
• How can you find rate of change given a graph?

Task 2
• In each part, what are you given?
• How does the information given help you decide which form of a linear equation to use to write the equation?

Task 3
• Is there a trend in the data?
• Does the data have a positive correlation, negative correlation, or neither? What does that tell you about the slope of the equations that model the data?

BIG idea Proportionality
In the graph of a line, the ratio for the slope indicates the rate of change.

Task 1

Find the rate of change for each table, equation, or graph. How did you find the rate of change?

a.

x	2	4	6
y	10	20	30

b. $5x + 3y = -2$

c.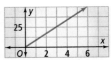

BIG idea Functions
There are several forms for the equation of a line. Each form communicates different information. For instance, from the point-slope form, you can determine a point and the slope of a line.

Task 2

Write an equation in slope-intercept, point-slope, or standard form for the line with the given information. Explain why you chose the form you used.

a. passes through $(-1, 4)$ and $(-5, 2)$
b. slope 2, y-intercept -4
c. has an x-intercept of 6 and a y-intercept of 3
d. passes through $(1, 2)$ with slope $-\frac{5}{3}$

BIG idea Modeling
You can model the trend of the real-world data in a scatter plot with an equation of a line. You can use the equation to estimate or to make predictions.

Task 3

At the beginning of a 20-month period, Stacie owns one clothing store. During that period, she opens a second clothing store in a different location. The table shows the total monthly sales of Stacie's clothing stores for the 20-month period.

Monthly Sales (in thousands of dollars)										
Month	2	4	6	8	10	12	14	16	18	20
Sales	3	5	4	6	5	12	16	22	26	32

a. Make a scatter plot of the data in the table.
b. What are two equations that model the data? What are the domain and range of each equation? Explain your process.
c. About how much money did Stacie's stores earn in the fifth month? How much money do you expect the stores to earn in the twenty-fourth month? Explain.

Assess Performance   UbD

Pull It All Together

See p. 67 for a holistic scoring rubric to gauge a student's progress on Understanding the Problem, Planning a Solution, Getting an Answer, and Assessing Autonomy.

SOLUTION OUTLINES

1. a. Find the ratio of the change in the y-values to the change in the x-values. Notice that the result is the same whether you use the first and second, first and third, or second and third columns of the table. (Answer: 5)

b. Write the equation in slope-intercept form by solving for y $\left(y = -\frac{5}{3}x - \frac{2}{3}\right)$. The slope, or rate of change, is the coefficient of x. $\left(\text{Answer: } -\frac{5}{3}\right)$

c. Pick two points on the graph. Count the units of vertical and horizontal change. $\left(\text{Answer: } \frac{25}{3}\right)$

2. a. Use point-slope form because you know the coordinates of points on the line. You can use the two points to find the slope $\left(\frac{4-2}{-1-(-5)} = \frac{2}{4} = \frac{1}{2}\right)$. You can use the coordinates of either point to write the equation. $\left(\text{Answer: } y - 4 = \frac{1}{2}(x + 1)\right)$

b. Use slope-intercept form because the slope and y-intercept are given. (Answer: $y = 2x - 4$)

c. Use slope-intercept form because the slope is easy to calculate and the y-intercept is given. The intercepts tell you that the points $(6, 0)$ and $(0, 3)$ are on the line. Use the slope formula to find the slope $\left(\frac{0-3}{6-0} = \frac{-3}{6} = -\frac{1}{2}\right)$. $\left(\text{Answer: } y = -\frac{1}{2}x + 3\right)$

d. Use point-slope form because the slope and a point are given. $\left(\text{Answer: } y - 2 = -\frac{5}{3}(x - 1)\right)$

3. a. Possible plan: Use the horizontal axis for the month. A reasonable scale is 0 to 20 with every 2 months labeled. Use the vertical axis for the sales (in thousands of dollars). A reasonable scale is 0 to 35 with every $5000 labeled.

3b–3c. See next page.

5 Chapter Review

Connecting BIG ideas and Answering the Essential Questions

1 Proportionality
In the graph of a line, the ratio for the slope indicates the rate of change.

> **Rate of Change and Slope (Lesson 5-1)**
> $$\text{slope} = \frac{\text{rise}}{\text{run}} = \frac{y_2 - y_1}{x_2 - x_1}$$

> **Parallel and Perpendicular Lines (Lesson 5-6)**
> Parallel lines have the same slope. The product of the slopes of perpendicular lines is -1.

2 Functions
There are several forms for the equation of a line. Each form communicates different information. For instance, from the point-slope form, you can determine a point and the slope of a line.

> **Slope-Intercept Form (Lesson 5-3)**
> $$y = mx + b$$

> **Point-Slope Form (Lesson 5-4)**
> $$y - y_1 = m(x - x_1)$$

> **Standard Form (Lesson 5-5)**
> $$Ax + By = C$$

3 Modeling
You can model the trend of the real-world data in a scatter plot with the equation of a line. You can use the equation to estimate or to make predictions.

> **Scatter Plots and Trend Lines (Lesson 5-7)**
> The trend line that shows the relationship between two sets of data most accurately is called the line of best fit.

Chapter Vocabulary

- absolute value function (p. 342)
- direct variation (p. 299)
- extrapolation (p. 334)
- interpolation (p. 334)
- linear equation (p. 306)
- line of best fit (p. 336)
- negative correlation (p. 333)
- no correlation (p. 333)
- opposite reciprocals (p. 328)
- parallel lines (p. 327)
- perpendicular lines (p. 328)
- point-slope form (p. 313)
- positive correlation (p. 333)
- rate of change (p. 292)
- scatter plot (p. 333)
- slope (p. 293)
- slope-intercept form (p. 306)
- standard form of a linear equation (p. 320)
- trend line (p. 334)
- x-intercept (p. 320)
- y-intercept (p. 306)

Choose the vocabulary term that correctly completes the sentence.

1. Estimating a value between two known values in a data set is called ? .

2. The slope of a line models the ? of a function.

3. The form of a linear equation that shows the slope and one point is the ? .

4. Two lines are perpendicular when their slopes are ? .

5. The line that most accurately models data in a scatter plot is the ? .

Essential Questions UbD

BIG idea Proportionality
ESSENTIAL QUESTION What does the slope of a line indicate about the line?
ANSWER In a graph of a line, the ratio for the slope indicates the rate of change.

BIG idea Function
ESSENTIAL QUESTION What information does the equation of a line give you?
ANSWER There are several forms for the equation of a line. Each form communicates different information. For instance, from the point-slope form, you can determine a point and the slope of a line.

BIG idea Modeling
ESSENTIAL QUESTION How can you make predictions based on a scatter plot?
ANSWER You can model the trend of the real-world data in a scatter plot with an equation of a line. You can use the equation to estimate or to make predictions.

SOLUTION OUTLINES (continued)

b. Possible plan: The sales become much greater between 10 and 12 months, so this is probably when the second store opened. Use one line to model the data from 0 to 10 months. Use another line to model the data from 12 to 20 months. Write equations for the lines. (Answers may vary. Samples: $y = \frac{1}{2}x + 2, 0 \le x \le 10$, $2 \le y \le 5$; $y = 3x - 26$, $x \ge 12, y \ge 12$)

c. Possible plan: Use the equation that models the sales from 0 to 10 months to interpolate the sales in the fifth month. (Answer based on equation given in part (b): about $4500) Use the equation that models the sales from 12 to 20 months to extrapolate the sales in the twenty-fourth month. (Answer based on equation given in part (b): about $46,000)

Answers

Chapter Review

1. interpolation
2. rate of change
3. point-slope form
4. opposite reciprocals
5. line of best fit

Summative Questions UbD

Use the following prompts as you review this chapter with your students. The prompts are designed to help you assess your students' understanding of the Big Ideas they have studied.

- Compare and contrast the three forms of a linear equation.
- How is the ratio for slope helpful in writing and graphing an equation?
- What does the slope of a trend line tell you about the data in a scatter plot?

Answers

Chapter Review (continued)

6. -1

7. 0

8. 3

9. undefined

10. 3

11. $-\frac{1}{2}$

12. $y = -2x;\ -14$

13. $y = \frac{5}{2}x;\ \frac{35}{2}$

14. $y = \frac{1}{3}x;\ \frac{7}{3}$

15. $y = -x;\ -7$

16. no

17. yes; $y = -2.5x$

5-1 Rate of Change and Slope

Quick Review

Rate of change shows the relationship between two changing quantities. The **slope** of a line is the ratio of the vertical change (the rise) to the horizontal change (the run).

$$\text{slope} = \frac{\text{rise}}{\text{run}} = \frac{y_2 - y_1}{x_2 - x_1}$$

The slope of a horizontal line is 0, and the slope of a vertical line is undefined.

Example

What is the slope of the line that passes through the points $(1, 12)$ and $(6, 22)$?

$$\text{slope} = \frac{y_2 - y_1}{x_2 - x_1} = \frac{22 - 12}{6 - 1} = \frac{10}{5} = 2$$

Exercises

Find the slope of the line that passes through each pair of points.

6. $(2, 2), (3, 1)$

7. $(4, 2), (0, 2)$

8. $(-1, 2), (0, 5)$

9. $(-3, -2), (-3, 2)$

Find the slope of each line.

10.

11.

5-2 Direct Variation

Quick Review

A function represents a **direct variation** if it has the form $y = kx$, where $k \neq 0$. The coefficient k is the **constant of variation**.

Example

Suppose y varies directly with x, and $y = 15$ when $x = 5$. Write a direct variation equation that relates x and y. What is the value of y when $x = 9$?

$y = kx$	Start with the general form of a direct variation.
$15 = k(5)$	Substitute 5 for x and 15 for y.
$3 = k$	Divide each side by 5 to solve for k.
$y = 3x$	Write an equation. Substitute 3 for k in $y = kx$.

The equation $y = 3x$ relates x and y. When $x = 9$, $y = 3(9)$, or 27.

Exercises

Suppose y varies directly with x. Write a direct variation equation that relates x and y. Then find the value of y when $x = 7$.

12. $y = 8$ when $x = -4$.

13. $y = 15$ when $x = 6$.

14. $y = 3$ when $x = 9$.

15. $y = -4$ when $x = 4$.

For the data in each table, tell whether y varies directly with x. If it does, write an equation for the direct variation.

16.

x	y
-1	-6
2	3
5	12
9	24

17.

x	y
-3	7.5
-1	2.5
2	-5
5	-12.5

5-3, 5-4, and 5-5 Forms of Linear Equations

Quick Review

The graph of a linear equation is a line. You can write a linear equation in different forms.

The **slope-intercept form** of a linear equation is $y = mx + b$, where m is the slope and b is the **y-intercept**.

The **point-slope form** of a linear equation is $y - y_1 = m(x - x_1)$, where m is the slope and (x_1, y_1) is a point on the line.

The **standard form** of a linear equation is $Ax + By = C$, where A, B, and C are real numbers, and A and B are not both zero.

Example

What is an equation of the line that has slope -4 and passes through the point $(-1, 7)$?

$y - y_1 = m(x - x_1)$	Use point-slope form.
$y - 7 = -4(x - (-1))$	Substitute $(-1, 7)$ for (x_1, y_1) and -4 for m.
$y - 7 = -4(x + 1)$	Simplify inside grouping symbols.

An equation of the line is $y - 7 = -4(x + 1)$.

Exercises

Write an equation in slope-intercept form of the line that passes through the given points.

18. $(-3, 4), (1, 4)$ **19.** $(3, -2), (6, 1)$

Write an equation of each line.

20.   **21.**

Graph each equation.

22. $y = 4x - 3$ **23.** $y = 2$

24. $y + 3 = 2(x - 1)$ **25.** $x + 4y = 10$

5-6 Parallel and Perpendicular Lines

Quick Review

Parallel lines are lines in the same plane that never intersect. Two lines are **perpendicular** if they intersect to form right angles.

Example

Are the graphs of $y = \frac{4}{3}x + 5$ and $y = -\frac{3}{4}x + 2$ parallel, perpendicular, or neither? Explain.

The slope of the graph of $y = \frac{4}{3}x + 5$ is $\frac{4}{3}$.

The slope of the graph of $y = -\frac{3}{4}x + 2$ is $-\frac{3}{4}$.

$$\frac{4}{3}\left(-\frac{3}{4}\right) = -1$$

The slopes are opposite reciprocals, so the graphs are perpendicular.

Exercises

Write an equation of the line that passes through the given point and is parallel to the graph of the given equation.

26. $(2, -1); y = 5x - 2$ **27.** $(0, -5); y = 9x$

Determine whether the graphs of the two equations are *parallel, perpendicular,* or *neither.* Explain.

28. $y = 6x + 2$ **29.** $2x - 5y = 0$
$18x - 3y = 15$ $y + 3 = \frac{5}{2}x$

Write an equation of the line that passes through the given point and is perpendicular to the graph of the given equation.

30. $(3, 5); y = -3x + 7$ **31.** $(4, 10); y = 8x - 1$

18. $y = 4$

19. $y = x - 5$

20. $y = \frac{2}{3}x + 1$

21. $y = -x - 1$

22.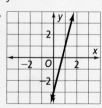

23.

24.

25.

26. $y = 5x - 11$

27. $y = 9x - 5$

28. Parallel; the slopes are equal.

29. Neither; the slopes are not equal or opposite reciprocals.

30. $y = \frac{1}{3}x + 4$

31. $y = -\frac{1}{8}x + \frac{21}{2}$

Answers

Chapter Review (continued)

32. negative correlation

33. no correlation

34. positive correlation

35. a.

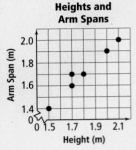

Heights and Arm Spans

b–d. Answers may vary. Samples are given.

b. $y = 0.96x - 0.01$

c. about 1.5 m

d. about 2.1 m

36.

37.

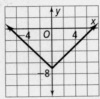

38.

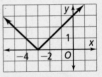

39.

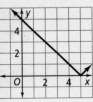

40. $y = |x| - 5.5$

41. $y = |x + 11|$

42. $y = |x| + 13$

43. $y = |x - 6.5|$

44. $y = |x| + 2$

5-7 Scatter Plots and Trend Lines

Quick Review

A **scatter plot** displays two sets of data as ordered pairs. A **trend line** for a scatter plot shows the correlation between the two sets of data. The most accurate trend line is the **line of best fit**. To estimate or predict values on a scatter plot, you can use **interpolation** or **extrapolation**.

Example

Estimate the length of the kudzu vine in Week 3.

When $w = 3$, $\ell \approx 10$. So in Week 3, the length of the kudzu vine was about 10 ft.

Predict the length of the kudzu vine in Week 11.

$\ell = 3.5w$ Use the equation of the trend line.

$\ell = 3.5(11)$ Substitute 11 for w.

$\ell = 38.5$ Simplify.

The length of the vine in Week 11 will be about 38.5 ft.

Kudzu Vine Growth

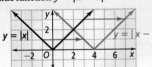

Exercises

Describe the type of correlation the scatter plot shows.

32.   **33.**   **34.**

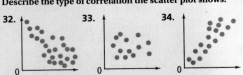

35. a. Make a scatter plot of the data below.

Heights and Arm Spans						
Height (m)	1.5	1.8	1.7	2.0	1.7	2.1
Arm Span (m)	1.4	1.7	1.7	1.9	1.6	2.0

b. Write an equation of a reasonable trend line or use a graphing calculator to find the equation of the line of best fit.

c. Estimate the arm span of someone who is 1.6 m tall.

d. Predict the arm span of someone who is 2.2 m tall.

5-8 Graphing Absolute Value Functions

Quick Review

The graph of an **absolute value function** is a V-shaped graph that opens upward or downward.

A **translation** shifts a graph either vertically, horizontally, or both. To graph an absolute value function, you can translate $y = |x|$.

Example

Graph the absolute value function $y = |x - 4|$.

Start with the graph of $y = |x|$. Translate the graph right 4 units.

Exercises

Graph each function by translating $y = |x|$.

36. $y = |x| + 2$ **37.** $y = |x| - 7$

38. $y = |x + 3|$ **39.** $y = |x - 5|$

Write an equation for each translation of $y = |x|$.

40. 5.5 units down   **41.** 11 units left

42. 13 units up   **43.** 6.5 units right

44. Write an equation for the absolute value function at the right.

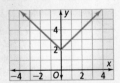

MathXL® for School
Go to PowerAlgebra.com

Do you know HOW?

Write an equation in slope-intercept form of each line.

1.   **2.**

Write an equation in point-slope form of the line through the given point and with the given slope.

3. $(5, 1)$; $m = \frac{1}{3}$

4. $(-2, 3)$; $m = -2$

Write each equation in standard form using integers.

5. $y = \frac{3}{4}x + 5$

6. $y + 4 = \frac{1}{3}(x + 6)$

Graph each equation.

7. $y = 4x - 3$

8. $y = 7$

9. $y + 3 = \frac{1}{2}(x + 2)$

10. $-3x + 5y = 15$

Determine whether each equation represents a direct variation. If it does, find the constant of variation.

11. $2x + 3y = 0$

12. $4x + 6y = 3$

Graph each function.

13. $y = |x - 4|$

14. $y = |x| + 3$

15. Pet Grooming You start a pet grooming service. You spend $30 on supplies. You plan to charge $5 to groom each pet.
  a. Write an equation to relate your profit y to the number of pets x you groom.
  b. Graph the equation. What are the x- and y-intercepts?

16. Make a scatter plot and draw a trend line for the data in the table. Interpolate or extrapolate to estimate the number of inventors applying for patents in 2006 and in 2015.

17. What is an equation of the line parallel to $y = -x + 1$ and through $(4, 4)$?

18. What is an equation of the line perpendicular to $y = -x - 2$ and through $(-2, 4)$?

Number of Inventors Applying for Patents

Year	Inventors
1999	22,052
2001	20,588
2003	18,462
2005	14,039
2007	13,748

Source: U.S. Patent Office

Do you UNDERSTAND?

19. Writing How are lines of best fit and other trend lines used with scatter plots?

20. Open-Ended Write an equation whose graph is parallel to the graph of $y = 0.5x - 10$.

21. Compare and Contrast Is an equation that represents a direct variation a type of linear equation? Explain.

22. Vocabulary What does it mean when a line of best fit has a correlation coefficient close to 1?

23. Reasoning How many lines can you draw that are parallel to the line and through the point shown at the right? Explain.

14.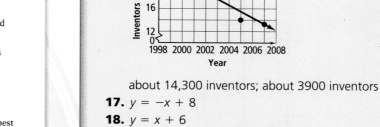

15. a. $y = 5x - 30$

b.

6, −30

16. Answers may vary. Sample:

Number of Inventors Applying for Patents

about 14,300 inventors; about 3900 inventors

17. $y = -x + 8$

18. $y = x + 6$

19. Lines of best fit and other trend lines are used to represent the trend in the data so that you can estimate and predict values.

20. Answers may vary. Sample: $y = 0.5x + 1$

21. Yes; a direct variation is a linear function with y-intercept 0.

22. The data have a positive correlation and cluster very closely around the line of best fit.

23. One; there are an infinite number of lines that contain the given point, but only one that is parallel to the given line.

Answers

Chapter Test

1. $y = -\frac{2}{3}x + 5$

2. $y = \frac{1}{2}x + 4$

3. $y - 1 = \frac{1}{3}(x - 5)$

4. $y - 3 = -2(x + 2)$

5. $3x - 4y = -20$

6. $x - 3y = 6$

7.

8.

9.

10.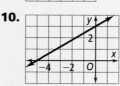

11. yes; $-\frac{2}{3}$

12. no

13.

MathXL for School
Prepare students for the Mid-Chapter Quiz and Chapter Test with online practice and review.

Item Number	Lesson
1	5-3
2	4-6
3	1-7
4	5-1
5	4-2
6	5-5
7	2-5
8	5-5
9	4-6
10	5-7
11	5-3
12	3-8
13	3-3
14	4-1
15	5-4
16	5-6
17	2-5
18	1-2
19	5-5
20	3-8
21	2-5
22	2-4
23	1-5
24	2-3
25	3-3
26	5-6
27	2-5

5 Cumulative Test Prep

Vocabulary Builder

As you solve test items, you must understand the meanings of mathematical terms. Choose the correct term to complete each sentence.

A. The (*dependent*, *independent*) variable provides the output values of a function.

B. The set of all possible values for the dependent variable is called the (*domain*, *range*).

C. The (*slope*, *y-intercept*) of a line is determined by the ratio $\frac{rise}{run}$.

D. An (*equation*, *inequality*) is a math sentence that shows the relationship between two quantities that may not have the same value.

E. (*Parallel*, *Perpendicular*) lines are lines in the same plane that never intersect.

Multiple Choice

Read each question. Then write the letter of the correct answer on your paper.

1. Which is an equation of a line with slope 3?
(A) $y = 3x - 4$ (C) $y = 4x - 3$
(B) $y = -3x + 3$ (D) $y = -3x - 5$

2. Ben has a cell phone plan where he pays $12 per month plus $.10 per minute of talk time. The equation $y = 0.10x + 12$ can be used to find his monthly phone bill y given the number of minutes x he spends talking. Which set or inequality represents a reasonable range of the function?
(F) $\{0, 12\}$ (H) $12 \le y$
(G) $0 \le y \le 12$ (I) $0 \le y$

Answers

Cumulative Test Prep

A. dependent

B. range

C. slope

D. inequality

E. parallel

1. A

2. H

3. Which expression is equivalent to
$3(12x + 2) - 2(10x + 3)$?

 (A) $16x$ (C) $16x + 9$

 (B) $16x + 5$ (D) $16x + 12$

4. What is the slope of the line at the right?

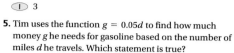

 (F) -2

 (G) $\frac{2}{3}$

 (H) $\frac{3}{2}$

 (I) 3

5. Tim uses the function $g = 0.05d$ to find how much money g he needs for gasoline based on the number of miles d he travels. Which statement is true?

 (A) The number of miles Tim travels depends on how much money he needs for gasoline.

 (B) The number of miles Tim travels depends on the price of a gallon of gasoline.

 (C) The amount of money Tim needs for gasoline depends on the number of miles he travels.

 (D) The amount of money Tim needs for gasoline is constant.

6. Which equation is *not* a function?

 (F) $y = 0$ (H) $x = -3$

 (G) $y = 2x - 4$ (I) $y = -x$

7. The perimeter P of a rectangle can be found using the formula $P = 2(\ell + w)$, where ℓ represents the length and w represents the width. Which equation represents the width in terms of P and ℓ?

 (A) $w = 2(P - \ell)$ (C) $w = 2P - \ell$

 (B) $w = \frac{P - \ell}{2}$ (D) $w = \frac{P}{2} - \ell$

8. Use the graph at the right. If the y-intercept increases by 2 and the slope remains the same, what will the x-intercept be?

 (F) -3 (H) 1

 (G) -2 (I) 4

9. The U.S. Mint charges $25 for a limited edition coin, plus a $6 shipping charge. The cost c of purchasing n coins can be found using the function $c = 25n + 6$. There is a limit of 5 coins per purchase. What is a reasonable domain of the function?

 (A) $\{5\}$

 (B) $\{1, 2, 3, 4, 5\}$

 (C) $\{25, 50, 75, 100, 125\}$

 (D) $\{31, 56, 81, 106, 131\}$

10. A financial advisor collected data on the amount of money earned and saved each year by people ages 20–29. The results are shown in the scatter plot. Which best describes the slope of the line of best fit?

 (F) positive   (H) zero

 (G) negative   (I) undefined

11. Which graph shows a line with slope $\frac{1}{3}$ and y-intercept -1?

12. Which set is the intersection of $X = \{3, 4, 5, 6, 7, 8\}$ and $Y = \{1, 2, 5, 6, 7, 8, 11\}$?

 (F) $\emptyset$ (H) $\{3, 4, 5, 6, 7\}$

 (G) $\{5, 6, 7, 8\}$ (I) $\{5, 6, 7, 8, 11\}$

13. If a, b, and c are real numbers where $b > c$, for which values of a is the expression $\frac{b}{a} < \frac{c}{a}$ always true?

 (A) $a > 0$ (C) $a < 0$

 (B) $a \geq 0$ (D) $a \leq 0$

3. A
4. G
5. C
6. H
7. D
8. G
9. B
10. F
11. B
12. G
13. C

Answers

14. H

15. A

16. $\frac{1}{2}$

17. 45

18. 9.715

19. 9

20. 240

21. 24

22. 1

23. 1.75

24. 5.75

25. [2] sometimes true

If x is negative and y is positive such that $x + y > 0$, then xy will not be greater than 0. For example, $-2 + 5 = 3 > 0$, but $(-2)(5) < 0$.

If either x or y equals 0, then xy will not be greater than 0.

However, if x and y both are positive, then $xy > 0$.

So the statement is sometimes true.

[1] correct answer but no explanation given

26. [2] Since line p has a slope of 0, then it is a horizontal line. Line q is parallel to line p, so it too must be horizontal. The equation of line q is $y = -9$.

[1] appropriate method but with one minor error

27. [4] Since the square has a perimeter of 16 in., then one side must be equal to 4 in. This means that the area of the square is $A = s^2 = (4 \text{ in.})^2 = 16 \text{ in.}^2$.

The area of a trapezoid is $\frac{1}{2}h(b_1 + b_2)$. This trapezoid

has area 16 in.^{2}. Its height is the same as the side of the square, 4 in. It has a base of 3 in.

Substituting, $16 = \frac{1}{2} \cdot 4(3 + b_2)$. So the length of the other base is 5 in.

[3] appropriate procedures, but with one computational error

[2] incorrect side of square, but with correct results for trapezoid given that answer OR correct side of square found, with incorrect answer for base of trapezoid

[1] correct answer, without work shown

---

14. The graph shows the relationship between the total price of tomatoes and the number of pounds of tomatoes purchased. Which statement is true?

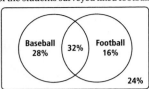
Price of Tomatoes

(F) The number of pounds depends on the total price.

(G) The number of tomatoes depends on the total price.

(H) The total price depends on the number of pounds.

(I) The number of tomatoes depends on the number of pounds.

15. A line passes through the point (2, 1) and has a slope of $-\frac{3}{5}$. What is an equation of the line?

(A) $y - 1 = -\frac{3}{5}(x - 2)$

(B) $y - 1 = -\frac{5}{3}(x - 2)$

(C) $y - 2 = -\frac{3}{5}(x - 1)$

(D) $y - 2 = -\frac{5}{3}(x - 1)$

GRIDDED RESPONSE

Record your answers in a grid.

16. What is the slope of a line that is perpendicular to the line shown at the right?

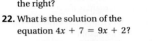

17. Fran makes a rectangular tablecloth that has an area of 5 ft^2. Her mother makes a tablecloth that is three times the length and three times the width of Fran's. What is the area, in square feet, of her mother's tablecloth?

18. In a gymnastics competition, a floor routine must last no longer than 90 s. For every second over 90 s, 0.05 point is deducted from an athlete's score. Suppose Jenny would have earned 9.865 points for her routine, but it lasted 93 s. What was the actual number of points that she earned?

19. The points $(-2, 11)$ and $(6, 3)$ lie on the same line. What is the x-intercept of the line?

20. Hannah took a survey of 500 students at her school to find out whether they liked baseball or football. The results are shown in the Venn diagram below. How many of the students surveyed liked football?

21. What is the volume, in cubic inches, of the rectangular prism at the right?

22. What is the solution of the equation $4x + 7 = 9x + 2$?

23. Corporate bond prices are quoted in fourths of a point. The price of a bond increases from $84\frac{1}{2}$ to $86\frac{1}{4}$. By how many points did the price increase?

24. An online bookseller charges $3 per order plus $1 per book for shipping. John places an order for four books that have the same price. The total cost of his order is $30. What is the price, in dollars, of each book?

Short Response

25. Determine whether the following statement is *always*, *sometimes*, or *never* true: If $x + y > 0$, then $xy > 0$. Justify your answer.

26. Line p passes through the point $(5, -2)$ and has a slope of 0. Line q passes through the point $(-13, -9)$ and is parallel to line p. What is an equation of line q? Show your work.

Extended Response

27. The perimeter of a square is 16 in. A trapezoid has the same area and height as the square. The area of a trapezoid is $\frac{1}{2}h(b_1 + b_2)$, where h is the height and b_1 and b_2 are the lengths of the bases. If one base of the trapezoid is 3 in. long, what is the length of the other base? Show your work.

Get Ready!

CHAPTER 6

Lesson 2-4 ◆ **Solving Equations**

Solve each equation. If the equation is an identity, write *identity*. If it has no solution, write *no solution*.

1. $3(2 - 2x) = -6(x - 1)$ **2.** $3p + 1 = -p + 5$

3. $4x - 1 = 3(x + 1) + x$ **4.** $\frac{1}{2}(6c - 4) = 4 + c$

5. $5x = 2 - (x - 7)$ **6.** $v + 5 = v - 5$

Lesson 3-4 ◆ **Solving Inequalities**

Solve each inequality.

7. $5x + 3 < 18$ **8.** $-\frac{r}{5} + 1 \geq -6$

9. $-3t - 5 < 34$ **10.** $-(7f + 18) - 2f \leq 0$

11. $8s + 7 > -3(5s - 4)$ **12.** $\frac{1}{2}(x + 6) + 1 \geq -5$

Lesson 4-5 ◆ **Writing Functions**

13. The height of a triangle is 1 cm less than twice the length of the base. Let $x =$ the length of the base.
   a. Write an expression for the height of the triangle.
   b. Write a function rule for the area of the triangle.
   c. What is the area of such a triangle if the length of its base is 16 cm?

Lessons 5-3, 5-4, and 5-5 ◆ **Graphing Linear Equations**

Graph each equation.

14. $2x + 4y = -8$ **15.** $y = -\frac{2}{3}x + 3$ **16.** $y + 5 = -2(x - 2)$

Looking Ahead Vocabulary

17. Two answers to a question are said to be *inconsistent* if they could not both be true. Two answers to a question are said to be *consistent* if they could both be true. If there is no solution that makes both equations in a system of two linear equations true, do you think the system is *inconsistent* or *consistent*?

18. After a team loses a game, they're *eliminated* from a tournament. The *elimination method* is a way to solve a system of equations. Do you think using the elimination method adds or deletes a variable from a system of equations?

PowerAlgebra.com   Chapter 6   Systems of Equations and Inequalities   357

Get Ready!

Assign this diagnostic assessment to determine if students have the prerequisite skills for Chapter 6.

Lesson	Skill
2-4	Solving Equations
3-4	Solving Inequalities
4-5	Writing Functions
5-3, 5-4, and 5-5	Graphing Linear Equations

To remediate students, select from these resources (available for every lesson).
- Online Problems (PowerAlgebra.com)
- Reteaching (All-in-One Teaching Resources)
- Practice (All-in-One Teaching Resources)

Why Students Need These Skills

SOLVING EQUATIONS
Solving equations will be extended to systems of equations.

SOLVING INEQUALITIES
Students will graph and solve systems of linear inequalities.

WRITING FUNCTIONS
Students write functions to solve real-world systems of equations.

GRAPHING LINEAR EQUATIONS
Students will solve systems of equations by graphing.

Looking Ahead Vocabulary

INCONSISTENT Ask students to give real-world examples of situations that are inconsistent.

CONSISTENT Ask students to give real-world examples of situations that are consistent.

ELIMINATED Ask students what it means to be eliminated.

Answers

Get Ready!

1. identity   **2.** 1

3. no solution   **4.** 3

5. 1.5   **6.** no solution

7. $x < 3$ **8.** $r \leq 35$

9. $t > -13$ **10.** $f \geq -2$

11. $s > \frac{5}{23}$ **12.** $x \geq -18$

13. a. $2x - 1$

   b. $A = \frac{1}{2}x(2x - 1)$

   c. 248 cm^2

14.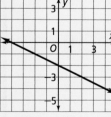

15.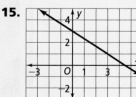

16.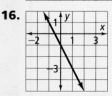

17. inconsistent   **18.** deletes

Get Ready!   357

Chapter 6 Overview

UbD Understanding by Design

Chapter 6 connects and extends the concepts associated with equations and inequalities to systems of equations and inequalities. In this chapter, students will develop the answers to the Essential Questions posed on the opposite page as they learn the concepts and skills bulleted below.

BIG idea Solving Equations and Inequalities

ESSENTIAL QUESTION How can you solve a system of equations or inequalities?
- Students will learn to solve systems of equations or inequalities by graphing.
- Students will learn to solve systems of equations or inequalities by substitution.
- Students will learn to solve systems of equations or inequalities by elimination.

BIG idea Modeling

ESSENTIAL QUESTION Can systems of equations model real-world situations?
- Students will write equations and inequalities to represent situations.
- Students will examine constraints placed on real-world situations.

Indiana Academic Standards

A1.2.5 Solve problems that can be modeled using linear equations and inequalities, interpret the solutions, and determine whether the solutions are reasonable.

A1.2.6 Graph a linear inequality in two variables.

A1.3.1 Understand the relationship between a solution of a pair of linear equations in two variables and the graphs of the corresponding lines and solve pairs of linear equations in two variables by graphing, substitution or elimination.

A1.3.2 Graph the solution set for a pair of linear inequalities in two variables with and without technology and use the graph to find the solution set.

A1.3.3 Solve problems that can be modeled using pairs of linear equations in two variables, interpret the solutions, and determine whether the solutions are reasonable.

CHAPTER 6

Systems of Equations and Inequalities

These pandas look like they're the same size. Does that mean they're the same age? Not necessarily!

Individuals grow at different rates.

In this chapter, you'll learn how to solve problems involving more than one equation, like finding out when two animals that grow at different rates will be the same size.

Vocabulary

English/Spanish Vocabulary Audio Online:

English	Spanish
consistent, p. 361	consistente
dependent, p. 361	dependiente
elimination method, p. 374	eliminación
inconsistent, p. 361	inconsistente
independent, p. 361	independiente
linear inequality, p. 390	desigualdad lineal
solution of an inequality, p. 390	solución de una desigualdad
solution of a system of linear equations, p. 360	solución de un sistema de ecuaciones lineales
solution of a system of linear inequalities, p. 396	solución de un sistema de desigualdades lineales
substitution method, p. 368	método de sustitución

Chapter 6 Overview

Use these online assets to engage your students. There is support for the Solve It and step-by step solutions for Problems.

 Show the student-produced video demonstrating relevant and engaging applications of the new concepts in the chapter.

 Find online definitions for new terms in English and Spanish.

 Start each lesson with an attention-getting Problem. View the Problem online with helpful hints.

My Math Video

00:04:04

BIG ideas

1 **Solving Equations and Inequalities**
   Essential Question: How can you solve a system of equations or inequalities?

2 **Modeling**
   Essential Question: Can systems of equations model real-world situations?

Chapter Preview

PowerAlgebra.com   Chapter 6   Systems of Equations and Inequalities   359

 Increase students' depth of knowledge with interactive online activities.

 Show Problems from each lesson solved step by step. Instant replay allows students to go at their own pace when studying online.

 Assign homework to individual students or to an entire class.

 Prepare students for the Mid-Chapter Quiz and Chapter Test with online practice and review.

My Math Video

FACILITATE Use this photo to discuss the concept of multiple equations that describe the same variables. The growth rate of each panda can be approximated by an equation. In this chapter, students will learn how to solve a system of equations to find an ordered pair that satisfies all equations in the system, and thereby assigns values to each variable.

Q Do you think all the pandas are the same age? Explain. **[Answers may vary. Sample: Not necessarily. The pandas could be different ages, but all adults.]**

Q How could the growth rate of an individual panda be represented in algebra? **[The growth rate could be represented using an equation.]**

Q Would the equation be the same for each panda? Why or why not? **[No, because individuals all grow at different rates.]**

Q If the equations were graphed and they intersected at one point, what would the point represent? **[The point would represent the time and size when the pandas were the same size.]**

ERROR PREVENTION

Remind students to check their answers to systems of equations. They should substitute the solution into both equations to verify that the ordered pair satisfies both equations.

UbD

Solving Equations & Inequalities

BIG idea Solving an equation is the process of rewriting the equation to make what it says about its variable(s) as simple as possible. Properties of numbers and equality can be used to transform an equation (or inequality) into equivalent, simpler equations (or inequalities) in order to find solutions. Useful information about equations and inequalities (including solutions) can be found by analyzing graphs or tables. The numbers and types of solutions vary predictably, based on the type of equation.

ESSENTIAL UNDERSTANDINGS

6-1 to 6-3 Systems of linear equations can be used to model problems. Systems of equations can be solved by graphing, substitution, or eliminating a variable.

6-5 to 6-6 A linear inequality in two variables has an infinite number of solutions. These solutions can be represented in the coordinate plane as the set of all points on one side of a boundary line. The solutions of a system of linear inequalities can be represented by the region where the graphs of the individual inequalities overlap.

Modeling

BIG idea Many real-world mathematical problems can be represented algebraically. These representations can lead to algebraic solutions. A function that models a real-world situation can then be used to make estimates or predictions about future occurrences.

ESSENTIAL UNDERSTANDINGS

6–1 Some problems can be modeled by systems of linear equations.

6-5 to 6-6 Solutions to a linear inequality in two variables can be represented in the coordinate plane as the set of all points on one side of a boundary line. The solutions of a system of linear inequalities can be represented by the region where the graphs of the individual inequalities overlap.

Solving Systems of Equations Graphically

To solve a linear system by graphing, graph each equation and look for the point at which the lines intersect.

There are three possibilities when solving a linear system.

1 One Solution This occurs when the graphs of the equations intersect in one point. In this case, the coordinates of the intersection point are the solution to the system.

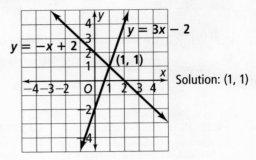

Solution: (1, 1)

2 Infinite Solutions This occurs when two equations have the same graph. All points that lie on the line are solutions to the system.

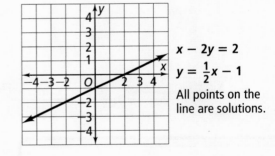

$x - 2y = 2$

$y = \frac{1}{2}x - 1$

All points on the line are solutions.

3 No Solutions If the graphs of the equations are parallel, then the system has no solutions.

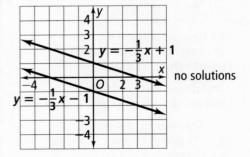

no solutions

Common Errors With Solving Systems of Equations Graphically

Students may mistake a system with infinite solutions for a system with no solutions.

Solving Systems of Equations Algebraically

Systems of equations can be solved algebraically as well as graphically. When finding solutions algebraically, you can use the substitution method or the elimination method.

The substitution method is particularly well suited for systems in which at least one of the equations is solved for one of the variables or can be easily solved for one of the variables, such as the system

$2y + 12x = 44$

$y = 5x.$

The equation $y = 5x$ is solved for y, so substitute $5x$ for y in the other equation.

$2y + 12x = 44$

$2(5x) + 12x = 44$

The elimination method is particularly well suited for systems in which the coefficients of one of the variables can easily be made the same. Consider the system

$4y + 3x = 12$

$2y + 2x = 8.$

The second equation can be multiplied by 2, resulting in the system

$4y + 3x = 12$

$4y + 4x = 16.$

Subtracting the second equation from the first cancels out the y terms leaving $-x = -4$ or $x = 4$. Now substitute 4 for x into either equation to solve for y.

Common Errors With Solving Systems of Equations by Substitution

When solving by substitution, students may substitute into the same equation they used to isolate a variable.

The example below illustrates this common error:

$3y = x + 1$ $x = 3y - 1$

$2x + y = 12$ $3y = (3y - 1) + 1$

$0 = 0$

$3y - 1$ should be substituted into the second equation, not the first.

Systems of Inequalities

Like systems of linear equations, you can solve systems of inequalities by graphing. To solve the system

$y > \frac{1}{2}x + 1$

$y \leq -\frac{1}{3}x + 1$

first graph each line. Then shade the areas above or below each line, as appropriate. The solution to the system is the area where the shaded regions overlap.

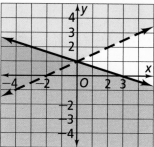

The dotted line in the graph corresponds to the inequality ($>$) in the first inequality, while the solid line corresponds to the inequality ($\leq$) in the second inequality.

The solution of the system of inequalities $y > \frac{1}{2}x + 1$ and $y \leq -\frac{1}{3}x + 1$ is the set of all ordered pairs that makes both inequalities true. The solutions are represented on a graph by the overlapping shaded areas. The dotted line indicates that points that lie on the line $y = \frac{1}{2}x + 1$ are not part of the solution set, while points that lie on the solid line $y = -\frac{1}{3}x + 1$ are part of the solution set.

Like systems of equations, it is possible that systems of inequalities do not have solution sets. Consider the following graph.

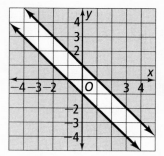

The shaded regions do not intersect, and so there are no solutions to the system of inequalities that corresponds to the graph.

Common Errors With Systems of Inequalities

When students are graphing a system of inequalities, they might shade the wrong side of the line. Using a test point can help avoid this mistake. The origin is often a good point to use.

SYSTEMS OF EQUATIONS AND INEQUALITIES
Pacing and Assignment Guide

		TRADITIONAL			BLOCK
Lesson	Teaching Day(s)	Basic	Average	Advanced	Block
6-1	1	Problems 1-3 Exs. 10–34, 36, 38, 43–57	Problems 1-3 Exs. 11–29 odd, 31–40, 43–57	Problems 1-3 Exs. 11–29 odd, 31–57	**Day 1** Problems 1-3 Exs. 11–29 odd, 31–40, 43–57
6-2	1	Problems 1-2 Exs. 11–22, 44–57	Problems 1-4 Exs. 11–31 odd, 32–41, 44–57	Problems 1-4 Exs. 11–31 odd, 32–57	Problems 1-4 Exs. 11–31 odd, 32–41, 44–57
	2	Problems 3-4 Exs. 23–31, 33–38			
6-3	1	Problems 1-2 Exs. 7–14 all, 45–56	Problems 1-2 Exs. 7–13 odd, 45–56	Problems 1-2 Exs. 7–13 odd, 45–56	**Day 2** Problems 1-5 Exs. 7–25 odd, 27–40 45–56
	2	Problems 3-5 Exs. 15–30 all, 32–38 even	Problems 3-5 Exs. 15–25 odd, 27–40	Problems 3-5 Exs. 15–25 odd, 27–44	
6-4	1	Problems 1-3 Exs. 7–12, 13–16, 18–21, 23, 25, 29–37	Problems 1-3 Exs. 7–11 odd, 13–26, 29–37	Problems 1-3 Exs. 7–11 odd, 13–37	**Day 3** Problems 1-3 Exs. 7–11 odd, 13–26, 29–37
6-5	1	Problems 1-2 Exs. 8–21, 42–49	Problems 1-2 Exs. 9–21 odd, 42–49	Problems 1-2 Exs. 9–21 odd, 42–49	Problems 1-2 Exs. 9–21 odd, 42–49
	2	Problems 3-5 Exs. 22–37, 42–49	Problems 3-5 Exs. 23–33 odd, 35–38	Problems 3-5 Exs. 23–33 odd, 35–41	**Day 4** Problems 3-5 Exs. 23–33 odd, 35–38
6-6	1	Problems 1-3 Exs. 7–27, 28, 30, 31, 33, 39–48	Problems 1-3 Exs. 7–27 odd, 28–35, 39–48	Problems 1-3 Exs. 7–27 odd, 28–48	Problems 1-3 Exs. 7–27 odd, 28–35, 39–48
Review	1	Chapter 6 Review	Chapter 6 Review	Chapter 6 Review	**Day 5** Chapter 6 Review
Assess	1	Chapter 6 Test	Chapter 6 Test	Chapter 6 Test	Chapter 6 Test
Total		**11 Days**	**10 Days**	**10 Days**	**5 Days**

Note: Pacing does not include Concept Bytes and other feature pages.

Resources

	For the Chapter	6-1	6-2	6-3	6-4	6-5	6-6
Planning							
Teacher Center Online Planner & Grade Book	I	I	I	I	I	I	I
Interactive Learning & Guided Instruction							
My Math Video	I						
Solve It!		I TM	I TM	I TM	I TM	I TM	I TM
Student Companion (SP)*		P M	P M	P M	P M	P M	
Vocabulary Support		I P M	I P M	I P M	I P M	I P M	I P M
Got It? Support		I P	I P	I P	I P	I P	I P
Dynamic Activity	I				I	I	I
Online Problems	I	I	I	I	I	I	I
Additional Problems		M	M	M	M	M	M
English Language Learner Support (TR)		E P M	E P M	E P M	E P M	E P M	E P M
Activities, Games, and Puzzles		E M	E M	E M	E M	E M	E M
Teaching With TI Technology With CD-ROM		✓ P	✓ P			✓ P	✓ P
TI-Nspire™ Support CD-ROM		✓	✓	✓	✓	✓	✓
Lesson Check & Practice							
Student Companion (SP)*		P M	P M	P M	P M	P M	P M
Lesson Check Support		I P	I P	I P	I P	I P	I P
Practice and Problem Solving Workbook (SP)		P	P	P	P	P	P
Think About a Plan (TR)*		E P M	E P M	E P M	E P M	E P M	E P M
Practice Form G (TR)*		E P M	E P M	E P M	E P M	E P M	E P M
Standardized Test Prep (TR)*		P M	P M	P M	P M	P M	P M
Practice Form K (TR)*		E P M	E P M	E P M	E P M	E P M	E P M
Extra Practice	E M						
Find the Errors!	M						
Enrichment (TR)		E P M	E P M	E P M	E P M	E P M	E P M
Answers and Solutions CD-ROM	✓	✓	✓	✓	✓	✓	✓
Assess & Remediate							
ExamView CD-ROM	✓	✓	✓	✓	✓	✓	✓
Lesson Quiz		I TM	I TM	I TM	I TM	I TM	I TM
Quizzes and Tests Form G (TR)*	E P M				E P M		E P M
Quizzes and Tests Form K (TR)*	E P M				E P M		E P M
Reteaching (TR)*		E P M	E P M	E P M	E P M	E P M	E P M
Performance Tasks (TR)*	P M						
Cumulative Review (TR)*	P M						
Progress Monitoring Assessments	I P M						

(TR) Available in All-In-One Teaching Resources   *Spanish available

1 Interactive Learning

Solve It!

PURPOSE To determine if two linear equations that represent a real-world situation intersect within a specified domain

PROCESS Students may make a table of values, use the formula $r \cdot t = d$, or write a linear equation to model each skier.

> ### FACILITATE
>
> **Q** How long does it take Skier 1 to finish the course? Skier 2? Explain. **[50 s; He travels 100 feet every second; 45.46 s; He travels 110 feet every second.]**
>
> **Q** If a stopwatch starts when Skier 1 leaves the chute, what will the stopwatch read when Skier 1 crosses the finish line? when Skier 2 crosses the finish line? **[50 s; 50.46 s]**

ANSWER See Solve It in Answers on next page.

CONNECT THE MATH The speeds are like the slopes of lines. When two lines have different slopes, the lines intersect. The point of intersection represents when one skier catches up with the other skier.

2 Guided Instruction

Problem 1

> **Q** How are the solutions to the two equations represented graphically? **[Every point on each line is a solution to the respective equation.]**
>
> **Q** Is it possible for two lines to have exactly two, three, or four points in common? Explain. **[No, two lines can only intersect in zero, one, or infinitely many points.]**

6-1 Solving Systems by Graphing

Indiana Academic Standard
A1.3.1 Understand the relationship between a solution of a pair of linear equations in two variables and the graphs of the corresponding lines and solve pairs of linear equations in two variables by graphing, substitution or elimination.

Objectives To solve systems of equations by graphing
To analyze special systems

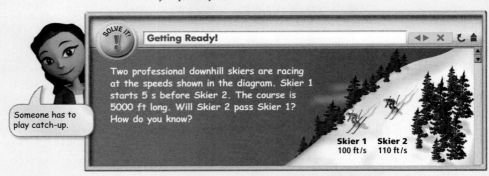

Someone has to play catch-up.

Two professional downhill skiers are racing at the speeds shown in the diagram. Skier 1 starts 5 s before Skier 2. The course is 5000 ft long. Will Skier 2 pass Skier 1? How do you know?

Skier 1   Skier 2
100 ft/s   110 ft/s

You can model the problem in the Solve It with two linear equations. Two or more linear equations form a **system of linear equations.** Any ordered pair that makes *all* of the equations in a system true is a **solution of a system of linear equations.**

Essential Understanding You can use systems of linear equations to model problems. Systems of equations can be solved in more than one way. One method is to graph each equation and find the intersection point, if one exists.

Lesson Vocabulary
• system of linear equations
• solution of a system of linear equations
• consistent
• independent
• dependent
• inconsistent

Think

How does graphing each equation help you find the solution?
A line represents the solutions of *one* linear equation. The intersection point is a solution of *both* equations.

Problem 1   Solving a System of Equations by Graphing

What is the solution of the system? Use a graph. $y = x + 2$
$y = 3x - 2$

Graph both equations in the same coordinate plane.

   The slope is 1. The y-intercept is 2.

$y = 3x - 2$ The slope is 3. The y-intercept is -2.

Find the point of intersection. The lines appear to intersect at (2, 4). Check to see if (2, 4) makes both equations true.

$$y = x + 2$$
$$4 \stackrel{?}{=} 2 + 2$$
$$4 = 4 \ ✔$$

Substitute (2, 4) for (x, y).

$$y = 3x - 2$$
$$4 \stackrel{?}{=} 3(2) - 2$$
$$4 = 4 \ ✔$$

The solution of the system is (2, 4).

6-1 Preparing to Teach

UbD

BIG ideas Solving Equations & Inequalities
Modeling

ESSENTIAL UNDERSTANDINGS
• Systems of linear equations can be used to model problems.
• Systems of equations can be solved in more than one way.
• One method is to graph each equation and find the intersection point, if one exists.

Math Background

The use of graphing to solve a system of equations has become a powerful investigative tool. With graphing calculators and graphing software, technology has opened the door to quickly and easily make changes to equations and see how these changes impact the location and steepness of a line. For instance, if students graph the lines of the equations $y = 3x - 6$ and $x - \frac{y}{3} = 2$; they will see that the equations represent the same line.

Changing the -6 in the first equation displays two parallel lines. Changing the slope of one of the lines results in two lines that intersect in one point. The ease of making changes to the equation being graphed invites students to experiment to see what changes result in intersection in each of the four quadrants.

Any equation in one variable can be written as a system of equations in two variables. For example, the equation $-4x + 9 = x + 3$ can be written as the system of equations $y = -4x + 9$ and $y = x + 3$. If the original equation is not in simplified form, a graphing calculator can be used to graph both equations and locate their point(s) of intersection.

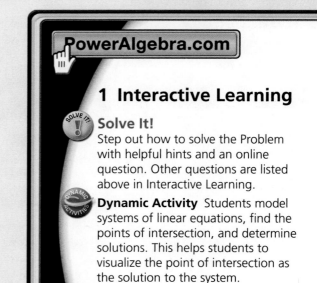

PowerAlgebra.com

1 Interactive Learning

Solve It!
Step out how to solve the Problem with helpful hints and an online question. Other questions are listed above in Interactive Learning.

Dynamic Activity Students model systems of linear equations, find the points of intersection, and determine solutions. This helps students to visualize the point of intersection as the solution to the system.

Got It? **1.** What is the solution of the system? Use a graph. $\quad y = 2x + 4$

Check your answer. $\qquad\qquad\qquad\qquad y = x + 2$

Problem 2 Writing a System of Equations

Biology Scientists studied the weights of two alligators over a period of 12 months. The initial weight and growth rate of each alligator are shown below. After how many months did the alligators weigh the same amount?

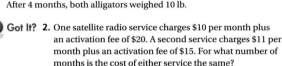

ALLIGATOR 1
Initial Weight: 4 lb
Rate of Growth:
1.5 lb per month

ALLIGATOR 2
Initial Weight: 6 lb
Rate of Growth:
1 lb per month

Dynamic Activity
Solving Linear
Systems by
Graphing

Think

Is there another way to solve this problem?
Yes. You can make a *table*. Show the weight of each alligator after 1 month, 2 months, and so on.

Relate | alligator weight | is | initial weight | plus | growth rate | times | time |

Define Let w = alligator weight.
Let t = time in months.

Write Alligator 1: $\quad w \quad = \quad 4 \quad + \quad 1.5 \quad \cdot \quad t$

Alligator 2: $\quad w \quad = \quad 6 \quad + \quad 1 \quad \cdot \quad t$

Graph both equations in the same coordinate plane.

$w = 4 + 1.5t$ The slope is 1.5. The w-intercept is 4.

$w = 6 + t$ The slope is 1. The w-intercept is 6.

The lines intersect at (4, 10).

After 4 months, both alligators weighed 10 lb.

Alligator Weights

Weight, w (lb)

(4, 10)

12
10
8
6
4
2
0
0 1 2 3 4 5 6 7
Time, t (months)

 Got It? **2.** One satellite radio service charges $10 per month plus an activation fee of $20. A second service charges $11 per month plus an activation fee of $15. For what number of months is the cost of either service the same?

A system of equations that has at least one solution is **consistent.** A consistent system can be either *independent* or *dependent*.

A consistent system that is **independent** has exactly one solution. For example, the systems in Problems 1 and 2 are consistent and independent. A consistent system that is **dependent** has infinitely many solutions.

A system of equations that has no solution is **inconsistent.**

---

2 Guided Instruction

Each Problem is worked out and supported online.

Problem 1
Solving a System of Equations by Graphing
Animated

Problem 2
Writing a System of Equations
Animated

Problem 3
Systems With Infinitely Many Solutions or No Solution

Alternative Problem 3
Systems With Infinitely Many Solutions or No Solution
Animated

Support in Algebra 1 Companion
• Vocabulary
• Key Concepts
• Got It?

Got It?

Q How do you know that these lines intersect? **[The slopes are different.]**

Problem 2

Q What are the independent and dependent variables for the situation? **[Weight, in pounds, is the dependent variable. Time, in months, is the independent variable.]**

Q What are the rates of change for each alligator? **[Alligator 1: 1.5 pounds per month, Alligator 2: 1 pound per month]**

Q What method of graphing will you use to graph the equations? Why? **[Answers may vary. Sample answer: slope-intercept method because the equations are written in slope-intercept form]**

Q When is graphing an efficient method for solving a system of equations? **[Answers may vary. Sample answer: when the point of intersection is at integral points on the grid and the point of intersection is included in the coordinate grid on which you graph the lines]**

Got It? SYNTHESIZING

Show students that this problem can also be solved by creating a table of values for both services. The solution is determined by finding the table entry in which the dependent variables are equivalent.

Answers

Solve It!
No; Skier 1 will reach the finish line 50 ft ahead of Skier 2; explanations may vary.

Got It?
1. (−2, 0)
2. 5 months

Problem 3

Q What method will you use to graph the first equation? Explain. **[the intercept method because the equation is in a form that makes substituting 0 for *x* and *y* easy]**

Q What is the most efficient method for graphing the second equation? Explain. **[the slope-intercept method because the equation is in slope-intercept form]**

Q If you write the first equation in slope-intercept form, what can you find out about the solution to the system? **[The equations represent that same line because they have equal slopes and the same *y*-intercept.]**

Got It?   ELL SUPPORT

Explain the concept of an infinite number of solutions. Make sure that students understand the difference between an infinite number of solutions for 3b, and the statement that *all* ordered pairs are solutions. Only ordered pairs that lie on the line are solutions to the system of equations.

Take Note

Q What is an example of an independent system of linear equations written in slope-intercept form? **[Check that students' work shows two equations of lines with different slopes.]**

Q What is an example of a dependent system of linear equations written in slope-intercept form? **[Check that students' work shows two equations of lines with the same slopes and the same *y*-intercepts.]**

Q What is an example of an inconsistent system of linear equations written in slope-intercept form? **[Check that students' work shows two different equations of lines with the same slopes, but different *y*-intercepts.]**

Think
If two equations have the same slope and *y*-intercept, their graphs will be the same line. If two equations have the same slope but different *y*-intercepts, their graphs will be parallel lines.

 Problem 3 Systems With Infinitely Many Solutions or No Solution

What is the solution of each system? Use a graph.

A $2y - x = 2$
$y = \frac{1}{2}x + 1$

Graph the equations $2y - x = 2$ and $y = \frac{1}{2}x + 1$ in the same coordinate plane.

The equations represent the same line. Any point on the line is a solution of the system, so there are infinitely many solutions. The system is consistent and dependent.

B $y = 2x + 2$
$y = 2x - 1$

Graph the equations $y = 2x + 2$ and $y = 2x - 1$ in the same coordinate plane.

The lines are parallel, so there is no solution. The system is inconsistent.

✓ **Got It?** **3.** What is the solution of each system in parts (a) and (b)? Use a graph. Describe the number of solutions.

   a. $y = -x - 3$ **b.** $y = 3x - 3$
        $y = -x + 5$ $3y = 9x - 9$

   c. **Reasoning** Before graphing the equations, how can you determine whether a system of equations has exactly one solution, infinitely many solutions, or no solution?

---

take note ➤ **Concept Summary**   **Systems of Linear Equations**

One solution	Infinitely many solutions	No solution
The lines intersect at one point. The lines have different slopes. The equations are consistent and independent.	The lines are the same. The lines have the same slope and *y*-intercept. The equations are consistent and dependent.	The lines are parallel. The lines have the same slope and different *y*-intercepts. The equations are inconsistent.

Additional Problems

1. What is the solution of the system? Use a graph.

$y = 2x - 1$
$y = 4x - 7$

ANSWER (3, 5)

2. Suppose one puppy weighs 5 pounds at birth and grows at a rate of 0.25 pound per month over the first several months. Another puppy weighs 4 pounds at birth and grows at a rate of 0.5 pound per month. After how many months will the puppies weigh the same amount?

ANSWER 4

3. What is the solution of each system? Use a graph.

a. $3y = x - 2$
    $-6y = -2x + 4$

b. $y = 5x - 6$
    $y = 5x + 4$

ANSWER a. infinitely many solutions; **b.** no solution

Answers

Got It? (continued)

3. a. no solution

   b. infinitely many solutions

   c. Systems with one solution have lines with different slopes. Systems with no solutions have the same slope but different *y*-intercepts. Systems with infinitely many solutions have the same slope and the same *y*-intercept.

Lesson Check

Do you know HOW?

Solve each system by graphing.

1. $y = x + 7$
$y = 2x + 1$

2. $y = \frac{1}{2}x + 6$
$y = x - 2$

3. $y = -3x - 3$
$y = 2x + 2$

4. $y = -x - 4$
$4x - y = -1$

5. Concert Tickets Tickets for a concert cost $10 each if you order them online, but you must pay a service charge of $8 per order. The tickets are $12 each if you buy them at the door on the night of the concert.

  a. Write a system of equations to model the situation. Let c be the total cost. Let t be the number of tickets.

  b. Graph the equations and find the intersection point. What does this point represent?

Do you UNDERSTAND?

6. Vocabulary Match each type of system with the number of solutions the system has.

  A. inconsistent   **I.** exactly one
  B. consistent and dependent   **II.** infinitely many
  C. consistent and independent   **III.** no solution

7. Writing Suppose you graph a system of linear equations. If a point is on only one of the lines, is it a solution of the system? Explain.

8. Reasoning Can a system of two linear equations have exactly two solutions? Explain.

9. Reasoning Suppose you find that two linear equations are true when $x = -2$ and $y = 3$. What can you conclude about the graphs of the equations? Explain.

Practice and Problem-Solving Exercises

Ⓐ Practice

Solve each system by graphing. Check your solution.   ◀ See Problem 1.

10. $y = 2x$
$y = -2x + 8$

11. $y = \frac{1}{2}x + 7$
$y = \frac{3}{2}x + 3$

12. $y = \frac{1}{3}x + 1$
$y = -3x + 11$

13. $y = x - 4$
$y = -x$

14. $y = -x + 3$
$y = x + 1$

15. $4x - y = -1$
$-x + y = x - 5$

16. $y = -\frac{1}{2}x + 2$
$y = \frac{1}{2}x + 6$

17. $2x - y = -5$
$-2x - y = -1$

18. $x = -3$
$y = 5$

19. Student Statistics The number of right-handed students in a mathematics class   ◀ See Problem 2.
is nine times the number of left-handed students. The total number of students in the class is 30. How many right-handed students are in the class? How many left-handed students are in the class?

20. Plants A plant nursery is growing a tree that is 3 ft tall and grows at an average rate of 1 ft per year. Another tree at the nursery is 4 ft tall and grows at an average rate of 0.5 ft per year. After how many years will the trees be the same height?

21. Fitness At a local fitness center, members pay a $20 membership fee and $3 for each aerobics class. Nonmembers pay $5 for each aerobics class. For what number of aerobics classes will the cost for members and nonmembers be the same?

---

3 Lesson Check

Do you know HOW?

- If students have difficulty graphing these Exercises 1–4, then remind them that once the equations are written in slope-intercept form, they can determine by visual inspection if the equations have 0, 1, or an infinite number of solutions and the corresponding relationship between the graphs of the lines.

Do you UNDERSTAND?

- If students have difficulty with Exercise 8, then have them try to draw a graphical representation of two lines that have exactly two solutions (intersect in two points).

Close

Q How is graphing used to solve a system of equations? **[When both equations in a system of equations are graphed on the same coordinate grid, you can determine the solution of the system by locating the point(s) that the two lines have in common.]**

Lesson Check

1. (6, 13)
2. (16, 14)
3. (−1, 0)
4. (−1, −3)
5. a. $c = 10t + 8$
$c = 12t$

  b. (4, 48); the cost is the same whether you buy 4 tickets for a cost of $48 online or at the door.

6. A, III; B, II; C, I

7. No; a solution to the system must be on both lines.

8. No; two lines intersect in no points, one point, or an infinite number of points.

9. The graphs of the equations both contain the point (−2, 3).

Practice and Problem-Solving Exercises

10. (2, 4)
11. (4, 9)
12. (3, 2)
13. (2, −2)
14. (1, 2)
15. (−3, −11)
16. (−4, 4)
17. (−1, 3)
18. (−3, 5)
19. 27 students; 3 students
20. 2 yr
21. 10 classes

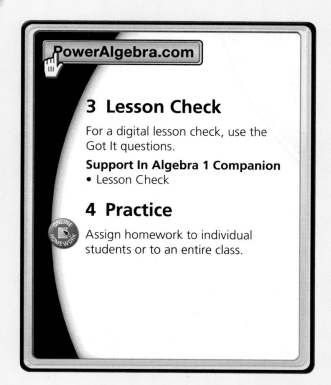

PowerAlgebra.com

3 Lesson Check

For a digital lesson check, use the Got It questions.

Support In Algebra 1 Companion
- Lesson Check

4 Practice

Assign homework to individual students or to an entire class.

4 Practice

ASSIGNMENT GUIDE

Basic: 10–34, 36, 38

Average: 11–29 odd, 31–40

Advanced: 11–29 odd, 31–42

Standardized Test Prep: 43–45

Mixed Review: 46–57

Reasoning exercises have blue headings.

Applications exercises have red headings.

EXERCISE 34: Use the Think About a Plan worksheet in the **Practice and Problem Solving Workbook** (also available in the Teaching Resources in print and online) to further support students' development in becoming independent learners.

HOMEWORK QUICK CHECK

To check students' understanding of key skills and concepts, go over Exercises 11, 25, 31, 33, and 34.

Solve each system by graphing. Tell whether the system has *one solution*, *infinitely many solutions*, or *no solution*. See Problem 3.

22. $y = x + 3$
$y = x - 1$

23. $y = 2x - 1$
$3y = 6x - 5$

24. $3x + y = 2$
$4y = 12 - 12x$

25. $2x - 2y = 5$
$y = x - 4$

26. $y = 2x - 2$
$2y = 4x - 4$

27. $y - x = 5$
$3y = 3x + 15$

28. $2x + 2y = 4$
$12 - 3x = 3y$

29. $2y = x - 2$
$3y = \frac{3}{2}x - 3$

30. $3x - y = 2$
$4y = -x + 5$

 Apply

31. Think About a Plan You are looking for an after-school job. One job pays $9 per hour. Another pays $12 per hour, but you must buy a uniform that costs $39. After how many hours of work would your net earnings from either job be the same?
• What equations can you write to model the situation?
• How will graphing the equations help you solve the problem?

32. Error Analysis A student graphs the system $y = -x + 3$ and $y = -2x - 1$ as shown at the right. The student concludes there is no solution. Describe and correct the student's error.

33. Reasoning Suppose you graph a system of linear equations and the intersection point appears to be (3, 7). Can you be sure that the ordered pair (3, 7) is the solution? What must you do to be sure?

34. Cell Phone Plans A cell phone provider offers a plan that costs $40 per month plus $.20 per text message sent or received. A comparable plan costs $60 per month but offers unlimited text messaging.
a. How many text messages would you have to send or receive in order for the plans to cost the same each month?
b. If you send or receive an average of 50 text messages each month, which plan would you choose? Why?

Without graphing, decide whether each system has *one solution*, *infinitely many solutions*, or *no solution*. Justify your answer.

35. $y = x - 4$
$y = x - 3$

36. $x - y = -\frac{1}{2}$
$2x - 2y = -1$

37. $y = 5x - 1$
$10x = 2y + 2$

38. $3x + 2y = 1$
$4y = 6x + 2$

39. Banking The graph at the right shows the balances in two bank accounts over time. Use the graph to write a system of equations giving the amount in each account over time. Let $t = $ the time in weeks and let $b = $ the balance in dollars. If the accounts continue to grow as shown, when will they have the same balance?

40. Open-Ended One equation in a system is $y = \frac{1}{2}x - 2$.
a. Write a second equation so that the system has one solution.
b. Write a second equation so that the system has no solution.
c. Write a second equation so that the system has infinitely many solutions.

Account Balances

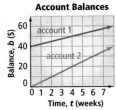

Answers

Practice and Problem-Solving Exercises
(continued)

22.

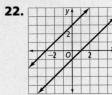

no solution

23.

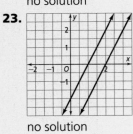

no solution

24.

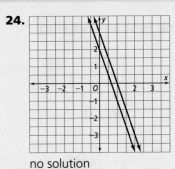

no solution

25.

no solution

26.

infinitely many solutions

27.

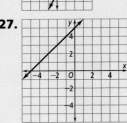

infinitely many solutions

28.

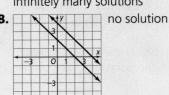 no solution

41. Reasoning Consider the system at the right.
$$y = gx + 3$$
$$y = hx + 7$$
a. If $g \geq h$, will the system *always, sometimes,* or *never* have exactly one solution? Explain your reasoning.
b. If $g \leq h$, will the system *always, sometimes,* or *never* have infinitely many solutions? Explain your reasoning.

42. Hiking Two hikers are walking along a marked trail. The first hiker starts at a point 6 mi from the beginning of the trail and walks at a speed of 4 mi/h. At the same time, the second hiker starts 1 mi from the beginning and walks at a speed of 3 mi/h.
a. What is a system of equations that models the situation?
b. Graph the two equations and find the intersection point.
c. Is the intersection point meaningful in this situation? Explain.

Standardized Test Prep

SAT/ACT

43. Which ordered pair is the solution of the system?
$$2x + 3y = -17$$
$$3x + 2y = -8$$
Ⓐ $(2, -7)$ Ⓑ $(-4, 2)$ Ⓒ $(-2, -1)$ Ⓓ $\left(-\frac{4}{3}, -2\right)$

44. Which expression is equivalent to $5(m - 12) + 8$?
Ⓕ $5m - 68$ Ⓖ $5m - 20$ Ⓗ $5m - 4$ Ⓘ $5m - 52$

Extended Response

45. The costs for parking in two different parking garages are given in the table at the right.
a. What is a system of equations that models the situation?
b. How many hours of parking would cost the same parking in either garage?
c. If you needed to park a car for 3 h, which garage would you choose? Why?

Garage Parking Fees

Garage	Flat Fee	Hourly Fee
A	$5	$2.50
B	$20	$0

Mixed Review

Graph each function by translating the graph of $y = |x|$.   ◀ See Lesson 5-8.

46. $y = |x| - 2$ **47.** $y = |x| - 1$ **48.** $y = |x + 3|$ **49.** $y = |x + 2|$

Find the slope of a line that is parallel to the graph of the equation.   ◀ See Lesson 5-6.

50. $y = x + 3$ **51.** $y = -\frac{1}{2}x - 4$ **52.** $3y + 2x = 7$ **53.** $3x = 5y + 10$

Get Ready! To prepare for Lesson 6-2, do Exercises 54–57.

Solve each equation for y.   ◀ See Lesson 2-5.

54. $4x + 2y = 38$ **55.** $\frac{1}{2}x + \frac{1}{3}y = 5$ **56.** $\frac{3}{2}y = \frac{4}{5}x$ **57.** $1.5x - 4.5y = 21$

29.
infinitely many solutions

30.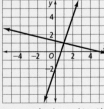
one solution: $(1, 1)$

31. 13 h

32. The student did not show enough of the graph. If you continue the graph to the left, the lines will intersect at the point $(-4, 7)$.

33. You should substitute the values of x and y into both equations to make sure that true statements result.

34. a. 100 messages
b. the plan that costs $40 per month and $.20 per text message

35. No solution; the lines have the same slope and different y-intercepts so they are parallel.

36. Infinitely many solutions; the lines are the same.

37. Infinitely many solutions; the lines are the same.

38. One solution; the lines have different slopes so they intersect.

39. $b = 2.5t + 40$; 16 weeks
$b = 5t$

40. a. Answers may vary. Sample:
$y = 2x + 8$
b. Answers may vary: Sample:
$y = \frac{1}{2}x + 7$
c. Answers may vary: Sample:
$2y = x - 4$

---

41. a. Sometimes; if $g > h$, the lines intersect at one point, but if $g = h$, the lines never intersect.
b. Never; if $g < h$, the lines intersect at one point, but if $g = h$, the lines never intersect.

42. a. $y = 4x + 6$
$y = 3x + 1$
where x is the number of hours hiking and y is the distance from the beginning of the trail
b. $(-5, -14)$

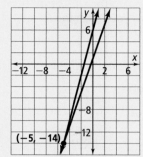

c. No; -14 represents 14 mi before the beginning of the trail.

43. A   **44.** I

45. [4] **a.** $C = 20$
$C = 2.5h + 5$
b. 6 h
c. Garage A; it costs less for the time given.
[3] appropriate methods with one calculation error
[2] system correct but graphed incorrectly OR system incorrect but graphed appropriately given work
[1] correct answers with no work shown

46. 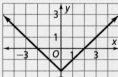   **47.**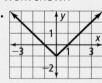

48.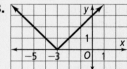

49.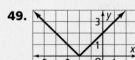

50. 1   **51.** $-\frac{1}{2}$
52. $-\frac{2}{3}$ **53.** $\frac{3}{5}$
54. $y = -2x + 19$ **55.** $y = -\frac{3}{2}x + 15$
56. $y = \frac{8}{15}x$ **57.** $y = \frac{1}{3}x - \frac{14}{3}$

Additional Instructional Support

Algebra 1 Companion

Students can use the **Algebra 1 Companion** worktext (4 pages) as you teach the lesson. Use the Companion to support

- New Vocabulary
- Key Concepts
- Got It for each Problem
- Lesson Check

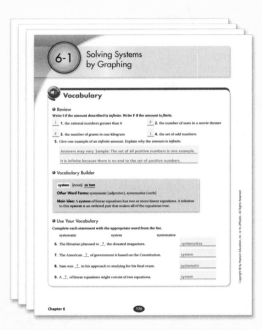

ELL Support

Focus on Language Place students in groups with different levels of language proficiency. Say: Write *consistent* on an index card. Have each student also write the words *inconsistent*, *dependent*, and *independent* on index cards. Ask students, What do all four words have in common? [end in *ent*]. What do two of the words have in common? [begin with *in*] Have students work with their group. On the back of each card, they should write a definition and an illustration of the concept (including graphs and sample equations).

Say: In your groups, write equations to illustrate each of the words. Pair groups and say: Have the other group decide which of the words *consistent*, *inconsistent*, *dependent*, and *independent* describe each of your equations.

5 Assess & Remediate

Lesson Quiz

1. What is the solution of the system?

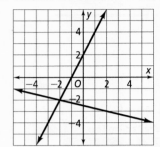

2. Do you UNDERSTAND? One electrician charges a $50 service call fee plus $25 per hour for labor. Another electrician charges a $35 service call fee plus $27.50 per hour for labor. How long would a job take if the total cost for each electrician is the same?

3. What is the solution of the system of equations? Explain.

$$y = \frac{1}{2}x + 4$$

$$2y + 4 = x$$

ANSWERS TO LESSON QUIZ

1. $(-2, -2)$

2. 6 h

3. There is no solution. The lines are parallel.

PRESCRIPTION FOR REMEDIATION
Use the student work on the Lesson Quiz to prescribe a differentiated review assignment.

Points	Differentiated Remediation
0–1	Intervention
2	On-level
3	Extension

PowerAlgebra.com

5 Assess & Remediate

Assign the Lesson Quiz. Appropriate intervention, practice, or enrichment is automatically generated based on student performance.

Intervention

- **Reteaching** (2 pages) Provides reteaching and practice exercises for the key lesson concepts. Use with struggling students or absent students.

- **English Language Learner Support** Helps students develop and reinforce mathematical vocabulary and key concepts.

All-in-One Resources/Online
Reteaching

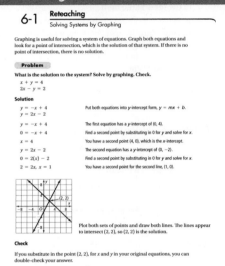

All-in-One Resources/Online
English Language Learner Support

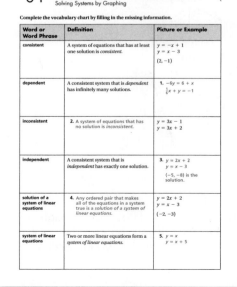

Differentiated Remediation *continued*

On-Level

- **Practice** (2 pages) Provides extra practice for each lesson. For simpler practice exercises, use the Form K Practice pages found in the All-in-One Teaching Resources and online.

- **Think About a Plan** Helps students develop specific problem-solving skills and strategies by providing scaffolded guiding questions.

- **Standardized Test Prep** Focuses on all major exercises, all major question types, and helps students prepare for the high-stakes assessments.

Extension

- **Enrichment** Provides students with interesting problems and activities that extend the concepts of the lesson.

- **Activities, Games, and Puzzles** Worksheets that can be used for concepts development, enrichment, and for fun!

Practice and Problem Solving WKBK/ All-in-One Resources/Online
Practice page 1

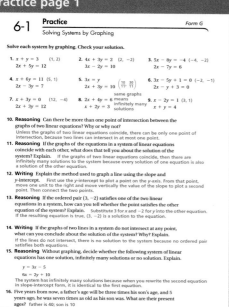

Practice and Problem Solving WKBK/ All-in-One Resources/Online
Practice page 2

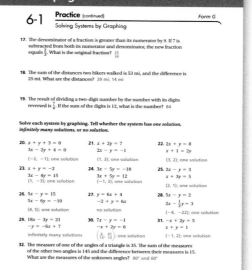

All-in-One Resources/Online
Enrichment

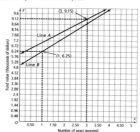

Practice and Problem Solving WKBK/ All-in-One Resources/Online
Think About a Plan

Practice and Problem Solving WKBK/ All-in-One Resources/Online
Standardized Test Prep

Online Teacher Resource Center
Activities, Games, and Puzzles

Guided Instruction

PURPOSE To use the table and graphing functions on a graphing calculator to solve a system of linear equations

PROCESS Students will
- use the table function on a graphing calculator to solve systems of equations.
- use the graph function on a graphing calculator to solve systems of equations.

DISCUSS Discuss the advantages and disadvantages of solving systems of equations using a table and a graph. When is one method preferred?

Activity
In this Activity students focus on using tables to find solutions to a system of equations.

> **Q** When entering more than one equation into the $Y=$ screen, does it matter which equation is entered first? **[No, the order of the equations does not matter.]**
>
> **Q** What is the difference between the Auto and Ask options on the table setup screen on the graphing calculator? **[The Auto option automatically calculates the table starting with the x-value at 0. The Ask options asks the user to enter a number to indicate what number the x-value on the table should use to begin.]**

Activity
In this Activity students focus on using graphs to find solutions to a system of equations.

> **Q** When graphing more than one equation, how do you know which line represents which equation? **[The first equation's line will be drawn first; the second equation's line will be drawn second.]**
>
> **Q** What calculator function do you use to find the solution of a system of equations? **[INTERSECT]**

Concept Byte
Use With Lesson 6-1
TECHNOLOGY

Solving Systems Using Tables and Graphs

Indiana Academic Standard
A1.3.1 Understand the relationship between a solution of a pair of linear equations in two variables and the graphs of the corresponding lines and solve pairs of linear equations in two variables by graphing, substitution or elimination.

Activity
Solve the system using a table.
$$y = 3x - 7$$
$$y = -0.5x + 7$$

Step 1
Enter the equations in the **y=** screen.

```
Plot1   Plot2   Plot3
\Y1 ▣ 3X - 7
\Y2 ▣ -0.5X + 7
\Y3 = 5
\Y4 = 0
\Y5 = 1
\Y6 = 1
\Y7 = 1
```

Step 2
Use the **tblset** function. Set TblStart to 0 and $\triangle$ Tbl to 1.

```
TABLE SETUP
 TblStart = 0
  △ Tbl = 1
 Indpnt : Auto Ask
 Depend : Auto Ask
```

Step 3
Press **table** to show the table on the screen.

X	Y₁	Y₂
0	-7	7
1	-4	6.5
2	-1	6
3	2	5.5
4	5	5
5	8	4.5
6	11	4

X=0

1. Which x-value gives the same value for Y_1 and Y_2?

2. What ordered pair is the solution of the system?

Activity
Solve the system using a graph.
$$y = -5x + 6$$
$$y = -x - 2$$

Step 1 Enter the equations in the **y=** screen.

Step 2 Graph the equations. Use a standard graphing window.

Step 3 Use the **calc** feature. Choose **INTERSECT** to find the point where the lines intersect.

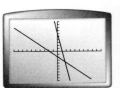

3. Copy and complete: The lines intersect at (_?_ , _?_), so this point is the solution of the system.

Exercises
Use a table and a graph to solve each system. Sketch your graph.

4. $y = 5x - 3$
$y = 3x + 1$

5. $y = 2x - 13$
$y = x - 9$

6. $2x - y = 1.5$
$y = -\frac{1}{2}x - 1.5$

Answers

Activity

1. 4   **2.** (4, 5)

Activity

3. 2, −4

Exercises

4. (2, 7)   **5.** (4, −5)   **6.** (0, −1.5)

Solving Systems Using Algebra Tiles

Indiana Academic Standard
A1.3.1 Understand the relationship between a solution of a pair of linear equations in two variables and the graphs of the corresponding lines and solve pairs of linear equations in two variables by graphing, substitution or elimination.

Just as algebra tiles can help you solve linear equations in one variable, they can also help you solve systems of linear equations in two variables.

Activity

Model and solve the system.

$-x + 2y = 4$
$y = x + 1$

Since $y = x + 1$, use tiles for $x + 1$ to model y.

Equation	Algebra Tiles	Steps
$-x + 2y = 4$ $-x + 2(x + 1) = 4$ $-x + 2x + 2 = 4$	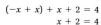	Substitute $x + 1$ for y in the first equation.
$(-x + x) + x + 2 = 4$ $x + 2 = 4$		Remove the zero pair x and $-x$.
$x + 2 - 2 = 4 - 2$		Subtract 2 from each side. Remove zero pairs.
$x = 2$		Solve for x.
$y = x + 1$		Model the second equation.
$y = 2 + 1$ $y = 3$		Substitute 2 for x and simplify.

The solution of the system is $(2, 3)$.

Exercises

Model and solve each system.

1. $y = x + 1$
$2x + y = 10$

2. $x + 4y = 1$
$x + 4 = y$

3. $y = 2x - 1$
$y = x + 2$

Guided Instruction

PURPOSE To use algebra tiles to solve systems of linear equations

PROCESS Students will
• model equations using algebra tiles.
• use algebra tiles to solve systems.

DISCUSS Have students discuss the concept of substitution. Ask why, in the example, the second equation was used to substitute into the first equation instead of the second equation. Highlight that y was already isolated in the second equation which makes it easier to be used for substitution.

Activity

In this Activity students focus on using substitution with algebra tiles to solve systems.

Q In the example, what was the first step? **[Substitution; $(x + 1)$ was substituted for y in the $-x + 2y = 4$ equation.]**

Q In the second picture, why are the red and green rectangles, representing x and $-x$, on the left side of the equals sign circled with an arrow attached? **[The rectangles are circled to represent the zero pair. The arrow indicates that the zero pair will be taken away from the equation.]**

ERROR PREVENTION
If students have difficulty following the illustrations, have them model the process with manipulatives.

Answers

Exercises

1. $(3, 4)$ **2.** $(-3, 1)$ **3.** $(3, 5)$

1 Interactive Learning

Solve It!

PURPOSE To use substitution to solve a real-world situation that can be represented by a system of linear equations

PROCESS Students may write a system of equations and solve by graphing, use substitution as mathematical reasoning, or use trial and error.

FACILITATE

Q In the second trade, what can you substitute in place of each house? **[3 cars and $100]**

Q According to the second diagram, what combination of cars and cash can you trade for a hotel? **[7 cars and $300]**

Q Given that a hotel is worth $2400 cash, how much cash are 7 cars worth? **[$2100]**

ANSWER See Solve It in Answers on next page.
CONNECT THE MATH Each trade can be modeled by an equation written in two variables. Together the equations become a system of equations and can be solved to find a solution for each variable that satisfies both equations.

2 Guided Instruction

Problem 1

Q What does a solution to both equations look like? How many solutions does each equation have? **[an ordered pair; infinite]**

Q What does $x = -8$ represent? **[the *x*-coordinate of the point where the two lines intersect]**

Q What does $y = -24$ represent? **[the *y*-coordinate of the point where the two lines intersect]**

6-2 Solving Systems Using Substitution

Indiana Academic Standard
A1.3.1 Understand the relationship between a solution of a pair of linear equations in two variables and the graphs of the corresponding lines and solve pairs of linear equations in two variables by graphing, substitution or elimination.

Objective To solve systems of equations using substitution

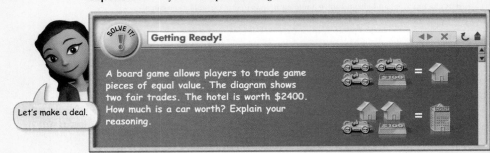

Let's make a deal.

Getting Ready!

A board game allows players to trade game pieces of equal value. The diagram shows two fair trades. The hotel is worth $2400. How much is a car worth? Explain your reasoning.

Lesson Vocabulary
• substitution method

You can model fair trades with a linear system. You can solve linear systems by solving one of the equations for one of the variables. Then substitute the expression for the variable into the other equation. This is called the **substitution method.**

Essential Understanding Systems of equations can be solved in more than one way. When a system has at least one equation that can be solved quickly for a variable, the system can be solved efficiently using substitution.

Problem 1 Using Substitution

What is the solution of the system? Use substitution.
$$y = 3x$$
$$x + y = -32$$

Plan

How can you get started?
If one equation is already solved for one variable, use it for the substitution. If both equations are solved for a variable, you can use either one.

Step 1 Because $y = 3x$, you can substitute $3x$ for y in $x + y = -32$.

$x + y = -32$	Write the second equation.
$x + 3x = -32$	Substitute $3x$ for y.
$4x = -32$	Simplify.
$x = -8$	Divide each side by 4.

Step 2 Substitute -8 for x in either equation and solve for y.

$y = 3x$	Write either equation.
$y = 3(-8) = -24$	Substitute -8 for x and solve.

The solution is $(-8, -24)$. Check by substituting $(-8, -24)$ into each equation.

UbD

BIG idea **Solving Equations & Inequalities**
ESSENTIAL UNDERSTANDINGS
• Systems of equations can be solved in more than one way.
• When a system has at least one equation that can be solved quickly for a variable, the system can be solved efficiently using substitution.

Math Background

Graphing is the first method introduced for solving systems of linear equations because graphing provides students with a visual representation of the common solution for the two equations. The substitution method is introduced next as an alternative using simple algebraic methods. Substitution depends on substituting an equal value into an equation. Although the topic of systems of equations is relatively new, the algebraic skills used to find a solution are basic.

Support Student Learning

Use the **Algebra 1 Companion** to engage and support students during instructions. See Lesson Resources at the end of this lesson for details.

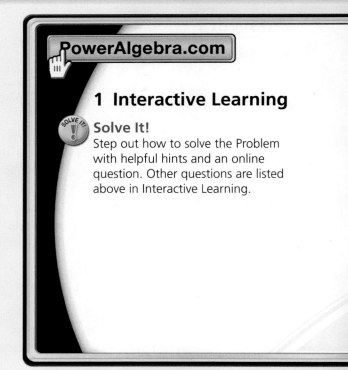

PowerAlgebra.com

1 Interactive Learning

Solve It!
Step out how to solve the Problem with helpful hints and an online question. Other questions are listed above in Interactive Learning.

Check

$$y = 3x \qquad\qquad x + y = -32$$
$$-24 \stackrel{?}{=} 3(-8) \qquad -8 + (-24) \stackrel{?}{=} -32$$
$$-24 = -24 \checkmark \qquad\qquad -32 = -32 \checkmark$$

 Got It? **1.** What is the solution of the system? Use substitution. $y = 2x + 7$
Check your answer. $\qquad\qquad\qquad\qquad\qquad y = x - 1$

To use substitution to solve a system of equations, one of the equations must be solved for a variable.

Problem 2 **Solving for a Variable and Using Substitution**

What is the solution of the system? Use substitution. $\quad 3y + 4x = 14$
$\qquad\qquad\qquad\qquad\qquad\qquad\qquad\qquad\qquad\qquad\qquad\qquad -2x + y = -3$

Know	**Need**	**Plan**
Neither equation is solved for one of the variables.	The solution of the system	Solve one of the equations for one of the variables. Then use the substitution method to find the solution of the system.

Think

Which variable should you solve for?
If one equation has a variable with a coefficient of 1 or −1, solve for that variable. It is generally easier to solve for a variable with a coefficient of 1 or −1.

Step 1 Solve one of the equations for one of the variables.

$$-2x + y = -3 \qquad \text{Write the second equation.}$$
$$-2x + y + 2x = -3 + 2x \qquad \text{Add } 2x \text{ to each side.}$$
$$y = 2x - 3 \qquad \text{Simplify.}$$

Step 2 Substitute $2x - 3$ for y in the other equation and solve for x.

$$3y + 4x = 14 \qquad \text{Write the first equation.}$$
$$3(2x - 3) + 4x = 14 \qquad \text{Substitute } 2x - 3 \text{ for } y. \text{ Use parentheses.}$$
$$6x - 9 + 4x = 14 \qquad \text{Distributive Property}$$
$$10x = 23 \qquad \text{Add 9 to each side. Simplify.}$$
$$x = 2.3 \qquad \text{Divide each side by 10.}$$

Step 3 Substitute 2.3 for x in either equation and solve for y.

$$-2x + y = -3 \qquad \text{Write either equation.}$$
$$-2(2.3) + y = -3 \qquad \text{Substitute 2.3 for } x.$$
$$-4.6 + y = -3 \qquad \text{Simplify.}$$
$$y = 1.6 \qquad \text{Add 4.6 to each side.}$$

The solution is (2.3, 1.6).

 Got It? **2. a.** What is the solution of the system? Use substitution. $\quad 6y + 5x = 8$
$\qquad\qquad\qquad\qquad\qquad\qquad\qquad\qquad\qquad\qquad\qquad\qquad\qquad x + 3y = -7$

b. Reasoning In your first step in part (a), which variable did you solve for? Which equation did you use to solve for the variable?

PowerAlgebra.com | **Lesson 6-2** Solving Systems Using Substitution | **369**

---

2 Guided Instruction

 Each Problem is worked out and supported online.

Problem 1
Using Substitution

Problem 2
Solving for a Variable and Using Substitution
Animated

Alternative Problem 2
Solving for a Variable and Using Substitution

Problem 3
Using Systems of Equations
Animated

Problem 4
Systems With Infinitely Many Solutions or No Solution
Animated

Alternative Problem 4
Systems With Infinitely Many Solutions or No Solution
Animated

Support in Algebra 1 Companion
• Vocabulary
• Key Concepts
• Got It?

Answers

Solve It!
$300; explanations may vary.

Got It?
1. $(-8, -9)$
2. a. $\left(7\frac{1}{3}, -4\frac{7}{9}\right)$
   b. x; $x + 3y = -7$

Problem 3

> **Q** Why is it impossible for either coordinate to be a non-whole number? **[Because it is not possible to sell part of a snack pack.]**
>
> **Q** Why is substituting the point into each equation not the best way to check your answer? How should you check your answer? **[Because you may have written your equations incorrectly. You should check your answer by making sure your answer satisfies the original situation.]**

Got It? SYNTHESIZING

In earlier lessons, students could have solved this problem by writing one linear equation letting x = the number of new games and $6 - x$ = the number of old games. Ask students how this is the same as the method of substitution.

Problem 4

> **Q** In 4A if you write each equation in slope-intercept form, what will you notice? What does this mean? **[The equations are the same. The graph of the equations is a single line.]**
>
> **Q** In 4B if you write each equation in slope-intercept form, what will you notice? What does this mean? **[The equations have the same slopes, but different y-intercepts. The lines are parallel.]**

Got It?

> **Q** Without solving or graphing, how do the coefficients and constant terms lead you to know there are an infinite number of solutions? **[The coefficient on each variable term and the constant term in the first equation is twice the corresponding terms in the second equation.]**

 Problem 3 Using Systems of Equations   GRIDDED RESPONSE

Snack Bar A snack bar sells two sizes of snack packs. A large snack pack is $5, and a small snack pack is $3. In one day, the snack bar sold 60 snack packs for a total of $220. How many small snack packs did the snack bar sell?

Step 1 Write the system of equations. Let x = the number of large $5 snack packs, and let y = the number of small $3 snack packs.

$x + y = 60$ Represent the total number of snack packs.

$5x + 3y = 220$ Represent the amount earned from 60 snack packs.

Step 2 $x + y = 60$ Use the first equation to solve for y.

$y = 60 - x$ Subtract x from each side.

Step 3 $5x + 3(60 - x) = 220$ Substitute $60 - x$ for y in the second equation.

$5x + 180 - 3x = 220$ Distributive Property

$2x = 40$ Simplify.

$x = 20$ Divide each side by 2.

Step 4 $20 + y = 60$ Substitute 20 for x in the first equation.

$y = 40$ Subtract 20 from each side.

Think

What does the solution represent in the real world?
Check what the assigned variables represent. Here, (20, 40) represents 20 large snack packs and 40 small snack packs.

The system's solution is (20, 40). The snack bar sold 40 small snack packs.

Got It? **3.** You pay $22 to rent 6 video games. The store charges $4 for new games and $2 for older games. How many new games did you rent?

If you get an identity, like $2 = 2$, when you solve a system of equations, then the system has infinitely many solutions. If you get a false statement, like $8 = 2$, then the system has no solution.

 Problem 4 Systems With Infinitely Many Solutions or No Solution

How many solutions does each system have?

Think

How many solutions can a system of linear equations have?
A system can have exactly one solution, infinitely many solutions, or no solution.

A $x = -2y + 4$
$3.5x + 7y = 14$

Substitute $-2y + 4$ for x in $3.5x + 7y = 14$.

$3.5x + 7y = 14$
$3.5(-2y + 4) + 7y = 14$
$-7y + 14 + 7y = 14$
$14 = 14$ ✔

The system has infinitely many solutions.

B $y = 3x - 11$
$y - 3x = -13$

Substitute $3x - 11$ for y in $y - 3x = -13$.

$y - 3x = -13$
$(3x - 11) - 3x = -13$
$-11 = -13$ ✗

The system has no solution.

Got It? **4.** How many solutions does the system have? $6y + 5x = 8$
$2.5x + 3y = 4$

Additional Problems

1. What is the solution of the system? Use substitution.

$y = 5x$
$x + y = 12$

ANSWER (2, 10)

2. What is the solution of the system? Use substitution.

$7x - 3y = 2$
$-2y + x = -6$

ANSWER (2, 4)

3. The school bookstore sells T-shirts for $8 and sweatshirts for $12. Last month, the bookstore sold 37 T-shirts and sweatshirts for a total of $376. How many T-shirts were sold?

ANSWER 17

4. How many solutions does each system have?

a. $x = -3y + 4$
$6y + 2x = 8$

b. $y = 4x - 9$
$y - 4x = 6$

ANSWER a. infinitely many solutions;
b. no solution

Answers

Got It? (continued)

3. 5 new games

4. infinitely many

Lesson Check

Do you know HOW?

Solve each system using substitution. Check your solution.

1. $4y = x$
$3x - y = 70$

2. $-2x + 5y = 19$
$3x - 4 = y$

Tell whether the system has *one solution, infinitely many solutions*, or *no solution*.

3. $y = 2x + 1$
$4x - 2y = 6$

4. $-x + \frac{1}{2}y = 13$
$x + 15 = \frac{1}{2}y$

5. Talent Show In a talent show of singing and comedy acts, singing acts are 5 min long and comedy acts are 3 min long. The show has 12 acts and lasts 50 min. How many singing acts and how many comedy acts are in the show?

Do you UNDERSTAND?

6. Vocabulary When is the substitution method a better method than graphing for solving a system of linear equations?

For each system, tell which equation you would first use to solve for a variable in the first step of the substitution method. Explain your choice.

7. $-2x + y = -1$
$4x + 2y = 12$

8. $2.5x - 7y = 7.5$
$6x - y = 1$

Tell whether each statement is *true* or *false*. Explain.

9. When solving a system using substitution, if you obtain an identity, then the system has no solution.

10. You cannot use substitution to solve a system that does not have a variable with a coefficient of 1 or -1.

Practice and Problem-Solving Exercises

Ⓐ Practice Solve each system using substitution. Check your answer. ◄ **See Problems 1 and 2.**

11. $x + y = 8$
$y = 3x$

12. $2x + 2y = 38$
$y = x + 3$

13. $x + 3 = y$
$3x + 4y = 7$

14. $y = 8 - x$
$7 = 2 - y$

15. $y = -2x + 6$
$3y - x + 3 = 0$

16. $3x + 2y = 23$
$\frac{1}{2}x - 4 = y$

17. $y - 2x = 3$
$3x - 2y = 5$

18. $4x = 3y - 2$
$18 = 3x + y$

19. $2 = 2y - x$
$23 = 5y - 4x$

20. $4y + 3 = 3y + x$
$2x + 4y = 18$

21. $7x - 2y = 1$
$2y = x - 1$

22. $4y - x = 5 + 2y$
$3x + 7y = 24$

23. Theater Tickets Adult tickets to a play cost \$22. Tickets for children cost \$15. ◄ **See Problem 3.** Tickets for a group of 11 people cost a total of \$228. Write and solve a system of equations to find how many children and how many adults were in the group.

24. Transportation A school is planning a field trip for 142 people. The trip will use six drivers and two types of vehicles: buses and vans. A bus can seat 51 passengers. A van can seat 10 passengers. Write and solve a system of equations to find how many buses and how many vans will be needed.

25. Geometry The measure of one acute angle in a right triangle is four times the measure of the other acute angle. Write and solve a system of equations to find the measures of the acute angles.

Answers

Lesson Check

1. $\left(25\frac{5}{11}, 6\frac{4}{11}\right)$ **2.** $(3, 5)$

3. no solution **4.** no solution

5. 7 singing, 5 comedy

6. Answers may vary. Sample: Graphing a system can be inexact, and it is very difficult to read the intersection, especially when there are noninteger solutions. The substitution method is better, as it can always give an exact answer.

7. $-2x + y = -1$ because it is easily solved for y.

8. $6x - y = 1$ because it is easily solved for y.

9. False; it has infinitely many solutions.

10. False; you can use it, but the arithmetic may be harder.

Practice and Problem-Solving Exercises

11. $(2, 6)$ **12.** $(8, 11)$

13. $\left(-\frac{5}{7}, 2\frac{2}{7}\right)$ **14.** $(13, -5)$

15. $(3, 0)$ **16.** $\left(7\frac{3}{4}, -\frac{1}{8}\right)$

17. $(-11, -19)$ **18.** $(4, 6)$

19. $(-12, -5)$ **20.** $(5, 2)$

21. $\left(0, -\frac{1}{2}\right)$ **22.** $(1, 3)$

23. 2 children, 9 adults

24. 2 buses, 4 vans

25. 18°, 72°

---

3 Lesson Check

Do you know HOW?

• If students have difficulty with Exercise 5, then guide students to identify their two variables and write one equation related to the time of the show and another equation related to the number of acts.

Do you UNDERSTAND?

• If students have difficulty with Exercise 10, then ask them how to solve an equation for a specific variable. Elicit a response that the coefficient on the variable for which you are solving is the divisor in the last step of the process.

Close

Q What is a good situation for using the substitution method? What is a difficult situation? **[Answers may vary. Sample: A good situation is when one of the equations is already solved for a variable. A difficult situation is when neither equation can be easily solved for one of the variables.]**

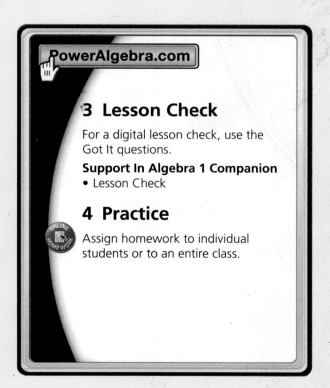

PowerAlgebra.com

3 Lesson Check

For a digital lesson check, use the Got It questions.

Support In Algebra 1 Companion
• Lesson Check

4 Practice

Assign homework to individual students or to an entire class.

ASSIGNMENT GUIDE

Basic: 11–31, 33–38

Average: 11–31 odd, 32–41

Advanced: 11–31 odd, 32–43

Standardized Test Prep: 44–48

Mixed Review: 49–57

Reasoning exercises have blue headings.

Applications exercises have red headings.

EXERCISE 36: Use the Think About a Plan worksheet in the **Practice and Problem Solving Workbook** (also available in the Teaching Resources in print and online) to further support students' development in becoming independent learners.

HOMEWORK QUICK CHECK

To check students' understanding of key skills and concepts, go over Exercises 13, 27, 33, 36, and 37.

 See Problem 4.

Tell whether the system has *one solution, infinitely many solutions,* or *no solution.*

26. $y = \frac{1}{2}x + 3$
    $2y - x = 6$

27. $6y = -5x + 24$
    $2.5x + 3y = 12$

28. $x = -7y + 34$
    $x + 7y = 32$

29. $5 = \frac{1}{2}x + 3y$
    $10 - x = 6y$

30. $17 = 11y + 12x$
    $12x + 11y = 14$

31. $1.5x + 2y = 11$
    $3x + 6y = 22$

 Apply

32. **Geometry** The rectangle shown has a perimeter of 34 cm and the given area. Its length is 5 more than twice its width. Write and solve a system of equations to find the dimensions of the rectangle.

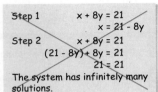

33. **Writing** What would your first step be in solving the system below? Explain.
    $$1.2x + y = 2$$
    $$1.4y = 2.8x + 1$$

34. **Coins** You have $3.70 in dimes and quarters. You have 5 more quarters than dimes. How many of each type of coin do you have?

35. **Error Analysis** Describe and correct the error at the right in finding the solution of the following system:
    $$7x + 5y = 14$$
    $$x + 8y = 21$$

    Step 1 $x + 8y = 21$
            $x = 21 - 8y$
    Step 2 $x + 8y = 21$
            $(21 - 8y) + 8y = 21$
            $21 = 21$
    The system has infinitely many solutions.

36. **Art** An artist is going to sell two sizes of prints at an art fair. The artist will charge $20 for a small print and $45 for a large print. The artist would like to sell twice as many small prints as large prints. The booth the artist is renting for the day costs $510. How many of each size print must the artist sell in order to break even at the fair?

37. **Think About a Plan** At a certain high school, 350 students are taking an algebra course. The ratio of boys to girls taking algebra is 33 : 37. How many more girls are taking algebra than boys?
    - How can you write a system of equations to model the situation?
    - Which equation will you solve for a variable in the first step of solving the system? Why?
    - How can you interpret the solution in the context of the problem?

38. **Compare and Contrast** How can you tell when a system of linear equations has no solution using a graph? How can you tell when a system of linear equations has no solution using substitution?

39. **Fireworks** A pyrotechnician plans for two fireworks to explode together at the same height in the air. They travel at speeds shown at the right. Firework B is launched 0.25 s before Firework A. How many seconds after Firework B launches will both fireworks explode?

Firework A
220 ft/s

Firework B
200 ft/s

Answers

Practice and Problem-Solving Exercises (continued)

26. infinitely many solutions
27. infinitely many solutions
28. no solution
29. infinitely many solutions
30. no solution
31. one solution
32. $2\ell + 2w = 34$
    $\ell = 2w + 5$
    4 cm by 13 cm
33. Solve $1.2x + y = 2$ for y because then you can solve the system using substitution.
34. 7 dimes and 12 quarters

35. The student solved an equation for x but then substituted it into the same equation, not the other equation.
    $x + 8y = 21$, so $x = 21 - 8y$
    $$7(21 - 8y) + 5y = 14$$
    $$147 - 56y + 5y = 14$$
    $$-51y = -133$$
    $$y = \frac{-133}{-51} = 2\frac{31}{51}$$
    So,
    $$x = 21 - 8\left(2\frac{31}{51}\right) = 21 - \frac{1064}{51} = \frac{7}{51}$$
    The solution is $\left(\frac{7}{51}, 2\frac{31}{51}\right)$.

36. 6 large, 12 small
37. 20 more girls
38. The lines will be parallel; a false statement results.
39. 2.75 s

40. Writing Let a be any real number. Will the system at the right *always*, *sometimes*, or *never* have a solution? Explain.

$$y = ax$$
$$y = ax + 4$$

41. Reasoning Explain how you can use substitution to show that the system at the right has no solution.

$$y + x = x$$
$$\frac{3x}{2y} = 4$$

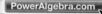

Challenge

42. Agriculture A farmer grows corn, tomatoes, and sunflowers on a 320-acre farm. This year, the farmer wants to plant twice as many acres of tomatoes as acres of sunflowers. The farmer also wants to plant 40 more acres of corn than of tomatoes. How many acres of each crop should the farmer plant?

43. Track and Field Michelle and Pam are running a 200-m race. Michelle runs at an average of 7.5 m/s. Pam averages 7.8 m/s, but she starts 1 s after Michelle.
   a. How long will it take Pam to catch up to Michelle?
   b. Will Pam overtake Michelle before the finish line? Explain.

Standardized Test Prep

GRIDDED RESPONSE

SAT/ACT

44. What is the value of the x-coordinate of the solution of the given system?
$$2x + 3y = 144$$
$$y - x = 24$$

45. You are making blueberry muffins and need to buy a muffin tin and baking cups. Each package of baking cups has 50 baking cups and costs $1.25. The muffin tin costs $15. If you have $22 to spend, at most how many baking cups can you buy?

46. What is the x-intercept of $2y - 3x = 24$?

47. An online store charges 4% of the cost of an order to cover shipping costs. How much would you pay in dollars for shipping on an order that costs $146?

48. What is the solution of the equation $2x - 3 = 8$?

Mixed Review

Solve each system by graphing. Tell whether the system has *one solution*, *infinitely many solutions*, or *no solution*.

◀ **See Lesson 6-1.**

49. $y = 3x + 3$
    $y = x - 3$

50. $y = x + 1$
    $2x + y = 10$

51. $y = -x + 2$
    $x + y = 3$

Find the slope of a line perpendicular to the graph of each equation.

◀ **See Lesson 5-6.**

52. $y = 3x$

53. $y = -\frac{1}{4}x$

54. $\frac{1}{3}x - y = 2$

Get Ready! To prepare for Lesson 6-3, do Exercises 55–57.

Solve each equation. Check your answer.

◀ **See Lesson 2-4.**

55. $5x + 1 = 3x - 5$

56. $4c - 7 = -c + 3$

57. $5k + 7 = 3k + 10$

---

40. Never; the lines are parallel.

41. Answers may vary. Sample: Solve the first equation, $y + x = x$, for y, so $y = x - x = 0$. But the second equation is not defined for $y = 0$; therefore, there is no solution.

42. corn: 152 acres; tomatoes: 112 acres; sunflowers: 56 acres

43. a. 25 s after Pam starts, 26 s after Michelle starts
   b. Yes; 26 s after Michelle starts, both runners will be at 195 m. Pam, who is running at a faster rate, will go on to win.

44. 14.4
45. 250
46. −8
47. $5.84
48. 5.5
49. one solution: $(-3, -6)$
50. one solution: $(3, 4)$
51. no solution
52. $-\frac{1}{3}$
53. 4
54. −3
55. −3
56. 2
57. $\frac{3}{2}$

Additional Instructional Support

Algebra 1 Companion

Students can use the **Algebra 1 Companion** worktext (4 pages) as you teach the lesson. Use the Companion to support

- New Vocabulary
- Key Concepts
- Got It for each Problem
- Lesson Check

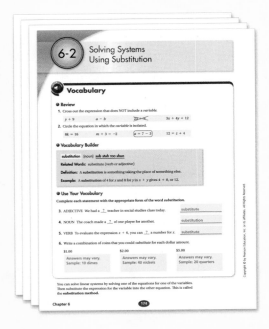

ELL Support

Focus on Communication Have students work in groups of four. Write the equations $y = -2x$ and $y - x = 3$ on the board. Say: Two students in each group should solve the equations by graphing; the other students should solve the equations by substitution. Have the students compare their solutions. Say: "In your group, decide which method was easier." Write down two reasons why that method was easier. Ask: "Which groups decided that substitution was easier? Which groups decided that graphing was easier?" Have a member of each group read one reason their way was easier. Write the reasons on the board. Have a volunteer write two linear equations on the board. Say: Use the method that you think is easier to solve this system of equations.

5 Assess & Remediate

Lesson Quiz

1. What is the solution of the system? Use substitution.
$$y = -3x$$
$$x + y = -4$$

2. What is the solution of the system? Use substitution.
$$-4y - 3x = -11$$
$$x - 2y = 17$$

3. A movie theater charges $6.50 for matinee showings and $8.75 for evening showings. Yesterday the theater sold 378 tickets for a total revenue of $2,929.50. How many matinee tickets were sold?

4. **Do you UNDERSTAND?** How many solutions does the system $y = -7x + 3$ and $y + 7x = 10$ have? Explain.

ANSWERS TO LESSON QUIZ

1. $(2, -6)$
2. $(9, -4)$
3. 168
4. No solutions; the lines are parallel.

PRESCRIPTION FOR REMEDIATION
Use the student work on the Lesson Quiz to prescribe a differentiated review assignment.

Points	Differentiated Remediation
0–2	Intervention
3	On-level
4	Extension

PowerAlgebra.com

5 Assess & Remediate

Assign the Lesson Quiz. Appropriate intervention, practice, or enrichment is automatically generated based on student performance.

Intervention

- **Reteaching** (2 pages) Provides reteaching and practice exercises for the key lesson concepts. Use with struggling students or absent students.

- **English Language Learner Support** Helps students develop and reinforce mathematical vocabulary and key concepts.

All-in-One Resources/Online
Reteaching

Differentiated Remediation *continued*

On-Level

- **Practice** (2 pages) Provides extra practice for each lesson. For simpler practice exercises, use the Form K Practice pages found in the All-in-One Teaching Resources and online.

- **Think About a Plan** Helps students develop specific problem-solving skills and strategies by providing scaffolded guiding questions.

- **Standardized Test Prep** Focuses on all major exercises, all major question types, and helps students prepare for the high-stakes assessments.

Extension

- **Enrichment** Provides students with interesting problems and activities that extend the concepts of the lesson.

- **Activities, Games, and Puzzles** Worksheets that can be used for concepts development, enrichment, and for fun!

Practice and Problem Solving WKBK/All-in-One Resources/Online
Practice page 1

6-2 Practice   Form G
Solving Systems Using Substitution

Solve each system by substitution. Check your solution.

1. $x = y$ (1, 1)
   $x + 2y = 3$

2. $y = -x + 4$ (1, 3)
   $y = 3x$

3. $y = 2x - 10$ (4, −2)
   $2y = x - 8$

4. $2y = x + 1$ (−3, −1)
   $-2x - y = 7$

5. $x + 2y = 14$ (6, 4)
   $y = 3x - 14$

6. $2x - 3y = 13$ (5, −1)
   $y = \frac{1}{2}x - \frac{7}{2}$

7. $-3x - 2y = 5.5$ (−4.5, 4)
   $x + 3y = 7.5$

8. $6x - 4y = 54$ (7, −3)
   $-9x + 2y = -69$

9. $y = \frac{-x}{3} - 4$ (6, −7)
   $-2x - y = -5$

10. **Writing** How do you know that substitution gives the answer to a system of equations? Explain.
   You can verify your answer by substituting the x- and y- values into the original equations.

11. **Reasoning** With the substitution method, which variable should you solve for first? Explain.
   You should solve for a variable that already has a coefficient of 1 or −1.

12. **Writing** How can you use substitution method to solve a system of equations that does not have a variable with a coefficient of 1 or −1?
   You can solve for a variable by isolating that term and then dividing by the coefficient.

13. **Writing** When solving the system of equations $\begin{array}{l} 6y + 2x = 3 \\ 2x + y = 8 \end{array}$ using substitution, which variable will you solve for and which equation will you use to substitute into? You would solve the second equation for y and then substitute back into the first equation.

14. **Reasoning** Can you tell that there is no solution for a system by just looking at the equations? Explain and give an example. If two equations are identical but with a different constant, then there is no solution to the system.

15. If the difference in the side lengths of two squares is 10, and the sum of the side lengths is 18, what are the side lengths? 14 and 4

16. A shopper purchased 8 T-Shirts and 5 pairs pants for $220. The next day, he purchased 5 T-shirts and 1 pair of pants for $112. How much does each T-shirt and each pair of pants cost? t-shirts: $20; pants: $12

Practice and Problem Solving WKBK/All-in-One Resources/Online
Practice page 2

6-2 Practice (continued)   Form G
Solving Systems Using Substitution

17. A student bought 1 box of crayons and 5 reams of paper for $54. She bought 5 boxes of crayons and 3 reams of paper for $50. What is the cost of each box of crayons and each ream of paper? crayons: $4; paper: $10

18. Suppose you got 8 mangoes and 5 apples for $18 and 3 mangoes and 5 apples for $14.50. How much does each mango and each apple cost?
   mango: $1.50; apple: $2.00

19. A shopper purchased 4 tables and 2 chairs for $200 and 2 tables and 7 chairs for $400. What is the cost of each table and each chair? tables: $25; chairs: $50

20. If the length of the rectangle is twice the width, and the perimeter of the rectangle is 30 cm, what is length and width of the rectangle? 10 cm; 5 cm

21. The population of a city is 2,500. If the number of males is 240 more than the number of females, how many males and females are there in the city? 1130 females and 1370 males

Solve each system by substitution. Tell whether the system has one solution, infinitely many solutions, or no solution.

22. $7x + 2y = -13$
   $-3x - 8y = -23$
   (−3, 4); one solution

23. $x - 9y = -10$
   $6x + y = -5$
   (−1, 1); one solution

24. $x = \frac{y}{4} + 1$
   $y = 4x - 5$
   no solution

25. $x - 2y - 1 = 0$
   $y - 5x + 14 = 0$
   (3, 1); one solution

26. $y = -8x - 37$
   $x + 3y = 4$
   (−5, 3); one solution

27. $3x + 6y = 18$
   $3y - \frac{3}{2}x + 9$
   infinitely many solutions

28. $5x - 9y = 29$
   $12x + y = 47$
   (4, −1); one solution

29. $2x = 3y - 9$
   $-3x + y = 10$
   (−3, 1); one solution

30. $5y = 7x + 22$
   $x = -6y + 17$
   (−1, 3); one solution

31. $x = 6y + 16$
   $9x - 2y = -12$
   (−2, −3); one solution

32. $4x - y - 4 = 0$
   $3x + 2y - 14 = 0$
   (2, 4); one solution

33. $x + 3y = -5$
   $-2x - y = 5$
   (−2, −1); one solution

All-in-One Resources/Online
Enrichment

6-2 Enrichment
Solving Systems Using Substitution

You can use technology (for example, a graphing calculator) to solve systems of equations, whether the solution needs to be exact or approximate.

Problem

At your fundraiser, you served an all-you-can-eat barbeque. You served 210 people and raised $930. If the amount for each adult was $6 and for each child was $3, the equation for money raised is $6x + 3y = 930$. The equation for the total number of adult and child dinners that were served is $x + y = 210$.
Solve the system $\begin{array}{l} 6x + 3y = 930 \\ x + y = 210 \end{array}$ using substitution.

$x = 210 - y$ Write the second equation in terms of x and substitute into the first equation.
$6(210 - y) + 3y = 930$ Simplify.
$330 = 3y$
$110 = y$

Substitute the value of y into the second equation and you find that $x = 100$.
Double check both answers into the first equation with a graphing calculator.
$6(100) + 3(110) \overset{?}{=} 930$
$930 = 930$ ✓

You could also graph this system of equations on your graphing calculator. How many adult and child dinners were served? You should have gotten approximately (100, 110) as you did using substitution.

Exercises

1. **Writing** What are the disadvantages and advantages of using one method over the other for the problem above and in general? Substitution lets you calculate an exact answer, but graphing is quicker.

Solve for x and y using substitution. Check your answer using a graphing calculator.

2. $x + 2y + 3z = 8$ (4, −1)
   $y + 2z = 3$
   $z = 2$

3. $x = y - a$ (a − 3b, 3b)
   $2y = 6b$

4. $2x - y + 4z = 9$ $\left(\frac{2}{3}, 12\frac{1}{3}\right)$
   $x + y - 3z = -2$
   $z = 5$

5. $x - y - d = 0$ (−d, −2d)
   $6x - 4y = 2d$

6. $2x - 2y = 2d$ $\left(\frac{3}{2} + d, \frac{3}{2} + d\right)$
   $x + y - d = 5$

7. $2x + y + 4z = 18$ (2, 2)
   $y + z = 5$
   $z = 3$

Practice and Problem Solving WKBK/All-in-One Resources/Online
Think About a Plan

6-2 Think About a Plan
Solving Systems Using Substitution

Art An artist is going to sell two sizes of prints at an art fair. The artist will charge $20 for a small print and $45 for a large print. The artist would like to sell twice as many small prints as large prints. The booth the artist is renting for the day costs $510. How many of each size print must the artist sell in order to break even at the fair?

Understanding the Problem

1. How much will the artist spend to rent a booth? $520

2. What do you know about selling prices of the prints? small print: $20; large print: $45

3. What do you know about the number of prints the artist would like to sell? The artist wants to sell twice as many small prints as large prints.

4. What is the problem asking you to determine? how many of each size print the artist must sell to break even

Planning the Solution

5. What variables are needed? s = number of small prints sold; l= number of large prints sold.

6. What equation can be used to determine the number of prints that the artist would like to sell based on size? $s = 2d$

7. What equation can be used to determine how many prints the artist has to sell to break even? $20s + 45d = 510$

Getting an Answer

8. What is the solution to the system of equations?
   The artist must sell 6 large prints and 12 small prints to break even.

Practice and Problem Solving WKBK/All-in-One Resources/Online
Standardized Test Prep

6-2 Standardized Test Prep
Solving Systems Using Substitution

Gridded Response

Solve each exercise and enter your answer on the grid provided.

1. For the following system of equations, what is the x-value of the solution? 0
   $-x + 2y = 6$
   $6y = x + 18$

2. The sum of the measures of angle X and angle Y is 90. If the measure of angle X is 30 less than twice the measure of angle Y, what is the measure of angle X? 50

3. One number is 4 less than 3 times a second number. If 3 more than two times the first number is decreased by 2 times the second number, the result is 11. Use the substitution method. What is the first number? 8

4. An investor bought 3 shares of stock A and 2 shares of stock B for a total of $41. Stock A costs $2.00 more per share than stock B. What is the cost of a share of stock A in dollars? 9

5. Solve the following system of equations using substitution. What is the value of y? 25
   $2x + 3y = 105$
   $x + 2y = 65$

Online Teacher Resource Center
Activities, Games, and Puzzles

6-2 Puzzle: The Shortest Path
Solving Systems Using Substitution

A collection of systems of linear equations is shown below. Each system has an ordered pair of whole numbers as its solution.

- Plot the solution to each system on the grid. Label each point using the letter of the system.
- Draw a line segment from point O to point T.
- You should have four letters on $\overline{OT}$ after you have plotted all the points.
- Answer the following question by placing these four letters and the letters O and T in the correct places at the bottom of the page.

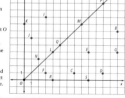

Economists use systems of linear equations to represent supply and demand. What is the name of the point where the supply graph and the demand graph intersect?

A. $y = 12$; $y = x + 11$ A(1, 12)

B. $y = 2x - 19$; $y = 7$ B(13, 7)

C. $y = 2x - 13$; $y = x - 6$ C(7, 1)

D. $y = 2x - 21$; $y = x - 10$ D(11, 1)

E. $y = -x + 13$; $y = 4$ E(9, 4)

F. $y = x - 2$; $y = -x + 4$ F(3, 1)

G. $y = x - 9$; $y = 2x - 22$ G(13, 4)

H. $y = 2x + 2$; $y = x + 7$ H(5, 12)

I. $y = x + 6$; $y = 3x$ I(3, 9)

J. $y = x + 5$; $y = 6x$ J(1, 6)

K. $y = 8$; $y = 10x + 8$ K(0, 8)

L. $y = -x + 8$; $y = x$ L(4, 4)

M. $y = x$; $y = x$ M(8, 8)

N. $y = 7x - 11$; $y = 2x - 1$ N(2, 3)

P. $y = -x + 22$; $y = 3x - 22$ P(11, 11)

Q. $y = 2x - 5$; $y = 3x - 10$ Q(5, 5)

R. $y = 4x - 16$; $y = 2x - 1$ R(4, 0)

S. $x = 9$; $y = -x + 9$ S(9, 0)

E Q U I L I B R I U M
P O I N T

---

1 Interactive Learning

Solve It!

PURPOSE To use the properties of equality to solve a real-world problem that can be represented by a system of linear equations

PROCESS Students may write a system of equations and solve by graphing or substitution, use the notion of subtracting common elements as part of mathematical reasoning, or use trial and error.

FACILITATE

Q What is the difference in the number of ounces between the two scales? **[14]**

Q How does the collection of fruit on the first scale compare to the second scale? **[There are 2 more oranges on the second scale.]**

Q How much do the two oranges weigh? **[14 ounces]**

ANSWER See Solve It in Answers on next page.
CONNECT THE MATH Each scale can be modeled by an equation written in two variables. Each equation has a term with equal coefficients, which is a situation that lends itself to using a method for combining the linear equations.

2 Guided Instruction

Problem 1

Q How can you tell that these lines have different slopes? How does that affect the number of solutions? **[The ratio of the coefficient of *y* to the coefficient of *x* is not the same for both equations. The lines intersect in one point.]**

Q What property are you using when you add the two equations together in Step 1? **[Addition Property of Equality]**

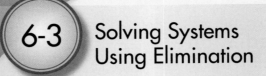

6-3 Solving Systems Using Elimination

Indiana Academic Standard
A1.3.1 Understand the relationship between a solution of a pair of linear equations in two variables and the graphs of the corresponding lines and solve pairs of linear equations in two variables by graphing, substitution or elimination.

Objective To solve systems by adding or subtracting to eliminate a variable

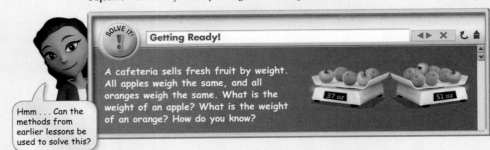

Getting Ready!

A cafeteria sells fresh fruit by weight. All apples weigh the same, and all oranges weigh the same. What is the weight of an apple? What is the weight of an orange? How do you know?

Hmm . . . Can the methods from earlier lessons be used to solve this?

Lesson Vocabulary
• elimination method

By the Addition and Subtraction Properties of Equality, if $a = b$ and $c = d$, then $a + c = b + d$ and $a - c = b - d$. For example, $5 + 1 = 6$ and $3 + 4 = 7$, so $(5 + 1) + (3 + 4) = 6 + 7$. In the **elimination method**, you use these properties to add or subtract equations in order to eliminate a variable in a system.

Essential Understanding There is more than one way to solve a system of equations. Some systems are written in a way that makes eliminating a variable a good method to use.

Plan

Which variable should you eliminate?
You can eliminate either variable. Since the coefficients of *y* are opposites, you can add the equations to eliminate *y* in one step.

Problem 1   Solving a System by Adding Equations

What is the solution of the system? Use elimination. $2x + 5y = 17$
                                         $6x - 5y = -9$

Step 1 Eliminate one variable. Since the sum of the coefficients of *y* is 0, add the equations to eliminate *y*.

$$2x + 5y = 17$$
$$\underline{6x - 5y = -9}$$
$$8x + 0 = 8 \qquad \text{Add the two equations.}$$
$$x = 1 \qquad \text{Solve for } x.$$

Step 2 Substitute 1 for *x* to solve for the eliminated variable.

$$2x + 5y = 17 \qquad \text{You can use the first equation.}$$
$$2(1) + 5y = 17 \qquad \text{Substitute 1 for } x.$$
$$2 + 5y = 17 \qquad \text{Simplify.}$$
$$y = 3 \qquad \text{Solve for } y.$$

Since $x = 1$ and $y = 3$, the solution is $(1, 3)$.

6-2 Preparing to Teach

UbD

BIG idea Solving Equations & Inequalities
ESSENTIAL UNDERSTANDINGS

• Systems of equations can be solved in more than one way.

• Some equations are written in a way that makes eliminating a variable a good method to use.

Math Background

To solve systems of equations using elimination, students will use several skills they have previously learned. Students will particularly use these skills: least common multiple, adding like terms, solving one-step equations, and substitution.

• Least common multiple is used to determine by what number each equation needs to be multiplied.

• Adding like terms is used when the linear equations are combined using addition or subtraction.

• One-step equations are solved after one of the variables has been eliminated.

• Substitution is used after the first variable has been solved for to find the value of the second variable. The method of elimination is an important skill. Students will later learn how to write systems of equations as augmented matrices and solve the systems using the methods of Gaussian elimination and/or Gauss-Jordan elimination.

Support Student Learning

Use the **Algebra 1 Companion** to engage and support students during instructions. See Lesson Resources at the end of this lesson for details.

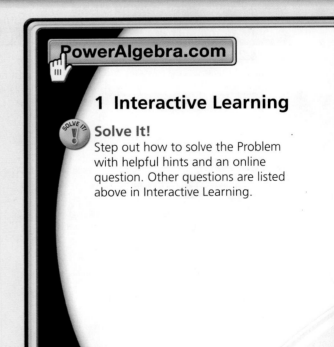

PowerAlgebra.com

1 Interactive Learning

Solve It!

Step out how to solve the Problem with helpful hints and an online question. Other questions are listed above in Interactive Learning.

Got It? 1. What is the solution of each system? Use elimination.

    a. $5x - 6y = -32$ **b.** $-3x - 3y = 9$
           $3x + 6y = 48$ $3x - 4y = 5$

Problem 2   **Solving a System by Subtracting Equations**

Multiple Choice The theater club sells a total of 101 tickets to its first play. A student ticket costs \$1. An adult ticket costs \$2.50. Total ticket sales are \$164. How many student tickets were sold?

   Ⓐ 25   Ⓑ 42   Ⓒ 59   Ⓓ 76

Define   Let a = the number of adult tickets sold.
           Let s = the number of student tickets sold.

Relate   total number of tickets   total ticket sales

Write $a + s = 101$ $2.5a + s = 164$

Think

How is this problem similar to Problem 1?
In each problem, you are looking for coefficients of one variable that are either the same or opposites. Here, the coefficients of s are the same, so eliminate s.

Step 1 Eliminate one variable. Since the difference of the coefficients of s is 0, eliminate s.

$$a + s = 101$$
$$\underline{2.5a + s = 164}$$
$$-1.5a + 0 = -63 \quad \text{Subtract the equations.}$$
$$a = 42 \quad \text{Solve for } a.$$

Step 2 Solve for the eliminated variable. Use either equation.

$$a + s = 101 \quad \text{You can use the first equation.}$$
$$42 + s = 101 \quad \text{Substitute 42 for } a.$$
$$s = 59 \quad \text{Solve for } s.$$

There were 59 student tickets sold. The correct answer is C.

Check   42 is close to 40 and 59 is close to 60. The total number of tickets is about $40 + 60 = 100$, which is close to 101. The total sales are about $\$2.50(40) + \$60 = \$160$, which is close to \$164. The solution is reasonable.

 Got It? 2. Washing 2 cars and 3 trucks takes 130 min. Washing 2 cars and 5 trucks takes 190 min. How long does it take to wash each type of vehicle?

From Problems 1 and 2 you can see that to eliminate a variable, its coefficients must have a sum or difference of zero. Sometimes you have to multiply one or both of the equations by a constant so that adding or subtracting the equations will eliminate one variable.

---

2 Guided Instruction

 Each Problem is worked out and supported online.

Problem 1
Solving a System by Adding Equations

Problem 2
Solving a System by Subtracting Equations
                  Animated

Problem 3
Solving a System by Multiplying One Equation
                  Animated

Problem 4
Solving a System by Multiplying Both Equations
                  Animated

Problem 5
Finding the Number of Solutions

Support in Algebra 1 Companion
• Vocabulary
• Key Concepts
• Got It?

Got It?   SYNTHESIZING

For 1a and 1b, ask students the following questions.

Q Which variable will be eliminated when the equations are added? **[in 1a, y; in 1b, x]**

Q What equation do you solve as the final step? **[in 1a, $8x = 16$; in 1b, $-7y = 14$]**

Problem 2

Q What property justifies the subtraction of the two equations? **[Subtraction Property of Equality]**

Q What equation would you get if the order of the equations were reversed when you performed the subtraction in Step 1? **[$1.5a = 63$]**

Q Would you still arrive at the same value for a? Explain. **[Yes, because $63 \div 1.5 = -63 \div (-1.5)$.]**

Q If a student answered Choice B, what error was made? **[The student indicated the number of adult tickets sold rather than the number of student tickets sold.]**

Q Can you solve this problem without writing a system of equations? Explain. **[Yes, you could use trial and error with the four answer choices.]**

Got It?   SYNTHESIZING

Q If x represents the number of cars and y represents the number of trucks, what two equations represent the situation? **[$2x + 3y = 130$ and $2x + 5y = 190$]**

Ask students to solve the system first using elimination and then by substitution. Have students explain the complications of solving this system using substitution.

Answers

Solve It!
8 oz, 7 oz; explanations may vary.

Got It?
  1. a. $(2, 7)$
     b. $(-1, -2)$
  2. car: 20 min; truck: 30 min

Problem 3

> **Q** Why is graphing not a convenient method for solving this system? **[The equations are not in slope-intercept form, and the y-intercepts are not whole numbers.]**
>
> **Q** If you were to add or subtract the equations as written, would either of the variables drop out of the resulting equation? Explain. **[No, the coefficients for the same variables are neither identical nor opposite.]**
>
> **Q** How do you know to eliminate y instead of x? **[The coefficient of y in one equation is a multiple of the coefficient of y in the other.]**
>
> **Q** If you were to multiply by -3 rather than 3, would the variable be eliminated? Explain. **[Yes, you would have to subtract the equations rather than add the equations.]**

Got It? ERROR PREVENTION

If students find that $x = \frac{5}{6}$, then they probably forgot to multiply the right side of the equation by 3.

Problem 4

> **Q** Is 4 a multiple of 3? Is 3 a multiple of 2? Explain. **[No, 3 cannot be multiplied by a whole number to get 4; No, 2 cannot be multiplied by a whole number to get 3.]**
>
> **Q** By multiplying the first equation by 3 and the second equation by 2, what variable will be eliminated when the equations are subtracted? **[y]**
>
> **Q** If you choose to multiply by 6 and 4 instead of 3 and 2, would you still arrive at the same solution? Explain. **[Yes, because the equation $2x = 14$ is equivalent to the equation $x = 7$.]**

 Problem 3 Solving a System by Multiplying One Equation

What is the solution of the system? Use elimination.
$$-2x + 15y = -32$$
$$7x - 5y = 17$$

Know	Need	Plan
A system of equations that can't quickly be solved by graphing or substitution	The solution of the system	Multiply one or both equations by a constant so that the coefficients of one variable are the same or opposites. Then eliminate the variable.

Think
You can eliminate either variable. You can eliminate y in fewer steps than x because you only need to multiply one equation.

Step 1 To eliminate one variable, you can multiply $7x - 5y = 17$ by 3 and then add.

$$-2x + 15y = -32 \qquad\qquad -2x + 15y = -32$$
$$7x - 5y = 17 \quad \text{Multiply by 3.} \quad \underline{21x - 15y = 51}$$
$$19x + 0 = 19 \quad \text{Add the equations.}$$
$$x = 1 \quad \text{Solve for } x.$$

Step 2 Solve for the eliminated variable. Use either of the original equations.

$$7x - 5y = 17 \quad \text{You can use the second equation.}$$
$$7(1) - 5y = 17 \quad \text{Substitute 1 for } x.$$
$$y = -2 \quad \text{Solve for } y.$$

The solution is $(1, -2)$.

 Got It? 3. a. What is the solution of the system? Use elimination.
$$-5x - 2y = 4$$
$$3x + 6y = 6$$

b. Reasoning Describe another way to solve the system in part (a).

 Problem 4 Solving a System by Multiplying Both Equations

What is the solution of the system? Use elimination.
$$3x + 2y = 1$$
$$4x + 3y = -2$$

Plan
How can you get started?
Find the LCM of the coefficients of the variable that you want to eliminate. Multiply to make the coefficients equal to the LCM.

Step 1 Multiply each equation so you can eliminate one variable.

$$3x + 2y = 1 \quad \text{Multiply by 3.} \quad 9x + 6y = 3$$
$$4x + 3y = -2 \quad \text{Multiply by 2.} \quad \underline{8x + 6y = -4}$$
$$x + 0 = 7 \quad \text{Subtract the equations.}$$

Step 2 Solve for the eliminated variable. Use either of the original equations.

$$3x + 2y = 1 \quad \text{You can use the first equation.}$$
$$3(7) + 2y = 1 \quad \text{Substitute 7 for } x.$$
$$2y = -20 \quad \text{Subtract 21 from each side. Simplify.}$$
$$y = -10 \quad \text{Solve for } y.$$

The solution is $(7, -10)$.

376   Chapter 6   Systems of Equations and Inequalities

Additional Problems

1. What is the solution of the system? Use elimination.
$$3x + 4y = -22$$
$$5x - 4y = 38$$

ANSWER $(2, -7)$

2. A concessions stand sold a total of 138 small and large popcorns. A small popcorn costs $2.50, and a large popcorn costs $4.00. Total popcorn sales were $466.50. How many large popcorns were sold?

ANSWER 81

3. What is the solution of the system? Use elimination.
$$-2x + 12y = -30$$
$$3x - 4y = 17$$

ANSWER $(3, -2)$

4. What is the solution of the system? Use elimination.
$$2x - 3y = -12$$
$$3x - 2y = 2$$

ANSWER $(6, 8)$

5. How many solutions does the system have?
$$12x - 8y = 20$$
$$3x - 2y = 5$$

ANSWER infinitely many

Answers

Got It? (continued)

3. a. $(-1.5, 1.75)$

b. Answers may vary. Sample: You could use substitution by solving the second equation for x.

Got It? **4.** What is the solution of the system? Use elimination.

$$4x + 3y = -19$$
$$3x - 2y = -10$$

Recall that if you get a false statement as you solve a system, then the system has no solution. If you get an identity, then the system has infinitely many solutions.

 Problem 5 **Finding the Number of Solutions**

How many solutions does the system have?

$$2x + 6y = 18$$
$$x + 3y = 9$$

Multiply the second equation by -2.

$$2x + 6y = 18 \qquad\qquad 2x + 6y = 18$$
$$x + 3y = 9 \quad \text{Multiply by } -2. \quad \underline{-2x - 6y = -18}$$
$$0 = 0 \quad \text{Add the equations.}$$

Because $0 = 0$ is an identity, there are infinitely many solutions.

Think
Could you have solved this problem another way?
Yes. For example, you could have multiplied the second equation by 2 and subtracted.

 Got It? **5.** How many solutions does the system have?

$$-2x + 5y = 7$$
$$-2x + 5y = 12$$

The flowchart below can help you decide which steps to take when solving a system of equations using elimination.

Can I eliminate a variable by adding or subtracting the given equations? — yes → Do so.
 — no →
Can I multiply one of the equations by a number, and then add or subtract the equations? — yes → Do so.
 — no →
Multiply both equations by different numbers. Then add or subtract the equations.

 Lesson Check

Do you know HOW?

Solve each system using elimination.

1. $3x - 2y = 0$
    $4x + 2y = 14$

2. $3p + q = 7$
    $2p - 2q = -6$

3. $3x - 2y = 1$
    $8x + 3y = 2$

Do you UNDERSTAND?

4. Vocabulary If you add two equations in two variables and the sum is an equation in one variable, what method are you using to solve the system? Explain.

5. Reasoning Explain how the Addition Property of Equality allows you to add equations.

6. Writing Explain how you would solve a system of equations using elimination.

 **PowerAlgebra.com** Lesson 6-3 Solving Systems Using Elimination 377

Got It?
Ask students to share their solution strategies, explain how they decided which variable to eliminate, and determined by what number to multiply the equations.

Problem 5

Q When both variables are eliminated, what possible situations describe the lines? **[The lines are either the same line or they are parallel lines.]**

Got It?

Q Do the equations need to be multiplied by a factor? Explain. **[No, the coefficients of both variables are the same.]**

Q How are the lines related when they are graphed? **[The lines are parallel.]**

3 Lesson Check

Do you know HOW?
- If students have difficulty with Exercise 3, then have them decide if they want to add the equations or subtract them. Be sure they understand that they can add and eliminate the y terms.

Do you UNDERSTAND?
- If students have difficulty with Exercise 5, then encourage them to include an example problem in their explanation.

Close

Q What kind of coefficients of x or y are needed to solve a system by adding equations? **[equal magnitude and opposite signs]**

Got It? (continued)

4. $(-4, -1)$

5. no solution

Lesson Check

1. $(2, 3)$

2. $(1, 4)$

3. $\left(\frac{7}{25}, -\frac{2}{25}\right)$

4. Elimination; the objective of the elimination method is to add (or subtract) two equations to eliminate a variable.

5. The Addition Property of Equality says that adding equals to equals gives you equals. This is what you are doing in the elimination method.

6. Answers may vary. Sample: Decide which variable to eliminate, and then multiply, if necessary, one or both equations so that the coefficients of the variable are the same (or opposites). Then subtract (or add) the two equations. This will result in one equation with a single variable that you can solve. Then substitute to find the value of the other variable.

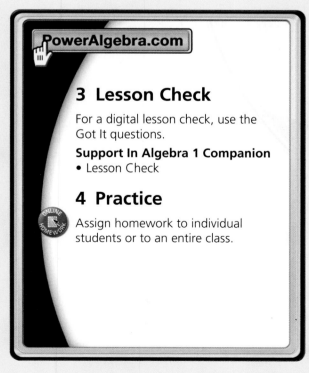

PowerAlgebra.com

3 Lesson Check

For a digital lesson check, use the Got It questions.

Support In Algebra 1 Companion
- Lesson Check

4 Practice

Assign homework to individual students or to an entire class.

4 Practice

ASSIGNMENT GUIDE

Basic: 7–30 all, 32–38 even

Average: 7–25 odd, 27–40

Advanced: 7–25 odd, 27–44

Standardized Test Prep: 45–49

Mixed Review: 50–56

Reasoning exercises have blue headings.

Applications exercises have red headings.

EXERCISE 30: Use the Think About a Plan worksheet in the **Practice and Problem Solving Workbook** (also available in the Teaching Resources in print and online) to further support students' development in becoming independent learners.

HOMEWORK QUICK CHECK

To check students' understanding of key skills and concepts, go over Exercises 7, 17, 27, 30, and 38.

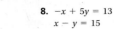

Practice and Problem-Solving Exercises

 Practice   Solve each system using elimination.   ◀ See Problems 1 and 2.

7. $3x + 3y = 27$
$x - 3y = -11$

8. $-x + 5y = 13$
$x - y = 15$

9. $2x + 4y = 22$
$2x - 2y = -8$

10. $4x - 7y = 3$
$x - 7y = -15$

11. $5x - y = 0$
$3x + y = 24$

12. $6x + 5y = 39$
$3x + 5y = 27$

13. Talent Show Your school's talent show will feature 12 solo acts and 2 ensemble acts. The show will last 90 min. The 6 solo performers judged best will give a repeat performance at a second 60-min show, which will also feature the 2 ensemble acts. Each solo act lasts x minutes, and each ensemble act lasts y minutes.
  a. Write a system of equations to model the situation.
  b. Solve the system from part (a). How long is each solo act? How long is each ensemble act?

14. Furniture A carpenter is designing a drop-leaf table with two drop leaves of equal size. The lengths of the table when one leaf is folded up and when both leaves are folded up are shown. How long is the table when no leaves are folded up?

5.5 ft   7 ft

Solve each system using elimination.   ◀ See Problems 3 and 4.

15. $2x + 3y = 9$
$x + 5y = 8$

16. $3x + y = 5$
$2x - 2y = -2$

17. $6x + 4y = 42$
$-3x + 3y = -6$

18. $3x + 2y = 17$
$2x + 5y = 26$

19. $6x - 3y = 15$
$7x + 4y = 10$

20. $5x - 9y = -43$
$3x + 8y = 68$

Tell whether the system has *one solution, infinitely many solutions,* or *no solution.*   ◀ See Problem 5.

21. $9x + 8y = 15$
$9x + 8y = 30$

22. $3x + 4y = 24$
$6x + 8y = 24$

23. $5x - 3y = 10$
$10x + 6y = 20$

24. $2x - 5y = 17$
$6x - 15y = 51$

25. $4x - 7y = 15$
$-8x + 14y = -30$

26. $4x - 8y = 15$
$-5x + 10y = -30$

 Apply   **27. Think About a Plan** A photo studio offers portraits in 8 × 10 and wallet-sized formats. One customer bought two 8 × 10 portraits and four wallet-sized portraits and paid $52. Another customer bought three 8 × 10 portraits and two wallet-sized portraits and paid $50. What is the cost of an 8 × 10 portrait? What is the cost of a wallet-sized portrait?
  • Can you eliminate a variable simply by adding or subtracting?
  • If not, how many of the equations do you need to multiply by a constant?

Answers

Practice and Problem-Solving Exercises

7. (4, 5)

8. (22, 7)

9. (1, 5)

10. (6, 3)

11. (3, 15)

12. (4, 3)

13. a. $12x + 2y = 90$
$6x + 2y = 60$

  b. solo act: 5 min; ensemble act: 15 min

14. 4 ft

15. (3, 1)

16. (1, 2)

17. (5, 3)

18. (3, 4)

19. (2, −1)

20. (4, 7)

21. no solution

22. no solution

23. one solution

24. infinitely many solutions

25. infinitely many solutions

26. no solution

27. $12; $7

28. Reasoning A toy store worker packed two boxes of identical dolls and plush toys for shipping in boxes that weigh 1 oz when empty. One box held 3 dolls and 4 plush toys. The worker marked the weight as 12 oz. The other box held 2 dolls and 3 plush toys. The worker marked the weight as 10 oz. Explain why the worker must have made a mistake.

29. Error Analysis A student solved a system of equations by elimination. Describe and correct the error made in the part of the solution shown.

$$5x + 4y = 2 \quad -\times 3 \rightarrow \quad 15x + 12y = 6$$
$$3x + 3y = -3 \quad \times 4 \rightarrow \quad \underline{12x + 12y = -3}$$
$$3x + 0 = 9$$
$$x = 3$$

30. Nutrition Half a pepperoni pizza plus three fourths of a ham-and-pineapple pizza contains 765 Calories. One fourth of a pepperoni pizza plus a whole ham-and-pineapple pizza contains 745 Calories. How many Calories are in a whole pepperoni pizza? How many Calories are in a whole ham-and-pineapple pizza?

31. Open-Ended Write a system of equations that can be solved efficiently by elimination. Explain what you would do to eliminate one of the variables. Then solve the system.

Solve each system using any method. Explain why you chose the method you used.

32. $y = 2.5x$
$2y + 3x = 32$

33. $2x + y = 4$
$6x + 7y = 12$

34. $3x + 2y = 5$
$4x + 5y = 16$

35. $y = \frac{2}{3}x + 1$
$2x + 3y = 27$

36. $x + y = 1.5$
$2x + y = 1$

37. $\frac{1}{3}x + \frac{1}{2}y = 0$
$\frac{1}{2}x + \frac{1}{5}y = \frac{11}{5}$

38. Compare and Contrast What do the substitution method and the elimination method have in common? Explain. Give an example of a system that you would prefer to solve using one method instead of the other. Justify your choice.

39. Vacations A hotel offers two activity packages. One costs $192 and includes 3 h of horseback riding and 2 h of parasailing. The second costs $213 and includes 2 h of horseback riding and 3 h of parasailing. What is the cost for 1 h of each activity?

40. Geometry Each of the squares in the figures shown at the right has the same area, and each of the triangles has the same area. The total area of Figure A is 141 cm². The total area of Figure B is 192 cm². What is the area of each square and each triangle?

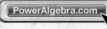

A   B

 Challenge **Solve each system using elimination.**

41. $\frac{2}{x} - \frac{3}{y} = -5$
$\frac{4}{x} + \frac{6}{y} = 14$

42. $2x = 5(2 - y)$
$y = 3(-x + 5)$

43. $2x - 3y + z = 0$
$2x + y + z = 12$
$y - z = 4$

---

28. The solution $(-3, 5)$ does not make sense because a plush toy can't have a negative weight.

29. The student forgot to multiply the constant in the second equation by 4.
$15x + 12y = 6$
$12x + 12y = -12$
so, $3x = 18$
$x = 6$

30. 660 Calories; 580 Calories

31. Answers may vary. Sample:
$3x - 2y = 7$
$5x + 2y = 33$
Because the coefficients of the y-terms are already opposites, simply add the two equations to get $8x = 40$, or $x = 5$. Substitute $x = 5$ into either equation to get $y = 4$. The solution is $(5, 4)$.

32. $(4, 10)$; Answers may vary. Sample: substitution; the first equation is already solved for y.

33. $(2, 0)$; Answers may vary. Sample: substitution; the first equation is easily solved for y.

34. $(-1, 4)$; Answers may vary. Sample: elimination; neither equation solves easily for x or y.

35. $(6, 5)$; Answers may vary. Sample: substitution; the first equation is already solved for y.

36. $(-0.5, 2)$; Answers may vary. Sample: elimination; you can subtract the equations as they are.

37. $(6, -4)$; Answers may vary. Sample: elimination; you can multiply each equation by the LCD of the denominators to eliminate the fractions. Then you can use elimination.

38. They both result in an equation with a single variable to solve. Check students' work.

39. parasailing: $51; horseback riding: $30

40. square: 81 cm²; triangle: 15 cm²

41. $\left(2, \frac{1}{2}\right)$

42. $(5, 0)$

43. $(5, 3, -1)$

Answers

Practice and Problem-Solving Exercises
(continued)

44. Yes; the problem can be represented by the system
$x + y = 7$
$19x + 8y = 100$
You can score 100 with four 19's and three 8's.

45. 7   **46.** 3
47. 5.46   **48.** 105
49. 390   **50.** (7, 3.5)
51. (34, 27)   **52.** (5, −3)
53. $a > 1$ **54.** $x \geq 7$
55. $b > 0.2$ **56.** 2.75 h

---

44. Reasoning Use the dartboard at the right. Can you score exactly 100 points with seven darts that all land on the board? Explain.

45. What is the value of the y-coordinate of the solution of the given system?

$4x + 3y = 33$
$3x + 2y = 23$

46. What is the y-intercept of $2x + 5y = 15$?

47. You buy a toothbrush for $2.83 and a tube of toothpaste for $2.37. There is a 5% sales tax. Including the tax, what is the total cost in dollars of your purchases?

48. Three fire trucks and 4 ambulances can fit into a parking lane 152 ft long. Two fire trucks and 5 ambulances can fit into a lane 136 ft long. How many feet long must a parking lane be for 1 fire truck and 5 ambulances? Assume there is 1 ft of space between each vehicle.

|← 152 ft →|

|← 136 ft →|

49. You are competing in a mountain bike race. Your average speed is 10 mi/h. If the racecourse is 65 mi long, how many minutes will it take you to finish the race?

Mixed Review

Solve each system using substitution.   See Lesson 6-2.

50. $y = \frac{1}{2}x$
$2y + 3x = 28$

51. $x - 7 = y$
$2x - y = 41$

52. $x + 2y = -1$
$3x - 5y = 30$

Solve each inequality.   See Lesson 3-4.

53. $4 - 2a < 3a - 1$

54. $3(2x - 1) \geq 5x + 4$

55. $2.7 + 2b > 3.4 - 1.5b$

Get Ready! To prepare for Lesson 6-4, do Exercise 56.

56. Two trains run on two sets of parallel tracks. The first train leaves a city $\frac{1}{2}$ h before the second train. The first train travels at 55 mi/h. The second train travels at 65 mi/h. How long does it take for the second train to pass the first train?   See Lesson 2-4.

Additional Instructional Support

Algebra 1 Companion

Students can use the **Algebra 1 Companion** worktext (4 pages) as you teach the lesson. Use the Companion to support

- New Vocabulary
- Key Concepts
- Got It for each Problem
- Lesson Check

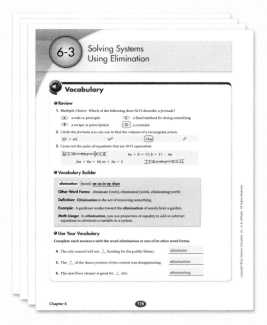

ELL Support

Use Graphic Organizers Divide students into groups of three. Say: "Make a graphic organizer showing the three methods for solving systems of equations, *graphing*, *substitution*, and *elimination*. You might give the organizer the title, 'Solving Systems of Equations'." Have the students include examples of each method in their graphic organizer. Say: "In your graphic organizer, show what is the same about all three methods. Then show what is different about the three methods." When students are finished, say: "Show your graphic organizer to another group. Tell them about your organizer." Have each group make changes to their graphic organizer based on what they learned from the other group.

5 Assess & Remediate

Lesson Quiz

1. What is the solution of the system? Use elimination.
$$7x + 5y = 19$$
$$-7x - 2y = -16$$

2. The cost of four scarves and six hats is $52. The cost of two hats is $1 more than the cost of one scarf. What are the costs of one scarf and one hat?

3. What is the solution of the system? Use elimination.
$$5x + 6y = 17$$
$$-10x - 9y = -43$$

4. **Do you UNDERSTAND?** How many solutions does the system have? Explain.
$$-3x + 6y = 10$$
$$-3x + 6y = -4$$

ANSWERS TO LESSON QUIZ

1. $(2, 1)$
2. $7; $4
3. $(7, -3)$
4. None; the two lines are parallel.

PRESCRIPTION FOR REMEDIATION
Use the student work on the Lesson Quiz to prescribe a differentiated review assignment.

Points	Differentiated Remediation
0–2	Intervention
3	On-level
4	Extension

PowerAlgebra.com

5 Assess & Remediate

Assign the Lesson Quiz. Appropriate intervention, practice, or enrichment is automatically generated based on student performance.

Intervention

- **Reteaching** (2 pages) Provides reteaching and practice exercises for the key lesson concepts. Use with struggling students or absent students.

- **English Language Learner Support** Helps students develop and reinforce mathematical vocabulary and key concepts.

All-in-One Resources/Online
Reteaching

6-3 Reteaching
Solving Systems Using Elimination

Elimination is one way to solve a system of equations. Think about what the word "eliminate" means. You can eliminate either variable, whichever is easiest.

Problem

Solve and check the following system of linear equations.
$$4x - 3y = -4$$
$$2x + 3y = 34$$

Solution The equations are already arranged so that like terms are in columns.

Notice how the coefficients of the y-variables have the opposite sign and the same value.

$$\begin{array}{ll} 4x - 3y = -4 & \\ \underline{2x + 3y = 34} & \text{Add the equations to eliminate } y. \\ 6x = 30 & \text{Divide both sides by 6 to solve for } x. \\ x = 5 & \\ 4(5) - 3y = -4 & \text{Substitute 5 for } x \text{ in one of the original equations} \\ 20 - 3y = -4 & \text{and solve for } y. \\ -3y = -24 & \\ y = 8 & \end{array}$$

The solution is (5, 8).

Check
$$\begin{array}{ll} 4x - 3y = -4 & \text{Substitute your solution into both of} \\ 4(5) - 3(8) \stackrel{?}{=} -4 & \text{the original equations to check.} \\ 20 - 24 \stackrel{?}{=} -4 & \\ -4 = -4 \checkmark & \end{array}$$

You can check the other equation.

Exercises

Solve and check each system.

1. $3x + y = 3$ (0, 3)
   $-3x + y = 3$

2. $6x - 3y = -14$ ($\frac{2}{3}$, 6)
   $6x - y = -2$

3. $3x - 2y = 10$ (2, -2)
   $x - 2y = 6$

4. $4x + y = 8$ (1, 4)
   $x + y = 5$

All-in-One Resources/Online
English Language Learner Support

6-3 ELL Support
Solving Systems Using Elimination

Tony is trying to find the solution of the system using elimination.
$$2x - 4y = 12 \qquad 3x + 4y = 48$$
He wrote these steps to solve the problem on note cards, but they got mixed up.

| Solve for x. |
| Eliminate one variable. Since the sum of the coefficients of y is 0, add the equations to eliminate y. |
| Simplify. |

| Substitute 12 for x to solve for the eliminated variable. |
| Solve for y. |
| Since $x = 12$ and $y = 3$, the solution is (12, 3). |

Use the note cards to complete the steps below.

1. First, eliminate one variable. Since the sum of the coefficients of y is 0, add the equations to eliminate y.

2. Second, solve for x.

3. Third, substitute 12 for x to solve for the eliminated variable.

4. Then, simplify.

5. Next, solve for y.

6. Finally, since $x = 12$ and $y = 3$, the solution is (12, 3).

Differentiated Remediation *continued*

On-Level

- **Practice** (2 pages) Provides extra practice for each lesson. For simpler practice exercises, use the Form K Practice pages found in the All-in-One Teaching Resources and online.

- **Think About a Plan** Helps students develop specific problem-solving skills and strategies by providing scaffolded guiding questions.

- **Standardized Test Prep** Focuses on all major exercises, all major question types, and helps students prepare for the high-stakes assessments.

Extension

- **Enrichment** Provides students with interesting problems and activities that extend the concepts of the lesson.

- **Activities, Games, and Puzzles** Worksheets that can be used for concepts development, enrichment, and for fun!

Practice and Problem Solving WKBK/ All-in-One Resources/Online
Practice page 1

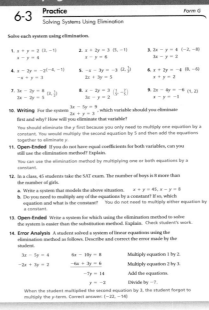

Practice and Problem Solving WKBK/ All-in-One Resources/Online
Practice page 2

All-in-One Resources/Online
Enrichment

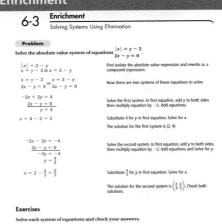

Practice and Problem Solving WKBK/ All-in-One Resources/Online
Think About a Plan

Practice and Problem Solving WKBK/ All-in-One Resources/Online
Standardized Test Prep

Online Teacher Resource Center
Activities, Games, and Puzzles

Matrices and Solving Systems

Indiana Academic Standard

A1.3.1 Understand the relationship between a solution of a pair of linear equations in two variables and the graphs of the corresponding lines and solve pairs of linear equations in two variables by graphing, substitution or elimination.

A *matrix* is a rectangular arrangement of numbers in rows and columns. The plural of *matrix* is *matrices*. You will learn more about matrix operations, including adding and subtracting matrices, in Chapter 12.

You can use a special type of matrix, called an *augmented matrix*, to solve a system of linear equations. An augmented matrix is formed using the coefficients and constants in the equations in a system. The equations must be written in standard form.

System of Equations

$$7x + 6y = 10$$
$$4x + 5y = -5$$

Augmented Matrix

$$\begin{bmatrix} 7 & 6 & | & 10 \\ 4 & 5 & | & -5 \end{bmatrix}$$

Recall the operations you performed when you solved systems using elimination. You can perform similar operations on the rows of an augmented matrix.

You can perform any of the following row operations on an augmented matrix to produce an equivalent augmented matrix.

Interchange two rows. $\begin{bmatrix} 7 & 6 & | & 10 \\ 4 & 5 & | & -5 \end{bmatrix} \rightarrow \begin{bmatrix} 4 & 5 & | & -5 \\ 7 & 6 & | & 10 \end{bmatrix}$

Multiply a row by any constant except 0. $\begin{bmatrix} 7 & 6 & | & 10 \\ 4 & 5 & | & -5 \end{bmatrix} \rightarrow \begin{bmatrix} 7 & 6 & | & 10 \\ 2(4) & 2(5) & | & 2(-5) \end{bmatrix} \rightarrow \begin{bmatrix} 7 & 6 & | & 10 \\ 8 & 10 & | & -10 \end{bmatrix}$

Add a multiple of one row to another row.

$\begin{bmatrix} 7 & 6 & | & 10 \\ 4 & 5 & | & -5 \end{bmatrix} \rightarrow \begin{bmatrix} 7 + 2(4) & 6 + 2(5) & | & 10 + 2(-5) \\ 4 & 5 & | & -5 \end{bmatrix} \rightarrow \begin{bmatrix} 15 & 16 & | & 0 \\ 4 & 5 & | & -5 \end{bmatrix}$

To solve a system using an augmented matrix, choose row operations that will transform the augmented matrix into a matrix with 1's along the main diagonal (top left to lower right) and 0's above and below the main diagonal, as shown below.

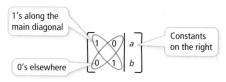

1's along the main diagonal

0's elsewhere

Constants on the right

$\begin{bmatrix} 1 & 0 & | & a \\ 0 & 1 & | & b \end{bmatrix}$

Guided Instruction

PURPOSE To use augmented matrices to solve systems of linear equations

PROCESS Students will

- write systems of equations as augmented matrices.
- compute row operations on matrices
- solve systems of equations using matrices.

DISCUSS Have students describe how the matrices are written in rows according to the equations. Ask why operations can only be performed on a row and not a column. Help students see how row operations are related to operations in equations.

The augmented matrix used to show the three operations is the matrix that represents the system given in the introduction. These matrices show examples of the operations and are not necessarily leading to the solutions to the system of equations.

Notice in the matrix showing the interchange of two rows that the order of the elements in each row does not change for any elements, just the vertical order of the elements of each column.

In the matrix that shows multiplication by a constant, the second row of the matrix is multiplied by 2. Ask students why the constant by which a row is multiplied should not be 0.

In the third matrix shown, a multiple of the second row of the matrix is added to the first row of the matrix. Ask students why the second row of the matrix is unchanged.

Example

In this activity students focus on solving systems of linear equations using an augmented matrix.

> **Q** What does the vertical line in an augmented matrix represent? **[It represents the equals sign from the equation.]**
>
> **Q** What would happen if an augmented matrix was written for a system in the form $C = Ax + By$? **[The solution matrix would have x and y values in the first column.]**
>
> **Q** When converting a linear equation into an augmented matrix, what equation form is needed? **[Standard form, $Ax + By = C$]**
>
> **Q** What is located on the left and right sides of the vertical line? **[The left side of the vertical line contains the coefficients of the variable terms, and the right side of the vertical line contains the constants of the equation.]**

Example

Solve the system using an augmented matrix. $3x + 2y = 11$
$4x + y = 18$

$$\begin{bmatrix} 3 & 2 & | & 11 \\ 4 & 1 & | & 18 \end{bmatrix}$$ Write the system as an augmented matrix.

$$\begin{bmatrix} 3 + (-2)(4) & 2 + (-2)(1) & | & 11 + (-2)(18) \\ 4 & 1 & | & 18 \end{bmatrix} \rightarrow \begin{bmatrix} -5 & 0 & | & -25 \\ 4 & 1 & | & 18 \end{bmatrix}$$ Multiply row 2 by -2 and add to row 1.

$$\begin{bmatrix} -\frac{1}{5}(-5) & -\frac{1}{5}(0) & | & -\frac{1}{5}(-25) \\ 4 & 1 & | & 18 \end{bmatrix} \rightarrow \begin{bmatrix} 1 & 0 & | & 5 \\ 4 & 1 & | & 18 \end{bmatrix}$$ Multiply row 1 by $-\frac{1}{5}$.

$$\begin{bmatrix} 1 & 0 & | & 5 \\ 4 + (-4)(1) & 1 + (-4)(0) & | & 18 + (-4)(5) \end{bmatrix} \rightarrow \begin{bmatrix} 1 & 0 & | & 5 \\ 0 & 1 & | & -2 \end{bmatrix}$$ Multiply row 1 by -4 and add to row 2.

$x = 5$ Write each row of the matrix as an equation.
$y = -2$

The solution of the system is $(5, -2)$.

Exercises

Solve each system using an augmented matrix.

1. $3x + 2y = 26$
$x + y = 7$

2. $-4x - 4y = 16$
$4x + 5y = 14$

3. $2x + 2y = 14$
$-x - 2y = -13$

4. Compare and Contrast Solve the system of equations in the example above using the elimination method. How are the row operations you have used in this activity like the operations you performed using the elimination method? How are they different?

5. Writing Are the row operations more like the substitution method or the elimination method? Explain.

6. Cosmetology A hairdresser finds that he can give 3 haircuts and 2 hair dyes in 315 min. Giving 2 haircuts and 4 hair dyes takes 450 min. How long does it take him to give a haircut? How long does it take him to dye a customer's hair? Write a system of equations and solve it using an augmented matrix.

7. Error Analysis A student says the augmented matrix at the right shows that the solution of the system is $(5, 3)$. What is the student's error? What is the correct solution of the system?

Answers

Exercises

1. $(12, -5)$ **2.** $(-34, 30)$

3. $(1, 6)$

4. Check students' work. Answers may vary. Sample: the row operations are like the ones used in the elimination method, where you multiply one of the equations by a constant and then add it to the other equation. Augmented matrices do not include variables like equations, even though they represent a system of equations.

5. Elimination; getting a zero in one row is like eliminating a variable.

6. haircut: 45 min; dye: 90 min

7. The augmented matrix is in the standard form of the system, so the solution is $x = 3$ and $y = 5$, or $(3, 5)$.

6-4 Applications of Linear Systems

Indiana Academic Standard
A1.3.3 Solve problems that can be modeled using pairs of linear equations in two variables, interpret the solutions, and determine whether the solutions are reasonable.

Objective To choose the best method for solving a system of linear equations

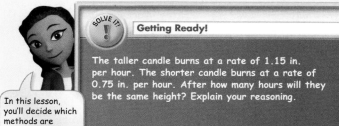
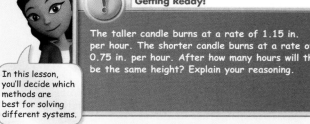

In this lesson, you'll decide which methods are best for solving different systems.

Getting Ready!

The taller candle burns at a rate of 1.15 in. per hour. The shorter candle burns at a rate of 0.75 in. per hour. After how many hours will they be the same height? Explain your reasoning.

9 in.   7 in.

Essential Understanding You can solve systems of linear equations using a graph, the substitution method, or the elimination method. The best method to use depends on the forms of the given equations and how precise the solution should be.

Dynamic Activity Modeling Linear Systems

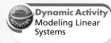

Concept Summary   **Choosing a Method for Solving Linear Systems**

Method	When to Use
Graphing	When you want a visual display of the equations, or when you want to estimate a solution
Substitution	When one equation is already solved for one of the variables, or when it is easy to solve for one of the variables
Elimination	When the coefficients of one variable are the same or opposites, or when it is not convenient to use graphing or substitution

Systems of equations are useful for modeling problems involving mixtures, rates, and break-even points.

The break-even point for a business is the point at which income equals expenses. The graph shows the break-even point for one business.

Notice that the values of y on the red line represent dollars spent on expenses. The values of y on the blue line represent dollars received as income. So y is used to represent both expenses and income.

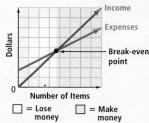

Income
Expenses
Break-even point

Dollars
Number of Items

☐ = Lose money   ☐ = Make money

1 Interactive Learning

Solve It!
PURPOSE To represent a real-world situation using a system of equations and to solve the system using a previously learned method
PROCESS Students may
• make a table of values.
• write a system and solve it graphically.
• write a system and solve it algebraically.
• use mathematical reasoning.

FACILITATE

Q What system of equations can be used to model this situation? [$y = 9 - 1.15x$ and $y = 7 - 0.75x$]

Q Which of the methods that you learned previously would you use to solve this system? Explain. **[Answers may vary. Sample: I would use substitution because both equations are already solved for y.]**

ANSWER See Solve It in Answers on next page.
CONNECT THE MATH Students write a system of equations related to the height of the two candles and their burning time. In this lesson, students evaluate whether the system is best solved using the graphing, substitution, or elimination method.

2 Guided Instruction

Take Note
Ask students to create an example of a system of equations for each method that matches the "When to Use" descriptions provided in the summary.

6-4 Preparing to Teach

BIG ideas Modeling
Solving Equations & Inequalities

ESSENTIAL UNDERSTANDINGS
• Systems of equations can be solved by graphing, substitution, or eliminating a variable.
• The best method to use depends on the forms of the given equations and how precise the solution should be.

Math Background
It is important for students to know when it is best to use each method for solving real-world equations. Any system can be solved using any of the methods. Finding a solution by graphing is more difficult when the values of the x- and y-coordinates of the point of intersection are not integers. Unfortunately, you will not know if the

UbD values are integers until the graph is complete. However, graphing provides additional information about the system of equations.

Substitution can be used to solve any system, but in some cases, fractions will be introduced in the first step and will require exceptional computational skills from that point forward.

Elimination is more difficult when the least common multiples of the coefficients are large.

Support Student Learning
Use the **Algebra 1 Companion** to engage and support students during instructions. See Lesson Resources at the end of this lesson for details.

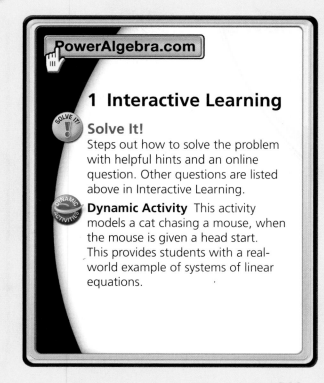

PowerAlgebra.com

1 Interactive Learning

Solve It!
Steps out how to solve the problem with helpful hints and an online question. Other questions are listed above in Interactive Learning.

Dynamic Activity This activity models a cat chasing a mouse, when the mouse is given a head start. This provides students with a real-world example of systems of linear equations.

Problem 1

Q If the designer sold 8 hats, what is her total expense, y? total income, y? **[y = $1444; y = $100]**

Q If the designer sold x hats, what expression represents her total expense, y? total income, y? **[y = 5.5x + $1400; y = 12.5x]**

Q What will be the designer's total revenue at the break-even point? Explain. **[$2500, because 12.5 · 200 = 2500]**

Got It?

Q What equation represents the expenses for the puzzle expert? the total revenue? **[y = 0.80x + 864; y = 2x]**

Problem 2

Q Is it possible to create 0.5% fat milk by combining the low-fat and whole milk? Explain. **[No, the minimum amount of fat in a combination would be 1% if all low-fat milk were used. Negative quantities will work algebraically, but not in the application.]**

Q Would it be possible to create 4.5% fat milk by combining the low-fat and whole milk? Explain. **[No, the maximum amount of fat in a combination would be 3.5% if all whole milk were used.]**

Q If you have 40 gallons of whole milk, how much fat does it contain? If you have y gallons of whole milk, how much fat does it contain? **[1.4 gallons; 0.035y]**

Q If you have 60 gallons of low-fat milk, how much fat does it contain? If you have x gallons of low-fat milk, how much fat does it contain? **[0.6 gallons; 0.01x]**

  Problem 1 Finding a Break-Even Point

Business A fashion designer makes and sells hats. The material for each hat costs $5.50. The hats sell for $12.50 each. The designer spends $1400 on advertising. How many hats must the designer sell to break even?

Step 1 Write a system of equations. Let x = the number of hats sold, and let y = the number of dollars of expense or income.

Expense: $y = 5.5x + 1400$ Income: $y = 12.5x$

Step 2 Choose a method. Use substitution since both equations are solved for y.

$y = 5.5x + 1400$	Start with one equation.
$12.5x = 5.5x + 1400$	Substitute 12.5x for y.
$7x = 1400$	Subtract 5.5x from each side.
$x = 200$	Divide each side by 7.

Since x is the number of hats, the designer must sell 200 hats to break even.

Got It? **1.** A puzzle expert wrote a new sudoku puzzle book. His initial costs are $864. Binding and packaging each book costs $.80. The price of the book is $2. How many copies must be sold to break even?

Think

What equations should you write? The break-even point is when income equals expenses, so write one equation for income and one equation for expenses.

 Problem 2 Solving a Mixture Problem

Dairy A dairy owner produces low-fat milk containing 1% fat and whole milk containing 3.5% fat. How many gallons of each type should be combined to make 100 gal of milk that is 2% fat?

Step 1 Write a system of equations. Let x = the number of gallons of low-fat milk, and let y = the number of gallons of whole milk.

Total gallons: $x + y = 100$ Fat content: $0.01x + 0.035y = 0.02(100)$

Step 2 The first equation is easy to solve for either x or y, so use substitution.

$x + y = 100$	Write the first equation.
$x = 100 - y$	Subtract y from each side.

Step 3 Substitute $100 - y$ for x in the second equation and solve for y.

$0.01x + 0.035y = 0.02(100)$	Write the second equation.
$0.01(100 - y) + 0.035y = 0.02(100)$	Substitute 100 − y for x.
$1 - 0.01y + 0.035y = 2$	Distributive Property
$0.025y = 1$	Subtract 1 from each side. Then simplify.
$y = 40$	Divide each side by 0.025.

Step 4 Substitute 40 for y in either equation and solve for x.

$x + 40 = 100$	Substitute 40 for y in the first equation.
$x = 60$	Solve for x.

The owner should mix 60 gal of low-fat milk with 40 gal of whole milk.

Think

What do the percents mean when used as coefficients? The percents describe the fat concentration in each type of milk. If you multiply the percents by some number of gallons, you'll get the amount of fat in that number of gallons.

Answers

Solve It!
5 h; explanations may vary.

Got It?
1. 720 books

 PowerAlgebra.com

2 Guided Instruction

Each Problem is worked out and supported online.

Problem 1 Finding a Break-Even Point *Animated*	**Problem 2** Solving a Mixture Problem *Animated*

Problem 3 Solving a Wind or Current Problem

Alternative Problem 1 Finding a Break-Even Point *Animated*

Support in Algebra 1 Companion
• Vocabulary
• Key Concepts
• Got It?

Got It? **2.** One antifreeze solution is 20% alcohol. Another antifreeze solution is 12% alcohol. How many liters of each solution should be combined to make 15 L of antifreeze solution that is 18% alcohol?

When a plane travels from west to east across the United States, the steady west-to-east winds act as tailwinds. This increases the plane's speed relative to the ground. When a plane travels from east to west, the winds act as headwinds. This decreases the plane's speed relative to the ground.

From West to East	**From East to West**
air speed + wind speed = ground speed	air speed − wind speed = ground speed

 Problem 3 Solving a Wind or Current Problem

Travel A traveler flies from Charlotte, North Carolina, to Los Angeles, California. At the same time, another traveler flies from Los Angeles to Charlotte. The air speed of each plane is the same. The ground speeds are shown below. What is the air speed? What is the wind speed?

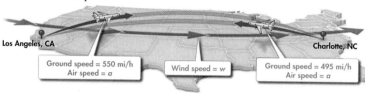

Los Angeles, CA

Charlotte, NC

Ground speed = 550 mi/h
Air speed = a

Wind speed = w

Ground speed = 495 mi/h
Air speed = a

Think

How are the speeds related?
The air speed is a plane's speed with no wind. Add wind speed and air speed to get the ground speed with a tailwind. Subtract wind speed from air speed to find the ground speed with a headwind.

Use the ground speed with the tailwind and with the headwind to write the system. Let a = the air speed of the planes. Let w = the wind speed.

$$\frac{\text{air}}{\text{speed}} + \frac{\text{wind}}{\text{speed}} = \frac{\text{ground speed}}{\text{with tailwind}} \qquad \frac{\text{air}}{\text{speed}} - \frac{\text{wind}}{\text{speed}} = \frac{\text{ground speed}}{\text{with headwind}}$$

$$a + w = 550 \qquad a - w = 495$$

Choose a method to solve the system. Use elimination.

$$a + w = 550$$
$$\underline{a - w = 495}$$
$$2a + 0 = 1045 \qquad \text{Add the equations.}$$
$$a = 522.5 \qquad \text{Solve for } a.$$

Substitute 522.5 for a in either equation and solve for w.

$$522.5 + w = 550 \qquad \text{Substitute 522.5 for } a \text{ in the first equation.}$$
$$w = 27.5 \qquad \text{Solve for } w.$$

The air speed is 522.5 mi/h. The wind speed is 27.5 mi/h.

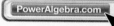
Got It?
The following table may help students organize the given information and write the equations.

	Solution 1	Solution 2	Solution 3
Total Volume	x	y	15
Volume of Alcohol	0.20x	0.12y	0.18(15)

Problem 3

Q If a plane has an air speed of 450 mph and has a tailwind of 30 mph, what is the groundspeed of the plane? **[480 mph]**

Q If the same plane turns around to fly in the opposite direction, what is the new ground speed? **[420 mph]**

Q Does the trip from Charlotte to Los Angeles have a tailwind or a headwind? **[headwind]**

Q Will the groundspeed from Los Angeles to Charlotte be greater than or less than the airspeed from Los Angeles to Charlotte? **[greater than]**

Q How could you eliminate the variable a from the system of equations rather than the variable w? **[Subtract the two equations.]**

Q Would the answer be the same if you solved by eliminating a? Explain. **[Yes. $2w$ would equal 55; so w would be 27.5 and a would be 522.5.]**

Additional Problems

1. A carpenter makes and sells rocking chairs. The material for each chair costs $22.50. The chairs sell for $75 each. If the carpenter spends $420 on advertising, how many chairs must she sell to break even?

ANSWER 8

2. A scientist has a container of 2% acid solution and a container of 5% acid solution. How many fluid ounces of each concentration should be combined to make 25 fl oz of 3.2% acid solution?

ANSWER 15 fl oz of 2% acid solution and 10 fl oz of 5% acid solution

3. The speed of a kayaker is 5.75 mi/h hour paddling with the river current and 3.25 mi/h paddling against it. What is the speed of the river current?

ANSWER 1.25 mi/h

Answers

Got It? (continued)
2. 11.25 L of 20% alcohol; 3.75 L of 12% alcohol

Got It?
Make sure students understand that rowing upstream is similar to flying with a headwind and that rowing downstream is similar to flying with a tailwind.

3 Lesson Check

Do you know HOW?
• If students have difficulty with Exercise 2, then encourage them to make a table to organize what is known.

Do you UNDERSTAND?
• If students have difficulty with Exercise 5, then have them review the concept summary box on page 383.

Close

> **Q** You have learned three methods for solving systems of equations. What types of conditions help you decide which method to use? **[If you want a visual display, you can graph the system. When one equation is solved for one of the variables, the best method is substitution. When the coefficients on one variable are the same or opposite (or can be easily changed to be the same or opposite) it is best to solve the system by elimination.]**

 Got It? 3. a. You row upstream at a speed of 2 mi/h. You travel the same distance downstream at a speed of 5 mi/h. What would be your rowing speed in still water? What is the speed of the current?

b. Reasoning Suppose your rowing speed in still water is 3 mi/h and the speed of the current is 4 mi/h. What happens when you try to row upstream?

 Lesson Check

Do you know HOW?

1. **Newsletters** Printing a newsletter costs $1.50 per copy plus $450 in printer's fees. The copies are sold for $3 each. How many copies of the newsletter must be sold to break even?

2. **Jewelry** A metal alloy is a metal made by blending 2 or more types of metal. A jeweler has supplies of two metal alloys. One alloy is 30% gold and the other is 10% gold. How much of each alloy should the jeweler combine to create 4 kg of an alloy containing 15% gold?

3. **Flying** With a tailwind, a bird flew at a ground speed of 3 mi/h. Flying the same path against the same wind, the bird travels at a ground speed of 1.5 mi/h. What is the bird's air speed? What is the wind speed?

Do you UNDERSTAND?

4. **Vocabulary** What is the relationship between income and expenses before a break-even point is reached? What is the relationship between income and expenses after a break-even point is reached?

5. **Reasoning** Which method would you use to solve the following system? Explain.
$$3x + 2y = 9$$
$$-2x + 3y = 5$$

6. **Reasoning** One brand of cranberry-apple drink is 15% cranberry juice. Another brand is 40% cranberry juice. You would like to combine the brands to make a drink that is 25% cranberry juice. Without calculating, which brand of juice will you need more of to make your drink? Explain.

 Practice and Problem-Solving Exercises

 Practice

7. **Business** A bicycle store costs $2400 per month to operate. The store pays an average of $60 per bike. The average selling price of each bicycle is $120. How many bicycles must the store sell each month to break even? ◆ See Problem 1.

8. **Theater** Producing a musical costs $88,000 plus $5900 per performance. One sold-out performance earns $7500 in revenue. If every performance sells out, how many performances are needed to break even?

9. **Investment** You split $1500 between two savings accounts. Account A pays annual 5% interest and Account B pays 4% annual interest. After one year, you have earned a total of $69.50 in interest. How much money did you invest in each account? ◆ See Problem 2.

10. **Metalwork** A metalworker has a metal alloy that is 20% copper and another alloy that is 60% copper. How many kilograms of each alloy should the metalworker combine to create 80 kg of a 52% copper alloy?

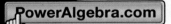 PowerAlgebra.com

3 Lesson Check

For a digital lesson check, use the Got It questions.

Support In Algebra 1 Companion
• Lesson Check

4 Practice

 Assign homework to individual students or to an entire class.

Answers

Got It? (continued)
3. a. 3.5 mi/h; 1.5 mi/h
b. You will be pushed backward.

Lesson Check
1. 300 copies
2. 1 kg of 30% gold, 3 kg of 10% gold
3. 2.25 mi/h; 0.75 mi/h
4. Before the break-even point, expenses exceed income. After the break-even point, income exceeds expenses.
5. Answers may vary. Sample: elimination; neither equation is easily solved for a variable.
6. You would need more of the 15% brand, since 25% is closer to 15% than 40%.

Practice and Problem-Solving Exercises
7. 40 bicycles
8. 55 performances
9. $950 at 5% and $550 at 4%
10. 16 kg of 20% copper, 64 kg of 60% copper

11. Airports A traveler is walking on a moving walkway in an airport. The traveler must walk back on the walkway to get a bag he forgot. The traveler's groundspeed is 2 ft/s against the walkway and 6 ft/s with the walkway. What is the traveler's speed off the walkway? What is the speed of the moving walkway?

◀ See Problem 3.

12. Kayaking A kayaker paddles upstream from camp to photograph a waterfall and returns. The kayaker's speed while traveling upstream and downstream is shown below. What is the kayaker's speed in still water? What is the speed of the current?

Apply

13. Money You have a jar of pennies and quarters. You want to choose 15 coins that are worth exactly $4.35.
    a. Write and solve a system of equations that models the situation.
    b. Is your solution reasonable in terms of the original problem? Explain.

Solve each system. Explain why you chose the method you used.

14. $4x + 5y = 3$
$3x - 2y = 8$

15. $2x + 7y = -20$
$y = 3x + 7$

16. $5x + 2y = 17$
$x - 2y = 8$

17. Reasoning Find A and B so that the system below has the solution $(2, 3)$.
$$Ax - 2By = 6$$
$$3Ax - By = -12$$

18. Think About a Plan A tugboat can pull a boat 24 mi downstream in 2 h. Going upstream, the tugboat can pull the same boat 16 mi in 2 h. What is the speed of the tugboat in still water? What is the speed of the current?
    • How can you use the formula $d = rt$ to help you solve the problem?
    • How are the tugboat's speeds when traveling upstream and downstream related to its speed in still water and the speed of the current?

Open-Ended Without solving, decide what method you would use to solve each system: *graphing*, *substitution*, or *elimination*. Explain.

19. $y = 3x - 1$
$y = 4x$

20. $3m - 4n = 1$
$3m - 2n = -1$

21. $4s - 3t = 8$
$t = -2s - 1$

22. Business A perfume maker has stocks of two perfumes on hand. Perfume A sells for $15 per ounce. Perfume B sells for $35 per ounce. How much of each should be combined to make a 3-oz bottle of perfume that can be sold for $63?

23. Chemistry In a chemistry lab, you have two vinegars. One is 5% acetic acid, and one is 6.5% acetic acid. You want to make 200 mL of a vinegar with 6% acetic acid. How many milliliters of each vinegar do you need to mix together?

ASSIGNMENT GUIDE

Basic: 7–12, 13–16, 18–21, 23, 25

Average: 7–11 odd, 13–26

Advanced: 7–11 odd, 13–28

Standardized Test Prep: 29–31

Mixed Review: 32–37

Reasoning exercises have blue headings.

Applications exercises have red headings.

EXERCISE 23: Use the Think About a Plan worksheet in the **Practice and Problem Solving Workbook** (also available in the Teaching Resources in print and online) to further support students' development in becoming independent learners.

HOMEWORK QUICK CHECK
To check students' understanding of key skills and concepts, go over Exercises 7, 11, 18, 20, and 23.

---

11. 4 ft/s; 2 ft/s

12. 5.5 mi/h; 1.5 mi/h

13. a. Let x = the number of pennies and let y = the number of quarters.
$x + y = 15$
$0.01x + 0.25y = 4.35$
The solution is 17.5 quarters and -2.5 pennies.
    b. No; you can't have a negative number of coins.

14. $(2, -1)$; elimination method because neither equation easily solves for a variable

15. $(-3, -2)$; substitution because the second equation is already solved for y

16. $\left(\frac{25}{6}, -\frac{23}{12}\right)$; Explanations may vary. Sample: substitution because one of the equations is easily solved for x

17. $A = -3$ and $B = -2$.

18. 10 mi/h; 2 mi/h

19–21. Answers may vary. Samples are given.

19. Substitution; both equations are already solved for y, so you can set them equal.

20. Elimination; you can just subtract the two equations, as the coefficients of x are the same.

21. Substitution; the second equation is already solved for y.

22. 2.1 oz of Perfume A, 0.9 oz of Perfume B

23. $66\frac{2}{3}$ mL of the 5% mixture; $133\frac{1}{3}$ mL of the 6.5% mixture

Answers

Practice and Problem-Solving Exercises
(continued)

24. 4.5 km/h

25. It can also be solved by the elimination method because the variables are lined up and the coefficients of the y-terms are the same. So one would simply have to subtract the second equation.

26. 13 correctly and 7 incorrectly

27. 37   **28.** 50 jars

29. C   **30.** G

31. [2] The slope of the line is $\frac{3-1}{4-3} = 2$.
So $y - 1 = 2(x - 3)$, or $y - 1 = 2x - 6$.
The equation of the line passing through the points (3, 1) and (4, 3) is $y = 2x - 5$.
[1] appropriate methods with one minor computational error

32. $(-7, 6)$ **33.** $(-2, -2)$

34. $(4, 2.5)$ **35.** $a > 5$

36. $d \leq -2.5$ **37.** $q \leq -4$

---

24. Boating A boat is traveling in a river with a current that has a speed of 1.5 km/h. In one hour, the boat can travel twice the distance downstream as it can travel upstream. What is the boat's speed in still water?

25. Reasoning A student claims that the best way to solve the system at the right is by substitution. Do you agree? Explain.

$y - 3x = 4$
$y - 6x = 12$

26. Entertainment A contestant on a quiz show gets 150 points for every correct answer and loses 250 points for each incorrect answer. After answering 20 questions, the contestant has 200 points. How many questions has the contestant answered correctly? Incorrectly?

 Challenge

27. Number Theory You can represent the value of any two-digit number with the expression $10a + b$, where a is the tens' place digit and b is the ones' place digit. For example, if a is 5 and b is 7, then the value of the number is $10(5) + 7$, or 57. What two-digit number is described below?
- The ones' place digit is one more than twice the tens' place digit.
- The value of the number is two more than five times the ones' place digit.

28. Mixed Nuts You want to sell 1-lb jars of mixed peanuts and cashews for $5. You pay $3 per pound for peanuts and $6 per pound for cashews. You plan to combine 4 parts peanuts and 1 part cashews to make your mix. You have spent $70 on materials to get started. How many jars must you sell to break even?

Standardized Test Prep

SAT/ACT

29. Last year, one fourth of the students in your class played an instrument. This year, 6 students joined the class. Four of the new students play an instrument. Now, one third of the students play an instrument. How many students are in your class now?

     Ⓐ 18   Ⓑ 24   Ⓒ 30   Ⓓ 48

30. Which answer choice shows $2x - y = z$ correctly solved for y?

     Ⓕ $y = 2x + z$ Ⓖ $y = 2x - z$ Ⓗ $y = -2x + z$ Ⓘ $y = -2x - z$

Short Response

31. What is an equation of a line passing through the points (3, 1) and (4, 3) written in slope-intercept form?

Mixed Review

Solve each system using elimination.   ◀ **See Lesson 6-3.**

32. $x + 3y = 11$
$2x + 3y = 4$

33. $2x + 4y = -12$
$-6x + 5y = 2$

34. $5x + 8y = 40$
$3x - 10y = -13$

Get Ready! To prepare for Lesson 6-5, do Exercises 35–37.

Solve each inequality. Check your solution.   ◀ **See Lesson 3-4.**

35. $3a + 5 > 20$ **36.** $2d - 3 \geq 4d + 2$ **37.** $3(q + 4) \leq -2q - 8$

Lesson Resources

Additional Instructional Support

Algebra 1 Companion

Students can use the **Algebra 1 Companion** worktext (4 pages) as you teach the lesson. Use the Companion to support

- New Vocabulary
- Key Concepts
- Got It for each Problem
- Lesson Check

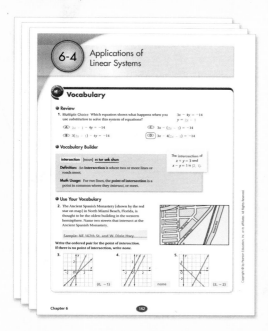

ELL Support

Use Role Playing Act out Problem 2. Assign students the roles of dairy owner, "1% fat milk," "3.5% fat milk," and "2% fat milk." Say: The gallons of 2% fat milk is the sum of the gallons of 1% fat milk and 3.5% fat milk. Have the dairy owner give "1% fat milk" and "3.5% fat milk" a paper with a number of gallons written on it. Have the dairy owner give "2% milk" the sum on another piece of paper. Ask students: What is the fat content for the 3.5% fat milk? [0.035 × the number of gallons] Have students state the fat content for the 1% fat milk [0.01 × gallons] and the 2% fat milk [sum of the 3.5% and 1% milk]. Ask: Does the fat content in the 2% fat milk equal 2%? Have students solve the problem and the dairy owner write the correct numbers.

5 Assess & Remediate

Lesson Quiz

1. The parent-teacher organization is selling baskets of cookies for a school fundraiser. The materials needed to make each basket cost $3.75, and the baskets are being sold for $10 each. If they spend $75 to advertise their sale, how many baskets must be sold in order to break even?

2. There is a beaker of 3.5% acid solution and a beaker of 6% acid solution in the science lab. Mr. Larson needs 200 mL of a 4.5% acid solution for an experiment. How many milliliters of each solution should he combine?

3. A plane flies at x miles per hour in still air. Flying with a tailwind, its speed is 485 mi/h. Against the wind, its air speed is only 445 mi/h. What is the speed of the wind?

4. **Do you UNDERSTAND?** What does it mean to break even?

ANSWERS TO LESSON QUIZ

1. 12
2. 120 mL of the 3.5% solution and 80 mL of the 6% solution
3. 20 mi/h
4. A business breaks even when income equals expenses.

PRESCRIPTION FOR REMEDIATION

Use the student work on the Lesson Quiz to prescribe a differentiated review assignment.

Points	Differentiated Remediation
0–2	Intervention
3	On-level
4	Extension

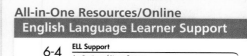

5 Assess & Remediate

Assign the Lesson Quiz. Appropriate intervention, practice, or enrichment is automatically generated based on student performance.

Intervention

- **Reteaching** (2 pages) Provides reteaching and practice exercises for the key lesson concepts. Use with struggling students or absent students.

- **English Language Learner Support** Helps students develop and reinforce mathematical vocabulary and key concepts.

All-in-One Resources/Online
Reteaching

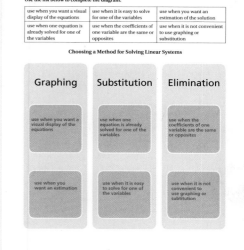

All-in-One Resources/Online
English Language Learner Support

Differentiated Remediation *continued*

On-Level

- **Practice** (2 pages) Provides extra practice for each lesson. For simpler practice exercises, use the Form K Practice pages found in the All-in-One Teaching Resources and online.
- **Think About a Plan** Helps students develop specific problem-solving skills and strategies by providing scaffolded guiding questions.
- **Standardized Test Prep** Focuses on all major exercises, all major question types, and helps students prepare for the high-stakes assessments.

Extension

- **Enrichment** Provides students with interesting problems and activities that extend the concepts of the lesson.
- **Activities, Games, and Puzzles** Worksheets that can be used for concepts development, enrichment, and for fun!

Practice and Problem Solving WKBK/ All-in-One Resources/Online

Practice page 1

6-4 Practice *Form G*

Applications of Linear Systems

Solve each word problem

1. You have $6000 to invest in two stock funds. The first fund pays 5% annual interest and the second account pays 9% annual interest. If after a year you have made $380 in interest, how much money did you invest in each account?
   $4000 at 5%; $2000 at 9%
2. During a sale at the local department store, you buy three sweatshirts and two pairs of sweatpants for $85.50. Later you return to the same store and buy three more sweatshirts and four more pairs of sweatpants for $123. What is the sale price of each sweatshirt and each pair of sweatpants?
   sweatshirt: $16; sweatpants: $18.75
3. The sum of two numbers is 27. The larger number is 3 more than the smaller number. What are the two numbers?
   (15, 12)
4. One plane at 520 feet is ascending at a rate of 40 feet per minute, while another plane at 3800 feet is descending at a rate of 120 feet per minute. How long will it take the two planes to be at the same altitude?
   20.5 min
5. The perimeter of a rectangle is 24 in. and its length is 3 times its width. What are the length and the width of the rectangle?
   length: 9 in.; width: 3 in.
6. You are getting ready to move and have asked some friends to help. For lunch, you buy the following sandwiches at the local deli for $30: six tuna sandwiches and six turkey sandwiches. Later at night, everyone is hungry again and you buy four tuna sandwiches and eight turkey sandwiches for $30.60. What is the price of each sandwich?
   tuna: $2.35; turkey: $2.65
7. You have a cable plan that costs $39 a month for a basic plan plus one movie channel. Your friend has the same basic plan plan plus two movie channels for $45.50. What is the basic plan charge that you both pay?
   $32.50
8. At an all-you-can-eat barbeque fundraiser that you are sponsoring, adults pay $6 for a dinner and children pay $4 for a dinner. 212 people attend and you raise $1128. What is the total number of adults and the total number of children attending?
   a. What is a system of equations that you can use to solve this problem? $x + y = 212$; $6x + 4y = 1128$
   b. What method would you use to solve the system? Why?
   I'd use substitution because in the first equation the coefficients are already 1.

Practice and Problem Solving WKBK/ All-in-One Resources/Online

Practice page 2

6-4 Practice (continued) *Form G*

Applications of Linear Systems

Solve each system. Explain why you chose the method you used.

9. $2y = x + 1$, $-2x - y = 7$ — $(-3, -1)$; substitution because there was a coefficient of 1
10. $6x - 4y = 54$, $-9x + 2y = -69$ — $(7, -3)$; elimination because no coefficients were 1 or -1.
11. $3y - 2y = 8$, $2x - 2y = 5$ — $\left(3, \frac{1}{2}\right)$; elimination because the y-coefficients are the same.
12. $2x - y = 4$, $3x - y = 2$ — $(-2, -8)$; elimination because the y-coefficients were the same.
13. $2x - 3y = 13$, $y = \frac{1}{2}x - \frac{7}{2}$ — $(5, -1)$; substitution because y is isolated in the second equation.
14. $-x - 3y = -3$, $2x + 3y = 5$ — $\left(2, \frac{1}{3}\right)$; elimination because the y-coefficients are opposites
15. **Open-Ended** What are three differences between an inconsistent system and a consistent and independent system? Explain.
    Answers may vary. Sample: There is one unique solution to an independent system, but no solution to an inconsistent system and infinitely many solutions to a dependent system. The graphs of the equations of an independent system have different slopes, but the slopes are the same for the lines of an inconsistent or dependent system. When solving a system algebraically, you get a specific value for each variable if the system is independent, but you get a false statement for an inconsistent system and a statement that is always true for a dependent system.
16. **Reasoning** One number is 4 less than 3 times a second number. If 3 more than two times the first number is decreased by two times the second, the result is 11. What are both numbers?
    (8, 4)
17. **Error Analysis** In Exercise 16, what kind of errors are likely to occur when solving the problem?
    Answers may vary. Sample: You might misinterpret the description. For instance, you might think "4 less than 3 times a number" means $4 - 3y$ instead of $3y - 4$.
18. A plane leaves Chicago and flies 750 miles to New York. If it takes 2.5 hours to get to New York flying against the wind, but only 2 hours to fly back to Chicago, what is the plane's rate of speed and what is the wind speed?
    wind: 37.5 mi/h; plane: 337.5 mi/h
19. A coin bank has 250 coins, dimes and quarters, worth $39.25. How many of each type of coin are there?
    155 dimes; 95 quarters
20. In 4 years, a mother will be 5 times as old as her daughter. At present, the mother is 9 times as old as the daughter. How old are the mother and the daughter today?
    mother: 36; daughter: 4

All-in-One Resources/Online

Enrichment

6-4 Enrichment

Applications of Linear Systems

The general form of the linear equation with three variables is $Ax + By + Cz = D$ where A, B, C and D are real numbers and do not equal 0.

Example

Solve the system of equations below.

$x + 2y - 3z = 1$ Equation (1)
$2x - 3y + 5z = 11$ Equation (2)
$x - y + 4z = 14$ Equation (3)

Solution

$x + 2y - 3z = 1$
$\underline{x - y + 4z = 14}$ — Subtract equation (3) from equation (1).
$3y - 7z = -13$ — Equation (4)

$2x - 2y + 8z = 28$
$\underline{2x - 3y + 5z = 11}$ — Multiply equation (3) by 2 and subtract equation (2).
$y + 3z = 17$ — Equation (5)

$3y + 9z = 51$
$\underline{3y - 7z = -13}$ — Multiply equation (5) by 3 and subtract equation (4).
$16z = 64$
$z = 4$ — Solve for z.

$y + 3(4) = 17$ — Substitute 4 for z in equation (5) and solve for y.
$y = 5$

$x + 2y - 3z = 1$
$x + 2(5) - 3(4) = 1$ — Substitute 5 for y and 4 for z in equation (1) and solve for x.
$x = 3$

The solution of the given system is $x = 3$, $y = 5$ and $z = 4$.

Practice

Solve each system of equations.

1. $3x - y + 2z = 4$, $x + 2y - 3z = -1$, $5x + 3y + z = 6$ — $\left(\frac{31}{35}, \frac{9}{35}, \frac{4}{5}\right)$
2. $-2x + 5y - 3z = 7$, $4x - 3y + 2z = 4$, $-3x - y - 4z = -7$ — $(3, 2, -1)$

Practice and Problem Solving WKBK/ All-in-One Resources/Online

Think About a Plan

6-4 Think About a Plan

Applications of Linear Systems

Chemistry In a chemistry lab, you have two vinegars. One is 5% acetic acid, and one is 6.5% acetic acid. You want to make 200 mL of a vinegar with 6% acetic acid. How many milliliters of each vinegar do you need to mix together?

Know

1. What types of vinegar do you have available?
   5% acetic acid and 6.5% acetic acid
2. What amount of mixed vinegar do you need?
   200 mL
3. What percentage of acetic acid do you want in the mixed vinegar?
   6%

Need

4. What do you need to find to solve the problem?
   the number of mL of each type of vinegar

Plan

5. How will you define the two variables for this problem?
   x = amount of 5% vinegar; y = amount of 6.5% vinegar
6. What is an equation for the total amount of vinegar you want to make?
   $x + y = 200$
7. What is an equation for the acetic acid content?
   $0.05x + 0.065y = 0.06(200)$
8. What method will you use to solve?
   Answers may vary. Sample: I will use substitution, because there are variable terms with coefficients of 1.
9. What is the solution of the system of equations?
   (66.67, 133.33)
10. How much of each type of vinegar should you mix together?
    You need 66.67 mL of 5% vinegar and 133.33 mL of 6.5% vinegar.

Practice and Problem Solving WKBK/ All-in-One Resources/Online

Standardized Test Prep

6-4 Standardized Test Prep

Applications of Linear Systems

Multiple Choice

For Exercises 1–5, choose the correct letter.

1. You solved a linear system with two equations and two variables and got the equation $-6 = -6$. How many solutions does the system of equations have? B
   A. no solution C. exactly 1 solution
   B. infinitely many solutions D. 2 solutions
2. The sum of two numbers is 12. The difference of the same two numbers is -4. What is the larger of the two numbers? I
   F. 4 H. 7 G. 5 I. 8
3. You solved a linear system and got the equation $-6 = 0$. How many solutions does the system of equations have? A
   A. no solution C. exactly 1 solution
   B. infinitely many solutions D. 2 solutions
4. What is the solution of the system of equations? $-y + 3x = 6$, $y = -6x + 12$ H
   F. $(-2, 0)$ H. $(2, 0)$ G. $(0, -2)$ I. $(0, 2)$
5. A kayaker paddles upstream for 1.5 hours, then turns his kayak around and returns to his tent in 1 hour. He travels 3 miles each way. What is the rate of the river's current? A
   A. 0.5 mi/h B. 2 mi/h C. 1 mi/h D. 1.5 mi/h

Short Response

6. Rectangle $EFGH$ has a perimeter of 24 inches, and triangle BCD has a perimeter of 18 inches.

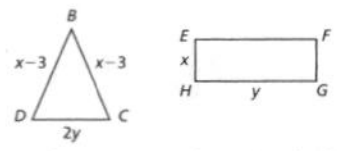

   a. What is a system of equations for the perimeters of the figures? $2x + 2y = 24$; $2(x - 3) + 2y = 18$
   b. Without solving, what method you would use to solve the system? Explain.
   I would use elimination because the y-coefficients are the same.
   [2] Both parts answered correctly. Explanation is clear.
   [1] One part answered correctly, or explanation is not clear or complete.
   [0] No parts answered correctly.

Online Teacher Resource Center

Activities, Games, and Puzzles

6-4 Activity: A Real-World Application

Applications of Linear Systems

Work with a partner in this activity.

A community theater is putting on a performance.

- An adult ticket sells for a dollars.
- A child's ticket sells for c dollars.
- The manager needs to collect $5000 in revenue to cover the theater's expenses.
- The theater can seat 800 people, and the manager expects the show to sell out.
- The manager wants to price the adult ticket at three times the cost of a child's ticket.

The manager wants to find the break-even point where the theater's income equals its expenses. Your teacher will assign you one of the four systems below. You need to determine the price of each ticket given the number of tickets sold.

	System A	System B	System C	System D
adults	600	700	500	650
children	200	100	300	150
Price: adult	$7.50	$6.81	$8.34	$7.14
Price: child	$2.50	$2.27	$2.78	$2.38

1. Write a system of equations that models your situation. Let a equal the price of an adult ticket and let c equal the price of a children's ticket.
   Answers may vary. Sample: $600a + 200c = 5000$; $a = 3c$
2. Now solve your system and find the price of an adult ticket and a children's ticket. Round to the nearest cent. Record your answers in the table.
   Answers may vary. Sample: The adult ticket price is $7.50 and the children's ticket is $2.50.
3. Discuss your findings with the rest of the class. Use the table to record the results from the other groups. Do all four systems satisfy the manager's conditions? If so, which system should the manager choose? Explain.
   Answers may vary. Sample: Yes; the manager should choose System C because the theater will collect about $5004, which is slightly more than they would collect with the other systems.

Do you know HOW?

Solve each system by graphing. Tell whether the system has *one solution*, *infinitely many solutions*, or *no solution*.

1. $y = x - 1$
$y = -3x - 5$

2. $y = \frac{4}{3}x - 2$
$3y - 4x = -6$

3. $y = 3x - 4$
$y - 3x = 1$

4. $y = 3x - 14$
$y - x = 10$

Solve each system using substitution.

5. $y = 2x + 5$
$y = 6x + 1$

6. $x = y + 7$
$y - 8 = 2x$

7. $4x + y = 2$
$3y + 2x = -1$

8. $4x + 9y = 24$
$y = -\frac{1}{3}x + 2$

Solve each system using elimination.

9. $2x + 5y = 2$
$3x - 5y = 53$

10. $4x + 2y = 34$
$10x - 4y = -5$

11. $11x - 13y = 89$
$-11x + 13y = 107$

12. $3x + 6y = 42$
$-7x + 8y = -109$

Write and solve a system of equations to solve each problem. Explain why you chose the method you used.

13. Geometry The length of a rectangle is 3 times the width. The perimeter is 44 cm. What are the dimensions of the rectangle?

14. Farming A farmer grows only pumpkins and corn on her 420-acre farm. This year she wants to plant 250 more acres of corn than pumpkins. How many acres of each crop should the farmer plant?

15. Coins You have a total of 21 coins, all nickels and dimes. The total value is $1.70. How many nickels and how many dimes do you have?

16. Business Suppose you start an ice cream business. You buy a freezer for $200. It costs you $.45 to make each single-scoop ice cream cone. You sell each cone for $1.25. How many cones do you need to sell to break even?

Do you UNDERSTAND?

Reasoning Without solving, tell which method you would choose to solve each system: *graphing*, *substitution*, or *elimination*. Explain your answer.

17. $y = 2x - 5$
$4y + 8x = 15$

18. $2y + 7x = 3$
$y - 7x = 9$

19. Reasoning If a system of linear equations has infinitely many solutions, what do you know about the slopes and *y*-intercepts of the graphs of the equations?

20. Open-Ended Write a system of equations that you would solve using substitution.

21. Reasoning Suppose you write a system of equations to find a break-even point for a business. You solve the system and find that it has no solution. What would that mean in terms of the business?

16. 250 cones

17. Answers may vary. Sample: Substitution; the first equation is already solved for *y*.

18. Answers may vary. Sample: Elimination; you can add the equations to eliminate *x*.

19. The slopes are the same and the *y*-intercepts are the same.

20. Check students' work.

21. Explanations may vary. Sample: It means that income never exceeds expenses, so the business never becomes profitable.

Answers

Mid-Chapter Quiz

1. one solution: $(-1, -2)$

2. infinitely many solutions

3. no solution

4. one solution: $(12, 22)$

5. $(1, 7)$

6. $(-15, -22)$.

7. $\left(\frac{7}{10}, -\frac{4}{5}\right)$

8. $(6, 0)$

9. $(11, -4)$

10. $(3.5, 10)$

11. no solution

12. $(15, -0.5)$

13. 5.5 cm by 16.5 cm; substitution because one of the equations was already solved for one of the variables

14. 85 acres of pumpkins and 335 acres of corn; substitution because one of the equations was already solved for one of the variables

15. 8 nickels and 13 dimes; elimination because neither equation can easily be solved for a variable

PowerAlgebra.com

MathXL for School
Prepare students for the Mid-Chapter Quiz and Chapter Test with online practice and review.

1 Interactive Learning

Solve It!

PURPOSE To show students a real-world problem represented by a linear inequality in two variables

PROCESS Students can solve the problem using a table, a linear equation or inequality in two variables, or by trial and error.

FACILITATE

Q If you bought one paperback book, what is the maximum number of hardcover books you could buy? Explain. [3; 3 · 4.50 + 2.50 = 16.]

Q What expression represents the total cost of h hardcover and p paperback books? [4.5h + 2.5p]

Q Do you have to buy the maximum number of books? What is the least number you could buy? [No; 0h + 0p]

ANSWER See Solve It in Answers on next page.

CONNECT THE MATH You can model the situation in the Solve It with $4.5x + 2.5y \leq 20$. In this lesson students will learn to solve linear inequalities and use them to model real-world problems.

2 Guided Instruction

Problem 1

Q Name a point on the line $y = x - 3$. Is the point also a solution of the inequality $y > x - 3$? Explain. [Answers may vary. Sample: (0, −3); No, since −3 > −3 is not true.]

Got It?   ERROR PREVENTION

If students answer that (3, 6) is not a solution, then they may have interpreted the inequality symbol as "less than" instead of "less than or equal to."

6-5 Linear Inequalities

Indiana Academic Standards
A1.2.5 Solve problems that can be modeled using linear equations and inequalities, interpret the solutions, and determine whether the solutions are reasonable.
A1.2.6 Graph a linear inequality in two variables.

Objectives To graph linear inequalities in two variables
To use linear inequalities when modeling real-world situations

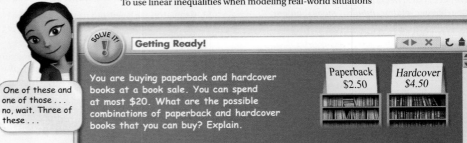

SOLVE IT!

Getting Ready!

You are buying paperback and hardcover books at a book sale. You can spend at most $20. What are the possible combinations of paperback and hardcover books that you can buy? Explain.

One of these and one of those . . . no, wait. Three of these . . .

Paperback $2.50

Hardcover $4.50

Lesson Vocabulary
• linear inequality
• solution of an inequality

A **linear inequality** in two variables, such as $y > x - 3$, can be formed by replacing the equals sign in a linear equation with an inequality symbol. A **solution of an inequality** in two variables is an ordered pair that makes the inequality true.

Essential Understanding A linear inequality in two variables has an infinite number of solutions. These solutions can be represented in the coordinate plane as the set of all points on one side of a boundary line.

Think

Have you tested solutions before?
Yes. You have tested whether ordered pairs are solutions of equations. Now you will test ordered pairs to see whether they satisfy an inequality.

Problem 1 **Identifying Solutions of a Linear Inequality**

Is the ordered pair a solution of $y > x - 3$?

A (1, 2)

$y > x - 3$ ← Write the inequality. → $y > x - 3$

$2 \overset{?}{>} 1 - 3$ ← Substitute. → $-7 \overset{?}{>} -3 - 3$

$2 > -2$ ✔   ← Simplify. → $-7 > -6$ ✗

B (−3, −7)

(1, 2) is a solution.

(−3, −7) is *not* a solution.

 Got It? 1. a. Is (3, 6) a solution of $y \leq \frac{2}{3}x + 4$?
b. Reasoning Suppose an ordered pair is not a solution of $y > x + 10$. Must it be a solution of $y < x + 10$? Explain.

390 Chapter 6 Systems of Equations and Inequalities

UbD

BIG idea Solving Equations & Inequalities

ESSENTIAL UNDERSTANDINGS

• A linear inequality in two variables has an infinite number of solutions.
• Solutions to a linear inequality in two variables can be represented in the coordinate plane as the set of all points on one side of a boundary line.

Math Background

Many real-world situations are better modeled by an inequality than an equation. An equation models situations in which a condition must be met exactly, while an inequality models situations in which a range of values is sufficient to meet a condition. While linear inequalities in one variable allow for modeling situations in which one variable has a range of values, a linear inequality in two variables allows for a situation in which an independent variable determines the value of a dependent variable.

In general, when an inequality is written in slope-intercept form (making certain that y is on the left side of the symbol), the direction of the inequality symbol indicates the region to shade. The symbols $<$ and $\leq$ mean the region below the boundary line should be shaded. The symbols $>$ and $\geq$ mean the region above the boundary line should be shaded. Before you use the direction of the symbol to determine where to shade, it is still best practice to test a point from the region in the original inequality.

Support Student Learning

Use the **Algebra 1 Companion** to engage and support students during instructions. See Lesson Resources at the end of this lesson for details.

PowerAlgebra.com

1 Interactive Learning

SOLVE IT! **Solve It!**
Step out how to solve the Problem with helpful hints and an online question. Other questions are listed above in Interactive Learning.

DYNAMIC ACTIVITIES **Dynamic Activity** Students graph linear inequalities and observe the effects of various characteristics. Students can test which areas of the graph satisfy the inequality.

The graph of a linear inequality in two variables consists of all points in the coordinate plane that represent solutions. The graph is a region called a *half-plane* that is bounded by a line. All points on one side of the boundary line are solutions, while all points on the other side are not solutions.

Each point on a *dashed* line is not a solution. A dashed line is used for inequalities with > or <.

Each point on a *solid* line is a solution. A solid line is used for inequalities with ≥ or ≤.

Problem 2 Graphing an Inequality in Two Variables

Problem 2

Think

Why does $y = x - 2$ represent the boundary line?
For any value of x, the corresponding value of y is the boundary between values of y that are greater than $x - 2$ and values of y that are less than $x - 2$.

What is the graph of $y > x - 2$?

First, graph the boundary line $y = x - 2$. Since the inequality symbol is >, the points on the boundary line are *not* solutions. Use a dashed line to indicate that the points are not included in the solution.

To determine which side of the boundary line to shade, test a point that is not on the line. For example, test the point $(0, 0)$.

$y > x - 2$

$0 \overset{?}{>} 0 - 2$ Substitute $(0, 0)$ for (x, y).

$0 > -2$ ✔ $(0, 0)$ is a solution.

Because the point $(0, 0)$ is a solution of the inequality, so are all the points on the same side of the boundary line as $(0, 0)$. Shade the area above the boundary line.

 Got It? 2. What is the graph of $y \le \frac{1}{2}x + 1$?

An inequality in one variable can be graphed on a number line or in the coordinate plane. The boundary line will be a horizontal or vertical line.

Problem 3 Graphing a Linear Inequality in One Variable

Think

Have you graphed inequalities like these before?
Yes. In Lesson 3-1, you graphed inequalities in one variable on a number line. Here you graph them in the coordinate plane.

What is the graph of each inequality in the coordinate plane?

A $x > -1$

Graph $x = -1$ using a dashed line.
Use $(0, 0)$ as a test point.

$x > -1$

$0 > -1$ ✔

Shade on the side of the line that contains $(0, 0)$.

B $y \ge 2$

Graph $y = 2$ using a solid line.
Use $(0, 0)$ as a test point.

$y \ge 2$

$0 \ge 2$ ✘

Shade on the side of the line that does *not* contain $(0, 0)$.

Problem 2

Problem 2

Q What is the most efficient method for graphing the equation $y = x - 2$? Explain. **[The slope-intercept method. The equation is already in slope-intercept form.]**

Q If you picked a point on the boundary line as a test point, would the test point be a solution to the inequality? Explain. **[No, The symbol is >, so the points on the boundary line are not solutions.]**

Q If you use $(3, -1)$ as a test point, how does it help you decide which side of the line to shade? **[$(3, -1)$ is not a solution to the inequality, so you should shade the opposite side of the boundary line.]**

Got It?

Q Is the boundary line solid or dashed? Explain. **[Solid; points on the boundary line solve the inequality.]**

Q Will selecting a point that is on the boundary line help you decide on which side of the line to shade? Explain. **[No, points on the boundary line solve the related equation. You need a point above or below the line to test the inequality.]**

Problem 3

Problem 3

Q What does the graph of $x > -1$ look like when graphed on a number line? **[Plot an open circle on a number line at −1, and shade from −1 to positive infinity.]**

Q What does the graph of $y \ge 2$ look like when graphed on a number line? **[Plot a closed circle on a number line at 2, and shade from 2 to positive infinity.]**

---

2 Guided Instruction

 Each Problem is worked out and supported online.

Problem 1
Identifying Solutions of a Linear Inequality

Problem 2
Graphing an Inequality in Two Variables
Animated

Problem 3
Graphing an Inequality in One Variable

Problem 4
Rewriting to Graph an Inequality
Animated

Problem 5
Writing an Inequality From a Graph
Animated

Support in Algebra 1 Companion
• Vocabulary
• Key Concepts
• Got It?

Answers

Solve It!

0 hardcover and up to 8 paperbacks, 1 hardcover and up to 6 paperbacks, 2 hardcovers and up to 4 paperbacks, 3 hardcovers and up to 2 paperbacks, 4 hardcovers and 0 paperbacks; explanations may vary.

Got It?

1. a. yes

   b. No; it could be on the line $y = x + 10$.

2.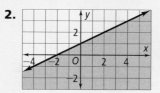

Got It?

ERROR PREVENTION

If students graph the boundary line in 3a as a horizontal line and the boundary line in 3b as a vertical line, remind them that equations of the form $x = a$ cross the x-axis and equations of the form $y = a$ cross the y-axis.

Problem 4

Q How can you determine the amount of wallpaper and tile needed for the project? **[Find the area of the wall that is to be covered with wallpaper and tile.]**

Q How do you determine the area of a rectangle? **[Multiply the base by the height.]**

Q If the wallpaper cost \$10 per square foot and the tile cost \$15 per square foot, what would be the total cost for the materials? **[\$420]**

Q If the wallpaper cost \$$x$ per square foot and the tile cost \$$y$ per square foot, what would be the total cost for the materials? **[24x + 12y]**

Q Is it possible to graph the equation $24x + 12y \leq 420$ without rewriting it into slope-intercept form? Explain. **[Yes, you could graph it using standard form.]**

Q How can you determine which side of the boundary line to shade? **[You use a test point.]**

Got It?

Q Are there any other limits on the possible values for x and y other than $2x + 4y \leq 12$? Explain. **[Both x and y must be greater than or equal to 0. You cannot buy a negative number of pounds of nuts.]**

 Got It? 3. What is the graph of each inequality?

a. $x < -5$ b. $y \leq 2$

When a linear inequality is solved for y, the direction of the inequality symbol determines which side of the boundary line to shade. If the symbol is $<$ or $\leq$, shade below the boundary line. If the symbol is $>$ or $\geq$, shade above it.

Sometimes you must first solve an inequality for y before using the method described above to determine where to shade.

Problem 4   Rewriting to Graph an Inequality

Interior Design An interior decorator is going to remodel a kitchen. The wall above the stove and the counter is going to be redone as shown. The owners can spend \$420 or less. Write a linear inequality and graph the solutions. What are three possible prices for the wallpaper and tiles?

Tiled Area
3 ft · 4 ft = 12 ft²

Papered Area
3 ft · 8 ft = 24 ft²

Let $x =$ the cost per square foot of the paper.

Let $y =$ the cost per square foot of the tiles.

Think

Which inequality symbol should you use?
You must read the problem statement carefully. Here "\$420 or less" means that the solution includes, but cannot exceed, \$420, so use $\leq$.

Write an inequality and solve it for y.

$24x + 12y \leq 420$ Total cost is \$420 or less.

$12y \leq -24x + 420$ Subtract 24x from each side.

$y \leq -2x + 35$ Divide each side by 12.

Graph $y \leq -2x + 35$. The inequality symbol is $\leq$, so the boundary line is solid and you shade below it. The graph only makes sense in the first quadrant. Three possible prices per square foot for wallpaper and tile are \$5 and \$25, \$5 and \$15, and \$10 and \$10.

Paper and Tile Costs

 Got It? 4. For a party, you can spend no more than \$12 on nuts. Peanuts cost \$2/lb. Cashews cost \$4/lb. What are three possible combinations of peanuts and cashews you can buy?

Additional Problems

1. Is the ordered pair a solution of $y < x + 2$?

a. $(-5, 2)$

b. $(4, 6)$

ANSWER a. no; **b.** no

2. What is the graph of $y < x - 1$?

ANSWER

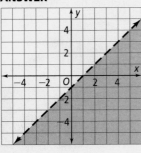

3. What is the graph of each inequality in the coordinate plane?

a. $x < 2$

b. $y \geq 3$

ANSWER

a.

b.

4. Suppose you can spend no more than \$20 for hot dogs and hamburgers for a picnic. Hot dogs cost \$5 per package, and hamburgers cost \$8 per package. What are three possible combinations of packages of hamburgers and hot dogs that you could buy?

ANSWER Answers may vary. Sample answer: 3 hot dogs, 2 hot dogs and 1 hamburger, 1 hot dog and 1 hamburger

5. Which inequality represents the graph below?

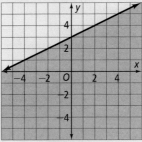

A. $y \geq \frac{1}{2}x + 3$

B. $y > \frac{1}{2}x + 3$

C. $y < \frac{1}{2}x + 3$

D. $y \leq \frac{1}{2}x + 3$

ANSWER D

Think

Can you eliminate choices?
Yes. The boundary line is solid and the region below it is shaded, so you know the inequality symbol must be ≤. You can eliminate choices C and D.

Problem 5 Writing an Inequality From a Graph

Multiple Choice Which inequality represents the graph at the right?

Ⓐ $y \leq 2x + 1$

Ⓒ $y \geq 2x + 1$

Ⓑ $y \leq x + 1$

Ⓓ $y < 2x + 1$

The slope of the line is 2 and the y-intercept is 1, so the equation of the boundary line is $y = 2x + 1$. The boundary line is solid, so the inequality symbol is either ≤ or ≥. The symbol must be ≤, because the region below the boundary line is shaded. The inequality is $y \leq 2x + 1$.

The correct answer is A.

Got It? 5. You are writing an inequality from a graph. The boundary line is dashed and has slope $\frac{1}{3}$ and y-intercept -2. The area above the line is shaded. What inequality should you write?

Lesson Check

Do you know HOW?

1. Is $(-1, 4)$ a solution of the inequality $y < 2x + 5$?

Graph each linear inequality.

2. $y \leq -2x + 3$

3. $x < -1$

4. What is an inequality that represents the graph at the right?

Do you UNDERSTAND?

5. **Vocabulary** How is a linear inequality in two variables like a linear equation in two variables? How are they different?

6. **Writing** To graph the inequality $y < \frac{3}{2}x + 3$, do you shade above or below the boundary line? Explain.

7. **Reasoning** Write an inequality that describes the region of the coordinate plane *not* included in the graph of $y < 5x + 1$.

Practice and Problem-Solving Exercises

Practice Determine whether the ordered pair is a solution of the linear inequality. ◀ See Problem 1.

8. $y \leq -2x + 1; (2, 2)$

9. $x < 2; (-1, 0)$

10. $y \geq 3x - 2; (0, 0)$

11. $y > x - 1; (0, 1)$

12. $y \geq -\frac{2}{5}x + 4; (0, 0)$

13. $3y > 5x - 12; (-6, 1)$

Graph each linear inequality. ◀ See Problem 2.

14. $y \leq x - 1$

15. $y \geq 3x - 2$

16. $y < -4x - 1$

17. $y > 2x - 6$

18. $y < 5x - 5$

19. $y \leq \frac{1}{2}x - 3$

20. $y > -3x$

21. $y \geq -x$

Problem 5

Q The graph shows a solid boundary line. Which answer choice should you eliminate? **[D]**

Q How can you use a test point to decide between Choices A and C? **[You can pick a test point in the shaded region of the graph and determine which of the two inequalities it satisfies.]**

Got It? VISUAL LEARNER
If students have difficulty with the problem, they should sketch the graph.

3 Lesson Check

Do you know HOW?
• If students have difficulty with Exercise 1, then remind them that the point can be tested in the inequality by substitution.

Do you UNDERSTAND?
• If students use $>$ in Exercise 7, then remind them that the points on the boundary line are not included in the solution of $y < 5x + 1$, so they must be included in the solution to the second inequality.

Close

Q How can you determine the correct side of the boundary line to shade when graphing an inequality? **[You can substitute a test point into the inequality.]**

Answers

Got It? (continued)

3. a.

b.

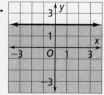

4. Answers may vary. Sample: 0 lb of peanuts and 3 lb of cashews; 6 lb of peanuts and 0 lb of cashews; 1 lb of peanuts and 1 lb of cashews

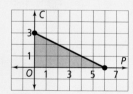

5. $y > \frac{1}{3}x - 2$

Lesson Check

1–7. See back of book.

Practice and Problem-Solving Exercises

8–21. See back of book.

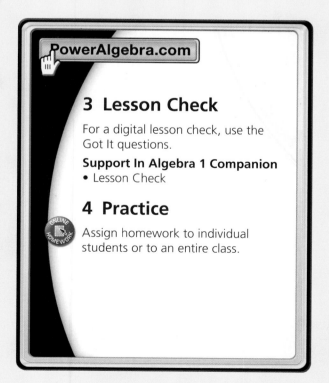

PowerAlgebra.com

3 Lesson Check

For a digital lesson check, use the Got It questions.

Support In Algebra 1 Companion
• Lesson Check

4 Practice

Assign homework to individual students or to an entire class.

4 Practice

ASSIGNMENT GUIDE

Basic: 8–37

Average: 9–33 odd, 35–38

Advanced: 9–33 odd, 35–41

Standardized Test Prep: 42–44

Mixed Review: 45–49

Reasoning exercises have blue headings.

Applications exercises have red headings.

EXERCISE 36: Use the Think About a Plan worksheet in the **Practice and Problem Solving Workbook** (also available in the Teaching Resources in print and online) to further support students' development in becoming independent learners.

HOMEWORK QUICK CHECK

To check students' understanding of key skills and concepts, go over Exercises 11, 27, 35, 36, and 37.

Graph each inequality in the coordinate plane.   ◀ See Problems 3 and 4.

22. $x \leq 4$ **23.** $y \geq -1$ **24.** $x > -2$ **25.** $y < -4$

26. $-2x + y \geq 3$ **27.** $x + 3y < 15$ **28.** $4x - y > 2$ **29.** $-x + 0.25y \leq -1.75$

30. Carpentry You budget $200 for wooden planks for outdoor furniture. Cedar costs $2.50 per foot and pine costs $1.75 per foot. Let x = the number of feet of cedar and let y = the number of feet of pine. What is an inequality that shows how much of each type of wood can be bought? Graph the inequality. What are three possible amounts of each type of wood that can be bought within your budget?

31. Business A fish market charges $9 per pound for cod and $12 per pound for flounder. Let x = the number of pounds of cod. Let y = the number of pounds of flounder. What is an inequality that shows how much of each type of fish the store must sell today to reach a daily quota of at least $120? Graph the inequality. What are three possible amounts of each fish that would satisfy the quota?

Write a linear inequality that represents each graph.   ◀ See Problem 5.

32.   **33.**   **34.**

B Apply

35. Think About a Plan A truck that can carry no more than 6400 lb is being used to transport refrigerators and upright pianos. Each refrigerator weighs 250 lb and each piano weighs 475 lb. Write and graph an inequality to show how many refrigerators and how many pianos the truck could carry. Will 12 refrigerators and 8 pianos overload the truck? Explain.
- What inequality symbol should you use?
- Which side of the boundary line should you shade?

36. Employment A student with two summer jobs earns $10 per hour at a cafe and $8 per hour at a market. The student would like to earn at least $800 per month.
a. Write and graph an inequality to represent the situation.
b. The student works at the market for 60 h per month and can work at most 90 h per month. Can the student earn at least $800 each month? Explain how you can you use your graph to determine this.

37. Error Analysis A student graphed $y \geq 2x + 3$ as shown at the right. Describe and correct the student's error.

38. Writing When graphing an inequality, can you always use $(0, 0)$ as a test point to determine where to shade? If not, how would you choose a test point?

C Challenge

39. Music Store A music store sells used CDs for $5 each and buys used CDs for $1.50 each. You go to the store with $20 and some CDs to sell. You want to have at least $10 left when you leave the store. Write and graph an inequality to show how many CDs you could buy and sell.

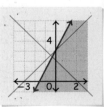

22.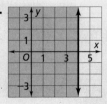

23.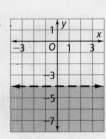

24.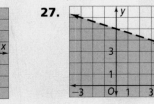

25.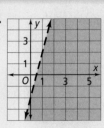

26.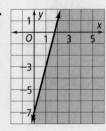

27.

28.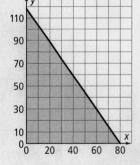

29.

Answers may vary. Sample: 10 ft of cedar and 80 ft of pine; 20 ft of cedar and 50 ft of pine; 60 ft of cedar and 20 ft of pine

30. $2.5x + 1.75y \leq 200$

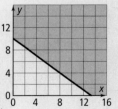

31. $9x + 12y \geq 120$

Answers may vary. Sample: 4 lb of cod and 12 lb of flounder; 10 lb of cod and 10 lb of flounder; 12 lb of cod and 4 lb of flounder

32. $y \geq -3x + 3$ **33.** $y > \frac{3}{2}x - 3$

34. $x < 3$

40. Groceries At your grocery store, milk normally costs $3.60 per gallon. Ground beef costs $3 per pound. Today there are specials: Milk is discounted $.50 per gallon, and ground beef is 20% off. You want to spend no more than $20. Write and graph a linear inequality to show how many gallons of milk and how many pounds of ground beef you can buy today.

41. Reasoning You are graphing a linear inequality of the form $y > mx + b$. The point $(1, 2)$ is not a solution, but $(3, 2)$ is. Is the slope of the boundary line *positive, negative, zero,* or *undefined*? Explain.

Standardized Test Prep

SAT/ACT

42. What is the equation of the graph shown?

- Ⓐ $y + x \geq -3$
- Ⓒ $x - y > -3$
- Ⓑ $y - x \geq 3$
- Ⓓ $y > -x + 3$

43. You secure pictures to your scrapbook using 3 stickers. You started with 24 stickers. There are now 2 pictures in your scrapbook. You write the equation $3(x + 2) = 24$ to find the number x of additional pictures you can put in your scrapbook. How many more pictures can you add?

- Ⓕ 4
- Ⓗ 8
- Ⓖ 6
- Ⓘ 12

Short Response

44. At Market A, 1-lb packages of rice are sold for the price shown. At Market B, rice is sold in bulk for the price shown. For each market, write a function describing the cost of buying rice in terms of the weight. How are the domains of the two functions different?

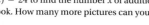

$2.00 $2.00/lb

Mixed Review

45. Small Business An electrician spends $12,000 on initial costs to start a new business. He estimates his expenses at $25 per day. He expects to earn $150 per day. If his estimates are correct, after how many working days will he break even?   ◀ **See Lesson 6-4.**

46. What compound inequality represents the phrase "all real numbers that are greater than 2 and less than or equal to 7"? Graph the solutions.   ◀ **See Lesson 3-6.**

Get Ready!   To prepare for Lesson 6-6, do Exercises 47–49.

Solve each system by graphing. Tell whether the system has *one solution,*   ◀ **See Lesson 6-1.**
infinitely many solutions, or *no solution.*

47. $y = \frac{3}{2}x$
$-2x + y = 3$

48. $3x + y = 6$
$2x - y = 4$

49. $x + y = 11$
$x + y = 16$

PowerAlgebra.com | Lesson 6-5   Linear Inequalities | **395**

---

35. $250x + 475y \leq 6400$, where x represents the number of refrigerators and y represents the number of pianos

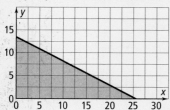

Yes; the point $(12, 8)$ is not in the shaded region.

36. a. Let $x =$ hours at the cafe and let $y =$ hours at the market; $10x + 8y \geq 800$

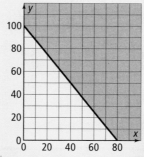

b. No; the point $(30, 60)$ does not lie in the shaded region of the graph.

---

37. The student graphed $y \leq 2x + 3$ instead of $y \geq 2x + 3$. The other side of the line should be shaded.

38. You could not use the point $(0, 0)$ in the case that $(0, 0)$ lies on the boundary line. If that were the case, you would have to choose any other point that was not on the boundary line.

39. $-5x + 1.5y \geq -10$, where x is the number of CDs bought and y is the number sold; actual solutions include only points representing whole numbers of CDs bought and sold.

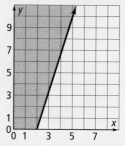

40. $3.10x + 2.40y \leq 20$, where x represents the number of gallons of milk and y represents the number of pounds of hamburger

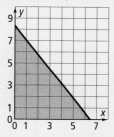

41. The slope must be negative; in order for the point $(3, 2)$ to be above the line and the point $(1, 2)$ to be below the line, the boundary line must be sloping downward. If the line had a positive slope, sloping upward, then the point $(1, 2)$ would be above the line and would satisfy $y > mx + b$, which is not what is given.

42. C

43. G

44. [2] The cost at Market A is given by $C(x) = 2x$, where x is a nonnegative integer. The cost at Market B is given by $C(x) = 2x$, where x is a nonnegative real number. In Market A you can only buy multiples of 1-lb packages; at Market B you can buy any amount.

[1] correct functions without explanation given.

45. 96 days

46. $2 < x \leq 7$

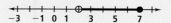

47. one solution: $(-6, -9)$

48. one solution: $(2, 0)$

49. no solution

Lesson 6-5   395

Lesson Resources

Additional Instructional Support

Algebra 1 Companion

Students can use the **Algebra 1 Companion** worktext (4 pages) as you teach the lesson. Use the Companion to support

- New Vocabulary
- Key Concepts
- Got It for each Problem
- Lesson Check

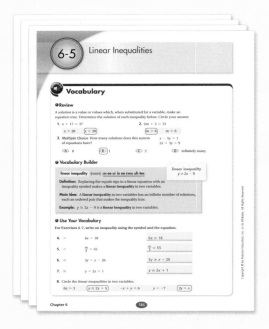

ELL Support

Connect to Prior Knowledge Have two students graph the inequalities $x > 3$ and $x < 2$ on number lines. Ask: "What does the open circle mean? What does the closed circle mean?" Have a student write the inequality $x + y \geq 3$ on the board. Say: First graph the equation $x + y = 3$. Have a student graph the equation. Ask: When will x plus y be greater than 3? [when either x or y is greater than the coordinates of the line] Have a student shade the upper right half of the graph. Say: The line is like the shaded circle. Have a student write the equation $x - y < 3$ on the board. Ask: What can we use instead of an open circle? [a dotted line] Have the class give instructions to a student who graphs $x - y < 3$ on the board.

5 Assess & Remediate

Lesson Quiz

1. Is the ordered pair a solution of $y \geq 2x - 5$?
   a. $(3, 1)$
   b. $(1, -4)$

2. What inequality is shown in the graph below?

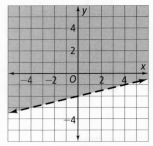

3. Do you UNDERSTAND? A storage shelf can hold no more than 250 lb. Carlos wants to stack boxes of paper that weigh 20 lb each and computer monitors that weigh 15 lb each on the shelf.
   a. Write an inequality that shows how many boxes of paper, x, and monitors, y, Carlos can stack on the shelf.
   b. Give 3 examples of paper and monitor combinations that Carlos can stack on the shelf.

ANSWERS TO LESSON QUIZ

1. a. yes; **b.** no   **2.** $y > \frac{1}{4}x - 2$

3. a. $20x + 15y \leq 250$; **b.** Answers may vary. Sample answers: 4 boxes of paper and 10 monitors, 6 boxes of paper and 3 monitors, 10 boxes of paper and 2 monitors

PRESCRIPTION FOR REMEDIATION

Use the student work on the Lesson Quiz to prescribe a differentiated review assignment.

Points	Differentiated Remediation
0–1	Intervention
2	On-level
3	Extension

5 Assess & Remediate

Assign the Lesson Quiz. Appropriate intervention, practice, or enrichment is automatically generated based on student performance.

Intervention

- **Reteaching** (2 pages) Provides reteaching and practice exercises for the key lesson concepts. Use with struggling students or absent students.

- **English Language Learner Support** Helps students develop and reinforce mathematical vocabulary and key concepts.

All-in-One Resources/Online
Reteaching

All-in-One Resources/Online
English Language Learner Support

Differentiated Remediation *continued*

On-Level

- **Practice** (2 pages) Provides extra practice for each lesson. For simpler practice exercises, use the Form K Practice pages found in the All-in-One Teaching Resources and online.

- **Think About a Plan** Helps students develop specific problem-solving skills and strategies by providing scaffolded guiding questions.

- **Standardized Test Prep** Focuses on all major exercises, all major question types, and helps students prepare for the high-stakes assessments.

Extension

- **Enrichment** Provides students with interesting problems and activities that extend the concepts of the lesson.

- **Activities, Games, and Puzzles** Worksheets that can be used for concepts development, enrichment, and for fun!

Practice and Problem Solving WKBK/All-in-One Resources/Online
Practice page 1

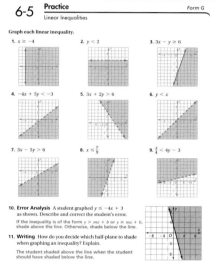

Practice and Problem Solving WKBK/All-in-One Resources/Online
Practice page 2

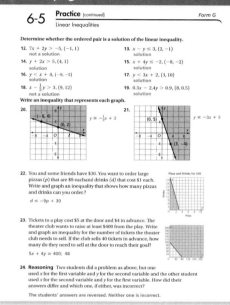

All-in-One Resources/Online
Enrichment

Practice and Problem Solving WKBK/All-in-One Resources/Online
Think About a Plan

6-5 Think About a Plan
Linear Inequalities

Employment A student with two summer jobs earns $10 per hour at a café and $8 per hour at a market. The student would like to earn at least $800 per month.
  a. Write and graph an inequality to represent the situation.
  b. The student works at the market for 60 h and can work at most 90 h per month. Can the student earn at least $800 each month? Explain how you can use your graph to determine this.

Understanding the Problem

1. What do you know about the student's hourly rates?
   The student makes $10/h at the café and $8/h at the market.

2. What do you know about how much the student would like to earn each month?
   The student would like to earn at least $800 a month.

3. What do you know about the number of hours the student can work each month?
   The student can work 60-90 hours per month.

Planning the Solution

4. What inequality represents the number of hours the student can work each month? _c + m ≤ 90_

5. What inequality represents the amount that the student can earn each month?
   10c + 8m ≥ 800

Getting an Answer

6. How can you use these two inequalities to find out if the student working 60 hours at the market can make $800 per month?
   Solve the first inequality for one of the variables and substitute it into the second inequality.

7. How can you determine the number of hours that the student should work each month? What are the number of hours the student should work at the market and at the café to earn at least $800 per month?
   The student would have to work 32 h at the cafe to make more than $800. Because the student can only work a maximum of 30 h at the café, the student cannot make $800 a month.

Practice and Problem Solving WKBK/All-in-One Resources/Online
Standardized Test Prep

6-5 Standardized Test Prep
Linear Inequalities

Multiple Choice

For Exercises 1–5, choose the correct letter.

1. What point on the axes satisfies the inequality $y < x$? C
   A. (0, 1)   B. (−1, 0)   C. (1, 0)   D. (0, 0)

2. For the graph of the inequality $x − 2y \geq 4$, what is a value of x for a point that is on the boundary line and the axes? F
   F. 4   G. 2   H. 2   I. −4

3. If $x \geq 0$ and $y \geq 0$, then which quadrant holds the solutions? C
   A. IV   B. III   C. I   D. II

4. Which is the y-value of a boundary point that is an intersecting point not on the axes for this region: $x \geq 0$, $y \geq 0$, $x \leq 4$ and $y \leq 3$? I
   F. 4   G. 0   H. 1   I. 3

5. How do you decide where to shade an inequality whose boundary does not go through the origin? B
   A. For <, shade above the boundary.
   B. If (0, 0) is a solution, shade where (0, 0) is.
   C. For <, shade below the boundary.
   D. If (0, 0) is a solution, shade where (0, 0) is not.

Short Response

6. A school fundraiser sells holiday cards and wrapping paper. They are trying to raise at least $400. They make a profit of $1.50 on each box of holiday cards and $1.00 on each pack of wrapping paper.
   a. What is an inequality for the profit the school wants to make for the fundraiser? 1.5x + y ≥ 400
   b. If the fundraiser sells 100 boxes of cards and 160 packs of wrapping paper, will they reach their goal? Show your work. No, they will not reach their goal.

   [2] Both parts answered correctly. Explanation is clear.
   [1] One part answered correctly, or explanation is not clear or complete.
   [0] No parts answered correctly.

Online Teacher Resource Center
Activities, Games, and Puzzles

6-5 Game: Above, On, or Below?
Linear Inequalities

This is a game in which one student competes against another. Your teacher or a student can serve as the host.

Rules: The host randomly chooses an item number from the list below, and players have 30 seconds to decide whether the given point is above, on, or below the graph of the equation shown. Your teacher will give you a coordinate plane to sketch your lines. To the right of the item, write "above," "on," or "below." Your teacher may decide to change the response time as needed.

All players begin with 50 points. Your opponent will check your answer and add or subtract points on the score sheet. If you are correct, you earn 5 points. If you are incorrect, you lose 5 points. Each of you will receive 10 points.
See Teacher Instructions Page.

Item Number	Item	Player 1 Points	Player 2 Points
	START	50	50
1	$y = 2x + 5$ and (3, 1)		
2	$y = -2$ and (−10, 3)		
3	$y = -x + 6$ and (5, −1)		
4	$y = 2x - 7$ and (−1, −4)		
5	$y = -5x + 3$ and (−2, 13)		
6	$y = 0.5x - 7$ and (−4, −9)		
7	$y = 7x - 1$ and (10, 70)		
8	$y = 6x - 30$ and (5, −3)		
9	$y = -x - 4$ and (6, 10)		
10	$y = -10x$ and (−1, 1)		
11	$y = 7x + 16$ and (12, 100)		
12	$y = 4x - 0.5$ and (1, 4)		
13	$y = 5x + 100$ and (10, 130)		
14	$y = -x - 100$ and (−100, 0)		
15	$y = 3x - 1.5$ and (7, 20)		
16	$y = 8x + 15$ and (5, 50)		
17	$y = 13x - 13$ and (−2, −39)		
18	$y = -9x - 100$ and (−10, −9)		
19	$y = 5.5x + 1$ and (4, 25)		
20	$y = 2(x - 1)$ and (−5, −13)		

1 Interactive Learning

Solve It!

PURPOSE To model a real-world situation with a system of linear inequalities in two variables

PROCESS Students may make a table or organized list, write linear inequalities in two variables, or use trial and error.

FACILITATE

Q Would the purchase of 4 Top 10 ring tones and 1 premium ring tone be a solution to this problem? Explain. **[No; the total cost is less than $15, but it does not satisfy the condition to buy at least 6 new ring tones.]**

Q What is one possible answer? Is that the only answer that meets the conditions? **[3 Top 10 and 4 Premium; no]**

ANSWER See Solve It in Answers on next page.

CONNECT THE MATH The situation in the Solve It has two conditions that must be met, a minimum number to buy and a maximum amount to spend. A system of inequalities can be used to solve problems involving more than one requirement.

2 Guided Instruction

Problem 1

Q Which regions represent the solutions to $2x + y > 2$? Explain. **[The blue and green regions; when the coordinates of any point chosen in these regions are substituted into the inequality, the inequality is true.]**

Q What region represents ordered pairs that satisfy the equation $2x + y > 2$, but do not satisfy $y < 2x - 3$? **[ordered pairs in the blue region that are not shaded green]**

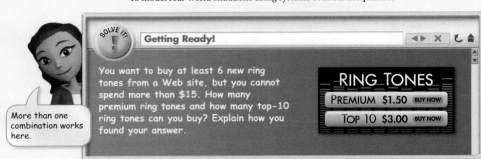

6-6 Systems of Linear Inequalities

Indiana Academic Standard
A1.3.2 Graph the solution set for a pair of linear inequalities in two variables with and without technology and use the graph to find the solution set.

Objectives To solve systems of linear inequalities by graphing
To model real-world situations using systems of linear inequalities

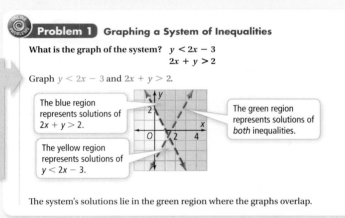

SOLVE IT!

Getting Ready!

More than one combination works here.

You want to buy at least 6 new ring tones from a Web site, but you cannot spend more than $15. How many premium ring tones and how many top-10 ring tones can you buy? Explain how you found your answer.

RING TONES
PREMIUM $1.50 BUY NOW
TOP 10 $3.00 BUY NOW

Lesson Vocabulary
- system of linear inequalities
- solution of a system of linear inequalities

A **system of linear inequalities** is made up of two or more linear inequalities. A **solution of a system of linear inequalities** is an ordered pair that makes *all* the inequalities in the system true. The graph of a system of linear inequalities is the set of points that represent all of the solutions of the system.

Essential Understanding You can graph the solutions of a system of linear inequalities in the coordinate plane. The graph of the system is the region where the graphs of the individual inequalities overlap.

Think
Have you seen a problem like this before?
Yes. The solution of a system of equations is shown by the intersection of two lines. The solutions of a system of inequalities are shown by the intersection of two shaded areas.

Problem 1 Graphing a System of Inequalities

What is the graph of the system? $y < 2x - 3$
$2x + y > 2$

Graph $y < 2x - 3$ and $2x + y > 2$.

The blue region represents solutions of $2x + y > 2$.

The green region represents solutions of *both* inequalities.

The yellow region represents solutions of $y < 2x - 3$.

The system's solutions lie in the green region where the graphs overlap.

6-6 Preparing to Teach

UbD

BIG idea Solving Equations & Inequalities
ESSENTIAL UNDERSTANDINGS
- Solutions of a system of linear inequalities can be graphed in the coordinate plane.
- The graph of the solution of a system of linear inequalities is the region where the graphs of the individual inequalities overlap.

Math Background
In order to visually show the solution set, students may use a different color or pattern to shade the region representing each inequality. To verify the solution, they should choose a test point from the solution set and check the point in each inequality.

Solving systems of linear inequalities underlies a mathematical process called linear programming. In resource allocation problems, linear programming finds the optimum value possible under various constraints. For example, a company may wish to maximize profits given limitations on materials

and labor. The topic of this lesson, defining the solution set for a system of linear inequalities, is the first of several steps in linear programming. Further investigations of linear programming occur in Algebra 2.

Support Student Learning
Use the **Algebra 1 Companion** to engage and support students during instructions. See Lesson Resources at the end of this lesson for details.

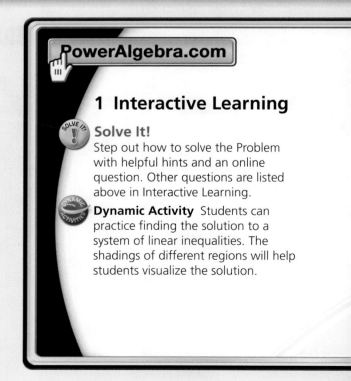

PowerAlgebra.com

1 Interactive Learning

Solve It!
Step out how to solve the Problem with helpful hints and an online question. Other questions are listed above in Interactive Learning.

Dynamic Activity Students can practice finding the solution to a system of linear inequalities. The shadings of different regions will help students visualize the solution.

Check (3, 0) is in the green region. See if (3, 0) satisfies both inequalities.

$y \overset{?}{\le} 2x - 3$ ← Write both inequalities. → $2x + y \overset{?}{\ge} 2$

$0 \overset{?}{\le} 2(3) - 3$ ← Substitute (3, 0) for (x, y). → $2(3) + 0 \overset{?}{\ge} 2$

$0 < 3$ ✔   ← Simplify. The solution checks. → $6 > 2$ ✔

 Got It? **1.** What is the graph of the system? $y \ge -x + 5$
$-3x + y \le -4$

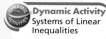 **Dynamic Activity**
Systems of Linear Inequalities

You can combine your knowledge of linear equations with your knowledge of inequalities to describe a graph using a system of inequalities.

Think

Have you seen a problem like this one before?
Yes. You wrote an inequality from a graph in Lesson 6-5. Now you'll write two inequalities.

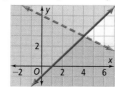 **Problem 2** **Writing a System of Inequalities From a Graph**

What system of inequalities is represented by the graph below?

To write a system that is represented by the graph, write an inequality that represents the yellow region and an inequality that represents the blue region.

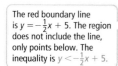
The red boundary line is $y = -\frac{1}{2}x + 5$. The region does not include the line, only points below. The inequality is $y < -\frac{1}{2}x + 5$.

The blue boundary line is $y = x - 1$. The region includes the boundary line and points above. The inequality is $y \ge x - 1$.

The graph shows the intersection of the system $y < -\frac{1}{2}x + 5$ and $y \ge x - 1$.

 Got It? **2. a.** What system of inequalities is represented by the graph?
b. Reasoning In part (a), is the point where the boundary lines intersect a solution of the system? Explain.

You can model many real-world situations by writing and graphing systems of linear inequalities. Some real-world situations involve three or more restrictions, so you must write a system of at least three inequalities.

PowerAlgebra.com   Lesson 6-6 Systems of Linear Inequalities   397

---

2 Guided Instruction

 Each Problem is worked out and supported online.

Problem 1
Graphing a System of Inequalities

Problem 2
Writing a System of Inequalities From a Graph
Animated

Problem 3
Using a System of Inequalities
Animated

Alternative Problem 3
Using a System of Inequalities
Animated

Support in Algebra 1 Companion
• Vocabulary
• Key Concepts
• Got It?

Got It? **VISUAL LEARNERS**
Encourage students to make a Venn diagram of the solution set for the system of inequalities. In the universal set, there are two overlapping circles, one for each equation. The points that satisfy each equation are in the overlapping region of the circles. Have the students add ordered pairs that belong in each region.

Problem 2

Q How can you determine the equations for the two boundary lines? **[Determine the slope and *y*-intercept for each line and write the equation in slope-intercept form.]**

Q What factors do you need to consider when determining the correct inequality symbol to use for each inequality? **[You need to consider if the boundary line is dashed or shaded and if the shading is above or below the boundary line.]**

Q How can you use test points to check your answer? **[Answers may vary. Sample: Pick a test point in the overlap region and check to make sure that it satisfies both inequalities.]**

Got It? **SYNTHESIZING**

Q If the point of intersection of the boundary lines is to be part of the solution of a system of inequalities, what must be true of the system? **[Both boundary lines must be solid, so both inequalities must have either the "≥" or "≤" symbol.]**

Answers

Solve It!
There are 15 possible combinations of at least 6 ring tones of the form (number of Premium, number of top 10): (10, 0), (9, 0), (8, 0), (8, 1), (7, 0), (7, 1), (6, 0), (6, 1), (6, 2), (5, 1), (5, 2), (4, 2), (4, 3), (3, 3), (2, 4); explanations may vary.

Got It?
1.

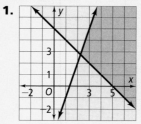

2. a. $y < -\frac{1}{2}x + 1$

$y \le \frac{1}{2}x + 1$

b. No; the red line is dashed, so points on that line are not included in the solution.

Problem 3

Q How many inequalities are needed to model the problem? Explain. **[3; there are three separate conditions that must be met.]**

Q Are non-integral ordered pairs reasonable solutions for the system of inequalities? Explain. **[Yes; time can be measured in fractions of an hour.]**

Got It?

ERROR PREVENTION

Encourage students to make a sketch and label the sides of the dog run prior to writing the inequalities. A common error is to write the incorrect inequality $x + y \leq 126$ rather than the correct inequality $2x + 2y \leq 126$ or $x + y \leq 63$.

3 Lesson Check

Do you know HOW?

• If students have difficulty with Exercise 1, then tell them to use different colors of shading for each inequality to find the overlapping region.

Do you UNDERSTAND?

• If students have difficulty with Exercise 5, then tell them to sketch multiple examples using > and < in different combinations. Shade each sketch differently to see all possibilities.

Close

Q Can the solutions of a system of linear inequalities be listed explicitly? Explain. **[No, the solution is a region on a coordinate plane. The points cannot be listed.]**

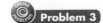 **Problem 3** Using a System of Inequalities

Time Management You are planning what to do after school. You can spend at most 6 h daily playing basketball and doing homework. You want to spend less than 2 h playing basketball. You must spend at least $1\frac{1}{2}$ h on homework. What is a graph showing how you can spend your time?

Know	Need	Plan
• At most 6 h playing basketball and doing homework • Less than 2 h playing basketball • At least $1\frac{1}{2}$ h doing homework	To find different ways you can spend your time	Write and graph an inequality for each restriction. Find the region where all three restrictions are met.

Let x = the number of hours playing basketball.

Let y = the number of hours doing homework.

Write a system of inequalities.

$x + y \leq 6$ At most 6 h of basketball and homework

$x < 2$ Less than 2 h of basketball

$y \geq 1\frac{1}{2}$ At least $1\frac{1}{2}$ h of homework

Graph the system. Because time cannot be negative, the graph makes sense only in the first quadrant. The solutions of the system are all of the points in the shaded region, including the points on the solid boundary lines.

 Got It? **3.** You want to build a fence for a rectangular dog run. You want the run to be at least 10 ft wide. The run can be at most 50 ft long. You have 126 ft of fencing. What is a graph showing the possible dimensions of the dog run?

Lesson Check

Do you know HOW?

1. What is the graph of the system?
$$y > 3x - 2$$
$$2y - x \leq 6$$

2. What system of inequalities is represented by the graph at the right?

3. Cherries cost $4/lb. Grapes cost $2.50/lb. You can spend no more than $15 on fruit, and you need at least 4 lb in all. What is a graph showing the amount of each fruit you can buy?

Do you UNDERSTAND?

4. **Vocabulary** How can you determine whether an ordered pair is a solution of a system of linear inequalities?

5. **Reasoning** Suppose you are graphing a system of two linear inequalities, and the boundary lines for the inequalities are parallel. Does that mean that the system has no solution? Explain.

6. **Writing** How is finding the solution of a system of inequalities different from finding the solution of a system of equations? How is it the same? Explain.

Additional Problems

1. What is the graph of the system?
$$y \geq 2x - 1$$
$$x + y < 2$$

ANSWER

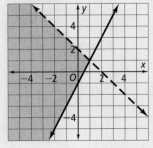

2. What system of inequalities is represented by the graph?

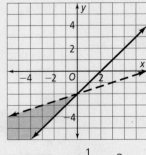

ANSWER $y < \frac{1}{3}x - 2$
$y \geq x - 2$

3. A dog walker earns $15 per hour. She also earns $12 per hour for babysitting. She wants to earn at least $300 next week, but can work no more than 30 hours. What is a graph showing how many hours she can work at each job?

ANSWER

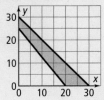

PowerAlgebra.com

3 Lesson Check

For a digital lesson check, use the Got It questions.

Support In Algebra 1 Companion
• Lesson Check

4 Practice

Assign homework to individual students or to an entire class.

Practice and Problem-Solving Exercises

A Practice

Determine whether the ordered pair is a solution of the given system.

See Problem 1.

7. $(2, 12)$;
$y > 2x + 4$
$y < 3x + 7$

8. $(8, 2)$;
$3x - 2y \leq 17$
$0.3x + 4y > 9$

9. $(-3, 17)$;
$y > -5x + 2$
$y \geq -3x + 7$

Solve each system of inequalities by graphing.

10. $y < 2x + 4$
$-3x - 2y \geq 6$

11. $y < 2x + 4$
$2x - y \leq 4$

12. $y > 2x + 4$
$2x - y \leq 4$

13. $y > \frac{1}{4}x$
$y \leq -x + 4$

14. $y < 2x - 3$
$y > 5$

15. $y \leq -\frac{1}{3}x + 7$
$y \geq -x + 1$

16. $x + 2y \leq 10$
$x + 2y \geq 9$

17. $y \geq -x + 5$
$y \leq 3x - 4$

18. $y \leq 0.75x - 2$
$y > 0.75x - 3$

19. $8x + 4y \geq 10$
$3x - 6y > 12$

20. $2x - \frac{1}{4}y < 1$
$4x + 8y > 4$

21. $6x - 5y < 15$
$x + 2y \geq 7$

Write a system of inequalities for each graph.

See Problem 2.

22.

23.

24.

25.

26. Earnings Suppose you have a job mowing lawns that pays $12 per hour. You also have a job at a clothing store that pays $10 per hour. You need to earn at least $350 per week, but you can work no more than 35 h per week. You must work a minimum of 10 h per week at the clothing store. What is a graph showing how many hours per week you can work at each job?

See Problem 3.

27. Driving Two friends agree to split the driving on a road trip from Philadelphia, Pennsylvania, to Denver, Colorado. One friend drives at an average speed of 60 mi/h. The other friend drives at an average speed of 55 mi/h. They want to drive at least 500 mi per day. They plan to spend no more than 10 h driving each day. The friend who drives slower wants to drive fewer hours. What is a graph showing how they can split the driving each day?

PowerAlgebra.com   **Lesson 6-6** Systems of Linear Inequalities   **399**

Answers

Got It? (continued)

3.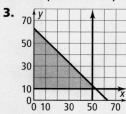

$2x + 2y \leq 126$, $x \leq 50$, $y \geq 10$

Lesson Check

1.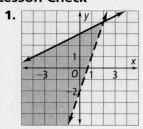

2. $y \geq 3x + 3$
$y < -x - 2$

3.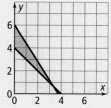

4. You can substitute the ordered pair into each inequality to make sure that it makes each true.

5. Not necessarily; as long as there is some overlap of the half-planes, then the system will have a solution.

6. You need to find the intersection of each of the two systems, but the intersections of lines will be a point or line and the intersections of inequalities will be a line or a planar section.

Practice and Problem-Solving Exercises

7. yes   **8.** no   **9.** no

10.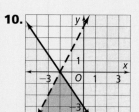

11.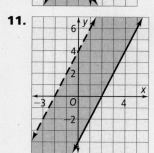

12–27. See back of book.

4 Practice

ASSIGNMENT GUIDE

Basic: 7–27, 28, 30, 31, 33

Average: 7–27 odd, 28–35

Advanced: 7–27 odd, 28–38

Standardized Test Prep: 39–42

Mixed Review: 43–48

Reasoning exercises have blue headings.

Applications exercises have red headings.

EXERCISE 31: Use the Think About a Plan worksheet in the **Practice and Problem Solving Workbook** (also available in the Teaching Resources in print and online) to further support students' development in becoming independent learners.

HOMEWORK QUICK CHECK

To check students' understanding of key skills and concepts, go over Exercises 11, 25, 28, 30, and 31.

Lesson 6-6   **399**

Answers

Practice and Problem-Solving Exercises
(continued)

28. Let x = length of garden in feet, let y = width of garden in feet.

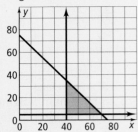

29. a.

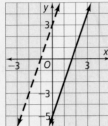

b. No; they have the same slope and different y-intercepts, so they will never intersect.

c. no

d. No; there are no points that satisfy both inequalities.

30. The student graphed $y \geq \frac{1}{2}x$, but he should have graphed $y \geq -\frac{1}{2}x$, and he shaded below $y = 2$, but he should have shaded above.

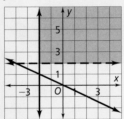

31. You can buy 5 T-shirts and 1 dress shirt or 2 T-shirts and 3 dress shirts.

32. a.

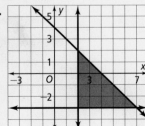

b. right triangle

c. $(2, 2)$, $(2, -3)$, $(7, -3)$

d. 12.5 units^2

33. C

34. Check students' work.

35. Check students' work.

 Apply

28. Think About a Plan You are fencing in a rectangular area for a garden. You have only 150 ft of fence. You want the length of the garden to be at least 40 ft. You want the width of the garden to be at least 5 ft. What is a graph showing the possible dimensions your garden could have?
- What variables will you use? What will they represent?
- How many inequalities do you need to write?

29. a. Graph the system $y > 3x + 3$ and $y \leq 3x - 5$.
   b. Writing Will the boundary lines $y = 3x + 3$ and $y = 3x - 5$ ever intersect? How do you know?
   c. Do the shaded regions in the graph from part (a) overlap?
   d. Does the system of inequalities have any solutions? Explain.

30. Error Analysis A student graphs the system as shown below. Describe and correct the student's error.

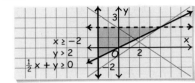

31. Gift Certificates You received a $100 gift certificate to a clothing store. The store sells T-shirts for $15 and dress shirts for $22. You want to spend no more than the amount of the gift certificate. You want to leave at most $10 of the gift certificate unspent. You need at least one dress shirt. What are all of the possible combinations of T-shirts and dress shirts you could buy?

32. a. Geometry Graph the system of linear inequalities.
   b. Describe the shape of the solution region.
   c. Find the vertices of the solution region.
   d. Find the area of the solution region.

$$x \geq 2$$
$$y \geq -3$$
$$x + y \leq 4$$

33. Which region represents the solution of the system?
   Ⓐ I   Ⓒ III
   Ⓑ II   Ⓓ IV

$$y \leq -\frac{3}{2}x - 2$$
$$3y - 9x \geq 6$$

Open-Ended Write a system of linear inequalities with the given characteristic.

34. All solutions are in Quadrant III.

35. There are no solutions.

Ⓒ **Challenge**

36. Business A jeweler plans to produce a ring made of silver and gold. The price of gold is about $25 per gram. The price of silver is approximately $.40 per gram. She considers the following in deciding how much gold and silver to use in the ring.
- The total mass must be more than 10 g but less than 20 g.
- The ring must contain at least 2 g of gold.
- The total cost of the gold and silver must be less than $90.
   a. Write and graph the inequalities that describe this situation.
   b. For one solution, find the mass of the ring and the cost of the gold and silver.

---

36. a. Let x = g of gold and let y = g of silver; $25x + 0.40y < 90$, $10 < x + y$, $x + y < 20$; $x \geq 2$.

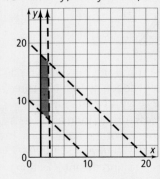

b. Answers may vary. Sample: One solution is $(3, 11)$, which represents 3 g of gold and 11 g of silver. $10 < 3 + 11 < 20$ and $3 > 2$. The cost of this ring will be $3(25) + 11(0.40) = 79.4$, or $79.40.

37. Solve $|y| \geq x$. (*Hint:* Write two inequalities and then graph them.)

38. Student Art A teacher wants to post a row of student artwork on a wall that is 20 ft long. Some pieces are 8.5 in. wide. Other pieces are 11 in. wide. She is going to leave 3 in. of space to the left of each art piece. She wants to post at least 16 pieces of art. Write and graph a system of inequalities that describes how many pieces of each size she can post.

Standardized Test Prep

SAT/ACT

39. The point $(-3, 11)$ is a solution of which of the following systems?

   Ⓐ $y \geq x - 2$ Ⓑ $y > x + 8$ Ⓒ $y > -x + 8$ Ⓓ $y \leq -3x + 1$
       $2x + y \leq 5$ $3x + y > 2$ $2x + 3y \geq 7$ $x - y \geq -15$

40. A plane has 18 passengers. Some have 1 bag and others have 2 bags. There are a total of 27 bags. Let $b =$ the number of passengers with 1 bag and $t =$ the number of passengers with 2 bags. Which system describes this situation?

   Ⓕ $b + t = 27$ Ⓖ $t = 18 - b$ Ⓗ $b + t = 18$ Ⓘ $b = 18 - t$
       $b + 2t = 18$ $b + 2t = 27$ $b = 27 + 2t$ $b + 2t = 18$

41. You fill your glass with ice and then add room-temperature water. Which graph best represents the change in temperature of the glass?

  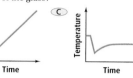

Extended Response

42. Suppose the line through points $(-1, 6)$ and $(x, 2)$ is perpendicular to the graph of $2x + y = 3$.

   a. Find the value of x. Show your work.
   b. What is an equation of the line perpendicular to the graph of $2x + y = 3$ and through the given points?
   c. What ordered pair is a solution of both equations? Explain.

Mixed Review

Graph each linear inequality.   ◀ **See Lesson 6-5.**

43. $y - x \leq 3$ **44.** $3y + x > 4$ **45.** $y \leq 5$

Get Ready!   To prepare for Lesson 7-1, do Exercises 46–48.

Simplify each expression.   ◀ **See Lesson 1-2.**

46. $(1 + 3)^2 - (1 + 3)$ **47.** $4^3 + 5^2 + (4 - 3)^1$ **48.** $7^2 + 2(3^3 + 5)$

---

c. Solve the system

$$2x + y = 3 \qquad 2(2x + y = 3)$$
$$4x + 2y = 6$$
$$x - 2y = -13 \qquad x - 2y = -13$$
$$x - 2y = -13$$

$$5x = -7 \text{ or } x = -\tfrac{7}{5}$$

Now substitute $x = -\tfrac{7}{5}$ into either equation to solve for y. $2\left(\tfrac{-7}{5}\right) + y = 3$, so $y = 3 + \tfrac{14}{5}$ or $y = \tfrac{29}{5}$.

So the point $\left(-\tfrac{7}{5}, \tfrac{29}{5}\right)$ is a solution of both equations.

[3]   appropriate methods with one minor calculation error

[2]   correct point and incorrect equation or incorrect point but corresponding correct equation

[1]   correct answers with no work shown

43. 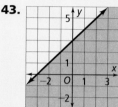   **44.**

45. 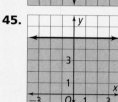   **46.** 12

47. 90   **48.** 113

37.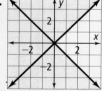

38. $11.5x + 14y \leq 240$
$x + y \geq 16$;

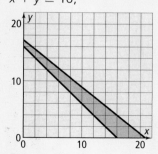

39. A   **40.** G   **41.** C

42. a. [4] $2x + y = 3$, so $y = -2x + 3$ and the slope of the line is -2. Therefore, the slope of the line containing the points must be equal to $\tfrac{1}{2}$.

$$\frac{2 - 6}{x - (-1)} = \frac{1}{2} \text{ or } \frac{-4}{x + 1} = \frac{1}{2}$$
$$(-4)(2) = 1(x + 1)$$
$$-8 = x + 1$$
$$-9 = x$$

b. $m = \tfrac{1}{2}$ and contains the points $(-1, 6)$ and $(-9, 2)$. Use the slope and either one of the points.

$$y - y_1 = m(x - x_1)$$
$$y - 6 = \tfrac{1}{2}(x - (-1))$$
$$y - 6 = \tfrac{1}{2}(x + 1)$$
$$y - 6 = \tfrac{1}{2}x + \tfrac{1}{2}$$
$$y = \tfrac{1}{2}x + \tfrac{13}{2} \text{ or } x - 2y = -13$$

Additional Instructional Support

Algebra 1 Companion

Students can use the **Algebra 1 Companion** worktext (4 pages) as you teach the lesson. Use the Companion to support

- New Vocabulary
- Key Concepts
- Got It for each Problem
- Lesson Check

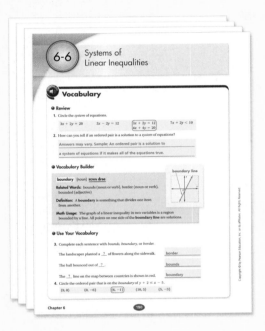

ELL Support

Use Manipulatives Write the inequalities $x + y \geq 2$ and $x + y \leq 7$ on the board. Have groups of students work together. Say: "Use pencils for x and books for y. Make a group of pencils and books that are a solution to the system of inequalities." After the groups have their solutions, ask: "Are the pencils and books more than 2? Are they less than 7?" Say: "Compare your solution with other groups. Is there only one solution?" Have each group write their own system of inequalities. Have them use pencils and books to model a solution to their system of inequalities. Demonstrate writing a note such as "I owe you 3 pencils" to represent a negative number. Have each group show its model to another group.

5 Assess & Remediate

Lesson Quiz

1. What is the graph of the system?

$$y > -x + 3$$
$$-2x + y < -1$$

2. **Do you UNDERSTAND?** What system of inequalities is represented by the graph? Is the point (2, 3) a solution of the system? Explain why or why not.

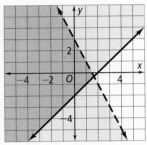

ANSWERS TO LESSON QUIZ

1.

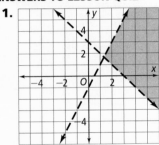

2. $y \geq x - 2$
   $y < -2x + 3$
   The point (2, 3) does not satisfy $y < -2x + 3$, so it is not a solution of the system.

PRESCRIPTION FOR REMEDIATION

Use the student work on the Lesson Quiz to prescribe a differentiated review assignment.

Points	Differentiated Remediation
0	Intervention
1	On-level
2	Extension

PowerAlgebra.com

5 Assess & Remediate

Assign the Lesson Quiz. Appropriate intervention, practice, or enrichment is automatically generated based on student performance.

Intervention

- **Reteaching** (2 pages) Provides reteaching and practice exercises for the key lesson concepts. Use with struggling students or absent students.
- **English Language Learner Support** Helps students develop and reinforce mathematical vocabulary and key concepts.

All-in-One Resources/Online
Reteaching

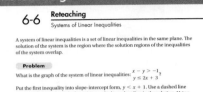

All-in-One Resources/Online
English Language Learner Support

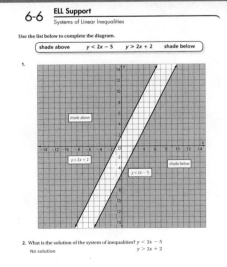

Differentiated Remediation *continued*

On-Level

- **Practice** (2 pages) Provides extra practice for each lesson. For simpler practice exercises, use the Form K Practice pages found in the All-in-One Teaching Resources and online.

- **Think About a Plan** Helps students develop specific problem-solving skills and strategies by providing scaffolded guiding questions.

- **Standardized Test Prep** Focuses on all major exercises, all major question types, and helps students prepare for the high-stakes assessments.

Extension

- **Enrichment** Provides students with interesting problems and activities that extend the concepts of the lesson.

- **Activities, Games, and Puzzles** Worksheets that can be used for concepts development, enrichment, and for fun!

Practice and Problem Solving WKBK/ All-in-One Resources/Online
Practice page 1

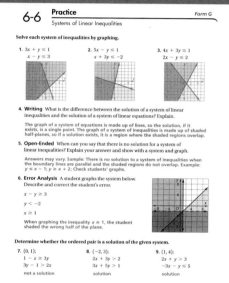

Practice and Problem Solving WKBK/ All-in-One Resources/Online
Practice page 2

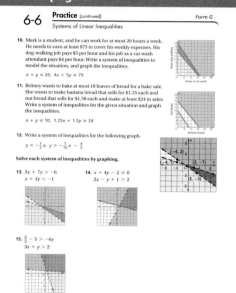

All-in-One Resources/Online
Enrichment

Practice and Problem Solving WKBK/ All-in-One Resources/Online
Think About a Plan

Practice and Problem Solving WKBK/ All-in-One Resources/Online
Standardized Test Prep

Online Teacher Resource Center
Activities, Games, and Puzzles

Guided Instruction

PURPOSE To use a graphing calculator to graph linear inequalities

PROCESS Students will

- graph inequalities and systems of inequalities using a graphing calculator.

DISCUSS Have students identify the differences between an equation and an inequality. Continue by discussing graphing for both equations and inequalities. Make sure students recognize that a solution to a system of equations is a point, whereas the solution to a system of inequalities is a region which includes many points.

Activity 1
In this activity students focus on using a graphing calculator to graph inequalities.

> **Q** How could you check whether a point is part of the solution of an inequality? **[Substitute the coordinates into the original inequality. If the statement is true, then the region containing that point is the solution.]**

Activity 2
In this activity students focus on using a graphing calculator to graph a system of inequalities.

> **Q** How is the solution identified by viewing a graph of the system? **[The solution is the overlapping section between the two regions.]**

Indiana Academic Standard
A1.3.2 Graph the solution set for a pair of linear inequalities in two variables with and without technology and use the graph to find the solution set.

A graphing calculator can show the solutions of an inequality or a system of inequalities. To enter an inequality, press **apps** and scroll down to select **INEQUAL**. Move the cursor over the = symbol for one of the equations. Notice the inequality symbols at the bottom of the screen, above the keys labeled **F2–F5**. Change the = symbol to an inequality symbol by pressing **alpha** followed by one of **F2–F5**.

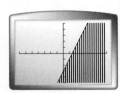

Activity 1

Graph the inequality $y < 3x - 7$.

1. Move the cursor over the = symbol for Y_1. Press **alpha** and **F2** to select the < symbol.
2. Enter the given inequality as Y_1.
3. Press **graph** to graph the inequality.

Activity 2

Graph the system. $y < -2x - 3$
$y \geq x + 4$

4. Move the cursor over the = symbol for Y_1. Press **alpha** and **F2** to select the < symbol. Enter the first inequality as Y_1.
5. Then move the cursor over the = symbol for Y_2, and press **alpha** and **F5** to select the ≥ symbol. Enter the second inequality as Y_2.
6. Press **graph** to graph the system of inequalities.

Exercises

Use a graphing calculator to graph each inequality. Sketch your graph.

7. $y \leq x$ **8.** $y > 5x - 9$ **9.** $y \geq -1$ **10.** $y < -x + 8$

Use a graphing calculator to graph each system of inequalities. Sketch your graph.

11. $y \geq -x + 3$ **12.** $y > x$ **13.** $y \geq -1$ **14.** $y \geq 2x - 2$
$y \leq x + 2$ $y \geq -2x + 5$ $y < 0.5x - 2$ $y \leq 2x - 4$

Answers

Activity 1 and 2
1–6. Check students' work.

Exercises
7.
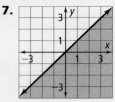

8.
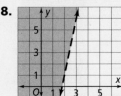

9.

10.
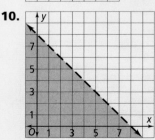

11.
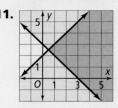

12–14. See back of book.

6

Pull It **All Together**

To solve these problems you will pull together many concepts and skills that you have studied about systems of equations and inequalities.

BIG idea Solving Equations and Inequalities

There are several ways to solve systems of equations and inequalities, including graphing and using equivalent forms of equations and inequalities within the system. The number of solutions depends on the type of system.

Task 1

Solve using two different methods. Explain which method you found to be more efficient.

a. $3x - 9y = 3$
$6x - 3y = -24$

b. $7x - 3y = 20$
$5x + 3y = 16$

c. $y = \frac{1}{2}x - 6$
$2x + 6y = 19$

Task 2

Solve. Show all your work and explain your steps.

The triangle on the left has a perimeter of 14. The triangle on the right has a perimeter of 21. What are x and y?

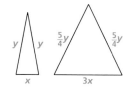

BIG idea Modeling

You can represent many real-world mathematical problems algebraically. When you need to find two unknowns, you may be able to write and solve a system of equations or inequalities.

Task 3

Solve the problem. Show all of your work and explain your steps.

A town is organizing a Fourth of July parade. There will be two sizes of floats in the parade, as shown below. A space of 10 ft will be left after each float.

a. The parade must be at least 150 ft long, but less than 200 ft long. What combinations of large and small floats are possible?

b. Large floats cost $600 to operate. Small floats cost $300 to operate. The town has a budget of $2500 to operate the floats. How does this change your answer to part (a)? What combinations of large and small floats are possible?

Assess Performance **UbD**

Pull It All Together

See p. 67 for a holistic scoring rubric to gauge a student's progress on Understanding the Problem, Planning a Solution, Getting an Answer, and Assessing Autonomy.

SOLUTIONS OUTLINES

Task 1

a. Method 1: Solve by substitution. Sample: Solve the first equation for x and substitute the result, $3y + 1$, for x in the second equation and solve for y. Use the value of y to solve for x. Method 2: Solve by elimination. Sample: First multiply the first equation by 2 and then subtract the equations to eliminate x. Solve for y and use its value in either equation to find the value of x. [Answer: $(-5, -2)$; elimination is more efficient.]

b. Method 1: Solve by substitution. Sample: Solve the second equation for x and substitute the result, $-0.6y + 3.2$, for x in the first equation and solve for y. Use the value of y to solve for x. Method 2: Solve by elimination. Sample: Add the two equations to eliminate x, and solve for y. Then use the value of y in either equation to find the value of x. [Answer: $\left(3, \frac{1}{3}\right)$; elimination is more efficient.]

c. Method 1: Solve by substitution. Sample: Substitute the expression for y found in the first equation, $\frac{1}{2}x - 6$, in the second equation and solve for x. Use the value of x to solve for y. Method 2: Solve by elimination. Sample: Rewrite the first equation with x and y on the left side of the equation. Then multiply the first equation by 6 and subtract the equations to eliminate y. Solve for x and use its value in either equation to find the value of y. [Answer: $\left(11, -\frac{1}{2}\right)$; substitution is more efficient.]

Pull It All Together

The concepts and skills required to solve these problems are from several lessons within this chapter and from the previous chapter. As students solve these problems, they will demonstrate their reasoning strategies and their growth as independent problem solvers.

The following questions are designed for you to:
• Help support students as they do the Tasks.
• Gauge the amount of support a student needs as they progress to becoming an independent problem solver.

Task 1
• When should you solve a system of equations by graphing?
• When should you solve a system of equations by substitution?
• When should you solve a system of equations by elimination?

Task 2
• How do you calculate perimeter?
• What is the relationship between the side lengths?

Task 3
• What do you know? What do you need?
• What does the problem require?
• What equations model those requirements?

Task 2

First step: Use a system of equations [Answer: $x + 2y = 14$; $3x + 2.5y = 21$]. Then substitute $14 - 2y$ for x in $3x + 2.5y = 21$. [Answer: $(2, 6)$]

Task 3

a. Possible plan: Represent the situation with a system of equations. Because each float is followed by 10 ft of space, represent a small float with $15 + 10 = 25$ and represent a large float with $30 + 10 = 40$. Let $x =$ number of small floats and $y =$ number of large floats. Write and graph the system $25x + 40y \geq 150$ and $25x + 40y < 200$. Note also that neither x nor y may be zero because the parade will have 2 kinds of floats as stated. [Answer: There are 7 possible combinations. Let (x, y) represent (number of small, number of large). $(1, 4), (2, 3), (3, 2), (3, 3), (4, 2), (5, 1), (6, 1)$]

b. Possible plan: Check the cost of each combination found in part (a). [Answer: There are now only 5 possible combinations. $(1, 4)$ and $(3, 3)$ are excluded because they cost more than the budget allows.]

Essential Questions

BIG idea Solving Equations and Inequalities

ESSENTIAL QUESTION How can you solve a system of equations or inequalities?

ANSWER There are several ways to solve systems of equations and inequalities, including graphing and using equivalent forms of equations and inequalities within the system. The number of solutions depends on the type of system.

BIG idea Modeling

ESSENTIAL QUESTION Can systems of equations model real-world situations?

ANSWER You can represent many real-world mathematical problems algebraically. When you need to find two unknowns, you may be able to write and solve a system of equations.

Connecting **BIG** ideas and Answering the Essential Questions

1 Solving Equations and Inequalities
There are several ways to solve systems of equations and inequalities, including graphing and using equivalent forms of equations and inequalities within the system. The number of solutions depends on the type of system.

Solving Systems of Equations
(Lessons 6-1, 6-2, and 6-3)

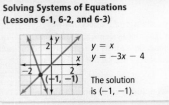

$y = x$
$y = -3x - 4$

The solution is $(-1, -1)$.

Linear Inequalities (Lessons 6-5 and 6-6)

2 Modeling
You can represent many real-world mathematical problems algebraically. When you need to find two unknowns, you may be able to write and solve a system of equations.

Applying Linear Systems
(Lesson 6-4)

income

expenses

break-even point

Chapter Vocabulary

- consistent (p. 361)
- dependent (p. 361)
- elimination method (p. 374)
- inconsistent (p. 361)
- independent (p. 361)
- linear inequality (p. 390)
- solution of an inequality (p. 390)
- solution of a system of linear equations (p. 360)
- solution of a system of linear inequalities (p. 396)
- substitution method (p. 368)
- system of linear equations (p. 360)
- system of linear inequalities (p. 396)

Choose the correct term to complete each sentence.

1. A system of equations that has no solution is said to be _?_ .

2. You can solve a system of equations by adding or subtracting the equations in such a way that one variable drops out. This is called the _?_ method.

3. Two or more linear equations together form a(n) _?_ .

Summative Questions

Use the following prompts as you review this chapter with your students. The prompts are designed to help you assess your students' understanding of the BIG Ideas they have studied.

- What three methods are used to solve systems of equations?
- What are the advantages and disadvantages to the methods of solving systems of equations?
- How do you show the solutions to a system of inequalities?

Answers

Chapter Review

1. inconsistent   **2.** elimination

3. system of linear equations

6-1 Solving Systems by Graphing

Quick Review

One way to solve a system of linear equations is by graphing each equation and finding the intersection point of the graph, if one exists.

Example

What is the solution of the system? $y = -2x + 2$
$y = 0.5x - 3$

$y = -2x + 2$ Slope is -2; y-intercept is 2.

$y = 0.5x - 3$ Slope is 0.5; y-intercept is -3.

The lines appear to intersect at $(2, -2)$. Check if $(2, -2)$ makes both equations true.

$-2 = -2(2) + 2$ ✔

$-2 = 0.5(2) - 3$ ✔

So, the solution is $(2, -2)$.

Exercises

Solve each system by graphing. Check your answer.

4. $y = 3x + 13$
$y = x - 3$

5. $y = -x + 4$
$y = 3x + 12$

6. $y = 2x + 3$
$y = \frac{1}{3}x - 2$

7. $y = 1.5x + 2$
$4.5x - 3y = -9$

8. $y = -2x - 21$
$y = x - 7$

9. $y = x + 1$
$2x - 2y = -2$

10. Songwriting Jay has written 24 songs to date. He writes an average of 6 songs per year. Jenna started writing songs this year and expects to write about 12 songs per year. How many years from now will Jenna have written as many songs as Jay? Write and graph a system of equations to find your answer.

11. Reasoning Describe the graph of a system of equations that has no solution.

6-2 Solving Systems Using Substitution

Quick Review

You can solve a system of equations by solving one equation for one variable and then substituting the expression for that variable into the other equation.

Example

What is the solution of the system? $y = -\frac{1}{3}x$
$3x + 3y = -18$

$3x + 3y = -18$ Write the second equation.

$3x + 3(-\frac{1}{3}x) = -18$ Substitute $-\frac{1}{3}x$ for y.

$2x = -18$ Simplify.

$x = -9$ Solve for x.

$y = -\frac{1}{3}(-9)$ Substitute -9 for x in the first equation.

$y = 3$

The solution is $(-9, 3)$.

Exercises

Solve each system using substitution. Tell whether the system has *one solution, infinitely many solutions*, or *no solution*.

12. $y = 2x - 1$
$2x + 2y = 22$

13. $-x + y = -13$
$3x - y = 19$

14. $2x + y = -12$
$-4x - 2y = 30$

15. $\frac{1}{3}y = \frac{7}{3}x + \frac{5}{3}$
$x - 3y = 5$

16. $y = x - 7$
$3x - 3y = 21$

17. $3x + y = -13$
$-2x + 5y = -54$

18. Business The owner of a hair salon charges $20 more per haircut than the assistant. Yesterday the assistant gave 12 haircuts. The owner gave 6 haircuts. The total earnings from haircuts were $750. How much does the owner charge for a haircut? Solve by writing and solving a system of equations.

4. $(-8, -11)$ **5.** $(-2, 6)$

6. $(-3, -3)$ **7.** no solution

8. $\left(-\frac{14}{3}, -\frac{35}{3}\right)$

9. infinitely many solutions

10. 4 yr

11. The lines will be parallel.

12. $(4, 7)$ **13.** $(3, -10)$

14. no solution   **15.** $(-1, -2)$

16. infinitely many solutions

17. $\left(-\frac{11}{17}, -\frac{188}{17}\right)$ **18.** $55

Answers

Chapter Review (continued)

19. no solution　　**20.** $(-1, 13)$

21. $(-11, -7)$　　**22.** $(5, 12)$

23. $(4.5, 3)$

24. infinitely many solutions

25. small centerpiece: 25 min, large centerpiece: 40 min

26.

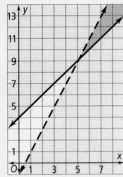

27.

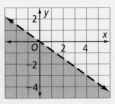

28.

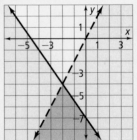

29.

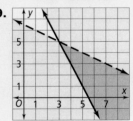

30.

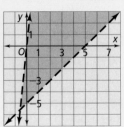

31.

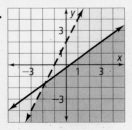

6-3 and 6-4 Solving Systems Using Elimination; Applications of Systems

Quick Review

You can add or subtract equations in a system to eliminate a variable. Before you add or subtract, you may have to multiply one or both equations by a constant to make eliminating a variable possible.

Example

What is the solution of the system?　$3x + 2y = 41$
$5x - 3y = 24$

$$
\begin{array}{lll}
3x + 2y = 41 & \text{Multiply by 3.} & 9x + 6y = 123 \\
5x - 3y = 24 & \text{Multiply by 2.} & \underline{10x - 6y = 48} \\
& & 19x + 0\ = 171 \\
& & \qquad\quad x = 9
\end{array}
$$

$3x + 2y = 41$　Write the first equation.

$3(9) + 2y = 41$　Substitute 9 for x.

$y = 7$　Solve for y.

The solution is $(9, 7)$.

Exercises

Solve each system using elimination. Tell whether the system has *one solution*, *infinitely many solutions*, or *no solution*.

19. $x + 2y = 23$
$5x + 10y = 55$

20. $7x + y = 6$
$5x + 3y = 34$

21. $5x + 4y = -83$
$3x - 3y = -12$

22. $9x + \frac{1}{2}y = 51$
$7x + \frac{1}{3}y = 39$

23. $4x + y = 21$
$-2x + 6y = 9$

24. $y = 3x - 27$
$x - \frac{1}{3}y = 9$

25. Flower Arranging It takes a florist 3 h 15 min to make 3 small centerpieces and 3 large centerpieces. It takes 6 h 20 min to make 4 small centerpieces and 7 large centerpieces. How long does it take to make each small centerpiece and each large centerpiece? Write and solve a system of equations to find your answer.

6-5 and 6-6 Linear Inequalities and Systems of Inequalities

Quick Review

A **linear inequality** describes a region of the coordinate plane with a boundary line. Two or more inequalities form a **system of inequalities**. The system's solutions lie where the graphs of the inequalities overlap.

Example

What is the graph of the system?　$y > 2x - 4$
$y \le -x + 2$

Graph the boundary lines $y = 2x - 4$ and $y = -x + 2$. For $y > 2x - 4$, use a dashed boundary line and shade above it. For $y \le -x + 2$, use a solid boundary line and shade below. The green region of overlap contains the system's solutions.

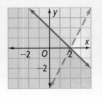

Exercises

Solve each system of inequalities by graphing.

26. $y \ge x + 4$
$y < 2x - 1$

27. $4y < -3x$
$y < -\frac{3}{4}x$

28. $2x - y > 0$
$3x + 2y \le -14$

29. $x + 0.5y \ge 5.5$
$0.5x + y < 6.5$

30. $y < 10x$
$y > x - 5$

31. $4x + 4 > 2y$
$3x - 4y \ge 1$

32. Downloads You have 60 megabytes (MB) of space left on your portable media player. You can choose to download song files that use 3.5 MB or video files that use 8 MB. You want to download at least 12 files. What is a graph showing the numbers of song and video files you can download?

32.

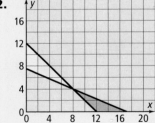

6 Chapter Test

MathXL® for School
Go to PowerAlgebra.com

Do you know HOW?

Solve each system by graphing. Tell whether the system has *one solution, infinitely many solutions,* or *no solution.*

1. $y = 3x - 7$
$y = -x + 1$

2. $x + 3y = 12$
$x = y - 8$

3. $x + y = 5$
$x + y = -2$

Solve each system using substitution.

4. $y = 4x - 7$
$y = 2x + 9$

5. $8x + 2y = -2$
$y = -5x + 1$

6. $y + 2x = -1$
$y - 3x = -16$

Solve each system using elimination.

7. $4x + y = 8$
$-3x - y = 0$

8. $2x + 5y = 20$
$3x - 10y = 37$

9. $3x + 2y = -10$
$2x - 5y = 3$

Solve each system of inequalities by graphing.

10. $y > 4x - 1$
$y \le -x + 4$

11. $x > -3$
$-3x + y \ge 6$

12. Garage Sale You go to a garage sale. All the items cost $1 or $5. You spend less than $45. Write and graph a linear inequality that models the situation.

13. Gardening A farmer plans to create a rectangular garden that he will enclose with chicken wire. The garden can be no more than 30 ft wide. The farmer would like to use at most 180 ft of chicken wire.
 a. Write a system of linear inequalities that models this situation.
 b. Graph the system to show all possible solutions.

Write a system of equations to model each situation. Solve by any method.

14. Education A writing workshop enrolls novelists and poets in a ratio of 5 : 3. There are 24 people at the workshop. How many novelists are there? How many poets are there?

15. Chemistry A chemist has one solution containing 30% insecticide and another solution containing 50% insecticide. How much of each solution should the chemist mix to get 200 L of a 42% insecticide?

Do you UNDERSTAND?

16. Open-Ended Write a system of two linear equations that has no solution.

17. Error Analysis A student concluded that $(-2, -1)$ is a solution of the inequality $y < 3x + 2$, as shown below. Describe and correct the student's error.

18. Reasoning Consider a system of two linear equations in two variables. If the graphs of the equations are not the same line, is it possible for the system to have infinitely many solutions? Explain.

Reasoning Suppose you add two linear equations that form a system, and you get the result shown below. How many solutions does the system have?

19. $x = 8$ **20.** $0 = 4$ **21.** $0 = 0$

10. 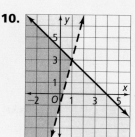   **11.**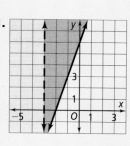

12. $1x + 5y < 45$

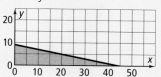

13. $2x + 2y \le 180$
$y \le 30$

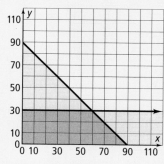

14. 15 novelists; 9 poets

15. 80 L of the 30% insecticide, 120 L of the 50% insecticide

16. Check students' work.

17. The student switched the values of x and y when substituting.
$y < 3x + 2$
$-1 < 3(-2) + 2$
$-1 < -6 + 2$
$-1 < -4$
This is false, so $(-2, -1)$ is not a solution of the inequality $y < 3x + 2$.

18. No; two lines can intersect in no points, one point, or infinitely many points. If they intersect in infinitely many points, then the two lines must be the same line.

19. one solution   **20.** no solution

21. infinitely many solutions

Answers

Chapter Test

1. one solution: $(2, -1)$

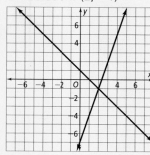

2. one solution: $(-3, 5)$

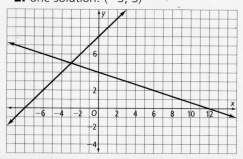

3. no solution

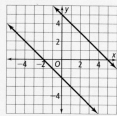

4. $(8, 25)$ **5.** $(2, -9)$
6. $(3, -7)$ **7.** $(8, -24)$
8. $(11, -0.4)$ **9.** $\left(-\frac{44}{19}, -\frac{29}{19}\right)$

PowerAlgebra.com

MathXL for School
Prepare students for the Mid-Chapter Quiz and Chapter Test with online practice and review.

Item Number	Lesson
1	6-3
2	2-7
3	1-7
4	5-3
5	6-1
6	2-5
7	4-6
8	3-4
9	2-5
10	2-8
11	4-6
12	5-3
13	6-1
14	6-4
15	2-1
16	2-5
17	2-3
18	2-1
19	2-3
20	5-6
21	2-8
22	5-1
23	6-4
24	2-9
25	2-6
26	1-2
27	1-8
28	5-6

Cumulative Test Prep

TIPS FOR SUCCESS

Some questions on tests ask you to solve a problem that involves a system of equations. Read the sample question at the right. Then follow the tips to answer the question.

TIP 1
When writing an equation, try to use variables that make sense for the problem. Instead of using x and y, use q for quarters and n for nickels.

Melissa keeps a jar for holding change. The jar holds 21 coins. All of the coins are quarters and nickels. The total amount in the jar is $3.85. How many quarters are in the jar?

- (A) 3
- (B) 7
- (C) 14
- (D) 21

TIP 2
Make sure to answer the question asked. Here you only need to find the number of quarters.

Think It Through
Write a system of equations.
$$q + n = 21$$
$$0.25q + 0.05n = 3.85$$
Solve the first equation for n and substitute to find q.
$$0.25q + 0.05n = 3.85$$
$$0.25q + 0.05(21 - q) = 3.85$$
$$0.2q + 1.05 = 3.85$$
$$q = 14$$
The correct answer is C.

Vocabulary Builder

As you solve test items, you must understand the meanings of mathematical terms. Choose the correct term to complete each sentence.

A. The (*substitution, elimination*) method is a way to solve a system of equations in which you replace one variable with an equivalent expression containing the other variable.

B. A linear (*equation, inequality*) is a mathematical sentence that describes a region of the coordinate plane having a boundary line.

C. A(n) (*x-intercept, y-intercept*) is the coordinate of a point where a graph intersects the *y*-axis.

D. The (*area, perimeter*) of a figure is the distance around the outside of the figure.

E. A (*function rule, relation*) is an equation that can be used to find a unique range value given a domain value.

Multiple Choice

Read each question. Then write the letter of the correct answer on your paper.

1. A group of students are going on a field trip. If the group takes 3 vans and 1 car, 22 students can be transported. If the group takes 2 vans and 4 cars, 28 students can be transported. How many students can fit in each van?
- (A) 2
- (B) 4
- (C) 6
- (D) 10

2. Greg's school paid $1012.50 for 135 homecoming T-shirts. How much would it cost the school to purchase 235 T-shirts?
- (F) $750.00
- (G) $1762.50
- (H) $2025.00
- (I) $2775.00

Answers

Cumulative Test Prep

A. substitution

B. inequality

C. *y*-intercept

D. perimeter

E. function rule

1. C

2. G

3. Which expression is equivalent to $64s - (8s - 4)$?

   (A) $52s$ (C) $56s + 4$

   (B) $60s$ (D) $56s - 4$

4. Which equation describes a line with slope 12 and y-intercept 4?

   (F) $y = 12x + 4$ (H) $y = 4x + 12$

   (G) $y = 12(x + 4)$ (I) $y = x + 3$

5. What is the solution of the system of equations shown at the right?

   (A) $(1, -1)$

   (B) $(-1, 1)$

   (C) $(-1, -1)$

   (D) $(1, 1)$

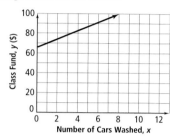

6. The width of Ben's rectangular family room is 3 ft less than the length. The perimeter is 70 ft. Which equation can be used to find the length ℓ of the room?

   (F) $70 = \ell - 3$ (H) $70 = 2(\ell - 3)$

   (G) $70 = 2\ell - 3$ (I) $70 = 2(2\ell - 3)$

7. Marisa's Flower Shop charges $3 per rose plus $16 for a delivery. Chris wants to have a bouquet of roses delivered to his mother. Which value is in the range of the function that gives the bouquet's cost in terms of the number of roses?

   (A) $16   (C) $34

   (B) $27   (D) $48

8. Which number is a solution of $8 > 3x - 1$?

   (F) 0 (H) 4

   (G) 3 (I) 6

9. The formula for the area A of a trapezoid is $A = \frac{1}{2}(b_1 + b_2)h$, where b_1 and b_2 represent the lengths of the bases and h represents the height. Which equation can be used to find the height of a trapezoid?

   (A) $h = 2A - b_1 - b_2$

   (B) $h = \frac{2A}{b_1 + b_2}$

   (C) $h = \frac{A(b_1 + b_2)}{2}$

   (D) $h = \frac{A - 2}{b_1 + b_2}$

10. Martin used 400 ft of fencing to enclose a rectangular area in his backyard. Isabella wants to enclose a similar area that is twice as long and twice as wide as the one in Martin's backyard. How much fencing does Isabella need?

   (F) 800 ft   (H) 1600 ft

   (G) 1200 ft   (I) 2000 ft

11. At the Conic Company, a new employee's earnings E, in dollars, can be calculated using the function $E = 0.05s + 30{,}000$, where s represents the employee's total sales, in dollars. All of the new employees earned between $50,000 and $60,000 last year. Which value is in the domain of the function?

   (A) $34,000   (C) $430,000

   (B) $300,000   (D) $3,400,000

12. Hilo's class fund has $65. The class is having a car wash to raise more money for a trip. The graph below models the amount of money the class will have if it charges $4 for each car washed.

How would the graph change if the class charged $5 per car washed?

   (F) The y-intercept would increase.

   (G) The slope would increase.

   (H) The y-intercept would decrease.

   (I) The slope would decrease.

13. A system has two linear equations in two variables. The graphs of the equations have the same slope but different y-intercepts. How many solutions does the system have?

   (A) 0 (C) 2

   (B) 1 (D) infinitely many

3. C
4. F
5. C
6. I
7. C
8. F
9. B
10. F
11. C
12. G
13. A

Answers

Cumulative Test Prep (continued)

14. I

15. C

16. 450

17. 3

18. 4.2

19. 64

20. $\frac{1}{5}$

21. 2.125

22. $\frac{1}{2}$

23. 4

24. 10,070

25. $\frac{1}{9}$

26. [2] 24 in. = 2 ft

$V = s^3$

$V = 2^3 = 8$

The volume of the cube is 8 ft³.

[1] appropriate method with one minor calculation error

27. [2] C = cost of envelopes + cost of stamps

$= 3.50 \times \frac{400}{50} + 0.42 \times 400$

$= 3.50 \times 8 + 0.42 \times 400$

$= 28 + 168$

$= 196$

The cost will be $196.

[1] appropriate methods with one minor calculation error

28. [4] **a.** Yes; $\overline{AD}$ and $\overline{BC}$ are parallel because $\overline{AD}$ has y-values of 5 and $\overline{BC}$ has y-values of 1, both sides being parallel to the x-axis. $\overline{AB}$ and $\overline{CD}$ are not parallel because $\overline{AB}$ is parallel to the y-axis and $\overline{CD}$ is not.

b. Going from point D to point C, the x-coordinate changes by 2 in the negative direction, so in order for ABCD to be a parallelogram, you have to move the x-coordinate of point B back 2 units to the point (−1, 5). Now two pairs of opposite sides are parallel.

[3] appropriate methods used with one minor error

[2] either part (a) or part (b) is incorrect

[1] correct answers with no work shown

---

14. Rhonda has 25 coins in her pocket. All of the coins are either dimes or nickels. If Rhonda has a total of $2.30, how many dimes does she have?

   (F) 4   (H) 18

   (G) 15   (I) 21

15. Which problem can be represented by the equation $19.2 = 3.2x$?

   (A) Elizabeth had $3.20, and she then received her paycheck. How much was her paycheck?

   (B) Jack bought some boxes of cereal at the store for $3.20 each. How much did he spend on cereal?

   (C) Mia spent $19.20 on socks. If each pair of socks cost $3.20, how many pairs did she buy?

   (D) Amos had $19.20 and spent $3.20 on lunch. How much money did Amos have after lunch?

GRIDDED RESPONSE

Record your answers in a grid.

16. An artist is putting a rectangular frame on a painting that is 12 in. wide and 19 in. long. The frame is 3 in. wide on each side. To the nearest square inch, what is the area of the painting with the frame?

17. What is the solution of $4(-3x + 6) - 1 = -13$?

18. In a regular polygon, all sides have the same length. Suppose a regular hexagon has a perimeter of 25.2 in. What is the length of each side in inches?

19. The sum of four consecutive integers is 250. What is the greatest of these integers?

20. What is the slope of a line that is perpendicular to the line with equation $y = -5x + 8$?

21. On a map, Julia's home is 8.5 in. from the library. If the map scale is 1 in. : 0.25 mi, how many miles from the library does Julia live?

22. The graph shows Jillian's distance from her house as she walks home from school. How many blocks per minute does Jillian walk?

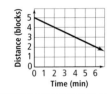

23. Sam is ordering pizza. Tony's Pizza charges $7 for a large cheese pizza plus $.75 for each additional topping. Maria's Pizza charges $8 for a large cheese pizza plus $.50 for each additional topping. For what number of toppings will the cost of a large pizza be the same at either restaurant?

24. Pam paid $9500 in college expenses this year. The college projects a 6% increase in expenses next year. What dollar amount should Pam expect to pay for college expenses next year?

25. A museum exhibit is showing various pieces of artwork created by an artist. The table below shows the number of each type of artwork shown.

Artwork	Number
Photographs	37
Paintings	43
Sculptures	10

What is the ratio of sculptures to all artwork? Give your answer as a fraction in lowest terms.

Short Response

26. The volume V of a cube is given by the formula $V = s^3$, where s represents the length of an edge of the cube. Suppose the edge length is 24 in. What is the volume of the cube in cubic feet?

27. You plan to mail surveys to different households. A box of 50 envelopes costs $3.50, and a postage stamp costs $.42. How much will it cost you to mail 400 surveys?

Extended Response

28. The vertices of quadrilateral ABCD are A(1, 1), B(1, 5), C(5, 5), and D(7, 1).

   a. A trapezoid is a four-sided figure with exactly one pair of parallel sides. Is ABCD a trapezoid? Explain your answer.

   b. You want to transform ABCD into a parallelogram by only moving point B. A parallelogram is a four-sided figure with both pairs of opposite sides parallel. What should be the new coordinates of point B? Explain.

Skills Handbook Contents

Skills **Handbook**

Prime Numbers and Composite Numbers

A prime number is a whole number greater than 1 that has exactly two factors, the number 1 and itself.

Prime number	2	5	17	29
Factors	1, 2	1, 5	1, 17	1, 29

A composite number is a number that has more than two factors. The number 1 is neither prime nor composite.

Composite number	6	15	48
Factors	1, 2, 3, 6	1, 3, 5, 15	1, 2, 3, 4, 6, 8, 12, 16, 24, 48

Example 1

Is 51 prime or composite?

$51 = 3 \cdot 17$ Try to find factors other than 1 and 51.

51 is a composite number.

You can use a factor tree to find the prime factors of a number. When all the factors are prime numbers, it is called the prime factorization of the number.

Example 2

Use a factor tree to write the prime factorization of 28.

The order of listing the factors may be different, but the prime factorization is the same.

The prime factorization of 28 is $2 \cdot 2 \cdot 7$.

Exercises

Is each number prime or composite?

1. 9	**2.** 16	**3.** 34	**4.** 61	**5.** 7	**6.** 13
7. 12	**8.** 40	**9.** 57	**10.** 64	**11.** 120	**12.** 700

List all the factors of each number.

13. 46	**14.** 32	**15.** 11	**16.** 65	**17.** 27	**18.** 29

Use a factor tree to write the prime factorization of each number.

19. 18	**20.** 20	**21.** 27	**22.** 54	**23.** 64	**24.** 96

Answers

Prime Numbers and Composite Numbers

1. composite   **2.** composite

3. composite   **4.** prime

5. prime   **6.** prime

7. composite   **8.** composite

9. prime   **10.** composite

11. composite   **12.** composite

13. 1, 2, 23, 46   **14.** 1, 2, 4, 8, 16, 32

15. 1, 11   **16.** 1, 5, 13, 65

17. 1, 3, 9, 27   **18.** 1, 29

19. $2 \cdot 3 \cdot 3$ **20.** $2 \cdot 2 \cdot 5$

21. $3 \cdot 3 \cdot 3$ **22.** $2 \cdot 3 \cdot 3 \cdot 3$

23. $2 \cdot 2 \cdot 2 \cdot 2 \cdot 2 \cdot 2$

24. $2 \cdot 2 \cdot 2 \cdot 17$

Factors and Multiples

A common factor is a number that is a factor of two or more numbers. The greatest common factor (GCF) is the greatest number that is a common factor of two or more numbers.

Example 1

Find the GCF of 24 and 64.

Method 1 List all the factors of each number.

Factors of 24   1, 2, 3, 4, 6, 8, 12, 24   Find the common factors: 1, 2, 4, 8.

Factors of 64   1, 2, 4, 8, 16, 32, 64   The greatest common factor is 8.

The GCF of 24 and 64 is 8.

Method 2 Use the prime factorization of each number.

$24 = 2 \cdot 2 \cdot 2 \cdot 3$ Find the prime factorization of each number.

$64 = 2 \cdot 2 \cdot 2 \cdot 2 \cdot 2 \cdot 2$

$GCF = 2 \cdot 2 \cdot 2 = 8$ The product of the common prime factors is the GCF.

A common multiple is a number that is a multiple of two or more numbers. The least common multiple (LCM) is the least number that is a common multiple of two or more numbers.

Example 2

Find the LCM of 12 and 18.

Method 1 List the multiples of each number.

Multiples of 12   12, 24, 36, . . .   List the multiples of each number until you find

Multiples of 18   18, 36, . . .   the first common multiple.

The LCM of 12 and 18 is 36.

Method 2 Use the prime factorization of each number.

$12 = 2 \cdot 2 \cdot 3$

$18 = 2 \cdot 3 \cdot 3$

$LCM = 2 \cdot 2 \cdot 3 \cdot 3 = 36$ Use each prime factor the greatest number of times it appears in either number.

Exercises

Find the GCF of each set of numbers.

1. 12 and 22   **2.** 7 and 21   **3.** 24 and 48   **4.** 42, 63, and 105

Find the LCM of each set of numbers.

5. 16 and 20   **6.** 14 and 21   **7.** 11 and 33   **8.** 6, 7, and 12

Factors and Multiples

1. 2   **2.** 7

3. 24   **4.** 21

5. 80   **6.** 42

7. 33   **8.** 84

Using Estimation

To make sure the answer to a problem is reasonable, you can estimate before you calculate. If the answer is close to your estimate, the answer is probably correct.

Example 1

Estimate to find whether each calculation is correct.

a. Calculation		Estimate		b. Calculation		Estimate
$126.91	$\approx$	$130		372.85	$\approx$	370
$14.05	$\approx$	$10		-227.31	$\approx$	-230
$+$25.14	$\approx$	$+$30		145.54		140
$266.10		$170				

The answer is not close to the estimate. It is not reasonable. The calculation is incorrect.

The answer is close to the estimate. It is reasonable. The calculation is correct.

For some situations, like estimating a grocery bill, you may not need an exact answer. A *front-end estimate* will give you a good estimate that is usually closer to the exact answer than an estimate you would get by rounding alone. Add the front-end digits, estimate the sum of the remaining digits by rounding, and then combine sums.

Example 2

Tomatoes cost $3.54, squash costs $2.75, and lemons cost $1.20. Estimate the total cost of the produce.

Add the	3.54	$\rightarrow$	0.50	Estimate by rounding. Then add.
front-end digits.	2.75	$\rightarrow$	0.80	
	$+1.20$	$\rightarrow$	$+0.20$	
	6		1.50	

Since $6 + 1.50 = 7.50$, the total cost is about $7.50.

Exercises

Estimate by rounding.

1. the sum of $15.70, $49.62, and $278.01

2. $563 - 125$

3. the sum of $163.90, $107.21, and $33.56

4. $824 - 467$

Use front-end estimation to find each sum or difference.

5. $1.65 + $5.42 + $9.89

6. $1.369 + 7.421 + 2.700$

7. $9.563 - 2.480$

8. $1.17 + 3.92 + 2.26$

9. $8.611 - 1.584$

10. $2.52 + $3.04 + $5.25

11. Ticket prices at an amusement park cost $11.25 for adults and $6.50 for children under 12. Estimate the cost for three children and one adult.

Answers

Using Estimation

Answers may vary for Exercises 1–11. Samples are given.

1. $350
2. 440
3. $300
4. 350
5. $17
6. 11.500
7. 6.90
8. 7.4
9. 7
10. $10.80
11. $30.80

Simplifying Fractions

A fraction can name a part of a group or region. The region below is divided into 10 equal parts and 6 of the equal parts are shaded.

$\dfrac{6}{10}$ ← Numerator
← Denominator   Read as "six tenths."

Two fractions that represent the same value are called equivalent fractions. You can find a fraction that is equivalent to a given fraction by multiplying the numerator and the denominator of the given fraction by the same nonzero number.

Example 1

Write five fractions that are equivalent to $\frac{3}{5}$.

$$\frac{3}{5} = \frac{3 \cdot 2}{5 \cdot 2} = \frac{6}{10} \qquad \frac{3}{5} = \frac{3 \cdot 3}{5 \cdot 3} = \frac{9}{15} \qquad \frac{3}{5} = \frac{3 \cdot 4}{5 \cdot 4} = \frac{12}{20} \qquad \frac{3}{5} = \frac{3 \cdot 5}{5 \cdot 5} = \frac{15}{25} \qquad \frac{3}{5} = \frac{3 \cdot 6}{5 \cdot 6} = \frac{18}{30}$$

The fraction $\frac{3}{5}$ is in simplest form because its numerator and denominator are relatively prime, which means their only common factor is 1. To write a fraction in simplest form, divide its numerator and its denominator by their greatest common factor (GCF).

Example 2

Write $\frac{6}{24}$ in simplest form.

Step 1 Find the GCF of 6 and 24.

$6 = 2 \cdot 3$ Multiply the common prime factors, 2 and 3.
$24 = 2 \cdot 2 \cdot 2 \cdot 3$ GCF = $2 \cdot 3 = 6$.

Step 2 Divide the numerator and the denominator of $\frac{6}{24}$ by the GCF, 6.

$\dfrac{6}{24} = \dfrac{6 \div 6}{24 \div 6} = \dfrac{1}{4}$ Simplify.

Exercises

Write five fractions that are equivalent to each fraction.

1. $\frac{4}{7}$ **2.** $\frac{9}{16}$ **3.** $\frac{3}{8}$ **4.** $\frac{8}{17}$ **5.** $\frac{5}{6}$ **6.** $\frac{7}{10}$

Complete each statement.

7. $\frac{3}{7} = \frac{\blacksquare}{21}$ **8.** $\frac{5}{8} = \frac{20}{\blacksquare}$ **9.** $\frac{11}{12} = \frac{44}{\blacksquare}$ **10.** $\frac{12}{16} = \frac{\blacksquare}{4}$ **11.** $\frac{50}{100} = \frac{1}{\blacksquare}$

Is each fraction in simplest form? If not, write the fraction in simplest form.

12. $\frac{4}{12}$ **13.** $\frac{3}{16}$ **14.** $\frac{5}{30}$ **15.** $\frac{9}{72}$ **16.** $\frac{11}{22}$ **17.** $\frac{24}{25}$

Write each fraction in simplest form.

18. $\frac{8}{16}$ **19.** $\frac{7}{14}$ **20.** $\frac{6}{9}$ **21.** $\frac{20}{30}$ **22.** $\frac{8}{20}$ **23.** $\frac{12}{40}$

Simplifying Fractions

1. $\frac{8}{14}, \frac{12}{21}, \frac{16}{28}, \frac{20}{35}, \frac{24}{42}$

2. $\frac{18}{32}, \frac{27}{48}, \frac{36}{64}, \frac{45}{80}, \frac{54}{96}$

3. $\frac{6}{16}, \frac{9}{24}, \frac{12}{32}, \frac{15}{40}, \frac{18}{48}$

4. $\frac{16}{34}, \frac{24}{51}, \frac{32}{68}, \frac{40}{85}, \frac{48}{102}$

5. $\frac{10}{12}, \frac{15}{18}, \frac{20}{24}, \frac{25}{30}, \frac{30}{36}$

6. $\frac{14}{20}, \frac{21}{30}, \frac{28}{40}, \frac{35}{50}, \frac{42}{60}$

7. 9   **8.** 32

9. 48   **10.** 3

11. 2   **12.** no; $\frac{1}{3}$

13. yes   **14.** no; $\frac{1}{6}$

15. no; $\frac{1}{8}$ **16.** no; $\frac{1}{2}$

17. yes   **18.** $\frac{1}{2}$

19. $\frac{1}{2}$ **20.** $\frac{2}{3}$

21. $\frac{2}{3}$ **22.** $\frac{2}{5}$

23. $\frac{3}{10}$

Fractions and Decimals

You can write a fraction as a decimal.

Example 1

Write $\frac{3}{5}$ as a decimal.

$$5\overline{)3.0}^{\,0.6}$$ Divide the numerator by the denominator.

So $\frac{3}{5} = 0.6$.

You can write a decimal as a fraction.

Example 2

Write 0.38 as a fraction.

$0.38 = 38$ hundredths $= \frac{38}{100} = \frac{19}{50}$

Some fractions can be written as decimals that repeat, but do not end.

Example 3

Write $\frac{3}{11}$ as a decimal.

Divide the numerator by the denominator, as shown at the right. The remainders 8 and 3 keep repeating. Therefore 2 and 7 will keep repeating in the quotient.

$\frac{3}{11} = 0.2727\ldots = 0.\overline{27}$

$$
\begin{array}{r}
0.2727\ldots \\
11\overline{)3.0000\ldots} \\
\underline{2.2} \\
80 \\
\underline{77} \\
30 \\
\underline{22} \\
80 \\
\underline{77} \\
3
\end{array}
$$

You can write a repeating decimal as a fraction.

Example 4

Write $0.363636\ldots$ as a fraction.

Let $x = 0.363636\ldots$

$\quad 100x = 36.36363636\ldots$ When 2 digits repeat, multiply by 100.

$\quad\ 99x = 36$ Subtract $x = 0.363636$.

$\qquad x = \frac{36}{99},$ or $\frac{4}{11}$ Divide each side by 99.

Exercises

Write each fraction or mixed number as a decimal.

1. $\frac{3}{10}$ **2.** $\frac{13}{12}$ **3.** $\frac{4}{20}$ **4.** $\frac{25}{75}$ **5.** $\frac{5}{7}$ **6.** $4\frac{3}{25}$

Write each decimal as a fraction in simplest form.

7. 0.07 **8.** 0.25 **9.** 0.875 **10.** 0.4545 **11.** 6.333 **12.** 7.2626

Answers

Fractions and Decimals

1. 0.3 **2.** $1.08\overline{3}$

3. 0.2 **4.** $0.\overline{3}$

5. $0.\overline{714285}$ **6.** 4.12

7. $\frac{7}{100}$ **8.** $\frac{1}{4}$

9. $\frac{7}{8}$ **10.** $\frac{5}{11}$

11. $6\frac{1}{3}$ **12.** $7\frac{26}{99}$

Adding and Subtracting Fractions

You can add and subtract fractions when they have the same denominator.
Fractions with the same denominator are called like fractions.

Example 1

a. Add $\frac{4}{5} + \frac{3}{5}$.

b. Subtract $\frac{5}{9} - \frac{2}{9}$.

$\frac{4}{5} + \frac{3}{5} = \frac{4+3}{5} = \frac{7}{5} = 1\frac{2}{5}$ ← Add or subtract the numerators and keep the same denominator. → $\frac{5}{9} - \frac{2}{9} = \frac{5-2}{9} = \frac{3}{9} = \frac{1}{3}$

Fractions with unlike denominators are called unlike fractions. To add or subtract unlike fractions, find the least common denominator (LCD) and write equivalent fractions with the same denominator. Then add or subtract the like fractions.

Example 2

Add $\frac{3}{4} + \frac{5}{6}$.

$\frac{3}{4} + \frac{5}{6} = \frac{9}{12} + \frac{10}{12}$ Find the LCD. The LCD is the least common multiple (LCM) of the denominators. The LCD of 4 and 6 is 12. Write equivalent fractions.

$= \frac{9+10}{12} = \frac{19}{12}$, or $1\frac{7}{12}$ Add like fractions and simplify.

To add or subtract mixed numbers, add or subtract the fractions. Then add or subtract the whole numbers. Sometimes when subtracting mixed numbers you have to regroup so that you can subtract the fractions.

Example 3

Subtract $5\frac{1}{4} - 3\frac{2}{3}$.

$5\frac{1}{4} - 3\frac{2}{3} = 5\frac{3}{12} - 3\frac{8}{12}$ Write equivalent fractions with the same denominator.

$= 4\frac{15}{12} - 3\frac{8}{12}$ Write $5\frac{3}{12}$ as $4\frac{15}{12}$ so you can subtract the fractions.

$= 1\frac{7}{12}$ Subtract the fractions. Then subtract the whole numbers.

Exercises

Add or subtract. Write each answer in simplest form.

1. $\frac{2}{7} + \frac{3}{7}$ **2.** $\frac{3}{8} + \frac{7}{8}$ **3.** $\frac{6}{5} + \frac{9}{5}$ **4.** $\frac{4}{9} + \frac{8}{9}$ **5.** $6\frac{2}{3} + 3\frac{4}{5}$

6. $1\frac{4}{7} + 2\frac{3}{14}$ **7.** $4\frac{5}{6} + 1\frac{7}{18}$ **8.** $2\frac{4}{5} + 3\frac{6}{7}$ **9.** $4\frac{2}{3} + 1\frac{6}{11}$ **10.** $3\frac{7}{9} + 5\frac{4}{11}$

11. $8 + 1\frac{2}{3}$ **12.** $8\frac{1}{5} + 3\frac{2}{4}$ **13.** $11\frac{3}{8} + 2\frac{1}{16}$ **14.** $\frac{7}{8} - \frac{3}{8}$ **15.** $\frac{9}{10} - \frac{3}{10}$

16. $\frac{17}{5} - \frac{2}{5}$ **17.** $\frac{11}{7} - \frac{2}{7}$ **18.** $\frac{5}{11} - \frac{4}{11}$ **19.** $8\frac{5}{8} - 6\frac{1}{4}$ **20.** $3\frac{2}{3} - 1\frac{8}{9}$

21. $8\frac{5}{6} - 5\frac{1}{2}$ **22.** $12\frac{3}{4} - 4\frac{5}{6}$ **23.** $17\frac{2}{7} - 8\frac{2}{9}$ **24.** $7\frac{3}{4} - 3\frac{3}{8}$ **25.** $4\frac{1}{12} - 1\frac{11}{12}$

Adding and Subtracting Fractions

1. $\frac{5}{7}$ **2.** $1\frac{1}{4}$

3. 3   **4.** $1\frac{1}{3}$

5. $10\frac{7}{15}$ **6.** $3\frac{11}{14}$

7. $6\frac{2}{9}$ **8.** $6\frac{23}{35}$

9. $6\frac{7}{33}$ **10.** $9\frac{14}{99}$

11. $9\frac{2}{3}$ **12.** $11\frac{19}{20}$

13. $13\frac{7}{16}$ **14.** $\frac{1}{2}$

15. $\frac{3}{5}$ **16.** 3

17. $1\frac{2}{7}$ **18.** $\frac{1}{11}$

19. $2\frac{3}{8}$ **20.** $1\frac{7}{9}$

21. $3\frac{1}{3}$ **22.** $7\frac{11}{12}$

23. $9\frac{4}{63}$ **24.** $4\frac{3}{8}$

25. $2\frac{1}{6}$

Multiplying and Dividing Fractions

To multiply two or more fractions, multiply the numerators, multiply the denominators, and simplify the product, if necessary.

Example 1

Multiply $\frac{3}{7} \cdot \frac{5}{6}$.

Method 1 Multiply the numerators and the denominators. Then simplify.

$$\frac{3}{7} \cdot \frac{5}{6} = \frac{3 \cdot 5}{7 \cdot 6} = \frac{15}{42} = \frac{15 \div 3}{42 \div 3} = \frac{5}{14}$$

Method 2 Simplify before multiplying.

$$\frac{\overset{1}{3}}{7} \cdot \frac{5}{\underset{2}{6}} = \frac{1 \cdot 5}{7 \cdot 2} = \frac{5}{14}$$

To multiply mixed numbers, change the mixed numbers to improper fractions and multiply the fractions. Write the product as a mixed number.

Example 2

Multiply $2\frac{4}{5} \cdot 1\frac{2}{3}$.

$$2\frac{4}{5} \cdot 1\frac{2}{3} = \frac{14}{5} \cdot \frac{\overset{1}{5}}{3} = \frac{14}{3} = 4\frac{2}{3}$$

To divide fractions, change the division problem to a multiplication problem. Remember that $8 \div \frac{1}{4}$ is the same as $8 \cdot 4$. To divide mixed numbers, change the mixed numbers to improper fractions and divide the fractions.

Example 3

a. Divide $\frac{4}{5} \div \frac{3}{7}$.

$$\frac{4}{5} \div \frac{3}{7} = \frac{4}{5} \cdot \frac{7}{3} \qquad \text{Multiply by the reciprocal of the divisor.}$$
$$= \frac{28}{15} \qquad \text{Simplify.}$$
$$= 1\frac{13}{15} \qquad \text{Write as a mixed number.}$$

b. Divide $4\frac{2}{3} \div 7\frac{3}{5}$.

$$4\frac{2}{3} \div 7\frac{3}{5} = \frac{14}{3} \div \frac{38}{5} \qquad \text{Change to improper fractions.}$$
$$= \frac{14^{7}}{3} \cdot \frac{5}{38_{19}} \qquad \text{Simplify.}$$
$$= \frac{35}{57} \qquad \text{Multiply.}$$

Exercises

Multiply or divide. Write your answers in simplest form.

1. $\frac{2}{5} \cdot \frac{3}{4}$ 2. $\frac{3}{7} \cdot \frac{4}{3}$ 3. $1\frac{1}{2} \cdot 5\frac{3}{4}$ 4. $3\frac{4}{5} \cdot 10$ 5. $5\frac{1}{4} \cdot \frac{2}{3}$

6. $4\frac{1}{2} \cdot 7\frac{1}{2}$ 7. $3\frac{2}{3} \cdot 6\frac{9}{10}$ 8. $6\frac{1}{2} \cdot 7\frac{2}{3}$ 9. $2\frac{2}{5} \cdot 1\frac{1}{6}$ 10. $4\frac{1}{9} \cdot 3\frac{3}{8}$

11. $\frac{3}{5} \div \frac{1}{2}$ 12. $\frac{4}{5} \div \frac{9}{10}$ 13. $2\frac{1}{2} \div 3\frac{1}{2}$ 14. $1\frac{4}{5} \div 2\frac{1}{2}$ 15. $3\frac{1}{6} \div 1\frac{3}{4}$

16. $5 \div \frac{3}{8}$ 17. $\frac{4}{9} \div \frac{3}{5}$ 18. $\frac{5}{8} \div \frac{3}{4}$ 19. $2\frac{1}{5} \div 2\frac{1}{2}$ 20. $6\frac{1}{2} \div \frac{1}{4}$

Answers

Multiplying and Dividing Fractions

1. $\frac{3}{10}$ 2. $\frac{4}{7}$

3. $8\frac{5}{8}$ 4. 38

5. $3\frac{1}{2}$ 6. $33\frac{3}{4}$

7. $25\frac{3}{10}$ 8. $49\frac{5}{6}$

9. $2\frac{4}{5}$ 10. $13\frac{7}{8}$

11. $1\frac{1}{5}$ 12. $\frac{8}{9}$

13. $\frac{5}{7}$ 14. $\frac{18}{25}$

15. $1\frac{17}{21}$ 16. $13\frac{1}{3}$

17. $\frac{20}{27}$ 18. $\frac{5}{6}$

19. $\frac{22}{25}$ 20. 26

Fractions, Decimals, and Percents

Percent means per hundred. 50% means 50 per hundred. 50% $= \frac{50}{100} = 0.50$.

You can write a fraction as a percent by writing the fraction as a decimal first. Then move the decimal point two places to the right and write a percent sign.

Example 1

Write each number as a percent.

a. $\frac{3}{5}$

$\frac{3}{5} = 0.6$

$0.6 = 60\%$

b. $\frac{7}{20}$

$\frac{7}{20} = 0.35$

$0.35 = 35\%$

c. $\frac{2}{3}$

$\frac{2}{3} = 0.66\overline{6}$

$0.66\overline{6} = 66.\overline{6}\% \approx 66.7\%$

You can write a percent as a decimal by moving the decimal point two places to the left and removing the percent sign. You can write a percent as a fraction with a denominator of 100. Then simplify the fraction, if possible.

Example 2

Write each percent as a decimal and as a fraction or mixed number.

a. 25%

$25\% = 0.25$

$25\% = \frac{25}{100} = \frac{1}{4}$

b. $\frac{1}{2}\%$

$\frac{1}{2}\% = 0.5\% = 0.005$

$\frac{1}{2}\% = \frac{\frac{1}{2}}{100} = \frac{1}{2} \div 100$

$= \frac{1}{2} \cdot \frac{1}{100} = \frac{1}{200}$

c. 360%

$360\% = 3.6$

$360\% = \frac{360}{100} = \frac{18}{5} = 3\frac{3}{5}$

Exercises

Write each number as a percent. If necessary, round to the nearest tenth.

1. 0.56   **2.** 0.09   **3.** 6.02   **4.** 5.245   **5.** 8.2   **6.** 0.14

7. $\frac{1}{7}$ **8.** $\frac{9}{20}$ **9.** $\frac{1}{9}$ **10.** $\frac{5}{6}$ **11.** $\frac{3}{4}$ **12.** $\frac{7}{8}$

Write each percent as a decimal.

13. 7%   **14.** 8.5%   **15.** 0.9%   **16.** 250%   **17.** 83%   **18.** 110%

19. 15%   **20.** 72%   **21.** 0.03%   **22.** 36.2%   **23.** 365%   **24.** 101%

Write each percent as a fraction or mixed number in simplest form.

25. 19%   **26.** $\frac{3}{4}\%$ **27.** 450%   **28.** $\frac{4}{5}\%$ **29.** 64%   **30.** $\frac{2}{3}\%$

31. 24%   **32.** 845%   **33.** $\frac{3}{8}\%$ **34.** 480%   **35.** 60%   **36.** 350%

Fractions, Decimals, and Percents

1. 56%
2. 9%
3. 602%
4. 524.5%
5. 820%
6. 14%
7. 14.3%
8. 45%
9. 11.1%
10. 83.3%
11. 75%
12. 87.5%
13. 0.07
14. 0.085
15. 0.009
16. 2.5
17. 0.83
18. 1.10
19. 0.15
20. 0.72
21. 0.0003
22. 0.362
23. 3.65
24. 1.01
25. $\frac{19}{100}$
26. $\frac{3}{400}$
27. $4\frac{1}{2}$
28. $\frac{1}{125}$
29. $\frac{16}{25}$
30. $\frac{1}{150}$
31. $\frac{6}{25}$
32. $8\frac{9}{20}$
33. $\frac{3}{800}$
34. $4\frac{4}{5}$
35. $\frac{3}{5}$
36. $3\frac{1}{2}$

Exponents

You can express $2 \cdot 2 \cdot 2 \cdot 2 \cdot 2$ as 2^5. The raised number 5 shows the number of times 2 is used as a factor. The number 2 is the base. The number 5 is the exponent.

$2^5 \leftarrow$ **exponent**
$\uparrow$
base

Factored Form: $2 \cdot 2 \cdot 2 \cdot 2 \cdot 2$ Exponential Form: 2^5 Standard Form: 32

A number with an exponent of 1 is the number itself: $8^1 = 8$.
Any number, except 0, with an exponent of 0 is 1: $5^0 = 1$.

Example 1

Write each expression using exponents.

a. $8 \cdot 8 \cdot 8 \cdot 8 \cdot 8$ b. $2 \cdot 9 \cdot 9 \cdot 9 \cdot 9 \cdot 9 \cdot 9$ c. $6 \cdot 6 \cdot 10 \cdot 10 \cdot 10 \cdot 6 \cdot 6$

Count the number of times each number is used as a factor.

$= 8^5$ $= 2 \cdot 9^6$ $= 6^4 \cdot 10^3$

Example 2

Write each expression in standard form.

a. 2^3 b. $8^2 \cdot 3^4$ c. $10^3 \cdot 15^2$

Write each expression in factored form and multiply.

$2 \cdot 2 \cdot 2 = 8$ $8 \cdot 8 \cdot 3 \cdot 3 \cdot 3 \cdot 3 = 5184$ $10 \cdot 10 \cdot 10 \cdot 15 \cdot 15 = 225{,}000$

For powers of 10, the exponent tells how many zeros are in the number in standard form.

$10^1 = 10$ $10^3 = 10 \cdot 10 \cdot 10 = 1000$ $10^5 = 10 \cdot 10 \cdot 10 \cdot 10 \cdot 10 = 100{,}000$

You can use powers of 10 to write numbers in expanded form.

Example 3

Write 739 in expanded form using powers of 10.

$739 = 700 + 30 + 9 = (7 \cdot 100) + (3 \cdot 10) + (9 \cdot 1) = (7 \cdot 10^2) + (3 \cdot 10^1) + (9 \cdot 10^0)$

Exercises

Write each expression using exponents.

1. $6 \cdot 6 \cdot 6 \cdot 6$ 2. $7 \cdot 7 \cdot 7 \cdot 7 \cdot 7$ 3. $5 \cdot 2 \cdot 2 \cdot 2 \cdot 2$

4. $3 \cdot 3 \cdot 3 \cdot 3 \cdot 3 \cdot 14 \cdot 14$ 5. $4 \cdot 4 \cdot 3 \cdot 3 \cdot 2$ 6. $3 \cdot 5 \cdot 5 \cdot 7 \cdot 7 \cdot 7$

Write each number in standard form.

7. 4^3 8. 9^4 9. 12^2 10. $6^2 \cdot 7^1$ 11. $11^2 \cdot 3^3$

Write each number in expanded form using powers of 10.

12. 658   13. 1254   14. 7125   15. 83,401   16. 294,863

Answers

Exponents

1. 6^4
2. 7^5
3. $5 \cdot 2^4$
4. $3^5 \cdot 14^2$
5. $4^2 \cdot 3^2 \cdot 2$
6. $3 \cdot 5^2 \cdot 7^3$
7. 64
8. 6561
9. 141
10. 252
11. 3267
12. $(6 \cdot 10^2) + (5 \cdot 10^1) + (8 \cdot 10^0)$
13. $(1 \cdot 10^3) + (2 \cdot 10^2) + (5 \cdot 10^1) \cdot (4 \cdot 10^0)$
14. $(7 \cdot 10^3) + (1 \cdot 10^2) + (2 \cdot 10^1) + (5 \cdot 10^0)$
15. $(8 \cdot 10^4) + (3 \cdot 10^3) + (4 \cdot 10^2) + (0 \cdot 10^1) + (1 \cdot 10^0)$
16. $(2 \cdot 10^5) + (9 \cdot 10^4) + (4 \cdot 10^3) + (8 \cdot 10^2) + (6 \cdot 10^1) + (3 \cdot 10^0)$

Perimeter, Area, and Volume

The perimeter of a figure is the distance around the figure. The area of a figure is the number of square units contained in the figure. The volume of a three-dimensional figure is the number of cubic units contained in the figure.

Example 1

Find the perimeter of each figure.

a.
Add the measures of the sides.
$3 + 4 + 5 = 12$
The perimeter is 12 in.

b.
Use the formula $P = 2\ell + 2w$.
$P = 2(3) + 2(4)$
$= 6 + 8 = 14$
The perimeter is 14 cm.

Example 2

Find the area of each figure.

a.
Use the formula $A = bh$.
$A = 6 \cdot 5 = 30$
The area is 30 in.^{2}.

b.
Use the formula $A = \frac{1}{2}(bh)$.
$A = \frac{1}{2}(7 \cdot 6) = 21$
The area is 21 in.^{2}.

Example 3

Find the volume of each figure.

a.
Use the formula $V = Bh$.
$B =$ area of the base
$= 3 \cdot 5 = 15$
$V = 15 \cdot 6 = 90$ in.^{3}
The volume is 90 in.^{3}.

b.
Use the formula $V = \pi r^2 h$.
$V = 3.14 \cdot 2^2 \cdot 5$
$= 3.14 \cdot 4 \cdot 5 = 62.8$ in.^{3}
The volume is 62.8 in.^{3}.

Exercises

For Exercises 1–2, find the perimeter of each figure. For Exercises 3–4, find the area of each figure. For Exercises 5–7, find the volume of each figure.

1.
2.
3.
4. (image)

5.
6.
7.

Perimeter, Area, and Volume
1. 22 cm
2. 22 in.
3. 24 cm^2
4. 56 in.^{2}
5. 216 cm^3
6. 48 cm^3
7. 352 cm^3

Line Plots

A line plot is created by placing a mark above a number line corresponding to each data value. Line plots have two main advantages:

- You can see the frequency of data values.
- You can see how the data values compare.

Example

The table at the right gives the heights, in inches, of a group of 25 adults. Display the data in a line plot. Describe the data shown in the line plot.

The data are graphed on a number line.

The title describes the data.

An **X** represents one element of the data set.

Heights of Adults (in.)

Heights of Adults (in.)				
59	60	63	63	64
64	64	65	65	65
67	67	67	67	68
68	68	69	70	70
71	72	73	73	77

The line plot shows that most of the heights are concentrated around 67 in., the maximum value is 77 in., and the minimum value is 59 in.

Exercises

Display each set of data in a line plot.

1. 3, 6, 4, 3, 6, 0, 4, 5, 0, 4, 6, 1, 5, 1, 0, 5, 5, 6, 5, 3

2. 19, 18, 18, 18, 19, 20, 19, 18, 18, 17, 18, 20, 19, 17

Draw a line plot for each frequency table.

3.

Number	1	2	3	4	5	6
Frequency	4	1	0	5	7	2

4.

Number	12	13	15	16	18	19
Frequency	2	5	1	3	6	3

5. Olympics The numbers of gold medals won by different countries during the 2002 Winter Olympics are listed below.

1, 1, 1, 2, 2, 2, 3, 3, 3, 3, 4, 4, 4, 5, 7, 10, 12, 13

Display the data in a line plot. Describe the data shown in the line plot.

Answers

Line Plots National

1.
```
                    X
                    X  X
        X       X  X  X  X
        X  X    X  X  X  X
        X  X    X  X  X  X
        0  1  2  3  4  5  6
```

2.
```
        X
        X
        X  X
        X  X
        X  X  X  X
        X  X  X  X
        17 18 19 20
```

3.
```
                    X
                    X
                    X  X
        X           X  X
        X           X  X
        X           X  X  X
        X  X        X  X  X
        1  2  3  4  5  6
```

4.
```
                          X
              X           X
              X           X
              X       X  X  X
        X  X  X    X  X  X  X
        X  X  X    X  X  X  X
        12 13 14 15 16 17 18 19
```

5.   **Gold Medals Won**
```
              X
        X  X  X  X
        X  X  X  X
        X  X  X  X  X    X       X          X
        0  1  2  3  4  5  6  7  8  9 10 11 12 13
```

The line plot shows that most of the countries won about 3 gold medals. The maximum number of gold medals that a country won was 13, and the minimum was 1.

Bar Graphs

Bar graphs are used to display and compare data. The horizontal axis shows categories and the vertical axis shows amounts. A multiple bar graph includes a key.

Example

Draw a bar graph for the data in the table below.

Median Household Income

Town	2 person	3 person	4 person
Mason	$62,690	$68,070	$77,014
Barstow	$68,208	$82,160	$99,584
York	$51,203	$58,902	$67,911
Rexford	$52,878	$54,943	$63,945
Onham	$54,715	$61,437	$69,260

The categories (in the first column) are placed on the horizontal scale. The amounts (in the second, third, and fourth columns) are used to create the scale on the vertical scale and to draw each bar.

Graph the data for each town. Use the values in the top row to create the key.

The highest median income is $99,584. A reasonable range for the vertical scale is $0 to $108,000.

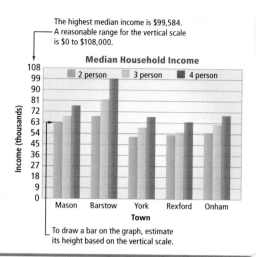

To draw a bar on the graph, estimate its height based on the vertical scale.

Exercises

1. Draw a bar graph for the data in the table below.

Highest Temperatures (°F)

Town	March	June	August
Mason	61	86	83
Barstow	84	104	101
York	89	101	102
Rexford	88	92	93
Onham	81	104	100

2. a. Reasoning If one more column of data were added to the table in the example, how would the bar graph be different?
  b. If one more row of data were added to the table in the example, how would the bar graph be different?

PowerAlgebra.com

Bar Graphs

1.

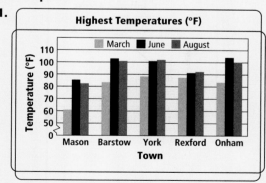

2. a. Each town would have one more bar and a new key element for the new month would be added.

  b. There would be another group of three bars added for the new town.

Line Graphs

Line graphs are used to display the change in a set of data over a period of time. A multiple-line graph shows change in more than one category of data over time. You can use a line graph to look for trends and make predictions.

Example

The data in the table below show the number of households, in thousands, that have cable TV and the number of households that subscribe to newspapers in a certain city. Graph the data.

Households With Cable TV and Newspapers (thousands)

Year	1980	1990	1995	2000	2005
Cable TV	15.2	51.9	60.5	68.6	73.9
Newspapers	62.2	62.3	58.2	55.8	53.3

Since the data show changes over time for two sets of data, use a double line graph. The horizontal scale displays years. The vertical axis shows the number of households for each category.

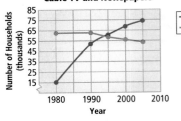

Notice that there is a *break* in the vertical axis. You can use a zigzag line to indicate a break from 0 to 15 since there is no data less than 15 to graph.

Exercises

Graph the data in each table.

1. Market Share (percent)

Year	2004	2005	2006	2007
Rap/Hip Hop	12.1	13.3	11.4	10.8
Pop	10.0	8.1	7.1	10.7

SOURCE: Recording Industry of America

2. Percent of Schools With Internet Access

Year	1997	1999	2001	2003
Elementary	75	94	99	100
Secondary	89	98	100	100

SOURCE: National Center for Education Statistics

Answers

Line Graphs

1.

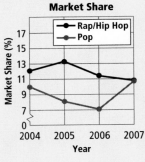

2.

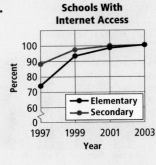

Circle Graphs

A circle graph is an efficient way to present certain types of data. The entire circle represents all of the data. Each section of the circle represents a part of the whole and can be labeled with the actual data or the data expressed as a fraction, decimal, or percent. The angles at the center are central angles, and each angle is proportional to the percent or fraction of the total.

Example

Students at a high school were asked to pick their favorite instrument. The table at the right shows the number of students who chose each instrument. Draw a circle graph for the data.

Favorite Musical Instruments

Instrument	Number of Students
Bass	35
Drums	103
Piano	150
Guitar	182

Step 1 Add to find the total number.

$$35 + 103 + 150 + 182 = 470$$

Step 2 For each central angle, set up a proportion to find the measure. Use a calculator to solve each proportion.

$\frac{35}{470} = \frac{a}{360°}$ $\frac{103}{470} = \frac{b}{360°}$ $\frac{150}{470} = \frac{c}{360°}$ $\frac{182}{470} = \frac{d}{360°}$

$a \approx 27°$ $b \approx 79°$ $c \approx 115°$ $d \approx 139°$

Step 3 Use a compass to draw a circle. Draw the approximate central angles using a protractor.

Step 4 Label each sector.

Favorite Musical Instruments

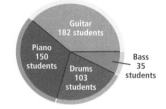

Exercises

1. **a.** Use the data in the table to draw a circle graph.
   b. Approximately what percent of students ride the bus?
   c. Approximately how many times more students walk than ride in a car?

Methods of Transportation

Transportation Method	Walk	Bicycle	Bus	Car
Number of Students	252	135	432	81

2. **Data Collection** Survey your class to find out how they get to school. Use the data to draw a circle graph.

Circle Graphs

1. a. Transportation Mode

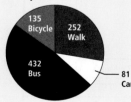

b. 48%

c. 3 times

2. Check students' work.

Stem-and-Leaf Plots

A stem-and-leaf plot is a display of data that uses the digits of the data values. To make a stem-and-leaf plot, separate each number into a stem and a leaf. A stem and leaf for the number 2.39 is shown at the right.

all digits
to the left of
last digit

last
digit

→ 2.3 | 9

↑   ↑
stem   leaf

You can use a stem-and-leaf plot to organize data. The data below describe the price for the same notebook at several stores.

Notebook Prices: $2.39 $2.47 $2.43 $2.21 $2.33 $2.28 $2.26

2.2	1 6 8
2.3	3 9
2.4	3 7

Key: 2.4 | 3 means 2.43

Use the first two digits for the "stems."

Use the corresponding last digits for the "leaves." Arrange the numbers in order.

You can use a back-to-back stem-and-leaf plot to display two related data sets. The stems are between two vertical bars, and the leaves are on each side. Leaves are in increasing order from the stems. In the back-to-back stem-and-leaf plot below, 3|4|1 represents a commute time of 43 min in Town A and a commute time of 41 min in Town B.

Daily Commute (min)

Town A		Town B
6 6 4 3	4	1 1 4 5 7
9 8 6 4 4 4	5	0 2 2 2 4
5 2 1 0	6	4 5 8 9
8 7 6 6 4 2	7	3 6 7 9 9 9

Key:

2 | 7 | 3

7 | 3 means 73

2 | 7 means 72

Exercises

Make a stem-and-leaf plot for each set of data.

1. 18 35 28 15 36 10 25 22 15

2. 18.6 18.4 17.6 15.7 15.3 17.5

3. 785 776 788 761 768 768 785

4. 0.8 0.2 1.4 3.5 4.3 4.5 2.6 2.2

5. Make a back-to-back stem-and-leaf plot of the test scores of the two classes below.
Class A: 98 78 85 72 94 81 68 83
Class B: 87 91 79 75 90 81 82 100

800

Answers

Stem-and-Leaf Plots

1.

1	0 5 5 8
2	2 5 8
3	5 6

Key: 1 | 0 means 10

2.

15	3 7
16	
17	5 6
18	4 6

Key: 15 | 3 means 15.3

3.

76	1 8 8
77	6
78	5 5 8

Key: 76 | 1 means 761

4.

0	2 8
1	4
2	2 6
3	5
4	3 5

Key: 0 | 2 means 0.2

5.

Test Scores

Class A		Class B
8	6	
8 2	7	5 9
5 3 1	8	1 2 7
8 4	9	0 1
	10	0

Key:

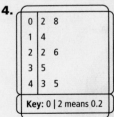

2 | 7 | 5

7 | 5 means 75

2 | 7 means 72

Reference

Table 1 Measures

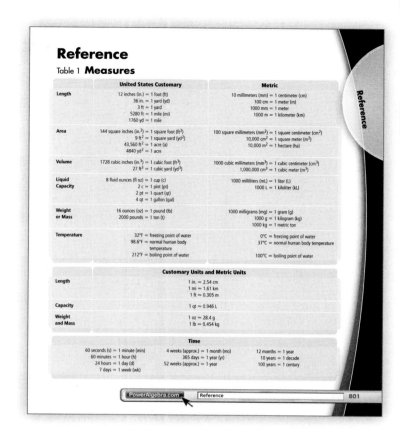

	United States Customary	Metric
Length	12 inches (in.) = 1 foot (ft) 36 in. = 1 yard (yd) 3 ft = 1 yard 5280 ft = 1 mile (mi) 1760 yd = 1 mile	10 millimeters (mm) = 1 centimeter (cm) 100 cm = 1 meter (m) 1000 mm = 1 meter 1000 m = 1 kilometer (km)
Area	144 square inches (in.^{2}) = 1 square foot (ft^2) 9 ft^2 = 1 square yard (yd^2) 43,560 ft^2 = 1 acre (a) 4840 yd^2 = 1 acre	100 square millimeters (mm^2) = 1 square centimeter (cm^2) 10,000 cm^2 = 1 square meter (m^2) 10,000 m^2 = 1 hectare (ha)
Volume	1728 cubic inches (in.^{3}) = 1 cubic foot (ft^3) 27 ft^3 = 1 cubic yard (yd^3)	1000 cubic millimeters (mm^3) = 1 cubic centimeter (cm^3) 1,000,000 cm^3 = 1 cubic meter (m^3)
Liquid Capacity	8 fluid ounces (fl oz) = 1 cup (c) 2 c = 1 pint (pt) 2 pt = 1 quart (qt) 4 qt = 1 gallon (gal)	1000 milliliters (mL) = 1 liter (L) 1000 L = 1 kiloliter (kL)
Weight or Mass	16 ounces (oz) = 1 pound (lb) 2000 pounds = 1 ton (t)	1000 milligrams (mg) = 1 gram (g) 1000 g = 1 kilogram (kg) 1000 kg = 1 metric ton
Temperature	32°F = freezing point of water 98.6°F = normal human body temperature 212°F = boiling point of water	0°C = freezing point of water 37°C = normal human body temperature 100°C = boiling point of water

	Customary Units and Metric Units
Length	1 in. ≈ 2.54 cm 1 mi ≈ 1.61 km 1 ft ≈ 0.305 m
Capacity	1 qt ≈ 0.946 L
Weight and Mass	1 oz ≈ 28.4 g 1 lb ≈ 0.454 kg

Time		
60 seconds (s) = 1 minute (min) 60 minutes = 1 hour (h) 24 hours = 1 day (d) 7 days = 1 week (wk)	4 weeks (approx.) = 1 month (mo) 365 days = 1 year (yr) 52 weeks (approx.) = 1 year	12 months = 1 year 10 years = 1 decade 100 years = 1 century

Table 2 Reading Math Symbols

Symbols	Words	Symbols	Words
·	multiplication sign, times (×)	∠A	angle A
=	equals	m∠A	measure of angle A
≟	Are the statements equal?	△ABC	triangle ABC
≈	is approximately equal to	(x, y)	ordered pair
≠	is not equal to	$x_1, x_2, \ldots$	specific values of the variable x
<	is less than	$y_1, y_2, \ldots$	specific values of the variable y
>	is greater than	$\bar{x}$	mean of data values of x
≤	is less than or equal to	σ	standard deviation
≥	is greater than or equal to	$f(x)$	f of x; the function value at x
≅	is congruent to	m	slope of a line
±	plus or minus	b	y-intercept of a line
( )	parentheses for grouping	a:b	ratio of a to b
[ ]	brackets for grouping	$\begin{bmatrix} 1 & 3 \\ 2 & 4 \end{bmatrix}$	matrix
{ }	set braces		
%	percent	sin A	sine of ∠A
|a|	absolute value of a	cos A	cosine of ∠A
…	and so on	tan A	tangent of ∠A
−a	opposite of a	n!	n factorial
π	pi, an irrational number, approximately equal to 3.14	$_nP_r$	permutations of n objects arranged r at a time
°	degree(s)	$_nC_r$	combinations of n objects chosen r at a time
a^n	nth power of a	P(event)	probability of an event
$\sqrt{x}$	nonnegative square root of x	^	raised to a power (in a spreadsheet formula)
$\frac{1}{a}, a \neq 0$	reciprocal of a	*	multiply (in a spreadsheet formula)
a^{-n}	$\frac{1}{a^n}, a \neq 0$	/	divide (in a spreadsheet formula)
$\overleftrightarrow{AB}$	line through points A and B		
$\overline{AB}$	segment with endpoints A and B		
AB	length of $\overline{AB}$; distance between points A and B		

Properties and Formulas

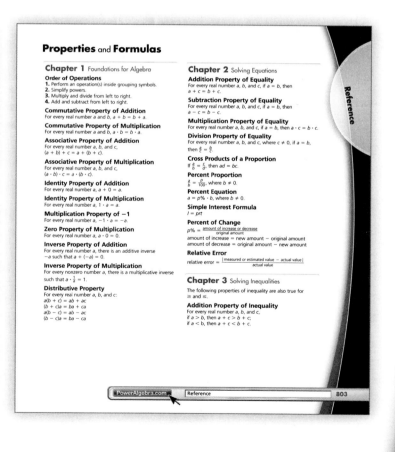

Chapter 1 Foundations for Algebra

Order of Operations
1. Perform an operation(s) inside grouping symbols.
2. Simplify powers.
3. Multiply and divide from left to right.
4. Add and subtract from left to right.

Commutative Property of Addition
For every real number a and b, a + b = b + a.

Commutative Property of Multiplication
For every real number a and b, a · b = b · a.

Associative Property of Addition
For every real number a, b, and c,
(a + b) + c = a + (b + c).

Associative Property of Multiplication
For every real number a, b, and c,
(a · b) · c = a · (b · c).

Identity Property of Addition
For every real number a, a + 0 = a.

Identity Property of Multiplication
For every real number a, 1 · a = a.

Multiplication Property of −1
For every real number a, −1 · a = −a.

Zero Property of Multiplication
For every real number a, a · 0 = 0.

Inverse Property of Addition
For every real number a, there is an additive inverse −a such that a + (−a) = 0.

Inverse Property of Multiplication
For every nonzero number a, there is a multiplicative inverse such that $a \cdot \frac{1}{a} = 1$.

Distributive Property
For every real number a, b, and c:
a(b + c) = ab + ac
(b + c)a = ba + ca
a(b − c) = ab − ac
(b − c)a = ba − ca

Chapter 2 Solving Equations

Addition Property of Equality
For every real number a, b, and c, if a = b, then a + c = b + c.

Subtraction Property of Equality
For every real number a, b, and c, if a = b, then a − c = b − c.

Multiplication Property of Equality
For every real number a, b, and c, if a = b, then a · c = b · c.

Division Property of Equality
For every real number a, b, and c, where c ≠ 0, if a = b, then $\frac{a}{c} = \frac{b}{c}$.

Cross Products of a Proportion
If $\frac{a}{b} = \frac{c}{d}$, then ad = bc.

Percent Proportion
$\frac{a}{b} = \frac{p}{100}$, where b ≠ 0.

Percent Equation
a = p% · b, where b ≠ 0.

Simple Interest Formula
I = prt

Percent of Change
$p\% = \frac{\text{amount of increase or decrease}}{\text{original amount}}$
amount of increase = new amount − original amount
amount of decrease = original amount − new amount

Relative Error
relative error $= \frac{|\text{measured or estimated value} - \text{actual value}|}{\text{actual value}}$

Chapter 3 Solving Inequalities

The following properties of inequality are also true for ≥ and ≤.

Addition Property of Inequality
For every real number a, b, and c,
if a > b, then a + c > b + c,
if a < b, then a + c < b + c.

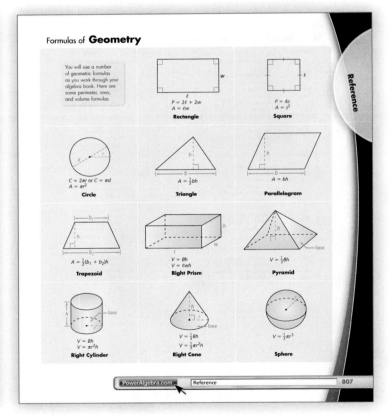

Subtraction Property of Inequality
For every real number a, b, and c,
if $a > b$, then $a - c > b - c$;
if $a < b$, then $a - c < b - c$.

Multiplication Property of Inequality
For every real number a, b, and c, where $c > 0$,
if $a > b$, then $ac > bc$;
if $a < b$, then $ac < bc$.
For every real number a, b, and c, where $c < 0$,
if $a > b$, then $ac < bc$;
if $a < b$, then $ac > bc$.

Division Property of Inequality
For every real number a, b, and c, where $c > 0$,
if $a > b$, then $\frac{a}{c} > \frac{b}{c}$;
if $a < b$, then $\frac{a}{c} < \frac{b}{c}$.
For every real number a, b, and c, where $c < 0$,
if $a > b$, then $\frac{a}{c} < \frac{b}{c}$;
if $a < b$, then $\frac{a}{c} > \frac{b}{c}$.

Reflexive Property of Equality
For every real number a, $a = a$.

Symmetric Property of Equality
For every real number a and b,
if $a = b$, then $b = a$.

Transitive Property of Equality
For every real number a, b, and c,
if $a = b$ and $b = c$, then $a = c$.

Transitive Property of Inequality
For every real number a, b, and c,
if $a < b$ and $b < c$, then $a < c$.

Chapter 4 An Introduction to Functions

Arithmetic Sequence
The form for the rule of an arithmetic sequence is
$A(n) = A(1) + (n - 1)d$, where $A(n)$ is the nth term,
$A(1)$ is the first term, n is the term number, and
d is the common difference.

Chapter 5 Linear Functions

Slope
slope $= \frac{\text{vertical change}}{\text{horizontal change}} = \frac{\text{rise}}{\text{run}}$

Direct Variation
A direct variation is a relationship that can be represented by
a function of the form $y = kx$, where $k \neq 0$.

Slope-Intercept Form of a Linear Equation
The slope-intercept form of a linear equation is
$y = mx + b$, where m is the slope and b is the
y-intercept.

Point-Slope Form of a Linear Equation
The point-slope form of the equation of a nonvertical line
that passes through the point (x_1, y_1) with slope m is
$y - y_1 = m(x - x_1)$.

Standard Form of a Linear Equation
The standard form of a linear equation is $Ax + By = C$,
where A, B, and C are real numbers and A and B are not
both zero.

Slopes of Parallel Lines
Nonvertical lines are parallel if they have the same slope and
different y-intercepts. Any two vertical lines are parallel.

Slopes of Perpendicular Lines
Two lines are perpendicular if the product of their slopes is
-1. A vertical line and horizontal line are perpendicular.

Chapter 6 Systems of Equations and Inequalities

Solutions of Systems of Linear Equations
A system of linear equations can have one solution, no
solution, or infinitely many solutions:
- If the lines have different slopes, the lines intersect, so
  there is one solution.
- If the lines have the same slopes and different
  y-intercepts, the lines are parallel, so there are no
  solutions.
- If the lines have the same slopes and the same
  y-intercepts, the lines are the same, so there are infinitely
  many solutions.

Chapter 7 Exponents and Exponential Functions

Zero as an Exponent
For every nonzero number a, $a^0 = 1$.

Negative Exponent
For every nonzero number a and integer n, $a^{-n} = \frac{1}{a^n}$.

Scientific Notation
A number in scientific notation is written as the product of
two factors in the form $a \times 10^n$, where n is an integer and
$1 \le a < 10$.

Multiplying Powers With the Same Base
For every nonzero number a and integers m and n,
$a^m \cdot a^n = a^{m + n}$.

Dividing Powers With the Same Base
For every nonzero number a and integers m and n,
$\frac{a^m}{a^n} = a^{m - n}$.

Raising a Power to a Power
For every nonzero number a and integers m and n,
$(a^m)^n = a^{mn}$.

Raising a Product to a Power
For every nonzero number a and b and integer n,
$(ab)^n = a^n b^n$.

Raising a Quotient to a Power
For every nonzero number a and b and integer n,
$\left(\frac{a}{b}\right)^n = \frac{a^n}{b^n}$.

Geometric Sequence
The form for the rule of a geometric sequence is
$A(n) = a \cdot r^{n - 1}$, where $A(n)$ is the nth term, a is the first
term, n is the term number, and r is the common ratio.

Exponential Growth and Decay
An exponential function has the form $y = a \cdot b^x$, where a is a
nonzero constant, b is greater than 0 and not equal to 1, and
x is a real number.
- The function $y = a \cdot b^x$, where b is the growth factor,
  models exponential growth for $a > 0$ and $b > 1$.
- The function $y = a \cdot b^x$, where b is the decay factor,
  models exponential decay for $a > 0$ and $0 < b < 1$.

Chapter 8 Polynomials and Factoring

Factoring Special Cases
For every nonzero number a and b:
$a^2 - b^2 = (a + b)(a - b)$
$a^2 + 2ab + b^2 = (a + b)(a + b) = (a + b)^2$
$a^2 - 2ab + b^2 = (a - b)(a - b) = (a - b)^2$

Chapter 9 Quadratic Functions and Equations

Graph of a Quadratic Function
The graph of $y = ax^2 + bx + c$, where $a \neq 0$, has the line
$x = \frac{-b}{2a}$ as its axis of symmetry. The x-coordinate of the
vertex is $\frac{-b}{2a}$.

Zero-Product Property
For every real number a and b, if $ab = 0$, then
$a = 0$ or $b = 0$.

Quadratic Formula
If $ax^2 + bx + c = 0$, where $a \neq 0$, then
$x = \frac{-b \pm \sqrt{b^2 - 4ac}}{2a}$

Property of the Discriminant
For the quadratic equation $ax^2 + bx + c = 0$, where $a \neq 0$,
the value of the discriminant $b^2 - 4ac$ tells you the number
of solutions.
- If $b^2 - 4ac > 0$, there are two real solutions.
- If $b^2 - 4ac = 0$, there is one real solution.
- If $b^2 - 4ac < 0$, there are no real solutions.

Chapter 10 Radical Expressions and Equations

The Pythagorean Theorem
In a right triangle, the sum of the squares of the lengths
of the legs is equal to the square of the length of the
hypotenuse: $a^2 + b^2 = c^2$.

The Converse of the Pythagorean Theorem
If a triangle has sides of lengths a, b, and c, and
$a^2 + b^2 = c^2$, then the triangle is a right triangle with
hypotenuse of length c.

Multiplication Property of Square Roots
For every number $a \ge 0$ and $b \ge 0$, $\sqrt{ab} = \sqrt{a} \cdot \sqrt{b}$.

Division Property of Square Roots
For every number $a \ge 0$ and $b > 0$, $\sqrt{\frac{a}{b}} = \frac{\sqrt{a}}{\sqrt{b}}$.

Trigonometric Ratios
sine of $\angle A = \frac{\text{length of leg opposite } \angle A}{\text{length of hypotenuse}}$
cosine of $\angle A = \frac{\text{length of leg adjacent to } \angle A}{\text{length of hypotenuse}}$
tangent of $\angle A = \frac{\text{length of leg opposite } \angle A}{\text{length of leg adjacent to } \angle A}$

The Distance Formula
The distance d between any two points (x_1, y_1) and
(x_2, y_2) is $d = \sqrt{(x_2 - x_1)^2 + (y_2 - y_1)^2}$.

The Midpoint Formula
The midpoint M of a line segment with endpoints
$A(x_1, y_1)$ and $B(x_2, y_2)$ is $\left(\frac{x_1 + x_2}{2}, \frac{y_1 + y_2}{2}\right)$.

Chapter 11 Rational Expressions and Functions

Inverse Variation
An inverse variation is a relationship that can be represented
by a function of the form $y = \frac{k}{x}$, where $k \neq 0$.

Chapter 12 Data Analysis and Probability

Mean
The mean of a set of data values $= \frac{\text{sum of the data values}}{\text{total number of data values}}$.

Standard Deviation
Standard deviation is a measure of how the values in a data
set vary, or deviate from the mean.
$\sigma = \sqrt{\frac{\sum(x - \bar{x})^2}{n}}$

Multiplication Counting Principle
If there are m ways to make a first selection and n ways to
make a second selection, there are $m \cdot n$ ways to make the
two selections.

Permutation Notation
The expression $_nP_r$ represents the number of permutations of
n objects arranged r at a time.
$_nP_r = \frac{n!}{(n - r)!}$

Combination Notation
The expression $_nC_r$ represents the number of combinations
of n objects chosen r at a time.
$_nC_r = \frac{n!}{r!(n - r)!}$

Theoretical Probability
$P(\text{event}) = \frac{\text{number of favorable outcomes}}{\text{number of possible outcomes}}$

Probability of an Event and Its Complement
$P(\text{event}) + P(\text{not event}) = 1$, or
$P(\text{not event}) = 1 - P(\text{event})$

Odds
Odds in favor of an event $= \frac{\text{number of favorable outcomes}}{\text{number of unfavorable outcomes}}$
Odds against an event $= \frac{\text{number of unfavorable outcomes}}{\text{number of favorable outcomes}}$

Experimental Probability
$P(\text{event}) = \frac{\text{number of times the event occurs}}{\text{number of times the experiment is done}}$

Probability of Mutually Exclusive Events
If A and B are mutually exclusive events, then
$P(A \text{ or } B) = P(A) + P(B)$.

Probability of Overlapping Events
If A and B are overlapping events, then
$P(A \text{ or } B) = P(A) + P(B) - P(A \text{ and } B)$.

Probability of Two Independent Events
If A and B are independent events, then
$P(A \text{ and } B) = P(A) \cdot P(B)$.

Probability of Two Dependent Events
If A and B are independent events, then
$P(A \text{ and } B) = P(A) \cdot P(B \text{ after } A)$.

Formulas of **Geometry**

You will use a number of geometric formulas as you work through your algebra book. Here are some perimeter, area, and volume formulas.

Rectangle
$P = 2\ell + 2w$
$A = \ell w$

Square
$P = 4s$
$A = s^2$

Circle
$C = 2\pi r$ or $C = \pi d$
$A = \pi r^2$

Triangle
$A = \frac{1}{2}bh$

Parallelogram
$A = bh$

Trapezoid
$A = \frac{1}{2}(b_1 + b_2)h$

Right Prism
$V = Bh$
$V = \ell wh$

Pyramid
$V = \frac{1}{3}Bh$

Right Cylinder
$V = Bh$
$V = \pi r^2 h$

Right Cone
$V = \frac{1}{3}Bh$
$V = \frac{1}{3}\pi r^2 h$

Sphere
$V = \frac{4}{3}\pi r^3$

Visual Glossary

English   A   Spanish

Absolute value (p. 31) The distance that a number is from zero on a number line.

Valor absoluto (p. 31) La distancia a la que un número está del cero en una recta numérica.

Example -7 is 7 units from 0, so $|-7| = 7$.

Absolute value function (p. 342) A function with a V-shaped graph that opens up or down. The parent function for the family of absolute value functions is $y = |x|$.

Función de valor absoluto (p. 342) Función cuya gráfica forma una V que se abre hacia arriba o hacia abajo. La función madre de la familia de funciones de valor absoluto es $y = |x|$.

Example

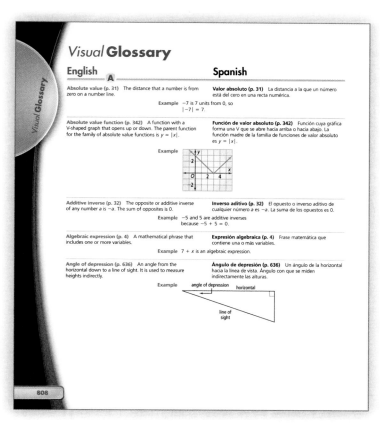

Additive inverse (p. 32) The opposite or additive inverse of any number a is $-a$. The sum of opposites is 0.

Inverso aditivo (p. 32) El opuesto o inverso aditivo de cualquier número a es $-a$. La suma de los opuestos es 0.

Example -5 and 5 are additive inverses because $-5 + 5 = 0$.

Algebraic expression (p. 4) A mathematical phrase that includes one or more variables.

Expresión algebraica (p. 4) Frase matemática que contiene una o más variables.

Example $7 + x$ is an algebraic expression.

Angle of depression (p. 636) An angle from the horizontal down to a line of sight. It is used to measure heights indirectly.

Ángulo de depresión (p. 636) Un ángulo de la horizontal hacia la línea de vista. Ángulo con que se miden indirectamente las alturas.

Example

English   Spanish

Angle of elevation (p. 636) An angle from the horizontal up to a line of sight. It is used to measure heights indirectly.

Ángulo de elevación (p. 636) Ángulo de la horizontal hacia la línea de vista. Ángulo con que se miden las alturas indirectamente.

Example

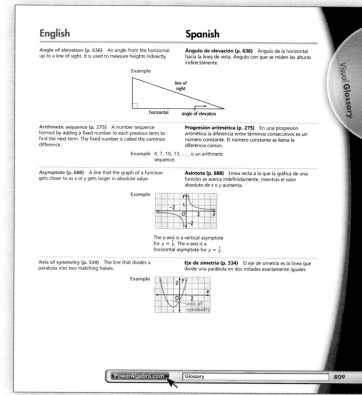

Arithmetic sequence (p. 275) A number sequence formed by adding a fixed number to each previous term to find the next term. The fixed number is called the common difference.

Progresión aritmética (p. 275) En una progresión aritmética la diferencia entre términos consecutivos es un número constante. El número constante se llama la diferencia común.

Example 4, 7, 10, 13, . . . is an arithmetic sequence.

Asymptote (p. 688) A line that the graph of a function gets closer to as x or y gets larger in absolute value.

Asíntota (p. 688) Línea recta a la que la gráfica de una función se acerca indefinidamente, mientras el valor absoluto de x o y aumenta.

Example

The y-axis is a vertical asymptote for $y = \frac{1}{x}$. The x-axis is a horizontal asymptote for $y = \frac{1}{x}$.

Axis of symmetry (p. 534) The line that divides a parabola into two matching halves.

Eje de simetría (p. 534) El eje de simetría es la línea que divide una parábola en dos mitades exactamente iguales.

Example

English   B   Spanish

Base (p. 10) A number that is multiplied repeatedly.

Base (p. 10) El número que se multiplica repetidas veces.

Example $4^5 = 4 \cdot 4 \cdot 4 \cdot 4 \cdot 4$. The base 4 is used as a factor 5 times.

Bias (p. 743) A sampling error that causes one option to seem better than another. Survey questions or samples can be biased.

Parcialidad (p. 743) Error de muestreo que hace que una opción parezca mejor que otra. Preguntas en una encuesta o muestras pueden ser parciales.

Binomial (p. 475) A polynomial of two terms.

Binomio (p. 475) Polinomio compuesto de dos términos.

Example $3x + 7$ is a binomial.

Bivariate (p. 742) A set of data that uses two variables is bivariate.

Bivariado (p. 742) Un conjunto de datos que usa dos variables es bivariado.

Box-and-whisker plot (p. 735) A graph that summarizes data along a number line. The left whisker extends from the minimum to the first quartile. The box extends from the first quartile to the third quartile and has a vertical line through the median. The right whisker extends from the third quartile to the maximum.

Gráfica de cajas (p. 735) Gráfica que resume los datos a lo largo de una recta numérica. El brazo izquierdo se extiende desde el valor mínimo del primer cuartil. La caja se extiende desde el primer cuartil hasta el tercer cuartil y tiene una línea vertical que atraviesa la mediana. El brazo derecho se extiende desde el tercer cuartil hasta el valor máximo.

Example

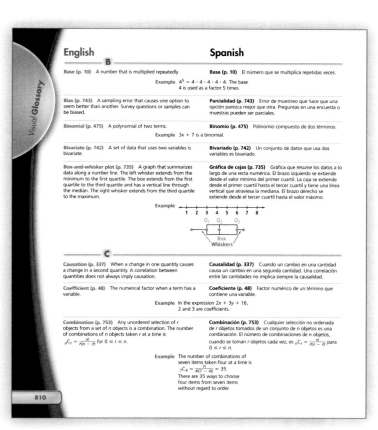

C

Causation (p. 337) When a change in one quantity causes a change in a second quantity. A correlation between quantities does not always imply causation.

Causalidad (p. 337) Cuando un cambio en una cantidad causa un cambio en una segunda cantidad. Una correlación entre las cantidades no implica siempre la causalidad.

Coefficient (p. 48) The numerical factor when a term has a variable.

Coeficiente (p. 48) Factor numérico de un término que contiene una variable.

Example In the expression $2x + 3y + 16$, 2 and 3 are coefficients.

Combination (p. 753) Any unordered selection of r objects from a set of n objects is a combination. The number of combinations of n objects taken r at a time is $_nC_r = \frac{n!}{r!(n-r)!}$ for $0 \le r \le n$.

Combinación (p. 753) Cualquier selección no ordenada de r objetos tomados de un conjunto de n objetos es una combinación. El número de combinaciones de n objetos, cuando se toman r objetos cada vez, es $_nC_r = \frac{n!}{r!(n-r)!}$ para $0 \le r \le n$.

Example The number of combinations of seven items taken four at a time is $_7C_4 = \frac{7!}{4!(7-4)!} = 35$. There are 35 ways to choose four items from seven items without regard to order.

English   Spanish

Common difference (p. 275) The difference between consecutive terms of an arithmetic sequence.

Diferencia común (p. 275) La diferencia común es la diferencia entre los términos consecutivos de una progresión aritmética.

Example The common difference is 3 in the arithmetic sequence 4, 7, 10, 13, . . .

Common ratio (p. 453) The fixed number used to find terms in a geometric sequence.

Razón común (p. 453) Número constante que se usa para hallar los términos en una progresión geométrica.

Example The common ratio is $\frac{1}{3}$ in the geometric sequence 9, 3, 1, $\frac{1}{3}$, . . .

Complement of an event (p. 758) All possible outcomes that are not in the event. P(complement of event) $= 1 - P$(event)

Complemento de un suceso (p. 758) Todos los resultados posibles que no se dan en el suceso. P(complemento de un suceso) $= 1 - P$(suceso)

Example The complement of rolling a 1 or a 2 on a number cube is rolling a 3, 4, 5, or 6.

Complement of a set (p. 196) The set of all elements in the universal set that are not in a given set.

Complemento de un conjunto (p. 196) Conjunto de todos los elementos en el conjunto universal que no se incluyen en el conjunto dado.

Example If $U = \{\ldots, -3, -2, -1, 0, 1, 2, 3, \ldots\}$ and $A = \{0, 1, 2, 3, \ldots\}$, then the complement of A is $A' = \{\ldots, -3, -2, -1\}$.

Completing the square (p. 561) A method of solving quadratic equations. Completing the square turns every quadratic equation into the form $x^2 = c$.

Completar el cuadrado (p. 561) Método para solucionar ecuaciones cuadráticas. Cuando se completa el cuadrado, se transforma la ecuación cuadrática a la fórmula $x^2 = c$.

Example $x^2 + 6x - 7 = 9$ is rewritten as $(x + 3)^2 = 25$ by completing the square.

Complex fraction (p. 516) A fraction that has a fraction in its numerator or denominator or in both its numerator and denominator.

Fracción compleja (p. 516) Una fracción compleja es una fracción que contiene otra fracción en el numerador o en el denominador, o en ambos.

Example $\frac{\frac{3}{4}}{\frac{5}{8}}$

Compound event (p. 764) An event that consists of two or more events linked by the word and or the word or.

Suceso compuesto (p. 764) Suceso que consiste en dos o más sucesos unidos por medio de la palabra y o la palabra o.

Examples Rolling a 5 on a number cube and then rolling a 4 is a compound event.

English | Spanish

Compound inequalities (p. 200) Two inequalities that are joined by *and* or *or*.

Desigualdades compuestas (p. 200) Dos desigualdades que están enlazadas por medio de una *y* o una *o*.

Examples $5 < x$ and $x < 10$
$14 < x$ or $x \le -3$

Compound interest (p. 456) Interest paid on both the principal and the interest that has already been paid.

Interés compuesto (p. 456) Interés calculado tanto sobre el capital como sobre los intereses ya pagados.

Example For an initial deposit of $1000 at a 6% interest rate with interest compounded quarterly, the function $y = 1000\left(\frac{0.06}{4}\right)^x$ gives the account balance y after x years.

Conclusion (p. 602) The conclusion is the part of an *if-then* statement (conditional) that follows *then*.

Conclusión (p. 602) La conclusión es lo que sigue a la palabra *entonces* en un enunciado condicional.

Example In the conditional "If an animal has four legs, then it is a horse," the conclusion is "it is a horse."

Conditional (p. 602) A conditional is an *if-then* statement.

Condicional (p. 602) Un enunciado condicional es del tipo *si . . . , entonces . . .*

Example If an animal has four legs, then it is a horse.

Conditional probability (p. 771) A probability that contains a condition that may limit the sample space for an event. The notation $P(B|A)$ is read "the probability of event B, given event A."

Probabilidad condicional (p. 771) Probabilidad que contiene una condición que puede limitar el espacio de muestra de un suceso. La notación $P(B|A)$ se lee "la probabilidad del suceso B, dado el suceso A."

Conjugates (p. 614) The sum and the difference of the same two terms.

Valores conjugados (p. 614) La suma y resta de los mismos dos términos.

Example $(\sqrt{3} + 2)$ and $(\sqrt{3} - 2)$ are conjugates.

Consistent system (p. 361) A system of equations that has at least one solution is consistent.

Sistema consistente (p. 361) Un sistema de ecuaciones que tiene por lo menos una solución es consistente.

Example

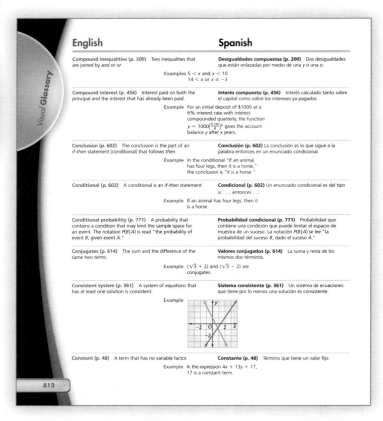

Constant (p. 48) A term that has no variable factor.

Constante (p. 48) Término que tiene un valor fijo.

Example In the expression $4x + 13y + 17$, 17 is a constant term.

English | Spanish

Constant of variation for direct variation (p. 299) The nonzero constant k in the function $y = kx$.

Constante de variación en variaciones directas (p. 299) La constante k cuyo valor no es cero en la función $y = kx$.

Example For the direct variation $y = 24x$, 24 is the constant of variation.

Constant of variation for inverse variation (p. 680) The nonzero constant k in the function $y = \frac{k}{x}$.

Constante de variación en variaciones inversas (p. 680) La constante k cuyo valor no es cero en la función $y = \frac{k}{x}$.

Example For the inverse variation $y = \frac{8}{x}$, 8 is the constant of variation.

Continuous graph (p. 255) A graph that is unbroken.

Gráfica continua (p. 255) Una gráfica continua es una gráfica ininterrumpida.

Example

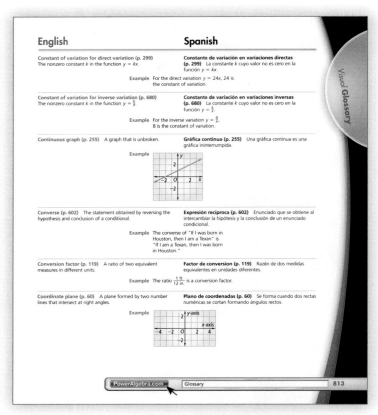

Converse (p. 602) The statement obtained by reversing the hypothesis and conclusion of a conditional.

Expresión recíproca (p. 602) Enunciado que se obtiene al intercambiar la hipótesis y la conclusión de un enunciado condicional.

Example The converse of "If I was born in Houston, then I am a Texan" is "If I am a Texan, then I was born in Houston."

Conversion factor (p. 119) A ratio of two equivalent measures in different units.

Factor de conversión (p. 119) Razón de dos medidas equivalentes en unidades diferentes.

Example The ratio $\frac{1\text{ ft}}{12\text{ in.}}$ is a conversion factor.

Coordinate plane (p. 60) A plane formed by two number lines that intersect at right angles.

Plano de coordenadas (p. 60) Se forma cuando dos rectas numéricas se cortan formando ángulos rectos.

Example

English | Spanish

Coordinates (p. 60) The numbers that make an ordered pair and identify the location of a point.

Coordenadas (p. 60) Números ordenados por pares que determinan la posición de un punto sobre un plano.

Example

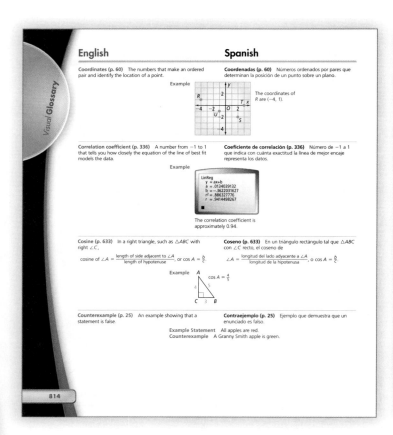

The coordinates of R are $(-4, 1)$.

Correlation coefficient (p. 336) A number from -1 to 1 that tells you how closely the equation of the line of best fit models the data.

Coeficiente de correlación (p. 336) Número de -1 a 1 que indica con cuánta exactitud la línea de mejor encaje representa los datos.

Example

LinReg
$y = ax+b$
$a = .01340039132$
$b = -.3622031627$
$r^2 = .886327776$
$r = .9414498267$

The correlation coefficient is approximately 0.94.

Cosine (p. 633) In a right triangle, such as $\triangle ABC$ with right $\angle C$,

Coseno (p. 633) En un triángulo rectángulo tal que $\triangle ABC$ con $\angle C$ recto, el coseno de

$\text{cosine of } \angle A = \frac{\text{length of side adjacent to } \angle A}{\text{length of hypotenuse}}$, or $\cos A = \frac{b}{c}$.

$\angle A = \frac{\text{longitud del lado adyacente a } \angle A}{\text{longitud de la hipotenusa}}$, o $\cos A = \frac{b}{c}$.

Example $\cos A = \frac{4}{5}$

Counterexample (p. 25) An example showing that a statement is false.

Contraejemplo (p. 25) Ejemplo que demuestra que un enunciado es falso.

Example Statement All apples are red.
Counterexample A Granny Smith apple is green.

English | Spanish

Cross product (of sets) (p. 220) The cross product of two sets A and B, denoted by $A \times B$, is the set of all ordered pairs with the first element in A and with the second element in B.

Producto cruzado (de dos conjuntos) (p. 220) El producto cruzado de dos conjuntos A y B, definido por $A \times B$, es el conjunto de todos los pares ordenados cuyo primer elemento está en A y cuyo segundo elemento está en B.

Cross products (of a proportion) (p. 125) In a proportion $\frac{a}{b} = \frac{c}{d}$, the products ad and bc. These products are equal.

Productos cruzados (de una proporción) (p. 125) En una proporción $\frac{a}{b} = \frac{c}{d}$, los productos ad y bc. Estos productos son iguales.

Example The cross products for $\frac{3}{4} = \frac{6}{8}$ are $3 \cdot 8$ and $4 \cdot 6$.

Cumulative frequency table (p. 722) A table that shows the number of data values that lie in or below the given intervals.

Tabla de frecuencia cumulativa (p. 722) Tabla que muestra el número de valores de datos que están dentro o por debajo de los intervalos dados.

Example

Interval	Frequency	Cumulative Frequency
0–9	5	5
10–19	8	13
20–29	4	17

— D —

Decay factor (p. 457) 1 minus the percent rate of change, expressed as a decimal, for an exponential decay situation.

Factor de decremento (p. 457) 1 menos la tasa porcentual de cambio, expresada como decimal, en una situación de reducción exponencial.

Example The decay factor of the function $y = 5(0.3)^x$ is 0.3.

Deductive reasoning (p. 25) A process of reasoning logically from given facts to a conclusion.

Razonamiento deductivo (p. 25) El razonamiento deductivo es un proceso de razonamiento lógico que parte de hechos dados hasta llegar a una conclusión.

Example Based on the fact that the sum of any two even numbers is even, you can deduce that the product of any whole number and any even number is even.

Degree of a monomial (p. 474) The sum of the exponents of the variables of a monomial.

Grado de un monomio (p. 474) La suma de los exponentes de las variables de un monomio.

Example $-4x^3y^2$ is a monomial of degree 5.

Degree of a polynomial (p. 475) The highest degree of any term of the polynomial.

Grado de un polinomio (p. 475) El grado de un polinomio es el grado mayor de cualquier término del polinomio.

Example The polynomial $P(x) = x^6 + 2x^3 - 3$ has degree 6.

English / Spanish

Page 816

Dependent events (p. 766) When the outcome of one event affects the probability of a second event, the events are dependent events.

Sucesos dependientes (p. 766) Dos sucesos son dependientes si el resultado de un suceso afecta la probabilidad del otro.

Example You have a bag with marbles of different colors. If you pick a marble from the bag and pick another without replacing the first, the events are dependent events.

Dependent system (p. 361) A system of equations that does not have a unique solution.

Sistema dependiente (p. 361) Sistema de ecuaciones que no tiene una solución única.

Example The system $\begin{cases} y = 2x + 3 \\ -4x + 2y = 6 \end{cases}$ represents two equations for the same line, so it has many solutions. It is a dependent system.

Dependent variable (p. 240) A variable that provides the output values of a function.

Variable dependiente (p. 240) Variable de la que dependen los valores de salida de una función.

Example In the equation $y = 3x$, y is the dependent variable.

Difference of squares (p. 513) A difference of two squares is an expression of the form $a^2 - b^2$. It can be factored as $(a + b)(a - b)$.

Diferencia de dos cuadrados (p. 513) La diferencia de dos cuadrados es una expresión de la forma $a^2 - b^2$. Se puede factorizar como $(a + b)(a - b)$.

Examples $25a^2 - 4 = (5a + 2)(5a - 2)$
$m^6 - 1 = (m^3 + 1)(m^3 - 1)$

Direct variation (p. 299) A linear function defined by an equation of the form $y = kx$, where $k \neq 0$.

Variación directa (p. 299) Una función lineal definida por una ecuación de la forma $y = kx$, donde $k \neq 0$, representa una variación directa.

Example $y = 18x$ is a direct variation.

Discrete graph (p. 255) A graph composed of isolated points.

Gráfica discreta (p. 255) Una gráfica discreta es compuesta de puntos aislados.

Example

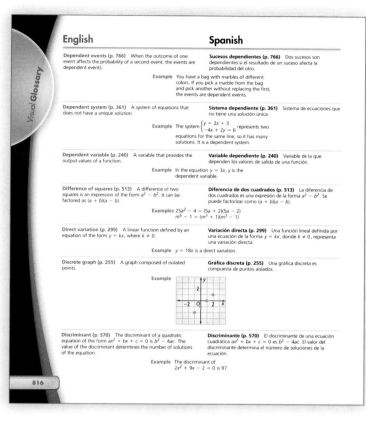

Discriminant (p. 570) The discriminant of a quadratic equation of the form $ax^2 + bx + c = 0$ is $b^2 - 4ac$. The value of the discriminant determines the number of solutions of the equation.

Discriminante (p. 570) El discriminante de una ecuación cuadrática $ax^2 + bx + c = 0$ es $b^2 - 4ac$. El valor del discriminante determina el número de soluciones de la ecuación.

Example The discriminant of $2x^2 + 9x - 2 = 0$ is 97.

Page 817

Disjoint sets (p. 215) Sets that do not have any elements in common.

Conjuntos ajenos (p. 215) Conjuntos que no tienen elementos en común.

Example The set of positive integers and the set of negative integers are disjoint sets.

Distance Formula (p. 605) The distance d between any two points (x_1, y_1) and (x_2, y_2) is $d = \sqrt{(x_2 - x_1)^2 + (y_2 - y_1)^2}$.

Fórmula de distancia (p. 605) La distancia d entre dos puntos cualesquiera (x_1, y_1) y (x_2, y_2) es $d = \sqrt{(x_2 - x_1)^2 + (y_2 - y_1)^2}$.

Example The distance between $(-2, 4)$ and $(4, 5)$ is
$d = \sqrt{(4 - (-2))^2 + (5 - 4)^2}$
$= \sqrt{(6)^2 + (1)^2}$
$= \sqrt{37}$

Distributive Property (p. 46) For every real number a, b, and c:
$a(b + c) = ab + ac \quad (b + c)a = ba + ca$
$a(b - c) = ab - ac \quad (b - c)a = ba - ca$

Propiedad Distributiva (p. 46) Para cada número real a, b y c:
$a(b + c) = ab + ac \quad (b + c)a = ba + ca$
$a(b - c) = ab - ac \quad (b - c)a = ba - ca$

Examples $3(19 + 4) = 3(19) + 3(4)$
$(19 + 4)3 = 19(3) + 4(3)$
$7(11 - 2) = 7(11) - 7(2)$
$(11 - 2)7 = 11(7) - 2(7)$

Domain (of a relation or function) (p. 268) The possible values for the input of a relation or function.

Dominio (de una relación o función) (p. 268) Posibles valores de entrada de una relación o función.

Example In the function $f(x) = x + 22$, the domain is all real numbers.

E

Element (of a matrix) (p. 714) An item in a matrix.

Elemento (de una matriz) (p. 714) Componente de una matriz.

Example $\begin{bmatrix} 5 & -2 \\ 7 & 3 \end{bmatrix}$
$5, 7, -2$, and 3 are the four elements of the matrix.

Elements (of a set) (p. 17) Members of a set.

Elementos (p. 17) Partes integrantes de un conjunto.

Example Cats and dogs are elements of the set of mammals.

Page 818

Elimination method (p. 374) A method for solving a system of linear equations. You add or subtract the equations to eliminate a variable.

Eliminación (p. 374) Método para resolver un sistema de ecuaciones lineales. Se suman o se restan las ecuaciones para eliminar una variable.

Example $3x + y = 19$
$2x - y = 1$
$5x + 0 = 20$ Add the equations to get $x = 4$.
$2(4) - y = 1 \rightarrow$ Substitute 4 for x in the second equation.
$8 - y = 1$
$y = 7 \rightarrow$ Solve for y.

Empty set (p. 195) A set that does not contain any elements.

Conjunto vacío (p. 195) Conjunto que no contiene elementos.

Example The intersection of the set of positive integers and the set of negative integers is the empty set.

Equation (p. 53) A mathematical sentence that uses an equal sign.

Ecuación (p. 53) Enunciado matemático que tiene el signo de igual.

Example $x + 5 = 3x - 7$

Equivalent equations (p. 81) Equations that have the same solution.

Ecuaciones equivalentes (p. 81) Ecuaciones que tienen la misma solución.

Example $\frac{a}{3} = 3$ and $\frac{a}{3} + a = 3 + a$ are equivalent equations.

Equivalent expressions (p. 23) Algebraic expressions that have the same value for all values of the variable(s).

Ecuaciones equivalentes (p. 23) Expresiones algebraicas que tienen el mismo valor para todos los valores de la(s) variable(s).

Example $3a + 2a$ and $5a$ are equivalent expressions.

Equivalent inequalities (p. 171) Inequalities that have the same set of solutions.

Desigualdades equivalentes (p. 171) Las desigualdades tienen el mismo conjunto de soluciones.

Example $x + 4 < 7$ and $x < 3$ are equivalent inequalities.

Evaluate (p. 12) To substitute a given number for each variable, and then simplify.

Evaluar (p. 12) Método de sustituir cada variable por un número dado para luego simplificar la expresión.

Example To evaluate $3x + 4$ for $x = 2$, substitute 2 for x and simplify.
$3(2) + 4 = 6 + 4 = 10$

Page 819

Event (p. 757) Any group of outcomes in a situation involving probability.

Suceso (p. 757) En la probabilidad, cualquier grupo de resultados.

Example When rolling a number cube, there are six possible outcomes. Rolling an even number is an event with three possible outcomes, 2, 4, and 6.

Excluded value (p. 646) A value of x for which a rational expression $f(x)$ is undefined.

Valor excluido (p. 646) Valor de x para el cual una expresión racional es indefinida.

Experimental probability (p. 759) The ratio of the number of times an event actually happens to the number of times the experiment is done.
$P(\text{event}) = \frac{\text{number of times an event happens}}{\text{number of times the experiment is done}}$

Probabilidad experimental (p. 759) La razón entre el número de veces que un suceso sucede en la realidad y el número de veces que se hace el experimento.
$P(\text{suceso}) = \frac{\text{número de veces que sucede un suceso}}{\text{número de veces que se hace el experimento}}$

Example A baseball player's batting average shows how likely it is that a player will get a hit, based on previous times at bat.

Exponent (p. 10) A number that shows repeated multiplication.

Exponente (p. 10) Denota el número de veces que debe multiplicarse.

Example $3^4 = 3 \cdot 3 \cdot 3 \cdot 3$
The exponent 4 indicates that 3 is used as a factor four times.

Exponential decay (p. 457) A situation modeled with a function of the form $y = ab^x$, where $a > 0$ and $0 < b < 1$.

Decremento exponencial (p. 457) Para $a > 0$ y $0 < b < 1$, la función $y = ab^x$ representa el decremento exponencial.

Example $y = 5(0.1)^x$

Exponential function (p. 447) A function that repeatedly multiplies an initial amount by the same positive number. You can model all exponential functions using $y = ab^x$, where a is a nonzero constant, $b > 0$, and $b \neq 1$.

Función exponencial (p. 447) Función que multiplica repetidas veces una cantidad inicial por el mismo número positivo. Todas las funciones exponenciales se pueden representar mediante $y = ab^x$, donde a es una constante con valor distinto de cero, $b > 0$ y $b \neq 1$.

Example

Exponential growth (p. 455) A situation modeled with a function of the form $y = ab^x$, where $a > 0$ and $b > 1$.

Incremento exponencial (p. 455) Para $a > 0$ y $b > 1$, la función $y = ab^x$ representa el incremento exponencial.

Example $y = 100(2)^x$

English | Spanish

Extraneous solution (p. 622) A solution of an equation derived from an original equation that is not a solution of the original equation.

Example $\frac{b}{b+4} = 3 - \frac{4}{b+4}$

$b = 3(b+4) - 4$ Multiply by $(b+4)$.

$b = 3b + 12 - 4$

$-2b = 8$

$b = -4$

Replace b with -4 in the original equation. The denominator is 0, so -4 is an extraneous solution.

Solución extraña (p. 622) Una solución extraña es una solución de una ecuación derivada que no es una solución de la ecuación original.

Extrapolation (p. 334) The process of predicting a value outside the range of known values.

Extrapolación (p. 334) Proceso que se usa para predecir un valor por fuera del ámbito de los valores dados.

F

Factor by grouping (p. 517) A method of factoring that uses the Distributive Property to remove a common binomial factor of two pairs of terms.

Example The expression $7x(x - 1) + 4(x - 1)$ can be factored as $(7x + 4)(x - 1)$.

Factor común por agrupación de términos (p. 517) Método de factorización que aplica la propiedad distributiva para sacar un factor común de dos pares de términos en un binomio.

Formula (p. 110) An equation that states a relationship among quantities.

Example The formula for the volume V of a cylinder is $V = \pi r^2 h$, where r is the radius of the cylinder and h is its height.

Fórmula (p. 110) Ecuación que establece una relación entre cantidades.

Frequency (p. 720) The number of data items in an interval.

Example In the data set 4, 7, 12, 4, 5, 8, 11, 2, the frequency of the interval 5–9 is 3.

Frecuencia (p. 720) Número de datos de un intervalo.

Frequency table (p. 720) A table that groups a set of data values into intervals and shows the frequency for each interval.

Example

Interval	Frequency
0–9	5
10–19	8
20–29	4

Tabla de frecuencias (p. 720) Tabla que agrupa un conjunto de datos en intervalos y muestra la frecuencia de cada intervalo.

English | Spanish

Function (p. 241) A relation that assigns exactly one value in the range to each value of the domain.

Example Earned income is a function of the number of hours worked. If you earn $4.50/h, then your income is expressed by the function $f(h) = 4.5h$.

Función (p. 241) La relación que asigna exactamente un valor del rango a cada valor del dominio.

Function notation (p. 269) To write a rule in function notation, you use the symbol $f(x)$ in place of y.

Example $f(x) = 3x - 8$ is in function notation.

Notación de una función (p. 269) Para expresar una regla en notación de función se usa el símbolo $f(x)$ en lugar de y.

Function rule (p. 262) An equation that describes a function.

Example $y = 4x + 1$ is a function rule.

Regla de función (p. 262) Ecuación que describe una función.

G

Geometric sequence (p. 453) A number sequence formed by multiplying a term in a sequence by a fixed number to find the next term.

Example 9, 3, 1, $\frac{1}{3}$, . . . is an example of a geometric sequence.

Progresión geométrica (p. 453) Tipo de sucesión numérica formada al multiplicar un término de la secuencia por un número constante, para hallar el siguiente término.

Growth factor (p. 455) 1 plus the percent rate of change for an exponential growth situation.

Example The growth factor of $y = 7(1.3)^x$ is 1.3.

Factor incremental (p. 455) 1 más la tasa porcentual de cambio en una situación de incremento exponencial.

H

Histogram (p. 721) A special type of bar graph that can display data from a frequency table. Each bar represents an interval. The height of each bar shows the frequency of the interval it represents.

Example

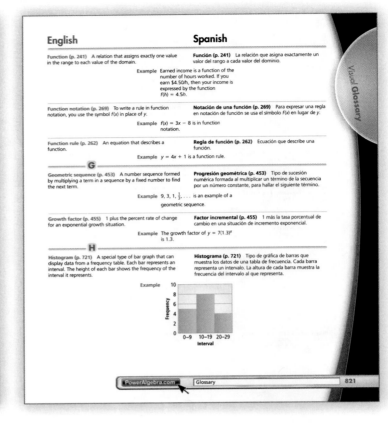

Histograma (p. 721) Tipo de gráfica de barras que muestra los datos de una tabla de frecuencia. Cada barra representa un intervalo. La altura de cada barra muestra la frecuencia del intervalo al que representa.

English | Spanish

Hypotenuse (p. 600) The side opposite the right angle in a right triangle. It is the longest side in the triangle.

Example

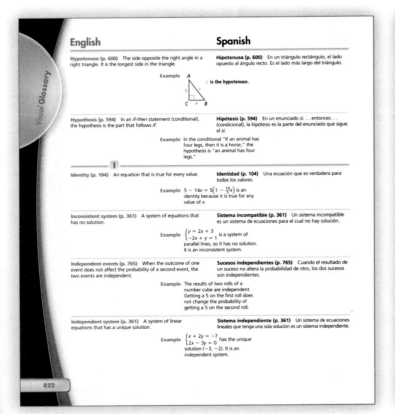

c is the hypotenuse.

Hipotenusa (p. 600) En un triángulo rectángulo, el lado opuesto al ángulo recto. Es el lado más largo del triángulo.

Hypothesis (p. 594) In an *if-then* statement (conditional), the hypothesis is the part that follows *if*.

Example In the conditional "If an animal has four legs, then it is a horse," the hypothesis is "an animal has four legs."

Hipótesis (p. 594) En un enunciado *sí. . . entonces. . .* (condicional), la hipótesis es la parte del enunciado que sigue el *sí*.

I

Identity (p. 104) An equation that is true for every value.

Example $5 - 14x = 5\left(1 - \frac{14}{5}x\right)$ is an identity because it is true for any value of x.

Identidad (p. 104) Una ecuación que es verdadera para todos los valores.

Inconsistent system (p. 361) A system of equations that has no solution.

Example $\begin{cases} y = 2x + 3 \\ -2x + y = 1 \end{cases}$ is a system of parallel lines, so it has no solution. It is an inconsistent system.

Sistema incompatible (p. 361) Un sistema incompatible es un sistema de ecuaciones para el cual no hay solución.

Independent events (p. 765) When the outcome of one event does not affect the probability of a second event, the two events are independent.

Example The results of two rolls of a number cube are independent. Getting a 5 on the first roll does not change the probability of getting a 5 on the second roll.

Sucesos independientes (p. 765) Cuando el resultado de un suceso no altera la probabilidad de otro, los sucesos son independientes.

Independent system (p. 361) A system of linear equations that has a unique solution.

Example $\begin{cases} x + 2y = -7 \\ 2x - 3y = 0 \end{cases}$ has the unique solution $(-3, -2)$. It is an independent system.

Sistema independiente (p. 361) Un sistema de ecuaciones lineales que tenga una sola solución es un sistema independiente.

English | Spanish

Independent variable (p. 240) A variable that provides the input values of a function.

Example In the equation $y = 3x$, x is the independent variable.

Variable independiente (p. 240) Variable de la que dependen los valores de entrada de una función.

Inductive reasoning (p. 63) Making conclusions based on observed patterns.

Razonamiento inductivo (p. 63) Sacar conclusiones a partir de patrones observados.

Inequality (p. 19) A mathematical sentence that compares the values of two expressions using an inequality symbol.

Example $3 < 7$

Desigualdad (p. 19) Expresión matemática que compara el valor de dos expresiones con el símbolo de desigualdad.

Input (p. 240) A value of the independent variable.

Example The input is any value of x you substitute into a function.

Entrada (p. 240) Valor de una variable independiente.

Integers (p. 18) Whole numbers and their opposites.

Example . . . -3, -2, -1, 0, 1, 2, 3, . . .

Números enteros (p. 18) Números que constan exclusivamente de una o más unidades, y sus opuestos.

Interpolation (p. 334) The process of estimating a value between two known quantities.

Interpolación (p. 334) Proceso que se usa para estimar el valor entre dos cantidades dadas.

Interquartile range (p. 734) The interquartile range of a set of data is the difference between the third and first quartiles.

Example The first and third quartiles of the data set 2, 3, 4, 5, 5, 6, 7, and 7 are 3.5 and 6.5. The interquartile range is $6.5 - 3.5 = 3$.

Intervalo intercuartil (p. 734) El rango intercuartil de un conjunto de datos es la diferencia entre el tercero y el primer cuartiles.

Intersection (p. 215) The set of elements that are common to two or more sets.

Example If $C = \{1, 2, 3, 4\}$ and $D = \{2, 4, 6, 8\}$, then the intersection of C and D, or $C \cap D$, is $\{2, 4\}$.

Intersección (p. 215) El conjunto de elementos que son comunes a dos o más conjuntos.

Interval notation (p. 203) A notation for describing an interval on a number line. The interval's endpoint(s) are given, and a parenthesis or bracket is used to indicate whether each endpoint is included in the interval.

Example For $-2 \le x < 8$, the interval notation is $[-2, 8)$.

Notación de intervalo (p. 203) Notación que describe un intervalo en una recta numérica. Los extremos del intervalo se incluyen y se usan un paréntesis o corchete para indicar si cada extremo está incluido en el intervalo.

English | Spanish

Inverse operations (p. 82) Operations that undo one another.

Operaciones inversas (p. 82) Las operaciones que se cancelan una a la otra.

Example Addition and subtraction are inverse operations. Multiplication and division are inverse operations.

Inverse variation (p. 680) An equation of the form $xy = k$ or $y = \frac{k}{x}$, where $k \neq 0$, is an inverse variation with constant of variation k.

Variación inversa (p. 680) La ecuación $y = \frac{k}{x}$, ó $xy = k$, donde $k \neq 0$, es una variación inversa con una constante de variación k.

Example The length x and the width y of a rectangle with a fixed area vary inversely. If the area is 40, $xy = 40$.

Irrational number (p. 18) A number that cannot be written as a ratio of two integers. Irrational numbers in decimal form are nonterminating and nonrepeating.

Número irracional (p. 18) Número que no puede expresarse como razón de dos números enteros. Los números irracionales en forma decimal no tienen término y no se repiten.

Example $\sqrt{11}$ and π are irrational numbers.

Isolate (p. 82) Using properties of equality and inverse operations to get a variable with a coefficient of 1 alone on one side of the equation.

Aislar (p. 82) Usar propiedades de igualdad y operaciones inversas para poner una variable con un coeficiente de 1 sola a un lado de la ecuación.

Example
$$x + 3 = 7$$
$$x + 3 - 3 = 7 - 3$$
$$x = 4$$

L

Leg (p. 600) Each of the sides that form the right angle of a right triangle.

Cateto (p. 600) Cada uno de los dos lados que forman el ángulo recto en un triángulo rectángulo.

Example

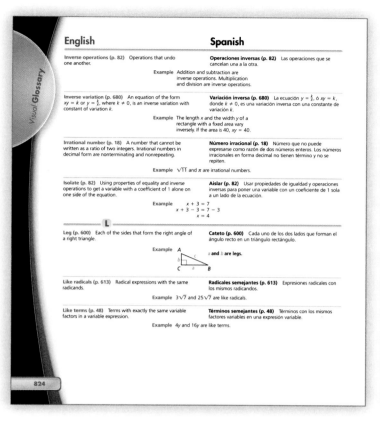

a and b are legs.

Like radicals (p. 613) Radical expressions with the same radicands.

Radicales semejantes (p. 613) Expresiones radicales con los mismos radicandos.

Example $3\sqrt{7}$ and $25\sqrt{7}$ are like radicals.

Like terms (p. 48) Terms with exactly the same variable factors in a variable expression.

Términos semejantes (p. 48) Términos con los mismos factores en una expresión variable.

Example $4y$ and $16y$ are like terms.

English | Spanish

Linear equation (p. 306) An equation whose graph forms a straight line.

Ecuación lineal (p. 306) Ecuación cuya gráfica es una línea recta.

Example

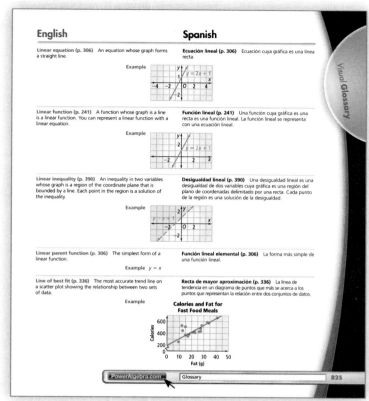

Linear function (p. 241) A function whose graph is a line is a linear function. You can represent a linear function with a linear equation.

Función lineal (p. 241) Una función cuya gráfica es una recta a una función lineal. La función lineal se representa con una ecuación lineal.

Example

Linear inequality (p. 390) An inequality in two variables whose graph is a region of the coordinate plane that is bounded by a line. Each point in the region is a solution of the inequality.

Desigualdad lineal (p. 390) Una desigualdad lineal es una desigualdad de dos variables cuya gráfica es una región del plano de coordenadas delimitado por una recta. Cada punto de la región es una solución de la desigualdad.

Example

Linear parent function (p. 306) The simplest form of a linear function.

Función lineal elemental (p. 306) La forma más simple de una función lineal.

Example $y = x$

Line of best fit (p. 336) The most accurate trend line on a scatter plot showing the relationship between two sets of data.

Recta de mayor aproximación (p. 336) La línea de tendencia en un diagrama de puntos que más se acerca a los puntos que representan la relación entre dos conjuntos de datos.

Example

Calories and Fat for Fast Food Meals

English | Spanish

Literal equation (p. 109) An equation involving two or more variables.

Ecuación literal (p. 109) Ecuación que incluye dos o más variables.

Example $4x + 2y = 18$ is a literal equation.

M

Matrix (p. 714) A matrix is a rectangular array of numbers written within brackets. A matrix with m horizontal rows and n vertical columns is an $m \times n$ matrix.

Matriz (p. 714) Una matriz es un conjunto de números encerrados en corchetes y dispuestos en forma de rectángulo. Una matriz que contenga m filas y n columnas es una matriz $m \times n$.

Example $\begin{bmatrix} 2 & 5 & 6.3 \\ -8 & 0 & -1 \end{bmatrix}$ is a 2×3 matrix.

Maximum (p. 535) The y-coordinate of the vertex of a parabola that opens downward.

Valor máximo (p. 535) La coordenada y del vértice en una parábola que se abre hacia abajo.

Example

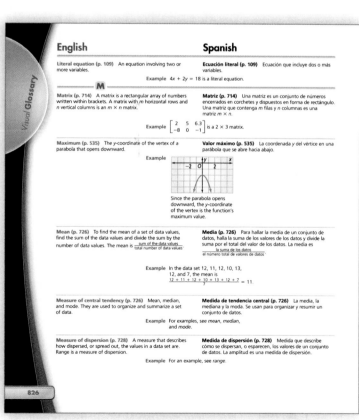

Since the parabola opens downward, the y-coordinate of the vertex is the function's maximum value.

Mean (p. 726) To find the mean of a set of data values, find the sum of the data values and divide the sum by the number of data values. The mean is $\frac{\text{sum of the data values}}{\text{total number of data values}}$.

Media (p. 726) Para hallar la media de un conjunto de datos, halla la suma de los valores de los datos y divide la suma por el total del valor de los datos. La media es $\frac{\text{la suma de los datos}}{\text{el número total de valores de datos}}$.

Example In the data set 12, 11, 12, 10, 13, 12, and 7, the mean is
$$\frac{12 + 11 + 12 + 10 + 13 + 12 + 7}{7} = 11$$

Measure of central tendency (p. 726) Mean, median, and mode. They are used to organize and summarize a set of data.

Medida de tendencia central (p. 726) La media, la mediana y la moda. Se usan para organizar y resumir un conjunto de datos.

Example For examples, see mean, median, and mode.

Measure of dispersion (p. 728) A measure that describes how dispersed, or spread out, the values in a data set are. Range is a measure of dispersion.

Medida de dispersión (p. 728) Medida que describe cómo se dispersan, o esparecen, los valores de un conjunto de datos. La amplitud es una medida de dispersión.

Example For an example, see range.

English | Spanish

Median (p. 726) The middle value in an ordered set of numbers.

Mediana (p. 726) El valor del medio en un conjunto ordenado de números.

Example In the data set 7, 10, 11, 12, 12, 12, and 13, the median is 12.

Midpoint (p. 605) The point M that divides a segment $\overline{AB}$ into two equal segments, $\overline{AM}$ and $\overline{MB}$.

Punto medio (p. 605) El punto M que divide un segmento $\overline{AB}$ en dos segmentos iguales, $\overline{AM}$ y $\overline{MB}$.

Example M is the midpoint of $\overline{XY}$.

Midpoint Formula (p. 605) The midpoint M of a line segment with endpoints $A(x_1, y_1)$ and $B(x_2, y_2)$ is $\left(\frac{x_1 + x_2}{2}, \frac{y_1 + y_2}{2} \right)$.

Fórmula del punto medio (p. 605) El punto medio M de un segmento con puntos extremos $A(x_1, y_1)$ y $B(x_2, y_2)$ es $\left(\frac{x_1 + x_2}{2}, \frac{y_1 + y_2}{2} \right)$.

Example The midpoint of a segment with endpoints $A(3, 5)$ and $B(7, 1)$ is $(5, 3)$.

Minimum (p. 535) The y-coordinate of the vertex of a parabola that opens upward.

Valor mínimo (p. 535) La coordenada y del vértice en una parábola que se abre hacia arriba.

Example

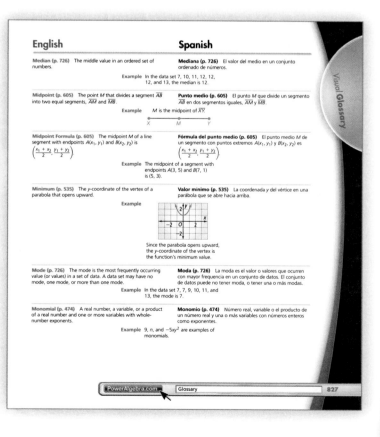

Since the parabola opens upward, the y-coordinate of the vertex is the function's minimum value.

Mode (p. 726) The mode is the most frequently occurring value (or values) in a set of data. A data set may have no mode, one mode, or more than one mode.

Moda (p. 726) La moda es el valor o valores que ocurren con mayor frecuencia en un conjunto de datos. El conjunto de datos puede no tener moda, o tener una o más modas.

Example In the data set 7, 7, 9, 10, 11, and 13, the mode is 7.

Monomial (p. 474) A real number, a variable, or a product of a real number and one or more variables with whole-number exponents.

Monomio (p. 474) Número real, variable o el producto de un número real y una o más variables con números enteros como exponentes.

Example 9, n, and $-5xy^2$ are examples of monomials.

English | Spanish

Multiplication Counting Principle (p. 751) If there are *m* ways to make the first selection and *n* ways to make the second selection, then there are *m* · *n* ways to make the two selections.

Principio de Conteo en la Multiplicación (p. 751) Si hay *m* maneras de hacer la primera selección y *n* maneras de hacer la segunda selección, quiere decir que hay *m* · *n* maneras de hacer las dos selecciones.

Example For 5 shirts and 8 pairs of shorts, the number of possible outfits is $5 \cdot 8 = 40$.

Multiplicative inverse (p. 40) Given a nonzero rational number $\frac{a}{b}$, the multiplicative inverse, or reciprocal, is $\frac{b}{a}$. The product of a nonzero number and its multiplicative inverse is 1.

Inverso multiplicativo (p. 40) Dado un número racional distinto de cero, el inverso multiplicativo, o recíproco, es $\frac{b}{a}$. El producto de un número distinto de cero y su inverso multiplicativo es 1.

Example $\frac{4}{3}$ is the multiplicative inverse of $\frac{3}{4}$ because $\frac{3}{4} \times \frac{4}{3} = 1$.

Mutually exclusive events (p. 764) When two events cannot happen at the same time, the events are mutually exclusive. If *A* and *B* are mutually exclusive events, then $P(A \text{ or } B) = P(A) + P(B)$.

Sucesos mutuamente excluyentes (p. 764) Cuando dos sucesos no pueden ocurrir al mismo tiempo, son mutuamente excluyentes. Si *A* y *B* son sucesos mutuamente excluyentes, entonces $P(A \text{ o } B) = P(A) + P(B)$.

Example Rolling an even number *E* and rolling a multiple of five *M* on a standard number cube are mutually exclusive events.

$$P(E \text{ or } M) = P(E) + P(M)$$
$$= \frac{3}{6} + \frac{1}{6}$$
$$= \frac{4}{6}$$
$$= \frac{2}{3}$$

--- **N** ---

Natural numbers (p. 18) The counting numbers.

Números naturales (p. 18) Los números que se emplean para contar.

Example 1, 2, 3, . . .

Negative correlation (p. 333) The relationship between two sets of data, in which one set of data decreases as the other set of data increases.

Correlación negativa (p. 333) Relación entre dos conjuntos de datos en la que uno de los conjuntos disminuye a medida que el otro aumenta.

Example
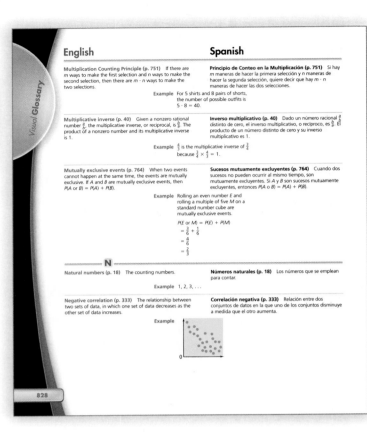

English | Spanish

Negative square root (p. 39) A number of the form $-\sqrt{b}$, which is the negative square root of *b*.

Raíz cuadrada negativa (p. 39) $-\sqrt{b}$ es la raíz cuadrada negativa de *b*.

Example -7 is the negative square root of $\sqrt{49}$.

n factorial (p. 752) The product of the integers from *n* down to 1, for any positive integer *n*. You write *n* factorial as *n*!. The value of 0! is defined to be 1.

n factorial (p. 752) Producto de todos los enteros desde *n* hasta 1, de cualquier entero positivo *n*. El factorial de *n* se escribe *n*!. El valor de 0! se define como 1.

Example $4! = 4 \times 3 \times 2 \times 1 = 24$

No correlation (p. 333) There does not appear to be a relationship between two sets of data.

Sin correlación (p. 333) No hay relación entre dos conjuntos de datos.

Example
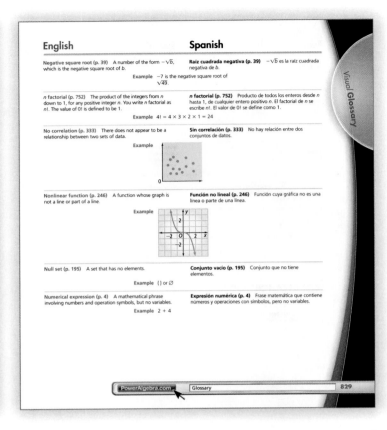

Nonlinear function (p. 246) A function whose graph is not a line or part of a line.

Función no lineal (p. 246) Función cuya gráfica no es una línea o parte de una línea.

Example

Null set (p. 195) A set that has no elements.

Conjunto vacío (p. 195) Conjunto que no tiene elementos.

Example { } or ∅

Numerical expression (p. 4) A mathematical phrase involving numbers and operation symbols, but no variables.

Expresión numérica (p. 4) Frase matemática que contiene números y operaciones con símbolos, pero no variables.

Example $2 + 4$

English O | Spanish

Odds (p. 759) A ratio that compares the number of favorable and unfavorable outcomes. Odds in favor are number of favorable outcomes : number of unfavorable outcomes. Odds against are number of unfavorable outcomes : number of favorable outcomes.

Probabilidad a favor (p. 759) Razón que compara el número de resultados favorables y no favorables. Las posibilidades a favor son el número de resultados favorables : número de resultados no favorables. Las posibilidades en contra son el número de resultados no favorables : número de resultados favorables.

Example You have 3 red marbles and 5 blue marbles. The odds in favor of selecting red are 3 : 5.

Open sentence (p. 53) An equation that contains one or more variables and may be true or false depending on the value of its variables.

Enunciado abierto (p. 53) Una ecuación es un enunciado abierto si contiene una o más variables y puede ser verdadera o falsa dependiendo del valor de sus variables.

Example $5 + x = 12$ is an open sentence.

Opposite (p. 32) A number that is the same distance from zero on the number line as a given number, but lies in the opposite direction.

Opuestos (p. 32) Dos números son opuestos si están a la misma distancia del cero en la recta numérica, pero en sentido opuesto.

Example -3 and 3 are opposites.

Opposite reciprocals (p. 328) A number of the form $-\frac{b}{a}$, where $\frac{a}{b}$ is a nonzero rational number. The product of a number and its opposite reciprocal is -1.

Recíproco inverso (p. 328) Número en la forma $-\frac{b}{a}$, donde $\frac{a}{b}$ es un número racional diferente de cero. El producto de un número y su recíproco inverso es -1.

Example $\frac{2}{5}$ and $-\frac{5}{2}$ are opposite reciprocals because $\left(\frac{2}{5}\right)\left(-\frac{5}{2}\right) = -1$.

Ordered pair (p. 60) Two numbers that identify the location of a point.

Par ordenado (p. 60) Un par ordenado de números que denota la ubicación de un punto.

Example The ordered pair $(4, -1)$ identifies the point 4 units to the right on the *x*-axis and 1 unit down on the *y*-axis.

Order of operations (p. 11)
1. Perform any operation(s) inside grouping symbols.
2. Simplify powers.
3. Multiply and divide in order from left to right.
4. Add and subtract in order from left to right.

Orden de las operaciones (p. 11)
1. Se hacen las operaciones que están dentro de símbolos de agrupación.
2. Se simplifican todos los términos que tengan exponentes.
3. Se hacen las multiplicaciones y divisiones en orden de izquierda a derecha.
4. Se hacen las sumas y restas en orden de izquierda a derecha.

Example $6 - (4^2 - [2 \cdot 5]) \div 3$
$= 6 - (16 - 10) \div 3$
$= 6 - 6 \div 3$
$= 6 - 2$
$= 4$

English | Spanish

Origin (p. 60) The point at which the axes of the coordinate plane intersect.

Origen (p. 60) Punto de intersección de los ejes del plano de coordenadas.

Example
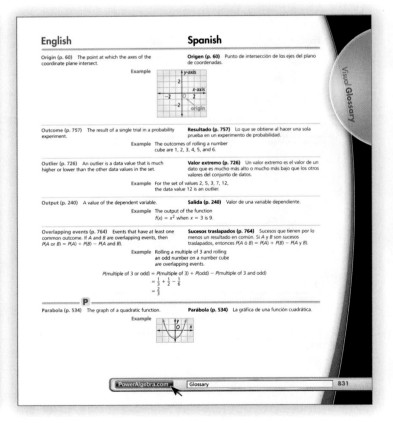

Outcome (p. 757) The result of a single trial in a probability experiment.

Resultado (p. 757) Lo que se obtiene al hacer una sola prueba en un experimento de probabilidad.

Example The outcomes of rolling a number cube are 1, 2, 3, 4, 5, and 6.

Outlier (p. 726) An outlier is a data value that is much higher or lower than the other data values in the set.

Valor extremo (p. 726) Un valor extremo es el valor de un dato que es mucho más alto o mucho más bajo que los otros valores del conjunto de datos.

Example For the set of values 2, 5, 3, 7, 12, the data value 12 is an outlier.

Output (p. 240) A value of the dependent variable.

Salida (p. 240) Valor de una variable dependiente.

Example The output of the function $f(x) = x^2$ when $x = 3$ is 9.

Overlapping events (p. 764) Events that have at least one common outcome. If *A* and *B* are overlapping events, then $P(A \text{ or } B) = P(A) + P(B) - P(A \text{ and } B)$.

Sucesos traslapados (p. 764) Sucesos que tienen por lo menos un resultado en común. Si *A* y *B* son sucesos traslapados, entonces $P(A \text{ ó } B) = P(A) + P(B) - P(A \text{ y } B)$.

Example Rolling a multiple of 3 and rolling an odd number on a number cube are overlapping events.

$P(\text{multiple of 3 or odd}) = P(\text{multiple of 3}) + P(\text{odd}) - P(\text{multiple of 3 and odd})$
$= \frac{1}{3} + \frac{1}{2} - \frac{1}{6}$
$= \frac{2}{3}$

--- **P** ---

Parabola (p. 534) The graph of a quadratic function.

Parábola (p. 534) La gráfica de una función cuadrática.

Example

English | Spanish

Parallel lines (p. 327) Two lines in the same plane that never intersect. Parallel lines have the same slope.

Rectas paralelas (p. 327) Dos rectas situadas en el mismo plano que nunca se cortan. Las rectas paralelas tienen la misma pendiente

Example

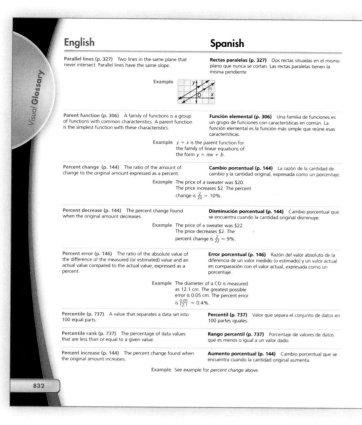

Parent function (p. 306) A family of functions is a group of functions with common characteristics. A parent function is the simplest function with these characteristics.

Función elemental (p. 306) Una familia de funciones es un grupo de funciones con características en común. La función elemental es la función más simple que reúne esas características.

Example $y = x$ is the parent function for the family of linear equations of the form $y = mx + b$.

Percent change (p. 144) The ratio of the amount of change to the original amount expressed as a percent.

Cambio porcentual (p. 144) La razón de la cantidad de cambio y la cantidad original, expresada como un porcentaje.

Example The price of a sweater was $20. The price increases $2. The percent change is $\frac{2}{20} = 10\%$.

Percent decrease (p. 144) The percent change found when the original amount decreases.

Disminución porcentual (p. 144) Cambio porcentual que se encuentra cuando la cantidad original disminuye.

Example The price of a sweater was $22. The price decreases $2. The percent change is $\frac{2}{22} \approx 9\%$.

Percent error (p. 146) The ratio of the absolute value of the difference of the measured (or estimated) value and an actual value compared to the actual value, expressed as a percent.

Error porcentual (p. 146) Razón del valor absoluto de la diferencia de un valor medido (o estimado) y un valor actual en comparación con el valor actual, expresada como un porcentaje.

Example The diameter of a CD is measured as 12.1 cm. The greatest possible error is 0.05 cm. The percent error is $\frac{0.05}{12.1} \approx 0.4\%$.

Percentile (p. 737) A value that separates a data set into 100 equal parts.

Percentil (p. 737) Valor que separa el conjunto de datos en 100 partes iguales.

Percentile rank (p. 737) The percentage of data values that are less than or equal to a given value.

Rango percentil (p. 737) Porcentaje de valores de datos que son menos o igual a un valor dado.

Percent increase (p. 144) The percent change found when the original amount increases.

Aumento porcentual (p. 144) Cambio porcentual que se encuentra cuando la cantidad original aumenta.

Example See example for *percent change* above.

English | Spanish

Perfect squares (p. 17) Numbers whose square roots are integers.

Cuadrado perfecto (p. 17) Número cuya raíz cuadrada es un número entero.

Example The numbers 1, 4, 9, 16, 25, 36, . . . are perfect squares because they are the squares of integers.

Perfect square trinomial (p. 511) Any trinomial of the form $a^2 + 2ab + b^2$ or $a^2 - 2ab + b^2$.

Trinomio cuadrado perfecto (p. 511) Todo trinomio de la forma $a^2 + 2ab + b^2$ ó $a^2 - 2ab + b^2$.

Example $(x + 3)^2 = x^2 + 6x + 9$

Permutation (p. 751) An arrangement of some or all of a set of objects in a specific order. You can use the notation $_nP_r$ to express the number of permutations, where n equals the number of objects available and r equals the number of selections to make.

Permutación (p. 751) Disposición de algunos o de todos los objetos en un conjunto en un orden determinado. El número de permutaciones se puede expresar con la notación $_nP_r$, donde n es igual al número total de objetos y r es igual al número de selecciones que han de hacerse.

Example How many ways can you arrange 5 objects 3 at a time?

$$_5P_3 = \frac{5!}{(5-3)!} = \frac{5!}{2!} = \frac{5 \cdot 4 \cdot 3 \cdot 2 \cdot 1}{2 \cdot 1} = 60$$

There are 60 ways to arrange 5 objects 3 at a time.

Perpendicular lines (p. 328) Lines that intersect to form right angles. Two lines are perpendicular if the product of their slopes is -1.

Rectas perpendiculares (p. 328) Rectas que forman ángulos rectos en su intersección. Dos rectas son perpendiculares si el producto de sus pendientes es -1.

Example

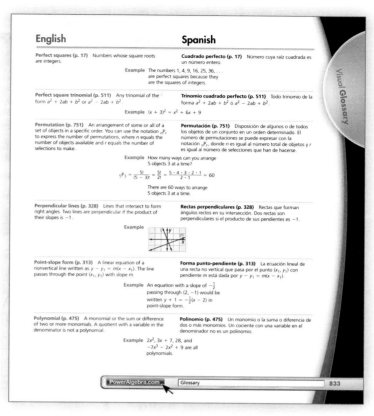

Point-slope form (p. 313) A linear equation of a nonvertical line written as $y - y_1 = m(x - x_1)$. The line passes through the point (x_1, y_1) with slope m.

Forma punto-pendiente (p. 313) La ecuación lineal de una recta no vertical que pasa por el punto (x_1, y_1) con pendiente m está dada por $y - y_1 = m(x - x_1)$.

Example An equation with a slope of $-\frac{1}{3}$ passing through $(2, -1)$ would be written $y + 1 = -\frac{1}{3}(x - 2)$ in point-slope form.

Polynomial (p. 475) A monomial or the sum or difference of two or more monomials. A quotient with a variable in the denominator is not a polynomial.

Polinomio (p. 475) Un monomio o la suma o diferencia de dos o más monomios. Un cociente con una variable en el denominador no es un polinomio.

Example $2x^2$, $3x + 7$, 28, and $-7x^3 - 2x^2 + 9$ are all polynomials.

English | Spanish

Population (p. 742) The entire group that you are collecting information about.

Población (p. 742) El grupo entero del cual juntas información.

Positive correlation (p. 333) The relationship between two sets of data in which both sets of data increase together.

Correlación positiva (p. 333) La relación entre dos conjuntos de datos en la que ambos conjuntos incrementan a la vez.

Example

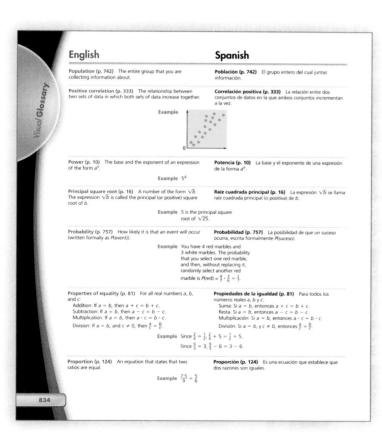

Power (p. 10) The base and the exponent of an expression of the form a^n.

Potencia (p. 10) La base y el exponente de una expresión de la forma a^n.

Example 5^4

Principal square root (p. 16) A number of the form $\sqrt{b}$. The expression $\sqrt{b}$ is called the principal (or positive) square root of b.

Raíz cuadrada principal (p. 16) La expresión $\sqrt{b}$ se llama raíz cuadrada principal (o positiva) de b.

Example 5 is the principal square root of $\sqrt{25}$.

Probability (p. 757) How likely is that an event will occur (written formally as P(event)).

Probabilidad (p. 757) La posibilidad de que un suceso ocurra, escrita formalmente P(suceso).

Example You have 4 red marbles and 3 white marbles. The probability that you select one red marble, and then, without replacing it, randomly select another red marble is P(red) $= \frac{4}{7} \cdot \frac{3}{6} = \frac{2}{7}$.

Properties of equality (p. 81) For all real numbers a, b, and c:
Addition: If $a = b$, then $a + c = b + c$.
Subtraction: If $a = b$, then $a - c = b - c$.
Multiplication: If $a = b$, then $a \cdot c = b \cdot c$.
Division: If $a = b$, and $c \neq 0$, then $\frac{a}{c} = \frac{b}{c}$.

Propiedades de la igualdad (p. 81) Para todos los números reales a, b y c:
Suma: Si $a = b$, entonces $a + c = b + c$.
Resta: Si $a = b$, entonces $a - c = b - c$.
Multiplicación: Si $a = b$, entonces $a \cdot c = b \cdot c$.
División: Si $a = b$, y $c \neq 0$, entonces $\frac{a}{c} = \frac{b}{c}$.

Example Since $\frac{3}{4} = \frac{3}{4}$, $\frac{3}{4} + 5 = \frac{3}{4} + 5$.
Since $\frac{9}{3} = 3$, $\frac{9}{3} - 6 = 3 - 6$.

Proportion (p. 124) An equation that states that two ratios are equal.

Proporción (p. 124) Es una ecuación que establece que dos razones son iguales.

Example $\frac{7.5}{9} = \frac{5}{6}$

English | Spanish

Pythagorean Theorem (p. 600) In any right triangle, the sum of the squares of the lengths of the legs is equal to the square of the length of the hypotenuse: $a^2 + b^2 = c^2$.

Teorema de Pitágoras (p. 600) En un triángulo rectángulo, la suma de los cuadrados de los catetos es igual al cuadrado de la hipotenusa: $a^2 + b^2 = c^2$.

Example $3^2 + 4^2 = 5^2$

Q

Quadrants (p. 60) The four parts into which the coordinate plane is divided by its axes.

Cuadrantes (p. 60) El plano de coordenadas está dividido por sus ejes en cuatro regiones llamadas cuadrantes.

Example

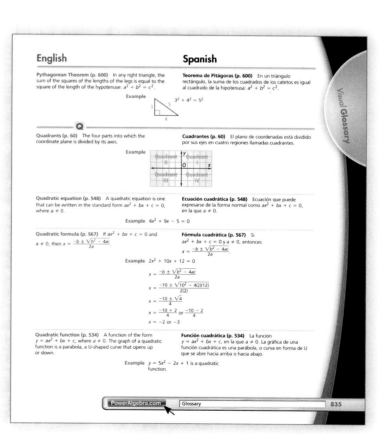

Quadratic equation (p. 548) A quadratic equation is one that can be written in the standard form $ax^2 + bx + c = 0$, where $a \neq 0$.

Ecuación cuadrática (p. 548) Ecuación que puede expresarse de la forma normal como $ax^2 + bx + c = 0$, en la que $a \neq 0$.

Example $4x^2 + 9x - 5 = 0$

Quadratic formula (p. 567) If $ax^2 + bx + c = 0$ and $a \neq 0$, then $x = \frac{-b \pm \sqrt{b^2 - 4ac}}{2a}$

Fórmula cuadrática (p. 567) Si $ax^2 + bx + c = 0$ y $a \neq 0$, entonces $x = \frac{-b \pm \sqrt{b^2 - 4ac}}{2a}$

Example $2x^2 + 10x + 12 = 0$

$$x = \frac{-b \pm \sqrt{b^2 - 4ac}}{2a}$$

$$x = \frac{-10 \pm \sqrt{10^2 - 4(2)(12)}}{2(2)}$$

$$x = \frac{-10 \pm \sqrt{4}}{4}$$

$$x = \frac{-10 + 2}{4} \text{ or } \frac{-10 - 2}{4}$$

$$x = -2 \text{ or } -3$$

Quadratic function (p. 534) A function of the form $y = ax^2 + bx + c$, where $a \neq 0$. The graph of a quadratic function is a parabola, a U-shaped curve that opens up or down.

Función cuadrática (p. 534) La función $y = ax^2 + bx + c$, en la que $a \neq 0$. La gráfica de una función cuadrática es una parábola, o curva en forma de U que se abre hacia arriba o hacia abajo.

Example $y = 5x^2 - 2x + 1$ is a quadratic function.

English | Spanish

Quadratic parent function (p. 534) The simplest quadratic function $f(x) = x^2$ or $y = x^2$.

Función cuadrática madre (p. 534) La función cuadrática más simple $f(x) = x^2$ ó $y = x^2$.

Example $y = x^2$ is the parent function for the family of quadratic equations of the form $y = ax^2 + bx + c$.

Qualitative (p. 741) Data that name qualities are qualitative.

Cualitativo (p. 741) Los datos que indican cualidades son cualitativos.

Example The data red, blue, red, green, blue, and blue are qualitative data.

Quantitative (p. 741) Data that measure quantity and can be described numerically are quantitative.

Cuantitativo (p. 741) Los datos que miden cantidades y pueden ser descritos numéricamente son cuantitativos.

Example The data 5 ft, 4 ft, 7 ft, 4 ft, 8 ft, and 10 ft are quantitative.

Quantity (p. 4) Anything that can be measured or counted.

Cantidad (p. 4) Cualquier cosa que se puede medir o contar.

Example A dozen is another way to describe a quantity of 12 eggs.

Quartile (p. 734) A quartile is a value that separates a finite data set into four equal parts. The second quartile (Q_2) is the median of the data set. The first and third quartiles $(Q_1$ and $Q_3)$ are the medians of the lower half and upper half of the data, respectively.

Cuartil (p. 734) Un cuartil es el valor que separa un conjunto de datos finitos en cuatro partes iguales. El segundo cuartil (Q_2) es la mediana del conjunto de datos. El primer cuartil y el tercer cuartil $(Q_1$ y $Q_3)$ son medianas de la mitad inferior y de la mitad superior de los datos, respectivamente.

Example For the data set 2, 3, 4, 5, 5, 6, 7, 7, the first quartile is 3.5, the second quartile (or median) is 5, and the third quartile is 6.5.

R

Radical (p. 16) An expression made up of a radical symbol and a radicand.

Radical (p. 16) Expresión compuesta por un símbolo radical y un radicando.

Example $\sqrt{a}$

Radical equation (p. 620) An equation that has a variable in a radicand.

Ecuación radical (p. 620) Ecuación que tiene una variable en un radicando.

Example
$$\sqrt{x} - 2 = 12$$
$$\sqrt{x} = 14$$
$$(\sqrt{x})^2 = 14^2$$
$$x = 196$$

Radical expression (p. 606) Expression that contains a radical.

Expresión radical (p. 606) Expresiones que contienen radicales.

Example $\sqrt{3}$, $\sqrt{5x}$, and $\sqrt{x-10}$ are examples of radical expressions.

English | Spanish

Radicand (p. 16) The expression under the radical sign is the radicand.

Radicando (p. 16) La expresión que aparece debajo del signo radical es el radicando.

Example The radicand of the radical expression $\sqrt{x+2}$ is $x + 2$.

Range (of a relation or function) (p. 268) The possible values of the output, or dependent variable, of a relation or function.

Rango (de una relación o función) (p. 268) El conjunto de todos los valores posibles de la salida, o variable dependiente, de una relación o función.

Example In the function $y = |x|$, the range is the set of all nonnegative numbers.

Range of a set of data (p. 728) The difference between the greatest and the least data values for a set of data.

Rango de un conjunto de datos (p. 728) Diferencia entre el valor mayor y el menor en un conjunto de datos.

Example For the set 2, 5, 8, 12, the range is $12 - 2 = 10$.

Rate (p. 118) A ratio of a to b where a and b represent quantities measured in different units.

Tasa (p. 118) La razón que existe entre a y b cuando a y b son cantidades medidas con distintas unidades.

Example Traveling 125 miles in 2 hours results in the rate $\frac{125 \text{ miles}}{2 \text{ hours}}$ or 62.5 mi/h.

Rate of change (p. 292) The relationship between two quantities that are changing. The rate of change is also called slope.

Tasa de cambio (p. 292) La relación entre dos cantidades que cambian. La tasa de cambio se llama también pendiente.

rate of change $= \frac{\text{change in the dependent variable}}{\text{change in the independent variable}}$

tasa de cambio $= \frac{\text{cambio en la variable dependiente}}{\text{cambio en la variable independiente}}$

Example Video rental for 1 day is $1.99. Video rental for 2 days is $2.99.
$$\text{rate of change} = \frac{2.99 - 1.99}{2 - 1}$$
$$= \frac{1.00}{1}$$
$$= 1$$

Ratio (p. 118) A ratio is the comparison of two quantities by division.

Razón (p. 118) Una razón es la comparación de dos cantidades por medio de una división.

Example $\frac{2}{3}$ and 7 : 3 are ratios.

Rational equation (p. 673) An equation containing rational expressions.

Ecuación racional (p. 673) Ecuación que contiene expresiones racionales.

Example $\frac{1}{x} = \frac{3}{2x-1}$ is a rational equation.

English | Spanish

Rational expression (p. 646) A ratio of two polynomials. The value of the variable cannot make the denominator equal to 0.

Expresión racional (p. 646) Una razón de dos polinomios. El valor de la variable no puede hacer el denominador igual a 0.

Example $\frac{3}{x^2 + x}$, where $x \neq 0$

Rational function (p. 687) A function that can be written in the form $f(x) = \frac{\text{polynomial}}{\text{polynomial}}$. The value of the variable cannot make the denominator equal to 0.

Función racional (p. 687) Función que puede expresarse de forma $f(x) = \frac{\text{polinomio}}{\text{polinomio}}$. El valor de la variable no puede hacer el denominador igual a 0.

Example $y = \frac{x}{x^2 + 2}$

Rationalize the denominator (p. 609) To rationalize the denominator of an expression, rewrite it so there are no radicals in any denominator and no denominators in any radical.

Racionalizar el denominador (p. 609) Para racionalizar el denominador de una expresión, ésta se escribe de modo que no haya radicales en ningún denominador y no haya denominadores en ningún radical.

Example $\frac{2}{\sqrt{5}} = \frac{2}{\sqrt{5}} \cdot \frac{\sqrt{5}}{\sqrt{5}} = \frac{2\sqrt{5}}{\sqrt{25}} = \frac{2\sqrt{5}}{5}$

Rational number (p. 18) A real number that can be written as a ratio of two integers. Rational numbers in decimal form are terminating or repeating.

Número racional (p. 18) Número real que puede expresarse como la razón de dos números enteros. Los números racionales en forma decimal son exactos o periódicos.

Example $\frac{2}{3}$, 1.548, and 2.292929 . . . are all rational numbers.

Real number (p. 18) A number that is either rational or irrational.

Número real (p. 18) Un número que es o racional o irracional.

Example 5, -3, $\sqrt{11}$, 0.666 . . . , $5\frac{4}{11}$, 0, and π are all real numbers.

Reciprocal (p. 41) Given a nonzero rational number $\frac{a}{b}$, the reciprocal, or multiplicative inverse, is $\frac{b}{a}$. The product of a nonzero number and its reciprocal is 1.

Recíproco (p. 41) El recíproco, o inverso multiplicativo, de un número racional $\frac{a}{b}$ cuyo valor no es cero es $\frac{b}{a}$. El producto de un número que no es cero y su recíproco es 1.

Example $\frac{2}{5}$ and $\frac{5}{2}$ are reciprocals because $\frac{2}{5} \times \frac{5}{2} = 1$.

Relation (p. 268) Any set of ordered pairs.

Relación (p. 268) Cualquier conjunto de pares ordenados.

Example {(0, 0), (2, 3), (2, -7)} is a relation.

English | Spanish

Relative error (p. 146) The ratio of the absolute value of the difference of a measured (or estimated) value and an actual value compared to the actual value.

Error relativo (p. 146) Razón del valor absoluto de la diferencia de un valor medido (o estimado) y un valor actual en comparación con el valor actual.

Example You estimated that a plant would be 5 in. tall 3 months after it was planted. The plant was actually 5.5 in. tall 3 months after it was planted. The relative error is
$$\frac{|5 - 5.5|}{5.5} = \frac{|-0.5|}{5.5} = \frac{0.5}{5.5} = \frac{1}{11},$$
or about 9%.

Root of the equation (p. 548) A solution of an equation.

Raíz de la ecuación (p. 548) Solucion de una ecuación.

Roster form (p. 194) A notation for listing all of the elements in a set using set braces and commas.

Lista (p. 194) Una notación en la que se enlistan todos los elementos en un conjunto usando llaves y comas.

Example The set of prime numbers less than 10, expressed in roster form, is {2, 3, 5, 7}.

S

Sample (p. 742) The part of a population that is surveyed.

Muestra (p. 742) Porción que se estudia de una población.

Example Let the set of all males between the ages of 19 and 34 be the population. A random selection of 900 males between those ages would be a sample of the population.

Sample space (p. 757) All possible outcomes in a situation.

Espacio muestral (p. 757) Todos los resultados posibles de una ecuación.

Example When you roll a number cube, the sample space is {1, 2, 3, 4, 5, 6}.

Scalar (p. 715) A real number is called a scalar for certain special uses, such as multiplying a matrix. See *Scalar multiplication*.

Escalar (p. 715) Un número real se llama escalar en ciertos casos especiales, como en la multiplicación de una matriz. Ver *Scalar multiplication*.

Example $2.5 \begin{bmatrix} 1 & 0 \\ -2 & 3 \end{bmatrix} = \begin{bmatrix} 2.5(1) & 2.5(0) \\ 2.5(-2) & 2.5(3) \end{bmatrix}$

$= \begin{bmatrix} 2.5 & 0 \\ -5 & 7.5 \end{bmatrix}$

Panel 1 (p. 840)

English	Spanish

Scalar multiplication (p. 715) Scalar multiplication is an operation that multiplies a matrix A by a scalar c. To find the resulting matrix cA, multiply each element of A by c.

Multiplicación escalar (p. 715) La multiplicación escalar es la que multiplica una matriz A por un número escalar c. Para hallar la matriz cA resultante, multiplica cada elemento de A por c.

Example $2.5\begin{bmatrix} 1 & 0 \\ -2 & 3 \end{bmatrix} = \begin{bmatrix} 2.5(1) & 2.5(0) \\ 2.5(-2) & 2.5(3) \end{bmatrix}$

$= \begin{bmatrix} 2.5 & 0 \\ -5 & 7.5 \end{bmatrix}$

Scale (p. 132) The ratio of any length in a scale drawing to the corresponding actual length. The lengths may be in different units.

Escala (p. 132) Razón de cualquier longitud de un dibujo a escala a la longitud real correspondiente. Las longitudes pueden tener diferentes unidades.

Example For a drawing in which a 2-in. length represents an actual length of 18 ft, the scale is 1 in. : 9 ft.

Scale drawing (p. 132) An enlarged or reduced drawing similar to an actual object or place.

Dibujo a escala (p. 132) Dibujo que muestra de mayor o menor tamaño un objeto o lugar dado.

Example

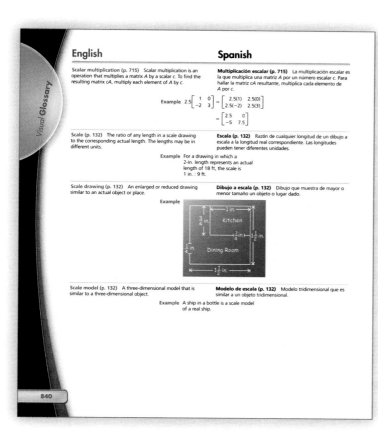

Scale model (p. 132) A three-dimensional model that is similar to a three-dimensional object.

Modelo de escala (p. 132) Modelo tridimensional que es similar a un objeto tridimensional.

Example A ship in a bottle is a scale model of a real ship.

840

Panel 2 (p. 841)

English	Spanish

Scatter plot (p. 333) A graph that relates two different sets of data by displaying them as ordered pairs.

Diagrama de puntos (p. 333) Gráfica que muestra la relación entre dos conjuntos. Los datos de ambos conjuntos se presentan como pares ordenados.

Example

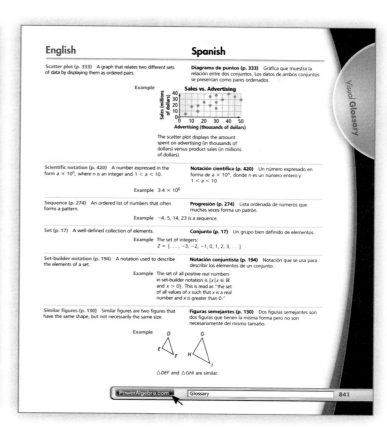

The scatter plot displays the amount spent on advertising (in thousands of dollars) versus product sales (in millions of dollars).

Scientific notation (p. 420) A number expressed in the form $a \times 10^n$, where n is an integer and $1 < a < 10$.

Notación científica (p. 420) Un número expresado en forma de $a \times 10^n$, donde n es un número entero y $1 < a < 10$.

Example 3.4×10^6

Sequence (p. 274) An ordered list of numbers that often forms a pattern.

Progresión (p. 274) Lista ordenada de números que muchas veces forma un patrón.

Example $-4, 5, 14, 23$ is a sequence.

Set (p. 17) A well-defined collection of elements.

Conjunto (p. 17) Un grupo bien definido de elementos.

Example The set of integers: $Z = \{\ldots, -3, -2, -1, 0, 1, 2, 3, \ldots\}$

Set-builder notation (p. 194) A notation used to describe the elements of a set.

Notación conjuntista (p. 194) Notación que se usa para describir los elementos de un conjunto.

Example The set of all positive real numbers in set-builder notation is $\{x \mid x \in \mathbb{R}$ and $x > 0\}$. This is read as "the set of all values of x such that x is a real number and x is greater than 0."

Similar figures (p. 130) Similar figures are two figures that have the same shape, but not necessarily the same size.

Figuras semejantes (p. 130) Dos figuras semejantes son dos figuras que tienen la misma forma pero no son necesariamente del mismo tamaño.

Example

$\triangle DEF$ and $\triangle GHI$ are similar.

Panel 3 (p. 842)

English	Spanish

Simple interest (p. 139) Interest paid only on the principal.

Interés simple (p. 139) Interés basado en el capital solamente.

Example The interest on $1000 at 6% for 5 years is $1000(0.06)5 = $300.

Simplify (p. 10) To replace an expression with its simplest name or form.

Simplificar (p. 10) Reemplazar una expresión por su versión o forma más simple.

Example $\dfrac{3 + 5}{8}$

Sine (p. 633) In a right triangle, such as $\triangle ABC$, with right $\angle C$,

$\text{sine of } \angle A = \dfrac{\text{length of side opposite } \angle A}{\text{length of hypotenuse}}$ or $\sin A = \dfrac{a}{c}$.

Seno (p. 633) En un triángulo rectángulo tal que $\triangle ABC$ con $\angle C$ recto,

el seno de $\angle A = \dfrac{\text{longitud del lado opuesto a } \angle A}{\text{longitud de la hipotenusa}}$, o $\text{sen } A = \dfrac{a}{c}$.

Example $\sin A = \dfrac{4}{5}$

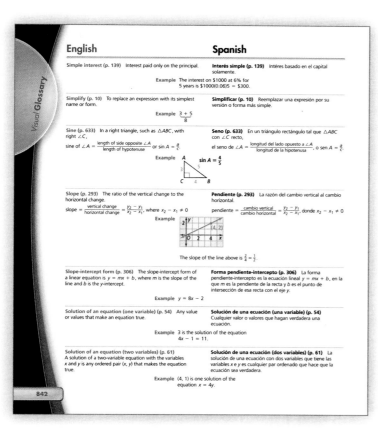

Slope (p. 293) The ratio of the vertical change to the horizontal change.

$\text{slope} = \dfrac{\text{vertical change}}{\text{horizontal change}} = \dfrac{y_2 - y_1}{x_2 - x_1}$, where $x_2 - x_1 \neq 0$

Pendiente (p. 293) La razón del cambio vertical al cambio horizontal.

$\text{pendiente} = \dfrac{\text{cambio vertical}}{\text{cambio horizontal}} = \dfrac{y_2 - y_1}{x_2 - x_1}$, donde $x_2 - x_1 \neq 0$

Example

The slope of the line above is $\dfrac{2}{4} = \dfrac{1}{2}$.

Slope-intercept form (p. 306) The slope-intercept form of a linear equation is $y = mx + b$, where m is the slope of the line and b is the y-intercept.

Forma pendiente-intercepto (p. 306) La forma pendiente-intercepto es la ecuación lineal $y = mx + b$, en la que m es la pendiente de la recta y b es el punto de intersección de esa recta con el eje y.

Example $y = 8x - 2$

Solution of an equation (one variable) (p. 54) Any value or values that make an equation true.

Solución de una ecuación (una variable) (p. 54) Cualquier valor o valores que hagan verdadera una ecuación.

Example 3 is the solution of the equation $4x - 1 = 11$.

Solution of an equation (two variables) (p. 61) A solution of a two-variable equation with the variables x and y is any ordered pair (x, y) that makes the equation true.

Solución de una ecuación (dos variables) (p. 61) La solución de una ecuación con dos variables que tiene las variables x e y es cualquier par ordenado que hace que la ecuación sea verdadera.

Example $(4, 1)$ is one solution of the equation $x = 4y$.

842

Panel 4 (p. 843)

English	Spanish

Solution of an inequality (one variable) (p. 165) Any value or values of a variable in the inequality that makes an inequality true.

Solución de una desigualdad (una variable) (p. 165) Cualquier valor o valores de una variable de la desigualdad que hagan verdadera la desigualdad.

Example The solution of the inequality $x < 9$ is all numbers less than 9.

Solution of an inequality (two variables) (p. 390) Any ordered pair that makes the inequality true.

Solución de una desigualdad (dos variables) (p. 390) Cualquier par ordenado que haga verdadera la desigualdad.

Example Each ordered pair in the yellow area and on the solid red line is a solution of $3x - 5y \le 10$.

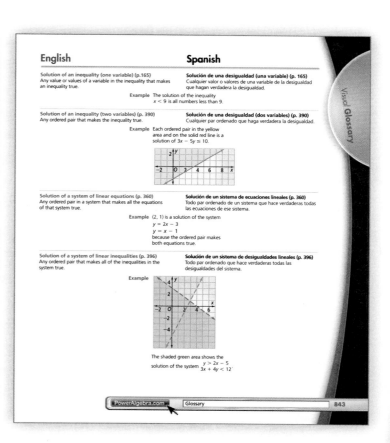

Solution of a system of linear equations (p. 360) Any ordered pair in a system that makes all the equations of that system true.

Solución de un sistema de ecuaciones lineales (p. 360) Todo par ordenado de un sistema que hace verdaderas todas las ecuaciones de ese sistema.

Example $(2, 1)$ is a solution of the system

$y = 2x - 3$
$y = x - 1$

because the ordered pair makes both equations true.

Solution of a system of linear inequalities (p. 396) Any ordered pair that makes all of the inequalities in the system true.

Solución de un sistema de desigualdades lineales (p. 396) Todo par ordenado que hace verdaderas todas las desigualdades del sistema.

Example

The shaded green area shows the solution of the system $\begin{cases} y > 2x - 5 \\ 3x + 4y < 12 \end{cases}$

English / Spanish (p. 844)

English	Spanish
Square root (p. 16) A number b such that $a^2 = b$. $\sqrt{b}$ is the principal square root. $-\sqrt{b}$ is the negative square root.	**Raíz cuadrada (p. 16)** Si $a^2 = b$, entonces a es la raíz cuadrada de b. $\sqrt{b}$ es la raíz cuadrada principal. $-\sqrt{b}$ es la raíz cuadrada negativa.

Example −3 and 3 are square roots of 9.

English	Spanish
Square root function (p. 629) A function that contains the independent variable in the radicand.	**Función de raíz cuadrada (p. 629)** Una función que contiene la variable independiente en el radicando.

Example $y = \sqrt{2x}$ is a square root function.

English	Spanish
Standard deviation (p. 733) A measure of how data varies, or deviates, from the mean.	**Desviación típica (p. 733)** Medida de cómo los datos varían, o se desvían, de la media.

Example Use the following formula to find the standard deviation.

$$\sigma = \sqrt{\frac{\sum(x-\bar{x})^2}{n}}$$

English	Spanish
Standard form of a linear equation (p. 320) The standard form of a linear equation is $Ax + By = C$, where A, B, and C are integers and A and B are not both zero.	**Forma normal de una ecuación lineal (p. 320)** La forma normal de una ecuación lineal es $Ax + By = C$, donde A, B y C son números reales, y donde A y B no son iguales a cero.

Example $6x - y = 12$

English	Spanish
Standard form of a polynomial (p. 475) The form of a polynomial that places the terms in descending order by degree.	**Forma normal de un polinomio (p. 475)** Cuando el grado de los términos de un polinomio disminuye de izquierda a derecha, está en forma normal, o en orden descendente.

Example $15x^3 + x^2 + 3x + 9$

English	Spanish
Standard form of a quadratic equation (p. 548) The standard form of a quadratic equation is $ax^2 + bx + c = 0$, where $a \neq 0$.	**Forma normal de una ecuación cuadrática (p. 548)** Cuando una ecuación cuadrática se expresa de forma $ax^2 + bx + c = 0$.

Example $-x^2 + 2x - 9 = 0$

English	Spanish
Standard form of a quadratic function (p. 534) The standard form of a quadratic function is $f(x) = ax^2 + bx + c$, where $a \neq 0$.	**Forma normal de una función cuadrática (p. 534)** La forma normal de una función cuadrática es $f(x) = ax^2 + bx + c$, donde $a \neq 0$.

Example $f(x) = 2x^2 - 5x + 2$

English	Spanish
Stem-and-leaf plot (p. 722) A display of data made by using the digits of the values.	**Diagrama de tallo y hojas (p. 722)** Un arreglo de los datos que use los dígitos de los valores.

Example

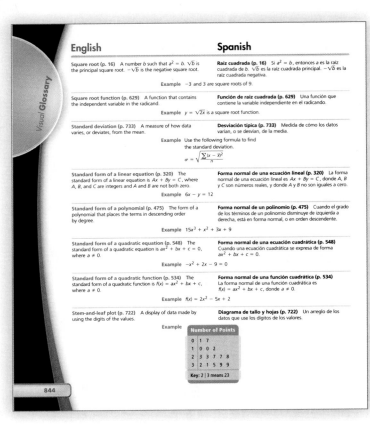

Number of Points

0	1 7
1	0 0 2
2	3 3 7 7 8
3	2 1 5 9 9

Key: 2 | 3 means 23

English / Spanish (p. 845)

English	Spanish
Subset (p. 17) A subset of a set consists of elements from the given set.	**Subconjunto (p. 17)** Un subconjunto de un conjunto consiste en elementos del conjunto dado.

Example If $B = \{1, 2, 3, 4, 5, 6, 7\}$ and $A = \{1, 2, 5\}$, then A is a subset of B.

English	Spanish
Substitution method (p. 368) A method of solving a system of equations by replacing one variable with an equivalent expression containing the other variable.	**Método de sustitución (p. 368)** Método para resolver un sistema de ecuaciones en el que se reemplaza una variable por una expresión equivalente que contenga la otra variable.

Example If $y = 2x + 5$ and $x + 3y = 7$, then $x + 3(2x + 5) = 7$.

English	Spanish
System of linear equations (p. 360) Two or more linear equations using the same variables.	**Sistema de ecuaciones lineales (p. 360)** Dos o más ecuaciones lineales que usen las mismas variables.

Example $y = 5x + 7$
$y = \frac{1}{2}x - 3$

English	Spanish
System of linear inequalities (p. 396) Two or more linear inequalities using the same variables.	**Sistema de desigualdades lineales (p. 396)** Dos o más desigualdades lineales que usen las mismas variables.

Example $y \leq x + 11$
$y < 5x$

T

English	Spanish
Tangent (p. 633) In a right triangle, such as $\triangle ABC$ with right $\angle C$, tangent of $\angle A = \frac{\text{length of side opposite } \angle A}{\text{length of side adjacent to } \angle A}$, or $\tan A = \frac{a}{b}$.	**Tangente (p. 633)** En un triángulo rectángulo tal que $\triangle ABC$, con $\angle C$ recto, la tangente de $\angle A = \frac{\text{longitud del lado opuesto a } \angle A}{\text{longitud del lado adyacente a } \angle A}$, o la $\tan A = \frac{a}{b}$.

Example

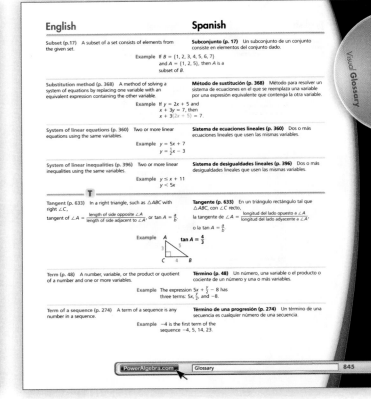

$\tan A = \frac{4}{3}$

English	Spanish
Term (p. 48) A number, variable, or the product or quotient of a number and one or more variables.	**Término (p. 48)** Un número, una variable o el producto o cociente de un número y una o más variables.

Example The expression $5x + \frac{y}{2} - 8$ has three terms: $5x$, $\frac{y}{2}$, and −8.

English	Spanish
Term of a sequence (p. 274) A term of a sequence is any number in a sequence.	**Término de una progresión (p. 274)** Un término de una secuencia es cualquier número de una secuencia.

Example −4 is the first term of the sequence −4, 5, 14, 23.

English / Spanish (p. 846)

English	Spanish
Theoretical probability (p. 757) The ratio of the number of favorable outcomes to the number of possible outcomes if all outcomes have the same chance of happening.	**Probabilidad teórica (p. 757)** Si cada resultado tiene la misma probabilidad de darse, la probabilidad teórica de un suceso se calcula como la razón del número de resultados favorables al número de resultados posibles.

$P(\text{event}) = \frac{\text{number of favorable outcomes}}{\text{number of possible outcomes}}$

$P(\text{suceso}) = \frac{\text{número de resultados favorables}}{\text{número de resultados posibles}}$

Example In tossing a coin, the events of getting heads or tails are equally likely. The likelihood of getting heads is $P(\text{heads}) = \frac{1}{2}$.

English	Spanish
Translation (p. 342) A transformation that shifts a graph horizontally, vertically, or both.	**Traslación (p. 342)** Proceso de mover una gráfica horizontalmente, verticalmente o en ambos sentidos.

Example

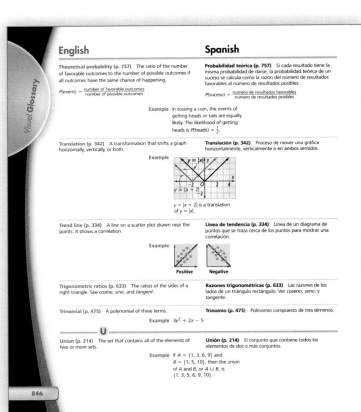

$y = |x + 2|$ is a translation of $y = |x|$.

English	Spanish
Trend line (p. 334) A line on a scatter plot drawn near the points. It shows a correlation.	**Línea de tendencia (p. 334)** Línea de un diagrama de puntos que se traza cerca de los puntos para mostrar una correlación.

Example

Positive   Negative

English	Spanish
Trigonometric ratios (p. 633) The ratios of the sides of a right triangle. See *cosine*, *sine*, and *tangent*.	**Razones trigonométricas (p. 633)** Las razones de los lados de un triángulo rectángulo. Ver *coseno*, *seno*, y *tangente*.

English	Spanish
Trinomial (p. 475) A polynomial of three terms.	**Trinomio (p. 475)** Polinomio compuesto de tres términos.

Example $3x^2 + 2x - 5$

U

English	Spanish
Union (p. 214) The set that contains all of the elements of two or more sets.	**Unión (p. 214)** El conjunto que contiene todos los elementos de dos o más conjuntos.

Example If $A = \{1, 3, 6, 9\}$ and $B = \{1, 5, 10\}$, then the union of A and B, or $A \cup B$, is $\{1, 3, 5, 6, 9, 10\}$.

English / Spanish (p. 847)

English	Spanish
Unit analysis (p. 119) Including units for each quantity in a calculation to determine the unit of the answer.	**Análisis de unidades (p. 119)** Incluir unidades para cada cantidad de un cálculo como ayuda para determinar la unidad que se debe usar para la respuesta.

Example To change 10 ft to yards, multiply by the conversion factor $\frac{1 \text{ yd}}{3 \text{ ft}}$.

$10 \text{ ft} \left(\frac{1 \text{ yd}}{3 \text{ ft}}\right) = 3\frac{1}{3} \text{ yd}$

English	Spanish
Unit rate (p. 119) A rate with a denominator of 1.	**Razón en unidades (p. 119)** Razón cuyo denominador es 1.

Example The unit rate for 120 miles driven in 2 hours is 60 mi/h.

English	Spanish
Univariate (p. 742) A set of data that uses only one variable is univariate.	**Univariado (p. 742)** Un conjunto de datos que tiene sólo una variable es univariado.

English	Spanish
Universal set (p. 196) The set of all possible elements from which subsets are formed.	**Conjunto universal (p. 196)** Conjunto de todos los posibles elementos específicos del cual se forma un subconjunto.

English	Spanish
Unlike radicals (p. 613) Radical expressions that do not have the same radicands.	**Radicales no semejantes (p. 613)** Expresiones radicales que no tienen radicandos semejantes.

Example $\sqrt{2}$ and $\sqrt{3}$ are unlike radicals.

V

English	Spanish
Variable (p. 4) A symbol, usually a letter, that represents one or more numbers.	**Variable (p. 4)** Símbolo, generalmente una letra, que representa uno o más valores de una cantidad.

Example x is the variable in the equation $9 - x = 3$.

English	Spanish
Vertex (p. 535) The highest or lowest point on a parabola. The axis of symmetry intersects the parabola at the vertex.	**Vértice (p. 535)** El punto más alto o más bajo de una parábola. El punto de intersección del eje de simetría y la parábola.

Example

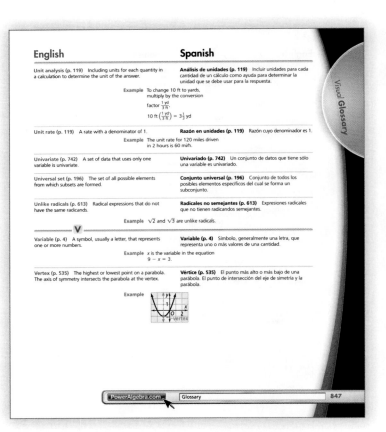

Vertical-line test (p. 269) The vertical-line test is a method used to determine if a relation is a function or not. If a vertical line passes through a graph more than once, the graph is not the graph of a function.

Prueba de la recta vertical (p. 269) La prueba de recta vertical es un método que se usa para determinar si una relación es una función o no. Si una recta vertical pasa por el medio de una gráfica más de una vez, la gráfica no es una gráfica de una función.

Example

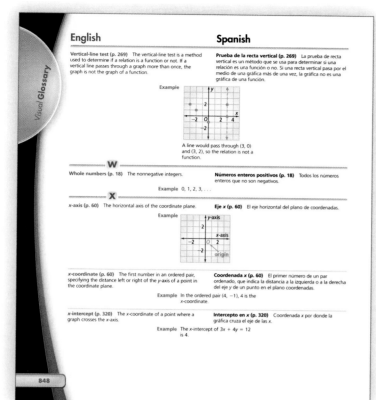

A line would pass through (3, 0) and (3, 2), so the relation is not a function.

W

Whole numbers (p. 18) The nonnegative integers.

Números enteros positivos (p. 18) Todos los números enteros que no son negativos.

Example   0, 1, 2, 3, . . .

X

x-axis (p. 60) The horizontal axis of the coordinate plane.

Eje x (p. 60) El eje horizontal del plano de coordenadas.

Example

x-coordinate (p. 60) The first number in an ordered pair, specifying the distance left or right of the y-axis of a point in the coordinate plane.

Coordenada x (p. 60) El primer número de un par ordenado, que indica la distancia a la izquierda o a la derecha del eje y de un punto en el plano coordenadas.

Example   In the ordered pair (4, −1), 4 is the x-coordinate.

x-intercept (p. 320) The x-coordinate of a point where a graph crosses the x-axis.

Intercepto en x (p. 320) Coordenada x por donde la gráfica cruza el eje de las x.

Example   The x-intercept of $3x + 4y = 12$ is 4.

---

y-axis (p. 60) The vertical axis of the coordinate plane.

Eje y (p. 60) El eje vertical del plano de coordenadas.

Example

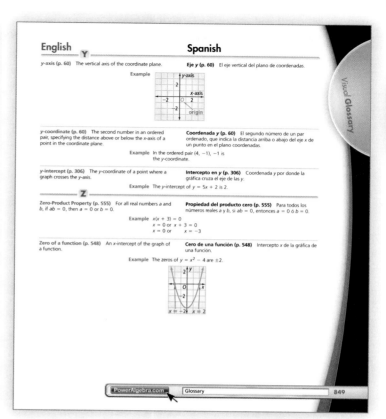

y-coordinate (p. 60) The second number in an ordered pair, specifying the distance above or below the x-axis of a point in the coordinate plane.

Coordenada y (p. 60) El segundo número de un par ordenado, que indica la distancia arriba o abajo del eje x de un punto en el plano coordenadas.

Example   In the ordered pair (4, −1), −1 is the y-coordinate.

y-intercept (p. 306) The y-coordinate of a point where a graph crosses the y-axis.

Intercepto en y (p. 306) Coordenada y por donde la gráfica cruza el eje de las y.

Example   The y-intercept of $y = 5x + 2$ is 2.

Z

Zero-Product Property (p. 555) For all real numbers a and b, if $ab = 0$, then $a = 0$ or $b = 0$.

Propiedad del producto cero (p. 555) Para todos los números reales a y b, si $ab = 0$, entonces $a = 0$ ó $b = 0$.

Example $x(x + 3) = 0$
$x = 0$ or $x + 3 = 0$
$x = 0$ or $x = -3$

Zero of a function (p. 548) An x-intercept of the graph of a function.

Cero de una función (p. 548) Intercepto x de la gráfica de una función.

Example   The zeros of $y = x^2 - 4$ are ±2.

Selected Answers

Chapter 1

Get Ready! p. 1

1. 6 **2.** 5 **3.** 1 **4.** 20 **5.** 15 **6.** 44 **7.** 72 **8.** 150 **9.** 400 **10.** 8 **11.** $294 **12.** $\frac{4}{5}$ **13.** $\frac{5}{7}$ **14.** $\frac{1}{7}$ **15.** $\frac{12}{13}$ **16.** 0.7 **17.** 0.6 **18.** 0.65 **19.** 0.93 **20.** $0.4\overline{6}$ **21.** $\frac{11}{14}$ **22.** $10\frac{7}{15}$ **23.** $\frac{1}{10}$ **24.** $3\frac{11}{12}$ **25.** Answers may vary. Sample: 20 + 15 **26.** Answers may vary. Sample: A simplified expression is one that is briefer or easier to work with than the original expression. **27.** Answers may vary. Sample: To evaluate an expression means to find its numeric value for given values of the variables.

Lesson 1-1 pp. 4–9

Got It? 1. $n + 18$ **2a.** $6n$ **b.** $\frac{18}{n}$ **c.** No; 6 less a number y means $6 - y$ and 6 less than a number y means $y - 6$. **3a.** $4x - 8$ **b.** $2(x + 8)$ **c.** $\frac{5}{12 + x}$ **4a.** the sum of a number x and 8.1 **b.** the sum of ten times a number x and 9 **c.** the quotient of a number n and 3 **d.** five times a number x less 1 **5.** subtract 2 from the number of sides in the polygon; $n - 2$

Lesson Check 1a. numerical **b.** algebraic **c.** numerical **2a.** $9t$ **b.** $x - \frac{1}{2}$ **c.** $m + 7.1$ **d.** $\frac{207}{n}$ **3.** six times a number c **4.** one less than a number x **5.** the quotient of a number t and 2 **6.** 4 less than the product of 3 and a number t **7.** Numerical expressions are mathematical phrases involving only numbers and operations. Algebraic expressions are mathematical phrases that include one or more variables. An algebraic expression includes at least one variable. A numerical expression does not include any variables. **8.** $49 + 0.75n$

Exercises 9. $p + 4$ **11.** $n - 12$ **13.** $\frac{n}{8}$ **15.** $x - 23$ **17.** $\frac{1}{3}n$ **19.** $2w + 2$ **21.** $(17 - k) + 9$ **23.** $37t - 9.85$ **25.** $15 + \frac{60}{w}$ **27.** 5 more than a number q **29.** the quotient of y and 5 **31.** 14.1 less a number w **33.** one more than the product of 9 and a number n **35.** the quotient of z and 8 less 9 **37.** the difference of 15 and the quotient of 1.5 and d **39.** 5 more than the product of 9 and a number n; $9n + 5$ **41.** $8 - 9r$ **43.** $\frac{3}{7}y - 4$ **45.** It should be "the Quotient of 5 and n." **47.** $4.50t$ **49.** A **59.** $\frac{3}{4}$ **60.** $\frac{5}{14}$ **61.** $\frac{7}{10}$ **62.** $\frac{1}{6}$ **63.** 3 **64.** 3 **65.** 1 **66.** 4

Lesson 1-2 pp. 10–15

Got It? 1a. 81 **b.** $\frac{8}{27}$ **c.** 0.125 **2a.** 27 **b.** 7 **c.** 17 **d.** A fraction bar acts as a grouping symbol since you simplify numerator and denominator before you divide. **3a.** 3 **b.** 11 **c.** 20; $(xy)^2 \neq xy^2$ **4.** $c + \frac{1}{10}c$; $47.30, $86.90, $104.50, $113.30

Lesson Check 1. 25 **2.** 8 **3.** $\frac{9}{16}$ **4.** 23 **5.** 1728 **6.** 0 **7.** exponent 3; base 4 **8.** The student subtracted before multiplying; $23 - 8 \cdot 2 + 3^2 = 23 - 8 \cdot 2 + 9 = 23 - 16 + 9 = 7 + 9 = 16$

Exercises 9. 243 **11.** 16 **13.** $\frac{8}{27}$ **15.** 0.004096 **17.** 2 **19.** 4.5 **21.** 53 **23.** 16 **25.** 1728 **27.** 1024 **29.** 1024 **31.** 496 **33.** 3458 **35.** mv; 15,000, 20,000, 25,000 **37.** 256 **39.** 5 **41.** 12 **43.** $\frac{3}{8}s$; 6 oz; 9 oz; 30 oz; 37.5 oz **45.** 27 **47.** 6 **49.** 68 **51.** 3 **53.** Yes; you can simplify the expression in the first set of parentheses first, or you can simplify the expression in the second set of parentheses first. **55.** 20; $14 - 5 \cdot 3 + 3^2$ **65.** $p + 4$ **66.** $5 - 3y$ **67.** $\frac{m}{10}$ **68.** $3(7 - d)$ **69.** prime **70.** composite **71.** prime **72.** composite **73.** 0.6 **74.** 0.875 **75.** $0.\overline{6}$ **76.** $0.\overline{571428}$ **77.** $\frac{7}{10}$ **78.** $\frac{7}{100}$ **79.** $4\frac{1}{4}$ or $\frac{17}{4}$ **80.** $\frac{17}{40}$

Lesson 1-3 pp. 16–22

Got It? 1a. 8 **b.** 5 **c.** $\frac{1}{6}$ **d.** $\frac{9}{11}$ **2.** about 6 **3a.** rational numbers, natural numbers, whole numbers, integers **b.** rational numbers **c.** rational numbers **d.** irrational numbers **4a.** $\sqrt{129} < 11.52$ **b.** Yes; $4\frac{1}{3} > \sqrt{17}$ also compares the two numbers.

5. 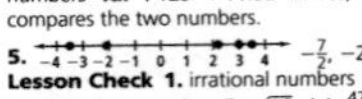

$-\frac{7}{2}, -2.1, \sqrt{5}, \sqrt{9}, 3.5$

Lesson Check 1. irrational numbers **2.** rational numbers, integers **3.** $-5, \sqrt{16}, 4.1, \frac{47}{10}$ **4.** about 4 in. **5.** rational numbers and irrational numbers **6.** Answers may vary. Sample: 0.5 **7.** Rational; its value is 10, which can be written as a ratio of two integers, $\frac{10}{1}$. **8.** Irrational; $\sqrt{0.29}$ is a nonrepeating, nonterminating number.

Exercises 9. 6 **11.** 4 **13.** $\frac{6}{7}$ **15.** $\frac{1}{3}$ **17.** 1.4 **19.** about 4 **21.** about 16 **23.** about 18 **25.** about 13 in. **27.** rational numbers **29.** rational numbers, integers **31.** irrational numbers **33.** rational numbers **35.** irrational numbers **37.** $5\frac{2}{3} > \sqrt{29}$ **39.** $\frac{4}{3} < \sqrt{2}$ **41.** $-\frac{7}{11} < -0.63$ **43.** $-\frac{22}{25} < -0.\overline{8}$ **45.** $-2, -\frac{7}{4}, \frac{1}{2}, \sqrt{5}, 2.4$ **47.** $-\frac{59}{9}, -6, 4.3, \sqrt{20}$ **49.** $-\frac{9}{4}, -\frac{13}{6}, -2.1, -\frac{26}{13}$ **51.** about 12 ft **53.** True; Answers may vary; any integer can be expressed as a rational number. **55.** False; Answers may vary; 2 is a positive number and an integer. **57.** $\frac{417}{1}$ **59.** $\frac{201}{100}$ **61.** $\frac{306}{100}$ **63.** about 12 ft **65.** $\frac{864}{275}$; its value 3.14181... is closer to the value of π than $\sqrt{10}$, which is 3.16227... **67.** no; no the real number line extends indefinitely in both the positive and negative direction. **75.** 16 **76.** 78 **77.** 512 **78.** $14 + x$ **79.** $4(y + 1)$ **80.** $\frac{3880}{z}$ **81.** $\frac{19}{3}t$ **82.** 18 **83.** 72 **84.** 442 **85.** 9

Lesson 1-4 pp. 23–28

Got It? 1a. Identity Prop. of Mult. **b.** Commutative Prop. of Add. **2.** 720 tennis balls **3a.** $9.45x$ **b.** $9 + 4h$ **c.** $\frac{2}{3n}$ **4a.** True; Commutative Prop. of Mult. and Identity Prop. of Add. **b.** False; answers may vary. Sample: $4(2 + 1) \neq 4(2) + 1$ **c.** No; it is true when a and b are both either 0 or 2.

Lesson Check 1. Comm. Prop. of Add. **2.** Assoc. Prop. of Mult. **3.** $4.45 **4.** $24d$ **5a.** no **b.** yes **6.** Comm. Prop. of Mult.; Assoc. Prop. of Mult.; multiply; multiply

Exercises 7. Comm. Prop. of Add. **9.** Ident. Prop. of Add. **11.** Comm. Prop. of Mult. **13.** 36 **15.** 9.7 **17.** 80 **19.** $110 **21.** $18x$ **23.** $110p$ **25.** $11 + 3x$ **27.** $1.2 + 7d$ **29.** $1.5n$ **31.** $11y$ **33.** False; answers may vary. Sample: $8 \div 4 \neq 4 \div 8$ **35.** true; Mult. Prop. of −1 **37a.** 497 mi **b.** 497 mi **c.** The Commutative Property of Addition applies to this situation. **39.** no **41.** yes **43.** yes **45.** no **47.** Hannah can only afford to give all her friends the same gift. **49.** 390 **51.** 0 **53.** no; $(a - b) - c \neq a - (b - c)$ **55.** no; $(a \div b) \div c \neq a \div (b \div c)$ **62.** $-6, 1.6, \sqrt{6}, 6^3$ **63.** $-17, 1.4, \frac{8}{5}, 10^2$ **64.** $-4.5, 1.75, \sqrt{4}, 14^1$ **65.** 14 **66.** 1 **67.** 1.1 **68.** $\frac{1}{18}$

Lesson 1-5 pp. 30–36

Got It? 1. −4 **2a.** −24 **b.** −2 **c.** −2 **d.** −8 **3a.** 13.5 **b.** any value where $a = b$ **4.** −2473 ft, or 2473 ft below sea level

Lesson Check 1. −3 **2.** −3 **3.** −3 **4.** −7 **5.** 2 **6.** −7 **7.** 0 **8.** Subtracting is the same as adding the opposite. **9.** The opposite of a number is the number that is added to it to equal 0. If a number is positive, its opposite is negative. However, if a number is negative, its opposite is positive.

Exercises

11. 5 **13.** −5 **15.** 3 **17.** −12

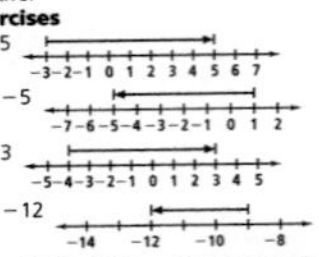

19. −11 **21.** 5 **23.** −11 **25.** 4.4 **27.** −3 **29.** $\frac{13}{36}$ **31.** −20 **33.** 48 **35.** −2 **37.** −20.3 **39.** 1.6 **41.** $\frac{15}{16}$ **43.** $48.54 **45.** −7.1 **47.** The sum of −4 and 5 is +1, not −1; $-4 - (-5) = -4 + 5 = 1$ **49.** $-\frac{1}{12}$ **51.** 1 **53.** positive **55.** negative **57.** Find the absolute value of each number. The sign of the number with the larger absolute value will be the sign of the sum. **59.** False; if both numbers are negative, the difference is larger than the sum. If the absolute values are equal, the sum is 0. **61.** 29.62 in. **63.** −2 **75.** yes **76.** no **77.** yes **78.** rational numbers **79.** rational numbers **80.** rational numbers, whole numbers, natural numbers, and integers **81.** rational numbers **82.** irrational numbers **83.** 18.75 **84.** 17 **85.** 318

Lesson 1-6 pp. 38–44

Got It? 1a. −90 **b.** 2.4 **c.** $-\frac{21}{50}$ **d.** 16 **2a.** 8 **b.** ±4 **c.** −11 **d.** $\pm\frac{1}{6}$ **3.** −$72 **4a.** $-\frac{3}{10}$ **b.** Yes; a positive divided by a negative is negative and the opposite of a positive divided by a positive is also negative.

Lesson Check 1. 36 **2.** $-\frac{5}{32}$ **3.** −16 **4.** $\frac{9}{8}$ **5.** −5

6. 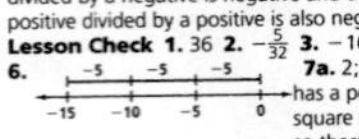

7a. 2; a positive number has a positive and negative square root. **b.** 1; 80 = 0, so there is one square root.

Exercises 9. 96 **11.** 20.5 **13.** −25 **15.** $\frac{1}{12}$ **17.** 1 **19.** 1.44 **21.** 13 **23.** −30 **25.** $-\frac{5}{9}$ **27.** $-\frac{11}{4}$ **29.** ±0.5 **31.** −6 **33.** −3 **35.** −0.9 **37.** −250 **39.** $115 **41.** 3 **43.** −1 **45.** $-\frac{25}{18}$ **47.** $\frac{1}{2}$ **49.** $-94\frac{1}{2}$ bushels **55.** −180 **57.** $38\frac{2}{5}$ **59.** −13°F **61.** First change $-2\frac{1}{2}$ to the improper fraction $-\frac{5}{2}$. Then multiply $-1\frac{2}{3}$ by the reciprocal of $-\frac{5}{2}$, which is $-\frac{2}{5}$. **63.** $\frac{800}{63}$, or $12\frac{44}{63}$ **65a.** If $0 \div x = y$, then $xy = 0$. Since $x \neq 0$, then $y = 0$ by the Zero Property of Multiplication. **b.** Suppose there is a value of y such that $x \div 0 = y$. Then $x = 0 \cdot y$, so $x = 0$. But this is a contradiction, since $x \neq 0$. So there is no value of y such that $x \div 0 = y$. **73.** 30 **74.** −10 **75.** −10 **76.** Ident. Prop. of Add. **77.** Comm. Prop. of Mult. **78.** Assoc. Prop. of Mult.

Lesson 1-7 pp. 46–52

Got It? 1a. $5x + 35$ **b.** $36 - 2t$ **c.** $1.2 + 3.3c$ **d.** $-2y^2 + y$ **2a.** $\frac{4}{3}x - \frac{16}{3}$ **b.** $\frac{11}{6} + \frac{1}{2}x$ **c.** $\frac{5}{4} + \frac{1}{2}x$ **d.** $\frac{1}{2} - \frac{1}{4}x$ **3a.** $-a - 5$ **b.** $x - 31$ **c.** $-4x + 12$ **d.** $-6m + 9n$ **4.** $29 **5a.** $2y$ **b.** $-12mn^4$ **c.** $8y^3z - 6yz^3$ **d.** No; it is already simplified since there are no like terms to combine.

Lesson Check 1a. $7j + 14$ **b.** $-8x + 24$ **c.** $-4 + c$ **d.** $-11 - 2b$ **2.** $-8x^2 + 3xy + (-9x) + (-3)$ **3.** $2ab + (-5ab^2) + (-9a^2b)$ **4.** yes **5.** no **6a.** yes **b.** no; Commutative Prop. of Mult. **c.** yes **d.** no; Associative Prop. of Add. **7.** 500 − 1; answers may vary. Sample: These numbers are easily multiplied by 5, making it possible to use the Distr. Prop. to solve this using mental math. **8a.** yes; no like terms **b.** This expression can be simplified by using the Distr. Prop. **c.** No; $12xy$ and $3yx$ are like terms.

Exercises 9. $6a + 60$ **11.** $25 + 5w$ **13.** $90 - 10t$ **15.** $112b + 96$ **17.** $4.5 - 12c$ **19.** $f - 2$ **21.** $12z + 15$ **23.** $\frac{3}{11} - \frac{7d}{17}$ **25.** $\frac{2}{5}x + \frac{7}{5}$ **27.** $\frac{8}{3} - 3x$ **29.** $5 - \frac{8}{5}t$ **31.** $11 - n$ **33.** $-20 - d$ **35.** $-9 + 7c$ **37.** $-18a + 17b$ **39.** $m - n - 1$ **41.** 40.8 **43.** 897 **45.** 23.4 **47.** 24.6 **49.** $49.50 **51.** $4725 **53.** $20x$ **55.** $-2t$ **57.** $17w^2$ **59.** $5y^2$ **61.** $-3x + y + 11$ **63.** $3h^2 - 11h - 3$ **65.** the product of 3 and the difference of t and 1; $3t - 3$ **67.** one-third the difference of 6 times x and 1; $2x - \frac{1}{3}$ **69.** The sum, not the product, of the terms should be found; $4(x + 5) = 4x + 4 \cdot 5 = 4x + 20$. **71.** $33x + 22$ **73.** $35n - 63$ **75.** 0 **77.** $-5m^3n + 5mn$ **79.** $23x^2y - 8x^2y^2 - 4x^3y^2 - 9xy^2$ **81.** $\frac{1}{3}(9 + 12n) = \frac{9}{3} + \frac{12n}{3} = 3 + 4n$ **95.** −25 **96.** $\frac{9}{16}$ **97.** 1.44 **98.** 10 less than a number x **99.** 18 less than the product of 5 and x **100.** 12 more than the quotient of 7 and y

Lesson 1-8 pp. 53–58

Got It? 1a. open **b.** true **c.** false **2.** yes **3.** $49 = 14h$ **4.** 9 **5a.** −10 **b.** Answers may vary. Sample: −5 **6.** The solution is between −8 and −9.

Lesson Check 1. no **2.** 15 **3.** $p = 1.5n$ **5.** Answers may vary. Sample: $\frac{x}{3} = 15$. **6.** 9

Exercises 7. false **9.** true **11.** false **13.** open **15.** open **17.** no **19.** yes **21.** no **23.** yes **25.** $4x + (-3) = 8$ **27.** $115d = 690$ **29.** 13 **31.** 6 **33.** 12 **35.** 6 **37.** 2 **39.** 4 **41.** 6 **43.** 4 **45.** 8 **47.** between −5 and −4 **49.** 2004 **51.** An expression describes the relationship between numbers and variables. An equation shows that two expressions are equal. An expression can be simplified but has no solution. **53.** −6 **55.** between 3 and 4 **57.** between −3 and −2 **59.** 0 **63.** 120 lb **71.** $28 + 14y$ **72.** $-18b - 66$ **73.** $-16.8 - 4.2t$ **74.** $-5 + 25x$ **75.** 10 **76.** −1 **77.** −12 **78.** 7 **79.** −9 **80.** −7 **81.** 2 **82.** $-7\frac{1}{2}$ **83.** 2 **84.** −1 **85.** 3 **86.** 0

Review p. 60

1. Answers may vary. Sample: For the sum −3 for the x-coordinate, you could roll a 4 on the negative cube and a 1 on the positive cube. For the sum 4 for the y-coordinate, you could roll a 1 on the negative cube and a 5 on the positive cube. **3.** Answers may vary. The number on the negative cube must be greater than the number on the positive cube.

Lesson 1-9 pp. 61–66

Got It? 1a. yes **b.** yes **c.** no **d.** yes

2a.

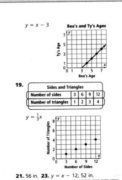

Megan's and Will's Laps

Megan's laps	1	2	3	4	5
Will's laps	7	8	9	10	11

$y = x + 6$

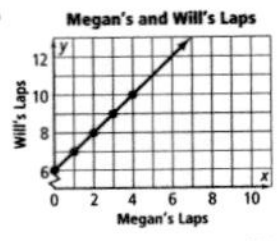

b. The graph would start at (0, 5) instead of (0, 2) and y would always be 5 greater than x.

3a.

Orange tiles	4	8	12	16
Total tiles	9	18	27	36

54 tiles

b.

Blue tiles	1	2	3	4
Yellow tiles	2	4	6	8

48 yellow tiles

Lesson Check 1. no **2.** yes

3.

Drink Cost

Drinks bought	1	2	3	4
Cost ($)	2.50	5	7.50	10

$y = 2.50x$

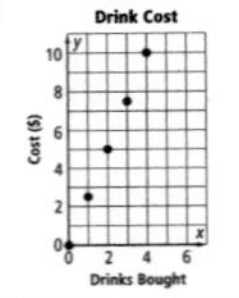

4. 110 Calories **5.** With inductive reasoning, conclusions are reached by observing patterns. With deductive reasoning, conclusions are reached by reasoning logically from given facts. **6.** Answers may vary. Sample: Both equations contain unknown values. An equation in one variable represents a situation with one unknown quantity. An equation in two variables represents a situation where two variable quantities have a relationship. **7.** All; y is 2 more than x.

Exercises 9. no **11.** no **13.** yes **15.** yes

17.

Bea's and Ty's Ages

Bea's age	4	5	6	7
Ty's age	1	2	3	4

$y = x - 3$

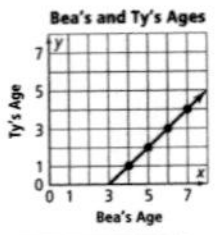

19.

Sides and Triangles

Number of sides	3	6	9	12
Number of triangles	1	2	3	4

$y = \frac{1}{3}x$

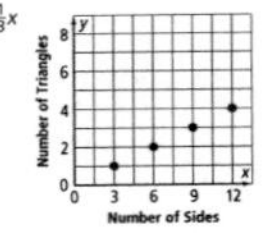

21. 56 in. **23.** $y = x - 12$; 52 in.

25.

Number of Houses	1	2	3	4	5
Number of Windows	4	8	12	16	20

36 windows

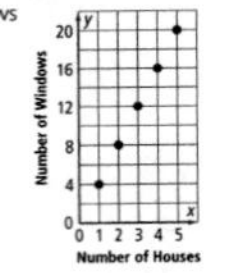

27. no **29.** no **31.** no **33.** no **35.** 13.5 h **37.** 11 h **46.** no **47.** yes **48.** yes **53.** 9 **54.** −3 **55.** −14 **56.** −27 **57.** 40 **58.** −30 **59.** −1 **60.** −81

Chapter Review pp. 68–72

1. irrational **2.** opposite **3.** like terms **4.** absolute value **5.** inductive reasoning **6.** $737w$ **7.** $q - 8$ **8.** $x + 84$ **9.** $51t + 9$ **10.** $\frac{63}{h} - 14$ **11.** $b - \frac{k}{5}$ **12.** the sum of 12 and a number a **13.** 31 less than a number r **14.** the product of 19 and a number t **15.** the quotient of b and 3 **16.** 3 less than the product of 7 and c **17.** the sum of 2 and the quotient of x and 8 **18.** 6 less than the quotient of y and 11 **19.** 13 more than the product of 21 and d **20.** 81 **21.** 125 **22.** $\frac{1}{36}$ **23.** 9.8 **24.** 100 **25.** 48 **26.** $8\frac{1}{3}$ **27.** 40 **28.** 79 **29.** 123 **30a.** 216 **b.** The surface area is reduced to a fourth of its previous value. **31.** 615 mi **32.** irrational **33.** rational **34.** irrational **35.** rational **36.** 10 **37.** 7 **38.** 5 **39.** rational numbers, integers **40.** rational numbers **41.** irrational numbers **42.** rational numbers, whole numbers, natural numbers, integers **43.** rational numbers **44.** rational numbers **45.** $-1\frac{4}{5}, -1\frac{2}{3}, 1.6$ **46.** $-0.8, \frac{7}{9}, \sqrt{3}$ **47.** $9w - 31$ **48.** −96 **49.** 0 **50.** $41 - 4t$ **51.** 1 **52.** yes **53.** no **54.** no **55.** no **56.** 5 **57.** −5 **58.** −9 **59.** 1.8 **60.** −144 **61.** 40 **62.** −3 **63.** −19 **64.** 3 **65.** −8 **66.** 60 **67.** 16 **68.** 12 **69.** −11 **70.** 19 **71.** −100 **72.** −56 **73.** 225 **74.** $-\frac{3}{10}$ **75.** $10x - 15$ **76.** $-14 + 2a$ **77.** $-\frac{1}{2}j + 4$ **78.** v^2 **79.** $6y - 6$ **80.** $\frac{3}{2}y - \frac{1}{4}$ **81.** $6 - 6y$ **82.** $y - 3$ **83.** $-\frac{1}{3}y + 6t$ **84.** $-2ab^2$ **85.** $2850 **86.** Yes; the variable parts of the terms are the same. **87.** yes **88.** no **89.** no **90.** yes **91.** 10 **92.** between 12 and 13 **93.** between 2 and 3 **94.** between 3 and 4 **95.** yes **96.** no **97.** no **98.** no **99.** y is 5 more than the product of 10 and x; $y = 10x + 5$. 55, 65, 75

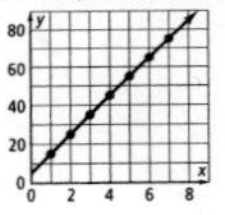

Chapter 2

Get Ready! p. 77

1. Answers may vary. Sample: For each lawn mowed, $7.50 is earned; $y = 7.50x$. **2.** Answers may vary. Sample: 30 pages are read each hour; $y = 30x$. **3.** 3 **4.** −10 **5.** 8 **6.** −8 **7.** 7.14 **8.** 16.4 **9.** $-\frac{9}{20}$ **10.** $-\frac{7}{15}$ **11.** 17 **12.** −3 **13.** 576 **14.** −2.75 **15.** $16k^2$ **16.** $13xy$ **17.** $2t + 2$ **18.** $12x - 4$ **19.** Answers may vary. Sample: The shirts might look the same but be different sizes or different colors; the triangles will be the same shape but different sizes. **20.** Answers may vary. Sample: The model ship is the same shape but just a smaller size than the actual ship.

Lesson 2-1 pp. 81–87

Got It? 1a. −8 **b.** The Subtr. Prop. of Eq. states that subtracting the same number from each side of an equation produces another equation that is equivalent. **2a.** −6 **b.** 2 **3a.** $\frac{2}{3}$ **b.** −4.375 **4a.** 57 **b.** −72 **5a.** 16 **b.** Yes; multiplying each side of the second equation by the

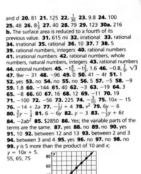

Page 854

reciprocal of $\frac{2}{5}$ produces the first equation. **6.** 6 months
Lesson Check 1. -4 **2.** 13 **3.** $4\frac{4}{5}$ **4.** $\frac{1}{2}b = 117$; 351 pages **5.** Subtr. Prop. of Eq. **6.** Div. Prop. of Eq. **7.** Add. Prop. of Eq. **8.** Mult. Prop. of Eq. **9.** Check students' work.
Exercises 11. 19 **13.** -9 **15.** 26 **17.** 7.5 **19.** 132 **21.** 13.5 **23.** 2 **25.** -4 **27.** -4 **29.** 0.16 **31.** 5 **33.** $-\frac{1}{3}$ **35.** 175 **37.** -117 **39.** 81 **41.** -34 **43.** 12 **45.** -2.5 **47.** 81 **49.** 24 **51.** p = city's population at start of three-year period; $p - 7525 = 581{,}600$; 589,125 **53.** $4500 **55.** $-\frac{7}{11}$ **57.** $7\frac{1}{3}$ **59.** $31\frac{1}{3}$ **61.** $\frac{1}{2}$ **63.** 0.8 **65.** $2\frac{1}{2}$ **67.** -25 **69.** $-\frac{1}{7}$ **71.** Each side of the equation should be multiplied by 9, not $\frac{1}{3}$; $(9)(-36) = (9)\left(\frac{1}{3}\right)$, so $x = -324$. **73.** 21 aces **75.** 2450 letters **82.** 10,000 **83.** $52x$ **84.** $6 - x$ **85.** $m + 4$ **86.** 2 **87.** $\frac{23}{36}$ **88.** 1

Lesson 2-2 pp. 88-93
Got It? 1. 16 **2.** 56 ads **3a.** 26 **b.** $6 = \frac{2}{3} \cdot 2$; 26; answers may vary. Sample: The equation in part (a) is easier because it uses fewer fractions.
4. $\frac{x}{3} - 5 + 5 = 4 + 5$ Add. Prop. of Eq.
$\frac{x}{3} = 9$ Use addition to simplify.
$\frac{x}{3} \cdot 3 = 9 \cdot 3$ Mult. Prop. of Eq.
$x = 27$ Use multiplication to simplify.
Lesson Check 1. -5 **2.** 63 **3.** -7 **4.** -13 **5.** $62 **6.** Subtr. Prop. of Eq. and Mult. Prop. of Eq.; subtr. **7.** Add. Prop. of Eq. and Div. Prop. of Eq.; add. **8.** Add. Prop. of Eq. and Mult. Prop. of Eq.; add. **9.** Subtr. Prop. of Eq. and Div. Prop. of Eq.; subtr. **10.** Answers may vary. Sample: No, you must either multiply both sides by 5 first or write the left side as the difference of two fractions and then add $\frac{2}{5}$ to both sides.
Exercises 11. -12 **13.** -1 **15.** -2 **17.** -27 **19.** 126 **21.** -3 **23.** 16 boxes **25.** $1150 **27.** 29 **29.** -2 **31.** -8 **33.** 8 **35.** 6 **37.** -15 **39.** 2.7 **41.** 4.5 **43.** -3.8 **45.** 0.449 **47.** $15 - 9 = 9 - 3p - 9$ Subt. Prop. of Eq.
$\frac{6}{-3} = \frac{-3p}{-3}$ Div. Prop. of Eq.
$-2 = p$ Use division to simplify.
49. $9 + \frac{-c}{5} - 9 = -5 - 9$ Sub. Prop. of Eq.
$\frac{-c}{5} = -14$ Use subtraction to simplify.
$\frac{-c}{5} \cdot -5 = -14 \cdot -5$ Mult. Prop. of Eq.
$c = 70$ Use multiplication to simplify.
51. 4 should be added to each side; $2x - 4 + 4 = 8 + 4$ so $2x = 12$ and $x = 6$. **53a.** 4 **b.** yes **c.** Answers may vary. Sample: The method in part (a) is easier because it doesn't involve fractions. **55.** 10.5 **57.** 4 **59.** about 2 km **69.** 5 **70.** 3.8 **71.** 144 **72.** 6.5 **73.** false; sample:

$|-5| - |2| \neq -5 - 2$ **74.** false; sample: $-4 + 1 = -3$, $|-4| = 4$ and $|-3| = 3$ **75.** $35 - 7t$ **76.** $4x - 10$ **77.** $-6 + 3b$ **78.** $10 - 25n$

Lesson 2-3 pp. 94-100
Got It? 1a. 6 **b.** 3 **2.** $14 **3a.** 6 **b.** Yes; divide both sides of the equation by 3 first. **4a.** $2\frac{18}{19}$ **b.** $2\frac{1}{6}$ **5.** 12.55
Lesson Check 1. $4\frac{11}{12}$ **2.** -7 **3.** 2 **4.** 2.5 **5.** 16 ft **6.** Answers may vary. Sample: Subtract 1.3 from each side, and then divide each side by 0.5. **7.** Answers may vary. Sample: Apply the Distr. Prop., and then add 28 to each side and divide each side by 21. **8.** Answers may vary. Sample: Multiply each side by the common denominator 18 to clear the fractions. Add 72 to each side and then divide by -4. **9.** Answers may vary. Sample: Amelia's method: it does not involve working with fractions until the end.
Exercises 11. $2\frac{5}{9}$ **13.** 6 **15.** $5\frac{5}{7}$ **17.** -10 **19.** $3x + 6x + 20 = 92$; $8 per h **21.** 6 **23.** 3.75 or $3\frac{3}{4}$ **25.** $7\frac{3}{7}$ **27.** $-\frac{1}{3}$ **29.** 9.75 or $9\frac{3}{4}$ **31.** $-\frac{1}{3}$ **33.** 2 **35.** $56\frac{2}{3}$ **37.** $\frac{1}{2}$ **39.** 3.5 **41.** 5 **43.** 4.27 **45.** $43\frac{1}{3}$ **47.** $3\frac{3}{10}$ **49.** 1.5 or $1\frac{1}{2}$ **51.** 2 **53.** 5 **55.** $15 **57.** Answers may vary. Sample: Combine the like terms on the left side of the equation. **59.** 3 games **61.** 15 **63.** 20 **65.** 4 weeks **72.** -5 **73.** 7 **74.** 4 **75.** Inv. Prop. of Add. **76.** Assoc. Prop. of Mult. **77.** Mult. Prop. of Zero **78.** $3y$ **79.** $-3y$ **80.** 0

Lesson 2-4 pp. 102-108
Got It? 1a. -4 **b.** The answer is the same, -4. **2.** about 27 months **3a.** -5 **b.** **4.** infinitely many solutions **b.** no solution
Lesson Check 1. 7 **2.** -3 **3.** infinitely many solutions **4.** no solutions **5.** 100 business cards **6.** C **7.** A **8.** B **9.** If the numeric values are the same on both sides, it is an identity. If they are different, there is no solution.
Exercises 11. -9 **13.** 6 **15.** -1 **17.** $-1\frac{1}{3}$ **19.** 22 ft **21.** 25 **23.** -37 **25.** 18 **27.** no solution **29.** no solution **31.** identity **33.** $\frac{4}{5}$ **35.** -19 **37.** no solution **39.** -3 **41a.** $\frac{4}{60}$ **b.** $\frac{4}{60}$ **c.** $\frac{4}{60} + 1 = \frac{5}{60}$; 120 mi; 48 mi/h **43.** Subtraction should be used to isolate the variable, not division by the variable. $2x = 4x$, so $= 4x$, and $x = 0$. **45.** 2 months **47.** always **49a.** always true **b.** sometimes true **c.** sometimes true **61.** -6 **62.** 1 **63.** 0.9 m **64.** 22 **65.** 9 **66.** 11.2

Lesson 2-5 pp. 109-114
Got It? 1a. $\frac{4 + 5x}{x}$, -3; 2, 7 **b.** $y = 10$; $y = 4$
2. $x = \frac{-t - t}{2}$ **3.** 6 in. **4.** about 55 days

Page 855

Lesson Check 1. $y = \frac{2x + 12}{5}$ **2.** $b = \frac{a + 10}{}$ **3.** $x = \frac{p}{m + 2n}$ **4.** $F = \frac{9}{5}C + 32$ **5.** 40 gal **6.** literal equation **7.** literal equation **8.** both **9.** both **10.** Answers may vary. Sample: They are the same in each case since you are isolating a variable by using inverse operations. They are different because, in an equation in one variable, to isolate the variable, inverse operations are used on numbers only. In a literal equation, inverse operations are used on variables as well as numbers.
Exercises 11. $y = -2x + 5$; 7; 5; -1 **13.** $y = \frac{3x - 9}{}$, $-\frac{12}{}$, $-\frac{6}{}$, $-\frac{5}{}$ **15.** $y = -\frac{5x - 4}{4}$, $-\frac{1}{4} - $, $-\frac{11}{}$ **17.** $y = \frac{x + 4}{4}$, $\frac{1}{2}$; 2; **19.** $x = \frac{p}{m + n}$ **21.** $x = r + s$ **23.** $x = \frac{5 - c}{2}$ **25.** $x = \frac{A - c}{}$ **27.** $x = 2y - 4$ **29.** 4.5 in. **31.** 7 cm **33.** 0.4 h **35.** $h = \frac{r}{t}$; 8 ft **37.** $x = \frac{9t}{r} + a$ **39.** $h = \frac{3V}{}$ **41.** $a = 2b - x$ **43.** $-108.4°F$ **45.** 3 was added to the left side of the equation instead of subtracted; $2m - 3 = -6n$, $\frac{2m - 3}{-6} = n$. **47.** 5 cm³ **54.** 5 **55.** 3 **56.** -4 **57.** 3 **58.** identity **59.** no solution **60.** 147 **61.** -40 **62.** 567 **63.** 100 **64.** 3 **65.** $\frac{4}{5}$ **66.** $\frac{7}{25}$

Lesson 2-6 pp. 118-123
Got It? 1. No; Store C is still the lowest. **2.** 12.5 m **3a.** about 442 m **b.** about 205 euros **4a.** about 22 mi/h **b.** Yes; $\frac{60.1}{1\,\text{min}} \cdot \frac{60\,\text{min}}{1\,\text{h}}$ is the same as $\frac{3600.5}{}$.
Lesson Check 1. 8 bagels for $4.15 **2.** 116 oz **3.** 12 m **4.** $80\frac{2}{3}$ ft/s **5.** not a unit rate **6.** unit rate **7.** No; a conversion factor is a ratio of two equivalent measures in different units and is always equal to 1. **8.** Greater; to convert you multiply by 16.
Exercises 7. Olga **11.** 189 ft **13.** 40 oz **15.** 240 s **23.** 1.875 gal/h **25.** 39,304 nm **27.** Yes; sample: 100 mi **33.** 5 oz **35.** recipe B **37.** Miles; kilometers cancel out and miles are left. **39.** 1580.82 INR; 19.98 GBP **41.** Answers may vary. Sample: Estimating the size to the nearest inch is appropriate because the carpenter is leaving an estimated amount on either side of the television, not an exact amount. **48.** 5 cm **49.** 15 in. **50.** 5 **51.** 6 **52.** 0.5 **53.** 3 **54.** 7 **55.** $\frac{1}{12}$ **56.** 20m **57.** $\frac{7}{2}$

Lesson 2-7 pp. 124-129
Got It? 1. 5.6 **2a.** 1.8 **3.** -5 **4.** 145.5 mg **5.** 5.6 **6.** 6.75 h **7.** m and q **7.** n and p **8.** mg and np **9.** Yes; sample: One method creates an equation using the fact that the cross products are equal, and the other method creates an equivalent equation using the Mult. Prop. of Eq. to clear the denominators.
Exercises 11. -19.5 **13.** 4.2 **15.** 112.5 **17.** $16\frac{2}{3}$ **19.** 10 **21.** 14 **23.** $26\frac{2}{3}$ **25.** -15 **27.** 4.75 **29.** 11 **31.** $-6\frac{3}{4}$ **33.** -5 **35.** 8 dozen **37.** about 17 people **39.** $\frac{\$5.07}{1\,\text{kWh}} = \frac{\$143.32}{x\,\text{kWh}}$, 2047.4 kWh **41.** at the same time as you **43.** 1.8 **45.** 2.7 **47.** 4.2 **49.** $-\frac{1}{3}$ **51.** 3 was not fully distributed when multiplying 3 and $x + 3$; $16 = 3x + 9$, $7 = 3x$, $x = \frac{7}{3}$ **63.** 4 **65.** 90 **66.** 190 **67.** no solution **68.** $\frac{1}{3}$ **69.** identity **70.** $2\frac{3}{5}$ or 2.8 **71.** $2\frac{1}{5}$ or 2.13 **72.** $6\frac{2}{3}$ or 6.6 **73.** $\frac{2}{3}$ or 0.6

Lesson 2-8 pp. 130-136
Got It? 1. 24 **2.** 30 ft **3a.** about 66 mi **b.** Write and solve the proportion $\frac{x}{250} = \frac{x}{1}$; 1 in. represents 125 mi. **4.** 300 ft
Lesson Check 1a. 32.5 cm **b.** 1 : 2.5 **2.** 225 km **3.** The order of the letters in each triangle tells which parts are corresponding. **4a.** yes **b.** no **c.** yes **5.** Answers may vary. Sample: No, it is greater than 100 times since 100 mi is more than 100 times greater than 1 in.
Exercises 7. $\angle F \cong \angle K$, $\angle G \cong \angle L$, $\angle H \cong \angle M$, $\angle I \cong \angle N$, $\frac{FG}{KL} = \frac{GH}{LM} = \frac{HI}{MN} = \frac{FI}{KN}$ **9.** 40 **11.** 100 **13.** 37.5 km **15.** 225 km **17.** 67.5 ft **19.** $6\frac{2}{3}$ ft $\times$ $2\frac{1}{3}$ ft **21.** no **23a.** The student used CJ instead of AJ. **b.** $\frac{BC}{} = \frac{GH}{}$ **25.** 39,304 cm **27.** Yes; all squares will have sides that are in proportion (the same length), and the measures of corresponding $\angle$s are equal (90°). **35.** 34 **36.** 4.5 **37.** -8 **38.** $-\frac{5}{}$ **39.** 1.5 **40.** 8 **41.** 0.4 **42.** 0.25 **43.** 2.9

Lesson 2-9 pp. 137-143
Got It? 1. 60% **2.** 75%; the answers are the same. **3.** $3600 **4.** $41\frac{2}{3}$ **5.** 4 yr
Lesson Check 1. 30% **2.** 120% **3.** 28 **4.** 48 **5.** $180 **6.** 100 **7.** $75 **8.** Answers may vary. Sample: 12 is what percent of 10?
Exercises 9. 20% **11.** 62.5% **13.** $41\frac{1}{3}\%$ **15.** 36 **17.** 13 **19.** 16 **21.** $52 **23.** 400 **25.** 22.5 **27.** $22\frac{2}{3}$ **29.** $108 **31.** part; 5.04 **33.** part; 142.5 **35.** percent; $1333\frac{1}{3}$ **37.** 66,000 mi² **39.** 16 **41.** 75 **43.** 8 **45.** 121%; it costs more to make a penny than the penny is worth. **47.** The values for a and b are reversed; $\frac{3}{15} = \frac{n}{100}$; $1.5p = 300$, $p = 200\%$ **49.** $181 **51.** $29\frac{2}{5}\%$ **57.** 14.4 cm **58.** 18 cans **59.** $c = 1.75 + 2.4\left(m - \frac{1}{8}\right)$; $2\frac{2}{3}$ mi **60.** 1250% **61.** 0.6 **62.** 175%

Page 856

Lesson 2-10 pp. 144-150
Got It? 1. about 32% **2.** about 17% **3.** about 16% **4.** 65.5 in. and 66.5 in. **5.** It would be smaller since the measurement of each dimension is closer to the actual value of each dimension.
Lesson Check 1. about 2% **2.** about 61% **3.** 7.25 ft and 7.75 ft **4a.** percent decrease **b.** percent decrease **c.** percent increase **5.** 0.05 m **6.** A percent increase involves an increase of the original amount and a percent decrease involves a decrease of the original amount.
Exercises 7. increase; 50% **9.** decrease; 7% **11.** decrease; 4% **13.** increase; 54% **15.** increase; 27% **17.** about 55% **19.** about 13% **21.** 1.05 kg; 1.15 kg **23.** about 28% **25.** 175% increase **27.** 42% decrease **29.** 39% increase **31.** 48.75 m²; 63.75 m² **33.** 550.25 ft²; 551.25 ft² **37.** The original amount is 12, not 18; $\frac{18 - 12}{12} = \frac{6}{12} = 0.5 = 50\%$. **39.** 12.63 **45.** $66\frac{2}{3}\%$ **46.** 64.75 **47.** 21
48-51.
-2.8, $\frac{1}{2}$
-3, -2.8, $\frac{1}{2}$, 2

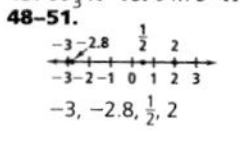

Chapter Review pp. 153-156
1. inverse operations **2.** identity **3.** rate **4.** scale **5.** cross products **6.** -7 **7.** 7 **8.** 14 **9.** 65 **10.** 3.5 **11.** -4 **12.** -5 **13.** -8 **14.** $6.50 **15.** Add. Prop. of Eq.; Simplify; Div. Prop. of Eq.; Simplify. **16.** 11 **17.** 8 **18.** -7.5 **19.** $3\frac{3}{8}$ **20.** 28 **21.** 14.7 **22.** $4h + 8h + 50 = 164$; $9.50 **23.** $37t + 8.50t + 14.99 = 242.49$; 5 tickets **24.** -90 **25.** 7.2 **26.** identity **27.** no solution **28.** $8h = 16 + 6h$; 8 ft **29.** $\frac{x}{65} = \frac{1}{130} + 3$; 390 mi **30.** $x = \frac{-c}{}$ **31.** $x = -t - t$ **32.** $x = \frac{m - p}{}$ **33.** $x = \frac{pqs}{r}$ **34.** 40 cm **35.** 15 mm **36.** 16 in. **37.** 78 in. **38.** 71 oz **39.** 2.25 min **40.** 3960 yd **41.** 240 loaves **42.** about 6 lb **43.** $\frac{1}{11}$ s or about 0.45 s **44.** 21 **45.** -4 **46.** 1.6 **47.** 21 **48.** 39 **49.** -1 **50.** 12 in. **51.** 42 in. **52.** 300% **53.** 108 **54.** 170 **55.** 60 seeds **56.** 30% **57.** 72 students **58.** increase; 11% **59.** decrease; 20% **60.** decrease; 11% **61.** increase; 32% **62.** about 47% **63.** about 39% **64.** Yes; 50% of 38° is 19° and $38° + 19° = 57°$.

Chapter 3

Get Ready! p. 161
1. $>$ **2.** $\geq$ **3.** $>$ **4.** $<$ **5.** 7 **6.** -4 **7.** 1.8 **9.** 3 **10.** -12 **11.** 32.4 **12.** 23 **13.** 29.5 **14.** -28 **15.** -12

16. 48 **17.** 5 **18.** -24 **19.** -10 **20.** 1.85 **21.** -24 **22.** -2 **23.** 3 **24.** 60 **25.** -4 **26.** 3 **27.** $\frac{1}{2}$ **28.** 2.5 **29.** 4.1 **30.** 24 **31.** Answers may vary. Sample: Two inequalities are joined together. **32.** Answers may vary. Sample: the part that the two groups of objects have in common

Lesson 3-1 pp. 164-170
Got It? 1a. $p \geq 1.5$ **b.** $t + 7 < -3$ **2a.** 1 and 3 **b.** The solution of the inequality is -2. The solution of the inequality is all real numbers greater than -2.
3a. [number line]
b. [number line]
c. [number line]
4a. $x < -3$ **b.** $x \geq 0$ **5.** No; the speed limit can only be nonnegative real numbers.
Lesson Check 1. $y \geq 12$ **2a.** no **b.** no **c.** yes **d.** yes **3.** Substitute the number for the variable and simplify. If the number makes the inequality true, then it is a solution of the inequality. **6.** Answers may vary. Sample: $x \geq 0$, whole numbers, a baseball team's score during an inning, amount in cubic centimeters of liquid in a chemistry beaker; $x > 0$, counting numbers, length of a poster, distance in blocks between your house and a park
Exercises 9. $b < 4$ **11.** $\frac{2}{3} > 1\frac{1}{2}$ **13a.** yes **b.** no **c.** yes **15a.** yes **b.** no **c.** no **17.** D **19.** A
21. [number line]
23. [number line]
25. [number line]
27. [number line]
29. $x > -4$ **31.** $x \geq 2$ **33.** $x \leq 3$ **35.** Let p = number of people seated; $p \leq 172$. **37.** Let w = number of watts of the light bulb; $w \leq 75$. **39.** Let m = amount of money earned; $m > 20{,}000$. **45.** b is greater than 0. **47.** z is greater than or equal to 25.6. **49.** 21 is greater than or equal to m. **51.** 2 less than g is less than 7. **53.** r more than 6 is greater than -2. **55.** 1.2 is greater than k. **57.** Answers may vary. Sample: No more than means "is less than or equal to," since the amount cannot be greater than the given number. No less than means "is greater than or equal to," since the amount cannot be less than the given number. **59.** $998 > 978$, so Option A > Option B. **69.** increase; 20% **70.** decrease; 10% **71.** decrease; 67% **72.** 44 **73.** $-\frac{5}{24}$ **74.** -3 **75.** $-1\frac{3}{}$ **76.** 11 **77.** -2 **78.** -11 **79.** $-\frac{1}{9}$

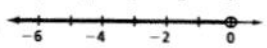

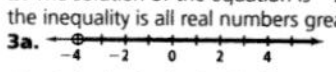

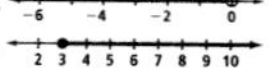

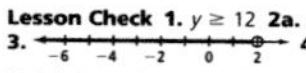

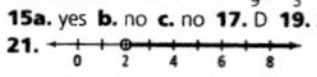

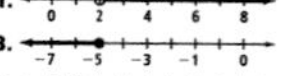

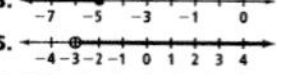

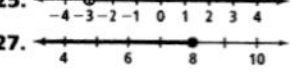

Page 857

Lesson 3-2 pp. 171-177
Got It? 1. $n < 2$
[number line, point at 2]
2. $m \geq 9$ [number line]
3. $y \leq -13$ [number line]
4a. $p \geq 8$ **b.** Yes. The $\geq$ symbol can be used to represent all 3 phrases.
Lesson Check
1. $p < 5$ [number line]
2. $d \leq 10$ [number line]
3. $y < -12$ [number line]
4. $c > 3$ [number line]
5. $w \leq 524$ **6.** Add or subtract the same number from each side of the inequality. **7a.** Subtract 4 from each side. **b.** Add 1 to each side. **c.** Subtract 3 from each side. **d.** Add 2 to each side. **8.** They are similar in that one inequality adds 4 and the other subtracts 4.
Exercises 9. 6 **11.** 3.3
13. $y > 13$ [number line]
15. $t \leq -4$ [number line]
17. $t \geq -3$ [number line]
19. $p > 12$ [number line]
21. $f > \frac{1}{3}$ [number line]
23. $r < 0$ [number line]
25. $s < 4.7$ [number line]
27. $c < 1\frac{2}{3}$ [number line]
29. 3 **31.** 4.2
33. $x \leq 5$ [number line]
35. $c > -7$ [number line]
37. $a \geq -1$ [number line]

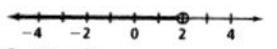

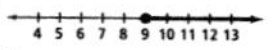

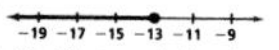

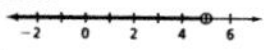

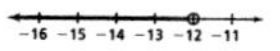

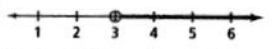

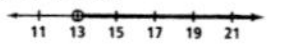

39. $n > -2\frac{2}{3}$ [number line]
41. $d \geq -1$ [number line]
43. $3 + 4 + g \geq 10$; $g \geq 3$ **45.** Add 4 to each side. **47.** Add $\frac{1}{2}$ to each side. **49.** yes
51. [box diagram: 51, 17, x]
53. [diagram: 3, 13]
55. $d \leq 2$ **57.** $-4\frac{2}{3}$ **59.** $-1.2 > z$ **61.** $p > 12$ **63.** $b \geq -2\frac{1}{4}$ **65.** $5\frac{1}{6} \geq m$ **67a.** yes **b.** No; in the first inequality, r is greater than or equal to the amount. In the second inequality, r is less than or equal to the amount. In part (a), these are equations with only one solution. In part (b), because the inequality relationship is different, there is no relationship between the two inequalities. **69.** Answers may vary. Sample: 94, 95, or 96. **71.** The graph should be shaded to the right, not the left.
[number line]
73a. No; the solution should be $a \geq 8.6 - 3.2$, or $a \geq 5.4$. **b.** Answers may vary. Sample: Other numbers that are not substituted could also be solutions to the inequality. **75.** at least $88.74 **85.** Let h = distance in miles the hummingbird migrates; $h > 1850$. **86.** Let o = length of octopus in feet; $o \leq 18$. **87.** 72 **88.** -1 **89.** 0.56 **90.** 20 **91.** $-\frac{1}{}$ **92.** -24

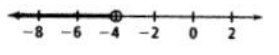

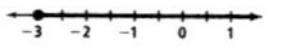

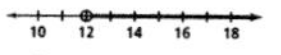

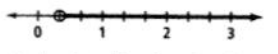

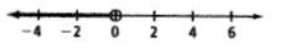

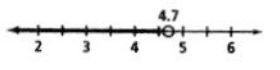

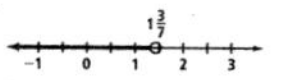

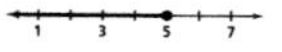

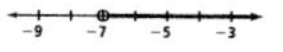

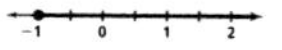

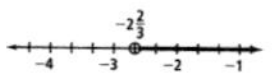

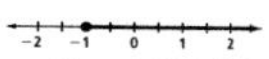

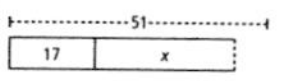

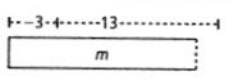

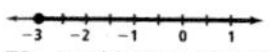

Lesson 3-3 pp. 178-183
Got It? 1. $c > 2$ [number line]
2. $n > 3$ [number line]
3a. 1, 2, 3, or 4 cases **b.** $\frac{x}{50} = 16\frac{2}{3}$, but you cannot walk $\frac{2}{3}$ of a dog. If you round down to 16, you will only make $72. So round up to 17.
4. $x < 2$ [number line]
Lesson Check 1. D **2.** B **3.** A **4.** C **5a.** Multiplication by -2; it is the inverse of division by -2. **b.** Addition of 4; it is the inverse of subtraction of 4. **c.** Division by -6; it is the inverse of multiplication by -6. **6.** The inequality symbol was not reversed when multiplying by a negative.
$-5\left(-\frac{c}{5}\right) < -5(2)$, $n < -10$

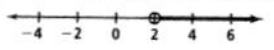

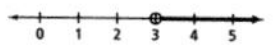

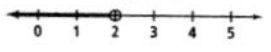

9. $p < 32$ [number line 28 30 32 34 36]
11. $v \le -3$ [number line -5 -4 -3 -2 -1 0]
13. $x \ge -3$ [number line]
15. $m \le 0$ [number line -2 -1 0 1 2]
17. $m \le -3$
19. $m \ge 2$ [number line 0 1 2 3 4 5]
21. $c > 6$ [number line 0 2 4 6 8 10]
23. $z > -3$ [number line]
25. $b \le -\frac{1}{6}$ [number line -6 -5 -4 -3 -2 -1 0]
27. $h > -13$ [number line -15 -14 -13 -12 -11 -10]
29. $q \le 9$ [number line 6 7 8 9 10]
31. no more than 66 text messages 33–35. Answers may vary. Samples are given. 33. $-5, -4, -3, -2$ 35. $-6, -5, -4, -3$ 37. Multiply each side by -4 and reverse the inequality symbol. 39. Divide each side by 5.
41. -2 43. 4 45. Sometimes true; sample: It is true when $x = 4$ and $y = 0.5$ but false when $x = 4$ and $y = -2$. 47. Sometimes true; sample: It is true when $x = 4$ and $y = 2$ but false when $x = 0$ and $y = 2$. 49. at least 0.08 mi per min
51. $3(-1) \le 3(\frac{1}{3})$ Mult. Prop. of Ineq.
    $-3 \le t$ Simplify.
53. $2(0.5) \le 2(\frac{1}{2}c)$ Mult. Prop. of Ineq.
    $1 \le c$ Simplify.
55. $5(\frac{1}{5}) \le 5(-2)$ Mult. Prop. of Ineq.
    $n \le -10$ Simplify.
57. $-\frac{7}{6}(1) > -\frac{7}{6}(-\frac{2}{9}s)$ Mult. Prop. of Ineq.
    $-\frac{7}{6} > s$ Simplify.
59. If the most expensive sandwiches and drinks are ordered, the cost is $3(7) + 3(2) = 27$, leaving \$3. If the most expensive snack is bought, the least number of snacks you can afford is 1. If the least expensive sandwiches and drinks are ordered, the cost is $3(4) + 3(1) = 15$, leaving \$15. If the least expensive snack is bought, the greatest number of snacks you can afford is 15. 61. $x < 20, x < 30, x < 40, \ldots$; any inequality following the one that a is a solution to. This is because each following inequality has the same solutions

as the previous inequalities, with more values as solutions.
68. $x \le -11$ 69. $y \ge 13.6$ 70. $q < 5$ 71. $-\frac{1}{4} > c$
72. $-1 < b$ 73. $y \le 75$ 74. $z \ge 76$ 75. -2 76. 1

Lesson 3-4 pp. 186–192
Got It? 1a. $a \ge -4$ b. $n < 3$ c. $x < 25$ 2. any width greater than 0 ft and less than or equal to 6 ft 3. $m \le -3$
4a. $b > 3$ b. Answers may vary. Sample: adding 1 to each side. This would gather the constant terms onto one side of the inequality. 5a. no solution b. all real numbers
Lesson Check 1. $a > 2$ 2. $t \le 5$ 3. $x < 13$ 4. no solution 5. greater than 0 cm and less than or equal to 8 cm 6. The variable terms cancel each other out and a false inequality results. 7. Yes; each side can be divided by 2 first. 8. No; there is no solution, since -6 is not greater than itself. If the inequality symbol were $\ge$, your friend would be correct.
Exercises 9. $f \le 3$ 11. $y > -2$ 13. $r \ge 3.5$
15. $5s \ge 250$; $s \ge 50$ mph 17. $k \ge 1$ 19. $j < -1$
21. $z < 9$ 23. $x < 3$ 25. $f \le 6$ 27. $m \ge -5$ 29. all real numbers 31. all real numbers 33. all real numbers
35. $x \ge -4$ 37. $t \ge \frac{7}{2}$ 39. $n \ge -2$ 41. $a \ge 0.5$
43. $k \le \frac{13}{2}$ 45. 5.5 h 47. D 49a. $v \ge v$ b. $4 \le v$
c. They are equivalent. 51. at least \$3750 53. $3y$ was subtracted from instead of added to each side; $7y \le 2$, $y \le \frac{2}{7}$. 62. $m \le -4$ 63. $y \ge 28$ 64. $y > -20$
65. $t \ge -3$ 66. whole numbers 67. natural numbers
68. integers

Lesson 3-5 pp. 194–199
Got It? 1. $N = \{2, 4, 6, 8, 10, 12\}$; $N = \{x \mid x$ is an even natural number, $x \le 12\}$ 2. $\{n \mid n < 3\}$
3a. $\{ \}$ or $\varnothing$, $\{a\}$, $\{b\}$, $\{a, b\}$; $\{ \}$ or $\varnothing$, $\{a\}$, $\{b\}$, $\{c\}$, $\{a, b\}$, $\{a, c\}$, $\{b, c\}$, $\{a, b, c\}$ b. Yes; every element of set A is part of set B, since $-3 < 0$. 4. $A' = \{$February, April, June, September, November$\}$
Lesson Check 1. $G = \{1, 3, 5, 7, 9, 11, 13, 15, 17\}$; $G = \{x \mid x$ is an odd natural number, $x < 18\}$
2. $\{d \mid d \le 3\}$ 3. $\{ \}$ or $\varnothing$, $\{4\}$, $\{8\}$, $\{12\}$, $\{4, 8\}$, $\{4, 12\}$, $\{8, 12\}$, $\{4, 8, 12\}$ 4. $W' = \{$spring, summer, fall$\}$ 5. A; its complement is the set of all elements in the universal set that are not in A'. 6a. Yes; the empty set is a subset of every set. b. No; the number 5 in the first set is not an element of the second set. c. Yes; the element in the first set is also an element of the second set. 7. sometimes
8. The student forgot that D is also a whole number.
Exercises 9. $\{0, 1, 2, 3\}$; $\{m \mid m$ is an integer, $-1 < m < 4\}$ 11. $\{1, 2, 3, 4, 5, 6, 7, 8, 9, 10\}$; $\{p \mid p$ is a natural number, $p < 11\}$ 13. $\{y \mid y \ge 4\}$ 15. $\{m \mid m > -5\}$ 17. $\{p \mid p \ge 1\}$ 19. $\{ \}$ or $\varnothing$, $\{a\}$, $\{e\}$, $\{i\}$, $\{o\}$, $\{a, e\}$, $\{a, i\}$, $\{a, o\}$, $\{e, i\}$, $\{e, o\}$, $\{i, o\}$, $\{a, e, i\}$, $\{a, e, o\}$, $\{a, i, o\}$, $\{e, i, o\}$, $\{a, e, i, o\}$ 21. $\{ \}$ or $\varnothing$, $\{$dog$\}$, $\{$cat$\}$, $\{$fish$\}$, $\{$dog, cat$\}$, $\{$dog, fish$\}$, $\{$cat, fish$\}$, $\{$dog, cat, fish$\}$ 23. $\{ \}$ or $\varnothing$, $\{1\}$

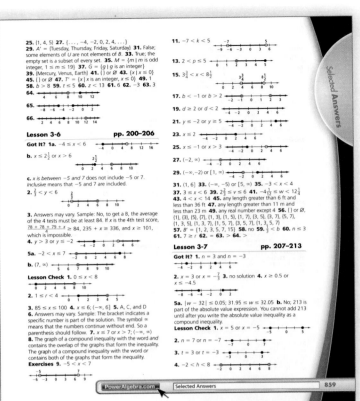

25. $\{1, 4, 5\}$ 27. $\{\ldots, -4, -2, 0, 2, 4, \ldots\}$
29. $A' = \{$Tuesday, Thursday, Friday, Saturday$\}$ 31. False; some elements of U are not elements of B. 33. True; the empty set is a subset of every set. 35. $M = \{m \mid m$ is odd integer, $1 \le m \le 19\}$ 37. $G = \{g \mid g$ is an integer$\}$
39. $\{$Mercury, Venus, Earth$\}$ 41. $\{ \}$ or $\varnothing$ 43. $\{x \mid x \le 0\}$
45. $\{ \}$ or $\varnothing$ 47. $T' = \{x \mid x$ is an integer, $x \le 0\}$ 49. 1
58. $b > $ 59. $t \le 5$ 60. $z < 13$ 61. 6 62. -3 63. 3
64. [number line -8 -6 -4 -2 0 2]
65. [number line -8 -6 -4 -2 0]
66. [number line 2 4 6 8 10 12 14]

Lesson 3-6 pp. 200–206
Got It? 1a. $-4 \le x < 6$ [number line -4 0 4 8 12 16]
b. $x \le 2\frac{1}{2}$ or $x > 6$ [number line 2 4 6 8 10]
c. x is between -5 and 7 does not include -5 or 7. Inclusive means that -5 and 7 are included.
2. $\frac{5}{2} < y < 6$ [number line 2 4 6 8 10]
3. Answers may vary. Sample: No; to get a 8, the average of the 4 tests must be at least 84. If x is the 4th test score, $\frac{78 + 78 + 79 + x}{4} \ge 84$, $235 + x \ge 336$, and $x \ge 101$, which is impossible.
4. $y > 3$ or $y \le -2$ [number line]
5a. $-2 < x \le 7$ [number line -2 0 2 4 6 8]
b. $(7, \infty)$ [number line]
Lesson Check 1. $0 \le x < 8$ [number line]
2. $1 \le r < 4$ [number line 0 1 2 3 4 5]
3. $85 \le x \le 100$ 4. $x \le 6$; $(-\infty, 6]$ 5. A, C, and D
6. Answers may vary. Sample: The bracket indicates a specific number is part of the solution. The symbol ∞ means that the numbers continue without end. So a parenthesis should follow. 7. $x \le 7$ or $x > 7$; $(-\infty, \infty)$
8. The graph of a compound inequality with the word *and* contains the overlap of the graphs that form the inequality. The graph of a compound inequality with the word *or* contains both of the graphs that form the inequality.
Exercises 9. $-5 < x < 7$ [number line -6 -3 0 3 6 9]

11. $-7 < k < 5$ [number line -9 -6 -3 0 3 6]
13. $2 < p \le 5$ [number line 0 1 2 3 4 5]
15. $3\frac{3}{4} < x < 8\frac{1}{2}$ [number line 0 4 8 12]
17. $b < -1$ or $b > 2$ [number line -4 -2 0 2 4 6]
19. $d \ge 2$ or $d < 2$ [number line 0 1 2 3 4 5]
21. $y \le -2$ or $y \ge 5$ [number line]
23. $x \le 2$ [number line -4 -2 0 2 4]
25. $x \le -1$ or $x > 3$ [number line -4 -2 0 2 4]
27. $(-2, \infty)$ [number line]
29. $(-\infty, -2]$ or $[1, \infty)$ [number line]
31. $(1, 6]$ 33. $(-\infty, -5)$ or $[5, \infty)$ 35. $-3 < x < 4$
37. $3 \le x < 6$ 39. $2\frac{2}{3} \le v \le 6$ 41. $-4\frac{1}{3} \le w < 12\frac{1}{3}$
43. $4 < x < 14$ 45. any length greater than 6 ft and less than 23 m 49. any real number except 4 56. $\{ \}$ or $\varnothing$, $\{1\}$, $\{3\}$, $\{5\}$, $\{7\}$, $\{1, 3\}$, $\{1, 5\}$, $\{1, 7\}$, $\{3, 5\}$, $\{3, 7\}$, $\{5, 7\}$, $\{1, 3, 5\}$, $\{1, 3, 7\}$, $\{1, 5, 7\}$, $\{3, 5, 7\}$, $\{1, 3, 5, 7\}$ 57. $B' = \{1, 2, 3, 5, 7, 15\}$ 58. No 59. $\frac{1}{3} < b$ 60. $n \le 3$
61. $7 \ge r$ 62. -6 63. $>$ 64. $>$

Lesson 3-7 pp. 207–213
Got It? 1. $n = 3$ and $n = -3$ [number line -4 -2 0 2 4]
2. $x = 3$ or $x = -\frac{7}{3}$ 3. no solution 4. $x \ge 0.5$ or $x \le -4.5$
5a. $|w - 32| \le 0.05$; $31.95 \le w \le 32.05$ b. No; 213 is part of the absolute value expression. You cannot add 213 until after you write the absolute value inequality as a compound inequality.
Lesson Check 1. $x = 5$ or $x = -5$ [number line]
2. $n = 7$ or $n = -7$ [number line]
3. $t = 3$ or $t = -3$ [number line]
4. $-2 < h < 8$ [number line -2 0 2 4 6 8]

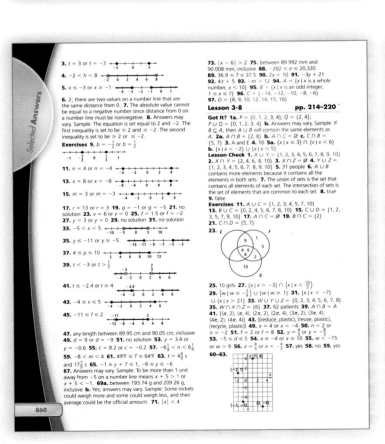

3. $t = 3$ or $t = -3$ [number line -3 0 3]
4. $-2 < h < 8$ [number line -2 ... 8]
5. $x \le -3$ or $x \ge -1$ [number line -4 -3 -2 -1 0 1]
6. 2; there are two values on a number line that are the same distance from 0. 7. The absolute value cannot be equal to a negative number since distance from 0 on a number line must be nonnegative. 8. Answers may vary. Sample: The equation is set equal to 2 and -2. The first inequality is set to be ≤ 2 and ≥ -2. The second inequality is set to be ≥ 2 or ≤ -2.
Exercises 9. $b = -\frac{1}{2}$ or $b = \frac{1}{2}$ [number line]
11. $n = 4$ or $n = -4$ [number line]
13. $x = 8$ or $x = -8$ [number line]
15. $m = 3$ or $m = -3$ [number line]
17. $r = 13$ or $r = 3$ 19. $g = -1$ or $g = -5$ 21. no solution 23. $v = 6$ or $v = 0$ 25. $f = 1.5$ or $f = -2$ 27. $y = 3$ or $y = 0$ 29. no solution 31. no solution
33. $-5 < x < 5$ [number line]
35. $y \le -11$ or $y \ge -5$ [number line]
37. $4 \le p \le 10$ [number line]
39. $t < -3$ or $t > \frac{7}{3}$ [number line]
41. $t \le -2.4$ or $t \ge 4$ [number line]
43. $-4 \le v \le 5$ [number line]
45. $-11 \le f \le 2$ [number line]
47. any length between 89.95 cm and 90.05 cm, inclusive 49. $d = 9$ or $d = -9$ 51. no solution 53. $y = 3.4$ or $y = -0.6$ 55. $c = 8.2$ or $c = -0.2$ 57. $-6\frac{1}{4} < n < 6\frac{1}{4}$
59. $-8 < m < 4$ 61. $49°F \le T \le 64°F$ 63. $T = 4\frac{4}{5}$ and $17\frac{4}{5}$ 65. $-1 \le y + 7 \le 1$, $-8 \le y \le -6$
67. Answers may vary. Sample: To be more than 1 unit away from -5 on a number line means $x + 5 > 1$ or $x + 5 < -1$. 69a. between 193.74 g and 209.26 g, inclusive b. Yes; answers may vary. Sample: Some nickels could weigh more and some could weigh less, and their average could be the official amount. 71. $|x| < 4$

73. $|x - 6| > 2$ 75. between 89.992 mm and 90.008 mm, inclusive 88. $-282 \le e \le 20{,}320$
89. $36.9 \le T \le 37.5$ 90. $2x + 10$ 91. $-3y + 21$
92. $4t + 5$ 93. $-m - 12$ 94. $A = \{x \mid x$ is a whole number, $x < 10\}$ 95. $B = \{x \mid x$ is an odd integer, $1 \le x \le 7\}$ 96. $C = \{-14, -12, -10, -8, -6\}$
97. $D = \{8, 9, 10, 12, 14, 15, 16\}$

Lesson 3-8 pp. 214–220
Got It? 1a. $P = \{0, 1, 2, 3, 4\}$; $Q = \{2, 4\}$;
$P \cup Q = \{0, 1, 2, 3, 4\}$ b. Answers may vary. Sample: If $B \subseteq A$, then $A \cup B$ will contain the same elements as A. 2a. $A \cap B = \{2, 8\}$ b. $A \cap C = \varnothing$ c. $C \cap B = \{5, 7\}$ 3. A and E 4. 10 5a. $\{x \mid x \ge 3\} \cap \{x \mid x < 6\}$ b. $\{x \mid x < -2\} \cup \{x \mid x > 5\}$
Lesson Check 1. $X \cup Y = \{1, 2, 3, 4, 5, 6, 7, 8, 9, 10\}$ 2. $X \cap Y = \{2, 4, 6, 8, 10\}$ 3. $A \cap Z = \varnothing$ 4. $Y \cup Z = \{1, 2, 3, 4, 5, 6, 7, 8, 9, 10\}$ 5. 31 people 6. $A \cup B$ contains more elements because it contains all the elements in both sets. 7. The union of sets is the set that contains all elements of each set. The intersection of sets is the set of elements that are common to each set. 8. true
9. false
Exercises 11. $A \cup C = \{1, 2, 3, 4, 5, 7, 10\}$
13. $B \cup C = \{0, 2, 4, 5, 6, 7, 8, 10\}$ 15. $C \cup D = \{1, 2, 3, 5, 7, 9, 10\}$ 17. $A \cap C = \varnothing$ 19. $B \cap C = \{2\}$
21. $C \cap D = \{5, 7\}$
23. [Venn diagram E F G with 9, 7, 4, 6, 8, 3, 5, 1, 10]
25. 10 girls 27. $\{x \mid x > -3\} \cap \{x \mid x < \frac{13}{2}\}$
29. $\{w \mid w \le -\frac{1}{3}\} \cup \{w \mid w \ge 1\}$ 31. $\{x \mid x < -7\} \cup \{x \mid x > 21\}$ 33. $W \cup Y \cup Z = \{0, 2, 3, 4, 5, 6, 7, 8\}$
35. $W \cap X \cap Z = \{6\}$ 37. 62 patients 39. $A \cap B = A$
41. $\{(\pi, 2), (\pi, 4), (2\pi, 2), (2\pi, 4), (3\pi, 2), (3\pi, 4), (4\pi, 2), (4\pi, 4)\}$ 43. $\{(\text{reduce, plastic}), (\text{reuse, plastic}), (\text{recycle, plastic})\}$ 49. $x = 4$ or $x = -4$ 50. $n = 2$ or $n = -2$ 51. $f = 2$ or $f = 8$ 52. $y = \frac{4}{9}$ or $y = -\frac{3}{9}$
53. $-5 \le d \le 5$ 54. $x \le -4$ or $x \ge 10$ 55. $w < -15$ or $w > 9$ 56. $x \le -4\frac{1}{3}$ or $x \ge -\frac{4}{3}$ 57. yes 58. no 59. yes
60–63. [coordinate grid]

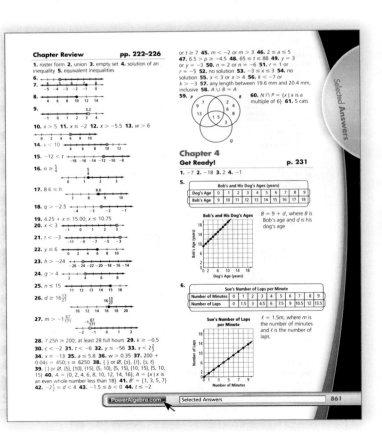

Chapter Review pp. 222–226
1. roster form 2. union 3. empty set 4. solution of an inequality 5. equivalent inequalities
6. [number line]
7. [number line]
8. [number line]
9. [number line]
10. $x > 5$ 11. $x \le -2$ 12. $x > -5.5$ 13. $w > 6$
14. $v < 10$ [number line]
15. $-12 < t$ [number line]
16. $n \ge \frac{5}{4}$ [number line]
17. $8.6 \le h$ [number line]
18. $q > -2.5$ [number line]
19. $4.25 + x \ge 15.00$; $x \le 10.75$
20. $x < 3$ [number line]
21. $t < -3$ [number line]
22. $y \le 6$ [number line]
23. $h > -24$ [number line]
24. $g > 4$ [number line]
25. $n \le 15$ [number line]
26. $d \ge 16\frac{13}{22}$ [number line]
27. $m > -1\frac{67}{171}$ [number line]
28. $7.25n \ge 200$; at least 28 full hours 29. $k \ge -0.5$
30. $x < -2$ 31. $t < -6$ 32. $y \le -56$ 33. $x < 2\frac{1}{3}$
34. $x \le -13$ 35. $a \le 5$ 36. $w > 0.35$ 37. $200 + 0.04s \le 450$; $s \ge 6250$ 38. $\{ \}$ or $\varnothing$, $\{s\}$, $\{t\}$, $\{s, t\}$
39. $\{ \}$ or $\varnothing$, $\{5\}$, $\{10\}$, $\{15\}$, $\{5, 10\}$, $\{5, 15\}$, $\{10, 15\}$, $\{5, 10, 15\}$ 40. $A = \{0, 2, 4, 6, 8, 10, 12, 14, 16\}$; $A = \{x \mid x$ is an even whole number less than 18$\}$ 41. $B' = \{1, 3, 5, 7\}$
42. $-2\frac{2}{3} \le d < 4$ 43. $-1.5 \le b < 0$ 44. $t \le -2$

or $t \ge 7$ 45. $m < -2$ or $m > 3$ 46. $2 \le a \le 5$
47. $6.5 > p \ge -4.5$ 48. $65 \le t \le 88$ 49. $y = 3$ or $y = -3$ 50. $n = 2$ or $n = -6$ 51. $r = 1$ or $r = -5$ 52. no solution 53. $-3 \le s \le 3$ 54. no solution 55. $x < 3$ or $x > 4$ 56. $x < -7$ or $k > 3$ 57. any length between 19.6 mm and 20.4 mm, inclusive 58. $A \cup B = A$
59. [Venn diagram P Q R with 13, 3, 7, 4, 2, 6, 1, 5, 8, 9] $N \cap P = \{x \mid x$ is a multiple of 6$\}$ 61. 5 cats

Chapter 4
Get Ready! p. 231
1. -7 2. -18 3. 2 4. -1
5.

Bob's and His Dog's Ages (years)

Dog's Age	0	1	2	3	4	5	6	7	8	9
Bob's Age	9	10	11	12	13	14	15	16	17	18

$B = 9 + d$, where B is Bob's age and d is his dog's age

[graph: Bob's and His Dog's Ages]

6.

Sue's Number of Laps per Minute

Number of Minutes	0	1	2	3	4	5	6	7	8	9
Number of Laps	0	1.5	3	4.5	6	7.5	9	10.5	12	13.5

$\ell = 1.5m$, where m is the number of minutes and ℓ is the number of laps.

[graph: Sue's Number of Laps per Minute]

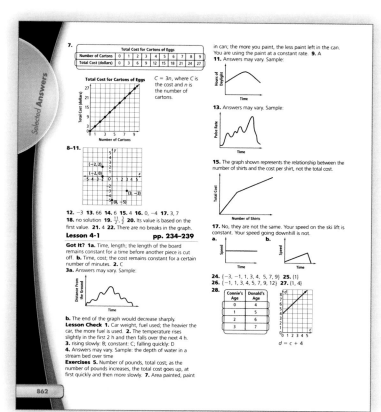

7.

Total Cost for Cartons of Eggs										
Number of Cartons	0	1	2	3	4	5	6	7	8	9
Total Cost (dollars)	0	3	6	9	12	15	18	21	24	27

$C = 3n$, where C is the cost and n is the number of cartons.

8–11.

12. -3 **13.** 66 **14.** 6 **15.** 4 **16.** 0, -4 **17.** 3, 7
18. no solution **19.** $1\frac{1}{2}$, $\frac{3}{2}$ **20.** Its value is based on the first value. **21.** 4 **22.** There are no breaks in the graph.

Lesson 4-1 pp. 234–239
Got It? 1a. Time, length; the length of the board remains constant for a time before another piece is cut off. **b.** Time, cost; the cost remains constant for a certain number of minutes. **2.** C
3a. Answers may vary. Sample:

b. The end of the graph would decrease sharply.
Lesson Check 1. Car weight, fuel used; the heavier the car, the more fuel is used. **2.** The temperature rises slightly in the first 2 h and then falls over the next 4 h.
3. rising slowly: B; constant: C; falling quickly: D
4. Answers may vary. Sample: the depth of water in a stream bed over time
Exercises 5. Number of pounds, total cost; as the number of pounds increases, the total cost goes up, at first quickly and then more slowly. **7.** Area painted, paint

in can; the more you paint, the less paint left in the can. You are using the paint at a constant rate. **9.** A
11. Answers may vary. Sample:

13. Answers may vary. Sample:

15. The graph shown represents the relationship between the number of shirts and the cost per shirt, not the total cost.

17. No, they are not the same. Your speed on the ski lift is constant. Your speed going downhill is not.
a. **b.**

24. $\{-3, -1, 1, 3, 4, 5, 7, 9\}$ **25.** $\{1\}$
26. $\{-1, 1, 3, 4, 5, 7, 9, 12\}$ **27.** $\{1, 4\}$
28.

Connie's Age	Donald's Age
0	4
1	5
2	6
3	7

$d = c + 4$

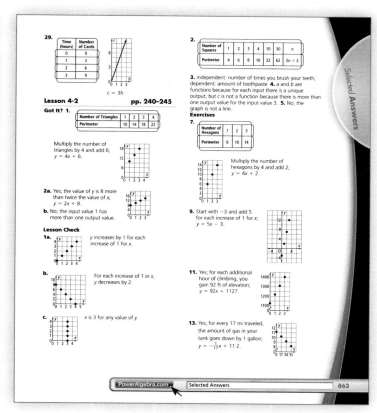

29.

Time (hours)	Number of Cards
0	0
1	3
2	6
3	9

$c = 3h$

Lesson 4-2 pp. 240–245
Got It? 1.

Number of Triangles	1	2	3	4
Perimeter	10	14	18	22

Multiply the number of triangles by 4 and add 6; $y = 4x + 6$.

2a. Yes; the value of y is 8 more than twice the value of x; $y = 2x + 8$.
b. No; the input value 1 has more than one output value.

Lesson Check
1a. y increases by 1 for each increase of 1 for x.

b. For each increase of 1 in x, y decreases by 2.

c. x is 3 for any value of y.

2.

Number of Squares	1	2	3	4	10	30	n
Perimeter	4	6	8	10	22	62	2n + 2

3. independent: number of times you brush your teeth; dependent: amount of toothpaste **4.** a and b are functions because for each input there is a unique output, but c is not a function because there is more than one output value for the input value 3. **5.** No; the graph is not a line.
Exercises
7.

Number of Hexagons	1	2	3
Perimeter	6	10	14

Multiply the number of hexagons by 4 and add 2; $y = 4x + 2$.

9. Start with -3 and add 5 for each increase of 1 for x; $y = 5x - 3$.

11. Yes; for each additional hour of climbing, you gain 92 ft of elevation; $y = 92x + 1127$.

13. Yes; for every 17 mi traveled, the amount of gas in your tank goes down by 1 gallon; $y = -\frac{1}{17}x + 11.2$.

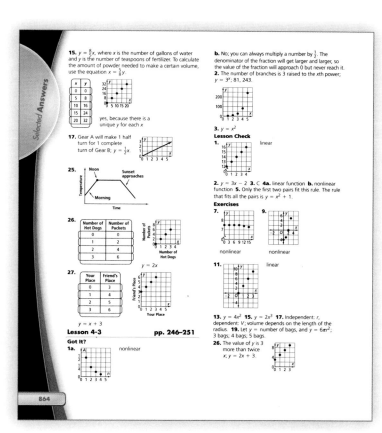

15. $y = \frac{8}{5}x$, where x is the number of gallons of water and y is the number of teaspoons of fertilizer. To calculate the amount of powder needed to make a certain volume, use the equation $x = \frac{8}{5}y$.

x	y
0	0
5	8
10	16
15	24
20	32

yes, because there is a unique y for each x

17. Gear A will make 1 half turn for 1 complete turn of Gear B; $y = \frac{1}{2}x$.

25. Noon, Sunset approaches, Morning

26.

Number of Hot Dogs	Number of Packets
0	0
1	2
2	4
3	6

$y = 2x$

27.

Your Place	Friend's Place
0	3
1	4
2	5
3	6

$y = x + 3$

Lesson 4-3 pp. 246–251
Got It?
1a. nonlinear

b. No; you can always multiply a number by $\frac{1}{3}$. The denominator of the fraction will get larger and larger, so the value of the fraction will approach 0 but never reach it.
2. The number of branches is 3 raised to the xth power; $y = 3^x$; 81, 243.

3. $y = x^2$
Lesson Check
1. linear

2. $y = 3x - 2$ **3.** C **4a.** linear function **b.** nonlinear function **5.** Only the first two pairs fit this rule. The rule that fits all the pairs is $y = x^2 + 1$.
Exercises
7. nonlinear **9.** nonlinear

11. linear

13. $y = 4x^2$ **15.** $y = 2x^3$ **17.** Independent: r, dependent: V; volume depends on the length of the radius. **19.** Let y = number of bags, and $y = 6\pi r^2$; 3 bags; 4 bags; 5 bags.
26. The value of y is 3 more than twice x; $y = 2x + 3$.

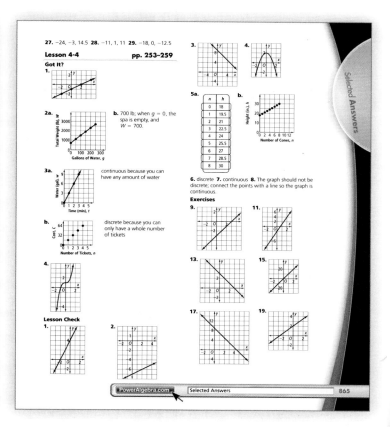

27. -24, -3, 14.5 **28.** -11, 1, 11 **29.** -18, 0, -12.5
Lesson 4-4 pp. 253–259
Got It?
1.

2a. (Total Weight (lb), W vs Gallons of Water, g) **b.** 700 lb; when $g = 0$, the spa is empty, and $W = 700$.

3a. (Water (gal), w vs Time (min), t) continuous because you can have any amount of water

b. (Cost, C vs Number of Tickets, n) discrete because you can only have a whole number of tickets

4.

Lesson Check
1. **2.**

3. **4.**

5a.

n	h
0	18
1	19.5
2	21
3	22.5
4	24
5	25.5
6	27
7	28.5
8	30

b. (Height (in.), h vs Number of Cones, n)
6. discrete **7.** continuous **8.** The graph should not be discrete; connect the points with a line so the graph is continuous.
Exercises
9. **11.**

13. **15.**

17. **19.**

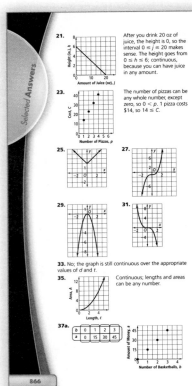

21.
After you drink 20 oz of juice, the height is 0, so the interval $0 \le j \le 20$ makes sense. The height goes from 0 to $h \le 6$; continuous, because you can have juice in any amount.

23.
The number of pizzas can be any whole number, except zero, so $0 < p$. 1 pizza costs \$14, so $14 \le C$.

25. **27.**

29. **31.**

33. No; the graph is still continuous over the appropriate values of d and t.

35.
Continuous; lengths and areas can be any number.

37a.

b	0	1	2	3
a	0	15	30	45

Discrete; you can only have whole numbers of basketballs.
b. 8 **39.** between 2 and 3 **46.** nonlinear **47.** linear **48.** −2, 12 **49.** −7, 1 **50.** 1, 13 **51.** −31, 9 **52.** no solution **53.** −4, 4 **54.** −2, 4 **55.** no solution **56.** −3, 1 **57.** Let x = number of cones purchased at \$4. Then $14 = 4x − 2$; 4. **58.** Let x = cost of each yard of mulch. Then $200 = 35 + 5x$; \$33.

Lesson 4-5 pp. 262–267

Got It? 1. $W = 50{,}000 + 420m$
2a. $C = 12 + 15n$; \$162 **b.** No; making the stay shorter only halves the daily charge, not the bath charge.
3a. $A = b^2 + 2b$; 288 in.^{2}
b. The graph is not a line.

Lesson Check 1. $C = 3.57p$ **2.** $f = \frac{h}{12}$
3. $y = x + 2$ **4.** $V = (d + 1)^3$ **5.** dependent, a; independent, b **6.** You can't add holes and minutes. The correct rule is $t = 15n$. **7.** Continuous; side length and area can be any positive real numbers.
Exercises 9. $C = 8 + \frac{1}{4}n$ **11.** $\frac{9}{5} + 2.5 = w$
13. $p = 6.95 + 0.95t$ **15.** $a = 8 − \frac{7}{8}b$
17. $d = −10 − 50t$; −160 ft **19.** $A = \frac{3}{2}h + \frac{3}{2}h^2$; 99 cm^2 **21.** $A = 3w^2 − 2w$; 8 ft^2 **23.** Answers may vary. Sample: The rule covers all values, whereas the table only represents some of the values.
25. $d = −3.5 − 108m$; −435.5 m
27a.

Cost of Meal	\$15	\$21	\$24	\$30
Money Left	\$37.75	\$30.85	\$27.40	\$20.50

b. $m = 55 − 1.15c$
c.

29a. $d = 1.8w$ **b.** No; the room is not wide enough.
c. $6\frac{2}{3}$ ft

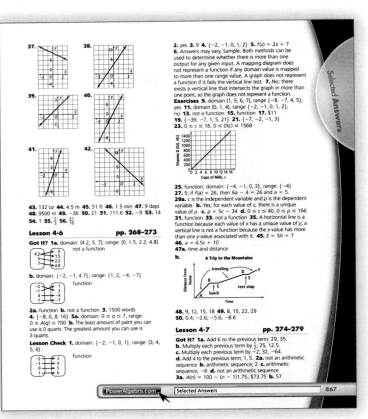

37. **38.**

39. **40.**

41. **42.**

43. 132 oz **44.** 4.5 m **45.** 51 ft **46.** 1.5 min **47.** 9 days **48.** 9500 m **49.** −36 **50.** 21 **51.** 111.6 **52.** −9 **53.** 14 **54.** 1 **55.** $\frac{3}{8}$ **56.** $\frac{22}{15}$

Lesson 4-6 pp. 268–273

Got It? 1a. domain: {4.2, 5, 7}; range: {0, 1.5, 2.2, 4.8} not a function

b. domain: {−2, −1, 4 7}; range: {1, 2, −4, −7} function

2a. function **b.** not a function **3.** 1500 words **4.** {−8, 0, 8, 16} **5a.** domain: $0 \le q \le 7$, range: $0 \le A(q) \le 700$ **b.** The least amount of paint you can use is 0 quarts. The greatest amount you can use is 3 quarts.
Lesson Check 1. domain: {−2, −1, 0, 1}, range: {3, 4, 5, 6}

function

2. yes **3.** 9 **4.** {−2, −1, 0, 1, 2} **5.** $f(x) = 2x + 7$
6. Answers may vary. Sample: Both methods can be used to determine whether there is more than one output for any given input. A mapping diagram does not represent a function if any domain value is mapped to more than one range value. A graph does not represent a function if it fails the vertical line test. **7.** No; there exists a vertical line that intersects the graph in more than one point, so the graph does not represent a function.
Exercises 9. domain {1, 5, 6, 7}, range {−8, −7, 4, 5}; yes **11.** domain {0, 1, 4}, range {−2, −1, 0, 1, 2}; no **13.** not a function **15.** function **17.** \$11 **19.** {−39, −7, 1, 5, 21} **21.** {−7, −2, −1, 3} **23.** $0 \le c \le 16$, $0 \le D(c) \le 1568$

25. function; domain: {−4, −1, 0, 3}, range: {−4} **27.** 5; if $f(a) = 26$, then $6a − 4 = 26$ and $a = 5$. **29a.** c is the independent variable and p is the dependent variable. **b.** Yes; for each value of c, there is a unique value of p. **c.** $p = 5c − 34$ **d.** $0 \le c \le 40$, $0 \le p \le 166$ **31.** function **33.** not a function **35.** A horizontal line is a function because each value of x has a unique value of y; a vertical line is not a function because the x-value has more than one y-value associated with it. **45.** $E = 5h + 7$
46. $a = 4.5s + 10$
47a. time and distance
b.

A Trip to the Mountains

48. 9, 12, 15, 18 **49.** 8, 15, 22, 29 **50.** 0.4, −2.6, −5.6, −8.6

Lesson 4-7 pp. 274–279

Got It? 1a. Add 6 to the previous term; 29, 35.
b. Multiply each previous term by $\frac{1}{2}$; 25, 12.5.
c. Multiply each previous term by −2; 32, −64.
d. Add 4 to the previous term; 1, 5. **2a.** not an arithmetic sequence **b.** arithmetic sequence; 2 **c.** arithmetic sequence; −6 **d.** not an arithmetic sequence
3a. $A(n) = 100 − (n − 1)1.75$; \$73.75 **b.** 57

Lesson Check 1. Add 8 to the previous term; 35, 43. **2.** Multiply the previous term by −2; 48, −96. **3.** not an arithmetic sequence **4.** arithmetic sequence; 9 **5.** $A(n) = 9 − 2(n − 1)$; −3 **6.** −6; the pattern is "add −6 to the previous term." **7.** Evaluate $A(n) = 4 + (n − 1)8$ for $n = 10$; $A(10) = 4 + (10 − 1)8 = 76$. **8.** Yes; $A(1) + (n − 1)d = A(1) + nd − d$ by the Distributive Property.
Exercises 9. Add 7 to the previous term; 34, 41. **11.** Add 4 to the previous term; 18, 22. **13.** Add −2 to the previous term; 5, 3. **15.** Add 1.1 to the previous term; 5.5, 6.6. **17.** Multiply the previous term by 2; 72, 144. **19.** not an arithmetic sequence **21.** not an arithmetic sequence **23.** yes; 1.3 **25.** not an arithmetic sequence **27.** yes; −0.5 **29.** not an arithmetic sequence **31.** $A(n) = 50 − 3.25(n − 1)$; \$11 **33.** 2, 12, 47 **35.** 17, 33, 89 **37.** −2, 8, 43 **39.** −3.2, −5.4, −13.1 **41.** Yes; the common difference is −4; $A(n) = −3 + (n − 1)(−4)$. **43.** No; there is no common difference. **45.** Yes; the common difference −0.8; $A(n) = 0.2 + (n − 1)(−0.8)$. **47.** Answers may vary. Sample: $A(n) = 15 + 2(n − 1)$ **49.** 350, 325, 300, 275, 250, 225; you owe \$225 at the end of six weeks.
51a. 1, 6, 15, 20, 15, 6, 1 **b.** 1, 2, 4, 8, 16; 64
53a. 11, 14 **b.**
c. The points all lie on a line.

61. {12, 4.8, 0, −4, −40} **62.** {13, 5.8, 1, −3, −19} **63.** {27, 4.32, 0, 3, 300} **64.** {−2.5, 8.84, 11, 9.5, −139} **65.** {−19, −2.8, 8, 17, 98} **66.** {−7.25, −5.9, −5, −4.25, 2.5} **67.** 480 gal/h **68.** 132 ft/s **69.** \$6

Chapter Review pp. 281–284

1. independent variable **2.** linear **3.** discrete **4.** range **5.** Answers may vary. Sample:

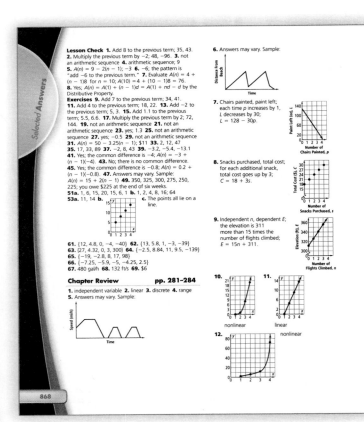

6. Answers may vary. Sample:

7. Chairs painted, paint left; each time p increases by 1, L decreases by 30; $L = 128 − 30p$.

8. Snacks purchased, total cost; for each additional snack, total cost goes up by 3; $C = 18 + 3s$.

9. Independent n, dependent E; the elevation is 311 more than 15 times the number of flights climbed; $E = 15n + 311$.

10. **11.** nonlinear linear

12. nonlinear

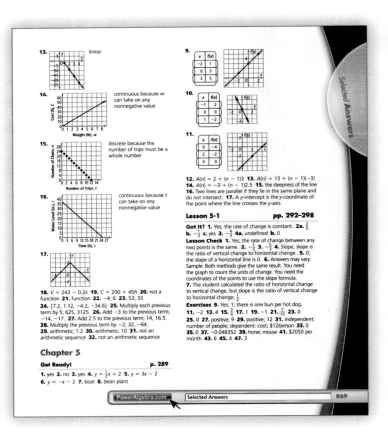

13. linear

14. continuous because w can take on any nonnegative value

15. discrete because the number of trips must be a whole number

16. continuous because t can take on any nonnegative value

17.

18. $V = 243 − 0.2s$ **19.** $C = 200 + 45h$ **20.** not a function **21.** function **22.** −4; 6 **23.** 53; 33 **24.** {7.2, 1.12, −4.2, −34.6} **25.** Multiply each previous term by 5; 625, 3125. **26.** Add −3 to the previous term; −14, −17. **27.** Add 2.5 to the previous term; 14, 16.5. **28.** Multiply the previous term by −2; 32, −64. **29.** arithmetic; 1.2 **30.** arithmetic; 10 **31.** not an arithmetic sequence **32.** not an arithmetic sequence

Chapter 5

Get Ready! p. 289

1. yes **2.** no **3.** yes **4.** $y = \frac{1}{3}x + 2$ **5.** $y = 3x − 2$ **6.** $y = −x − 2$ **7.** boat **8.** bean plant

9.

x	$f(x)$
−2	1
0	3
2.5	5

10.

x	$f(x)$
−1	5
0	3
1	2

11.

x	$f(x)$
0	−4
2	0
4	0

12. $A(n) = 2 + (n − 1)3$ **13.** $A(n) = 13 + (n − 1)(−3)$ **14.** $A(n) = −3 + (n − 1)2.5$ **15.** the steepness of the line **16.** Two lines are parallel if they lie in the same plane and do not intersect. **17.** A y-intercept is the y-coordinate of the point where the line crosses the y-axis.

Lesson 5-1 pp. 292–298

Got It? 1. Yes; the rate of change is constant. **2a.** $\frac{2}{5}$ **b.** $−\frac{1}{3}$ **c.** yes **3.** $−\frac{4}{7}$ **4a.** undefined **b.** 0
Lesson Check 1. Yes; the rate of change between any two points is the same. **2.** $−\frac{1}{3}$ **3.** $−\frac{9}{2}$ **4.** Slope; slope is the ratio of vertical change to horizontal change. **5.** 0; the slope of a horizontal line is 0. **6.** Answers may vary. Sample: Both methods give the same result. You need the graph to count the units of change. You need the coordinates of the points to use the slope formula. **7.** The student calculated the ratio of horizontal change to vertical change, but slope is the ratio of vertical change to horizontal change; $\frac{1}{3}$.
Exercises 9. Yes; 1; there is one bun per hot dog. **11.** $−2$ **13.** 4 **15.** $\frac{1}{3}$ **17.** 1 **19.** −1 **21.** $\frac{9}{10}$ **23.** 0 **25.** 0 **27.** positive; 9 **29.** positive; 12 **31.** independent: number of people; dependent: cost; \$12/person **33.** 0 **35.** 0 **37.** −0.048352 **39.** horse; mouse **41.** \$2050 per month **43.** 6 **45.** 4 **47.** 3

49a. 5 **b.**

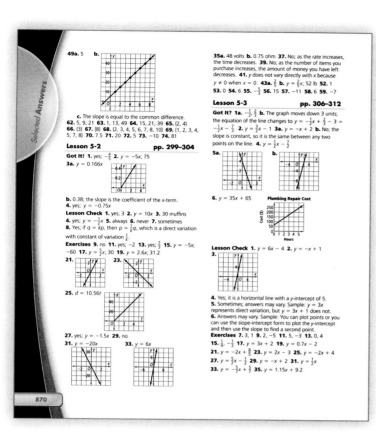

c. The slope is equal to the common difference.
62. 5, 9, 21 **63.** 1, 13, 49 **64.** 15, 21, 39 **65.** (2, 4)
66. (3) **67.** (8) **68.** (2, 3, 4, 5, 6, 7, 8, 10) **69.** (1, 2, 3, 4, 5, 7, 8) **70.** 7.5 **71.** 20 **72.** 5 **73.** −10 **74.** 81

Lesson 5-2   pp. 299–304

Got It? 1. yes; $-\frac{4}{5}$ **2.** $y = -5x$; 75
3a. $y = 0.166x$

b. 0.38; the slope is the coefficient of the x-term.
4. yes; $y = -0.75x$
Lesson Check 1. yes; 3 **2.** $y = 10x$ **3.** 30 muffins
4. yes; $y = -\frac{1}{3}x$ **5.** always **6.** never **7.** sometimes
8. Yes; if $q = kp$, then $p = \frac{1}{k}q$, which is a direct variation with constant of variation $\frac{1}{k}$.
Exercises 9. no **11.** yes; -2 **13.** yes; $\frac{7}{3}$ **15.** $y = -5x$; −60 **17.** $y = \frac{5}{3}x$; 30 **19.** 2.6x; 31.2
21.   **23.**

25. $d = 10.56t$

27. yes; $y = -1.5x$ **29.** no
31. $y = -20x$ **33.** $y = 6x$

35a. 48 volts **b.** 0.75 ohm **37.** No; as the rate increases, the time decreases. **39.** No; as the number of items you purchase increases, the amount of money you have left decreases. **41.** y does not vary directly with x because $y \neq 0$ when $x = 0$. **43a.** $\frac{2}{3}$ **b.** $y = \frac{2}{3}x$; 52 lb **52.** 1
53. 0 **54.** 6 **55.** $-\frac{3}{2}$ **56.** 15 **57.** −11 **58.** 6 **59.** −7

Lesson 5-3   pp. 306–312

Got It? 1a. $-\frac{1}{2}$, $\frac{5}{2}$ **b.** The graph moves down 3 units; the equation of the line changes to $y = -\frac{1}{2}x + \frac{5}{2} - 3 = -\frac{1}{2}x - \frac{1}{2}$. **2.** $y = \frac{3}{4}x - 1$ **3a.** $y = -x + 2$ **b.** No; the slope is constant, so it is the same between any two points on the line. **4.** $y = \frac{1}{2}x - \frac{7}{2}$
5a.   **b.**

6. $y = 35x + 65$

Plumbing Repair Cost

Lesson Check 1. $y = 6x - 4$ **2.** $y = -x + 1$
3.

4. Yes; it is a horizontal line with a y-intercept of 5.
5. Sometimes; answers may vary. Sample: $y = 3x$ represents direct variation, but $y = 3x + 1$ does not.
6. Answers may vary. Sample: You can plot points or you can use the slope-intercept form to plot the y-intercept and then use the slope to find a second point.
Exercises 7. 3, 1 **9.** 2, −5 **11.** 5, −3 **13.** 0, 4
15. $\frac{1}{4}$, $-\frac{1}{3}$ **17.** $y = 3x + 2$ **19.** $y = 0.7x - 2$
21. $y = -2x + \frac{8}{3}$ **23.** $y = 2x - 3$ **25.** $y = -2x + 4$
27. $y = \frac{2}{3}x - \frac{1}{2}$ **29.** $y = -x + 2$ **31.** $y = \frac{1}{2}x$
33. $y = -\frac{5}{7}x + \frac{2}{7}$ **35.** $y = 1.15x + 9.2$

---

37.   **39.**

41.   **43.**

45.   **47.**

49. $y = 7.5x - 5$ **51.** −3, 2
53. 9, $\frac{1}{3}$
Price of Fabric   **55.** 9, −15
57. 2 − a, a
59. 2030

61a. $y = 35x + 50$ **b.**
c. The amount of time the repair takes and the cost must be positive.

63.   **65.**   **67.**

71a. $y = 10x + 175$
b. 675 pieces

81. $y = 5x$; 50 **82.** $y = 2x$; 20 **83.** $y = 3x$; 30
84. $t = -9$ **85.** $q = 27$ **86.** $x = 7$ **87.** $-3x + 15$
88. $5x + 10$ **89.** $-\frac{4}{9}x + \frac{8}{9}$ **90.** $1.5x + 18$

Lesson 5-4   pp. 313–318

Got It? 1. $y + 4 = \frac{2}{3}(x - 8)$ **2.**

3a. $y + 3 = \frac{2}{5}(x + 2)$ **b.** They are both equal to $y = \frac{2}{5}x + \frac{2}{5}$; you can use any point on a line to write an equation of the line in point-slope form. **4a.** Answers may vary. Sample: $y - 3320 = 1250(x - 2)$; the rate at which water is being added to the tank, in gallons per hour **b.** $y = 1250x + 820$; the initial number of gallons of water in the tank
Lesson Check 1. $\frac{4}{9}$, $(-7, 12)$ **2.** $y + 8 = -2(x - 3)$
3.

4. Answers may vary. Sample: $y + 2 = 2(x + 1)$
5. the slope m of the line and a point (x_1, y_1) on the line
6. yes; $1 - 4 = 3(-2 + 1)$ **7.** Yes; answers may vary. Sample: $y - a = m(x - b)$, $y = mx - mb + a$, $y = mx + (a - mb)$
Exercises 9. $y - 2 = -\frac{2}{3}(x - 4)$
11. $y = -1(x - 4)$
13.   **15.**

17. Answers may vary. Sample: $y - 1 = -\frac{3}{4}(x - 1)$
19–21. Point-slope forms may vary. Samples are given.
19. $y - 4 = \frac{2}{3}(x - 1)$; $y = \frac{2}{3}x + \frac{10}{3}$ **21.** $y - 6 = -\frac{1}{2}(x + 6)$; $y = -\frac{1}{2}x + 3$ **23.** $y = 8.5x$; the slope 8.5 represents the hourly wage in dollars; the y-intercept 0 represents the amount earned for working 0 h.

25.

27. The student graphed the point (2, 0) instead of (0, 2).

29a. Answers may vary. Sample: $y - 5 = x + 2$
b. Infinitely many; you can use any value for the slope.
31. $b = -0.0018a + 212$; 207.5°F **39.** 6, 0
40. −1, −13 **41.** $y = \frac{z}{7x}$ **42.** $y = \frac{7b + 3}{a}$
43. $y = \frac{6x - c}{6}$

Lesson 5-5   pp. 320–326

Got It? 1a. 12; −10 **b.** 4; $\frac{3}{2}$ **2.**

3a.   **b.**

c.   **d.**

4. $x + 3y = 0$ **5a.** $x + 15y = 60$ **b.** domain: nonnegative integers less than or equal to 60; range: {0, 1, 2, 3, 4}
Lesson Check 1. 3, $-\frac{9}{4}$
2.   **3.** horizontal line
4. $x - 2y = -6$
5. $10x + 25y = 285$; answers may vary. Sample: 1 $10 card and 11 $25 cards, 6 $10 cards and 9 $25 cards, 11 $10 cards and 7 $25 cards

6a. point-slope form **b.** slope-intercept form **c.** point-slope form **d.** standard form **7.** Answers may vary. Sample: slope-intercept form; it is easy to find the y-intercept and calculate the slope from the graph.
Exercises 9. 2, −1 **11.** $-\frac{20}{3}$, 4 **13.** 1.5, −2.5
15.   **17.**

19.   **21.**

23. horizontal **25.** horizontal
27.   **29.**

31. $2x - y = -5$ **33.** $2x + y = 10$ **35.** $2x + 3y = -3$
37. $5j + 5x = 250$
Points   Answers may vary. Sample: 50 jewels and 0 stars, 48 jewels and 5 stars, 42 jewels and 20 stars
Number of Jewels

39. When you have a slope and the y-intercept, use the slope-intercept form. When you have two points or a slope and a point, use the point-slope form. When you have the standard form, it is easy to graph.
41.

Two lines have the same slope but different y-intercepts.
Two lines have the same y-intercept but different slopes.
43. The student did not subtract 1 from each side of the equation. The correct equation is $4x - y = -1$.

---

45.   **47.**

49.   **51.** 4, 3; $3x + 4y = 12$
53. −3, −2; $x + y = -3$
55. 10, $-\frac{10}{3}$ **57.** 6, 6
59. 4, $-\frac{8}{5}$

71–73. Point-slope forms may vary. Samples are given.
71. $y + 1 = -\frac{3}{8}(x - 5)$; $y = -\frac{3}{8}x + \frac{17}{8}$
72. $y + 2 = \frac{3}{4}x$; $y = \frac{3}{4}x - 2$
73. $y + 1 = x + 2$; $y = x + 1$
74. $-2 < t \leq 3$

75. $1.7 \leq y < 12.5$

76. $x \leq -1$ or $x > 3$

77. 2 **78.** 3 **79.** 0

Lesson 5-6   pp. 327–332

Got It? 1. $y = 2x + 5$ **2a.** Neither; the slopes are not equal or opposite reciprocals. **b.** Parallel; the slopes are equal. **3.** $y = -\frac{1}{2}x + \frac{17}{2}$ **4.** $y = -\frac{2}{3}x + 10$
Lesson Check 1. $y = 6x$ and $y = 6x - 2$; $y = -\frac{1}{6}x$ and $y = 6x$, $y = -\frac{1}{6}x$ and $y = 6x - 2$; $y = -4x + 11$
3. $y = -x - 1$ **4a.** yes **b.** no **c.** no **6.** In both cases, you compare the slopes of the lines. If the slopes are equal, then the lines are parallel. If the slopes are opposite reciprocals, the lines are perpendicular.
Exercises 7. $y = 3x$ **9.** $y = 4x - 7$ **11.** $y = \frac{2}{3}x$
13. Perpendicular; the slopes are opposite reciprocals.
15. Parallel; the slopes are equal. **17.** Perpendicular; one line is vertical and the other line is horizontal. **19.** $y = \frac{1}{3}x$
21. $y = \frac{1}{2}x - \frac{9}{2}$ **23.** $y = -\frac{1}{3}x$ **25.** $y = -\frac{1}{3}x + 4$
27. a and f; b and d, c and e **29.** Sometimes; if the slopes are equal and the y-intercepts are not equal, then the lines are parallel. **31.** Answers may vary. Samples: $y = 1$; $x = 1$
33. $x = 3$ **35.** $y = -100x + 600$, $y = -100x + 1000$; parallel; the slopes are the same.
41.   **42.**

43.   **44.** $y = 3x - 2$
45. $y = -\frac{2}{5}x + \frac{29}{5}$
46. $y = 0.25x + 1.875$
47. $y = -\frac{9}{5}x + \frac{660}{?}$

Lesson 5-7   pp. 333–340

Got It? 1a.
Gasoline Purchases   positive correlation
Gallons Bought / **Dollars Spent**

b. No correlation; the length of a city's name and the population are not related. **2a.** Answers may vary. Sample: $y = 2.23x + 8.8$; about 24.4 in. **b.** No; an adult panda does not grow at the same rate as a young panda.
Body Length of a Panda
Body Length (in.) / **Age (month)**

3a. about $9964 **b.** The slope tells you that the cost increases at a rate of about $409.43 per year. **4a.** There may be a positive correlation, but it is not causal because a more expensive vacation does not cause a family to own a bigger house. **b.** There is a positive correlation and a causal relationship. The more time you spend exercising, the more Calories you burn.
Lesson Check
1.
Average Maximum Daily Temperature in January for Northern Latitudes   negative correlation
Temperature (°F) / **Latitude (°N)**

2–3. Answers may vary. Samples are given.
2. $y = -2x + 120$ **3.** about 20°F **4.** You use interpolation to estimate a value between two known values. You use extrapolation to predict a value outside the range of the known values. **5.** Both the trend line and the line of best fit show a correlation between two sets of data. The line of best fit is the most accurate trend line. **6.** If y decreases as x

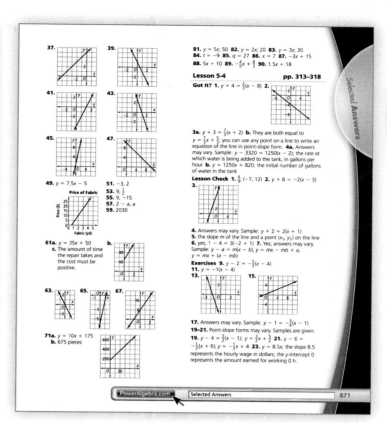
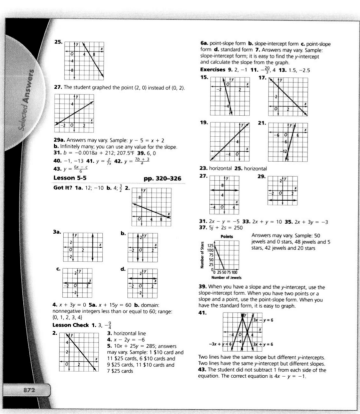
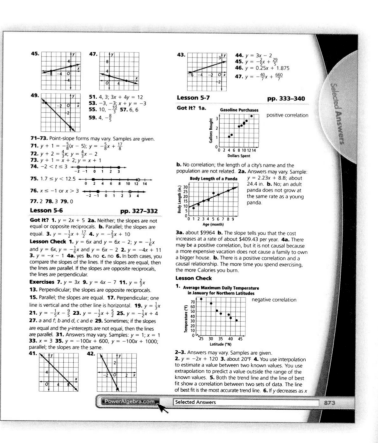

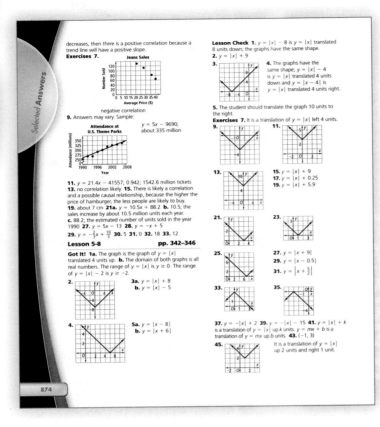

decreases, then there is a positive correlation because a trend line will have a positive slope.

Exercises 7.

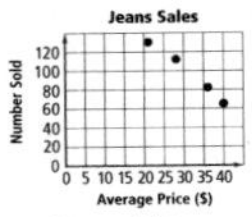

Jeans Sales
Number Sold
120
100
80
60
40
20
0
0 5 10 15 20 25 30 35 40
Average Price ($)

negative correlation

9. Answers may vary. Sample:

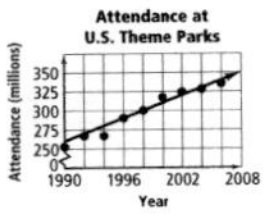

Attendance at U.S. Theme Parks
Attendance (millions)
350
325
300
275
250
0
1990 1996 2002 2008
Year

$y = 5x - 9690$; about 335 million

11. $y = 21.4x - 41557$; 0.942; 1542.6 million tickets **13.** no correlation likely **15.** There is likely a correlation and a possible causal relationship, because the higher the price of hamburger, the less people are likely to buy. **19.** about 7 cm **21a.** $y = 10.5x + 88.2$ **b.** 10.5; the sales increase by about 10.5 million units each year. **c.** 88.2; the estimated number of units sold in the year 1990 **27.** $y = 5x - 13$ **28.** $y = -x + 5$ **29.** $y = -\frac{2}{3}x + \frac{10}{3}$ **30.** 5 **31.** 0 **32.** 18 **33.** 12

Lesson 5-8 pp. 342–346

Got It! 1a. The graph is the graph of $y = |x|$ translated 4 units up. **b.** The domain of both graphs is all real numbers. The range of $y = |x|$ is $y \geq 0$. The range of $y = |x| - 2$ is $y \geq -2$.

2.

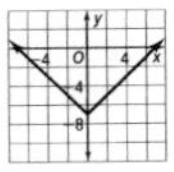

3a. $y = |x| + 8$ **b.** $y = |x| - 5$

4.

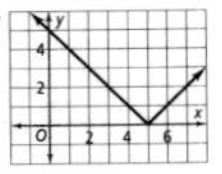

5a. $y = |x - 8|$ **b.** $y = |x + 6|$

Lesson Check 1. $y = |x| - 8$ is $y = |x|$ translated 8 units down; the graphs have the same shape. **2.** $y = |x| + 9$

3.

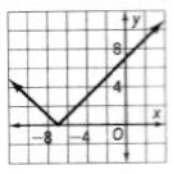

4. The graphs have the same shape; $y = |x| - 4$ is $y = |x|$ translated 4 units down and $y = |x - 4|$ is $y = |x|$ translated 4 units right.

5. The student should translate the graph 10 units to the right.

Exercises 7. It is a translation of $y = |x|$ left 4 units.

9.

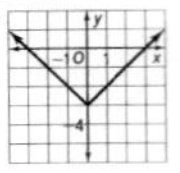

11.

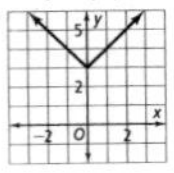

13.

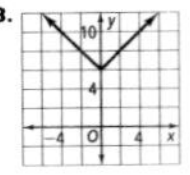

15. $y = |x| + 9$ **17.** $y = |x| + 0.25$ **19.** $y = |x| + 5.9$

21.

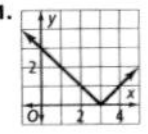

23.

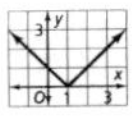

25.

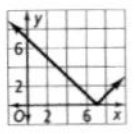

27. $y = |x + 9|$ **29.** $y = |x - 0.5|$ **31.** $y = \left|x + \frac{5}{2}\right|$

33.

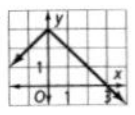

35.

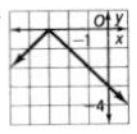

37. $y = -|x| + 2$ **39.** $y = -|x| - 15$ **41.** $y = |x| + k$ is a translation of $y = |x|$ up k units. $y = mx + b$ is a translation of $y = mx$ up b units. **43.** $(-1, 3)$

45.

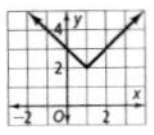

It is a translation of $y = |x|$ up 2 units and right 1 unit.

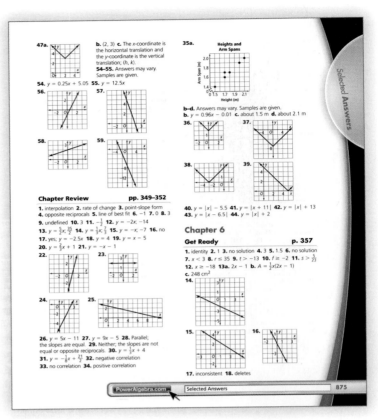

47a.

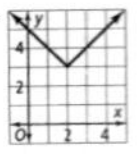

b. (2, 3) **c.** The x-coordinate is the horizontal translation and the y-coordinate is the vertical translation; (h, k).

54–55. Answers may vary. Samples are given.

54. $y = 0.25x + 5.05$ **55.** $y = 12.5x$

56.

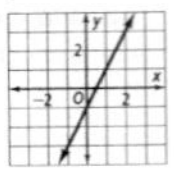

57.

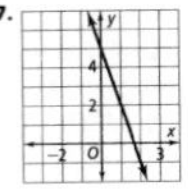

58.

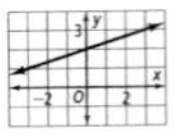

59.

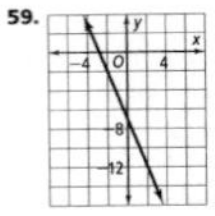

Chapter Review pp. 349–352

1. interpolation **2.** rate of change **3.** point-slope form **4.** opposite reciprocals **5.** line of best fit **6.** −1 **7.** 0 **8.** 3 **9.** undefined **10.** 3 **11.** $-\frac{1}{2}$ **12.** $y = -2x$; −14 **13.** $y = \frac{5}{2}x$; $\frac{35}{2}$ **14.** $y = \frac{1}{3}x$; $\frac{7}{3}$ **15.** $y = -x$; −7 **16.** no **17.** yes; $y = -2.5x$ **18.** $y = 4$ **19.** $y = x - 5$ **20.** $y = \frac{2}{3}x + 1$ **21.** $y = -x - 1$

22.

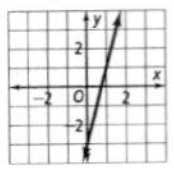

23.

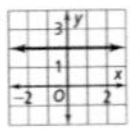

24.

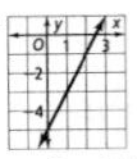

25.

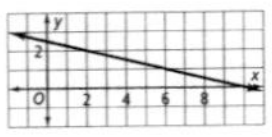

26. $y = 5x - 11$ **27.** $y = 9x - 5$ **28.** Parallel; the slopes are equal. **29.** Neither; the slopes are not equal or opposite reciprocals. **30.** $y = \frac{1}{3}x + 4$ **31.** $y = -\frac{1}{8}x + \frac{21}{2}$ **32.** negative correlation **33.** no correlation **34.** positive correlation

35a.

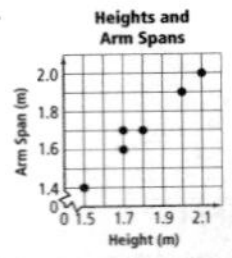

Heights and Arm Spans
Arm Span (m)
2.0
1.8
1.6
1.4
0
0 1.5 1.7 1.9 2.1
Height (m)

b–d. Answers may vary. Samples are given.
b. $y = 0.96x - 0.01$ **c.** about 1.5 m **d.** about 2.1 m

36.

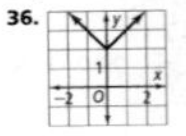

37.

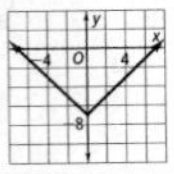

38.

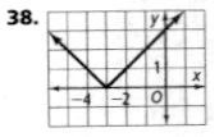

39.

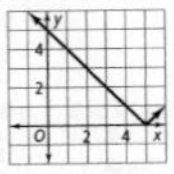

40. $y = |x| - 5.5$ **41.** $y = |x + 11|$ **42.** $y = |x| + 13$ **43.** $y = |x - 6.5|$ **44.** $y = |x| + 2$

Chapter 6

Get Ready p. 357

1. identity **2.** 1 **3.** no solution **4.** 3 **5.** 1.5 **6.** no solution **7.** $x < 3$ **8.** $r \leq 35$ **9.** $t > -13$ **10.** $f \geq -2$ **11.** $s > \frac{5}{23}$ **12.** $x \geq -18$ **13a.** $2x - 1$ **b.** $A = \frac{1}{2}x(2x - 1)$ **c.** 248 cm^2

14.

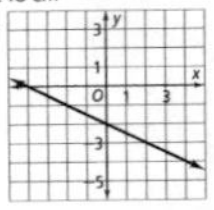

15.

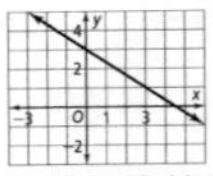

16.

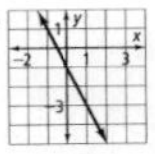

17. inconsistent **18.** deletes

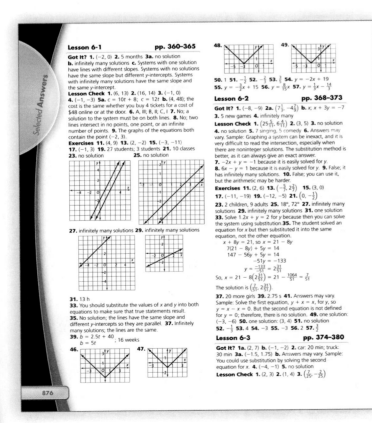

Lesson 6-1 pp. 360–365

Got It? 1. (−2, 0) **2.** 5 months **3a.** no solution **b.** infinitely many solutions **c.** Systems with one solution have lines with different slopes. Systems with no solutions have the same slope but different y-intercepts. Systems with infinitely many solutions have the same slope and the same y-intercept.

Lesson Check 1. (6, 13) **2.** (16, 14) **3.** (−1, 0) **4.** (−1, −3) **5a.** $c = 10t + 8$; $c = 12t$ **b.** (4, 48); the cost is the same whether you buy 4 tickets for a cost of $48 online or at the door. **6.** A, III; B, II; C, I **7.** No; a solution to the system must be on both lines. **8.** No; two lines intersect in no points, one point, or an infinite number of points. **9.** The graphs of the equations both contain the point (−2, 3).

Exercises 11. (4, 9) **13.** (2, −2) **15.** (−3, −11) **17.** (−1, 3) **19.** 27 students; 3 students **21.** 10 classes

23. no solution **25.** no solution

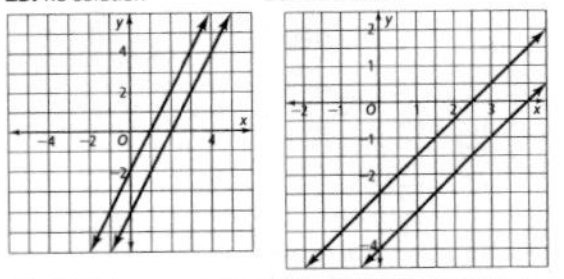

27. infinitely many solutions **29.** infinitely many solutions

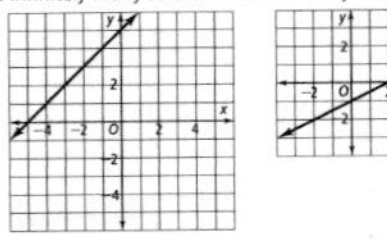

31. 13 h
33. You should substitute the values of x and y into both equations to make sure that true statements result.
35. No solution; the lines have the same slope and different y-intercepts so they are parallel. **37.** Infinitely many solutions; the lines are the same.
39. $b = 2.5t + 40$, $b = 5t$; 16 weeks

46. **47.**

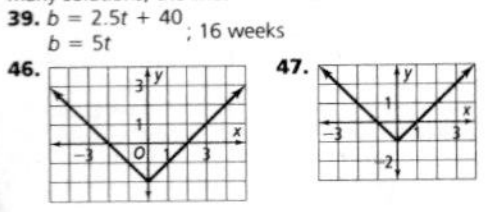

48. **49.**

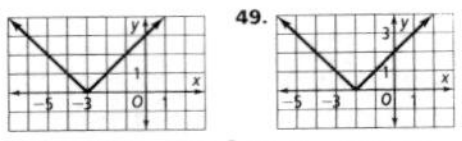

50. 1 **51.** $-\frac{1}{2}$ **52.** $-\frac{2}{3}$ **53.** $\frac{3}{5}$ **54.** $y = -2x + 19$ **55.** $y = -\frac{3}{2}x + 15$ **56.** $y = \frac{8}{15}x$ **57.** $y = \frac{1}{3}x - \frac{14}{3}$

Lesson 6-2 pp. 368–373

Got It? 1. (−8, −9) **2a.** $\left(7\frac{1}{3}, -4\frac{7}{9}\right)$ **b.** x; $x + 3y = -7$ **3.** 5 new games **4.** infinitely many

Lesson Check 1. $\left(25\frac{5}{11}, 6\frac{4}{11}\right)$ **2.** (3, 5) **3.** no solution **4.** no solution **5.** 7 singing, 5 comedy **6.** Answers may vary. Sample: Graphing a system can be inexact, and it is very difficult to read the intersection, especially when there are noninteger solutions. The substitution method is better, as it can always give an exact answer.
7. $-2x + y = -1$ because it is easily solved for y.
8. $6x - y = 1$ because it is easily solved for y. **9.** False; it has infinitely many solutions. **10.** False; you can use it, but the arithmetic may be harder.

Exercises 11. (2, 6) **13.** $\left(-\frac{5}{7}, 2\frac{2}{7}\right)$ **15.** (3, 0) **17.** (−11, −19) **19.** (−12, −5) **21.** $\left(0, -\frac{1}{2}\right)$
23. 2 children, 9 adults **25.** 18°, 72° **27.** infinitely many solutions **29.** infinitely many solutions **31.** one solution **33.** Solve $1.2x + y = 2$ for y because then you can solve the system using substitution. **35.** The student solved an equation for x but then substituted it into the same equation, not the other equation.

$$x + 8y = 21, \text{ so } x = 21 - 8y$$
$$7(21 - 8y) + 5y = 14$$
$$147 - 56y + 5y = 14$$
$$-51y = -133$$
$$y = \frac{-133}{-51} = 2\frac{31}{51}$$

So, $x = 21 - 8\left(2\frac{31}{51}\right) = 21 - \frac{1064}{51} = \frac{7}{51}$

The solution is $\left(\frac{7}{51}, 2\frac{31}{51}\right)$.

37. 20 more girls **39.** 2.75 s **41.** Answers may vary. Sample: Solve the first equation, $y + x = x$, for y, so $y = x - x = 0$. But the second equation is not defined for $y = 0$; therefore, there is no solution. **49.** one solution: (−3, −6) **50.** one solution: (3, 4) **51.** no solution **52.** $-\frac{1}{3}$ **53.** 4 **54.** −3 **55.** −3 **56.** 2 **57.** $\frac{3}{2}$

Lesson 6-3 pp. 374–380

Got It? 1a. (2, 7) **b.** (−1, −2) **2.** car: 20 min; truck: 30 min **3a.** (−1.5, 1.75) **b.** Answers may vary. Sample: You could use substitution by solving the second equation for x. **4.** (−4, −1) **5.** no solution

Lesson Check 1. (2, 3) **2.** (1, 4) **3.** $\left(\frac{7}{25}, -\frac{2}{25}\right)$

4. Elimination; the objective of the elimination method is to add (or subtract) two equations to eliminate a variable. **5.** The Addition Property of Equality says that adding equals to equals gives you equals. This is what you are doing in the elimination method. **6.** Answers may vary. Sample: Decide which variable to eliminate, and then multiply, if necessary, one or both equations so that the coefficients of the variable are the same (or opposites). Then subtract (or add) the two equations. This will result in one equation with a single variable that you can solve. Then substitute to find the value of the other variable.

Exercises 7. (4, 5) **9.** (1, 5) **11.** (3, 15)
13a. $12x + 2y = 90$, $6x + 2y = 60$ **b.** solo act: 5 min; ensemble act: 15 min
15. (3, 1) **17.** (5, 3) **19.** (2, −1) **21.** no solution **23.** one solution **25.** infinitely many solutions **27.** $12; $7 **29.** The student forgot to multiply the constant in the second equation by 4.

$15x + 12y = 6$
$12x + 12y = -12$
so, $3x = 18$
$x = 6$

31. Answers may vary. Sample:
$3x - 2y = 7$
$5x + 2y = 33$
Because the coefficients of the y-terms are already opposites, simply add the two equations to get $8x = 40$, or $x = 5$. Substitute $x = 5$ into either equation to get $y = 4$. The solution is (5, 4).
33. (2, 0); answers may vary. Sample: Substitution; the first equation is easily solved for y. **35.** (6, 5); answers may vary. Sample: Substitution; the first equation is already solved for y. **37.** (6, −4); answers may vary. Sample: Elimination; you can multiply each equation by the LCD of the denominators to eliminate the fractions. Then you can use elimination. **39.** parasailing: $51; horseback riding: $30 **50.** (7, 3.5) **51.** (34, 27) **52.** (5, −3) **53.** $a > 1$ **54.** $x \geq 7$ **55.** $b > 0.2$ **56.** 2.75 h

Lesson 6-4 pp. 383–388

Got It? 1. 720 books **2.** 11.25 L of 20% alcohol; 3.75 L of 12% alcohol **3a.** 3.5 mi/h; 1.5 mi/h **b.** You will be pushed backward.

Lesson Check 1. 300 copies **2.** 1 kg of 30% gold, 3 kg of 10% gold **3.** 2.25 mi/h; 0.75 mi/h **4.** Before the break-even point, expenses exceed income. After the break-even point, income exceeds expenses. **5.** Answers may vary. Sample: elimination; neither equation is easily solved for a variable. **6.** You would need more of the 15% brand, since 25% is closer to 15% than 40%.

Exercises 7. 40 bicycles **9.** $950 at 5% and $550 at 4% **11.** 4 ft/s; 2 ft/s
13a. Let x = the number of pennies and let y = the number of quarters.
$x + y = 15$
$0.01x + 0.25y = 4.35$
The solution is 17.5 quarters and −2.5 pennies.
b. No; you cannot have a negative number of coins.
15. (−3, −2); substitution because the second equation is already solved for y **17.** $A = -3$ and $B = -2$.
19–21. Answers may vary. Samples are given.
19. Substitution; both equations are already solved for y, so you can set them equal. **21.** Substitution; the second equation is already solved for y. **23.** $66\frac{2}{3}$ mL of the 5% mixture; $133\frac{1}{3}$ mL of the 6.5% mixture **25.** It can also be solved by the elimination method because the variables are lined up and the coefficients of the y-terms are the same. So one would simply have to subtract the second equation. **32.** (−7, 6) **33.** (−2, −2) **34.** (4, 2.5) **35.** $a > 5$ **36.** $d \leq -2.5$ **37.** $q \leq -4$

Lesson 6-5 pp. 390–395

Got It? 1a. yes **b.** No; it could be on the line $y = x + 10$.

2.

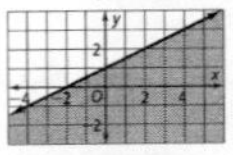

3a. **b.**

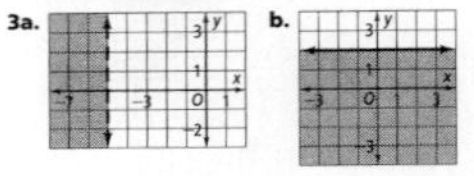

4. Answers may vary. Sample: 0 lb of peanuts and 3 lb of cashews; 6 lb of peanuts and 0 lb of cashews; 1 lb of peanuts and 1 lb of cashews

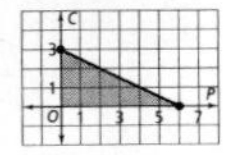

5. $y > \frac{1}{3}x - 2$

Lesson Check 1. no

2. **3.**

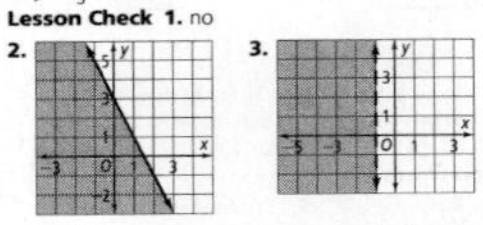

4. $y < \frac{1}{2}x - 1$ **5.** Answers will vary. Sample: The solutions of a linear equation and a linear inequality are coordinates of the points that make the equation or inequality true. The graph of a linear equation is a line, but the graph of a linear inequality is a region of the coordinate plane. **6.** Since the inequality is already solved for y, the < symbol means you should shade

below the boundary line. All of these shaded points will make the inequality true. **7.** $y \geq 5x + 1$

Exercises **9.** solution **11.** solution **13.** solution

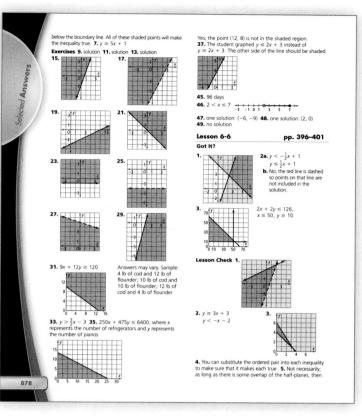

15. **17.** **19.** **21.** **23.** **25.** **27.** **29.**

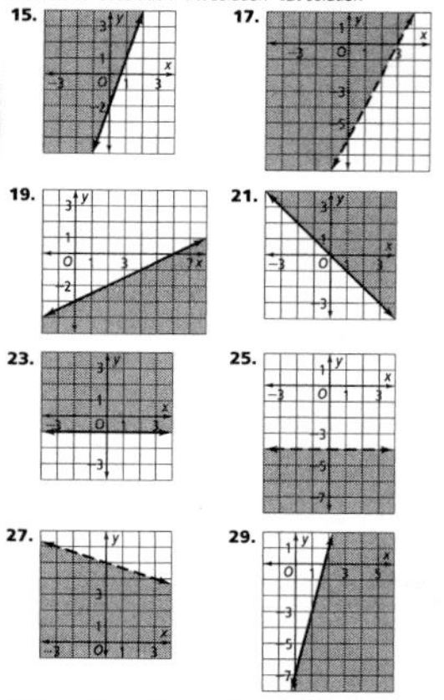

31. $9x + 12y \geq 120$

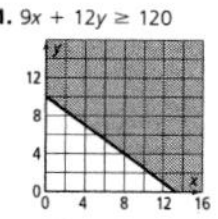

Answers may vary. Sample: 4 lb of cod and 12 lb of flounder; 10 lb of cod and 10 lb of flounder; 12 lb of cod and 4 lb of flounder

33. $y > \frac{3}{2}x - 3$ **35.** $250x + 475y \leq 6400$, where x represents the number of refrigerators and y represents the number of pianos

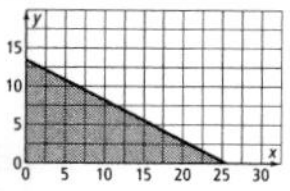

Yes; the point (12, 8) is not in the shaded region. **37.** The student graphed $y \leq 2x + 3$ instead of $y \geq 2x + 3$. The other side of the line should be shaded.

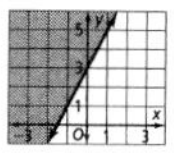

45. 96 days

46. $2 < x \leq 7$

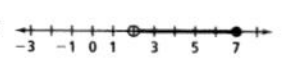

47. one solution: (−6, −9) **48.** one solution: (2, 0) **49.** no solution

Lesson 6-6 pp. 396–401

Got It?

1.

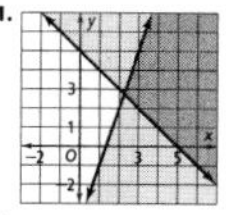

2a. $y < -\frac{1}{2}x + 1$, $y \leq \frac{1}{2}x + 1$ **b.** No; the red line is dashed so points on that line are not included in the solution.

3.

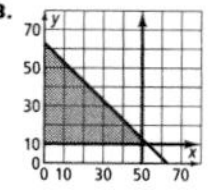

$2x + 2y \leq 126$, $x \leq 50$, $y \geq 10$

Lesson Check **1.**

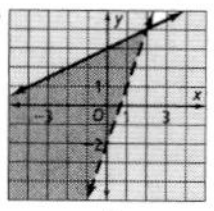

2. $y \geq 3x + 3$, $y < -x - 2$ **3.**

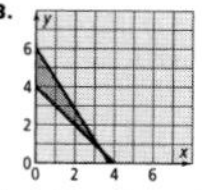

4. You can substitute the ordered pair into each inequality to make sure that it makes each true. **5.** Not necessarily; as long as there is some overlap of the half-planes, then the system will have a solution. **6.** You need to find the intersection of each of the two systems, but the intersections of lines will be a point or line and the intersections of inequalities will be a line or a planar section.

Exercises **7.** yes **9.** no

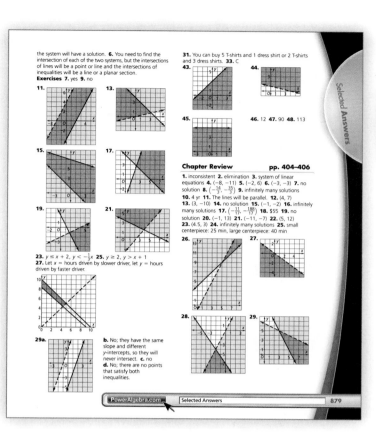

11. **13.** **15.** **17.** **19.** **21.**

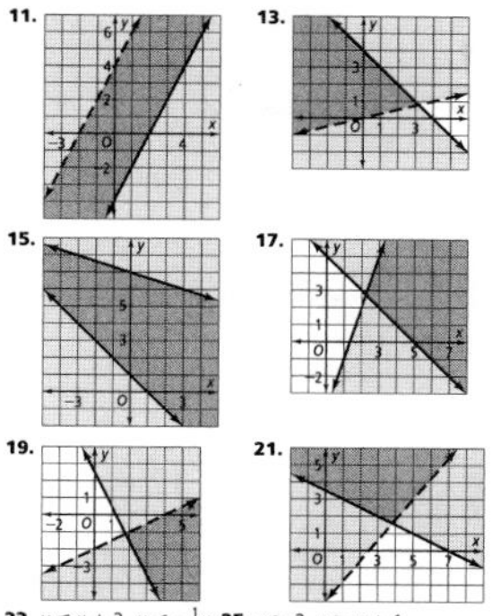

23. $y \leq x + 2$, $y < -\frac{1}{3}x$ **25.** $y \geq 2$, $y > x + 1$

27. Let x = hours driven by slower driver, let y = hours driven by faster driver.

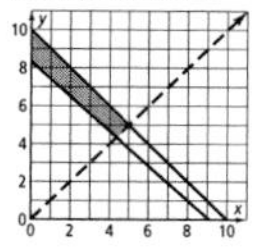

29a.

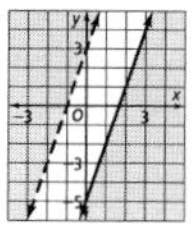

b. No; they have the same slope and different y-intercepts, so they will never intersect. **c.** no **d.** No; there are no points that satisfy both inequalities.

31. You can buy 5 T-shirts and 1 dress shirt or 2 T-shirts and 3 dress shirts. **33.** C

43. **44.** **45.**

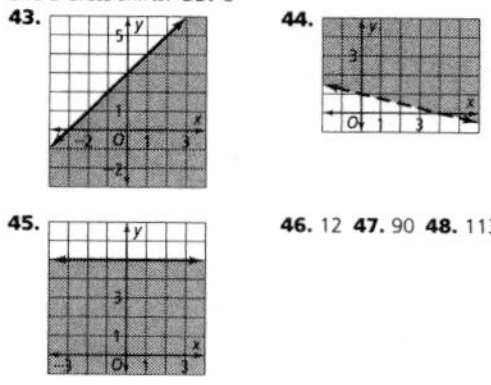

46. 12 **47.** 90 **48.** 113

Chapter Review pp. 404–406

1. inconsistent **2.** elimination **3.** system of linear equations **4.** (−8, −11) **5.** (−2, 6) **6.** (−3, −3) **7.** no solution **8.** $\left(-\frac{14}{3}, -\frac{35}{3}\right)$ **9.** infinitely many solutions **10.** 4 yr **11.** The lines will be parallel. **12.** (4, 7) **13.** (3, −10) **14.** no solution **15.** (−1, −2) **16.** infinitely many solutions **17.** $\left(-\frac{11}{17}, -\frac{188}{17}\right)$ **18.** $55 **19.** no solution **20.** (−1, 13) **21.** (−11, −7) **22.** (5, 12) **23.** (4.5, 3) **24.** infinitely many solutions **25.** small centerpiece: 25 min, large centerpiece: 40 min

26. **27.** **28.** **29.**

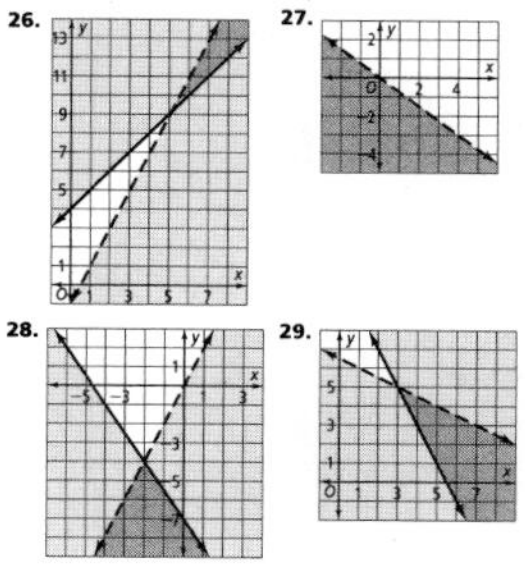

30. **31.**

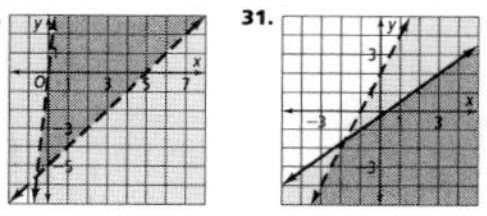

32.

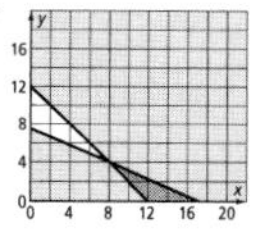

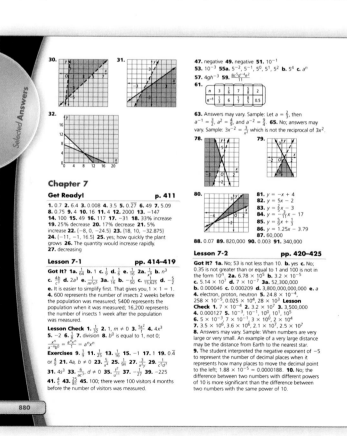

Chapter 7

Get Ready! p. 411

1. 0.7 **2.** 6.4 **3.** 0.008 **4.** 3.5 **5.** $0.\overline{27}$ **6.** 49 **7.** 5.09 **8.** 0.75 **9.** 4 **10.** 16 **11.** 4 **12.** 2000 **13.** −147 **14.** 100 **15.** 49 **16.** 117 **17.** −31 **18.** 33% increase **19.** 25% decrease **20.** 17% decrease **21.** 5% increase **22.** {−8, 0, −24.5} **23.** {18, 10, −32.875} **24.** {−11, −1, 16.5} **25.** yes; how quickly the plant grows **26.** The quantity would increase rapidly. **27.** decreasing

Lesson 7-1 pp. 414–419

Got It? **1a.** $\frac{1}{64}$ **b.** 1 **c.** $\frac{1}{9}$ **d.** $\frac{1}{6}$ **e.** $\frac{1}{16}$ **2a.** $\frac{1}{x^9}$ **b.** n^3 **c.** $\frac{4b}{c^3}$ **d.** $2a^3$ **e.** $\frac{1}{m^2n^5}$ **3a.** $\frac{1}{16}$ **b.** $-\frac{1}{50}$ **c.** $\frac{1}{15{,}625}$ **d.** $-\frac{5}{2}$ **e.** It is easier to simplify first. That gives you, 1 × 1 = 1. **4.** 600 represents the number of insects 2 weeks before the population was measured; 5400 represents the population when it was measured; 16,200 represents the number of insects 1 week after the population was measured.

Lesson Check **1.** $\frac{1}{32}$ **2.** 1, $m \neq 0$ **3.** $\frac{5s^2}{t}$ **4.** $4x^3$ **5.** −2 **6.** $\frac{1}{8}$ **7.** division **8.** b^0 is equal to 1, not 0; $\frac{x^n}{a^{-n}b^0} = \frac{a^nx^n}{1} = a^nx^n$

Exercises **9.** $\frac{1}{9}$ **11.** $\frac{1}{25}$ **13.** $\frac{1}{16}$ **15.** −1 **17.** 1 **19.** $0.\overline{4}$ or $\frac{4}{9}$ **21.** $4a$, $b \neq 0$ **23.** $\frac{5}{x^4}$ **25.** $\frac{1}{9n}$ **27.** $\frac{3}{x^2y}$ **29.** $\frac{1}{c^5d^7}$ **31.** $4s^3$ **33.** $\frac{6}{ac^3}$, $d \neq 0$ **35.** $\frac{t^7}{u^{11}}$ **37.** $-\frac{1}{27}$ **39.** −225 **41.** $\frac{4}{5}$ **43.** $\frac{25}{81}$ **45.** 100; there were 100 visitors 4 months before the number of visitors was measured.

47. negative **49.** negative **51.** 10^{-1} **53.** 10^{-3} **55a.** $5^{-2}, 5^{-1}, 5^0, 5^1, 5^2$ **b.** 5^4 **c.** a^n **57.** $4gh^{-3}$ **59.** $\frac{8c^5d^{-4}e^2}{11}$

61.

n	3	$\frac{1}{6}$	7	$\frac{5}{8}$	2
n^{-1}	$\frac{1}{3}$	6	$\frac{1}{7}$	$\frac{8}{5}$	0.5

63. Answers may vary. Sample: Let $a = \frac{2}{3}$, then $a^{-1} = \frac{3}{2}$, $a^2 = \frac{4}{9}$, and $a^{-2} = \frac{9}{4}$. **65.** No; answers may vary. Sample: $3x^{-2} = \frac{3}{x^2}$ which is not the reciprocal of $3x^2$.

78. **79.**

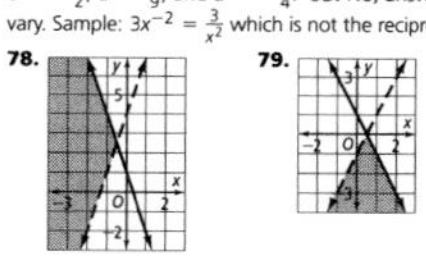

80.

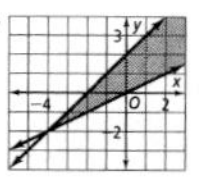

81. $y = -x + 4$
82. $y = 5x - 2$
83. $y = \frac{2}{5}x - 3$
84. $y = -\frac{3}{11}x - 17$
85. $y = \frac{5}{9}x + \frac{1}{3}$
86. $y = 1.25x - 3.79$
87. 60,000

88. 0.07 **89.** 820,000 **90.** 0.003 **91.** 340,000

Lesson 7-2 pp. 420–425

Got It? **1a.** No; 53 is not less than 10. **b.** yes **c.** No; 0.35 is not greater than or equal to 1 and 100 is not in the form 10^n. **2a.** 6.78×10^5 **b.** 3.2×10^{-5} **c.** 5.14×10^7 **d.** 7×10^{-7} **3a.** 52,300,000 **b.** 0.000046 **c.** 0.000209 **d.** 3,800,000,000,000 **e.** a **4.** electron, proton, neutron **5.** 24.8×10^{-4}, 258×10^{-5}, 0.025×10^4, 28×10^3 **Lesson Check** **1.** 7×10^{-4} **2.** 3.2×10^7 **3.** 3,500,000 **4.** 0.000127 **5.** $10^{-3}, 10^{-1}, 10^0, 10^1, 10^5$ **6.** $5 \times 10^{-3}, 7 \times 10^{-1}, 3 \times 10^0, 2 \times 10^4$ **7.** $3.5 \times 10^6, 3.6 \times 10^6, 2.1 \times 10^7, 2.5 \times 10^7$ **8.** Answers may vary. Sample: When numbers are very large or very small. An example of a very large distance may be the distance from Earth to the nearest star. **9.** The student interpreted the negative exponent of −5 to represent the number of decimal places when it represents how many places to move the decimal point to the left; $1.88 \times 10^{-5} = 0.0000188$. **10.** No; the difference between two numbers with different powers of 10 is more significant than the difference between two numbers with the same power of 10.

Exercises **11.** No; 44 is not less than 10 **13.** No; 0.9 is not greater than 1. **15.** yes **17.** No; 457 is not less than 10. **19.** 9.04×10^9 **21.** 9.3×10^6 **23.** 3.25×10^{-3} **25.** 9.2×10^{-4} **27.** 500 **29.** 2040 **31.** 0.897 **33.** 274,000 **35.** 6×10^{-10}, 8×10^{-8}, 9×10^{-7}, 7×10^{-6} **37.** 0.52×10^{-3}, 4.8×10^{-3}, 50.1×10^{-3}, 56×10^{-3} **39.** ^{232}U, ^{234}U, ^{236}U, ^{235}U **41.** 2.4×10^{15} **43.** 3.18×10^{-3} **45.** 3.4×10^5 **47.** 436 billion is 436,000,000,000 so in scientific notation it becomes 4.36×10^{11} because it must be the product of a number greater than or equal to 1 and less than 10 and a power of 10. **49.** It increases by 2 because 100 is 10^2. Sample: $100(3.46 \times 10^5) = 346 \times 10^5 = 3.46 \times 10^7$ **56.** $\frac{c}{d^6}$ **57.** b^3 **58.** $\frac{9}{w^3}$ **59.** $4mn^5$ **60.** $\frac{k^5}{9}$

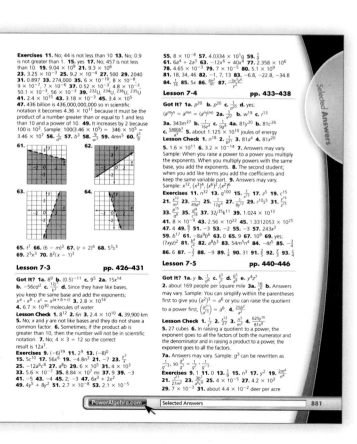

61. **62.**

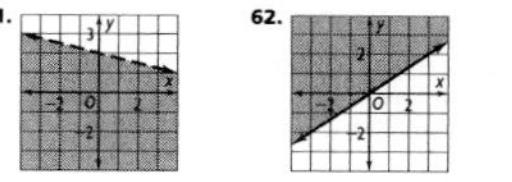

63. **64.**

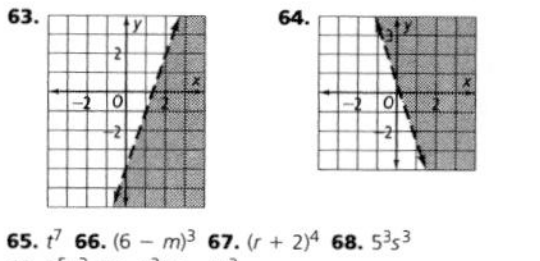

65. t^7 **66.** $(6 - m)^3$ **67.** $(r + 2)^4$ **68.** 5^3s^3 **69.** 2^5x^3 **70.** $8^2(x - 1)^3$

Lesson 7-3 pp. 426–431

Got It? **1a.** 8^9 **b.** $(0.5)^{-11}$ **c.** 9^5 **2a.** $15x^{14}$ **b.** $-56cd^2$ **c.** $\frac{12j^3}{k^2}$ **d.** Since they have like bases, you keep the same base and add the exponents; $x^a \cdot x^b \cdot x^c = x^{(a+b+c)}$ **3.** 2.8×10^{14} **4.** 6.7×10^{30} molecules of water

Lesson Check **1.** 8^{12} **2.** $6n$ **3.** 2.4×10^{10} **4.** 39,900 km **5.** No; x and y are not like bases and they do not share a common factor. **6.** Sometimes; if the product ab is greater than 10, then the number will not be in scientific notation. **7.** No; 4 × 3 = 12 so the correct result is $12a^7$.

Exercises **9.** $(-6)^{19}$ **11.** 2^9 **13.** $(-8)^0$ **15.** $5c^{10}$ **17.** $56x^6$ **19.** $-4.8n^3$ **21.** −7 **23.** $\frac{y^3}{x}$ **25.** $-12a^6c^8$ **27.** a^8b **29.** 6×10^5 **31.** 4×10^3 **33.** 5.6×10^{-7} **35.** 8.84×10^7 mi **37.** 9 **39.** −3 **41.** −5 **43.** −4 **45.** 2; −3 **47.** $6x^3 + 2x^2$ **49.** $4y^5 + 8y^2$ **51.** 2.7×10^{-8} **53.** 2.1×10^{-5} **55.** 8×10^{-8} **57.** 4.0334×10^1g **59.** $\frac{1}{a}$ **61.** $6a^4 + 2a^3$ **63.** $-12x^6 + 40x^4$ **77.** 2.358×10^6 **78.** 4.65×10^{-3} **79.** 7×10^{-5} **80.** 5.1×10^9 **81.** 18, 34, 46 **82.** −1, 7, 13 **83.** −6.8, −22.8, −34.8 **84.** $\frac{1}{16}$ **85.** $5x$ **86.** $\frac{4n^2}{m}$ **87.** $\frac{-3x^3z^6}{y^2}$

Lesson 7-4 pp. 433–438

Got It? **1a.** p^{20} **b.** p^{20} **c.** $\frac{1}{p^{20}}$ **d.** yes; $(a^m)^n = a^{mn} = (a^n)^{(m)}$ **2a.** $\frac{1}{x^{22}}$ **b.** w^{19} **c.** r^{13} **3a.** $343m^{27}$ **b.** $\frac{1}{16z^4}$ **c.** $\frac{1}{9g^8}$ **4a.** $81y^{20}$ **b.** $81c^{26}$ **c.** $\frac{5400b^3}{a^3}$ **5.** about 1.125×10^{10} joules of energy **Lesson Check** **1.** n^{18} **2.** $\frac{1}{b^{21}}$ **3.** $81a^4$ **4.** $81x^{20}$ **5.** 1.6×10^{11} **6.** 3.2×10^{-14} **7.** Answers may vary. Sample: When you raise a power to a power you multiply the exponents. When you multiply powers with the same base, you add the exponents. **8.** The second student; when you add like terms you add the coefficients and keep the same variable part. **9.** Answers may vary. Sample: $x^{12}, (x^3)^4, (x^6)^2, (x^2)^6$

Exercises **11.** n^{32} **13.** q^{100} **15.** $\frac{1}{x^{15}}$ **17.** z^5 **19.** c^{15} **21.** $\frac{x^{10}}{m^3}$ **23.** $\frac{1}{49a^2}$ **25.** $\frac{1}{12g^4}$ **27.** $\frac{1}{8y^{12}}$ **29.** $r^{10}s^5$ **31.** $\frac{y^{16}}{z^{15}}$ **33.** $\frac{p^{15}}{q^9}$ **35.** $\frac{d^8}{c^{18}}$ **37.** $32j^{35}k^{11}$ **39.** 1.024×10^{13} **41.** 8×10^{-9} **43.** 2.56×10^{22} **45.** 1.3312053×10^{25} **47.** 4 **49.** $\frac{6}{7}$ **51.** −3 **53.** −2 **55.** −3 **57.** $243x^3$ **59.** b^{17} **61.** $-8a^9b^6$ **63.** 0 **65.** 9 **67.** 10^9 **69.** yes; $(7xyz)^2$ **81.** $\frac{b^4}{c^6}$ **82.** a^8b^3 **83.** $54m^5n^4$ **84.** $-4t^5$ **85.** $-\frac{3}{4}$ **86.** 6 **87.** $-\frac{3}{2}$ **88.** −9 **89.** $\frac{1}{4}$ **90.** 31 **91.** $\frac{2}{5}$ **92.** $\frac{y}{3}$ **93.** $\frac{c}{4}$

Lesson 7-5 pp. 440–446

Got It? **1a.** y **b.** $\frac{1}{d^6}$ **c.** $\frac{k^5}{j^3}$ **d.** $\frac{b^5}{a^8}$ **e.** y^4z^7 **2.** about 169 people per square mile **3a.** $\frac{16}{x^6}$ **b.** Answers may vary. Sample: You can simplify within the parentheses first to give you $(a^2)^3 = a^6$ or you can raise the quotient to a power first, $\left(\frac{a^{21}}{a^{15}}\right) = a^6$. **4.** $\frac{25b^2}{a^2}$

Lesson Check **1.** $\frac{1}{y^7}$ **2.** $\frac{x^{12}}{27}$ **3.** $\frac{n^3}{m^3}$ **4.** $\frac{625y^{16}}{81x^8}$ **5.** 27 cubes **6.** In raising a quotient to a power, the exponent goes to all the factors of both the numerator and the denominator and in raising a product to a power, the exponent goes to all the factors.

7a. Answers may vary. Sample: g^3 can be rewritten as $\frac{1}{g^{-3}}$, so $\frac{g^3}{g^7} = \frac{1}{g^7} \cdot \frac{1}{g^{-3}}$.

Exercises **9.** 1 **11.** 0 **13.** $\frac{1}{9}$ **15.** n^3 **17.** y^2 **19.** $\frac{2m^4}{n^4}$ **21.** $\frac{t^{11}}{27m^2}$ **23.** $\frac{3b^7}{a^6c^8}$ **25.** 4×10^{-5} **27.** 4.2×10^3 **29.** 7×10^{-3} **31.** about 4.4×10^{-2} deer per acre

33. $\frac{9}{64}$ **35.** $\frac{81x^4}{y^4}$ **37.** $\frac{216}{15{,}625}$ **39.** $\frac{262{,}144}{n^{30}}$ **41.** $\frac{5}{2}$ **43.** $\frac{25y^8}{49x^{10}}$
45. $\frac{x^6}{25}$ **47.** b^{15} **49.** 5^3 should be 125. **51.** Each factor should be raised to the fourth power and simplified.
53. The base d should only appear once.
55a. about 1636 h **b.** about 31 h **57.** dividing powers with the same base, definition of negative exponent
59. raising a power to a power, dividing powers with the same base, definition of negative exponent **61.** $\frac{1}{16m^8}$
63. a^4 **65.** $\frac{1}{a^9}$ **67.** $\frac{y^{10}}{2x^5}$ **69.** Answers may vary. Samples are given.

I. $\left(\frac{3}{x^2}\right)^{-3} = \left(\frac{x^2}{3}\right)^3$ Rewrite using the reciprocal.
$= \frac{(x^2)^3}{3^3}$ Raise the numerator and denominator to the third power.
$= \frac{x^6}{27}$ Simplify.

II. $\left(\frac{3}{x^2}\right)^{-3} = \frac{3^{-3}}{(x^2)^{-3}}$ Raise a quotient to a power rule
$= \frac{3^{-3}}{x^{-6}}$ Power to a power rule
$= \frac{x^6}{3^3}$ Definition of negative exponent
$= \frac{x^6}{27}$ Simplify.

III. $\left(\frac{3}{x^2}\right)^{-3} = \left(\frac{x^2}{3}\right)^3$ Rewrite using the reciprocal.
$= \frac{x^2}{3} \cdot \frac{x^2}{3} \cdot \frac{x^2}{3}$ Definition of an exponent
$= \frac{x^6}{27}$ Simplify.

71. $\frac{x^6}{9y^8}$ **73.** $\frac{2}{27}$ **75.** $\frac{c^6}{a^{18}b^6}$ **77.** $\frac{y^6}{256x^2}$ **79.** about $3\frac{1}{3}$ m
81. $x = 7$ and $y = 4$; use the two given expressions to find the system of equations, $x - y = 3$ and $x - 3y = -5$. Solve the system to find the values of x and y. **83.** $\left(\frac{m}{n}\right)^7$ **85.** $\left(\frac{3x}{2y}\right)^3$ **87a.** a^{-n} **b.** $\frac{1}{a^n}$
c. Since $\frac{a^0}{a^n}$ equals both a^{-n} and $\frac{1}{a^n}$, a^{-n} must equal $\frac{1}{a^n}$, which is the definition of a negative exponent.
98. $\frac{8}{m^{21}}$ **99.** $\frac{2s^6}{27}$ **100.** $\frac{1}{64c^2}$ **101.** $9r^{10}$ **102.** n^{15}
103. (0, 0)

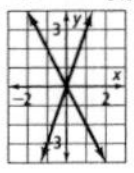

104. (−4, −7)

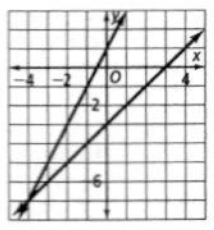

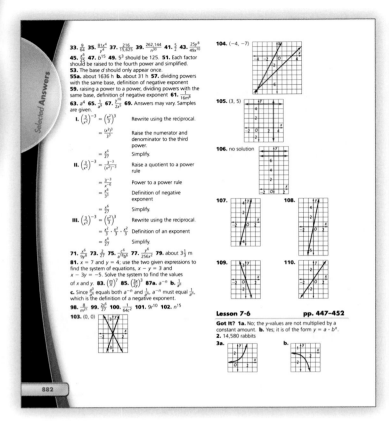

105. (3, 5)

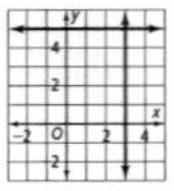

106. no solution

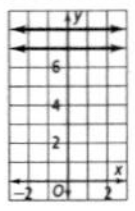

107.

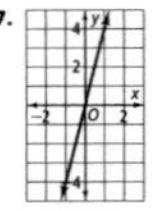

108.

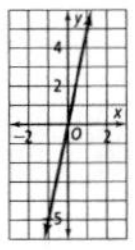

109.

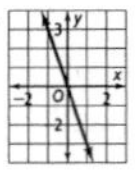

110.

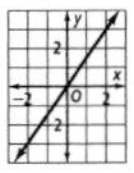

Lesson 7-6 pp. 447–452

Got It? 1a. No; the y-values are not multiplied by a constant amount. **b.** Yes; it is of the form $y = a \cdot b^x$.
2. 14,580 rabbits
3a.

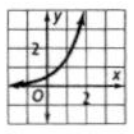

b.

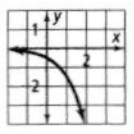

4a.

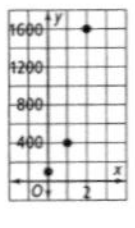

b. 300%

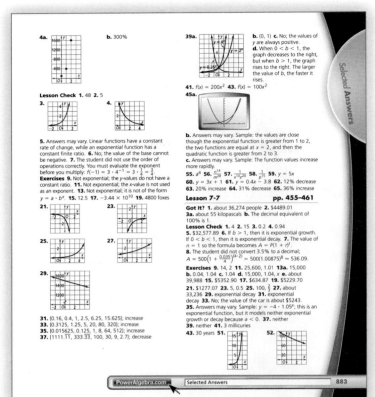

Lesson Check 1. 48 **2.** 5
3.

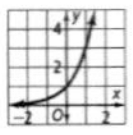

4.

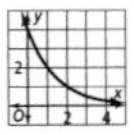

5. Answers may vary. Linear functions have a constant rate of change, while an exponential function has a constant finite ratio. **6.** No; the value of the base cannot be negative. **7.** The student did not use the order of operations correctly. You must evaluate the exponent before you multiply: $f(-1) = 3 \cdot 4^{-1} = 3 \cdot \frac{1}{4} = \frac{3}{4}$.
Exercises 9. Not exponential; the y-values do not have a constant ratio. **11.** Not exponential; the x-value is not used as an exponent. **13.** Not exponential; it is not of the form $y = a \cdot b^x$. **15.** 12.5 **17.** -3.44×10^{10} **19.** 4800 foxes
21.

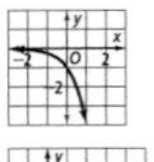

23.

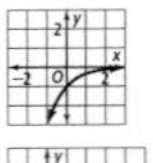

25.

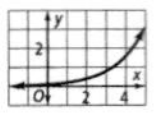

27.

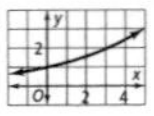

29.

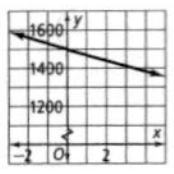

31. {0.16, 0.4, 1, 2.5, 6.25, 15.625}; increase
33. {0.3125, 1.25, 5, 20, 80, 320}; increase
35. {0.015625, 0.125, 1, 8, 64, 512}; increase
37. {$1111.\overline{11}$, $333.\overline{33}$, 100, 30, 9, 2.7}; decrease

39a.

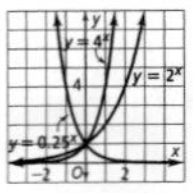

b. (0, 1) **c.** No; the values of y are always positive.
d. When $0 < b < 1$, the graph decreases to the right, but when $b > 1$, the graph rises to the right. The larger the value of b, the faster it rises.
41. $f(x) = 200x^2$ **43.** $f(x) = 100x^2$
45a.

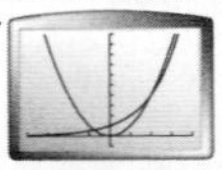

b. Answers may vary. Sample: the values are close though the exponential function is greater from 1 to 2, the two functions are equal at $x = 2$, and then the quadratic function is greater from 2 to 3.
c. Answers may vary. Sample: The function values increase more rapidly.
55. a^4 **56.** $\frac{n^{14}}{m^{28}}$ **57.** $\frac{1}{x^{10}z^{20}}$ **58.** $\frac{1}{p^{15}}$ **59.** $y = 5x$
60. $y = 3x + 1$ **61.** $y = 0.4x - 3.8$ **62.** 12% decrease
63. 20% increase **64.** 31% decrease **65.** 36% increase

Lesson 7-7 pp. 455–461

Got It? 1. about 36,274 people **2.** \$4489.01
3a. about 55 kilopascals **b.** The decimal equivalent of 100% is 1.
Lesson Check 1. 4 **2.** 15 **3.** 0.2 **4.** 0.94
5. \$32,577.89 **6.** If $b > 1$, then it is exponential growth. If $0 < b < 1$, then it is exponential decay. **7.** The value of $n = 1$ so the formula becomes $A = P(1 + r)^t$.
8. The student did not convert 3.5% to a decimal; $A = 500\left(1 + \frac{0.035}{4}\right)^{(4 \cdot 2)} = 500(1.00875)^8 \approx 536.09$.
Exercises 9. 14, 2 **11.** 25,600, 1.01 **13a.** 15,000 **b.** 0.04, 1.04 **c.** 1.04 **d.** 15,000, 1.04, x **e.** about 39,988 **15.** \$5352.90 **17.** \$634.87 **19.** \$5229.70
21. \$1277.07 **23.** 5, 0.5 **25.** 100, $\frac{2}{3}$ **27.** about 33,236 **29.** exponential decay **31.** exponential decay **33.** No; the value of the car is about \$5243.
35. Answers may vary. Sample: $y = -4 \cdot 1.05^x$; this is an exponential function, but it models neither exponential growth or decay because $a < 0$. **37.** neither
39. neither **41.** 3 millicuries
43. 30 years **51.**

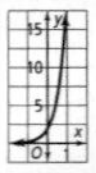

52.

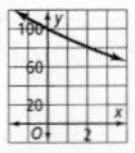

53.

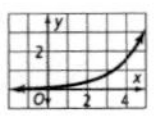

54. $x < 2$ **55.** $t \geq 12$
56. $k < 0.2$ **57.** $19t$
58. $-8k$ **59.** $11b - 6$
60. $-3n^2$ **61.** $9x^2$

Chapter Review pp. 463–466

1. scientific notation **2.** growth factor **3.** decay factor
4. exponential growth **5.** exponential decay **6.** 1
7. $\frac{1}{49}$ **8.** $\frac{4y^8}{x^2}$ **9.** $\frac{q^4}{p^2}$ **10.** 9 **11.** $\frac{9}{16}$ **12.** 1 **13.** 45 **14.** $\frac{25}{9}$
15. $-\frac{20}{9}$ **16.** No; −3 should be raised to the fourth power instead of multiplying it by 4. **17.** No; 950 is not between 1 and 10. **18.** No; 100 is not written as a power of 10. **19.** yes **20.** No; 0.84 is not between 1 and 10.
21. 2.793×10^6 **22.** 1.89×10^8 **23.** 4.3×10^{-5}
24. 2.7×10^{-9} **25.** 3.86×10^{12} **26.** 4.78×10^{-6}
27. 8 **28.** 2 **29.** 3; 6 **30.** 3 **31.** −5 **32.** 2 **33.** $2d^5$
34. $q^{12}r^4$ **35.** $-20c^4m^2$ **36.** 1.7956 **37.** $\frac{243x^3y^{11}}{16}$
38. $-\frac{4}{3r^{10}z^8}$ **39.** 7.8×10^3 pores **40.** $\frac{1}{w^3}$ **41.** $7x^4$
42. $\frac{n^{35}}{v^{21}}$ **43.** $\frac{e^{20}}{81c^{12}}$ **44.** 2×10^{-3} **45.** 2.5×10^2
46. 5×10^{-5} **47.** 3×10^3
48. Answers may vary. Sample:
1) Simplify the expression within the parentheses.
2) Take the reciprocal of the rational expression raised to the third power.
3) Use the quotient raised to a power rule by applying the exponent to both the numerator and denominator.
4) Simplify the numerator.
5) Simplify the denominator using the power rule.

49. 4, 16, 64 **50.** 0.01, 0.0001, 0.000001 **51.** 20, 10, 5
52. 6, 12, 24
53.

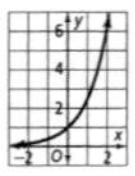

54.

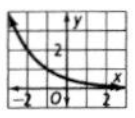

55.

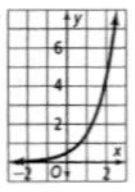

56.

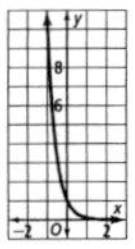

57a. 800 bacteria **b.** about 1.4×10^{16} bacteria
58. exponential growth; 3 **59.** exponential decay; 0.32
60. exponential growth; $\frac{3}{2}$ **61.** exponential decay; $\frac{1}{4}$
62. \$2697.20 **63.** 463 people

Chapter 8

Get Ready! p. 471

1. 1, 2, 3, 4, 6, 12 **2.** 1, 2, 3, 6, 9, 18 **3.** 1, 2, 4, 5, 10, 20, 25, 50, 100 **4.** 1, 3, 9, 27, 81 **5.** 1, 2, 3, 4, 6, 8, 9, 12, 18, 24, 36, 72 **6.** 1, 2, 3, 4, 5, 6, 10, 12, 15, 20, 25, 30, 50, 60, 75, 100, 150, 300 **7.** 1, 2, 5, 10, 25, 50, 125, 250
8. 1, 3, 9, 23, 69, 207 **9.** $x^2 - 9x$ **10.** $3d + 15$
11. $24r^2 - 15r$ **12.** $34m - 29$ **13.** $-36a^2 - 6a$
14. $-s^2 - 7s - 2$ **15.** $25x^2$ **16.** $9v^3$ **17.** $64c^6$
18. $56m^7$ **19.** $81b^6$ **20.** $36p^2q^2$ **21.** $7n^4$ **22.** $-125t^{12}$
23. p^2q^3 **24.** $5x$ **25.** $-\frac{1}{8n^5}$ **26.** $3y^2$ **27.** 3
28. A binomial is an expression with two terms.
29. b; $(x + 4)(x + 4) = (x + 4)^2$, which is a square, and $(x + 4)(x + 4) = x^2 + 8x + 16$, which is a trinomial.

Lesson 8-1 pp. 474–479

Got It? 1a. 2 **b.** 5 **c.** 0 **2.** $5x^4$, $-5x^2y^4$
3a. $8x^2 + 2x - 3$, quadratic trinomial **b.** Answers may vary. Sample: Writing a polynomial in standard form allows you to see which monomial term has the greatest degree and how many terms the polynomial has.
4. $-12x^3 + 120x^2 - 255x + 6022$
5. $-4m^3 - 4m^2 - 2m + 21$
Lesson Check 1. 4 **2.** 5 **3.** $11r^3 + 11$
4. $x^2 - 3x - 7$ **5.** quadratic trinomial **6.** linear binomial **7.** The coefficient of the sum of like monomials is the sum of the coefficients. To add polynomials, you group like terms and add their coefficients. A monomial has only one term and a polynomial can have more than one term.
Exercises 9. 3 **11.** 10 **13.** 0 **15.** no degree
17. $11m^3n^3$ **19.** $14t^4$ **21.** $18v^4w^3$
23. $-8bc^4$ **25.** $-2q + 7$; linear binomial
27. $-7x^2 - 4x + 4$; quadratic trinomial
29. $3z^4 - 2z^2 - 5z$; fourth degree trinomial
31. $9x^2 + 8$ **33.** $20x^2 + 5$ **35.** $-18x^2 + 228x + 2300$
37. $2x^3 + 8$ **39.** $5h^4 + h^3$ **41.** $9x - 1$
43. The student forgot to distribute the negative sign to all the terms in the second set of parentheses.
$(4x^2 - x + 3) - (3x^2 - 5x - 6) =$
$4x^2 - x + 3 - 3x^2 - (-5x) - (-6) =$
$4x^2 - 3x^2 - x + 5x + 3 + 6 =$
$x^2 + 4x + 9$ **45.** $-5y^3 + 2y^2 - 6$
47. $3z^3 + 15z^2 - 10z - 5$ **49.** No. Answers may vary. Sample: $(x^2 - x + 3) + (x - x^2 + 1) = 4$,

which is a monomial. **56.** 3 **57.** 2.1 **58.** 4
59. 5 **60.** $-\frac{2}{5}$ **61.** 8 **62.** $-\frac{8}{3}$ **63.** $-\frac{2}{3}$
64. a^5 **65.** $18r^3$ **66.** $28x^8$ **67.** $-10t^6$

Lesson 8-2 pp. 480–484

Got It? 1. $15n^4 - 5n^3 + 40n$ **2.** $3x$
3a. $3x^2(3x^4 + 5x^2 + 4)$ **b.** $-6x^2(x^2 + 3x + 2)$
4. $9x^2(4 - \pi)$
Lesson Check 1. $12x^4 + 42x^2$ **2.** $2a^2$ **3.** $3m(2m - 5)$
4. $4x(x^2 + 2x + 3)$ **5.** B **6.** C **7.** A **8.** Answers may vary. Sample: $18x^3 + 27x^2$
Exercises 9. $7x^2 + 28x$ **11.** $30m^2 + 3m^3$ **13.** $8x^4 - 28x^3 + 4x^2$ **15.** 4 **17.** 9 **19.** 4 **21.** $3(3x - 2)$
23. $7(2n^3 - 5n^2 + 4)$ **25.** $2x(7x^2 - x + 4)$
27. $25x^2(9 - \pi)$ **29.** $-10x^3 + 8x^2 - 26x$
31. $-60a^3 + 20a^2 - 70a$ **33.** $-t^3 + t^2 + t$
35. $20x^2 + 5x$; $5x(4x + 1)$ **37.** $17xy^3(y + 3x)$
39. $a^5(31ab^3 + 63)$ **41.** 49; $p = 7a$ and $q = 7b$, where a and b have no common factors other than 1, so $p^2 = 49a^2$ and $q^2 = 49b^2$. Since a^2 and b^2 have no common factors other than 1, the GCF of p^2 and q^2 is 49. **49.** $8x^2 + 4x + 5$ **50.** $7x^4 + 3x^2 - 1$
51. $-5x^3 - 6x$ **52.** $7x^4 + 2x^3 - 8x^2 + 4$
53. $y \leq \frac{4}{5}x - 2$ **54.** $y \geq \frac{7}{2}x - 4$

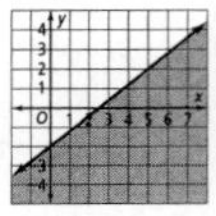

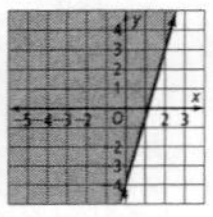

55. $y < -\frac{1}{3}x - 3$

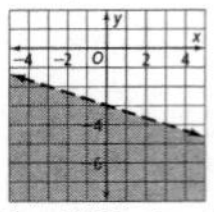

56. $8x - 40$ **57.** $-3w - 12$ **58.** $1.5c + 4$

Lesson 8-3 pp. 486–491

Got It? 1. $4x^2 - 21x - 18$ **2.** $3x^2 + 13x + 4$
3a. $3x^2 + 2x - 8$ **b.** $4n^2 - 31n + 42$
c. $4p^3 - 10p^2 + 6p - 15$ **4.** $4\pi x^2 + 20\pi x + 24\pi$

5a. $2x^3 - 9x^2 + 10x - 3$ **b.** Answers may vary. Sample: Distribute the trinomial to each term of the binomial. Then continue distributing and combining like terms as needed.
Lesson Check 1. $x^2 + 9x + 18$ **2.** $2x^2 + x - 15$
3. $x^3 + 5x^2 + 2x - 8$ **4.** $x^2 + 2x - 15$ **5.** Find the sum of the products of the FIRST terms, OUTER terms, INNER terms, and LAST terms. **6.** $3x^2 + 11x + 8$ **7.** The degree of the product is the sum of the degrees of the two polynomials.
Exercises 9. $y^2 + 5y - 24$ **11.** $c^2 - 15c + 50$
13. $6x^2 + 13x - 28$ **15.** $a^2 - 12a + 11$
17. $2h^2 + 11h - 63$ **19.** $6p^2 + 23p + 20$
21. $4x^2 + 11x - 20$ **23.** $b^2 - 12b + 27$
25. $45z^2 - 7z - 12$ **27.** $4w^2 + 21w + 26$
29. $4\pi x^2 + 22\pi x + 28\pi$ **31.** $x^3 + 2x^2 - 14x + 5$
33. $10a^3 + 12a^2 + 9a - 20$ **35.** $x^2 + 200x + 9375$
37. $-n^3 - 3n^2 - n - 3$ **39.** $2m^3 + 10m^2 + m + 5$
41. $12z^4 + 4z^3 + 3z^2 + z$ **45a. i.** $x^2 + 2x + 1$, 121
ii. $x^2 + 3x + 2$, 132 **iii.** $x^2 + 4x + 3$, 143
b. The digits in the product of the two integers are the coefficients of the terms in the product of the two binomials. **55.** $2(3x - 2)$ **56.** $b(b + 8)$
57. $5t(2t^2 - 5t + 4)$ **58.** $36x^2$ **59.** $4y^2$ **60.** $9m^2$
61. $25n^2$

Lesson 8-4 pp. 492–497

Got It? 1a. $n^2 - 14n + 49$ **b.** $4x^2 + 36x + 81$
2. $(16x + 64)$ ft^2 **3a.** 7225 **b.** Answers may vary. Sample: You could write 85 as (80 + 5) or as (100 − 15).
4a. $x^2 - 81$ **b.** $36 - m^4$ **c.** $9c^2 - 16$ **5.** 2496
Lesson Check 1. $c^2 + 6c + 9$ **2.** $g^2 - 8g + 16$
3. $4r^2 - 9$ **4.** $4x^2 + 12x + 9$ in.^{2} **5.** The Square of a Binomial **6.** The Product of a Sum and Difference
7. The Square of a Binomial **8.** Answers may vary. Sample: You can use the rule for the product of a sum and difference to multiply two numbers when one number can be written as $a + b$ and the other number can be written as $a - b$.
Exercises 9. $w^2 + 10w + 25$ **11.** $9s^2 + 54s + 81$
13. $a^2 - 16a + 64$ **15.** $25m^2 - 20m + 4$
17. $(10x + 15)$ units^2 **19.** $36 - x^2$ in.^{2} **21.** 6241
23. 162,409 **25.** $v^2 - 36$ **27.** $z^2 - 25$ **29.** $100 - y^2$
31. 1596 **33.** 3591 **35.** 89,991 **37.** $4a^2 + 4ab + b^2$
39. $g^2 - 14gh + 49h^2$ **41.** $64r^2 - 80rs + 25s^2$
43. $p^8 - 18p^4q^2 + 81q^4$ **45.** $a^2 - 36b^2$ **47.** $r^4 - 9s^2$
49. $9w^6 - z^4$ **51.** $8x^2 + 32x + 32$

53. Answers may vary. Sample:
$a^2 = b(a-b) + b^2 + (a-b)^2 + b(a-b)$ Area of big square = sum of areas of the 4 interior rectangles
$= 2b(a-b) + b^2 + (a-b)^2$ Combine like terms.
$= 2ab - 2b^2 + b^2 + (a-b)^2$ Distributive Property
$= 2ab - b^2 + (a-b)^2$ Combine like terms.
So, $(a-b)^2 = a^2 - 2ab + b^2$ by the Add. and Subtr. Prop. of =.
55. No; $\left(3\frac{1}{2}\right)^2 = \left(3+\frac{1}{2}\right)^2 = \left(3+\frac{1}{2}\right)\left(3+\frac{1}{2}\right) = 3^2 + 2(3)\left(\frac{1}{2}\right) + \left(\frac{1}{2}\right)^2 = 9 + 3 + \frac{1}{4} = 12\frac{1}{4} \neq 9\frac{1}{4}$
62. $6x^2 - 11x - 10$ **63.** $24m^2 - 34m + 7$ **64.** $5x^2 + 53x + 72$ **65.** decrease of 25% **66.** increase of 25% **67.** increase of 25% **68.** decrease of 12.5% **69.** $6x(2x^3 + 5x^2 + 7)$ **70.** $9(8x^3 + 6x^2 + 3)$ **71.** $7x(5x^2 + x + 9)$

Lesson 8-5 pp. 500–505

Got It? 1. $(r+8)(r+3)$ **2a.** $(y-4)(y-2)$ **b.** No. There are no factors of 2 with sum −1. **3a.** $(n+12)(n-3)$ **b.** $(c-7)(c+3)$ **4.** $x+8$ and $x-9$ **5.** $(m+9n)(m-3n)$

Lesson Check 1. $(x+4)(x+3)$ **2.** $(r-7)(r-6)$ **3.** $(p+8)(p-5)$ **4.** $(a+4b)(a+8b)$ **5.** $n-7$ and $n+4$ **6.** positive **7.** positive **8.** negative **9.** when the constant term is positive and the coefficient of the second term is negative

Exercises 11. 2 **13.** 2 **15.** $(t+2)(t+8)$ **17.** $(n-7)(n-8)$ **19.** $(q-6)(q-2)$ **21.** 6 **23.** 1 **25.** $(w+1)(w-8)$ **27.** $(x+6)(x-1)$ **29.** $(n+2)(n-5)$ **31.** $r-4$ and $r+1$ **33.** A **35.** $(r+9s)(r+10s)$ **37.** $(m-7n)(m+4n)$ **39.** $(w-10z)(w-4z)$ **41a.** p and q must have the same sign. **b.** p and q must have opposite signs. **43.** $x-12$ **45.** $4x^2+12x+5$; $(2x+5)(2x+1)$ **47a.** They are opposites. **b.** Since the coefficient of the middle term is negative, the number with the greater absolute value must be negative. So, p must be a negative integer. **49.** $(x+25)(x+2)$ **51.** $(k-21)(k+3)$ **53.** $(s+5t)(s-15t)$ **65.** $c^2+8c+16$ **66.** $4v^2-36v+81$ **67.** $9w^2-49$ **68.** $\frac{ad}{b}$ **69.** $\frac{8d}{7}$ **70.** $mn-c$ **71.** $7x$ **72.** 6 **73.** 3

Lesson 8-6 pp. 506–510

Got It? 1a. $(3x+5)(2x+1)$ **b.** The factors are both negative. **2.** $(2x+7)(5x-2)$ **3.** $2x+3$ and $4x+5$ **4.** $4(2x+1)(x-5)$
Lesson Check 1. $(3x+1)(x+5)$ **2.** $(5q+2)(2q+1)$ **3.** $(2w-1)(2w+3)$ **4.** $3x+8$ and $2x-9$ **5.** There are no factors of 20 with sum 7. **6.** 24 **7.** Answers may vary. Sample: If $a = 1$, you look for factors of c whose sum is b. If $a \neq 1$, you look for factors of ac whose sum is b.

Exercises 9. $(3d+2)(d+7)$ **11.** $(4p+3)(p+1)$ **13.** $(2g-3)(4g-1)$ **15.** $(2k+3)(k-8)$ **17.** $(3x-4)(x+9)$ **19.** $(2d+5)(2d-7)$ **21.** $5x+2$ and $3x-4$ **23.** $2(4v-3)(v+5)$ **25.** $5(w-2)(4w-1)$ **27.** $3(3r-5)(r+2)$ **29–33.** Answers may vary. Samples are given. **29.** −31, $(5v+3)(3v-8)$; 31, $(5v-3)(3v+8)$ **31.** 20, $(3g+2)(3g+2)$; 15, $(3g+1)(3g+4)$ **33.** 41, $(8r-7)(r+6)$; −5, $(8r-21)(r+2)$ **35.** $6x+4$ **37a.** $(2x+2)(x+2)$; $(x+1)(2x+4)$ **b.** yes **c.** Answers may vary. Sample: Neither factoring is complete. Each one has a common factor, 2. **39.** $3(11k+4)(2k+1)$ **41.** $28(h-1)(h+2)$ **43.** $(11n-6)(5n-2)$ **45.** $(9g-5)(7g-6)$ **47.** 2; explanations may vary. Sample: ax^2+bx+c factors to $(ax+1)(x+c)$ or $(ax+c)(x+1)$ so $b = ac+1$ or $b = a+c$. **57.** $(w+4)(w+11)$ **58.** $(t-7)(t+4)$ **59.** $(x-5)(x-12)$ **60.** 12.5 **61.** 12 **62.** 37.5 **63.** 21 **64.** $a^2+18a+81$ **65.** $q^2-30q+225$ **66.** h^2-100 **67.** $4x^2-49$

Lesson 8-7 pp. 511–516

Got It? 1a. $(x+3)^2$ **b.** $(x-7)^2$ **2.** $4m-9$ **3a.** $(v-10)(v+10)$ **b.** $(s-4)(s+4)$ **4a.** $(5d+8)(5d-8)$ **b.** No; $25d^2+64$ is not a difference of two squares. **5a.** $12(t+2)(t-2)$ **b.** $3(2x+1)^2$
Lesson Check 1. $(y-8)^2$ **2.** $(3q+2)^2$ **3.** $(p+6)(p-6)$ **4.** $6w+5$ **5.** perfect-square trinomial **6.** perfect-square trinomial **7.** difference of two squares **8.** In a difference of two squares, both terms are perfect squares separated by a subtraction symbol.
Exercises 9. $(h+4)^2$ **11.** $(d-10)^2$ **13.** $(q+1)^2$ **15.** $(8x+7)^2$ **17.** $(3n-7)^2$ **19.** $(5z+4)^2$ **21.** $10r-11$ **23.** $5r+3$ **25.** $(a+7)(a-7)$ **27.** $(t+5)(t-5)$ **29.** $(m+15)(m-15)$ **31.** $(9r+1)(9r-1)$ **33.** $(8q+9)(8q-9)$ **35.** $(3n+20)(3n-20)$ **37.** $3(3w+2)(3w-2)$ **39.** $3(3x+5)^2$ **41.** $8(s-4)^2$ **43.** Answers may vary. Sample: Rewrite the absolute value of both terms as squares. The factorization is the product of two binomials. The first is the sum of square roots of the squares. The second is the difference of the square roots of the squares. Example 1: $x^2-4 = (x+2)(x-2)$; Example 2: $4y^2-25 = (2y+5)(2y-5)$
45. [1] Subtract by combining like terms.
$(49x^2-56x+16)-(16x^2+24x+9) =$
$(49x^2-16x^2)+(-56x-24x)+(16-9) =$
$33x^2-80x+7$
[2] Factor each expression, then use the rule for factoring the difference of two squares. $(49x^2-56x+16) - (16x^2+24x+9) = (7x-4)^2-(4x+3)^2 =$
$[(7x-4)-(4x+3)]-[(7x-4)+(4x+3)] =$
$(3x-7)(11x-1) = 33x^2-80x+7$

47. 11, 9 **49.** 14, 6 **51a.** Answers may vary. Sample: x^2+6x+9 **b.** because the first term x^2 is a square, the last term 3^2 is a square, and the middle term is $2(x)(3)$ **64.** $(6x+7)(3x-2)$ **65.** $(2x+3)(4x+3)$ **66.** $(4x-7)(3x-5)$ **67.** 2 **68.** $3m$ **69.** $4h^2$

Lesson 8-8 pp. 517–521

Got It? 1a. $(2t^2+5)(4t+7)$ **b.** Answers may vary. Sample: In Lesson 8-6, you rewrote the middle term as the sum of two terms and then factored by grouping. In this problem, there were already two middle terms.
2. $3h(h^2+2)(2h+3)$ **3.** Answers may vary. Sample: $2x$, $5x+2$, and $6x+1$
Lesson Check 1. $(4r^2+3)(5r+2)$ **2.** $(3d^2-5)(2d+1)$ **3.** $6(2x^2+3)(2x+5)$ **4.** Answers may vary. Sample: $4x$, $3x+1$, and $3x+2$ **5.** No; the polynomial is a perfect square. **6.** Yes; when you write $23w$ as $20w+3w$ the resulting two groups of terms have the same factor, $w+5$. **7.** Yes; two groups of terms have the same factor, $4t-7$. **8.** No; when you factor out the GCF from each pair of terms, there is no common factor.
Exercises 9. $2z^2$, 3 **11.** $2r^2$, −5 **13.** $(5q^2+1)(3q+8)$ **15.** $(7z^2+8)(2z-5)$ **17.** $(2m+1)(2m-1)(2m+3)$ **19.** $(4v^2-5)(5v+6)$ **21.** $(4y^2-3)(3y+1)$ **23.** $w(w^2+6)(3w-2)$ **25.** $3q(q+2)(q-2)(2q+1)$ **27.** $2(d^2+4)(2d-3)$ **29.** Answers may vary. Sample: $4c$, $c+8$, and $c+5$ **31.** $9t(t-8)(t-2)$ **33.** $8(m^2+5)(m+4)$ **35.** The factorization is correct, but it is not complete. The GCF of all the terms is $4x$, not 4. $4x^4+12x^3+8x^2+24x = 4x(x^3+3x^2+2x+6) = 4x[x^2(x+3)+2(x+3)] = 4x(x^2+2)(x+3)$ **37.** Answers may vary. Sample: Split the expression into three binomials. Find the GCF of each binomial, then factor again. **39.** Answers may vary. Sample: $30x^3+36x^2+40x+48 = 2(3x^2+4)(5x+6)$ **52.** $(m+6)^2$ **53.** $(8x-9)^2$ **54.** $(7p+2)(7p-2)$ **55.** not a function **56.** function **57.** function

58.
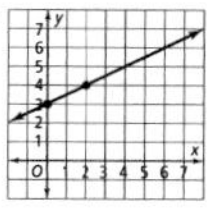

59.
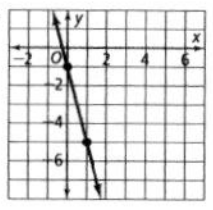

60.
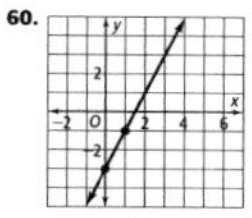

61.
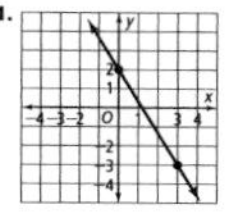

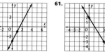

Chapter Review pp. 523–526

1. binomial **2.** polynomial **3.** monomial **4.** perfect-square trinomial **5.** degree of the monomial **6.** $-9r^2+11r+3$; quadratic trinomial **7.** b^3+b^2+3; cubic trinomial **8.** $8t^2+3$; quadratic binomial **9.** $4n^5+n$; fifth degree binomial **10.** $6x+8$; linear binomial **11.** p^3q^3; sixth degree monomial **12.** v^3+5 **13.** $14s^4-4s^2+9s+7$ **14.** $9h^3-3h+3$ **15.** $7z^3-2z^2-16$ **16.** $-20k^2+15k$ **17.** $36m^3+8m^2-24m$ **18.** $6g^3-48g^2$ **19.** $3d^3+18d^2$ **20.** $-8n^4-10n^3+18n^2$ **21.** $-2q^3+8q^2+11q$ **22.** $4p(3p^3+4p^2+2)$ **23.** $3b(b^3-3b+2)$ **24.** $9c(5c^4-7c^2+3)$ **25.** $4g(g+2)$ **26.** $3(t^4-2t^3-3t+4)$ **27.** $3h^3(10h^2-2h-5)$ **28.** 30; if the GCF of p and q is 5, then the GCF of $6p$ and $6q$ is $6(5) = 30$. **29.** $w^2+13w+12$ **30.** $10s^2-7s-12$ **31.** $9r^2-12r+4$ **32.** $6g^2-41g-56$ **33.** $21q^2+62q+16$ **34.** $12n^4+20n^3+15n+25$ **35.** $t^2+6t-27$ **36.** $36c^2+60c+25$ **37.** $49h^2-9$ **38.** $3y^2-11y-42$ **39.** $32a^2-44a-21$ **40.** $16b^2-9$ **41.** $(3x+5)(x+7)$; $3x^2+26x+35$ **42.** $(g-7)(g+2)$ **43.** $(2n-1)(n+2)$ **44.** $2(3k-2\ell)(k-\ell)$ **45.** $(p+6)(p+2)$ **46.** $(r+10)(r-4)$ **47.** $(2m+n)(3m+11n)$ **48.** $(t+2)(t-15)$ **49.** $(2g-1)(g-17)$ **50.** $3(x+2)(x-1)$ **51.** $(d-3)(d-15)$ **52.** $(w+3)(w-18)$ **53.** $7(3z-7)(z-1)$ **54.** $-2(h-7)(h+5)$ **55.** $(x+2)(x+19)$ **56.** $(5v+8)(2v-1)$ **57.** $5(g+2)(g+1)$ **58.** Answers may vary. Sample: If the expression is factorable then there must be factors of 18 whose sum is $b = 15$. The factors of 18 are 1 and 18, 2 and 9, 3 and 6. None of these have a sum equal to 15, so the expression is not factorable. **59.** $(s-10)^2$ **60.** $(4q+7)^2$ **61.** $(r+8)(r-8)$ **62.** $(3z+4)(3z-4)$ **63.** $(5m+8)^2$ **64.** $(7n+2)(7n-2)$ **65.** $(g+15)(g-15)$ **66.** $(3p-7)^2$ **67.** $(6h-1)^2$ **68.** $(w+12)^2$ **69.** $8(2v+1)(2v-1)$

70. $(5x-6)(5x+6)$ **71.** $3n+9$ **72.** It is a perfect-square trinomial. **73.** $3y^2$; 1 **74.** $8m^2$; 3 **75.** $2d(d+1)(d-1)(3d+2)$ **76.** $(b^2+1)(11b-6)$ **77.** $(5z^2+1)(9z+4)$ **78.** $3(a^2+2)(3a-4)$

Chapter 9

Get Ready! p. 531

1. −13 **2.** −3.5 **3.** −9 **4.** −0.5 **5.** −23 **6.** −3

7.
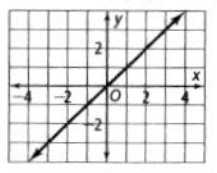

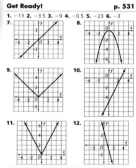

8.
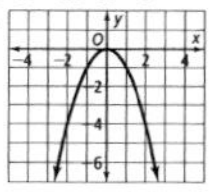

9.
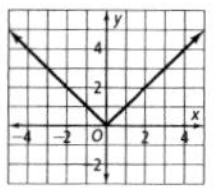

10.
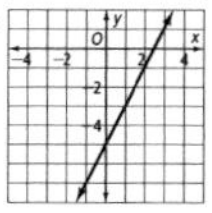

11.
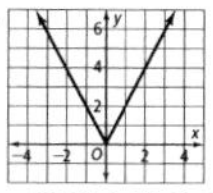

12.
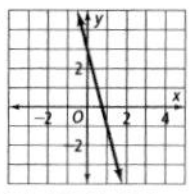

13. −108 **14.** 0 **15.** 49 **16.** 25 **17.** 24 **18.** 144 **19.** $(2x+1)^2$ **20.** $(5x-3)(x+7)$ **21.** $(4x-3)(2x-1)$ **22.** $(x-9)^2$ **23.** $(6y-5)(2y+3)$ **24.** $(m-9)(m+2)$ **25.** A quadratic function is of the form $f(x) = ax^2+bx+c$, where $a \neq 0$. **26.** Answers will vary. Sample: You can fold the graph along the axis of symmetry and the two halves of the graph will match. **27.** Answers will vary. Sample: the product of two factors can only be zero if at least one of the factors is zero.

Lesson 9-1 pp. 534–540

Got It? 1. $(-2, -3)$; minimum

2.
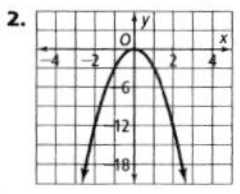

domain: all real numbers, range: $y \le 0$

3. $f(x) = -\frac{1}{3}x^2$, $f(x) = -x^2$, $f(x) = 3x^2$

4.
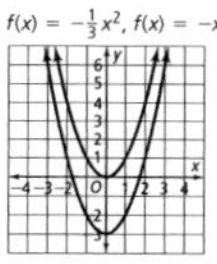

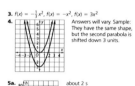

Answers will vary. Sample: They have the same shape, but the second parabola is shifted down 3 units.

5a.
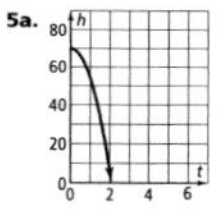

about 2 s

b. domain: $0 \le t \le 1.2$; range: $0 \le h \le 20$

Lesson Check

1.
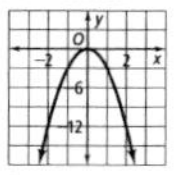

(0, 0)

2.
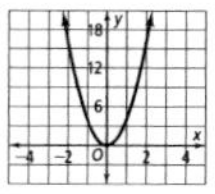

(0, 0)

3.
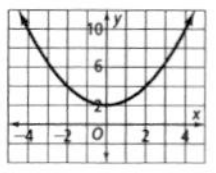

(0, 2)

4.
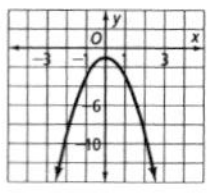

(0, −1)

5. If $a > 0$, the vertex is a minimum. If $a < 0$, the vertex is a maximum. **6.** Answers will vary. Sample: They have the same shape, but the second graph is shifted up 1 unit.
Exercises 7. (2, 3); maximum **9.** (2, 1); minimum

11.
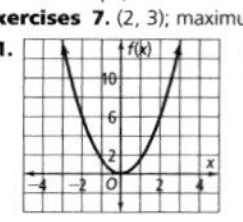

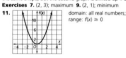

domain: all real numbers; range: $f(x) \ge 0$

13.
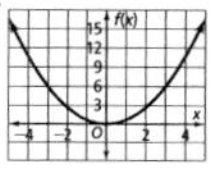

domain: all real numbers; range: $f(x) \ge 0$

15.
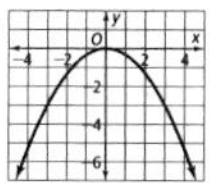

domain: all real numbers; range: $y \le 0$

17. $f(x) = x^2$, $f(x) = -3x^2$, $f(x) = 5x^2$
19. $f(x) = -\frac{2}{3}x^2$, $f(x) = -2x^2$, $f(x) = -4x^2$

21.
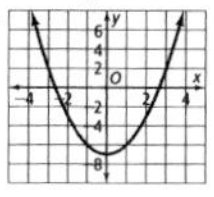

23.
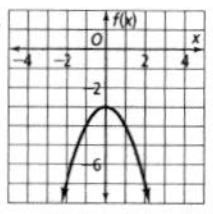

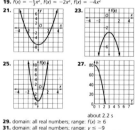

25.
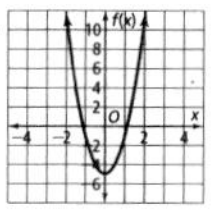

27.
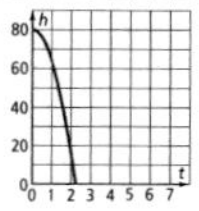

about 2.2 s

29. domain: all real numbers; range: $f(x) \ge 6$
31. domain: all real numbers; range: $y \le -9$
33. Answers will vary. Sample: If $a > 0$, the parabola opens upward. If $a < 0$, the parabola opens downward. The vertex of the parabola is $(0, c)$. **35.** D **37.** F **39.** C

41.
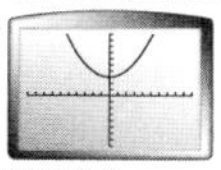

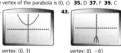

vertex: (0, 3)
axis of symmetry: $x = 0$

43.
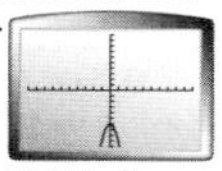

vertex: (0, −6)
axis of symmetry: $x = 0$

45. M **47.** M **57.** $3r(5r+1)(2r+3)$ **58.** $(3q^2-2)(5q-6)$ **59.** $(7b^3+1)(b+2)$ **60.** 0.75 **61.** −0.4 **62.** $-\frac{3}{8}$ **63.** $\frac{7}{20}$ **64.** $\frac{1}{8}$ **65.** −2

Lesson 9-2 pp. 541–546

Got It?

1a.
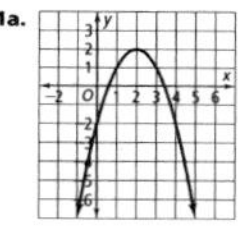

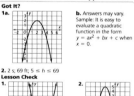

b. Answers may vary. Sample: It is easy to evaluate a quadratic function in the form $y = ax^2+bx+c$ when $x = 0$.

2. 2 s; 69 ft; $5 \le h \le 69$

Lesson Check

1.
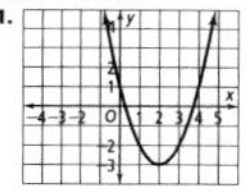

2.
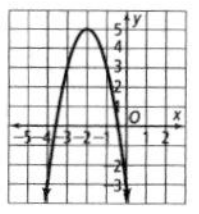

3.
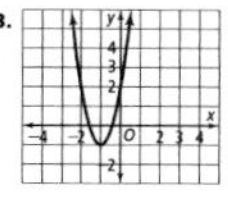

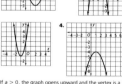

4.
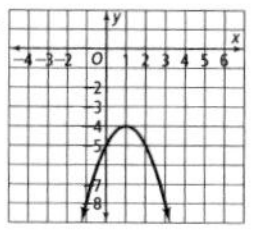

5. If $a > 0$, the graph opens upward and the vertex is a minimum. If $a < 0$, the graph opens downward and the vertex is a maximum. The greater the value of $|a|$, the narrower the parabola is. The axis of symmetry is the line $x = -\frac{b}{2a}$. The x-coordinate of the vertex is $-\frac{b}{2a}$. The y-intercept of the parabola is c. **6.** First graph the vertex and then graph the y-intercept. Reflect the y-intercept over the axis of symmetry to get a third point. Then sketch the parabola through these three points.
Exercises 7. $x = 0$; (0, 3) **9.** $x = -1$; (−1, −3) **11.** $x = 1.5$; (1.5, −4.75) **13.** $x = 0.3$; (0.3, 2.45) **15.** $x = -0.5$; (−0.5, −6.5) **17.** B **19.** A

21.
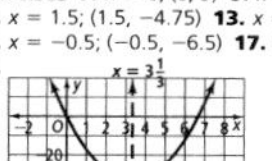

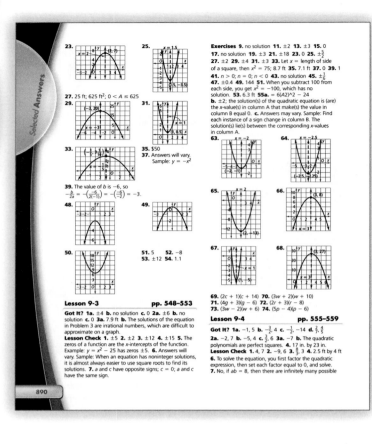

23. **25.**

27. 25 ft; 625 ft²; 0 < A ≤ 625

29. **31.**

33. **35.** $50
37. Answers will vary.
Sample: $y = -x^2$

39. The value of b is −6, so
$-\frac{b}{2a} = -\left(\frac{-6}{2(-1)}\right) = -\left(\frac{-6}{-2}\right) = -3.$

48. **49.**

50. **51.** 5 **52.** −8
53. ±12 **54.** 1.1

Lesson 9-3   pp. 548–553

Got It? 1a. ±4 **b.** no solution **c.** 0 **2a.** ±6 **b.** no
solution **c.** 0 **3a.** 7.9 ft **b.** The solutions of the equation
in Problem 3 are irrational numbers, which are difficult to
approximate on a graph.
Lesson Check 1. ±5 **2.** ±2 **3.** ±12 **4.** ±15 **5.** The
zeros of a function are the x-intercepts of the function.
Example: $y = x^2 - 25$ has zeros ±5. **6.** Answers will
vary. Sample: When an equation has noninteger solutions,
it is almost always easier to use square roots to find its
solutions. **7.** a and c have opposite signs; c = 0; a and c
have the same sign.

Exercises 9. no solution **11.** ±2 **13.** ±3 **15.** 0
17. no solution **19.** ±3 **21.** ±18 **23.** ±5 **25.** ±$\frac{2}{3}$
27. ±2 **29.** ±4 **31.** ±3 **33.** Let x = length of side
of a square, then $x^2 = 75$; 8.7 ft **35.** 7.1 ft **37.** 0 **39.** 1
41. n > 0; n = 0; n < 0 **43.** no solution **45.** ±$\frac{1}{6}$
47. ±0.4 **49.** 144 **51.** When you subtract 100 from
each side, you get $x^2 = -100$, which has no
solution. **53.** 6.3 ft **55a.** = 6(42)^2 − 24
b. ±2; the solution(s) of the quadratic equation is (are)
the x-value(s) in column A that make(s) the value in
column B equal 0. **c.** Answers may vary. Sample: Find
each instance of a sign change in column A. The
solution(s) lie(s) between the corresponding x-values
in column A.

63. **64.**

65. **66.**

67. **68.**

69. $(2c + 1)(c + 14)$ **70.** $(3w + 2)(w + 10)$
71. $(4g + 3)(g - 6)$ **72.** $(2r + 3)(r - 8)$
73. $(3w - 2)(w + 6)$ **74.** $(5p - 4)(p - 6)$

Lesson 9-4   pp. 555–559

Got It? 1a. −1, 5 **b.** −$\frac{3}{2}$, 4 **c.** −$\frac{1}{3}$, −14 **d.** $\frac{3}{2}$, $\frac{7}{5}$
2a. −2, 7 **b.** −5, 4 **c.** $\frac{3}{2}$, 6 **3a.** −7 **b.** The quadratic
polynomials are perfect squares. **4.** 17 in. by 23 in.
Lesson Check 1. 4, 7 **2.** −9, 6 **3.** $\frac{8}{3}$, 3 **4.** 2.5 ft by 4 ft
6. To solve the equation, you first factor the quadratic
expression, then set each factor equal to 0, and solve.
7. No, if ab = 8, then there are infinitely many possible

---

values of a and b, such as a = 2 and b = 4 or a = −1
and b = −8.
Exercises 9. −$\frac{5}{4}$, −7 **11.** 0, 2.5 **13.** −$\frac{7}{4}$, −$\frac{8}{3}$ **15.** −8, 4
17. −1.5, 12 **19.** −$\frac{3}{2}$, 8 **21.** −3, 7 **23.** 1.5, 4 **25.** ±$\frac{4}{3}$
27. 4 ft by 6 ft **29.** (−4, −2) **31.** (−5, −2) **33.** $q^2 +$
$7q - 18 = 0$; −9, 2 **35.** Answers will vary. Sample:
$6x^2 + 5x - 4 = 0$ **37.** 2; ±k **39.** 0, 4, 6 **41.** 0, 3
51. ±12 **52.** no solution **53.** 0 **54.** ±4 **55.** ±7
56. ±3 **57.** $(y - 5)^2$ **58.** $(g - 7)^2$ **59.** $(m + 9)^2$

Lesson 9-5   pp. 561–566

Got It? 1. 100 **2.** −13, 19 **3a.** −2.21, −6.79 **b.** No,
there are no factors of 15 with a sum of 9. **4.** 5.77 ft
Lesson Check 1. −18, 10 **2.** −11, 15 **3.** −21, 14
4. −9, 7.5 **5.** Answers will vary. Samples are given.
a. factoring; $k^2 - 3k - 304 = (k - 19)(k + 16)$
b. completing the square **6.** Answers will vary. Sample:
You have to know how to solve using square roots in
order to solve by completing the square. There are more
steps involved in completing the square.
Exercises 7. 81 **9.** 225 **11.** $\frac{289}{4}$ **13.** −16, 9
15. −10.24, −5.76 **17.** −28.70, 10.70 **19.** −5, 7
21. 1, 13 **23.** −5.82, 4.82 **25.** −1.65, 3.65 **27.** −1.96,
2.56 **29.** −7, 1 **31.** about 13.3 **33a.** 75 − 2w **b.** 11.6 ft
or 25.9 ft **c.** 51.9 ft or 23.1 ft **35.** no solution **37.** 2.27,
5.73 **39.** no solution **41.** −0.11, 9.11 **43.** She forgot to
divide each side by 4 to make the coefficient of the x^2-term 1.
47. −0.45, 4.45 **57.** −6, −5 **58.** ±$\frac{4}{3}$ **59.** −$\frac{1}{6}$, $\frac{3}{2}$
60. m^{12} **61.** −$\frac{1}{12}$ **62.** t^{13} **63.** y^{29} **64.** 81 **65.** 0 **66.** −15

Lesson 9-6   pp. 567–573

Got It? 1. −3, 7 **2.** 144.8 ft **3a.** Factoring; the
equation is easily factorable. **b.** Square roots; there is no
x-term. **c.** Quadratic formula, graphing; the equation
cannot be factored. **4a.** 2 **b.** 2; if a > 0 and c < 0, then
−4ac > 0 and $b^2 - 4ac > 0$.
Lesson Check 1. −4, $\frac{1}{3}$ **2.** −0.94, 1.22 **3.** 2 **4.** If the
discriminant is positive, there are 2 x-intercepts. If the
discriminant is 0, there is 1 x-intercept. If the discriminant
is negative, there are no x-intercepts. **5.** Factoring
because the equation is easily factorable; quadratic
formula or graphing because the equation cannot be
factored. **6.** If you complete the square for
$ax^2 + bx + c = 0$, you will get the quadratic formula.
Exercises 7. −1.5, −1 **9.** −3, 1.25 **11.** −$\frac{5}{6}$, $\frac{10}{3}$
13. −11, 15 **15.** −2.6, 12 **17.** −2.56, 0.16
19. −0.47, 1.34 **21.** −2.26, 0.59 **23.** Quadratic
formula, completing the square, or graphing; the
coefficient of the x^2-term is 1, but the equation cannot be

---

factored. **25.** Quadratic formula, graphing; the equation
cannot be factored. **27.** Factoring; the equation is easily
factorable. **29.** 0 **31.** 0 **33.** 2 **35.** ±4 **37.** ±1.73
39. 2 **41.** No, there are no real-number solutions of the
equation (14 − x)(50 + 5x) = 750. **43.** Find values of a,
b, and c such that $b^2 - 4ac > 0$. **45a.** 16; 1, 5
b. 81; −5, 4 **c.** 73; −0.39, 3.89 **d.** Rational; if the
discriminant is a perfect square, then its square root is an
integer, and the solutions are rational. **55.** 1.54, 8.46
56. −2, −1 **57.** −6.06, 0.06

58.

60. **61.**

Lesson 9-7   pp. 574–580

Got It?
1a. **b.**

exponential   quadratic

2. exponential **3a.** exponential; $y = 6(0.2)^x$ **b.** You have
already used them to write the equation. **4.** Answers
will vary. Sample: linear; $y = 480.7x + 18,252.4$
Lesson Check 1. quadratic **2.** linear **3.** exponential
4. No, a function cannot be both linear and exponential.
5. Graph the points, or test ordered data for a
common difference (linear function), a common ratio
(exponential function), or a common second difference
(quadratic function).

Exercises

7. **9.**

linear   quadratic

11. **13.** linear
15. quadratic; $y = 2.8x^2$
17. linear; $y = -0.5x + 2$
19. exponential;
$y = 540(1.03)^x$

linear

21b. The second common difference is twice the
coefficient of the x^2-term. **c.** When second differences
are the same, the data are quadratic. The coefficient
of the x^2-term is one-half the second difference.
23. Answers will vary. Sample: (0, 5), (2, 13), (4, 29), (6, 53)
25a. linear

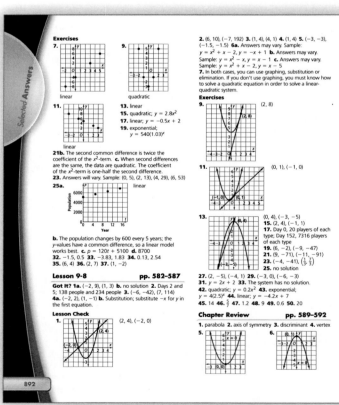

b. The population changes by 600 every 5 years; the
y-values have a common difference, so a linear model
works best. **c.** $p = 120t + 5100$ **d.** 8700
32. −1.5, 0.5 **33.** −3.83, 1.83 **34.** 0.13, 2.54
35. (6, 4) **36.** (2, 7) **37.** (1, −2)

Lesson 9-8   pp. 582–587

Got It? 1a. (−2, 9), (1, 3) **b.** no solution **2.** Days 2 and
5; 138 people and 234 people **3.** (−6, −42), (7, 114)
4a. (−2, 2), (1, −1) **b.** Substitution; substitute −x for y in
the first equation.
Lesson Check 1.

(2, 4), (−2, 0)

2. (6, 10), (−7, 192) **3.** (1, 4), (4, 1) **4.** (1, 4) **5.** (−3, −3),
(−1.5, −1.5) **6a.** Answers may vary. Sample:
$y = x^2 + x - 2$, $y = -x + 1$ **b.** Answers may vary.
Sample: $y = x^2 - x$, $y = x - 1$ **c.** Answers may vary.
Sample: $y = x^2 + x - 2$, $y = x - 5$
7. In both cases, you can use graphing, substitution or
elimination. If you don't use graphing, you must know how
to solve a quadratic equation in order to solve a linear-
quadratic system.

Exercises

9. (2, 8)

11. (0, 1), (−1, 0)

13. (0, 4), (−3, −5)
15. (2, 4), (−1, 1)
17. Day 0, 20 players of each
type; Day 152, 7316 players
of each type
19. (6, −2), (−9, −47)
21. (9, −71), (−11, −91)
23. (−4, −41), ($\frac{1}{3}$, $\frac{7}{3}$)
25. no solution

27. (2, −5), (−4, 1) **29.** (−3, 0), (−6, −3)
31. $y = 2x + 2$ **33.** The system has no solution.
42. quadratic; $y = 0.2x^2$ **43.** exponential;
$y = 4(2.5)^x$ **44.** linear; $y = -4.2x + 7$
45. 14 **46.** $\frac{1}{2}$ **47.** 1.2 **48.** 9 **49.** 0.6 **50.** 20

Chapter Review   pp. 589–592

1. parabola **2.** axis of symmetry **3.** discriminant **4.** vertex
5.

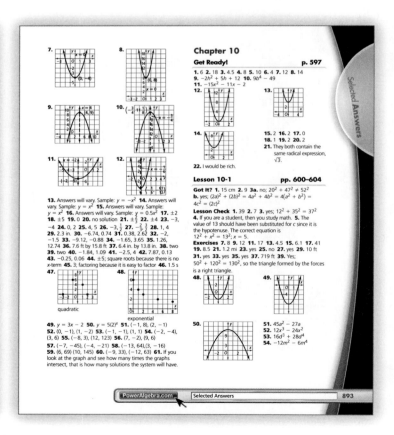

7. **8.**

9. **10.**

11. **12.**

13. Answers will vary. Sample: $y = -x^2$ **14.** Answers will
vary. Sample: $y = -x^2$ **15.** Answers will vary. Sample:
$y = x^2$ **16.** Answers will vary. Sample: $y = 0.5x^2$ **17.** ±2
18. ±5 **19.** 0 **20.** no solution **21.** ±$\frac{1}{3}$ **22.** ±4 **23.** −3,
−4 **24.** 0, 2 **25.** 4, 5 **26.** −3, $\frac{1}{2}$ **27.** −$\frac{1}{3}$, $\frac{2}{5}$ **28.** 1, 4
29. 2.3 in. **30.** −6.74, 0.74 **31.** 0.38, 2.62 **32.** −2,
−1.5 **33.** −9.12, −0.88 **34.** −1.65, 3.65 **35.** 1.26,
12.74 **36.** 7.6 ft by 15.8 ft **37.** 6.4 in. by 13.8 in. **38.** two
39. two **40.** −1.84, 1.09 **41.** −2.5, 4 **42.** 7.87, 0.13
43. −0.25, 0.06 **44.** ±5; square roots because there is no
x-term **45.** 3; factoring because it is easy to factor **46.** 1.5 s
47. **48.**

quadratic   exponential

49. $y = 3x - 2$ **50.** $y = 5(2)^x$ **51.** (−1, 8), (2, −1)
52. (0, −1), (1, −2) **53.** (−1, −1), (1, 1) **54.** (−2, −4),
(3, 6) **55.** (−8, 3), (12, 123) **56.** (7, −2), (9, 6)
57. (−7, −45), (−4, −21) **58.** (−13, 64),(3, −16)
59. (6, 69) (10, 145) **60.** (−9, 33), (−12, 63) **61.** If you
look at the graph and see how many times the graphs
intersect, that is how many solutions the system will have.

Chapter 10

Get Ready!   p. 597

1. 6 **2.** 18 **3.** 4.5 **4.** 8 **5.** 10 **6.** 4 **7.** 12 **8.** 14
9. −$2h^2$ + 5h + 12 **10.** $9b^4$ − 49
11. −$15x^2$ − 11x − 2
12. **13.**

14. **15.** 2 **16.** 2 **17.** 0
18. 1 **19.** 2 **20.** 2
21. They both contain the
same radical expression,
$\sqrt{3}$.
22. I would be rich.

Lesson 10-1   pp. 600–604

Got It? 1. 15 cm **2.** 9 **3a.** no; $20^2 + 47^2 \neq 52^2$
b. yes; $(2a)^2 + (2b)^2 = 4a^2 + 4b^2 = 4(a^2 + b^2) =$
$4c^2 = (2c)^2$
Lesson Check 1. 39 **2.** 7 **3.** yes; $12^2 + 35^2 = 37^2$
4. If you are a student, then you study math. **5.** The
value of 13 should have been substituted for c since it is
the hypotenuse. The correct equation is
$12^2 + x^2 = 13^2$; x = 5.
Exercises 7. 8 **9.** 12 **11.** 7 **13.** 4.5 **15.** 6.1 **17.** 41
19. 8.5 **21.** 1.2 mi **23.** yes **25.** no **27.** yes **29.** 10 ft
31. yes **33.** yes **35.** yes **37.** 719 ft **39.** Yes;
$50^2 + 120^2 = 130^2$, so the triangle formed by the forces
is a right triangle.
48. **49.**

50. **51.** $45a^2 - 27a$
52. $12x^3 - 24x^2$
53. $16d^3 + 28d^4$
54. $-12m^2 - 6m^4$

Lesson 10-2 pp. 606–612

Got It? 1. $6\sqrt{2}$ **2.** $-4m^5\sqrt{5m}$ **3a.** $18\sqrt{3}$ **b.** $3a^2\sqrt{2}$ **c.** $210x^3$ **d.** yes; $\sqrt{14t^2} = t\sqrt{14}$ **4.** $w\sqrt{17}$ **5a.** 4 **b.** $\frac{3}{a}$ **c.** $\frac{5y\sqrt{y}}{z}$ **6a.** $\frac{\sqrt{6}}{3}$ **b.** $\frac{\sqrt{10m}}{6m}$ **c.** $\frac{\sqrt{21s}}{3}$
Lesson Check 1. $7\sqrt{2}$ **2.** $4b^2\sqrt{b}$ **3.** $12m^2$ **4.** $\frac{\sqrt{15}}{x}$ **5.** $\frac{\sqrt{15}}{3}$ **6.** $\frac{\sqrt{3n}}{n}$ **7a.** Yes; there are no perfect-square factors in 31, there are no fractions in the radicand, and there are no radicals in the denominator. **b.** No; there is a fraction in the radicand. **c.** No; 25 is a perfect-square factor of 175. **8.** Answers may vary. Sample:
$\frac{3}{\sqrt{12}} = \frac{3}{2\sqrt{3}} \cdot \frac{\sqrt{3}}{\sqrt{3}} = \frac{3\sqrt{3}}{6} = \frac{\sqrt{3}}{2}$;
$\frac{3}{\sqrt{12}} = \frac{3}{\sqrt{12}} \cdot \frac{\sqrt{12}}{\sqrt{12}} = \frac{3\sqrt{12}}{12} = \frac{\sqrt{12}}{4} = \frac{2\sqrt{3}}{4} = \frac{\sqrt{3}}{2}$
9. A radical expression is in simplified form if the radicand has no perfect-square factors other than 1, the radicand contains no fractions, and no radicals appear in the denominator of a fraction.
Exercises 11. $3\sqrt{11}$ **13.** $-2\sqrt{15}$ **15.** $50\sqrt{7}$ **17.** $5t^2\sqrt{2t}$ **19.** $-63x^4\sqrt{3x}$ **21.** $-18y\sqrt{3y}$ **23.** 4 **25.** 30 **27.** $42n^2$ **29.** $16y^3$ **31.** $-126a\sqrt{a}$ **33.** $24c^7$ **35.** $w\sqrt{26}$ **37.** $\frac{7\sqrt{3}}{4}$ **39.** $\frac{\sqrt{3x}}{8}$ **41.** $\frac{77a}{2}$ **43.** $\frac{\sqrt{10x}}{4x}$ **45.** $2\sqrt{11}$ **47.** $\frac{4}{3}$ **49.** $2\sqrt{6}$ in. **51.** not simplest form; radical in the denominator of a fraction **53.** Simplest form; radicand has no perfect-square factors other than 1. **55a.** $f\sqrt{3f}$ **b.** $\frac{1}{x^2}$ **c.** $\frac{\sqrt{2a}}{2a}$ **d.** $\frac{\sqrt{2m}}{4m}$ **57a.** $\sqrt{18 \cdot 10} = \sqrt{180} = \sqrt{36} \cdot \sqrt{5} = 6\sqrt{5}$ **b.** Answers may vary. Sample: 4 and 45 **59.** $2\sqrt{13}$ **61.** $\frac{-2\sqrt{a}}{a^2}$ **63.** $\frac{x\sqrt{y}}{y^2}$ **65.** $4\sqrt{5}$ **67.** $ab^2c\sqrt{abc}$ **69.** $\frac{8\sqrt{6a}}{3a}$ **71.** $1 \pm \sqrt{5}$ **73.** Answers may vary. Sample: 12, 27, 48 **83.** yes **84.** yes **85.** no **86.** $(8y + 3)(8y - 3)$ **87.** $(a + 9)(a - 9)$ **88.** $(5 + 4b)(5 - 4b)$ **89.** $6a^2 - 5a - 4$ **90.** $-4m^2 + 14mn - 12n^2$ **91.** $4x^2 + 16x + 15$

Lesson 10-3 pp. 613–618

Got It? 1a. $-\sqrt{2}$ **b.** $7\sqrt{5}$ **2a.** $8\sqrt{7}$ **b.** $8\sqrt{2}$ **c.** No; if they are unlike and have no common factors other than 1, even if they can be simplified, they still will not be like. **3a.** $2\sqrt{3} + 5\sqrt{2}$ **b.** $15 - 4\sqrt{11}$ **c.** $-6\sqrt{2} - 6$ **4.** $\frac{-3\sqrt{10} + 3\sqrt{5}}{5}$ **5.** $(6\sqrt{5} - 6)$ in., or about 7.4 in.
Lesson Check 1. $5\sqrt{3}$ **2.** $\sqrt{6}$ **3.** $\sqrt{21} - 2\sqrt{7}$ **4.** $41 - 12\sqrt{5}$ **5.** $3\sqrt{5} - \sqrt{10}$ **6.** $2\sqrt{7} - 4$ **7a.** $\sqrt{13} + 2$ **b.** $\sqrt{6} - \sqrt{3}$ **c.** $\sqrt{5} + \sqrt{10}$ **8.** $\sqrt{3} \cdot \sqrt{3} \neq 9$; $\frac{\sqrt{3} + 1}{3 - 1} = \frac{\sqrt{3} + 1}{2}$
Exercises 9. $7\sqrt{5}$ **11.** $8\sqrt{3}$ **13.** 0 **15.** $-7\sqrt{5}$ **17.** $9\sqrt{10}$ **19.** $\frac{19\sqrt{5}}{2}$ **21.** $2\sqrt{3} + 3\sqrt{2}$ **23.** $3\sqrt{7} - 21$ **25.** $5\sqrt{33} - 15\sqrt{22}$ **27.** -6 **29.** $62 - 20\sqrt{6}$ **31.** $\frac{3\sqrt{7} + 3\sqrt{3}}{4}$ **33.** $-2\sqrt{5} - 5$ **35.** $\frac{7\sqrt{13} - 7\sqrt{5}}{8}$ **37.** $\frac{23\sqrt{5} - 23}{2}$ ft, or about 14.2 ft **39.** $-\frac{4}{3}$; -1.3 **41.** $\frac{-1 + \sqrt{7}}{4}$; -0.4 **43.** $9 + 6\sqrt{2} + 4\sqrt{5} + 3\sqrt{10}$; 35.9 **45.** No; yes; you can simplify $\sqrt{12}$ to $2\sqrt{3}$ and then combine the like radicals. **47.** $5\sqrt{10}$ **49.** $22\sqrt{3} - 6$ **51.** $\frac{13 + \sqrt{65} + \sqrt{130} + 5\sqrt{2}}{8}$ **53.** -24 **55.** $4\sqrt{3} + 4\sqrt{2} + 3\sqrt{6} + 6$ **57.** $s\sqrt{3}$ **59a.** $x^{\frac{n}{2}}$ **b.** $x^{\frac{n-1}{2}}\sqrt{x}$ **68.** $6\sqrt{3}$ **69.** $15\sqrt{6}$ **70.** $\frac{2\sqrt{2}}{3c}$ **71.** 15 **72.** 8^{16} **73.** 2^{11} **74.** 5^{27} **75.** 3^3 **76.** -1 **77.** $-4, 3$ **78.** $-5, 3$ **79.** $-3, \frac{2}{3}$ **80.** $-2, \frac{1}{2}$ **81.** -7

Lesson 10-4 pp. 620–625

Got It? 1. 9 **2.** 0.825 ft **3.** 7 **4.** -2 **5a.** no solution **b.** The principal root of a number is never negative.
Lesson Check 1. 12 **2.** 3 **3.** 1 **4.** no solution **5.** C **6.** If $x^2 = y^2$, then $x = y$; no, if $x = -1$ and $y = 1$, then $x^2 = y^2$, but $x \neq y$.
Exercises 7. 4 **9.** 36 **11.** 8 **13.** 16 **15.** -2 **17.** about 5.2 ft **19.** 4.5 **21.** 7 **23.** 4 **25.** 2 **27.** none **29.** -7 **31.** 3 **33.** no solution **35.** no solution **37.** The student did not check the solutions in the original equations. Both of those solutions are extraneous, so the equation has no solution. **39a.** 25 **b.** 11.25 **41.** Add $\sqrt{y + 2}$ to each side of the equation. Square each side of the equation. Solve for y. Check each apparent solution in the original equation. **43.** 3 **45.** no solution **47.** 1.5 **49.** 1600 ft **57.** $5\sqrt{2}$ **58.** -24 **59.** $-\frac{2\sqrt{3} - 4\sqrt{2}}{5}$ **60.** no solution **61.** $-2, 2$ **62.** $-\frac{3}{2}, -\frac{2}{3}$

63. 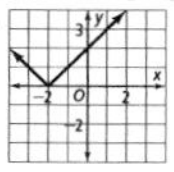

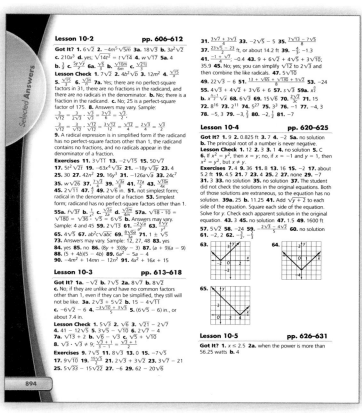

64. 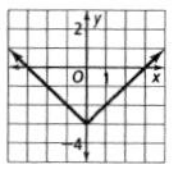

65. 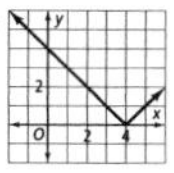

Lesson 10-5 pp. 626–631

Got It? 1. $x \leq 2.5$ **2a.** when the power is more than 56.25 watts **b.** 4

3. 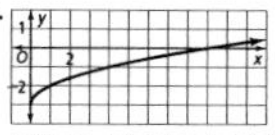

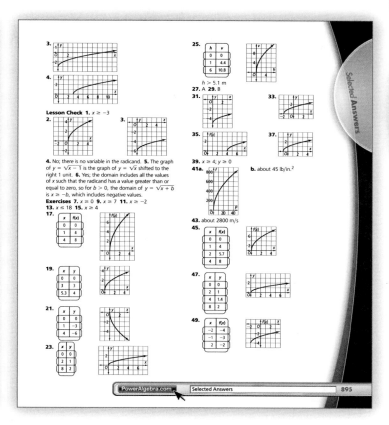

4. 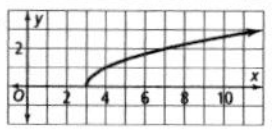

Lesson Check 1. $x \geq -3$

2. 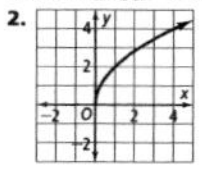

3. 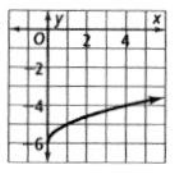

4. No; there is no variable in the radicand. **5.** The graph of $y = \sqrt{x - 1}$ is the graph of $y = \sqrt{x}$ shifted to the right 1 unit. **6.** Yes; the domain includes all the values of x such that the radicand has a value greater than or equal to zero, so for $b > 0$, the domain of $y = \sqrt{x + b}$ is $x \geq -b$, which includes negative values.
Exercises 7. $x \geq 0$ **9.** $x \geq 7$ **11.** $x \geq -2$ **13.** $x \leq 18$ **15.** $x \geq 4$

17.

x	f(x)
0	0
1	4
4	8

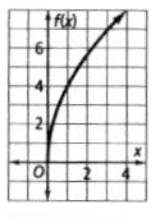

19.

x	y
0	0
3	3
5.3	4

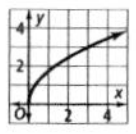

21.

x	y
0	0
1	−3
4	−6

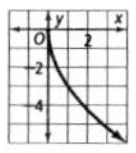

23.

x	y
0	0
2	1
8	2

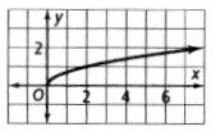

25.

h	v
0	0
1	4.4
6	10.8

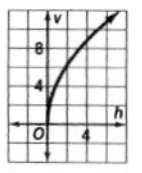

$h > 5.1$ m
27. A **29.** B

31. 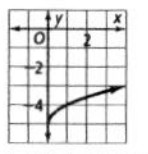

33. 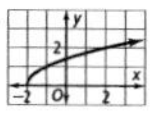

35. 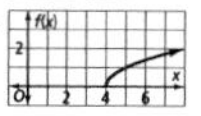

37. 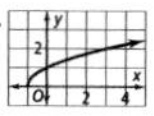

39. $x \geq 4$; $y \geq 0$

41a. 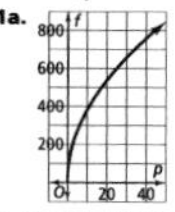

b. about 45 lb/in.^{2}

43. about 2800 m/s

45.

x	f(x)
0	0
1	4
2	5.7
4	8

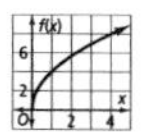

47.

x	y
0	0
2	1
4	1.4
8	2

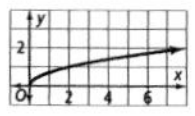

49.

x	f(x)
−2	−4
−1	−3
2	−2

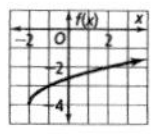

51.

x	y
−3	1
−2	2.4
−1	3
0	3.4

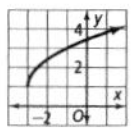

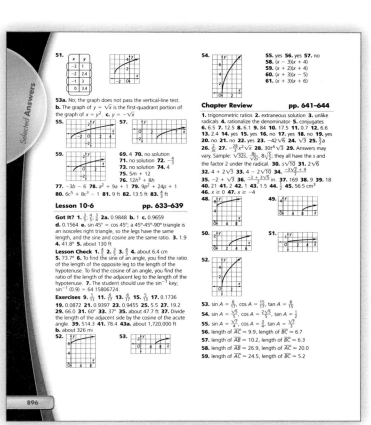

53a. No; the graph does not pass the vertical-line test. **b.** The graph of $y = \sqrt{x}$ is the first-quadrant portion of the graph of $x = y^2$. **c.** $y = -\sqrt{x}$

55. 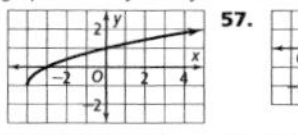

57. 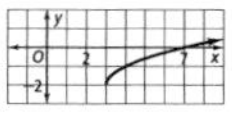

59. 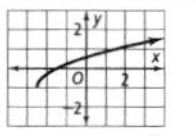

69. 4 **70.** no solution **71.** no solution **72.** $-\frac{4}{3}$ **73.** no solution **74.** 4 **75.** $5m + 12$ **76.** $12h^3 + 8h$ **77.** $-3b - 6$ **78.** $a^2 + 9a + 1$ **79.** $9p^2 + 24p + 1$ **80.** $6c^5 + 8c^3 - 1$ **81.** 9 ft **82.** 13.5 ft **83.** $\frac{4}{3}$ ft

Lesson 10-6 pp. 633–639

Got It? 1. $\frac{3}{5}$; $\frac{4}{5}$; $\frac{3}{4}$ **2a.** 0.9848 **b.** 1 **c.** 0.9659 **d.** 0.1564 **e.** $\sin 45° = \cos 45°$; a 45°-45°-90° triangle is an isosceles right triangle, so the legs have the same length, and the sine and cosine are the same ratio. **3.** 1.9 **4.** 41.8° **5.** about 130 ft
Lesson Check 1. $\frac{4}{5}$ **2.** $\frac{3}{5}$ **3.** $\frac{4}{3}$ **4.** about 6.4 cm **5.** 73.7° **6.** To find the sine of an angle, you find the ratio of the length of the opposite leg to the length of the hypotenuse. To find the cosine of an angle, you find the ratio of the length of the adjacent leg to the length of the hypotenuse. **7.** The student should use the $\sin^{-1}$ key; $\sin^{-1}(0.9) = 64.15806724$.
Exercises 9. $\frac{5}{13}$ **11.** $\frac{8}{17}$ **13.** $\frac{8}{17}$ **15.** $\frac{5}{13}$ **17.** 0.1736 **19.** 0.0872 **21.** 0.9397 **23.** 0.9455 **25.** 5.5 **27.** 19.2 **29.** 66.0 **31.** 60° **33.** 37° **35.** about 47.7 ft **37.** Divide the length of the adjacent side by the cosine of the acute angle. **39.** 514.3 **41.** 78.4 **43a.** about 1,720,000 ft **b.** about 326 mi

52. 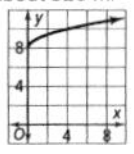

53. 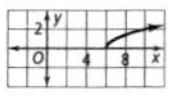

54. 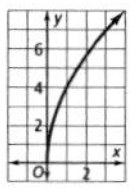

55. yes **56.** yes **57.** no **58.** $(x - 3)(x + 4)$ **59.** $(x + 2)(x + 4)$ **60.** $(x + 3)(x - 5)$ **61.** $(x + 3)(x + 6)$

Chapter Review pp. 641–644

1. trigonometric ratios **2.** extraneous solution **3.** unlike radicals **4.** rationalize the denominator **5.** conjugates **6.** 6.5 **7.** 12.5 **8.** 6.1 **9.** 84 **10.** 17.5 **11.** 0.7 **12.** 6.6 **13.** 2.4 **14.** yes **15.** yes **16.** no **17.** yes **18.** no **19.** yes **20.** no **21.** no **22.** yes **23.** $-42\sqrt{6}$ **24.** $\sqrt{3}$ **25.** $\frac{5}{2}a$ **26.** $\frac{2}{3s}$ **27.** $-\frac{28}{3}x^2\sqrt{x}$ **28.** $30t^4\sqrt{3}$ **29.** Answers may vary. Sample: $\sqrt{32s}$, $\frac{8s}{\sqrt{2s}}$, $8\sqrt{\frac{s}{2}}$; they all have the s and the factor 2 under the radical. **30.** $s\sqrt{10}$ **31.** $2\sqrt{6}$ **32.** $4 + 2\sqrt{3}$ **33.** $4 - 2\sqrt{10}$ **34.** $\frac{-3\sqrt{2} + 9}{7}$ **35.** $-2 + \sqrt{3}$ **36.** $\frac{-3 + 3\sqrt{5}}{2}$ in. **37.** 169 **38.** 9 **39.** 18 **40.** 21 **41.** 2 **42.** 1 **43.** 1.5 **44.** $\frac{1}{2}$ **45.** 56.5 cm^3 **46.** $x \geq 0$ **47.** $x \geq -4$

48. 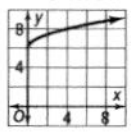

49. 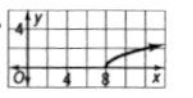

50. 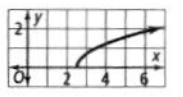

51. 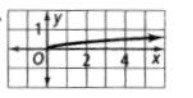

52. 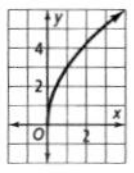

53. $\sin A = \frac{8}{17}$, $\cos A = \frac{15}{17}$, $\tan A = \frac{8}{15}$
54. $\sin A = \frac{\sqrt{5}}{5}$, $\cos A = \frac{2\sqrt{5}}{5}$, $\tan A = \frac{1}{2}$
55. $\sin A = \frac{\sqrt{7}}{4}$, $\cos A = \frac{3}{4}$, $\tan A = \frac{\sqrt{7}}{3}$
56. length of $\overline{AC} \approx 9.9$, length of $\overline{BC} \approx 6.7$
57. length of $\overline{AB} \approx 10.2$, length of $\overline{BC} \approx 6.3$
58. length of $\overline{AB} \approx 26.9$, length of $\overline{AC} \approx 20.0$
59. length of $\overline{AC} \approx 24.5$, length of $\overline{BC} \approx 5.2$

Chapter 11

Get Ready! p. 649

1. $2\frac{1}{30}$ **2.** $3\frac{1}{4}$ **3.** $-\frac{73}{120}$ **4.** $\frac{11}{35}$ **5.** $\frac{q^6}{p^5}$ **6.** $6\frac{30}{49}$ **7.** $\frac{64}{729}$ **8.** $\frac{8yz^6}{5x^6}$ **9.** $-7, 9$ **10.** $-\frac{5}{3}, \frac{7}{4}$ **11.** -13 **12.** 0, 3 **13.** $-\frac{4}{3}, 5$ **14.** $-5, -\frac{2}{3}$ **15.** $-10, -1$ **16.** $-3, 7$ **17.** $-\frac{1}{2}, \frac{5}{3}$ **18.** no solution **19.** 1 **20.** 4 **21.** The excluded values are not allowed. **22.** A rational expression involves a ratio. **23.** One is decreasing as the other increases.

Lesson 11-1 pp. 652–657

Got It? 1a. $\frac{3}{a}$, $a \neq 0$ **b.** $\frac{9d^2}{2d + 4}$, $d \neq -2$ **c.** $\frac{1}{3}$, $n \neq \frac{3}{2}$ **d.** 13c, none **2a.** $\frac{2}{x + 2}$; $x \neq -2$, $x \neq 4$ **b.** $\frac{a - 2}{3}$; $a \neq 1$ **c.** $\frac{6}{2z + 3}$; $z \neq -2$, $z \neq -\frac{3}{2}$ **d.** $\frac{c - 3}{c + 3}$; $c \neq -3$, $c \neq -2$ **3a.** -1; $x \neq 2.5$ **b.** $-y - 4$; $y \neq 4$ **c.** $-\frac{3}{2d + 1}$; $d \neq -\frac{1}{2}$, $d \neq \frac{1}{3}$ **d.** $-\frac{3}{2z + 2}$; $z \neq \pm 1$ **4a.** $12x + 4$ **b.** No, h must be greater than 2π in order for the value of a to be greater than 0. If h is less than or equal to 2π, then a will be negative, and length cannot be negative.
Lesson Check 1. 3; $x \neq -3$ **2.** $-\frac{1}{x + 3}$; $x \neq -3$, $x \neq 5$ **3.** $4x$ **4a.** No, the expression is not the ratio of two polynomials. **b.** Yes, the expression is the ratio of two polynomials. **5.** If the denominator contains a polynomial, there may be values of the variable that make the denominator equal to zero, and division by zero is undefined. **6.** The only way the rational expression is not in simplest form is if the numerator and the denominator are equal. **7a.** yes, $3 - x = -(x - 3)$ **b.** no, $2 - y = -(y - 2)$
Exercises 9. $\frac{1}{7x}$, $x \neq 0$ **11.** $\frac{1}{2}$, $p \neq 12$ **13.** $\frac{x + 2}{x^2}$, $x \neq 0$ **15.** $\frac{2}{b + 4}$, $b \neq \pm 4$ **17.** $\frac{w}{w - 7}$, $w \neq \pm 7$ **19.** $\frac{m + 3}{m + 2}$, $m \neq -4$, $m \neq -2$ **21.** $b + 3$, $b \neq -5$ **23.** -1, $n \neq \frac{5}{4}$ **25.** -2, $m \neq 2$ **27.** $\frac{-1}{v + 5}$, $v \neq \pm 5$ **29.** $w + 1$ **31.** $\frac{2r - 1}{r + 5}$, $r \neq -5$ **33.** $\frac{5t - 4}{3t - 1}$, $t \neq -2$, $t \neq \frac{1}{3}$ **35.** $\frac{3(z + 4)}{z^3}$, $z \neq 0$ **37.** $-\frac{2a + 1}{a + 3}$, $a \neq -3$, $a \neq \frac{5}{2}$ **39.** $-\frac{c(3c + 5)}{5c + 4}$, $c \neq -\frac{4}{5}$, $c \neq 2$ **41.** No, $y = \frac{x^2 - 9}{x + 3}$ is not defined for $x = -3$ but $x - 3$ is. **43.** The student canceled terms instead of factors; $\frac{x^2 + 2x}{2x} = \frac{x(x + 2)}{2x} = \frac{x + 2}{2}$. **45.** Answers may vary. Sample: $\frac{1}{(x - 4)(x + 3)}$ **47.** $\frac{5w}{5w + 6}$ **58.** $\frac{15}{17}$ **59.** $\frac{15}{17}$ **60.** $\frac{8}{15}$ **61.** $10\sqrt{2}$ **62.** $a^2b^3c^4\sqrt{b}$ **63.** $3x\sqrt{11}$ **64.** $\frac{\sqrt{2}}{5m^2}$ **65.** $2\sqrt{2}$ **66.** $2y\sqrt{y}$ **67.** $(2c + 1)(c + 7)$ **68.** $(15t - 11)(t - 1)$ **69.** $(3q + 2)^2$ **70.** $(2c - 1)(2c - 5)$ **71.** $(6t + 1)(4t - 3)$ **72.** $(3q - 7)(q + 2)$

Lesson 11-2 pp. 658–664

Got It? 1a. $\frac{15}{y^4}$, $y \neq 0$ **b.** $\frac{x(x + 1)}{(x - 2)(x - 3)}$, $x \neq 3$, $x \neq 2$ **2a.** $3x(x + 1)$ **b.** Yes, but you will have to simplify the resulting expression. **3a.** $(x - 7)(3x - 2)$ **b.** $(x + 1)(x + 3)$ **4a.** $\frac{1}{y}$ **b.** $\frac{6}{k + 4}$ **5.** $\frac{z - 1}{z^2 + 2}$ **6.** $\frac{1}{q^2}$
Lesson Check 1. $\frac{6}{5t^6}$ **2.** $\frac{(2x + 5)(x - 5)}{4}$ **3.** $3k^2(k + 1)$ **4.** $\frac{4x}{(x + 7)(2x + 3)}$ **5.** $\frac{(a - 2)^2}{3a}$ **6.** x^2 **7.** no; $\frac{\frac{a}{b}}{c} = \frac{a}{b} \div c = \frac{a}{b} \cdot \frac{1}{c} = \frac{a}{bc}$, where $\frac{a}{\frac{b}{c}} = a \div \frac{b}{c} = a \cdot \frac{c}{b} = \frac{ac}{b}$
8. The procedures are the same, but when you multiply rational expressions, there may be values of the variables for which the rational expressions are not defined. **9.** The variables b, c, and d appear in the denominators, and division by 0 is not defined. **10a.** Write the product of the rational expression and the polynomial, factor, divide out common factors, and write the product in factored form. **b.** Rewrite the quotient of the rational expression and the polynomial as the product of the rational expression and the reciprocal of the polynomial. Factor the numerators and denominators, divide out common factors, and write the answer in factored form.
Exercises 11. $\frac{35x}{36}$ **13.** $\frac{40}{3a^5}$ **15.** $\frac{2x(x - 1)}{3(x + 1)}$ **17.** $\frac{2c(c + 2)}{c - 1}$ **19.** $\frac{(r + 2)(r - 2)}{2r}$ **21.** $t - 4$ **23.** $4(t + 1)(t + 2)$ **25.** $\frac{(x - 1)(x - 2)}{3}$ **27.** $\frac{(h - 1)(h + 4)}{3}$ **29.** $\frac{x + 1}{2}$ **31.** $\frac{1}{c^2 - 1}$ **33.** 6 **35.** $-\frac{1}{2}$ **37.** $\frac{n - 3}{4n + 5}$ **39.** $\frac{11}{7k - 15}$ **41.** $\frac{b - 1}{3(b + 1)}$ **43.** 18 **45.** $\frac{1}{2(x + 1)}$ **47.** $\frac{2(3g + 1)}{g(3g - 1)}$ **49.** $\frac{1}{3z(z + 10)}$ **51.** $t + 3$ **53.** $\frac{3t - 5}{7t^2}$ **55.** $\frac{x - 2}{x - 3}$ **57.** \$88.71 **59.** \$518,011.65 **61.** The student forgot to rewrite the divisor as its reciprocal before canceling. $\frac{3a}{a + 2} \div \frac{(a + 2)^2}{a - 4} = \frac{3a}{a + 2} \cdot \frac{a - 4}{(a + 2)^2} = \frac{3a(a - 4)}{(a + 2)^3}$ **63.** 0, 4, and -4 make the denominators equal 0. **65.** $\frac{2m^2(m + 2)}{(m - 1)(m + 4)}$ **74.** $\frac{7}{3}$, $m \neq 2$ **75.** $\frac{1}{2a^2 - 3}$, $a \neq 0$, $a \neq \pm\frac{\sqrt{6}}{2}$ **76.** $\frac{2c - 9}{2c + 8}$, $c \neq -4$, $c \neq 4.5$ **77.** $2x^2 + 10x + 12$ **78.** $-3n^2 + 11n + 20$ **79.** $6a^3 - 21a^2 + 2a - 7$

Lesson 11-3 pp. 666–671

Got It? 1a. $2a + 5 + \frac{3}{2a}$ **b.** $b - \frac{3}{b} + \frac{1}{5b^3}$ **c.** $2c^3 + 3c + \frac{3}{2}$ **2.** $2m - 3$ **3a.** $q^3 + q^2 + 2q + 3$ **b.** $h^2 - 3h + 5 - \frac{3}{h + 3}$ **4a.** $2y - \frac{19}{3} + \frac{55}{3(3y + 4)}$ **b.** $3a + 1 - \frac{3}{6a + 5}$ **c.** Check whether $(2x - 3)(2x + 2) - 7$ equals $4x^2 - 10x - 1$.

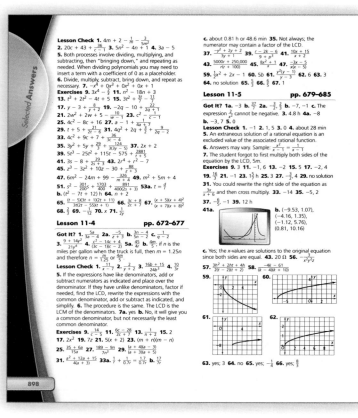

Lesson Check 1. $4m + 2 - \frac{1}{m} - \frac{3}{5m^2}$
2. $20c + 43 + \frac{36}{c - 1}$ **3.** $5n^2 - 4n + 1$ **4.** $3a - 5$
5. Both processes involve dividing, multiplying, and subtracting, then "bringing down," and repeating as needed. When dividing polynomials you may need to insert a term with a coefficient of 0 as a placeholder.
6. Divide, multiply, subtract, bring down, and repeat as necessary. **7.** $-x^4 + 0x^3 + 0x^2 + 0x + 1$
Exercises 9. $3x^4 - \frac{2}{5}$ **11.** $n^2 - 18n + 3$
13. $t^3 + 2t^2 - 4t + 5$ **15.** $3t^2 + \frac{3t}{7} - \frac{11}{7}$
17. $y - 3 + \frac{8}{y + 2}$ **19.** $-2q - 10 + \frac{22}{2q + 1}$
21. $2w^2 + 2w + 5 - \frac{10}{w - 1}$ **23.** $c^2 - \frac{1}{c - 1}$
25. $4c^2 - 8c + 16$ **27.** $a - 1 + \frac{1}{4a + 5}$
29. $t + 5 + \frac{21}{2t} - \frac{8}{7}$ **31.** $4q^2 + 2q + \frac{3}{2} + \frac{9}{2q - 2}$
33. $4c^2 + 9c + 7 + \frac{36}{3c - 4}$
35. $3y^2 + 5y + \frac{29}{3} + \frac{124}{3y - 5}$ **37.** $2x + 2$
39. $5s^3 - 25s^2 + 115t - 575 + \frac{2881}{t + 5}$
41. $3s - 8 + \frac{29}{2s + 3}$ **43.** $2r^4 + r^2 - 7$
45. $z^3 - 3z^2 + 10z - 30 + \frac{88}{z + 3}$
47. $6m^2 - 24m + 99 - \frac{326}{m + 4}$ **49.** $m^2 + 5m + 4$
51. $s^2 - \frac{301}{200s} + \frac{1703}{400} - \frac{891}{400(2s + 3)}$ **53a.** $t = \frac{d}{s}$
b. $(t^2 - 7t + 12)$ h **54.** $n + 2$
65. $\frac{(t^2 - 5x3t + 1)(2t + 11)}{3t(2r - 55Xt + 1)}$ **66.** $\frac{3c + x8}{2c + 7}$ **67.** $\frac{(x + 5Xx + 4)^2}{(x + 7Xx + 8)^2}$
68. $\frac{2}{3}$ **69.** $-\frac{1}{12}$ **70.** x **71.** $\frac{1}{2y}$

Lesson 11-4 pp. 672–677
Got It? 1. $\frac{5a}{3a} - \frac{4}{3}$ **2a.** $\frac{-5}{r + 3}$ **b.** $\frac{3n - 4}{5n - 2}$ **c.** $\frac{3}{q - 2}$
3. $\frac{9 + 14y^2}{21y^4}$ **4.** $\frac{c^2 - 14c + 4}{(3c - 1Xc - 2)}$ **5a.** $\frac{45}{4r}$ **b.** $\frac{4m}{5}$; if n is the miles per gallon when the truck is full, then $m = 1.25n$ and therefore $n = \frac{m}{1.25}$ or $\frac{4m}{5}$
Lesson Check 1. $\frac{11}{x - 7}$ **2.** $\frac{3}{y + 2}$ **3.** $\frac{16b + 15}{24b^3}$ **4.** $\frac{10}{3r}$
5. If the expressions have like denominators, add or subtract numerators as indicated and place over the denominator. If they have unlike denominators, factor if needed, find the LCD, rewrite the expressions with the common denominator, add or subtract as indicated, and simplify. **6.** The procedure is the same. The LCD is the LCM of the denominators. **7a.** yes **b.** No, it will give you a common denominator, but not necessarily the least common denominator.
Exercises 9. $-\frac{14}{x - 5}$ **11.** $\frac{6c - 28}{2c}$ **13.** $\frac{1}{n + 2}$ **15.** 2
17. $2x^2$ **19.** $7z$ **21.** $5(x + 2)$ **23.** $(m + n)(m - n)$
25. $\frac{35 + 6a}{15a}$ **27.** $\frac{189 - 9n}{7n^3}$ **29.** $\frac{(a + 4Xa - 3)}{(a + 33Xa + 5)}$
31. $\frac{a^2 + 12a + 15}{4(a + 3)}$ **33a.** $\frac{1}{y} + \frac{1}{0.7t} = \frac{1.7}{0.7t}$ **b.** $\frac{17}{7t}$

c. about 0.81 h or 48.6 min **35.** Not always; the numerator may contain a factor of the LCD.
37. $\frac{-y^2 + 2y + 2}{3y + 1}$ **39.** $\frac{c - 2x - 6}{9 + p^3}$ **41.** $\frac{10x + 15}{x + 2}$
43. $\frac{5000r + 250,000}{r(r + 100)}$ **45.** $\frac{8x^2 + 1}{x^2}$ **47.** $\frac{-3x - 5}{x(x - 5)}$
59. $\frac{1}{2}x^2 + 2x - 1$ **60.** 5b **61.** $\frac{y^2(y - 1)}{y - 3}$ **62.** 6.3 **63.** 3
64. no solution **65.** $\frac{5}{9}$ **66.** $\frac{5}{6}$ **67.** 1

Lesson 11-5 pp. 679–685
Got It? 1a. -3 **b.** $\frac{37}{12}$ **2a.** $-\frac{3}{2}, \frac{2}{3}$ **b.** $-7, -1$ **c.** The expression $\frac{4}{x^2}$ cannot be negative. **3.** 4.8 h **4a.** -8
b. $-3, 7$ **5.** 0
Lesson Check 1. -1 **2.** 1, 5 **3.** 0 **4.** about 28 min
5. An extraneous solution of a rational equation is an excluded value of the associated rational function.
6. Answers may vary. Sample: $\frac{x^2}{x - 1} = \frac{1}{x - 1}$
7. The student forgot to first multiply both sides of the equation by the LCD, 5m.
Exercises 9. 3 **11.** $-1, 6$ **13.** -2 **15.** 5 **17.** $-2, 4$
19. $\frac{16}{7}$ **21.** -1 **23.** $1\frac{3}{5}$ **25.** 3 **27.** $-\frac{3}{4}$, 4 **29.** no solution
31. You could rewrite the right side of the equation as $\frac{3r}{x + 6}$ and then cross multiply. **33.** -14 **35.** -5, 2
37. $-\frac{6}{5}$, -1 **39.** 12 h
41a.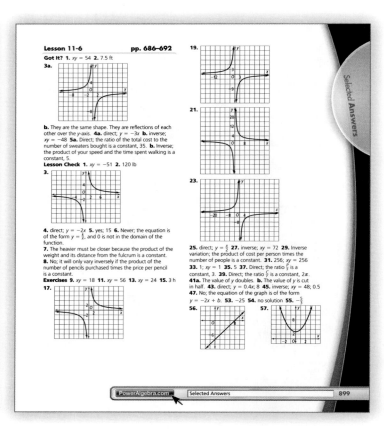

b. $(-9.53, 1.07)$, $(-4.16, 1.35)$, $(-1.12, 5.76)$, $(0.81, 10.16)$

c. Yes; the x-values are solutions to the original equation since both sides are equal. **43.** 20 Ω **56.** $-\frac{3}{x^3y^2z}$
57. $\frac{3h^2 + 2ht + 4h}{2(t - 2Xt + 2)}$ **58.** $\frac{-4k - 61}{(k - 4Xk + 10)}$

59.

60.

61.

62.

63. yes; 3 **64.** no **65.** yes; $-\frac{1}{4}$ **66.** yes; $\frac{a}{3}$

Lesson 11-6 pp. 686–692
Got It? 1. $xy = 54$ **2.** 7.5 ft
3a.

b. They are the same shape. They are reflections of each other over the y-axis. **4a.** direct; $y = -3x$ **b.** inverse; $xy = -48$ **5a.** Direct; the ratio of the total cost to the number of sweaters bought is a constant, 35. **b.** Inverse; the product of your speed and the time spent walking is a constant, 5.
Lesson Check 1. $xy = -51$ **2.** 120 lb
3.

4. direct; $y = -2x$ **5.** yes; 15 **6.** Never; the equation is of the form $y = \frac{k}{x}$, and 0 is not in the domain of the function.
7. The heavier must be closer because the product of the weight and its distance from the fulcrum is a constant.
8. No; it will only vary inversely if the product of the number of pencils purchased times the price per pencil is a constant.
Exercises 9. $xy = 18$ **11.** $xy = 56$ **13.** $xy = 24$ **15.** 3 h
17.

19.

21.

23.

25. direct; $y = \frac{5}{2}x$ **27.** inverse; $xy = 72$ **29.** Inverse variation; the product of cost per person times the number of people is a constant. **31.** 256; $xy = 256$
33. 1; $xy = 1$ **35.** 5 **37.** Direct; the ratio $\frac{p}{s}$ is a constant, 3. **39.** Direct; the ratio $\frac{y}{x}$ is a constant, 2π.
41a. The value of y doubles. **b.** The value of y is cut in half. **43.** direct; $y = 0.4x$; 8 **45.** inverse; $xy = 48$; 0.5
47. No; the equation of the graph is of the form $y = -2x + b$. **53.** -25 **54.** no solution **55.** $-\frac{5}{3}$
56.

57.

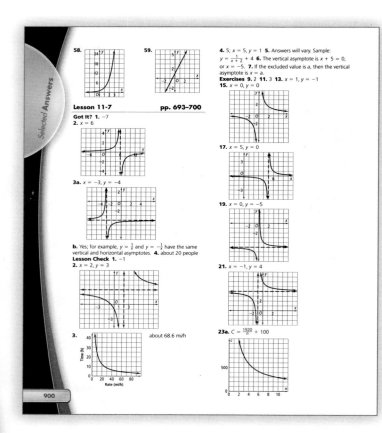

58.

59.

Lesson 11-7 pp. 693–700
Got It? 1. -7
2. $x = 6$

3a. $x = -3, y = -4$

b. Yes; for example, $y = \frac{1}{x}$ and $y = -\frac{1}{x}$ have the same vertical and horizontal asymptotes. **4.** about 20 people
Lesson Check 1. -1
2. $x = 2, y = 3$

3.

about 68.6 mi/h

4. 5; $x = 5, y = 1$ **5.** Answers will vary. Sample:
$y = \frac{1}{x + 2} + 4$ **6.** The vertical asymptote is $x + 5 = 0$, or $x = -5$. **7.** If the excluded value is a, then the vertical asymptote is $x = a$.
Exercises 9. 2 **11.** 3 **13.** $x = 1, y = -1$
15. $x = 0, y = 0$

17. $x = 5, y = 0$

19. $x = 0, y = -5$

21. $x = -1, y = 4$

23a. $C = \frac{1920}{n} + 100$

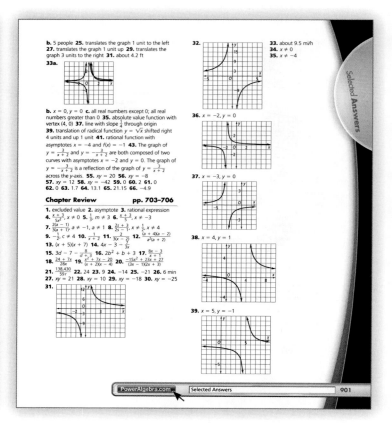

b. 5 people **25.** translates the graph 1 unit to the left
27. translates the graph 1 unit up **29.** translates the graph 3 units to the right **31.** about 4.2 ft
33a.

b. $x = 0, y = 0$ **c.** all real numbers except 0; all real numbers greater than 0 **35.** absolute value function with vertex (4, 0) **37.** line with slope $\frac{1}{4}$ through origin
39. translation of radical function $y = \sqrt{x}$ shifted right 4 units and up 1 unit **41.** rational function with asymptotes $x = -4$ and $f(x) = -1$ **43.** The graph of $y = \frac{3}{x + 2}$ and $y = -\frac{3}{x + 2}$ are both composed of two curves with asymptotes $x = -2$ and $y = 0$. The graph of $y = -\frac{3}{x + 2}$ is a reflection of the graph of $y = \frac{3}{x + 2}$ across the y-axis. **55.** $xy = 20$ **56.** $xy = -8$
57. $xy = 12$ **58.** $xy = -42$ **59.** 0 **60.** 2 **61.** 0
62. 0 **63.** 1.7 **64.** 13.1 **65.** 21.15 **66.** -4.9

Chapter Review pp. 703–706
1. excluded value **2.** asymptote **3.** rational expression
4. $\frac{x + 3}{5x^2}$, $x \neq 0$ **5.** $\frac{1}{m + 3}$, $m \neq 3$ **6.** $\frac{x - 3}{x + 3}$, $x \neq -3$
7. $\frac{2(a - 1)}{3(a + 1)}$; $a \neq -1, a \neq 1$ **8.** $\frac{2x + 3}{2x - 1}$, $x \neq \frac{1}{2}, x \neq 4$
9. $-\frac{1}{2}$, $c \neq 4$ **10.** $\frac{1}{x + 2}$ **11.** $\frac{2}{3(x - 2)}$ **12.** $\frac{(a + 4Xa - 2)}{a^2(a + 2)}$
13. $(x + 5)(x + 7)$ **14.** $4x - 3 - \frac{1}{3x}$
15. $3d - 7 - \frac{8}{d + 3}$ **16.** $2b^2 + b + 3$ **17.** $\frac{8x - 3}{x^2}$
18. $\frac{24}{28x} + \frac{5}{7}$ **19.** $\frac{x^2 + 7x - 20}{(x + 23Xx - 4)}$ **20.** $\frac{-15x^3 + 23x + 27}{(3x - 1X2x + 3)}$
21. $\frac{138,430}{59r}$ **22.** 24 **23.** 9 **24.** -14 **25.** -21 **26.** 6 min
27. $xy = 21$ **28.** $xy = 10$ **29.** $xy = -18$ **30.** $xy = -25$
31.

32.

33. about 9.5 mi/h
34. $x \neq 0$
35. $x \neq -4$

36. $x = -2, y = 0$

37. $x = -3, y = 0$

38. $x = 4, y = 1$

39. $x = 5, y = -1$

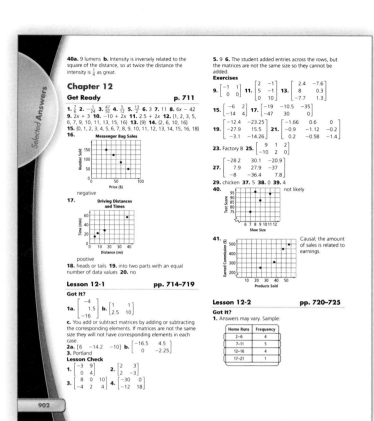

40a. 9 lumens **b.** Intensity is inversely related to the square of the distance, so at twice the distance the intensity is $\frac{1}{4}$ as great.

Chapter 12
Get Ready p. 711
1. $\frac{7}{6}$ **2.** $-\frac{7}{6}$ **3.** $\frac{47}{12}$ **4.** $\frac{5}{9}$ **5.** $-\frac{13}{2}$ **6.** 3 **7.** 11 **8.** $6x - 42$
9. $2x + 3$ **10.** $-10 + 2x$ **11.** $2.5 + 2x$ **12.** {1, 2, 3, 5, 6, 7, 9, 10, 11, 13, 15, 16} **13.** {9} **14.** {2, 6, 10, 16}
15. {0, 1, 2, 3, 4, 5, 6, 7, 8, 9, 10, 11, 12, 13, 14, 15, 16, 18}
16.

negative

17.

positive

18. heads or tails **19.** into two parts with an equal number of data values **20.** no

Lesson 12-1 pp. 714–719
Got It?
1a. $\begin{bmatrix} -4 \\ 1.5 \\ -16 \end{bmatrix}$ **b.** $\begin{bmatrix} 1 & 1 \\ 2.5 & 10 \end{bmatrix}$
c. You add or subtract matrices by adding or subtracting the corresponding elements. If matrices are not the same size they will not have corresponding elements in each case. **2a.** $\begin{bmatrix} 6 & -14.2 & -10 \end{bmatrix}$ **b.** $\begin{bmatrix} -16.5 & 4.5 \\ 0 & -2.25 \end{bmatrix}$
3. Portland
Lesson Check
1. $\begin{bmatrix} -3 & 9 \\ 0 & 4 \end{bmatrix}$ **2.** $\begin{bmatrix} 2 & 3 \\ 2 & -3 \end{bmatrix}$
3. $\begin{bmatrix} 8 & 0 & 10 \\ -4 & 2 & 4 \end{bmatrix}$ **4.** $\begin{bmatrix} -30 & 0 \\ -12 & 18 \end{bmatrix}$

5. 9 **6.** The student added entries across the rows, but the matrices are not the same size so they cannot be added.
Exercises
9. $\begin{bmatrix} -1 & 1 \\ 0 & 0 \end{bmatrix}$ **11.** $\begin{bmatrix} 2 & -1 \\ 5 & -1 \\ 0 & 10 \end{bmatrix}$ **13.** $\begin{bmatrix} 2.4 & -7.6 \\ 8 & 0.3 \\ -7.7 & 1.3 \end{bmatrix}$
15. $\begin{bmatrix} -6 & 2 \\ -14 & 4 \end{bmatrix}$ **17.** $\begin{bmatrix} -19 & -10.5 & -35 \\ -47 & 30 & 0 \end{bmatrix}$
19. $\begin{bmatrix} -12.4 & -23.25 \\ -27.9 & 15.5 \\ -3.1 & -14.26 \end{bmatrix}$ **21.** $\begin{bmatrix} -1.66 & 0.6 & 0 \\ -0.9 & -1.12 & -0.2 \\ 0.2 & -0.58 & -1.4 \end{bmatrix}$
23. Factory B **25.** $\begin{bmatrix} 9 & 1 & 2 \\ 10 & 2 & 0 \end{bmatrix}$
27. $\begin{bmatrix} -28.2 & 30.1 & -20.9 \\ 7.9 & 27.9 & -37 \\ -8 & -36.4 & 7.8 \end{bmatrix}$
29. chicken **37.** 5 **38.** 0 **39.** 4
40. not likely

41. Causal; the amount of sales is related to earnings.

Lesson 12-2 pp. 720–725
Got It?
1. Answers may vary. Sample:

Home Runs	Frequency
2–6	4
7–11	5
12–16	4
17–21	1

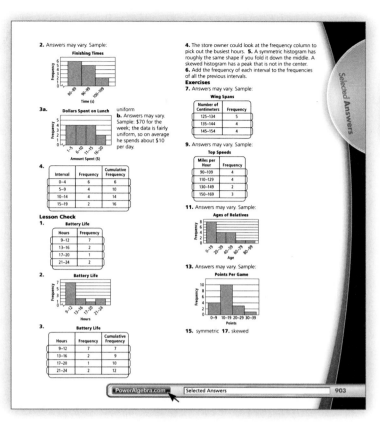

2. Answers may vary. Sample:

3a. uniform **b.** Answers may vary. Sample: $70 for the week; the data is fairly uniform, so on average he spends about $10 per day.
4.

Interval	Frequency	Cumulative Frequency
0–4	6	6
5–9	4	10
10–14	4	14
15–19	2	16

Lesson Check
1.

Hours	Frequency
9–12	7
13–16	2
17–20	1
21–24	2

2. Battery Life

3.

Hours	Frequency	Cumulative Frequency
9–12	7	7
13–16	2	9
17–20	1	10
21–24	2	12

4. The store owner could look at the frequency column to pick out the busiest hours. **5.** A symmetric histogram has roughly the same shape if you fold it down the middle. A skewed histogram has a peak that is not in the center.
6. Add the frequency of each interval to the frequencies of all the previous intervals.
Exercises
7. Answers may vary. Sample:

Number of Centimeters	Frequency
125–134	5
135–144	4
145–154	4

9. Answers may vary. Sample:

Miles per Hour	Frequency
90–109	4
110–129	4
130–149	2
150–169	3

11. Answers may vary. Sample:

13. Answers may vary. Sample:

15. symmetric **17.** skewed

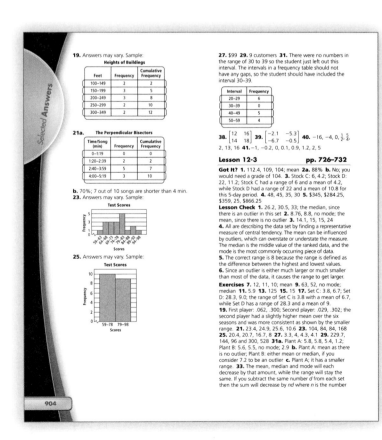

19. Answers may vary. Sample:

Feet	Frequency	Cumulative Frequency
100–149	2	2
150–199	3	5
200–249	3	8
250–299	2	10
300–349	2	12

21a. The Perpendicular Bisectors

Time/Song (min)	Frequency	Cumulative Frequency
0–1:19	0	0
1:20–2:39	2	2
2:40–3:59	5	7
4:00–5:19	3	10

b. 70%; 7 out of 10 songs are shorter than 4 min.
23. Answers may vary. Sample:

25. Answers may vary. Sample:

27. $99 **29.** 9 customers **31.** There were no numbers in the range of 30 to 39 so the student just left out this interval. The intervals in a frequency table should not have any gaps, so the student should have included the interval 30–39.

Interval	Frequency
20–29	6
30–39	0
40–49	5
50–59	4

38. $\begin{bmatrix} 12 & 16 \\ 14 & 16 \end{bmatrix}$ **39.** $\begin{bmatrix} -2.1 & -5.3 \\ -6.7 & -0.5 \end{bmatrix}$ **40.** $-16, -4, 0, \frac{1}{2}, \frac{5}{4}$, 2, 13, 16 **41.** $-1, -0.2, 0, 0.1, 0.9, 1.2, 2, 5$

Lesson 12-3 pp. 726–732
Got It? 1. 112.4, 109, 104; mean **2a.** 88% **b.** No; you would need a grade of 104. **3.** Stock C: 6, 4.2; Stock D: 22, 11.2; Stock C had a range of 6 and a mean of 4.2, while Stock D had a range of 22 and a mean of 10.8 for this 5-day period. **4.** 48, 45, 35, 30 **5.** $345, $284.25, $359.25, $866.25.
Lesson Check 1. 26.2, 30.5, 33; the median, since there is an outlier in this set **2.** 8.76, 8.8, no mode; the mean, since there is no outlier **3.** 14.1, 15, 15, 24
4. All are describing the data set by finding a representative measure of central tendency. The mean can be influenced by outliers, which can overstate or understate the measure. The median is the middle value of the ranked data, and the mode is the most commonly occurring piece of data.
5. The correct range is 8 because the range is defined as the difference between the highest and lowest values.
6. Since an outlier is either much larger or much smaller than most of the data, it causes the range to get larger.
Exercises 7. 12, 11, 10; mean **9.** 63, 52, no mode; median **11.** 5.9 **13.** 125 **15.** 15 **17.** Set C: 3.8, 6.7; Set D: 28.3, 9.0; the range of Set C is 3.8 with a mean of 6.7, while Set D has a range of 28.3 and a mean of 9.
19. First player: .062, .300; Second player: .029, .302; the second player had a slightly higher mean over the six seasons and was more consistent as shown by the smaller range. **21.** 23.4, 24.9, 25.6, 10.6 **23.** 104, 84, 84, 168 **25.** 20.4, 20.7, 16.7, 8 **27.** 3.3, 4, 4.3, 4.1 **29.** 229.7, 144, 96 and 300, 528 **31a.** Plant A: 5.8, 5.8, 5.4, 1.2; Plant B: 5.6, 5.5, no mode; 2.9 **b.** Plant A: mean as there is no outlier; Plant B: either mean or median, if you consider 7.2 to be an outlier **c.** Plant A; it has a smaller range. **33.** The mean, median and mode will each decrease by that amount, while the range will stay the same. If you subtract the same number d from each set then the sum will decrease by nd where n is the number

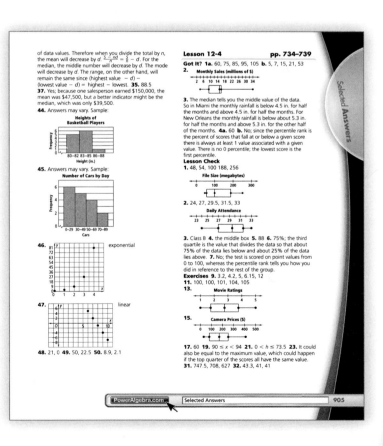

of data values. Therefore when you divide the total by n, the mean will decrease by d. $\frac{\Sigma - nd}{n} = \frac{\Sigma}{n} - d$. For the median, the middle number will decrease by d. The mode will decrease by d. The range, on the other hand, will remain the same since (highest value $- d$) $-$ (lowest value $- d$) = highest $-$ lowest. **35.** 88.5
37. Yes; because one salesperson earned $150,000, the mean was $47,500, but a better indicator might be the median, which was only $39,500.
44. Answers may vary. Sample:

45. Answers may vary. Sample:

46. exponential

47. linear

48. 21, 0 **49.** 50, 22.5 **50.** 8.9, 2.1

Lesson 12-4 pp. 734–739
Got It? 1a. 60, 75, 85, 95, 105 **b.** 5, 7, 15, 21, 53
2.

3. The median tells you the middle value of the data. So in Miami the monthly rainfall is below 4.5 in. for half the months and above 4.5 in. for half the months. For New Orleans the monthly rainfall is below 5.3 in. for half the months and above 5.3 in. for the other half of the months. **4a.** 60 **b.** No; since the percentile rank is the percent of scores that fall at or below a given score there is always at least 1 value associated with a given value. There is no 0 percentile; the lowest score is the first percentile.
Lesson Check
1. 48, 54, 100 188, 256
File Size (megabytes)

2. 24, 27, 29.5, 31.5, 33
Daily Attendance

3. Class B **4.** the middle box **5.** 88 **6.** 75%; the third quartile is the value that divides the data so that about 75% of the data lies below and about 25% of the data lies above. **7.** No; the test is scored on point values from 0 to 100, whereas the percentile rank tells you how you did in reference to the rest of the group.
Exercises 9. 3.2, 4.2, 5, 6.15, 12
11. 100, 100, 101, 104, 105
13. Movie Ratings

15. Camera Prices ($)

17. 60 **19.** $90 \le x < 94$ **21.** $0 < h \le 73.5$ **23.** It could also be equal to the maximum value, which could happen if the top quarter of the scores all have the same value.
31. 747.5, 708, 627 **32.** 43.3, 41, 41

33.

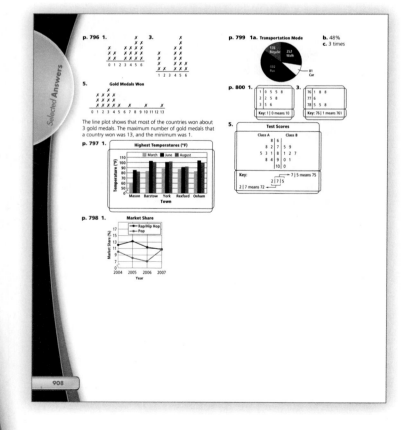

Answers may vary. Sample: $y = -81x + 167{,}509$; about 4300 bowling establishments

Lesson 12-5   pp. 741–747
Got It? 1a. quantitative; numerical quantities
b. qualitative; not numerical **2a.** Bivariate; there are two variables. **b.** Univariate; there is only one variable.
3. No; if you are using a stratified sampling method, you should sample at random from each group. **4.** Answers may vary. Sample: Do you prefer action movies or documentaries? **5.** Students who have e-mail may be more likely to have a cell phone.
Lesson Check 1. systematic **2.** random **3.** stratified **4.** quantitative **5.** The words *delicious* and *plain* are biased and might influence a respondent's answer.
6. Univariate data involves one variable and bivariate data involves two variables.
Exercises 7. qualitative **9.** quantitative **11.** univariate **13.** univariate **15.** stratified; not a good sample as it assumes each town has a similar number of voters **17.** random; good sample **19.** not biased; respondent is not influenced by question **21.** During the day many people are at work so your sample is not representative of the population. **23.** Because each sample is random, it would not be expected to be exactly the same.
25a. People at an airport are more likely to be travelers. **b.** Your question is influencing the result. Respondents might prefer "neither." **c.** The sample is biased as it includes mostly people who might prefer France.
27. people who are customers at the store; every fifteenth customer; systematic **29.** attendees at the game; random attendees; random **31.** quantitative **33.** quantitative; bivariate **35a.** Responses are voluntary and there are sports that are not listed. **b.** no for the reasons listed in part (a) **37.** Response is voluntary and only those who like the scent are probably going to return the card. **45.** 40 **46.** 60 **47.** $a > 1$ **48.** $x \geq -3$ **49.** $b > 0.2$ **50.** 20 **51.** 42 **52.** 6

Lesson 12-6   pp. 750–756
Got It? 1a. 48 **b.** No; the tree diagram would be very large, so using the Multiplication Counting Principle would be easier. **2.** 40,320 ways **3.** 20,160 **4.** 455 ways
Lesson Check 1. 5040 **2.** 6,227,020,800 **3.** 120 **4.** 5040 **5.** 10 **6.** 35 **7.** 24 outfits **8.** permutations **9.** Permutations are used to count in situations where order is important. Combinations are used to count in situations where selection, not order, is important.
10. There is only one way to take n things, n at a time. Also, ${}_nC_n = \frac{n!}{n!(n-n)!} = \frac{n!}{n!} = 1$.
Exercises 11a. 8, 10 **b.** 8×10^6 or 8,000,000
13. 3,628,800 **15.** 1680 **17.** 5040 **19.** 42 **21.** 6 **23.** 90 **25.** 5040 ways **27.** 1 **29.** 9 **31.** 56 **33.** 28 **35.** 10 **37.** 220 ways **39.** 142,506 groups **41.** ${}_9P_7$ **43.** ${}_9P_6$ **45.** ${}_8C_5$ **47a.** 24 ways **b.** No; there is a limited number of ways that you can arrange the letters so someone can figure it out. **49.** 60 **51.** 210
53. Combination; the order of the books does not matter. **55a.** 35,152 call signs **b.** 913,952 call signs **57.** 2 **59.** 4 **61.** 1 **70.** qualitative **71.** quantitative **72.** quantitative **73.** qualitative **74.** 0.81, −6.81 **75.** 6.70, 0.30 **76.** 1.46, −5.46 **77.** −1, −1.67 **78.** 32% **79.** 9% **80.** 22.5% **81.** 18%

Lesson 12-7   pp. 757–762
Got It? 1. $\frac{2}{3}$ **2.** It will be $1 - \frac{20}{60+x}$, where x is the number of other samples added. The probability will increase. **3.** 3 : 1 **4.** 98% **5.** about 34,995 light bulbs
Lesson Check 1. $\frac{1}{2}$ **2.** $\frac{1}{3}$ **3.** $\frac{2}{5}$ **4.** $\frac{1}{2}$ **5.** 1 : 5 **6.** 16%
7. Theoretical probability is based on the number of favorable outcomes when all of the outcomes are equally likely. Experimental probability is based on the results of an experiment. **8.** There are only two outcomes that are favorable, getting a 1 or a 2, therefore the probability is $\frac{2}{10}$, or $\frac{1}{5}$.
Exercises 11. 0 **13.** $\frac{2}{3}$ **15.** $\frac{1}{4}$ **17.** $\frac{2}{5}$ **19.** $\frac{2}{3}$ **21.** $\frac{1}{3}$ **23.** 5 : 1 **25.** 5 : 1 **27.** 1 : 5 **29.** 43% **31.** 85% **33.** about 201 trees **35.** 98.4% **39.** 40% **41.** 25% **50.** 840 **51.** 6 **52.** 30 **53.** 9 **54.** 5 **55.** {1, 4, 5, 6, 7, 10} **56.** {4, 6} **57.** {0, 2, 4, 5, 6, 7, 8, 10} **58.** {4, 10} **59.** {0, 1, 2, 4, 6, 7, 8, 10}

Lesson 12-8   pp. 764–770
Got It? 1a. $\frac{2}{9}$ **b.** $\frac{1}{2}$ **2.** $\frac{2}{13}$ **3.** $\frac{2}{5}$ **4.** Answers may vary. Sample: find the probability of spinning a number less than 5 that is even. **5.** Mutually exclusive; answers may vary. Sample: The complement of being even on a number die is being odd, and even and odd are mutually exclusive. **7.** Because a tile can be both yellow and a letter, the formula should be $P(\text{yellow or letter}) = P(\text{yellow}) + P(\text{letter}) - P(\text{yellow and letter}) = \frac{2}{5} + \frac{2}{5} - \frac{1}{5} = \frac{3}{5}$.

Exercises 9. $\frac{4}{5}$ **11.** $\frac{1}{2}$ **13.** $\frac{1}{2}$ **15.** $\frac{7}{9}$ **17.** $\frac{1}{2}$ **19.** $\frac{1}{6}$ **21.** $\frac{4}{81}$ **23.** $\frac{1}{9}$ **25.** $\frac{2}{9}$ **27.** $\frac{5}{9}$ **29.** $\frac{2}{9}$ **31.** $\frac{1}{12}$ **33.** 0 **35.** $\frac{3}{22}$ **37.** Dependent; the outcome of the first event affects the outcome of the second. **39.** For independent events, the outcome of the first event does not affect the outcome of the second event, while for dependent events, the outcome is affected. An example of two independent events is the rolling of two number cubes. An example of two dependent events is picking two cards from a deck without replacing the first one. **41.** about 4.7% **49.** $\frac{11}{21}$ **50.** $\frac{2}{21}$ **51.** $\frac{8}{21}$ **52.** $\frac{8}{21}$ **53.** −22
54. $\frac{a+5}{5(a-5)}$ **55.** $\frac{7(y+1)}{7y+1}$

Chapter Review   pp. 774–778
1. element **2.** frequency **3.** outlier **4.** quartile
5. $\begin{bmatrix} -12 & 7 \\ 4 & 6 \end{bmatrix}$ **6.** $\begin{bmatrix} 4.4 & 4.5 \\ 9.5 & -10.2 \\ 3.4 & -2.6 \end{bmatrix}$
7. $\begin{bmatrix} -12.6 & -4.62 \\ -12.6 & 8.4 \\ 4.2 & -12.18 \end{bmatrix}$ **8.** [graph: Customers]
9. [graph: Workout Times] **10.** skewed **11.** symmetric **12.** 26.3, 26, 23 and 25 and 29, 9 **13.** 12.1, 12, 12.2 **14.** 11.1, 11.3, 13.4; mean or median **15.** 27
16. [graph: Movie Lengths (min)]
17. [graph: Dog Weights (lb)]
18. [graph: Book Lengths (Number of Pages)]
19. B; the box in A is from about 90 to 110, where the box in B is from about 75 to 125. **20.** Systematic; good sample; do you plan on seeing more or fewer movies in the coming year? **21.** Stratified; good sample; who do you support for student council president? **22.** 15,120 **23.** 6 **24.** 336 **25.** 20 **26.** 360 **27.** 42 **28.** 28 **29.** 126 **30.** 10 **31.** 20 **32.** 35 **33.** 5 **34.** 10 **35.** 40,320 ways **36.** 126 outfits **37.** $\frac{1}{3}$ **38.** $\frac{1}{3}$ **39.** $\frac{1}{3}$ **40.** $\frac{1}{2}$ **41.** 0 **42.** $\frac{1}{2}$ **43.** about 93.3% **44.** $\frac{4}{7}$ **45.** $\frac{2}{7}$ **46.** $\frac{3}{8}$ **47.** $\frac{1}{4}$
48. Dependent; the outcome of the first event affects the outcome of the second event. **49.** Independent; the outcome of the spinner does not affect the outcome of the pick.

Skills Handbook
p. 786 1. composite **3.** composite **5.** prime **7.** composite **9.** prime **11.** composite **13.** 1, 2, 23, 46 **15.** 1, 11 **17.** 1, 3, 9, 27 **19.** $2 \cdot 3 \cdot 3$ **21.** $3 \cdot 3 \cdot 3$ **23.** $2 \cdot 2 \cdot 2 \cdot 2 \cdot 2$
p. 787 1. 2 **3.** 24 **5.** 80 **7.** 33
p. 788 1–11. Answers may vary. Samples are given.
p. 789 1. $\frac{8}{14}, \frac{16}{28}$; $\frac{20}{35}, \frac{24}{42}$ **3.** $\frac{1}{16}, \frac{2}{32}$; $\frac{12}{40}, \frac{15}{48}$
5. $\frac{15}{24}, \frac{20}{32}$; $\frac{30}{40}, \frac{36}{48}$ **9.** 48 **11.** 2 **13.** yes **15.** no; $\frac{5}{8}$
17. yes **19.** $\frac{2}{3}$ **21.** $\frac{2}{3}$ **23.** $\frac{3}{10}$
p. 790 1. 0.3 **3.** 0.2 **5.** $0.\overline{714285}$ **7.** $\frac{7}{100}$ **9.** $\frac{1}{6}$ **11.** $6\frac{1}{3}$
p. 791 1. $\frac{5}{3}$ **3.** 3 **5.** $10\frac{7}{15}$ **7.** $6\frac{2}{3}$ **9.** $9\frac{2}{3}$ **11.** $9\frac{2}{3}$ **13.** $13\frac{7}{16}$ **15.** $\frac{2}{7}$ **17.** $1\frac{9}{16}$ **19.** $2\frac{3}{8}$ **21.** $3\frac{1}{2}$ **23.** $9\frac{4}{63}$ **25.** $2\frac{1}{8}$
p. 792 1. $\frac{1}{10}$ **3.** $8\frac{2}{5}$ **5.** $3\frac{1}{2}$ **7.** $25\frac{1}{10}$ **9.** $2\frac{2}{5}$ **11.** $1\frac{1}{2}$ **13.** $1\frac{5}{16}$ **15.** $1\frac{1}{4}$ **17.** $2\frac{5}{12}$ **19.** $2\frac{19}{20}$
p. 793 1. 56% **3.** 602% **5.** 820% **7.** 14.3% **9.** 11.1% **11.** 75% **13.** 0.07 **15.** 0.009 **17.** 0.83 **19.** 0.15 **21.** 0.0003 **23.** 3.65 **25.** $\frac{7}{100}$ **27.** $4\frac{1}{2}$ **29.** $\frac{3}{20}$ **31.** $\frac{6}{25}$ **33.** $\frac{3}{800}$ **35.** $\frac{1}{3}$
p. 794 1. 6^4 **3.** $5 \cdot 2^4$ **5.** $4^2 \cdot 3^2 \cdot 2$ **7.** 64 **9.** 141 **11.** 3267 **13.** $(1 \cdot 10^3) + (2 \cdot 10^2) + (5 \cdot 10^1) + (4 \cdot 10^0)$ **15.** $(8 \cdot 10^4) + (3 \cdot 10^3) + (4 \cdot 10^2) + (0 \cdot 10^1) + (1 \cdot 10^0)$
p. 795 1. 22 cm **3.** 24 cm² **5.** 216 cm³ **7.** 352 cm³

p. 796 1. [line plot] **3.** [line plot]
5. Gold Medals Won [line plot]
The line plot shows that most of the countries won about 3 gold medals. The maximum number of gold medals that a country won was 13, and the minimum was 1.
p. 797 1. [bar graph: Highest Temperatures (°F)]
p. 798 1. [line graph: Market Share]
p. 799 1a. [pie chart: Transportation Mode] **b.** 48% **c.** 3 times
p. 800 1. [stem-and-leaf plot] **3.** [stem-and-leaf plot]
5. [back-to-back stem-and-leaf plot: Test Scores]

Additional Answers

Chapter 3

Lesson 3-2

Practice and Problem-Solving Exercises   page 174

13. $y > 13$

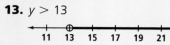

14. $v < 1$

15. $c < -4$

16. $f \geq 12$

17. $t \geq -3$

18. $s \leq 11$

19. $p > 12$

20. $x \leq -2$

21. $f > \frac{1}{3}$

22. $z \leq 8$

23. $r < 0$

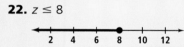

24. $y \geq 2.5$

25. $s < 4.7$

26. $n < -1.6$

27. $c < 1\frac{3}{7}$

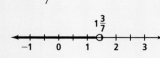

28. $p > 3$

Lesson 3-3

Practice and Problem-Solving Exercises   page 181

7. $x \geq -10$

8. $w < 6$

9. $p < 32$

10. $y \leq -\frac{4}{5}$

11. $v \leq -3$

12. $x > -9$

13. $x \geq -3$

14. $k < 12$

15. $m \leq 0$

16. $b > -4$

17. $m < 2$

18. $y \geq 9$

19. $m \geq 2$

20. $t < -3$

21. $c > 6$

22. $w \geq -5$

23. $z > -3$

24. $d < -8$

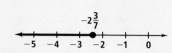

25. $b \leq -\frac{1}{6}$

26. $y \leq -2\frac{3}{7}$

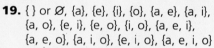

27. $h > -13$

28. $t \leq 8$

29. $q \leq 9$

30. $x < -11$

Lesson 3-5

Practice and Problem-Solving Exercises   page 197

19. { } or Ø, {a}, {e}, {i}, {o}, {a, e}, {a, i}, {a, o}, {e, i}, {e, o}, {i, o}, {a, e, i}, {a, e, o}, {a, i, o}, {e, i, o}, {a, e, i, o}

20. { } or Ø, {0}, {1}, {2}, {0, 1}, {0, 2}, {1, 2}, {0, 1, 2}

21. { } or Ø, {dog}, {cat}, {fish}, {dog, cat}, {dog, fish}, {cat, fish}, {dog, cat, fish}

22. { } or Ø, {−2}, {2}, {−2, 2}

Chapter 4

5.

Bob's and His Dog's Ages (years)										
Dog's Age	0	1	2	3	4	5	6	7	8	9
Bob's Age	9	10	11	12	13	14	15	16	17	18

Bob's and His Dog's Ages

$B = 9 + d$, where B is Bob's age and d is his dog's age

6.

Sue's Number of Laps per Minute										
Number of Minutes	0	1	2	3	4	5	6	7	8	9
Number of Laps	0	1.5	3	4.5	6	7.5	9	10.5	12	13.5

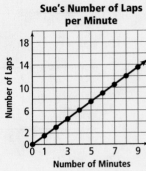

Sue's Number of Laps per Minute

$\ell = 1.5m$, where m is the number of minutes and ℓ is the number of laps.

7.

Total Cost for Cartons of Eggs										
Number of Cartons	0	1	2	3	4	5	6	7	8	9
Total Cost (dollars)	0	3	6	9	12	15	18	21	24	27

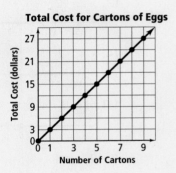

Total Cost for Cartons of Eggs

$C = 3n$, where C is the cost and n is the number of cartons.

8–11.

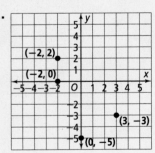

$(-2, 2)$
$(-2, 0)$
$(3, -3)$
$(0, -5)$

Lesson 4-2

Practice and Problem-Solving
Exercises page 243

6.

Number of Pentagons	1	2	3
Perimeter	5	8	11

Multiply the number of pentagons by 3 and add 2; $y = 3x + 2$.

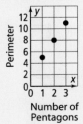

Number of Pentagons

7.

Number of Hexagons	1	2	3
Perimeter	6	10	14

Multiply the number of hexagons by 4 and add 2; $y = 4x + 2$.

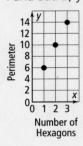

Number of Hexagons

8. Start with 5 and add 3 for each increase of 1 for x; $y = 3x + 5$.

9. Start with −3 and add 5 for each increase of 1 for x; $y = 5x − 3$.

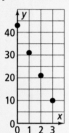

10. Start with 43 and subtract 11 for each increase of 1 for x; $y = −11x + 43$.

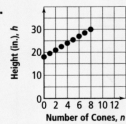

Lesson 4-4

Lesson Check   page 257

5. a.

n	h
0	18
1	19.5
2	21
3	22.5
4	24
5	25.5
6	27
7	28.5
8	30

b.

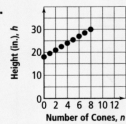

6. discrete

7. continuous

8. The graph should not be discrete; connect the points with a line so the graph is continuous.

Practice and Problem-Solving Exercises   page 257

9.

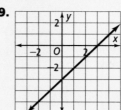

10.

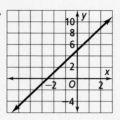

11.

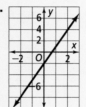

12.

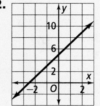

13.

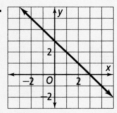

14.

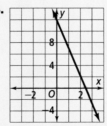

15.

16.

17.

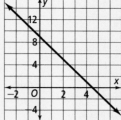

18.

19.

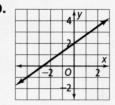

20.

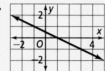

21.

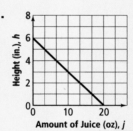

After you drink 20 oz of juice, the height is 0, so the interval $0 \le j \le 20$ makes sense. The height goes from $0 \le h \le 6$; continuous, because you can have juice in any amount.

22.

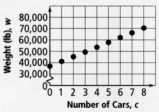

The truck can carry 8 cars, so the interval $0 \le t \le 8$ makes sense. The maximum weight is 70,600 lb, so an interval of $0 \le w \le 70,600$ makes sense. Discrete; the number of cars must be a whole number.

23.

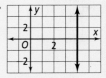

The number of pizzas can be any whole number except zero, so $0 < p$. 1 pizza costs $14, so $14 \leq C$.

Chapter 5

Lesson 5-5

Got It?   page 321

3. a.

b.

c.

d.

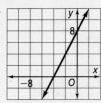

Practice and Problem-Solving
Exercises   page 324

20.

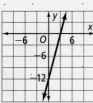

21.

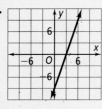

22.

23. horizontal   **24.** vertical
25. horizontal   **26.** vertical
27.

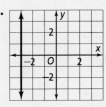

28.

29.

30.

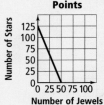

31. $2x - y = -5$ **32.** $4x - y = 7$
33. $2x + y = 10$ **34.** $x - 4y = 8$
35. $2x + 3y = -3$ **36.** $2x - 3y = -2$
37. $5j + 2s = 250$

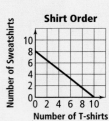

Points

Answers may vary. Sample: 50 jewels and 0 stars, 48 jewels and 5 stars, 42 jewels and 20 stars

38. $12t + 15s = 120$

Shirt Order

Answers may vary. Sample: 10 T-shirts and 0 sweatshirts, 0 T-shirts and 8 sweatshirts, 5 T-shirts and 4 sweatshirts

39. When you have a slope and the y-intercept, use the slope-intercept form. When you have two points or a slope and a point, use the point-slope form. When you have the standard form, it is easy to graph.

40.

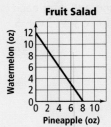

Fruit Salad

Lesson 5-8

Practice and Problem-Solving
Exercises   page 345

6. It is a translation of $y = |x|$ up 3 units.

7. It is a translation of $y = |x|$ left 4 units.

8. It is a translation of $y = |x|$ down 4 units.

9.

10.

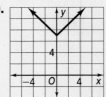

11.

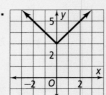

12.

13.

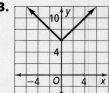

14.

15. $y = |x| + 9$ **16.** $y = |x| - 7$
17. $y = |x| + 0.25$
18. $y = |x| - 3.25$
19. $y = |x| + 5.9$ **20.** $y = |x| - 1$

21.   **22.**

23.

24.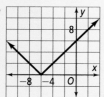

25.   **26.**

27. $y = |x + 9|$ **28.** $y = |x - 9|$
29. $y = |x - 0.5|$ **30.** $y = \left|x + \frac{3}{2}\right|$
31. $y = \left|x + \frac{5}{2}\right|$ **32.** $y = |x - 8.2|$

33.   **34.**

35.   **36.**

37. $y = -|x| + 2$
38. $y = -|x + 2.25|$
39. $y = -|x| - 15$
40. $y = -|x - 4|$
41. $y = |x| + k$ is a translation of $y = |x|$ up k units. $y = mx + b$ is a translation of $y = mx$ up b units.

42.

x	y = |x|	y = |x| + 5
−3	3	8
−2	2	7
−1	1	6
0	0	5
1	1	6
2	2	7
3	3	8

Each y-value of $y = |x| + 5$ is 5 more than the corresponding y-value of $y = |x|$.

Concept Byte Exercises   page 347

1a.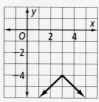

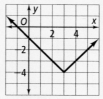

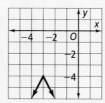

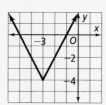

Chapter 6

Lesson 6-5

Lesson Check   page 393

1. no

2.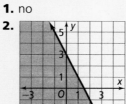

3.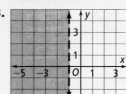

4. $y < \frac{1}{2}x - 1$

5. Answers will vary. Sample: The solutions of a linear equation and a linear inequality are coordinates of the points that make the equation or inequality true. The graph of a linear equation is a line, but the graph of a linear inequality is a region of the coordinate plane.

6. Since the inequality is already solved for y, the $<$ symbol means you should shade below the boundary line. All of these shaded points will make the inequality true.

7. $y \geq 5x + 1$

Practice and Problem-Solving Exercises   page 393

8. not a solution   **9.** solution
10. solution   **11.** solution
12. not a solution   **13.** solution

14.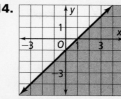

15.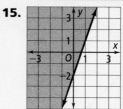

16.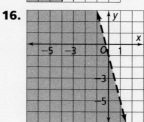

17.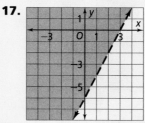

18.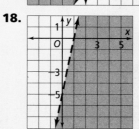

19.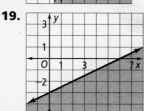

20.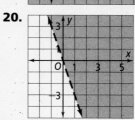

21.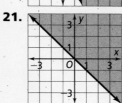

Lesson 6-6

Practice and Problem-Solving
Exercises   page 399

12.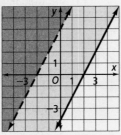

13.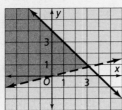

14.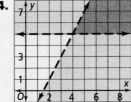

15.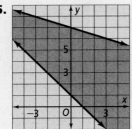

16.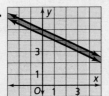

17.

18.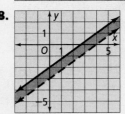

19.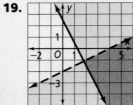

20.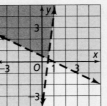

21.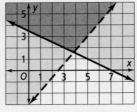

22. $y > 3x - 2$, $y \geq -2x + 2$

23. $y \leq x + 2$, $y < -\frac{1}{3}x$

24. $x < 1$, $y < -\frac{3}{2}x + 3$

25. $y \geq 2$, $y > x + 1$

26. Let x = hours worked at mowing lawns, let y = hours worked at clothing store.

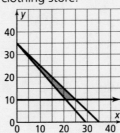

27. Let x = hours driven by slower driver, let y = hours driven by faster driver.

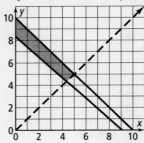

Exercises   page 402

12.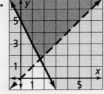

13.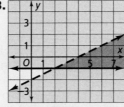

14.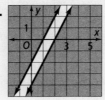

Chapter 9

Get Ready!

Get Ready!   page 531

7.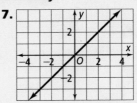

8.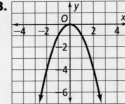

9.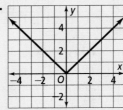

10.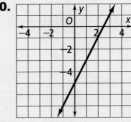

11.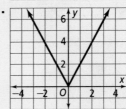

12.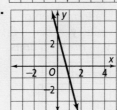

Chapter 10

Lesson 10-5

Lesson Check   page 622

2.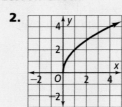

3.

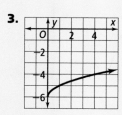

4. No; there is no variable in the radicand.

5. The graph of $y = \sqrt{x - 1}$ is the graph of $y = \sqrt{x}$ shifted to the right 1 unit.

6. Yes; the domain includes all the values of x such that the radicand has a value greater than or equal to zero, so for $b > 0$, the domain of $y = \sqrt{x + b}$ is $x \geq -b$, which includes negative values.

Practice and Problem-Solving Exercises **page 623**

21.

x	y
0	0
1	-3
4	-6

22.

x	f(x)
0	0
1	$\frac{1}{3}$
9	1

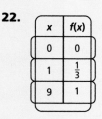

23.

x	y
0	0
2	1
8	2

24.

x	y
3	0
4	2
7	4

25.

h	v
0	0
1	4.4
6	10.8

$h > 5.1$ m

26. D   **27.** A   **28.** C   **29.** B

30.

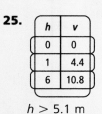

31.

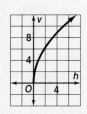

32.

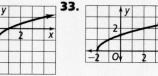

33.

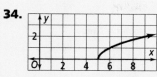

34.

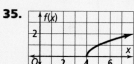

35.

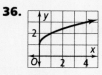

36.

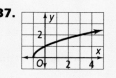

37.

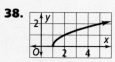

38.

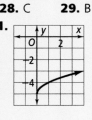

39. $x \geq 4; y \geq 0$ **40.** $x \leq 4; y \geq 0$

Chapter 11

Lesson 11-7

Practice and Problem-Solving Exercises **page 692**

14. $x = 0, y = 2$ **15.** $x = 0, y = 0$

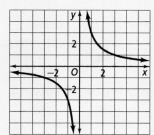

16. $x = 0, y = 0$

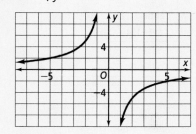

17. $x = 5, y = 0$

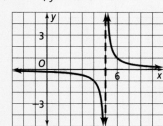

18. $x = -4, y = 0$

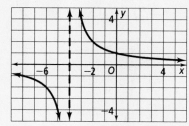

19. $x = 0, y = -5$

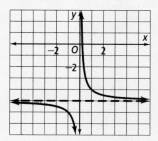

20. $x = 0, y = 6$

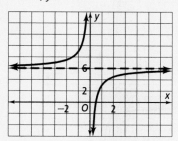

21. $x = -1, y = 4$

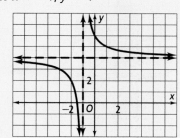

22. $x = 3, y = -5$

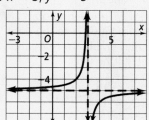

23. a. $C = \frac{1920}{n} + 100$

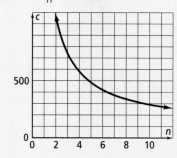

b. 5 people

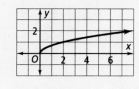
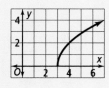

5.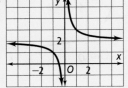

6.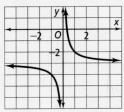

7.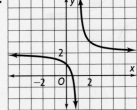

8.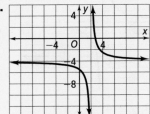

9. a.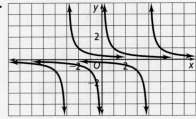

b. The graphs are the same shape as $y = \frac{1}{x}$. The second graph is a translation 4 units to the right. The third graph is a translation 3 units to the left.

10. a.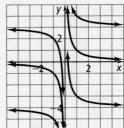

b. The graphs are the same shape as $y = \frac{1}{x}$. The second graph is a translation 4 units down. The third graph is a translation 3 units up.

Chapter 12

Lesson 12-2

Got It   page 721

2. Answers may vary. Sample:

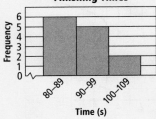

Finishing Times

Lesson 12-2 Lesson Chack

Practice and Problem-Solving Exercises   **page 692**

3.

Battery Life

Hours	Frequency	Cumulative Frequency
9–12	7	7
13–16	2	9
17–20	1	10
21–24	2	12

4. The store owner could look at the frequency column to pick out the busiest hours.

5. A symmetric histogram has roughly the same shape if you fold it down the middle. A skewed histogram has a peak that is not in the center.

6. Add the frequency of each interval to the frequencies of all the previous intervals.

Practice and Problem-Solving Exercises

7. Answers may vary. Sample:

Wing Spans

Number of Centimeters	Frequency
125–134	5
135–144	4
145–154	4

8. Answers may vary. Sample:

Marathon Times

Minutes	Frequency
130–149	1
150–169	2
170–189	2
190–209	3
210–229	2
230–249	2

9. Answers may vary. Sample:

Top Speeds

Miles per Hour	Frequency
90–109	4
110–129	4
130–149	2
150–169	3

10. Answers may vary. Sample:

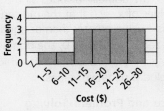

Costs of Items

11. Answers may vary. Sample:

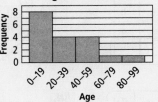

Ages of Relatives

12. Answers may vary. Sample:

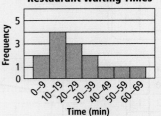

Restaurant Waiting Times

13. Answers may vary. Sample:

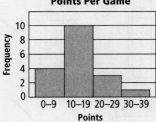

Points Per Game

14. skewed

15. symmetric

16. uniform

17. skewed

Index

Associative Property
of Addition, 23
of Multiplication, 23

astronomy, 156, 429, 439, 444, 446, 758

asymptote
defined, 694, 706
horizontal, 695
identifying, 695
vertical, 694–695

Auditory Learners, **47**

average, 726. *See also* mean

axes, 60, 234

axis of symmetry, 534, 590

B

Bar Graphs, 797

base
defined, 10
of exponent, 427
finding, 139
multiplying powers with same, 426

best fit, line of. *See* line of best fit

bias
defined, 743, 777
in samples, 744
in survey questions, 743

Big Ideas
Data Collection and Analysis, 713, 773, 774
Data Representation, 713, 773, 774
Equivalence, 79, 151, 152, 163, 221, 222, 413, 462, 463, 473, 522, 523, 599, 640, 641, 651, 702, 703
Functions, 233, 280, 281, 291, 348, 349, 413, 462, 533, 588, 589, 599, 640, 641, 651, 702, 703
Modeling, 233, 280, 281, 291, 348, 349, 359, 403, 404, 533, 588, 589
Probability, 713, 773, 774
Properties, 3, 67, 68, 413, 462, 463, 522, 523
Proportionality, 79, 151, 152, 291, 348, 349
Solving Equations and Inequalities, 79, 151, 152, 163, 359, 403, 404, 533, 588, 589, 599, 640, 641, 651, 702, 703
Variable, 3, 67, 68, 163, 221, 222

Big Ideas, 3A, 79A, 163A, 233A, 291A, 359A, 413A, 473A, 533A, 593A, 599A, 651A

binomials
dividing polynomials by, 667
modeling multiplication of, 485
multiplying, 486, 487
squaring, 492–493

biology, 17, 84, 111, 128, 191, 212, 335, 361, 421, 429, 466, 615, 616

bivariate, 742

Block Scheduling, See Pacing Assignment

box-and-whisker plot
defined, 735, 776
interpreting, 736
making, 736

braces, 17, 194

brackets, 11, 203

break-even point, 384

C

calc key, of graphing calculator, 261, 336, 366, 543, 554, 581, 584

calculator, 663. *See also* graphing calculator
degree mode, 634
equations in slope-intercept form, 305
exercises that use, 451, 460, 539, 544, 637
histograms, 721
linear inequalities, 402
line of best fit, 336
permutations, 752
rational functions, 695, 696, 701
regressions, 581
roots, 554
scientific notation, 420
systems of quadratic equations, 584
trigonometric ratios, 634
vertical motion model, 543

cards, 45

causation, 337

Challenge exercises, 9, 15, 22, 28, 36, 44, 52, 58, 66, 87, 93, 100, 108, 114, 123, 129, 136, 143, 150, 170, 177, 183, 192, 199, 206, 213, 220, 239, 245, 251, 259, 267, 273, 279, 298, 304, 311, 317, 325, 332, 340, 365, 373, 379, 388, 394, 400, 419, 431, 438, 452, 479, 484, 491, 497, 505, 510, 516, 521, 540, 546, 553, 559, 566, 573, 580, 586, 604, 612, 618, 625, 630, 639, 656, 664, 671, 677, 684, 700, 719, 725, 732, 739, 747, 756, 762, 770

Index

Acknowledgments

Staff Credits

The people who made up the High School Mathematics team—representing composition services, core design digital and multimedia production services, digital product development, editorial, editorial services, manufacturing, marketing, and production management—are listed below.

Dan Anderson, Scott Andrews, Christopher Anton, Carolyn Artin, Michael Avidon, Margaret Banker, Charlie Bink, Niki Birbilis, Suzanne Biron, Beth Blumberg, Kyla Brown, Rebekah Brown, Judith Buice, Sylvia Bullock, Stacie Cartwright, Carolyn Chappo, Christia Clarke, Tom Columbus, Andrew Coppola, AnnMarie Coyne, Bob Craton, Nicholas Cronin, Patrick Culleton, Damaris Curran, Steven Cushing, Sheila DeFazio, Cathie Dillender, Emily Dumas, Patty Fagan, Frederick Fellows, Jorgensen Fernandez, Mandy Figueroa, Suzanne Finn, Sara Freund, Matt Frueh, Jon Fuhrer, Andy Gaus, Mark Geyer, Mircea Goia, Andrew Gorlin, Shelby Gragg, Ellen Granter, Jay Grasso, Lisa Gustafson, Toni Haluga, Greg Ham, Marc Hamilton, Chris Handorf, Angie Hanks, Scott Harris, Cynthia Harvey, Phil Hazur, Thane Heninger, Aun Holland, Amanda House, Chuck Jann, Linda Johnson, Blair Jones, Marian Jones, Tim Jones, Gillian Kahn, Brian Keegan, Jonathan Kier, Jennifer King, Tamara King, Elizabeth Krieble, Meytal Kotik, Brian Kubota, Roshni Kutty, Mary Landry, Christopher Langley, Christine Lee, Sara Levendusky, Lisa Lin, Wendy Marberry, Dominique Mariano, Clay Martin, Rich McMahon, Eve Melnechuk, Cynthia Metallides, Hope Morley, Christine Nevola, Michael O'Donnell, Michael Oster, Ameer Padshah, Jeffrey Paulhus, Jonathan Penyack, Valerie Perkins, Brian Reardon, Wendy Rock, Marcy Rose, Carol Roy, Irene Rubin, Hugh Rutledge, Vicky Shen, Jewel Simmons, Ted Smykal, Emily Soltanoff, William Speiser, Jayne Stevenson, Richard Sullivan, Dan Tanguay, Dennis Tarwood, Susan Tauer, Tiffany Taylor-Sullivan, Catherine Terwilliger, Maria Torti, Mark Tricca, Leonid Tunik, Ilana Van Veen, Lauren Van Wart, John Vaughan, Laura Vivenzio, Samuel Voigt, Kathy Warfel, Don Weide, Laura Wheel, Eric Whitfield, Sequoia Wild, Joseph Will, Kristin Winters, Allison Wyss, Dina Zolotusky

Additional Credits: Michele Cardin, Robert Carlson, Kate Dalton-Hoffman, Dana Guterman, Narae Maybeth, Carolyn McGuire, Manjula Nair, Rachel Terino, Steve Thomas

Illustration

Kevin Banks: 330; **Jeff Grunewald:** 238, 265, 266, 534, 555, 566, 606, 608, 626, 633, 681; **Christopher Wilson:** 253, 268, 276, 325, 368, 390, 474, 492, 550, 663, 674, 714, 718, 720, 724, 726, 750, 751, 755, 757, 764, 766; **XNR Productions:** 4, 132, 142, 151, 169, 171, 385, 422, 449

Technical Illustration

GGS Book Services

Photography

All photographs not listed are the property of Pearson Education.

Back Cover, © Gary Bell/zefa/Corbis

Page 3, ©Joel Kiesel/Getty Images; **17,** www.src.le.ac.uk/projects/lobster/ov_optics.htm; **43,** Alamy; **54,** Satellite Imaging Corp.; **79,** Tobias Schwarz/Reuters/Landov; **84 T,** Livio Soares/Peter Arnold; **84 Bkgd.,** iStockphoto; **113,** Corbis; **133 R,** Franklin Institute; **133 L,** Photo Researchers; **133 M,** SuperStock; **163,** Michael Newman/PhotoEdit; **164,** Google; **167 R,** Shubroto Chattopadhyay/Corbis; **167 L,** Macduff Everton/Getty Images; **196,** iStockphoto; **221 T,** Corbis; **221 B,** Dorling Kindersley; **233,** Ed Ou/AP Photos; **255 R,** National Geographic; **255 L,** iStockphoto; **255 M,** Dorling Kindersley; **291,** Paul Kitagaki Jr./MCT/Landov; **300 B,** AP Images; **300 T,** Photo Researchers; **300 M,** NASA; **309,** Corbis; **309 Bkgd.,** iStockphoto; **359,** ©Wildlife GmbH/Alamy; **361 L,** Alamy; **361 R,** Animals, Animals; **413,** Jeff Vanuga/Corbis; **418,** Getty Images; **420 L,** Minden Pictures; **420 R, 451,** Photo Researchers; **473,** Stan Liu/Getty Images; **482 B,** Paulo Fridman/Corbis; **482 T,** Alamy; **500, 506,** iStockphoto; **512, both** Minden Pictures; **520,** Kyla Brown; **533,** Bernd Opitz/Getty Images; **557,** Dreamstime; **564,** Dorling Kindersley; **599,** Roine Magnusson/Getty Images; **601,** iStockphoto; **603,** Geoffrey Morgan/Alamy; **615,** Art Wolfe/Getty Images; **611,** iStockphoto; **617,** greeklandscapes.com; **651,** Peter Essick/Aurora Photos; **663,** iStockphoto; **713,** Jamie Wilson/iStockphoto.